THE OXFORD ENCYCLOPEDIA OF
INDUSTRIAL, WORK, AND ORGANIZATIONAL PSYCHOLOGY

THE OXFORD ENCYCLOPEDIA OF
INDUSTRIAL, WORK, AND ORGANIZATIONAL PSYCHOLOGY

José M. Peiró
EDITOR IN CHIEF

VOLUME 1

Oxford University Press is a department of the University of Oxford.
It furthers the University's objective of excellence in research, scholarship,
and education by publishing worldwide. Oxford is a registered trade mark of
Oxford University Press in the UK and in certain other countries.

Published in the United States of America by Oxford University Press
198 Madison Avenue, New York, NY 10016, United States of America.

© Oxford University Press 2024

All rights reserved. No part of this publication may be reproduced,
stored in a retrieval system, or transmitted, in any form or by any means,
without the prior permission in writing of Oxford University Press,
or as expressly permitted by law, by license or under terms agreed with
the appropriate reprographics rights organization. Inquiries concerning
reproduction outside the scope of the above should be sent to the
Rights Department, Oxford University Press, at the address above.

You must not circulate this work in any other form
and you must impose this same condition on any acquirer.

Library of Congress Cataloging-in-Publication Data
Names: Peiró, José M., editor.
Title: The Oxford Encyclopedia of Industrial, Work, and Organizational
Psychology / José M. Peiró, editor in chief.
Description: New York : Oxford University Press, 2024- |
Includes bibliographical references and index. | Contents: Vol 1—Vol 2
Identifiers: LCCN 2023037970 (print) | LCCN 2023037971 (ebook) |
ISBN 9780190641856 (set) | ISBN 9780190667689 (vol. 1 ; hardback) |
ISBN 9780190667832 (vol. 2 ; hardback) | ISBN 9780190866501 (ebk)
Subjects: LCSH: Work—Psychological aspects—Encyclopedias. |
Psychology, Industrial—Encyclopedias.
Classification: LCC BF481 .O943 2024 (print) | LCC BF481 (ebook) |
DDC 158.7—dc23/eng/20231218
LC record available at https://lccn.loc.gov/2023037970
LC ebook record available at https://lccn.loc.gov/2023037971

Sheridan Books, Inc., United States of America

About the *Oxford Research Encyclopedia of Psychology*

The Oxford Encyclopedia of Industrial, Work, and Organizational Psychology is published as part of the *Oxford Research Encyclopedia of Psychology*, a dynamic and scholarly digital resource. This online collection of overview articles provides in-depth, foundational essays on both core and emerging topics in psychology. All articles are commissioned under the editorial leadership of international experts of the highest caliber and are vetted through rigorous peer review. A living reference work, the online publication is updatable and enriched with crosslinking and multimedia features. The essays are intended for scholars, practitioners, and university-level readers, including advanced undergraduates, graduate students, and researchers.

Oxford Research Encyclopedia of Psychology
Editor in Chief: Ingrid Johnsrude

Previously published in print from the *Oxford Research Encyclopedia of Psychology*:

The Oxford Encyclopedia of the History of Modern Psychology
Edited by Wade E. Pickren

The Oxford Encyclopedia of Sport, Exercise, and Performance Psychology
Edited by Edmund O. Acevedo

The Oxford Encyclopedia of Psychology and Aging
Edited by Bob G. Knight

Contents

List of Articles   ix

Preface   xvii

THE OXFORD ENCYCLOPEDIA OF INDUSTRIAL, WORK,
AND ORGANIZATIONAL PSYCHOLOGY

Directory of Contributors (vol. 2)   1647

Index (vol. 2)   1655

List of Articles

VOLUME 1

FOUNDATIONS AND HISTORY

1. History of Organizational Psychology   3
   HELIO CARPINTERO
2. Evidence-Based Decision-Making and Practice in Organizations   24
   ALESSANDRA CAPEZIO AND PATRICK L'ESPOIR DECOSTA
3. Ethics in Work and Organizational Psychology   49
   JOEL LEFKOWITZ

MAIN THEORIES AND APPROACHES

4. The Sociotechnical Approach to Work Organization   77
   DAVID E. GUEST
5. Action Regulation Theory   97
   HANNES ZACHER
6. Goal Setting Theory: Causal Relationships, Mediators, and Moderators   110
   GARY P. LATHAM

x • LIST OF ARTICLES

7. Self-Determination Theory and Its Relation to Organizations 121
   ANJA H. OLAFSEN AND EDWARD L. DECI
8. Individual Differences in the Vitamin Model of Well-Being 140
   PETER WARR
9. A Selective Review of Developments in Positive Studies of Work and Organizations 160
   ARRAN CAZA
10. An Applied Approach to Psychology of Sustainability 172
    ROBERT G. JONES
11. Humanitarian Work and Organizational Psychology 184
    STUART C. CARR

RESEARCH METHODS

12. Mediator Variables 207
    MATTHEW S. FRITZ AND HOUSTON F. LESTER
13. Moderator Variables 228
    MATTHEW S. FRITZ AND ANN M. ARTHUR
14. Multilevel Modeling Methods 253
    VICENTE GONZÁLEZ-ROMÁ AND ANA HERNÁNDEZ
15. Temporal Dynamics in Organizational Psychology 280
    YANNICK GRIEP AND HANNES ZACHER
16. General Coding and Analysis in Qualitative Research 302
    MICHAEL G. PRATT

THE ENVIRONMENT OF ORGANIZATIONS

17. Industrial and Organizational Psychology From a Global Perspective 329
    MO WANG, CHENGQUAN HUANG, JUNHUI YANG, AND ZHEFAN HUANG
18. Cross-Cultural Issues in Industrial, Work, and Organizational Psychology 352
    SHARON GLAZER AND CATHERINE KWANTES
19. The Group Dynamics of Interorganizational Collaboration 371
    SANDRA SCHRUIJER

INDIVIDUALS IN ORGANIZATIONS

20. Judgment and Decision-Making Processes 391
    RICHARD P. LARRICK AND M. ASHER LAWSON
21. Work Motivation 411
    JAMES M. DIEFENDORFF, MEGAN E. KENWORTHY, FAITH C. LEE, AND
    LINH K. NGUYEN
22. Employee Work Experiences, Feelings, and Morality 429
    REMUS ILIES AND SHERRY AW
23. Emotions at Work 446
    NEAL M. ASHKANASY AND AGATA BIALKOWSKI

LIST OF ARTICLES • xi

24. Person–Environment Fit From an Organizational Psychology Perspective 465
    TOMOKI SEKIGUCHI AND YUNYUE YANG
25. Political Skill at Work and in Careers 485
    IRIS KRANEFELD, GERHARD BLICKLE, AND JAMES A. MEURS
26. Dark Personalities in the Workplace 506
    BIRGIT SCHYNS, SUSANNE BRAUN, AND BARBARA WISSE

DIVERSITY IN ORGANIZATIONS

27. Diversity in the Workplace 529
    REGINE BENDL, ASTRID HAINZL, AND HEIKE MENSI-KLARBACH
28. Individual Differences at Work 550
    ADRIAN FURNHAM
29. Gender in Organizations 570
    KARYSSA COUREY, MAKAI RUFFIN, MIKKI HEBL, DILLON STEWART,
    MERIDITH TOWNSEND, LEILANI SEGED, JORDYN WILLIAMS,
    CEDRIC PATTERSON, SARA MEI, AND EDEN KING
30. Work and Organizational Issues Affecting Young Workers 594
    BELGIN OKAY-SOMERVILLE, EVA SELENKO, AND ROSALIND H. SEARLE
31. Aging Workforce Issues From a Multilevel Approach 613
    LALE M. YALDIZ, FRANCO FRACCAROLI, AND DONALD M. TRUXILLO
32. Ageism in the Workplace 633
    DAVID M. CADIZ, AMY C. PYTLOVANY, AND DONALD M. TRUXILLO
33. Sexual Orientation (LGBTQ+) Issues in Industrial and Organizational Psychology 648
    JENNICA WEBSTER AND RAYMOND TRAU
34. Disabilities at Work 667
    FRED ZIJLSTRA AND HENNY MULDERS

JOBS AND WORK SYSTEMS

35. Job and Work Design 683
    ANJA VAN DEN BROECK AND SHARON K. PARKER
36. Job Crafting 708
    FANGFANG ZHANG, SABREEN KAUR, AND SHARON K. PARKER
37. Human–Computer Interaction 728
    AMON RAPP
38. Telework and Remote Work 753
    MATTI VARTIAINEN
39. Informal Work 779
    MAHIMA SAXENA

INTERPERSONAL RELATIONSHIPS, GROUPS, AND TEAMS

40. Impression Management 797
    DAVID M. LONG

xii • LIST OF ARTICLES

41. Social Comparison in Organizations 813
ABRAHAM P. BUUNK
42. Team Dynamics and Processes in the Workplace 830
TIFFANY M. BISBEY AND EDUARDO SALAS
43. Virtual Teams and Digital Collaboration 860
CONNY H. ANTONI
44. Justice in Teams 879
VINCENTE MARTÍNEZ-TUR AND CAROLINA MOLINER

VOLUME 2

LEADERSHIP IN ORGANIZATIONS

45. Positive Leadership in Organizations 901
LUCAS MONZANI AND ROLF VAN DICK
46. The Psychology of Abusive Supervision 920
KATRINA A. GRAHAM, GAHYUN YOO, AND EMMA K. KRISTAL
47. Ethical Leadership 937
SUZANNE VAN GILS AND NIELS VAN QUAQUEBEKE

ORGANIZATIONAL PROCESSES

48. Organizational Behavior 955
NEAL M. ASHKANASY AND ALANA D. DORRIS
49. Communication in Organizations 977
RYAN S. BISEL AND KATHERINE ANN RUSH
50. Organizational Sensemaking 992
RAVI S. KUDESIA
51. Conflict Management 1025
PATRICIA ELGOIBAR, MARTIN EUWEMA, AND LOURDES MUNDUATE
52. Organizational Climate and Culture 1044
MARK G. EHRHART AND BENJAMIN SCHNEIDER
53. Organizational Justice 1063
DIRK D. STEINER
54. Corporate Social Responsibility: An Overview From an Organizational and
Psychological Perspective 1078
ANTE GLAVAS AND MISLAV RADIC

HUMAN RESOURCES PSYCHOLOGY

55. Human Resource Management and Organizational Psychology 1105
DAVID E. GUEST
56. Psychological Contracts and the Employment Relationship 1125
KERSTIN ISAKSSON

LIST OF ARTICLES · xiii

57. Personnel Selection   1140
JESÚS F. SALGADO

58. Job Insecurity   1160
NELE DE CUYPER AND HANS DE WITTE

59. Training From an Organizational Psychology Perspective   1177
KURT KRAIGER

60. Overqualification in the Workplace   1195
BERRIN ERDOGAN, TALYA N. BAUER, AND AYSEGUL KARAEMINOGULLARI

61. Careers and Career Development   1218
JOS AKKERMANS, DANIEL SPURK, AND NADYA FOUAD

62. Retirement   1251
MO WANG AND VALERIA ALTERMAN

ORGANIZATIONAL OUTPUTS AND OUTCOMES

63. Work Performance Management and Assessment   1273
ROSE MUELLER-HANSON

64. The Psychology of Work Engagement   1292
MICHAEL P. LEITER

65. Creativity at Work   1305
KRISTINA POTOČNIK AND NEIL ANDERSON

66. Counterproductive Work Behaviors   1319
ROSALIND H. SEARLE

OCCUPATIONAL HEALTH PSYCHOLOGY

67. Occupational Health Psychology   1339
SHARON CLARKE

68. Work and Family   1368
MACKENNA L. PERRY AND LESLIE B. HAMMER

69. Work, Stress, Coping, and Stress Management   1394
SHARON GLAZER AND CONG LIU

70. Bullying and Harassment in the Workplace   1426
STALE EINARSEN AND KARI WIK ÅGOTNES

71. Burnout in Organizations   1447
MICHAEL P. LEITER AND JO WINTLE

72. Organizational Dehumanization   1459
NOÉMIE BRISON, FLORENCE STINGLHAMBER, AND GAËTANE CAESENS

73. Safety at Work   1480
GUDELA GROTE

74. Quality of Working Life   1498
DAVID E. GUEST

75. Well-Being at Work   1515
MAŁGORZATA W. KOŻUSZNIK, AIDA SORIANO, AND JOSÉ M. PEIRÓ

xiv • LIST OF ARTICLES

ORGANIZATIONAL CHANGE

76. Organization Change   1553
GEORGE P. HUBER AND JEAN M. BARTUNEK

77. Generative Emergence: Research and Praxis for Social Innovation   1572
BENYAMIN LICHTENSTEIN

78. Organizational Interventions   1595
KARINA NIELSEN

79. Organization Development   1614
W. WARNER BURKE

For my wife, Professor Alicia Salvador.

Preface

The current changes in our world, whether they be incremental or disruptive, are far-reaching. Globalization in its many forms, climate change and the challenges of sustainability, technological transformations and digitalization all have strong repercussions for many facets of society. Moreover, demographic changes, migrations, pandemics, war, and geopolitical changes impact multiple areas of social and personal life.

Labor and enterprises are particularly sensitive to all these changes and are therefore undergoing significant transformations. The automation of jobs due to digitalization and, above all, the impact of artificial intelligence, the significant shift in tasks and functions in a huge number of jobs, and the growth of green jobs are all important changes for today's environment. Alongside these, the increase in freelance work and gig work in platforms with no employment contracts redefine the nature of work and labor relations. It is therefore more necessary than ever to anticipate the future of work and how to face it.

Organizations themselves are also undergoing significant transformations. These social formations have diversified to a great extent and serve a large range of functions within societal and personal life. The traditional focus on industrial and some primary sector organizations (e.g. mining) has expanded to include design service organizations, public administration, non-profit organizations, non-governmental organizations and third sector organizations. Along with this, transitory organizational forms, temporary business units, and many other organizational structures such as networks, value chains, and loosely coupled systems emerge as innovative organizational configurations in an increasingly dynamic and transitory environment.

The social sciences, and especially psychology, have paid close attention to the psychological and social aspects of human behavior at work for over a century, and this attention has been extended to the collective behavior of organizations as a whole. Since the pioneering contributions of Münsterberg (1913) and other psychologists who have investigated human phenomena in the workplace, there have been many theoretical contributions and scientifically proven psychosocial interventions that have contributed to improving work and organizations. Especially since the Second World War, professional psychology has developed an impressive armamentarium of knowledge and tools aimed at improving organizations, in terms of efficiency and productivity as well as in terms of members' well-being. In fact, it was acknowledged early on that psychology, and more specifically work and organizational psychology, is a discipline that fits within both the natural and artificial sciences (Simon, 1969).

As complex, uncertain, and dynamic transformations take place in the world of work, much of the previously validated knowledge and interventions reveal their limitations and poor fit in the face of new demands. This opens up a vast horizon, which will require a serious rethinking of our discipline, in terms of its research, academic, and professional areas. For this reason, it is important to join efforts to open new paths and frontiers in order to cope with the needs, demands, and social challenges that are ever emerging.

To contextualize these changes, it is important to consider the multiple traditions within our discipline, which are even reflected in the labels that have been used in different regions over more than a century. Within the European tradition, the discipline was first called *psychotechnics* and later *applied psychology*. It has also been referred to as *personnel psychology* in some European countries. In later decades, the term *organization* was added to the label of *work psychology*. The British tradition has opted for the name *occupational psychology*, and more recently this label has been expanded to include the term *organizational*. From its beginnings, the North American tradition (United States and Canada) has opted for the denomination of *industrial psychology*, and again later on the term *organizational* was added. This denomination has been extended to countries in other continents (e.g. South Africa), while the briefer *organizational psychology* label has been used in Australia. Within this context, the title of this encyclopedia, *The Oxford Encyclopedia of Industrial, Work, and Organizational Psychology*, aims to integrate these different traditions and capture the multilaterality of the field.

The expansion of and diversity within the discipline and throughout the world requires us to combine global with local phenomena. Along with the more mainstream features of the discipline, there are many important scientific and professional developments ongoing in several regions of the world. Wider knowledge of these developments, however, is often restricted due to linguistic factors and editorial policies, among other reasons; dialogue within the discipline, on a worldwide scale, is therefore often limited. For example, developments that occur in Latin America or Asia often receive less attention than they deserve. To address this, we have explicitly asked the contributors to this encyclopedia to consider research contributions from different linguistic areas and regions of the world.

Work is undergoing strong transformations due to digitalization. The various forms of work without employment (e.g. the gig economy) and flexible work, in terms of time, place, function, and contractual terms, are no longer nonstandard work arrangements. These new forms of precarious and informal work have driven the need to prioritize decent work, as it is termed in Goal 8 of the Sustainable Development Goals. On the other hand, organizations with greater diversity in form and scope have also expanded the focus of their analyses. Broader consideration of the organizational environment, the multiplicity of stakeholders, and the inclusion of nonprofit organizations have led to new responses from the discipline, such as the formation of *humanitarian organizational psychology* as a cross-disciplinary field.

An important element in work and organizations is the relationships established between different stakeholders. These relationships have been the subject of extensive theoretical development and technological research in recent years. On the one hand, the importance of people is becoming more central. This has opened up a large field of development related to human resources management and development practices, with new labels that illustrate these conceptual transformations (talent, human capital, human-centric, etc.). On the other hand, the role of stakeholders, such as customers, or state requirements to promote sustainability and respect for the environment are also gaining in importance, and maintaining a balance between conflicting interests is a real challenge.

The results and impacts that are sought with the contributions of our discipline to the work of people and organizations have also been expanded. The types of performance and their results have been diversified: productivity and economic results, as well as innovation, quality, and leadership in the socioeconomic environment are valuable outcomes. The time perspective makes things even more complex, and a proper combination of short, medium, and long-term success is critical. The range of results required for organizational success has expanded. The well-being of workers, the prevention of labor risks, and the protection of the organizational members' health, including clients, are required results for a comprehensive measure of organizational success. A third area of success pertains to the competitive quality of the products and services offered, with compliance with legal and environmental requirements and the practices of corporate social responsibility. This perspective of integral sustainability requires innovative planning and implementation of organizational changes. Change management strategies have expanded and diversified: greater agility and the involvement of different stakeholders are increasingly necessary. Integration of change, cooperation, and harmony between public policies and business initiatives are also important.

All these changes are giving great vitality to our discipline and placing new demands and challenges on it. It is impossible to fully cover the extent of the discipline within a single work, and it is also difficult to make a meaningful selection that is useful for a readership seeking to understand recent developments within the main areas of the discipline. However, we have aimed to do just this with the encyclopedia, paying attention to the needs and interests of academics, students, researchers, professionals, and other interested people. The results are presented in the following thematic sections.

Section 1: Foundations and History
Section 2: Main Theories and Approaches
Section 3: Research Methods
Section 4: The Environment of Organizations
Section 5: Individuals in Organizations
Section 6: Diversity in Organizations

Section 7:   Jobs and Work Systems
Section 8:   Interpersonal Relationships, Groups, and Teams
Section 9:   Leadership in Organizations
Section 10:   Organizational Processes
Section 11:   Human Resources Psychology
Section 12:   Organizational Outputs and Outcomes
Section 13:   Occupational Health Psychology
Section 14:   Organizational Change

I have been fortunate to have a magnificent cast of prestigious authors, who are all specialists in the fields in which they have made their contributions. They come from multiple regions of the world, and all of them present prestigious profiles in the international arena of our discipline. Here I am pleased to express my thanks to each of them for their excellent contributions and for their willingness to take into consideration the main editorial lines of the work. My gratitude also extends to the large number of reviewers who have contributed to the improvement of each and every article in this encyclopedia. Finally, the support of the OUP editorial team since the beginning of this project has been excellent and essential. Without them this publication would not have been possible, and for this reason my most effusive thanks go to Ada Brunstein, Alyssa Callan, Matt Vitale, Sara Hales-Brittain, Rachel Utnage, and Alyssa Duck-Glen.

REFERENCES

Münsterberg, H. (1913). *Psychology and industrial efficiency*. Houghton Mifflin.
Simon, H. A. (1969). *The sciences of the artificial*. Massachusetts Institute of Technology.

José M. Peiró

Foundations and History

HISTORY OF ORGANIZATIONAL PSYCHOLOGY

INTRODUCTION

Organizational psychology (OP) is a psychological specialty that deals with the application of scientific concepts and interpretative models, consisting of devised technological interventions, upon mental and behavioral aspects of manmade organizations within modern societies.

It is today generally accepted that such a discipline covers approximately the same field that is also signified by the terms of *industrial psychology, work psychology, I-O psychology*, and similar areas of study. Here we adopt the one that has a convenient degree of generality. It takes, as its proper subject matter, social entities that may be considered organizations, whatever might be the nature of their constituent members.

"Organization" refers to a complex entity that contains a plurality of elements or members, forming a unity and operating as a certain whole that endeavors to reach some goals or ends, which represent the basic reason for its existence. (Its etymological root, the Greek *órganon*, signifies an instrument or means for attaining a certain goal.)

A well-known definition sees social organizations as "role systems," with interrelated people operating according to certain norms and looking for certain desired and valued goals (Katz & Kahn, 1966). Social organizations have been implemented over time to obtain a large

• 3

variety of results. Among them are hospitals, universities, newspapers, factories, trade companies, and so on. Each one includes certain working members, a leading group, a communication system, and definite goals to achieve with media and procedures. All of them are serving social needs and being supported by certain resources and supplies.

Most of the present-day life of society is mediated by organizations whose behavior is largely influenced by psychological factors. Once established in the late 19th century, the new science of psychology and its theorists and researchers, although primarily interested in scientific questions on the human mind and its biological basis, felt themselves forced to respond to the social demands for help from laypeople.

Problems that were arising in the industrial social network were of utmost importance. The industrial revolution had taken place in Western countries in the early decades of the 19th century. In order to attain a better adaptation to practical needs and actions, societies created organizations based on principles of impersonal work, labor division, cooperation, and competent leadership. Developed nations were based on masses of people operating under the leadership of certain elites that ruled countries. Natural science, gaining a growing control of the physical world, gave birth to a technology that enabled humans to create a world always based on human industry. This was a major revolution in Western societies. Their populations grew rapidly, industry favored urban life where factories were, and new demands appeared in need of solutions.

An artificial and technical world replaced the previous "natural" and "patriarchal" one. Power spread out in democratic societies, although fortunate men who had means and financial resources became the dominant class, imposing their will on the larger and less fortunate parts of society; this notwithstanding, the latter was capable of developing an enormous force and resistance through its unions. The class struggle characterized the typical climate of the 19th century in the more industrialized countries, the United Kingdom, France, the United States, and Germany being dominant. When conflicts and violence appeared in their powerful and productive organizations, management and owners tried to protect their own power, and many of them looked to science in search of a solution (Benjamin & Baker, 2004). Then psychology became, little by little, a very effective instrument in reconciling contrary viewpoints.

The history of organizational psychology is deeply rooted in the process of growth, increasing complexity and richness of both economic and industrial structures in our modern world.

PSYCHOLOGY APPLIED TO WORK SETTINGS AND INDIVIDUALS

At around the turning point of the 19th century, psychology was in its early stages, and its cultivators were being asked for help by people suffering from behavioral and mental problems. Wilhelm Wundt (1832–1920) had initiated a new epoch in Germany in the study of mental life and conscious experience and applied the experimental approach of physiology laboratories to these questions, instead of philosophical reflection. Psychological functions came to be analyzed in an objective and empirical way, discovering, piece by piece, the basic laws governing the human mind.

The relevance of individual differences among subjects was soon apparent. The pioneer work in Britain of Sir Francis Galton (1822–1911) that was soon followed by some of his disciples showed the possibility of measuring mental qualities through the application of some instruments and tests. This research paved the way for a psychotechnology focused on human subjects, looking at their traits, abilities, and deficiencies, and trying to determine their personal profiles in a new and scientific approach.

All sorts of people benefited from this new psychology. For instance, children profited from the new science of mind, as their capacities, intelligence, and degree of aptitude for schooling could be objectively assessed. Educational psychology worked to adapt students to the classroom environment. It also helped to make the aims of education more defined and objective, although social criticism was raised against an interpretation of intelligence as a fixed entity, totally dependent on heredity (Gould, 1981). Psychology was also soon utilized to adapt adults to their working places. This was an urgent question in a growing technological society. Here psychologists were preceded by well-trained and inspired technicians and engineers who began to analyze working behavior and elaborate a sophisticated body of knowledge.

THE SCIENTIFIC STUDY OF WORK ORGANIZATIONS

Industry was seen in the 19th century as the backbone of a nation's economy. Conflicts inside industrial settings were a continuous menace that required attention from governments and the ruling classes. European workers had learned from Karl Marx (1818–1883) and other reformers that class struggle was an efficient means for getting their economic demands satisfied by owners. The International Workingmen's Association (or First International) was established in 1864, and the Socialist (or Second) International was founded in 1884 (Stavrianos, 1991, p. 513). The economic world and workmen's behavior were in need of scientific-based solutions that would end the violence. It brought to the fore the question of work rationalization and the analysis of all factors implied in the production process.

Although organizations and groups were largely dependent on individuals, they exhibited characteristics and properties of a structural nature that required specific treatments. The British mathematician and engineer Charles Babbage (1791–1871) was a pioneer in asking for scientific analysis of enterprises and industrial settings. Some other U.S. scientists and engineers like Henry Metcalfe (1847–1917) and Henry R. Towne (1844–1924) initiated three different lines of exploration on this topic: (1) the study of the scientific organization of work; (2) the study of the formal organization of enterprises; and (3) the social theory of bureaucracy. It has to be noted that the first steps in our discipline's history were made by engineers who were deeply engaged in man/machine interactions and problems (Rodríguez, 1992).

The Study of the Scientific Organization of Work. A. D. Chandler pointed out that in American industry, the economic depression of the 1870s brought about a new interest in manufacturers, not because of technology but rather for organization techniques within firms and factories. This change precipitated the beginnings of the scientific management movement in the United States (Chandler, 1977, p. 272). The American Society for Mechanical Engineers was created in 1880 to face the problems raised by growing industrialization.

Soon after, in 1886, Henry R. Towne maintained that engineers' responsibility was not only in the technical aspects, but also in the management of people in production. Such ideas became very influential on Frederick Winslow Taylor (1856–1915), who developed the Taylor System and the core ideas of management in his *Principles of Scientific Management* (1911) and other well-known books (Taylor, 1947).

Striving against inefficiency, he analyzed all the productive processes with a scientific methodology. Although not a psychologist, he applied psychological techniques such as reaction-time measures and studies of movement and cooperation among workers, trying to find rationalized working procedures that would combine attractive salaries and incentives, personal satisfaction, and greater efficiency. He offered prescriptions for better results at the risk of being judged as an inhumane manager. In essence, he proposed the continuous presence of managers on workers in a way that actively combined knowledge, management and direction with physical capacities, energies, and mechanical efforts. A sort of mechanization was imposed on everybody, including managers, in the name of reason. The enterprise, as a real unit, worked thanks to the complete cooperation of all its members.

Taylorism became both a success and a threat; in any case, it was seen as a controversial theory. Workers' associations and critics rejected it as inhumane, while technicians and managers were in favor of it. Many distinguished researchers became his disciples: in the United States, Frank B. Gilbreth (1868–1924), Lillian M. Gilbreth (1878–1972), and Henry Gantt (1861–1919); in France, Charles Bedaux (1886–1944) and Henry Le Chatelier (1850–1936); in Russia, Aleksei Gastev (1882–1939), among others. All of them founded the Taylor Society in 1915 and, in 1923, the Council on Scientific Organization of Labor; it promoted several international conferences that analyzed all sorts of details of the productive process and largely contributed to the development of scientific management (Mallart, 1942; Kliksberg, 1975).

The Study of the Formal Organization of Enterprises. The study of individuals was not enough for solving all the problems encountered within companies. French engineer Henri Fayol (1841–1925), author of *General and Industrial Management* (1916), conceived the idea of an enterprise as a whole operating system, whose efficiency had to be raised to its highest level (Scheid, 1987). Such a goal was to be achieved through the governance, order, and control of such units, what he called their "administration." This function required the accomplishment of many different tasks that were to be fulfilled in accordance with some principles governing the system (Kliksberg, 1975).

Fayol's work tried to clarify the role of management and the need for competence and authority in organizations, far from any ineffective democratization. But his final model seemed to be an ideal construction that was far from effective, and its distance from the daily work of real enterprises was criticized by D. McGregor and other, later theorists.

The Social Theory of Bureaucracy. A further step in these types of studies on productivity and the formal traits of an enterprise may be represented by the bureaucratic theory of management, due to the German sociologist Max Weber (1864–1920). He, as part of his extraordinarily deep studies of society, economy, and *Weltanschauung*, and partly inspired by

F. W. Taylor's ideas, approached the analysis of social organizations as hierarchically built bodies, operating under impersonal and standardized procedures strictly followed by their members who operate at various levels and are charged with differential responsibilities and power. This is the "bureaucratic managerial model" that was widely influential in the field. Within it, emphasis had been placed on the traits of rationality, objectivity, formal rules, and well-defined methods, all based on the types of tasks to be accomplished, with an abstraction of its members' personal qualities (Mouzelis,1968; Peiró, 1983).

THE HUMAN SUBJECT AT WORK

The active man was at the core of all these problems of human performance at work, and psychology, as a new scientific knowledge of humans, began to be considered. At the beginning of the 20th century, this new science offered a plurality of perspectives—structuralism, functionalism, reflexology, and psychoanalysis. At the same time, some applied knowledge began to grow. German professor William Stern (1871–1938) defined this by its "practical utility." Applied interventions required a previous assessment period (*Psychognostik*) and a correlative procedure (*Psychotechnik*) based on knowledge gained (Dorsch, 1963; Rüegsegger, 1986).

Man-at-work problems were soon considered a psychological matter. Scientific research seemed to offer a valuable alternative to class-struggle options. Different facets began to be examined (Quintanilla, 1992). For instance, the study of worker fatigue made by Italian physiologist Angelo Mosso (1846–1910) suggested some measures to improve work rhythm and performance; German psychiatrist Emil Kraepelin (1856–1926) plotted a "fatigue curve" (1900) that gave a new dynamic view of working efforts. An initial evaluation of motives and aptitudes in young individuals applying for jobs, carried out by U.S. philanthropist Frank Parsons (1854–1908) at his Boston Vocation Bureau (1908), showed that a vocation test would benefit the professional adaptation of subjects through an effective process of personal guidance. Mechanical carriages began to invade modern life, bringing perils to city streets because of poor and unskilled drivers; concrete studies on people's driving abilities began to be made everywhere. German researchers Walter Moede (1888–1958) and Curt Piorkowski (1888–1939) provided some useful tests for detecting unsafe drivers. Other types of workers, like typists, operators, and telegraphers, were analyzed by French researcher Jean Maurice Lahy (1872–1943), who added new pieces of valuable practical knowledge to professional life. Psychologists in the United States were asked to influence consumer behavior through the use of persuasion techniques in advertising, a field in which they became very active; Walter Dill Scott (1869–1955) and Harry Hollingworth (1880–1956) did very important pioneer work on that topic.

It was Hugo Münsterberg (1863–1916), the German "father of psychotechnology," who was the first to face the problematic field in its entirety and find a certain solution. He conceived it (*psychotechnik*) as the "science of practical applications of psychology in the service of culture" (Münsterberg, 1913, 1914). From a functionalist perspective, he devised tests and testing situations that measured people's abilities relative to a certain job and favored an empirical-based personnel selection process. Person, situation, and means-ends relationships were the basic elements to consider in every practical intervention, and these were also the three factors interacting within the test. Simulated situations would allow evaluation of a subject's abilities and his reaction type, in a way that could allow predictions of his behavior in real circumstances.

In a parallel way, other colleagues, working on learning capacities in schoolchildren, had discovered ways to assess "intelligence" as a general ability to acquire knowledge. Its evaluation proved highly useful for an estimate of one man's learning capacity and practical potentialities. French researchers Alfred Binet (1857–1911) and Victor Henri (1872–1940) created a metric scale of intelligence, and British Charles Spearman (1863–1945) mapped human abilities and their interrelationships. On these grounds, German psychologist William Stern (1871–1938) coined the concept of the Intelligence Quotient (I.Q., the ratio of mental age to chronological age) that soon appeared as a good predictor of future performance in academic and daily settings. World War I, as we will see, furthered testing procedures and put psychology "on the table," as J. McKeen Cattell said.

THE IMPACT OF WORLD WAR I

As an enormous social proof of psychology's efficacy, World War I (1914–1918) showed that psychologists were able to test a large number of soldiers and, based on such tests, assign them to better-defined jobs. This selection process enormously favored the efficiency of the armies of various belligerent countries and, in some cases, it was accompanied by clinical interventions.

In the United States, a group of psychologists from the American Psychological Association (founded in 1892) led by its president Robert M. Yerkes (1876–1956) worked out a battery of tests ("Army Alpha" and "Army Beta") that proved to be very effective in assessing men. Another group, led by Walter Dill Scott (1889–1955) and Walter V. D. Bingham (1880–1952), with other outstanding psychologists such as J. B. Watson, E. L. Thorndike, and Lewis Terman, worked on personnel classification with excellent results (Katzell & Austin, 1992). In the clinical field, Robert S. Woodworth (1869–1962) built his "personal data sheet" (1918), a pioneer effective questionnaire for the detection of war neurosis in people.

Similar efforts were carried out in other countries. In Italy, Father Agostino Gemelli (1878–1959) examined pilots, and in France, doctors Jean Camus and Henri Nepper (1915), and in Germany, W. Stern (1916) did similar work. All these efforts represent the beginning of aviation psychology. Many new centers for selection and guidance were then created and benefited from that military experience and from the instruments produced for the war. Let us mention here the Laboratory for Industrial Psychotechnology from Charlottenburg (1918) in Germany; the Industrial Fatigue Research Board (1917) that was soon to become the National Institute of Industrial Psychology (1921) directed by Charles S. Myers (1873–1946) in the United Kingdom; the Institute of Professional Orientation of Barcelona (Spain, 1918); and many others. The time was also ripe for training professionals in specialized university centers; for instance, in the United States, the Division of Applied Psychology was established at the Carnegie Institute of Technology (now Carnegie-Mellon University) in Pittsburgh that turned into one of the leading research centers in the field; it was headed by Walter V. D. Bingham who was accompanied by W. D. Scott and other well-known specialists. Also, other private centers began to be created; Scott himself founded the Scott Company in Illinois in 1919, a pioneer consulting firm in the psychology of advertising and personnel selection; James McKeen Cattell (1860–1944) created The Psychological Corporation (1921), with analogous purposes, that was very active for more than half a century (Katzell & Austin, 1992). All these movements clearly revealed the vitality of this new field. Practitioners began to be hired by administrations, military services, and private industry; new concepts and mechanisms were added to previous ones (Koppes & Pickren, 2007).

Testing and interventions grew endlessly in the 1920s and 1930s (Salgado, 2001). Important journals were also created: *Journal of Applied Psychology* (1917), *Journal of Personnel Research* (1922), *Industrielle Psychotechnik* (1924), and many others. In all types of industrial and practical settings, knowledge of the human factor became indispensable.

The worker, his abilities, and his psychophysical constitution became central topics among applied psychologists, who could then give useful advice to workers and employers in order to achieve more efficient work practices. They also paid a lot of attention to the basic dimensions of individual human differences that built the framework for other phenomena, like the fatigue effect, the well-being of the worker, more effective selection procedures, job analysis, and the study of time and motion in working activities, as salient factors in this applied field. Typologies and profession descriptions and analyses were among the main benefits.

THE HUMAN RELATIONS MODEL AND THE STUDY OF GROUPS

Early psychotechnology tried to solve all sorts of conflicts in the job/person adaptation by comparing the psychological capacities of a person to the necessary functions for productive work. But unexpectedly, informal aspects of organizations and the interactions of members inside a group appeared as highly salient factors influencing productivity and became major objectives for research.

Some studies on work efficiency carried out among employees of the Western Electric Co. in Chicago, Illinois, between 1924 and 1932 offered a new perspective on the field. In a large series of experiments conducted between 1924 and 1927 by researchers at the company and the National Research Council of the National Academy of Sciences, they tried to determine the effect of workplace illumination on productivity, with poor results. In 1927, a group from the Harvard Business School headed by George Elton Mayo (1880–1949) with Fritz Roethlisberger (1898–1974) and William J. Dickson studied a sample of women working in a relay assembly test room—both an experimental and a control group; they were measured on certain tasks: for instance, manipulating telephone relays in special settings, while they were subjected to different stimuli changes. In the end, the data gathered seemed to imply that group efficiency was minimally affected by variations in physical factors in the workplace, while changes in social variables, such as informal rules, leadership, social climate, expectations, and fears, as well as the researchers' attention to subjects, seemed to have a large effect on group productivity (Mayo, 1945). Although harsh criticism ended these studies on the grounds of some ethical and methodological flaws (Adair, 1984), psychologists began to put the emphasis now on human relations in industry, stressing the importance of a holistic approach to work problems. Attention was now paid to the social dimensions of the production process, and researchers were urged to take into account the "human value" of work.

Most of the contributions made by the Chicago school on social problems are characterized by the attention paid to environment, mainly seen as a social network to be analyzed in terms of member interactions, all members belonging to one effective totality. There the anthropologist

William Lloyd Warner (1898–1970) with J. O. Low, working on modern urban life, wrote about the factory in connection with society, whose extra-organizational variables (technological and market changes, religion, race, and social class) threw light on productive processes. Detailed study of many types of interactions, mainly through interviews and surveys, would permit an understanding of work from a human perspective.

A great and newer impulse to this holistic perspective proceeded a few years later from the contributions of Kurt Lewin who immigrated to the United States from Nazi Germany. But it benefited also from other important sociological contributions, like Weber's bureaucratic model of management.

THE INFLUENCE OF WORLD WAR II

World War II (1939–1945) deeply changed the scenery of historical life, including psychology. In accordance with the experiences of World War I, the involved armies required rapid selection of people for all sorts of jobs, and convenient tests were applied by psychologists according to their acquired competences. In Germany, the assignment was done by a military psychology (*Wehrmacht Psychologie*) created in 1925 (Geuter, 1992, p. 199), while in the United States, a group of psychologists created the Army General Classification Test (AGCT), a group test for intelligence that was given to more than one million people.

After the war, many changes took place in the social context: U.S. psychology raised itself into a leading place that previously had been in European and mostly German hands; veterans returning home were in need of mental help and care, and many clinical psychologists were needed. Of course, many countries had to rebuild their economies, specifically the losing ones. The U.S. government implemented a very successful world plan for the recovery of the destroyed nations' economies (the Marshall Aid Plan, 1947), not without some criticisms about priorities and the possible predominance of U.S. policy over the European economy. Finally, an international confrontation between communism and capitalism, in both politics and economy, marked out the new era. New social phenomena then appeared: the "welfare state" (the state subsidizing disadvantaged people); and demands for egalitarianism, new forms of leadership, and work rationalization (Shimmin & van Strien, 1998). New technologies of information and communication rapidly began to change most human activities. Computers, whose roots can be traced back into the early 20th century, had already played an important role in the days of war (Colosus, 1943, in the United Kingdom; ENIAC, 1945, in the United States), but soon after the advent of peace, they were introduced into industries and administrations (e.g., UNIVAC I, 1951, in the United States) where they grew in an exponential way, widening the possibilities for operative work.

THE EXPANSION PERIOD

Man/machine problems had characterized all sorts of industrial activities and gave rise to industrial psychology as a specialty for many professionals. New types of economic structures began operating all over Western countries, giving a great shot in the arm to economies. In 1951, the European Coal and Steel Community was founded, and a few years later, the Treaty of Rome set the basis for the Common Market—or the European Economic Community

(EEC), which would become the seed of the present-day European Union. New potentials emerged for trade and industry. U.S. companies entered the European arena, and an enormous economic change took place in all fields, largely due to the new "American trial," as it was then called (Servan-Schreiber, 1967). New terms forcefully emerged at that time: "organization" and "organizational." The area of industrial activities was widened to receive those productive groups mainly operating with information and communication. Industrial *and* organizational psychology became the new discipline that has continuously grown since then. It symbolized the new zeitgeist. *Annual Review of Psychology* reviewed organizational studies for the first time in 1961. Significant books revealed the new inspiration: for instance, C. Argyris (1957), *Personality and Organization*, J. G. March and H. Simon (1958), *Organizations*, and E. H. Schein (1965), *Organizational Psychology*, among others.

New emphasis on organizations and management and their major tasks were studied by Peter Drucker (1909–2005) in his *The Practice of Management* (1958) and in many other works. Topics like direction, leadership, new forms of producing goods, and problems of worker adaptation to the new world demanded a deeper scientific understanding. Above all, the viewpoint related to individual differences that dominated industrial studies was now complemented by other research oriented toward group and social levels of phenomena (Porter & Schneider, 2014).

Among the most influential directions in these studies, according to some specialists (Peiró, 1983), were (1) the sociotechnical and holistic perspective, (2) the humanistic and motivational approach, and (3) the cognitive view of decision processes.

The Sociotechnical Perspective.   This doctrine stressed the importance of technology in all work processes. Its influence on social adjustment and the well-being of workers reinforced the view of organizations as systems in which a continuous interaction takes place between instruments and human operators.

In the United States, an important group developed under the inspiration of U.S.-German-born Gestalt psychologist Kurt Lewin (1890–1947), who emigrated from Germany. He was first at Iowa working on child behavior, and then at MIT, from where he moved to the University of Michigan, where he carried out a Gestalt-type research program on social groups and organizational behavior. He considered human situations, including working ones, as totalities determined by forces mediating man/field interactions, always taking place inside a certain field. Behavior's efficiency was largely determined by the organizational climates in families, schools, and enterprises. Leadership, the need for achievement, and levels of aspiration appeared as important factors influencing group efficiency, self-esteem, and satisfaction. He differentiated three possible climates within a group—authoritarian, democratic, and laissez faire—and then, with his collaborators R. Lippitt and R. K. White (1939), he evaluated their effects on various social environments.

An important development of these ideas was the theory and practice of group dynamics, which focuses on processes occurring either within a group or between groups. Operating forces, changes over time, the phenomena of leadership, communication, pressure, and resistance to change were some of the topics considered in his work; salient work in this field had been carried out by Dorwin Cartwright, Leon Festinger, and Murry Horwitz, among others (Cartwright & Zander, 1974). The war experience provided an opportunity to study social attitudes and group mentality in *The American Soldier* (1949) by Samuel A. Stouffer (1900–1960), taking the army as an idiosyncratic organization (Rodríguez, 1992) very different from industrial ones.

Another movement, also inspired by Lewin's Gestalt ideas, focused on the T-groups, or training groups, and was carried out in the United States at the National Training Laboratories in Bethel, Maine, in 1947. Here, the group dynamics were the center of attention, in order to create and strengthen team spirits and creative thinking when orienting a conflict situation and implementing a certain "people game" with rules and roles that imposed "objectivity" on the group. Some of these techniques had paved the way to the study of a more general field, organizational development, and its search for better ways to fortify a certain organization, consolidating the network of interactive relationships (Hollway, 1991, p. 112).

In the United Kingdom, an influential psychoanalytic group, the Tavistock Institute (London, 1947) was created to provide clinical treatment for people suffering from the effects of war, employing technological interactions. Wilfred R. Bion (1897–1979) tried to analyze and modify the "group mentality," made up of attitudes, desires, and expectations. Work activities, such as a project on coal mining, were examined by Eric L. Trist (1908–1993), who emphasized the role of interactions between instrumentation, attitudes, and productivity in that process. It has been noted that some studies of Elliott Jaques (1917–2003) at the Glacier Metal Co. (1951) could be viewed as laying the foundations for the action-research methodological model (Shimmin & van Strien, 1998); other researches on urban organizations, like those made by William F. Whyte (1914–2000), widely used the same "participative" model to understand social groups from the inside and combine theory and practice.

Humanistic Psychology. Another line of theoretical development in the field was due to humanistic psychology, the so-called "third force"—in-between behaviorism and psychoanalysis. In it, the motivational aspect of personal behavior was widely considered. Abraham Maslow (1908–1970) is one of its most representative figures. He stressed the importance of motivation in governing human behavior and presented, by means of a well-known pyramid, a hierarchy of motives (from physiological on the bottom to self-actualization on the top, through security, belongingness, and self-esteem). Groups and organizations provide people with security, belongingness, and membership. Nevertheless, each person also feels the need for developing his/her own personality and experiencing a sense of plenitude and happiness that should be reached within the organization itself. But organizations might be considered on many occasions as a limiting factor when a conflict breaks out. They should take into account such necessities, humanizing all interactions.

These ideas received great attention from another theoretician, Frederick Herzberg (1923–2000), who built a motivation-hygiene theory, in which human motivation is seen as having a double process, one of satisfaction and one of dissatisfaction, both unrelated and independent. The former relates the job to personal motivation (e.g., interest, values, and self-growth); the latter, on the contrary, relates to context dimensions (company policy, work conditions, and so on) that do not produce satisfaction but can bring about dissatisfaction if they are not conveniently disposed, in a kind of preventive or "hygienic situation." People have to learn to balance them in order to keep the whole working process running at a realistic level.

On these grounds, different aspects of the problem have been considered, adding new elements to it. Several theoreticians have developed salient contributions. Let us mention here those of MacGregor, Likert, and Argyris as representative of this way of thinking.

Douglas MacGregor (1906–1964) compared two basic ways of being a human in an organization, what he called theory X and theory Y, two different managerial styles. He called theory X the "classical" one, maintained by Taylor and others, according to which work is undesired by humans, who must accomplish their tasks always under supervision and evaluation from others. Theory Y, to the contrary, considers humans as self-directed operators, impelled by their own desires for self-esteem and self-actualization and looking for personal happiness achieved by creative realizations. MacGregor is well aware of the idealization implied in such a theory, but he considers it as an instrument for reaching the Y situation. Such managerial style would promote higher values of humanity in the world of work.

Rensis Likert (1903–1981), once head of the Institute for Social Research at the University of Michigan, found that productivity was largely based on the managerial style adopted in enterprises. Deeply interested in measurement techniques and their applications to attitudes, he developed some aspects of the Lewinian intellectual legacy. He differentiated four leadership styles—exploitative authoritative, benevolent authoritative, consultative, and participative—with totally different results, the last one being the most beneficial for members and the organization as a whole, as it promotes group cooperation that permits it to attain far-reaching goals.

Last but not least, Chris Argyris (1923–2013) maintained the idea of an organization as an open system interacting with its environment (in accordance with L. von Bertalanffy's "general systems theory"), adapting its goals to the demands from its administration. A degree of excellence would be reached when its members obtain personal enrichment. In such conditions, deviant or faulty behaviors do not take place, and productivity rises to higher levels.

Cognitive Studies on Decision Processes. A third line of studies has relied on the cognitive processes of decision-making and the various rationality degrees that may inspire managerial decisions. Practical decisions are not always based on pure logic due to other factors, such as experience and motivation (Lord & Maher, 1991). One important antecedent of such cognitive perspectives was Chester Barnard (1886–1961) in his *The Functions of the Executive* (1938). He relied on the idea that organizations, as systems of conscious activities, largely depended on the executives, whose main function was making rational, purposeful decisions in a quest for success. When making decisions, they had to combine formal rationality with informal knowledge and experience. A further and deeper analysis of the process was carried out some years later by Herbert Simon (1916–2001), a Noble Prize winner in economics (1978) and a leading researcher in sociology, economy, and computer science. He and his collaborators analyzed thinking and decision-making processes that they characterized as having a "bounded rationality." This means that problems are usually solved using explicit or tacit knowledge, without reaching the higher levels of conscious rationality. In the case of people entering into organizations to attain certain finalities, they generally tend to assume that membership gain will be enough to compensate for the accepted group requirements (such as the case of the "administrative man"), instead of trying to maximize his profit (as the "economic man" would have done). This sort of decision would

PERIOD OF CONSOLIDATION

In the last decades of the past century, the process of world globalization began to emerge, but not without internal conflicts. The European Union and Western democracies, allied with the United States, faced the political empire created by the USSR and communist regimes that divided international life with the Iron Curtain symbolized by the visible wall that divided the German city of Berlin from 1961 to 1989. Large conflicts sprang up, like the Vietnam War (1954–1975) and the Yom Kippur War between Syria and Egypt against Israel (1973); this was followed by an enormous oil crisis with deep economic consequences throughout the whole world. Moreover, U.S. society experienced the internal conflict of the civil rights movement (1955–1963), symbolized by the figure of Martin Luther King (1939–1968), that reinforced a growing humanism. An enormous technological effort was made by Western societies to lead toward historical movement; the landing of man on the moon (U.S. Apollo XI project, 1969) was to become a symbolic icon for a new era. At the same time, giant computers that had appeared during World War II became minicomputers in the 1960s and then personal computers in the 1970s and laid the basis for the internet (1990) and the current information society that has propelled the advent of effective globalization. The introduction of computers in industries and social corporations, and the internationalization of markets and operating companies required more and more flexible and complex organizations. These entities have acquired still greater significance than before in the economic and social world.

At the same time, U.S. psychology, now in the forefront of the field, experienced a great change: "cognitivism" replacing the previously dominant "behaviorism." New perspectives on the human mind were discovered as early as 1956 (Gardner, 1985), and they gave new meanings to the already established behavioral dimensions.

Both old and new paradigms had their echoes within I-O psychology. A fully cognitive organizational approach began to develop, considering both individual minds and organizations as information-processing systems managing physical and symbolic elements and making decisions for solving problems on the basis of previous information. Such activities would take place in many directions: personnel selection, social climate, leadership, and so on. J. Galbraith, K. E. Weick, and many other researchers have pointed to ambiguity as a main trait of social situations that organizations have to deal with. The study of decisions received new developments from the Nobel Prize winner for economics (2002) Daniel Kahneman (b. 1934) and his colleague Amos Tversky (1937–1996) in what they called the limited rationality that humans use to operate in uncertain or probabilistic situations because of their different expectations in concrete situations. New topics also began to emerge in the field (for instance, the influence of values on decision-making, the skills needed for information technology, and cognitive dimensions of performance, as well as the need for new assessment instruments adjusted to the new theoretical lines, among others).

Notwithstanding, behavioral theory was still alive in the field. Behavior modification, which explains individual and/or organizational behavior changes in terms of reinforcement contingencies (positive reinforcement versus punishment), revealed itself as a useful approach to some problems like absenteeism, lifestyle improvement, and task performance adaptation, among others (McShane & von Glinow, 2010). It should also be noted that the U.S. neo-behaviorist B. F. Skinner (1904–1990) imagined an organizational utopia in behavioral terms in his novel *Walden Two* (1948). In it, individuals and groups were controlled by operant conditioning that set the rules for the whole community. Some years later, in 1956, W. H. Whyte Jr. (1917–1999) wrote *The Organization Man*, a bestseller that presented many Americans as living under the protection of large organizations, instead of subscribing to traditional individualism, a very important social change.

TOWARD THE HUMANIZATION OF WORK, 1960s–1970s

Political movements and conflicts brought out some new humanitarian perspectives on humankind, work, and the economy. In the United States, as an understandable reaction, a deeper comprehension of other people began to emerge. A decisive step was the approval of the Civil Rights Act (1964), which outlawed any discrimination based on race, age, sex, color, and national origin. In the world of work, equal employment and the personal dignity of all employees and employers were the focus of attention. In this climate, some voices were raised in the United States against the pretended use of social sciences in industry, which was always biased in favor of the dominant entrepreneurial class, and asked for a fair policy (Baritz, 1960). The *One Dimensional Man*, Herbert Marcuse's bestseller (1964), criticized the one-dimensional type of thought, focusing on how to make the current production system work more effectively without any crises that always favored the dominant class.

Leadership became a central topic. Ideas like the existence of naturally endowed "great men" or charismatic leaders and behaviorally well-trained people gave way to more situational conceptions. Fred E. Fiedler (b. 1922) proposed in the 1960s a "contingency theory," according to which a person becomes a leader under certain personality and situational factors, and may have success in certain types of situations but not in others. Some leaders are "task-oriented," while others are "group-oriented"; situation, task, and leader/member relationships determine a structure that may affect various resulting possibilities. Many alternatives have been proposed in recent years, empirically exploring the multiple typologies of known leaders.

Studies on motivation, like the cognitive "expectancy theory" of Canadian Victor Vroom (b. 1932), of individuals operating according to their perceived expectations of their actions, were combined with others stressing the relevance of cross-cultural variables and the training of economic achievement motivation, as D. McClelland (1917–1998) and D. G. Winter have described (McClelland & Winter, 1969).

As Marvin D. Dunnette (1926–2007) pointed out in his *Handbook of Industrial and Organizational Psychology* (1976), a new emphasis in theorizing was already present that eventually widened the research field.

RECENT DEVELOPMENTS

A brand new historical context is now serving as a framework for recent developments in the field. Scientific progress and growing technical and informational advances are having deep effects upon economic agencies. The rise of new, gigantic economies (like the one seen in

China), the reappearance of strong nationalisms within Third World countries, the profound political changes of present-day Russia and the whole Islamic world, and the incorporation of many Third World countries into historical life are creating new conditions in the world of economics. New problems are demanding solutions from all professionals operating in the field. The new challenges imply the need to manage social change, attitudes, and desires, with models that "maximize human and machine resources" (Offermann & Gowing, 1990). I-O psychology has acquired immense weight. Classic topics have received continuous attention: personnel selection, labor socialization, and school-work transition processes (Peiró, 1983); motivation, work satisfaction, and the quality of life (Latham & Budworth, 2007); power participation and human performance (Fleishman & Quaintance, 1984); and the impact of new technologies and the multifactor problem of unemployment. Some other topics have been raised to the fore. One of these is organizational culture, a concept that emphasizes values, shared images, and empirical elements that give "uniqueness" to each organization. From the great diversity of studies on this topic, let us cite as an example some studies carried out by Michael Frese (b. 1949), who has shown the relevance of cultural factors to phenomena like personal initiative, entrepreneurial success, and innovation in both developed and underdeveloped countries (Frese et al., 2002).

Another important facet of today's research is organizational health psychology, a field in which the multiple dimensions of the labor world are interrelated with the mental health of workers, especially in stress, unemployment, or conflict situations. Accident-prone personalities, bullying, workplace violence, and other topics are currently receiving greater attention in order to establish intervention programs that modify conflict situations (Leka & Houdmont, 2010).

There have also been new theoretical approaches. Positive psychology focuses on positive and hedonistic dimensions of organizational behavior, instead of being centered on defective and deviant ones. It has appeared as an innovative viewpoint in the field, widening the I-O psychology area. It focuses on aspects related to positive emotions and positive subjective experiences and traits in workplaces and organizations while trying to improve the quality of life for both individuals and organizations (Nelson & Cooper, 2007; Salanova & Rodriguez-Sanchez, 2009).

A strong movement rapidly entering into all psychological areas is one based on present-day neurosciences. Biological, genetic, and neuropsychological dimensions of behavior are now being considered in workplace activities, attention and perception, emotions and motives in labor activity, stress, and many other concrete factors influencing productivity and worker feelings (Arvey & Zhang, 2015). In these matters, no doubt, research is on the first leg of a long journey.

Another salient trait of the current research situation is a strong tendency to combine some empirically well-grounded theoretical models with a great interest in hard and complex methodologies, well adapted to the collected data that have to be analyzed and clearly focused on concrete patterns (Peiró, 1990).

A content analysis of articles edited (1963–2007) in two of the most important journals in the field, the *Journal of Applied Psychology* (founded 1917) and *Personnel Psychology* (founded 1948), reveals that the following subject matters appear in both publications: research methods/psychometrics; predictors of performance; work motivation and attitudes; and performance measurement/work outcomes (from Cascio & Aguinis, 2008; see Porter & Schneider, 2014). Emphasis on methodological procedures was accompanied by psychological questions (motivation, attitudes) and objective measures of working activity and results (performance, outcomes), basic aspects taken into account since the birth of I-O psychology.

Apart from a continuously growing specialized literature, an endless list of treatises and works offering complete information about many matters may be easily found today. What follows is a list of several handbooks in which a detailed panorama of the rise and foundations of the discipline may be found. Apart from some fundamental works, like the classics Burtt's *Psychology and Industrial Efficiency* (1929), M. Viteles's *Industrial Psychology* (1932), and D. Katz and R. Kahn's *The Social Psychology of Organizations* (1966), we also cite J. G. March's *Handbook on Organizations* (1985) and another classic work, M. Dunnette's *Handbook of Industrial and Organizational Psychology* (1976, 1991). More recent treatises include P. J. D. Drenth et al., *Handbook of Work and Organizational Psychology* (1998), N. Anderson et al., *Handbook of Industrial, Work and Organizational Psychology* (2002), S. Zedeck, ed., *APA Handbook of Industrial and Organizational Psychology* (2010), and S. Kozlowski, ed., *The Oxford Handbook of Organizational Psychology* (2012). Moreover, an *International Review of Industrial and Organizational Psychology* has been published yearly (1986–2012), and an *Annual Review of Organizational Psychology and Organizational Behavior* has been recently launched (2014); many specialized review chapters have also appeared in *Annual Review of Psychology*, with detailed and critical views of I-O psychology.

SOME OTHER COUNTRIES' DEVELOPMENTS

I-O psychology has become one of the leading directions in contemporary research and intervention. The globalization of the economy and the existence of continuous interactions among cultures and nations have favored a multicultural approach to this field.

Let us now briefly consider a selection of views taken from I-O psychology in non-U.S. countries where I-O psychology has achieved a particular significance.

An Idiosyncratic Development in the USSR.   Ideas on work psychology have had an idiosyncratic evolution in the USSR, the big political unit created around the old Russian Empire after the communist revolution of 1917. The reason for this peculiarity is based on its Marxist view of economy and work as a state enterprise, far from the liberal views accepted by most Western democracies. In the initial days, some followers of Russian psychotechnology participated in the first congresses of the International Association of Psychotechnology (AIP) and even organized the fifth one that took place in Moscow in 1931. The president Isaak Spielrein (1891–1937) surprised his colleagues with an attack on "bourgeois" industrial psychology, while maintaining the superiority of the Marxist approach to work. The official thesis was against personnel selection procedures based on individual differences and, on that basis, tests were banned by the government through the decree "On Pedological Distortions" (1936) that required a democratic equality among all people and the rejection of "bourgeois evaluation" (McLeish, 1975). The model of a "new man," fully given to the ideals of a communist revolution, implied that industrial activities should not be guided by individual factors, but by the political direction of the Communist Party, the leading force of the nation. As Boris Pariguin

(1930–2012) put it, while the bourgeois psychologists were trying to manipulate workers in favor of "capitalist monopolies," the Marxist ones were contributing to establish the new man in an egalitarian socialist society (Pariguin, 1967).

It has been said that Western work-organizational (W-O) psychology could benefit greatly from certain Russian developments in the study of human "higher nervous activity" (the purposeful and conscious activity toward goals mainly based on brain functioning) for more than half a century, as well as those in the fields of ergonomics and industrial safety. But at the same time, the principles of "guaranteed labor" and "full employment" determined a totally different framework from the one existing in Western countries in the labor field (Roe, 1995). Notwithstanding this, during the 1950s, there was an increasing interest in man/machine adjustment problems, and ergonomics and engineering psychology became very active areas of research; Boris F. Lomov (1927–1989), head of the Institute of Psychology within the Academy of Sciences at Moscow, did significant work on the human operator, paying attention to various capacities and considering "man as the subject of work, cognition and generalization" (Lomov, 1969). Only after the Soviet Union breakup of the early 1990s (Warr, 2007) did the process of liberalization of the Russian society begin, in which the economy has paved the way to a reestablishment of scientific freedom and a liberalized exchange with other developed countries.

Russia clearly exhibits the paradigm of a society wherein certain political criteria have made freedom of thinking and analysis of social problems impossible. These are at the core of any study of working humankind and, in effect, Russia has banned all possibilities for developing an effective I-O psychology as long as that worldview is in force.

Some Other Countries and Cultures. It is not possible, given the editorial limitations of this article, to try to present a clear picture of the I-O psychology developments that would take into account all the significant national stories. Only some disjointed comments are presented here, with the hope of creating an impressionist landscape with some cross-cultural flavor and certain meaning.

As psychological science was born in Europe, and more precisely in Germany, since its early days, most of the problems have also had a presence in the European story, but not without certain peculiarities, as was aptly pointed out by the German professor Bernhard Wilpert (1936–2007) (Wilpert, 1990).

Germany had the first laboratory for experimental psychology in Leipzig in 1879, thanks to the efforts of Wilhelm Wundt (1832–1920), and around this nucleus, a great school of thought was established with a large number of distinguished disciples. In it, some of Wundt's students like Hugo Münsterberg and William Stern did pioneering work on applied science and succeeded in setting the scene for a psychotechnological network. They analyzed a variety of problems, from work fatigue to traffic safety, vocational guidance, and military psychology (by very well-known researchers like E. Kraepelin, W. Moede, K. Piorkowski, W. Stern, O. Lipmann, and many others). In the days of Nazi Germany in the 1930s, groups of professionals were able to offer psychotechnological help to industry and the army, creating specialized centers for industrial psychology, and eventually transferred to both the Deutsche Democratic Republic or East Germany, and West Germany during the hard times of the divided country (1946–1989). Since then, German professionals have been actively integrated into the European Association of Work and Organizational Psychology (EAWOP) and other associations of our discipline.

The development of I-O psychology in France cannot be forgotten here. The pioneer work on child psychology and intelligence testing, largely dependent on the extraordinary contributions of Alfred Binet (1857–1911), showed the possibilities offered to society by the new psychology, thanks to its objective knowledge on abilities and mental activity. Psychotechnological research was carried out by Jean Maurice Lahy (on professional abilities), E. Toulouse (in mental health, 1920), and other colleagues. They prepared the ground for the creation of the National Institute for the Study of Labor and Professional Guidance in Paris, thanks mainly to the efforts of Henri Piéron (1881–1964), an experimentalist who emphasized applied interventions to promote safe work and psychological health (Piéron, 1959). He also favored the creation of the AIP in 1920. Under his patronage, a new wave of specialists entered the field and brought new ideas to old problems: Claude Levy Leboyer (1928–2015), one of the major European contributors to organizational research; Raymond Bonnardel (1901–1988) industrial psychologist, and many others.

This French group was also connected with a Belgian nucleus, the important Institute of Ergology headed by Paul Sollier (1861–1933) that did significant work on psychotechnology. Another well-known researcher was the Polish-born Mrs. Iosefa Ioteyko (1866–1928), who worked in Brussels and whose book *The Science of Labor and Its Organization* (1919) was one of the first approaches to an organizational view of the working enterprise.

In Spain, there was a very peculiar development due to historical circumstances. As the so-called father of psychological guidance, Juan Huarte was a 16th-century Spanish physician who, for the first time, paid attention to individual differences and their effects on the professional training of individuals in his *The Examination of Men's Wits* (1575). This was a seminal work on vocational guidance that was deeply censored by the Spanish Inquisition, on the grounds of its fully naturalistic conception of man. Many centuries later, in 1918, a center for applied psychology was created in Barcelona, headed by Emilio Mira-y-Lopez (1896–1964), another active member of AIP. He explored many aspects of human activities, from war to sports, and devised a psychomotor projective test, the PMK or Myokinetic Apperception Test (1939). Jointly with another psychiatrist, Jose Germain (1897–1986), they promoted a national system for guidance, selection, and traffic safety in the 1920s. The Spanish Civil War (1936–1939) put an end to this initial psychotechnology and forced Mira-y-Lopez and many other colleagues to go into exile, mainly to Latin American countries, where applied psychology studies were resumed. In Spain, after some delay, psychology recovered its impetus, and applied research paved the way to new theoretical developments. Some students, M. Yela (1921–1994), J. L. Pinillos (1919–2013), and M. Siguan (1918–2010), brought psychology into the list of university careers. Soon after, specialized developments took place among those in I-O psychology (Peiró & Munduate, 1994). Of most significance were those promoted by José M. Peiró (b. 1950), head of one very active European center for organizational research and one of the leading researchers in the International Association of Applied Psychology (IAAP).

Attention to national traditions cannot be separated from recent developments in cross-cultural studies. Most I-O psychological problems, especially those related to values, job meaning, leadership, and interpersonal relationships, should always be considered from a point of view deeply embedded in a particular cultural framework, although a cross-cultural approach to them has proven fruitful in many cases. It has expanded the range of organizational behavior, reduced ethnocentrism, and tested the universality of theories (Aycan & Gelfand, 2012). Organizational phenomena are, in large part, culture-bound processes. Entrepreneurial ideologies and political views of humans and society have exerted deep influence upon concrete situations of working people. The system of forces defining a society (Marías, 1987) is always operating in a historical manner in all organizations that mediate the life of society itself.

Studies comparing, for instance, Japanese and U.S. organizational cultures have shown the need for some anthropological information in order to understand the differences that were observed (Misumi, 1985; Gelfand & Erez y Aycan, 2007). W. G. Ouchi (b. 1943) examined the climates of two organizations, one American and the other Japanese. Both greatly differed on employment policies, company-personnel identification, and some values rooted in the countries' worldviews (Ouchi, 1981; Garmendia, 1988). It has been noted that some Confucian doctrines on interpersonal relationships still influence certain Chinese ways of implementing social enterprises (Ralston et al., 1992). Or, in other studies, it has been observed that some cultural-specific traits had effects on decision-making processes and contingent punishments, something that appears in Japan, Korea, Taiwan, Mexico, and the United States (Bond & Smith, 1996).

Dimensions like gender self-concept, ethnic identity, personal perception, justice, and many others have a great effect on the way interpersonal interactions are structured and interpreted in work situations. The meaning of work holds a different position within the value constellation among peoples in differing cultures, from the West European world, Far East Asia, and East European countries—especially in the days of their Marxian political governments (Bond & Smith, 1996). Cognitive factors are operating in many aspects of organizational processes—performance appraisal, leadership, supervision, and employee participation, among others—and studies are now focusing on current cross-cultural research (Koppes & Vinchur, 2012).

In a world with changing cultural heterogeneity and more immigration in developed and industrial countries, this type of approach is needed in order to fulfill all the requirements of respect for the rights of people and cultures, and obtain an effective, in-depth knowledge of human interactions.

NETWORKS OF RESEARCHERS

The field of work-industrial-organizational (W-I-O) psychology has shown great potential and capacity for creating collaborative and professional networks, profiting from its interest in the creation of more effective ways for promoting personal self-development in workplaces and influencing society's well-being.

One of the oldest associations of professionals and researchers is the American Psychological Association (APA), founded in 1892 and now gaining large support in society. Industrial psychologists, as they were first called, did not find desired accommodation at the APA. They tried other associations and finally gave support to the establishment of an American Association of Applied Psychology (AAAP) in 1937, where they had their own department; this eventually merged with a reorganized APA in 1945, forming a specialized division 14,

Industrial and Business Psychology, a proper site for them that has not remained without changes: In 1962, "Business" disappeared from its name and, in 1973, the term "Organizational" was added; now it was known as the Division of Industrial and Organizational Psychology. In 1982, it adopted the form of a society, the SIOP or the Society for Industrial and Organizational Psychology, which is very active in its present form (Koppes, 2015).

Interest in associations has also grown in the European world. Psychologists felt the need for communication and cooperation. In looking for solutions, the AIP was established in 1920 under the leadership of Edouard Claparède (1873–1940), with the participation of well-known European psychologists like Giulio Cesare Ferrari, Emilio Mira-y-Lopez, Jean-Maurice Lahy, Ovide Decroly, George van Wayenburg, and Dimitre Katzaroff, among others. Since then, membership has continuously increased. AIP eventually changed its name to the present-day IAAP and has become a very active society, largely inspired by its predecessor. A division on O-psychology was established in 1978 (currently W-O psychology), with professor Bernard M. Bass (1925–2007), a well-known specialist in leadership, as its founding president, and other distinguished researchers like P. J. Drenth, F. Fiedler, and E. Fleishman as members; it has played an important role in reinforcing research and multiplying influences.

A European Network on Work and Organizational Psychology created in 1980 has driven many initiatives to enhance teaching and communication about research on current topics in the discipline. It eventually turned into the European Association of Work and Organizational Psychology (EAWOP). It was founded in 1991, and its first president, Robert Roe (1944–2016), a very active researcher on stress and organizational development, was able to strengthen professional training and establish links with the European Federation of Psychological Associations—a union of national psychological associations—that has provided additional support. In 2016, an Alliance for Organizational Psychology (AOP) was created, as a federation of Work, Industrial, and Organizational Psychology societies that include the IAAP special division, the EAWOP, and the SIOP, from the American Psychological Association. Its main purposes are to support the advancement of this discipline across the world, enhancing its scientific bases, promoting connections and cooperation among professionals, and strengthening interactions with society.

Organizational psychology is now a very active field involving both scientific researchers and applied professionals. It is seeking a consolidation of humanistic climates within organizations that will allow personal well-being for all members. At the same time, it seeks to keep productivity and efficiency at the highest levels as a means for creating prosperous, well-balanced, and equitable societies with the support of an updated scientific knowledge of organizations in our world.

FURTHER READING

Anderson, N., Ones, S. D., Sinangil H. K., & Viswesvaran, C. (Eds.). (2002). *Handbook of industrial, work, and organizational psychology*. Thousand Oaks, CA: SAGE.

Goleman, D. (1998). *Working with emotional intelligence*. New York: Bantham Books.

Jex, S. M., & Britt, T. V. (2008). *Organizational psychology*. Hoboken, NJ: Wiley.

Koppes, L. (Ed.). (2007). *Historical perspectives in industrial and organizational psychology*. London: Lawrence Erlbaum.

Pinder, C. C. (2008). *Work motivation in organizational behavior* (2d ed.). New York: Psychology Press.

Schultz, D., & Schultz, S. E. (2010). *Psychology and work today: An introduction to industrial and organizational psychology* (10th ed.). Hoboken, NJ: Prentice Hall.

Spector, P. E. (2011). *Industrial and organizational psychology: Research and practice* (6th ed.). Hoboken, NJ: Wiley.

Weiner, I. B., Schmitt, N., & Highhouse, S. (2012). *Handbook of psychology: Industrial and organizational psychology*. London: Wiley.

Whyte, W. H., Jr. (1957). *The organization man*. New York: Doubleday.

Yukl, G. (2010). *Leadership in organizations* (7th ed.). Upper Saddle River, NJ: Pearson.

Zedeck, S. (Ed). (2010). *APA handbook of industrial and organizational psychology*. Washington, DC: American Psychological Association.

REFERENCES

Adair, J. (1984). The Hawthorne effect: A reconsideration of the methodological artifact. *Journal of Applied Psychology, 69*, 334–345.

Arvey, R. D., & Zhang, Z. (2015). Biological factors in organizational behaviour and I-O psychology: An introduction to the special edition. *Applied Psychology, 64*(2), 281–285.

Aycan Z., & Gelfand, M. (2012). Cross-cultural organizational psychology. In S. W. J. Kozlowski (Ed.), *The Oxford handbook of organizational psychology* (Vol. I, pp. 1103–1160). New York: Oxford University Press.

Baritz, L. (1960). *The servants of power*. Middleton, CT: Wesleyan University Press.

Benjamin, L. T., & Baker, D. (2004). *From séance to science: A history of the profession of psychology in America*. Belmont, CA: Thomson Wadsworth.

Bond, M. H., & Smith, P. B. (1996). Cross-cultural organizational behavior. *Annual Review of Psychology, 47*, 205–235.

Carpintero, H. (2004). History of applied psychology. In C. Spielberger (Ed.), *Encyclopedia of applied psychology* (Vol. II, pp. 179–196). New York: Elsevier.

Cartwright, D., & Zander, A. (1974). *Dinámica de grupos. Investigación y teoría.* (*Group dynamics. Research and theory*). México: Trillas.

Cascio, W. F., & Aguinis, H. (2008). Research in industrial and organizational psychology from 1963 to 2007. *Journal of Applied Psychology, 93*, 1062–1081.

Chandler Jr., A. D. (1977). *The visible hand: The managerial revolution in American business*. Cambridge, MA: Harvard University Press.

Dorsch, F. (1963). *Geschichte und Probleme der angewandten Psychologie*. Bern, Switzerland: H. Huber Verlagt.

Dunnette, M. D., & Hough, S. L. (Eds.). (1991). *Handbook of industrial and organizational psychology* (2d ed.). Palo Alto, CA: Consulting Psychologist Press.

Fleishman, E., & Quaintance, M. (1984). *Taxonomies of human performance: The description of human tasks*. Orlando, FL: Academic Press.

Frese, M., Brantjes, A., & Hoorn, R. (2002). Psychological success factors of small scale businesses in Namibia: The roles of strategy process, entrepreneurial orientation and the environment. *Journal of Developmental Entrepreneurship, 7*(3), 259–282.

Gardner, H. (1985). *The mind's new science: A history of cognitive revolution*. New York: Basic Books.

Garmendia, J. A. (1988). La cultura de la empresa: Una aproximación teórica y practica. *Revista Española de investigaciones sociológicas, 41*, 7–23.

Gelfand, M., Erez, M., & Aycan, Z. (2007). Cross-cultural organizational behavior. *Annual Review of Psychology, 58*, 479–514.

Geuter, U. (1992). *The professionalization of psychology in Nazi Germany*. Cambridge, U.K.: Cambridge University Press.

Gould, S. J. (1981). *The mismeasure of man*. New York: Norton.

Hollway, W. (1991). *Work psychology and organizational behavior*. London: SAGE.

Katz, D., & Kahn, R. L. (1966). *The social psychology of organizations*. New York: Wiley.

Katzell, R. A., & Austin, J. T. (1992). From then to now: The development of industrial-organizational psychology in the United States. *Journal of Applied Psychology, 77*(6), 803–835.

Kliksberg, B. (1975). *El pensamiento organizativo: Del taylorismo a la teoría de la organización* (Organizational thought: From Taylorism to organizational theory). Buenos Aires: Paidós.

Koppes, L. L. (2003). Industrial-organizational psychology. In D. K. Freedheim, *Handbook of psychology. Volume I. History of psychology* (pp. 367–389). New York: Wiley.

Koppes, L. L. (Ed.). (2007). *Historical perspectives in industrial and organizational psychology*. London: Lawrence Erlbaum.

Koppes, L. L. (2015). *A brief history of the Society for Industrial and Organizational Psychology, Inc., a division of the APA* (at www.siop.org/History/historynew.aspx#narrative).

Koppes, L. L., & Pickren, W. (2007). Industrial and organizational psychology: An evolving science and practice. In L. L. Koppes (Ed.) (pp. 3–35).

Koppes, L. L., & Vinchur, A. J. (2012). A history of industrial and organizational psychology. In S. Kozlowski (Ed.). *The Oxford handbook of organizational psychology*, Vol. I. Oxford: Oxford University Press.

Latham, G., & Budworth, M. H. (2007). The study of work motivation in the 20th century. In L. Koppes (Ed.) (pp. 353–381).

Leka, S., & Houdmont, J. (Eds.). (2010). *Occupational health psychology*. Chichester, U.K.: Wiley-Blackwell.

Lomov, B. F. (1969). Engineering psychology in the USSR. In M. Cole & I. Maltzman (Eds.), *Handbook of contemporary Soviet psychology* (pp. 574–602). New York: Basic Books.

Lord, R. G., & Maher, K. (1991). Cognitive theory in industrial/organizational psychology. In Dunnette & Hough (Vol. II, pp. 1–62).

Mallart, J. (1942). *Organización científica del trabajo* (Scientific work organization). Barcelona: Labor.

Marías, J. (1987). *The structure of society*. Tuscaloosa: University of Alabama Press.

Mayo, E. (1945). *The social problems of an industrial civilization*. Boston: Harvard University Press.

McClelland, D., & Winter, D. G. (1969). *Motivating economic achievement*. New York: Free Press.

McLeish, J. (1975). *Soviet psychology: History, theory, content*. London: Methuen.

McShane, S. L., & von Glinow, M. A. (2010). *Organizational behavior: Emerging realities for the workplace revolution* (5th ed.). New York: McGraw Hill.

Misumi, J. (1985). *The behavioral science of leadership*. Ann Arbor: University of Michigan Press.

Mouzelis, N. (1968). *Organization and bureaucracy: An analysis of modern theories*. Chicago: Aldine.

Münsterberg, H. (1913). *Psychology and industrial efficiency*. Boston: Houghton Mifflin.

Münsterberg, H. (1914). *Gründzuge der psychotechnik* (Fundamentals of psychotechnology). Leipzig: Barth.

Nelson, D., & Cooper, C. L. (2007). *Positive organizational behavior*. London: SAGE.

Offermann, L. R., & Gowing, M. K. (1990). Organizations of the future: Changes and challenges. *American Psychologist, 45*(2), 95–108.

Ouchi, W. G. (1981). *Theory Z: How American business can meet the Japanese challenge*. Reading, PA: Addison-Wesley.

Pariguin, B. D. (1967). *La psicologia social como ciencia* (Social psychology as a science). Montevideo, Spain: Pueblos Unidos.

Peiró, J. M. (1983). *Psicología de la organización* (Organizational psychology). Madrid: UNED.

Peiró, J. M. (1990). *Organizaciones: Nuevas perspectivas psicosociológicas*, (Organizations: New psychosociological perspectives). Barcelona: PPU.

Peiró, J. M., & Munduate, L. (1994). Work and organizational psychology in Spain. *Applied Psychology, 43*(2), 231–274.

Piéron, H. (Ed.). (1959). *Traité de psychologie appliquée: Les grands domaines d'application de la psychologie* (Vol. VII). Paris: Presses Universitaires de France.

Porter, L. W., & Schneider, B. (2014). What was, what is, and what may be in OP/OB. *Annual Review of Organizational Psychology and Organizational Behavior, 1*, 1–21.

Quintanilla, I. (1992). *Teoria, aplicaciones y práctica de la psicologia del trabajo* (Theory, application and practice of work psychology). Valencia: Promolibro.

Ralston, D. A., Gustafson, D. J., Elsacs, P. M., Cheing, F. M., & Terpstra, R. H. (1992). Eastern values: A comparison of managers in the United States, Hong Kong and the People's Republic of China. *Journal of Applied Psychology, 77*, 664–671.

Rodríguez, A. (1992). *Psicología de las organizaciones: Teoría y método* (Organizational psychology: Theory and method). Barcelona: PPU.

Roe, R. A. (1995). Developments in Eastern Europe and work and organizational psychology. *International Review of Industrial and Organizational Psychology, 10*, 275–349.

Rüegsegger, R. (1986). *Die geschichte der angewandten psychologie, 1900–1940*. Bern, Switzerland: Hans Huber.

Salanova, M., & Rodriguez-Sanchez, A. (2009). *Looking for the positive side of occupational health at work* (e-book). Castellon, Spain: Universitat Jaume I.

Salgado, J. F. (2001). Some landmarks of 100 years of scientific personnel selection at the beginning of the new century. *International Journal of Selection and Assessment, 9*(1–2), 3–8.

Scheid, J. C. (1987). *Los grandes autores en administración* (Great authors in administration): Barcelona: Orbis.

Servan-Schreiber, J. J. (1967). *Le défi americain* (The American challenge). Paris: Denoël.

Shimmin, S., & van Strien, P. J. (1998). History of the psychology of work and organization. In P. J. D. Drenth, Henk Thierry and Charles Johannes Wolff (Eds.), *Handbook of work and organizational psychology* (2d ed., Vol. I, pp. 71–99). New York: Psychology Press.

Stavrianos, L. S. (1991). *A global history. From prehistory to the present* (5th ed.). Englewood, NJ: Prentice Hall.

Taylor. F. W. (1947). *Scientific management*. New York: Harper.

Warr, P. (2007). Some historical developments in I-O psychology outside the United States. In L. Koppes (Ed.) (pp. 81–107).

Wilpert, B. (1990). How European is work and organizational psychology? In P. J. D. Drenth et al. (Eds.), *European perspectives in psychology* (pp. 3–20). New York: Wiley.

Helio Carpintero

EVIDENCE-BASED DECISION-MAKING AND PRACTICE IN ORGANIZATIONS

INTRODUCTION

Managerial and organizational decision-making encompasses, inter alia, decisions about operations, resource allocation, leadership, human resources, governance, and strategy. These decision contexts are often characterized by significant causal ambiguity and complexity. However, relying on one source of evidence only (intuition, for example) will not provide sufficient information to adequately address most complex or "wicked" management and organizational problems. Evidence-based decision-making and practice (EDMP) in organizations, which is more commonly referred to as "evidence-based management" in the literature, involves using critical thinking and the best available evidence from multiple sources to identify problems and opportunities and their best solutions. In this sense, it draws on a plurality of information and sources to test claims and assumptions in order to identify organizational practice problems, opportunities, and their solutions. It considers relevant scientific evidence, stakeholder views and concerns, expert and professional opinion, and data and information inside and outside the organization including at an industry level and their attendant levels of trustworthiness. The terminology "evidence-based decision-making and practice in organizations" will be used to signal that evidence-based management is much broader than is implied, and that it encompasses different domains of business, management, and organizational decision-making and practice. It more specifically includes decisions and practice in organizations that address leadership, governance, business, marketing, management, strategy, change, operational decisions, and practice problems and opportunities. Importantly, the inclusion of "decision-making" helps ensure an understanding that EDMP in organizations encompasses both the elements and cognitive operations in decision-making, as well as practice, which involves the translation of evidence into practice, implementation, and the assessment of its efficacy. In this sense, it includes problematization, evidence-gathering, problem-solving, evidence translation, implementation, and evaluation elements.

Evidence-based practice in medicine came about in response to an overreliance on clinical expertise and intuition and a concomitant under-use of scientific evidence (Jenicek et al., 2011). In a controlled comparative analysis, physicians participating in continuing medical education aimed at improving scientific knowledge, skills, and practice decisions were more likely to make more evidence-based rather than intuitive clinical choices than those who did not (Casebeer et al., 2010). Strong appeals for a more evidence-based approach in management and organizations have been made as a response to decision neglect and suboptimal decisions made on the basis of limited and poor-quality information, and human errors in unaided decision-making and judgment (Pfeffer & Sutton, 2006; Rousseau, 2006, 2020). Such appeals are themselves supported by research indicating that managers make better informed decisions when they take a more evidence-based approach. For example, getting managers to gather multiple sources of critically appraised evidence to test claims, assumptions, and hypotheses, and to think more probabilistically, can help improve decision quality (Tetlock & Gardner, 2015) and entrepreneurial decisions (Camuffo et al., 2020).

Using evidence to take decisions, and being *perceived* to take decisions based on trustworthy evidence, is also an important, yet overlooked, leadership attribute. It is the basis upon which managerial and organizational decisions are perceived to be made that can greatly impact organizational behavior. Indeed, according to research by Jepsen and Rousseau (2022), the impacts of EDMP in organizations, particularly on employees who are critical to implementing decisions, warrant attention in leadership development. In their cross-sectional study of 308 aged-care employees, perceptions of managers' use of evidence in decision-making was positively associated with a number of work-related outcomes, including trust in supervisor, leader-member-exchange, and work-based learning.

Yet, management and organizational decisions and practice ostensibly reflect an entrenched and highly contagious "best practice" logic, decoupled from critical thought and trustworthy scientific research (Speicher-Bocija & Adams, 2012; Yaniv & Choshen-Hillel, 2012). In a survey of 2,789 managers in the Netherlands, the United Kingdom, the United States, Australia, and Belgium, 91% reported that they based their decisions on personal experience, 64% on intuition, very few made decisions based on scientific evidence (27%), and even fewer (14%) had ever read a peer-reviewed journal article (see Barends et al., 2017). The use of off-the-shelf products, fads, and quick fixes has resulted in the wastage of resources and the destruction of value in organizations. For instance, the misuse of personality-typing tools, training in emotional intelligence, poor selection methods, and a focus on employee engagement and millennial differences are just some examples of faddish organizational practices bereft of a strong evidence base. Another example of a prevalent yet evidence-decoupled management practice is the use of implicit-bias training to counteract discrimination and prejudice despite some research suggesting there are problems with the efficacy of such training (Tetlock & Mitchell, 2009).

Leadership development is often practiced in a faddish and evidence-decoupled way, even within universities. In interviews with 60 academic directors of leadership centers in universities, it was consistently reported that leadership development curricula are seldom evidence-based and evaluated (Leroy et al., 2022). This qualitative study further indicated that even in a business school context, there is a lack of understanding of what it means in practice to take an evidence-based approach. Leadership development curricula tend to inculcate claims about practice efficacy that are based on a small number of case studies, or a single empirical study, and not necessarily the best available evidence (Leroy et al., 2022). Also, in business school contexts and in practice, the concept of triangulation, and using multiple sources of evidence to test a claim or assumption, gets overlooked. Besides scientific evidence, evidence-based practice in management also considers stakeholders, professional expertise, and organizational and industry data as sources of evidence.

The focus on "best practice" in case studies, a legacy of the Harvard model of management education, further imbues a "craft" model of management education rather than a more scientific model teaching what works in practice (Speicher-Bocija & Adams, 2012). This is compounded by the lack of clear andragogic development and specification of the criterion domain (Knowledge, Skills, and Application of skills and knowledge [KSA] requirements) in the scholarship and field. Extant literature on evidence-based management does not provide an in-depth understanding of the KSAs and the curriculum framework that enables it (Briner et al., 2022). To this end, a nested capabilities model of EDMP in organizations is proposed, with a consideration of the hierarchical relationships and interdependencies among capabilities.

This article makes some much-needed contributions to organizational practice and decision-making, education, and scholarship. First, drawing on existing conceptualizations, it defines EDMP in organizations, evinces its key concepts and principles, and addresses common misconceptions. Second, it distills the key systemic barriers to the uptake and use of evidence, and the successful implementation of EDMP in organizations. The existing fragmented understanding of these barriers prompts us to develop a framework to provide a deeper and more structured understanding of the organizational- and individual-level barriers.

Informed by this framework, an EDMP capabilities framework for teaching and practicing EDMP in organizations is introduced. Building on extant work in this nascent field, the framework specifies the core and functional capability requirements for better-informed managerial decision-making through enhanced decision quality, decision awareness, and cognitive repair. The framework represents a transformative and critical paradigm shift in management and organization decision-making and practice and education as well as the unlearning of entrenched patterns of thinking and behaving that have limited progress in practice. By implication, the framework contributes to literature on decision-making and judgment that is informed by behavioral decision theory (see Kahneman, 2013), by elucidating the steps to debias decision-making, improve decision awareness, and circumvent decision neglect. Following a discussion of the capabilities framework, some important avenues for management research, practice, and education are canvassed.

A BRIEF OVERVIEW OF THE HISTORY OF EVIDENCE-BASED PRACTICE

Evidence-based practice originated in medicine in the 1990s to improve clinical decision-making, practice, and medical research (Guyatt et al., 1992). This approach emerged in response to an overreliance on idiosyncratic clinical expertise, rather than trustworthy scientific research amenable to nomothetic or more generalizable principles for clinical practice, diagnosis, and treatment.

Evidence-based medicine has been defined as "the conscientious and judicious use of current best evidence from clinical care research in the management of individual patients" (Sackett et al., 1996, p. 71). There are two central principles. The first is that *triangulating multiple sources of evidence* greatly improves clinical decision-making and practice and as such, clinical expertise should not be relied upon exclusively, as it is merely one source of evidence. Second, the notion of the *best available evidence* recognizes the limitations of different sources of information to inform clinical judgment. Decision-makers need to *critically appraise* the quality, reliability, and validity of the information they use to take decisions. Accuracy in causal inference, in particular, necessitates the use of information that is trustworthy and has a high level of internal validity. For this reason, the use of research from randomized control trials, systematic reviews, and meta-analyses with controlled studies are a preferred basis for causal inference. Evidence-based practice principles have since been applied in other domains, including nursing, social work, policing, education, and psychology, albeit somewhat inconsistently, particularly in clinical psychology (for more in-depth historical accounts of evidence-based practice in psychology, see Beck et al., 2014; Lilienfeld & Basterield, 2020; Spring, 2007).

EDMP IN ORGANIZATIONS: DEFINITION AND KEY FEATURES

Evidence-based practice has also been extended to the domain of management, leadership, organizational behavior, and human resource management practice. In her presidential address in 2005 to the Academy of Management, Denise Rousseau noted that management practice often reflects bad advice from touted management gurus and consultants rather than being grounded in scientific principles and trustworthy research (Rousseau, 2006). She also asserted that it is the very nature of decisions and practice in organizations, including long lags in effects of practice, complex cause-and-effect relationships, and complexities in implementation that necessitates the combination of local organizational knowledge with scientific principles (Rousseau, 2006). In organizations, evidence-based practice (or more simply referred to as evidence-based management) is defined as "the conscientious (effort), explicit (transparent) and judicious (critical of quality) use of evidence from multiple sources to increase the likelihood of a favourable outcome" (Briner et al., 2009, p. 19). It provides managers and leaders with the necessary structure and scaffolding to improve decision quality primarily through the combination of critical thinking with the best available evidence which helps address the limitations of unaided human judgment (Rousseau, 2020) and counteracts several constraints and limitations of human cognition (including judgment and information-processing). This article contributes to the evidence-based practice literature by articulating and extending the capabilities Rousseau (2006, 2020) believes managers and leaders need to acquire should they adopt evidence-based management.

Four Sources of Evidence.   Drawing on multiple sources of evidence, not just exclusively relying on a single source, is an important hallmark of evidence-based management. In evidence-based medicine and psychology, the sources of evidence include clinical expertise, scientific research, and patient preferences and values (Spring, 2007). In an organizational context, there are four key sources of evidence: (a) scientific and research literatures, (b) professional and personal expertise and experience-based knowledge, (c) organizational facts and figures, and (d) stakeholder views and perspectives regarding the problem or practical issue (see Barends et al., 2014). Multiple sources of evidence are used to answer questions and test claims and assumptions about problems and opportunities, and their best possible solutions in organizations. Decision quality improves when managers can make better decisions, risk assessments, and predictions because they do not rely exclusively on their own professional judgment but also on aggregate experience and information from multiple sources (Yaniv & Choshen-Hillel, 2012). This subsequently elevates the significance of *triangulation* (through multiple sources of evidence) as a fundamental principle of evidence-based practice. It is a research strategy used toward developing a comprehensive understanding of phenomena, and testing validity through the convergence of information from different sources in qualitative research (Patton, 1999). The process of triangulation is not linear with one occurrence. Rather, in EDMP it occurs iteratively to identify the problem and then to identify solutions. An additional benefit of relying on multiple sources of evidence to take decisions in organizations is that it reduces the risk of myopia, misdiagnosis, and poor practice and implementation because the information at hand is the best available or more trustworthy, and is also more variegated in terms of depth, breadth, scope, temporality, and contextual relevance. For example, the science may proffer information and insights on what works and what does not work in practice; however, on its own, it may not provide sufficient information about current and future challenges, dynamics, and discontinuities facing the organization.

Furthermore, there are problems that when translated into an answerable question may pertain to causal effects (more hypothesis-led) or non-effects (more exploratory) or descriptions (descriptive). For example, the question of *what impact does increasing job satisfaction have on task performance?* is a cause-and-effect question that relies more on evidence with a high level of internal validity. Therefore, more primacy is given to scientific studies with research designs conducive to causal inference such as randomized controlled trials and systematic reviews of controlled studies. It is also likely that, at the solution level, the most likely question to be posed is a cause-and-effect question. A question about frequency or incidence rates, however, may be best addressed via the descriptive analysis of organizational data. While the nature of the question and claim being addressed is an important consideration in EDMP in organizations, equally important is the availability of evidence from multiple sources.

Best Available Evidence. The Center for Evidence-Based Management (CEBMa), recognizes that EDMP in organizations can sometimes be impacted by the availability of evidence from multiple sources. In decision and practice problem contexts in organizations, the most methodologically appropriate evidence to test a claim may simply not be available. That is, scientific evidence with high levels of internal validity may not exist to test a claim about the efficacy of an intervention. Likewise, organizational data may not exist to more accurately diagnose problems. It could be in such cases that only stakeholder and expert evidence is available. In these circumstances, particularly if the question or claim pertains to the efficacy of practice and interventions, pilots and controlled field experiments can be conducted to generate additional evidence to validate decision-making and practice (see Dietz et al., 2014).

Six Skills in EDMP in Organizations. The CEBMa delineates six skills (based on the five skills identified in medicine; see Strauss et al., 2005) required to practice evidence-based management: ask, acquire, appraise, aggregate, apply, and assess. Alongside domain-specific knowledge, these skills are more precisely a set of capabilities that also include specific knowledge related to discrete activities that encompass procedural knowledge and skills that occur before, during, and after decision-making (Rousseau & Gunia, 2016). These skills also represent steps or a sequence of decision-making operations in evidence-based practice. *Asking* is about identifying and translating a problem, claim, or opportunity into an answerable question or a hypothesis. This is a particularly critical capability in evidence-based management because it enables decision-making that is hypothesis-led rather than data-driven. *Acquiring* is about the retrieval of evidence to address a question, claim, or hypothesis in relation to a practice problem. *Appraising* involves critically gauging the methodological quality and appropriateness of evidence acquired to address a practice problem. *Aggregating* involves pulling together and weighing up the evidence. *Applying* involves translating evidence into practice, and *assessing* involves determining the value of outcomes of the evidence-based decision taken.

COMMON MISCONCEPTIONS ABOUT EDMP IN ORGANIZATIONS

The advocacy of EDMP in management and organizational studies has not been without controversy and challenges, both of which reside not only in misconceptions about evidence-based management, but also in the misreading of its definition right from the beginning to ultimately impact the perception of its purview.

A major opposition to EDMP in organizations comes from several critics, including Morrell and Learmonth (2015) and Tourish (2013), arguing that its definition is too narrow and inflexible considering the diversity of perspectives in which management problems can be understood (Morrell & Learmonth, 2015). In fact, this denunciation naturally morphs into another misconception about evidence-based practice being couched in the supremacy of scientific research evidence to the detriment of the knowledge and expertise of practitioners. The first misconception thus ascribes a dogmatic label to evidence-based practice that limits the understanding of management problems under scrutiny, and ultimately negatively impacts the solution, decision-making process, and results. Interestingly, the insistence by Barends et al. (2014) that the definition of evidence-based management refers to the combination of the practitioner's experience with other sources of evidence to make decisions for better outcomes has met with critics' own bidding and interpretation that scientific evidence is not only supreme, but it can be based on any reasonable evidence. The latter criticism is a misconception easily clarified by the fact that evidence-based management is based on best available evidence made possible by one of its requirements, that is, the evaluation of the trustworthiness of all relevant evidence through the grading of its quality. Unfortunately, the latter requirement has given rise to another misconception that an evidence-based approach is all about numbers and statistics. In fact, an understanding of basic statistical concepts and statistical thinking can help in the evaluation of some types of evidence, but evidence-based management does not equate to statistics according to the Center for Evidence-Based Management (Barends et al., 2014). The natural ensuing misconception thus relates to the claim that only high-quality evidence can help in decision-making, when, in fact, evidence-based practice acknowledges that in some cases (contexts where changes are rapid and frequent) the practitioner must work with limited evidence supplemented with ongoing experience.

A ramification of the misconception about the reliance of evidence-based practice on quantitative data is that it also completely disregards qualitative data. However, valid and relevant evidence to provide an answer to the problem may also be of a qualitative nature depending on the type of question asked. Such an approach counters the popular misconception that evidence-based practice or management devalues stories or narrative forms of knowledge (Morrell & Learmonth, 2015). In fact, by giving due consideration to context and mindset, qualitative data in EDMP contribute to the quality of evidence, which, when made sense of, in turn help practitioners make decisions. Evidence in that sense can be of a plural nature. Furthermore, triangulation, which involves drawing on multiple sources of evidence to address different types of questions and claims related to problems and solutions in organizations, requires *methodological pluralism* via mixed-methods research involving both secondary and primary sources of data (see Alavi et al., 2018). This means that qualitative and quantitative research methods are combined to work in relationship to each other, in order to promote a holistic and integrative and unified understanding of social and organizational phenomena (see Alavi et al., 2018, p. 531). This approach affords decision-makers with methods to more systematically acquire evidence from different sources with variegated depth and breadth that address different types of questions about cause-and-effect, non-effects and processes, mediating mechanisms, and boundary conditions relevant to practice. This does, however, require knowledge about which research designs and methods of acquiring evidence are aligned to, and methodologically appropriate for, addressing particular types of questions and claims.

IN THE ABSENCE OF EDMP IN ORGANIZATIONS

In the absence of EDMP, organizations risk making suboptimal managerial decisions and practice solutions. It is therefore important to recognize and understand the key organizational and psychological barriers and sources of resistance to EDMP in organizations which is a representation of critical thinking and scientific thinking and decision-making more generally. A collective and integrative understanding of these barriers is lacking in the extant literature. Further, the absence and lack of adoption of EDMP in organizations can be understood at two levels of interacting organizational and psychological processes: (a) organizational norms and socialization processes and (b) unaided individual and group decision-making and judgment processes that are reflected in certain patterns of decision-making and practice. These processes are included in the framework shown in Figure 1, and work in concert to precipitate decision neglect, which, in turn, results in suboptimal managerial and organizational decision and practice outcomes.

Organizational Norms and Socialization Processes. Barriers (and enablers) of EDMP and the use and uptake of evidence can be examined at the organizational level and can be represented as elements of organizational norms and socialization processes.

Internalization of a "Craft" Model of Management Practice. The key misconceptions about EDMP suggest that a very different mindset and way of thinking and doing is needed in organizations—one that represents a significant departure from the dominant logic in management practice and education (Rousseau & Mccarthy, 2007). When considering management education and curricula, it becomes clear that most managers are socialized and inculcated in a *craft* model of management (Speicher-Bocija & Adams, 2012). In management, a prevailing mindset exists (socialized in management and leadership development and education programs), that it is important to emulate the behaviors and practices of high performing organizations or the best practitioners. This reflects a "craft" model, rather than a "science" model, of management (Speicher-Bocija & Adams, 2012). The problem with this approach is that it takes critical thinking out of management decision-making and practice. Managers therefore do not question the efficacy of best practice prescriptions and merely mimic what they think works in other organizations or what has worked for them in the past. EDMP in organizations directly challenges this approach in favor of decisions about problems and solutions being based on the *best available evidence*. Through a craft model of management education, business and management students learn to think in terms of principles from case studies rather than nomothetic and generalizable principles from scientific research and theory. This means management decisions and practice reflect a "best practice" logic resulting in *systematic uncritical emulation.*

The reliance on the best available evidence thus overrides the orthodoxy of best practice in management practice and organizational psychology. Rather than completely defenestrate a craft model of management entirely, it may be that such an approach is helpful for the development of specific skills or routine decisions and practices only, rather than being applied to complex decision and practice domains.

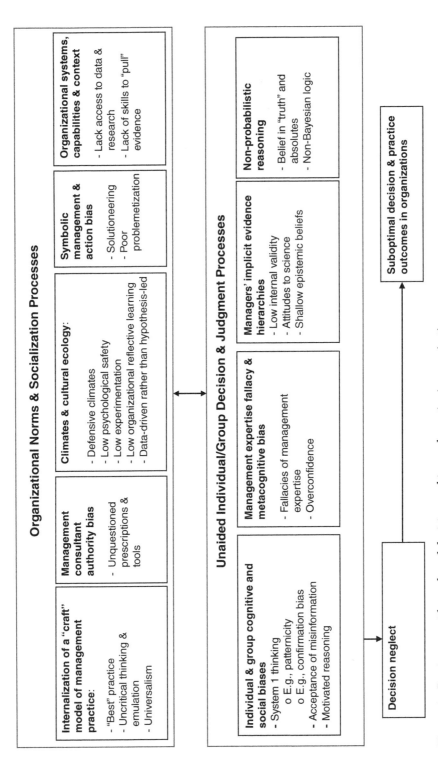

Figure 1. Barriers to evidence-based decision-making and practice in organizations.

Action Bias and Solutioneering.   Organizations can take a fairly reactive approach to their management practice problems, creating scope for action bias—an artifact of uncritical thinking. An action bias occurs when managers want to be seen to be doing something rather than nothing to address a practice issue or problem. Likewise, engaging in *symbolic management* ostensibly means that management decisions are highly reactive and reflect "box ticking" and "rubber stamping" rather than a genuine attempt to address the root causes of a problem. Relatedly, *solutioneering* can serve as a barrier to EDMP in organizations. This means that a solution to a management practice problem can be identified without carefully considering and understanding the magnitude, urgency, and root causes of problems (James 1980). That is, a solution may be applied to a problem that is ill-defined or that does not exist. In essence, it is a form of uncritical thinking, and the consequence is that management problems do not get adequately addressed, which can create internal cynicism about organizational change efforts and programs.

Management Consultant Authority Bias.   As shown in Figure 1, management consultant authority bias may also represent a barrier to EDMP in organizations. A quick and blind deference to the potentially evidence-decoupled advice and prescriptions and tools of reputable management consultancies and management gurus can also thwart evidence-based practice. Highly marketed off-the-shelf products offering a one-size-fits-all approach further entrench uncritical thinking, solutioneering, and contextually insensitive practice in organizations.

Climates and Cultural Ecology.   The prevailing organizational climates and cultural ecology of the organization, which encompass prevailing beliefs, norms, and behaviors in an organization, can impact the uptake and the adoption of evidence-based practice. Resistance to EDMP in organizations can also be explained by the prevalence of *defensive* climates in organizations that encompass low levels of psychological safety, innovation, experimentation, constructive questioning, and more generally aversion to change (Potworowski & Green, 2011). Constructive climates characterized by norms of achievement and motivation, and open to change and critical questioning, are associated with more favorable attitudes toward the adoption of EDMP, compared to defensive climates that maintain the status quo and are resistant to change and innovation (Aarons & Sawitsky, 2006). Collective attitudes toward the use of evidence and scientific research can also impact the prevalence of EDMP. According to a survey of managers across the globe, having an organizational climate that is supportive of the use of scientific research is perceived by some managers to be critical to its implementation (see Barends et al., 2017).

Data-Driven Rather Than Hypothesis-Led Decision-Making.   There is an internalized and socialized view in management practice that data-driven decisions confer a high level of decision validity, accountability, and legitimacy. However, the real danger of this approach is that it becomes all about the data and thus decision-makers neglect other sources of evidence. There are, unfortunately, several problems associated with data-driven decision-making. First, data become evidence only when they "test" a claim, assumption, or hypothesis in relation to a management practice problem. Second, there is a risk of analysis paralysis and metric fixation (see Muller, 2019). As a consequence, organizations can gather too much data and therefore waste a lot of money collecting, using, or maintaining data as an end in itself. Indeed, metrics can be used in ways that mimic science (Muller, 2019) and are decoupled from the problem and issue. According to Muller (2019), a *quantitative fallacy* results when organizations focus only on things that can be easily measured and disregard or ignore things that cannot. Furthermore, it is important for organizations to take an evidence-based and hypothesis-led rather than data-driven approach, and collect and analyze data only in the context of the management practice problem being solved. This also elevates the role of theory in practice, which in and outside the evidence-based practice literature has a fairly sanguine role. As a source of evidence, scientific studies represent the symbiosis between theory and research, with theory and related concepts, and nomological networks in particular, providing a way to understand and test complex social phenomena and particularly the mechanisms underlying cause and effect relationships (see Alavi et al., 2018). Theories and related concepts in the organizational sciences can help practitioners understand how and why things are the way they are in organizations, particularly the causal mechanisms linking interventions to outcomes. This knowledge then helps organizations develop logic models and theories of change so that practice in organizations is more purposive and evidence-based.

Organizational Systems, Capabilities, and Context. There may be other internal and external constraints on an organization to adopt EDMP. Organizational systems, including infrastructure and policies, and the context of the organization (the economic, legal, institutional, and cultural environments) can also limit the uptake and implementation of EDMP in organizations. It may also be the case that while an organization may wish to subscribe to EDMP, it may simply lack the capabilities, particularly in the upper echelons where decision rights are concentrated, to use and apply evidence. Leaders and managers are critical to role modeling EDMP and enabling climates that support it (Jepsen & Rousseau, 2022). More specifically, if organizations lack access to databases to "pull" scientific evidence, or reliable and valid data to diagnose problems, it will be difficult to enact evidence-based practice. Likewise, if they do not have the requisite skills to acquire and critically appraise evidence, they will have little choice but to rely on data and information that is potentially invalid and unreliable, and this in turn diminishes decision validity.

Unaided Individual and Group Decision and Judgment Processes.
To enable more EDMP in organizations, it is necessary to first understand the four key artifacts of unaided individual and group decision-making and judgment.

Individual and Group Cognitive and Social Biases. Nobel Prize winner Daniel Kahneman (2013) described two modes of thinking governing judgment and decision-making, which he referred to as *System 1* and *System 2 thinking*. He described System 1 as the brain's fast, intuitive, and emotional approach to thinking. This mode of thinking mainly occurs in the limbic system. System 1 operates automatically and very quickly, with little or no effort and no sense of voluntary control (Kahneman, 2013, p. 20). In contrast, System 2 thinking is the brain's slow, deliberate, and rational approach to thinking. System 2 allocates attention to the effortful mental activities that also demand focus and concentration (Kahneman, 2013, p. 20). However, it is System 1 that dominates thinking and is most influential in judgment. Though, as Kahneman suggested, the use of System 1 is adaptive, given that using System 2 would be exhaustive and resource-depleting if used all the time; thus, System 1 is sufficient for routine decisions or decisions where the stakes are low or when creative thinking is required to generate new ideas. However, System 2 thinking is important to solve practice problems that are highly complex and in which there is a high degree of uncertainty and risk.

System 1 thinking can give rise to a number of social and cognitive biases, including, for example, confirmation bias, recency error, patternicity, groupthink, and stereotyping and reinforces cognitive processes leading to acceptance of misinformation (Kahneman, 2013; Lewandowsky et al., 2012). These human cognitive constraints highlight the frailties of decision-making in organizations and have been empirically supported by decades of research informed by behavioral decision theory. The Carnegie School was instrumental in developing the concept of decision neglect in organizations to encapsulate the limited search and appraisal of information, incomplete survey of alternatives, selective attention, and failure to draw on the full range of resources and information available to make a decision (Cyert et al., 1956). Further work on motivated reasoning has highlighted that managers may be predisposed to selectively search for or interpret information in ways that confirm existing beliefs, expectations, and assumptions, and to ignore information to the contrary (Tetlock, 1983). According to Lewandowsky and others (2012) these processes also mean that misinformation can be quite resistant to correction and retraction, which is referred to as the continued influence effect.

Management Expertise Fallacy and Metacognitive Bias. Uncritical and automatic thinking in managerial decisions and judgment is further exacerbated by a *management expertise fallacy* or *metacognitive bias* where managers overstate their own rationality in decision-making (Highhouse, 2008). A management expertise fallacy can explain an overconfidence in one's experience causing decision neglect. Even a manager with 20 years of experience is prone to decision neglect and cognitive and social biases. In a clinical domain, experience is not enough to safeguard against systematic errors in decision-making (Jenicek et al., 2011). In any case, there are limits to which management expertise can be developed, as management expertise is inherently unreliable. Expertise is best developed through prolonged practice, highly controlled conditions and environments, and regular direct and objective feedback. As suggested by Barends and Rousseau (2018) expertise in management is hard to develop given the nature of management decision problems, issues, and opportunities. These are not the conditions under which most managers operate. The outcomes of managerial decisions and actions are not immediate and easy to measure. Relying on one's management expertise exclusively, rather than taking into account stakeholder concerns and scientific research, may also serve a functional purpose in that the decision-maker has greater control of decisions and their implementation.

Managers' Implicit Evidence Hierarchies. Managers' *implicit evidence hierarchies* can also mean that managers privilege case studies' anecdotal evidence, idiosyncratic small sample successes, over more generalizable, nomothic trustworthy scientific evidence. Experience and expert opinion are at the apex of the hierarchy along with best practice case studies. However, these sources of evidence on their own are not conducive to causal inference and generalization. This suggests that *managers' epistemic beliefs* may privilege knowledge that is not easily amenable to legitimate causal inference. Lilienfeld and Basterfield (2020) discussed the need to shift from naive empiricism to systematic empiricism that relies on scientific knowledge. Managers' shallow epistemic beliefs mean that they may not pay attention to the trustworthiness of their evidence. Managers also tend to have erroneous perceptions about generalizability and applicability of scientific research, thinking that only recent research has value. This recency bias means that they sometimes discredit and ignore earlier robust and trustworthy evidence, as well as misunderstand the cumulative nature of scientific knowledge.

Non-Probabilistic Reasoning. Managers' beliefs are important inputs for decision and judgments. Having absolute rather than degrees of belief is the norm rather than the exception. This means that beliefs can be dichotomous in nature. For instance, one believes something to be true or not true. However, having absolute certainty in something or in a claim means that beliefs are static and cannot be updated in light of new information. This has some very important and often overlooked implications for decision-making. This non-probabilistic and non-conditional reasoning is likely to result in an extension neglect or a base-rate fallacy, where important parameters for valuations and forecasting, including sample size, base rates, scope, duration, and incidence rates, are ignored, thus leading to misdetection or misdiagnosis (Kahneman, 2013). Thinking more in terms of probabilities and likelihoods than in absolute truth and certainty, means that decisions are taken based on information that is assumed to reflect fact and truth (Barends & Rousseau, 2018). Thinking in terms of probabilities and likelihoods, which is more Bayesian thinking, allows for the integration of evidence and information while considering the uncertainty and limitations associated with each source evidence (Ashby & Smith, 2000) or the possibility that information may be unreliable or invalid. Having a clearer and more in-depth understanding of such barriers is important for both the specification and the development of valid capabilities for EDMP and is therefore crucial for leadership and management curricula development.

INTRODUCING AN EDMP IN ORGANIZATIONS CAPABILITIES FRAMEWORK

Taking an evidence-based approach to decisions and practice in organizations requires the development of some important functional capabilities while reinforcing core capabilities. As discussed, EDMP in organizations requires a shift in the epistemic beliefs and thinking of managers and represents a significant departure from the dominant logic and mode of practice in management. To drive that shift toward performance effectiveness in a particular domain requires capability, which is a set of knowledge and skills, and the ability to apply said knowledge and skills as required.

Figure 2 presents an integrative and transdisciplinary EDMP in organizations process and capabilities framework. This framework describes the capability requirements as well as provides a structured decision-making process for evidence-based practice in organizations. The capabilities framework has three key aspects: (a) sources of evidence, (b) functional EBP capabilities, and (c) the hitherto underexplored core capabilities. The framework extends the specification of foundational and functional competencies of Rousseau and Gunia (2016) by (a) elucidating the role of metacognitions and (b) providing a more explicit specification, as well as finer granulation, of foundational and core evidence-based management capabilities.

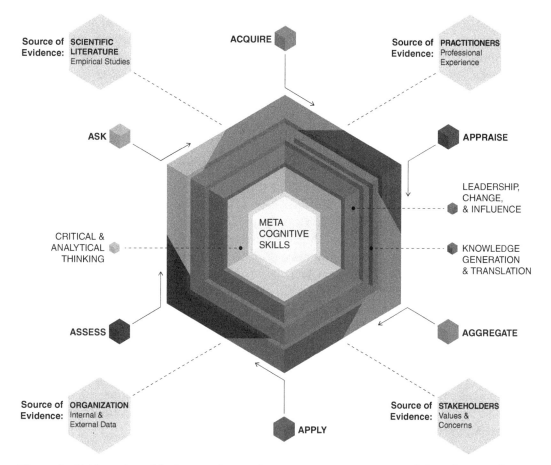

Figure 2. Evidence-based decision-making and practice in organizations capabilities framework.
Source: Developed by Capezio and L'Espoir Decosta and designed by Camilo Potocnjak-Oxman.

Both functional and foundational skills are dependent on the depth and breadth of domain-specific knowledge. Domain knowledge helps facilitate critical thinking, appraisal, and interpretation of evidence (Bailin, 2002; Rousseau & Gunia, 2016). The framework, which has broader appeal to evidence-based practice in other fields, makes explicit the capabilities required to take more evidence-based decisions.

Functional Capabilities. The six As that appear in Figure 2 represent the functional capabilities and steps required in evidence-based decision-making and practice. These capabilities build on core capabilities, and are also dependent on the depth and breadth of domain-specific knowledge (Rousseau & Gunia, 2016).

Ask. Asking requires problematization skills that include identifying the organizational problem by drawing on the four sources of evidence, and accurately translating a practical issue or problem into an answerable question. Managers need to be able to ask the right questions to identify both the problem and the solution. According to Barends and Rousseau (2018) these questions that need to be asked by managers must include *What is the organizational evidence for the assumed problem? What are the assumed causes and organizational consequences of the problem? Do stakeholders agree with the problem definition? How urgent is the problem? What is known in the scientific literature about the key causes of the problem?* In other words, decision-makers need to understand the nature of the problem as a network of relationships including its assumed causes, consequences, mechanisms, and moderators or boundaries in the organization. Asking the right questions includes questions about how dependable and reliable information is.

Acquire.   Acquiring involves search skills to efficiently retrieve relevant evidence including scientific, organizational, professional or experiential, and stakeholder evidence, depending on the problem under scrutiny. Decision-makers need to know where to source evidence to test their assumptions about the problem, and this means they need knowledge about both qualitative and quantitative research methods to know how to acquire the relevant and best evidence from different sources. For example, acquiring evidence from stakeholders means asking them about their perspective on the problem, including its urgency and severity. Having knowledge of different research methods and designs can help decision-makers target different types of scientific studies depending on their needs and the type of question they are asking.

Knowledge of different scientific databases is important when searching for scientific studies relevant to a problem or opportunity. Knowledge of search techniques, including Boolean operators and methodological filters, can help retrieve particular types of studies, for example meta-analyses (Barends & Rousseau, 2018). Decision-makers also need to know where to access organizational or industry data and information relevant to the problem or opportunity. This requires knowledge about the organization's business information systems and human resources information systems, or what industry data is available.

Appraise.   Appraising involves judging the trustworthiness and relevance of the evidence (i.e., scientific, organizational, professional, and stakeholder evidence). The notion of best available evidence in evidence-based management requires decision-makers to have some basic knowledge of research methodologies, particularly to both acquire and appraise scientific evidence. A critical step in the appraisal of evidence means that decision-makers need to know how to appraise the *methodological appropriateness* of the evidence to gauge its *trustworthiness*. In identifying problems and their best solutions, different types of questions are asked, requiring information with certain properties. Methodological appropriateness is about establishing whether information obtained is suitable for addressing the type of question asked. For example, managers may often want to know whether a particular course of action is effective or has been shown to have the desired practical impact as a way to mitigate risk. This type of question is about cause-and-effect. As such, decision-makers need to be able to ascertain the internal validity of their evidence to be able to draw legitimate inferences about the practical effects or impacts of an intervention. Other types of questions about the frequency of events in the organization, for example, do not require information with high levels of internal validity, nor do questions about how stakeholders feel about a particular course of action or change program. Questions about people's opinions, perceptions, and experiences with existing organizational practices, for example, *What do you think the organization needs to do in order to reduce bullying?* or questions exploring processes such as *How does an event or outcome occur and through what mechanisms?* (see Barends & Rousseau, 2018), are non-effect questions.

Aggregate. Aggregating involves weighing and pulling together the evidence pertaining to a problem and its solution. This requires summarizing and integrating different types of critically appraised evidence. Scientific evidence can be aggregated by using methodologies such as systematic reviews meta-analysis, rapid appraisals of evidence (REAs), and critically appraised topics (CAT) (see Barends & Rousseau, 2018). Both REAs and CATs are expedient forms of systematic reviews.

However, while methods exist to aggregate scientific evidence, formal methods to aggregate different sources of evidence are not well established. To diagnose practice problems or opportunities, scientific evidence needs to be integrated with other available evidence from the local context, experts, and stakeholder values and concerns. One method to aggregate multiple and sometimes conflicting sources of evidence, is to use Bayes's Theorem to estimate probabilities of outcomes given the available evidence (Barends & Rousseau, 2018). It can be used to aggregate evidence and estimate the probability of a claim or assumption in light of evidence at hand. Another way to pull evidence from different sources together is through a logic model. Figure 3 provides a template for a logic model that has several important features,

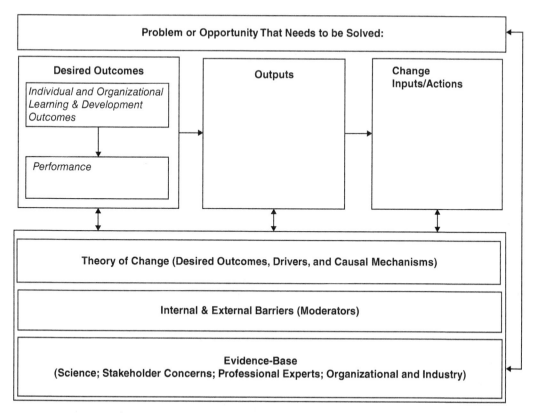

Figure 3. Logic model template for evidence-based practice.

including the specification of the desired behavior and outcomes, and the inputs, processes, and outputs through which desired outcomes are achieved. Not only can it be used as a tool to pull together different sources of evidence pertaining to a problem and its solution, but it is also a way to track and evaluate the outcomes of the decision taken or program of change specified in the logic model. Importantly, the logic model specifies key internal and external barriers to implementation, as well as assumptions underpinning an evidence-based theory of change encompassing the process and mechanisms through which inputs translate into desired outcomes and specified important boundary conditions. The theory of change is likely to be integrative and multi-theoretic for complex problems involving social and organizational phenomena, and the specific theories invoked will likely depend on the dependent variables or independent variables relevant to the practice problem.

Apply. Applying as a functional capability involves adapting relevant principles from the best available evidence to the contexts of practice. The evidence does not self-translate into practice in the local context or organization, nor does it automatically apply and take stock of the organization's internal and external complexities (Barends & Rousseau, 2018). Evidence does need to be translated into a set of practices, activities, and interventions that consider the unique social, environmental, cultural, and political system factors that can impact practice. The logic model framework in Figure 3 also serves as a helpful tool to translate evidence into practice. It gives explicit consideration to the internal and external barriers and enablers to implementing evidence-based practice, and to what resources, inputs, activities, and outputs are needed to achieve desired outcomes. Evidence-based management recognizes that evidence needs to be translated and applied with consideration to potential boundary conditions (firm size, industry, external and internal contingency factors). This localization of evidence also takes into account stakeholder perspectives and social and ethical implications of decisions including stakeholder concerns, power structures, and politics, as they are likely to impact implementation success (Kepes et al., 2014).

Assess. Assessing involves evaluating the outcome of the decision taken (Barends et al., 2014). This requires decision-makers to critically assess their actions, decision implementation, outcomes, and interventions. As suggested by Kepes et al. (2014), once a solution is put into action, further evidence needs to be gathered to assess the effectiveness of implementation. This then precipitates an iterative process whereby adjustments are made to implementation, and corrective action is taken to improve practice and optimize favorable outcomes. This also requires individuals and organizations to recast mistakes and failures as opportunities for learning. Organizations that take this approach make better decisions (Cannon & Edmondson, 2004). There is also research indicating that organizations can improve individual and team performance by using properly conducted debriefs ($d = 0.67$; medium to large effect size; Tannenbaum & Cerasoli, 2013).

Core Capabilities. In the proposed EDMP in organizations capabilities framework, the core capabilities refer to the knowledge and skills integral to functioning and sustenance. The core capabilities thus include metacognitive skills, critical thinking and appraisal, knowledge generation and translation, and leadership, change, and influence. Simply put, they represent the general knowledge and skills required to engage in all aspects of evidence-based decision-making and are fundamental to the functional capabilities. In fact, there is a two-way or mutually reinforcing and symbiotic relationship between core capabilities and functional capabilities. The proposed framework also illustrates the interdependencies and hierarchical relationships among core and functional capabilities. For example, metacognitive skills are foundational to critical thinking and appraisal, both of which are foundational to the six As (functional capabilities and steps in evidence-based decision-making).

Metacognitive Skills. Metacognitive skills are foundational all-functional capabilities in EDMP in organizations. While the importance of metacognitive skills in the literature has received some attention (Rousseau & Gunia, 2016), little systematic attention has been given to how to teach and help develop metacognitions, and how these link more explicitly to functional EDMP capabilities.

Metacognitive skills are higher-order thinking functions than regular cognitions and essentially involve having an awareness and management of one's own thinking and current cognitive and affective states, or "thinking about thinking" (Downing et al., 2009; Kuhn & Dean, 2004; Tetlock & Gardner, 2015).

First, metacognitive skills require managers to have metacognitive knowledge. That is because they know, and they can reflect on and surface, their own mental models, which involves introspection to gain understanding of personal knowledge, experiences, and values and beliefs that influence one's decisions, causal inferences, attributions, and judgments regarding management practice problems. It is also important to reflect on the reliability and validity of the information a manager has at hand to take decisions, and on the potential for misinformation. Such reflections rest on the application of philosophical knowledge regarding the nature of knowledge and evidence, and different epistemological and ontological perspectives. The more sophisticated rather than shallow epistemological beliefs are (Spray et al., 2013), the more evidence-based decisions will be.

Second, metacognitive skills require a person to *plan, monitor, and manage his or her own learning goals* to enhance evidence-based domain knowledge. This includes knowledge about procedures or useful strategies such as note-taking, slowing down for important information, skimming unimportant information, using mnemonics, summarizing main ideas, and periodic self-testing (Schraw et al., 2006). Of significance too is knowledge about factors that can limit learning. For example, knowing the limitations of our memory system can help us plan (our actions) accordingly (Schraw et al., 2006). Finally, seeking feedback is necessary to improve one's own thinking and to evaluate one's own learning.

Third, *self-regulation and self-management* relate to being one's own neuroplastician and regulating and changing one's cognitions, thinking, and learning (Allen & Armour-Thomas, 1993; Downing et al., 2009). This phase involves the use of heuristics, decision aids, and supports as tools to make more mindful judgments and decisions (e.g., decision awareness). It includes how to put what has been learned into practice (Downing et al., 2009; Schraw et al., 2006).

Critical and Analytical Thinking. Two other core capabilities underpinning the six functional capabilities (six As) in the framework are critical thinking and critical appraisal. They are also foundational to knowledge generation and translation as well as effective communication and influence. Additionally, critical thinking is a metacognitive process, consisting of the skills of analysis, evaluation, and inference. Through purposeful and reflective judgment, it increases the chances of producing a logical conclusion to an argument or solution to a problem (Dwyer et al., 2015). Critical thinking includes two components: (a) a set of information, belief-generating, and processing skills and (b) the habit and intellectual commitment of using skills to guide behavior (Mulnix, 2012).

Critical and analytical thinking is at the core of EDMP in organizations (Rousseau, 2012; Rousseau & Gunia, 2016) and ensures that decisions are made through the conscientious, explicit, and judicious use of the best available evidence. It has also been identified as being a critical capability in management education (Gosling & Mintzberg, 2006, p. 422). Critical thinking is defined as the intellectually disciplined process of actively and skillfully conceptualizing, analyzing, and evaluating and synthesizing information as a guide to belief and action (Facione & Facione, 2008). Critical appraisal is a specific type of critical thinking that is important in all aspects of EDMP in organizations. It involves ascertaining the degree to which different sources of evidence are conducive to causal inference and involves an assessment of the internal validity of evidence and potential confounders. Decisions about interventions and change efforts are based on assumptions about cause-and-effect and therefore require an evidence base conducive to valid causal inference. The evidence base of the decision must therefore be highly trustworthy in terms of internal validity. For this reason, EDMP involves the *critical appraisal* of different inputs in decision-making, an exercise that prioritizes scientific empiricism over naive empiricism (see Lilienfeld & Basterfield, 2020).

Another facet of critical thinking that is important in evidence-based practice in management is *probabilistic reasoning*. This is because the outcome of an evidence-based process is an estimate of a probability in relation to an intervention working given the available evidence, not the truth. The probability of a claim, assumption, or an hypothesis being true is always conditional on the available evidence. The process of critical appraisal in which managers consider information in terms of probabilities and likelihoods also means an enhancement in decision quality. There is some research suggesting that that probabilistic reasoning and training therein can help guard against bias and boost accuracy in prediction (Tetlock & Gardner, 2015).

Knowledge Generation and Translation. Knowing how to generate data and information to solve problems is also an important capability in evidence-based practice. Knowing the hallmarks of the scientific method and being versed in qualitative and quantitative research methods will certainly provide a manager with more options for generating information for the purpose of decision-making but also to assess the outcomes of decisions taken and to track implementation success. For example, knowing how to conduct interviews and administer questionnaires is important for acquiring evidence from stakeholders. If it is not clear whether an effect will apply to a local context, it may be necessary to pilot test the intervention locally (Dietz et al., 2014). Having knowledge about experimental methods can be helpful in the context of pilot testing interventions.

Arguably, critically appraised evidence in relation to a management practice problem does not automatically provide practice solutions or interventions. In fact, evidence from multiple sources needs to be translated and then implemented into practice in the local organizational context. The best available evidence needs to be interpreted and applied to the organizational context, and this requires a level of absorptive capacity, systems and conditional thinking, and knowledge about implementation science to enable *evidence-based implementation*. It is often wrongly assumed that organizations and targeted users have the capabilities to implement change or recommendations (Klein & Sorra, 1996), An organization that can identify, capture, and use new knowledge, and link it to an existing knowledge base, will be in a better position to assimilate these innovations (Greenhalgh et al., 2004). Here, the role of external validity of findings must be reconsidered, as the simpler controlled conditions of scientific research may not extrapolate to the complex local environment (Rousseau & Gunia, 2016). It is ecological validity that enables the questioning of how well evidence from a scientific study can generalize to a local context. Evidence may be very trustworthy and insightful, but it may have used a sample from a different industry or field, such as medicine, airline safety, or the military. The circumstances in those industries may or may not be relevant to the applicability of findings to the local context. Determining how different the local context (industry, firm size, organizational structure) is from the context in which the research was conducted is important, as the factors or boundary conditions may weaken or strengthen the effect of a particular intervention or practice. The next step of implementation of (translated) evidence refers to a purposefully designed set of actions for the application of a purposefully designed program or intervention to cause change (Palinkas & Soydan, 2012). Furthermore, it is up to the practitioner to translate findings from one context to another. For example, an organization facing a problem of low productivity may turn to evidence of pay-for-performance schemes and find experimental evidence that individual performance incentives increase motivation and productivity. However, such interventions are highly context-sensitive and there may be constraints in the local context that may interfere with successful implementation. For example, individual pay-for-performance schemes may not be feasible in a context where people work in groups. Therefore, the applicability of findings to a local context needs careful examination as there could be important local contextual and individual factors (i.e., in the organization) that may moderate the outcomes of the intervention.

Leadership, Change, and Influence. There are core sets of capabilities that get overlooked but are critical to the use of evidence in decision-making and practice in organizations. These capabilities involve leadership skills, change management skills, and social influence and communication skills. These capabilities are pivotal for the development of a collective and shared understanding of the importance and uptake of EDMP in organizations.

Leaders who are seen to take, and indeed communicate, decisions and enact change based on trustworthy evidence from multiple sources can not only help to model and embed a constructive climate that supports EDMP, but may also have more support from followers for such decisions, and thus greater implementation success (Jepsen & Rousseau, 2022). Furthermore, managers and leaders need the skills to communicate the vision and reasons for change, and transmit EDMP to their followers (Rousseau & ten Have, 2022).

Also, any decision to implement evidence-based practice requires first the identification of the target users who will be affected by such a decision. It is then important to determine any potential resistance to, or cynicism about, the change. Leaders enacting change need to have skills to assess the readiness for change in the organizations and to put in place planning and support for change, particularly in organizations that have a less than favorable change history among staff (Rousseau & ten Have, 2022). This analysis becomes important for developing an implementation plan and building commitment to the change (Klein & Sorra, 1996).

The adoption of an evidence-informed practice in an organization is more likely if both leaders and employees support the innovation (Greenhalgh et al., 2004). Local champions must be identified to support the implementation of evidence into practice (Kitson et al., 1998). Altogether, evidence-based management involves the explicit use of different sources of evidence, so managers must have the skills to communicate how different sources of evidence have come to bear on problem identification and decision-making. Indeed, those who are responsible for leading and implementing evidence-based practice need skills to communicate and influence to achieve positive outcomes from implementation.

FUTURE DIRECTIONS

There are several important future directions for EDMP scholarship, education, and practice in management and organizations. The first call to action is for management education, leadership development, and business schools within universities to overhaul their curricula with the integration of evidence-based management capabilities. There needs to be a strong recognition that the dominant "craft" model of management circumvents rather than enables training in decision-making that benefits business and society.

The evidence-based decision-making and practice capabilities framework introduced contributes to the broader literature of decision-making and judgment informed by behavioral decision theory (see Kahneman, 2013), by positioning evidence-based practice as a prescriptive model of decision-making outlining the capabilities and elements of evidence-based decision making. Even though the capabilities framework is evidence-based and builds on the extant literature, it would be helpful for future research to examine the impacts of applying these capabilities to the job domain and whether applying the capabilities results in better objective performance and career success. Examining whether the learning of the capabilities does indeed represent transformative development including shifts in epistemic beliefs, metacognitive skills, and probabilistic reasoning is important, as the learning benefits transcend work-life. It is suggested to study the effects of metacognitive skills in particular and their self-regulation on evidence-based decision-making. Another suggestion would be to examine over time changes in peoples' probabilistic reasoning and the effects on decision-making.

Further work is needed to integrate and test the efficacy of implementation science in educational psychology when teaching EDMP. Also, programs and courses taught from an evidence-based perspective must ensure that *how and what students learn* is evidence-based. Having more evidence-based instructional methods is likely to optimize learning and learning transfer to the job domain. There is a need for a framework of how this might be done and how evidence-based management education can be evaluated. This is of critical importance given that much of the teaching in business schools is not evidence-based. For example, descriptive research suggests that despite their low criterion-related validity, student satisfaction scores remain the dominant way to evaluate the efficacy of programs, as reported by 70% of 60 directors of leadership development programs in business schools that use student satisfaction as the dominant approach to course evaluation (Leroy et al., 2022). Furthermore, work is needed to identify the instructional methods and learning strategies that are most effective in operationalizing the capabilities framework, as well as evaluating its efficacy.

Education in evidence-based management should have three distinctive features:

1. It should enable transformative evidence-based capability development—an evidence-based approach to capability development focuses on capabilities that have practical importance in organizational settings.
2. Content of programs and courses should be transdisciplinary and evidence-based—the evidence base for course content is transdisciplinary and includes subdisciplines such as decision-making and judgment, cognitive neuroscience, Buddhist philosophy and mindfulness, systems thinking, implementation science, data science, social and industrial and organizational psychology, leadership and management, quantum science, fault lines, and social identity psychometrics. This transdisciplinarity needs to be made made more explicit.
3. Finally, professional bodies have a responsibility to encourage their members to be more evidence-based, particularly those providing consulting and advice. As a world authority for human resource professionals, the Chartered Institute of Personnel Development in the United Kingdom incorporates evidence-based practice into its membership model.

CONCLUDING REMARKS

EDMP in organizations requires a transformative and paradigmatic shift in management practice and education. However, the promise of this approach to reduce decision neglect and bias from unaided human decisions and judgment depends on whether managers have the right capabilities in the first place, and whether systemic barriers to critical thinking stemming from a "craft" model of management are addressed. Turmoil in management, the workplace, and organizations has highlighted the need for management education to question and reimagine itself through imminent changes. The EDMP capabilities framework provides the architecture for curriculum developments. The framework also provides organizations with a structured decision-making process for the integration of EDMP through three key aspects:

1. Four sources of evidence.
2. Functional EDMP capabilities (six As).
3. The hitherto unexplored core or foundational capabilities that include metacognitive skills, critical thinking and appraisal, knowledge generation and translation, and leadership, effective communication, and influence.

The EDMP in organizations capabilities framework has broad appeal to other fields and makes explicit the capabilities required to take more evidence-based decisions, which increases the likelihood of favorable outcomes.

REFERENCES

Aarons, G. A., & Sawitzky, A. C. (2006). Organizational culture and climate and mental health provider attitudes toward evidence-based practice. *Psychological Services, 3*(1), 61–72. https://doi.org/10.1037/1541-1559.3.1.61

Alavi, M., Archibald, M., McMaster, R., Lopez, V., & Cleary, M. (2018). Aligning theory and methodology in mixed methods research: Before design theoretical placement. *International Journal of Social Research Methodology, 21*(5), 527–540. https://doi.org/10.1080/13645579.2018.1435016

Allen, B. A., & Armour-Thomas, E. (1993). Construct validation of metacognition. *The Journal of Psychology, 127*(2), 203–211. https://doi.org/10.1080/00223980.1993.9915555

Ashby, D., & Smith, A. F. M. (2000). Evidence-based medicine as Bayesian decision-making. *Statistics in Medicine, 19*, 3291–3305. https://doi.org/10.1002/1097-0258(20001215)19:23%3c3291::AID-SIM627%3e3.0.CO;2-T

Bailin, S. (2002). Critical thinking and science education. *Science & Education, 11*(4), 361–375. https://doi.org/10.1023/A:1016042608621

Barends, E., & Rousseau, D. M. (2018). *Evidence-based management: How to use evidence to make better organizational decisions*. Kogan Page.

Barends, E., Rousseau, D. M., & Briner, R. B. (2014). *Evidence-based management: The basic principles*. Center for Evidence-Based Management.

Barends, E., Villanueva, J., Rousseau, D. M., Briner, R. B., Jepsen, D. M., Houghton, E., & Have, S. ten. (2017). Managerial attitudes and perceived barriers regarding evidence-based practice: An international survey. *PLOS ONE, 12*(10), e0184594. https://doi.org/10.1371/journal.pone.0184594

Beck, J. G., Castonguay, L. G., Chronis-Tuscano, A., Klonsky, E. D., McGinn, L. K., & Youngstrom, E. A. (2014). Principles for training in evidence-based psychology: Recommendations for the graduate curricula in clinical psychology. *Clinical Psychology: Science and Practice, 21*, 410–424. http://doi.org/10.1111/cpsp.12079

Briner, R. B., Capezio, A., & Decosta, P. L. (2022). Evidence-based management education. In *The future of management education* (pp. 102–125). Routledge.

Briner, R. B., Denyer, D., & Rousseau, D. M. (2009). Evidence-based management: Concept cleanup time? *Academy of Management Perspectives, 23*(4), 19–32. https://doi.org/10.5465/amp.2009.45590138

Camuffo, A., Cordova, A., Gambardella, A., & Spina, C. (2020). A scientific approach to entrepreneurial decision making: Evidence from a randomized control trial. *Management Science, 66*(2), 564–586. https://doi.org/10.1287/mnsc.2018.3249

Cannon, M., & Edmondson, A. (2004). Failing to learn and learning to fail (intelligently): How great organizations put failure to work to innovate and improve. *Long Range Planning, 38*, 299–319. https://doi.org/10.1016/j.lrp.2005.04.005

Casebeer, L., Brown, J., Roepke, N., Grimes, C., Henson, B., Palmore, R., Granstaff, U. S., & Salinas, G. D. (2010). Evidence-based choices of physicians: A comparative analysis of physicians participating in Internet CME and non-participants. *BMC Medical Education, 10*(1), 1–6. https://doi.org/10.1186/1472-6920-10-42

Cyert, R. M., Simon, H. A., & Trow, D. B. (1956). Observation of a business decision. *The Journal of Business, 29*(4), 237–248. https://www.jstor.org/stable/2350807

Dietz, J., Antonakis, J., Hoffrage, U., Krings, F., Marewski, J. N., & Zehnder, C. (2014). Teaching evidence-based management with a focus on producing local evidence. *Academy of Management Learning & Education, 13*(3), 397–414. https://www.jstor.org/stable/43696631

Downing, K., Kwong, T., Chan, S.-W., Lam, T.-F., & Downing, W.-K. (2009). Problem-based learning and the development of metacognition. *Higher Education, 57*(5), 609–621. https://doi.org/10.1007/s10734-008-9165-x

Dwyer, C. P., Hogan, M. J., & Stewart, I. (2015). The effects of argument mapping-infused critical thinking instruction on reflective judgement performance. *Thinking Skills and Creativity, 16*, 11–26. https://doi.org/10.1016/j.tsc.2014.12.002

Facione, N. C., & Facione, P. A. (2008). *Critical thinking and clinical reasoning in the health sciences: An international multidisciplinary teaching anthology*. California Academic Press.

Gosling, J., & Mintzberg, H. (2006). Management education as if both matter. *Management Learning, 37*(4), 419–428. https://doi.org/10.1177/1350507606070214

Greenhalgh, T., Robert, G., Macfarlane, F., Bate, P., & Kyriakidou, O. (2004). Diffusion of innovations in service organizations: Systematic review and recommendations. *The Milbank Quarterly, 82*(4), 581–629. https://doi.org/10.1111/j.0887-378X.2004.00325.x

Guyatt, G., Cairns, J., Churchill, D., Cook, D., Haynes, B., Hirsh, J., Irvine, J., Levine, M., Levine, M., Nishikawa, J., Sackett, D., Brill-Edwards, P., Gerstein, H., Gibson, J., Jaeschke, R., Kerigan, A., Neville, A., Panju, A., Detsky, A., … Tugwell, P. (1992). Evidence-based medicine: A new approach to teaching the practice of medicine. *Journal of the American Medical Association, 268*(17), 2420–2425. https://doi.org/10.1001/jama.1992.03490170092032

Highhouse, S. (2008). Stubborn reliance on intuition and subjectivity in employee selection. *Industrial and Organizational Psychology, 1*(3), 333–342. https://doi.org/10.1111/j.1754-9434.2008.00058.x

James, R. (1980). *Return to reason: Popper's thought in social life.* Open Books.

James, R. (1980). *Return to reason: Popper's thought in public life.* Open Books.

Jenicek, M., Croskerry, P., & Hitchcock, D. L. (2011). Evidence and its uses in health care and research: The role of critical thinking. *Medical Science Monitor, 17*(1), RA12–RA17. https://doi.org/10.12659/MSM.881321

Jepsen, D. M., & Rousseau, D. M. (2022). Perceived evidence use: Measurement and construct validation of managerial evidence use as perceived by subordinates. *PLOS ONE, 17*(4), e0266894. https://doi.org/10.1371/journal.pone.0266894

Kahneman, D. (2013). *Thinking, fast and slow.* Farrar, Straus & Giroux.

Kepes, S., Bennett, A. A., & McDaniel, M. A. (2014). Evidence-based management and the trustworthiness of our cumulative scientific knowledge: Implications for teaching, research, and practice. *Academy of Management Learning & Education, 13*(3), 446–466.

Kitson, A., Harvey, G., & McCormack, B. (1998). Enabling the implementation of evidence based practice: A conceptual framework. *BMJ Quality & Safety, 7*(3), 149–158. https://doi.org/10.1136/qshc.7.3.149

Kitson, A. L., Rycroft-Malone, J., Harvey, G., McCormack, B., Seers, K., & Titchen, A. (2008). Evaluating the successful implementation of evidence into practice using the PARiHS framework: Theoretical and practical challenges. *Implementation Science, 3*(1), 1. https://doi.org/10.1186/1748-5908-3-1

Klein, K. J., & Sorra, J. S. (1996). The challenge of innovation implementation. *Academy of Management Review, 21*(4), 1055–1080. https://doi.org/10.5465/amr.1996.9704071863

Kuhn, D., & Dean, D., Jr. (2004). Metacognition: A bridge between cognitive psychology and educational practice. *Theory Into Practice, 43*(4), 268–273. https://doi.org/10.1207/s15430421tip4304_4

Leroy, H. L., Anisman-Razin, M., Avolio, B. J., Bresman, H., Stuart Bunderson, J., Burris, E. R., Claeys, J., Detert, J. R., Dragoni, L., Giessner, S. R., Kniffin, K. M., Kolditz, T., Petriglieri, G., Pettit, N. C., Sitkin, S. B., Van Quaquebeke, N., & Vongswasdi, P. (2022). Walking our evidence-based talk: The case of leadership development in business schools. *Journal of Leadership & Organizational Studies, 29*(1), 5–32. https://doi.org/10.1177/15480518211062563

Lewandowsky, S., Ecker, U. K. H., Seifert, C. M., Schwarz, N., & Cook, J. (2012). Misinformation and its correction: Continued influence and successful debiasing. *Psychological Science in the Public Interest, 13*(3), 106–131. https://doi.org/10.1177/1529100612451018

Lilienfeld, S. O., & Basterfield, C. (2020, February 28). History of evidence-based practice. *Oxford Research Encyclopedia of Psychology.* https://doi.org/10.1093/acrefore/9780190236557.013.633

Morrell, K., & Learmonth, M. (2015). Against evidence-based management, for management learning. *Academy of Management Learning & Education, 14*(4), 520–533. https://www.jstor.org/stable/43698371

Muller, J. Z. (2019). *The tyranny of metrics.* Princeton University Press. https://doi.org/10.1515/9780691191263

Mulnix, J. W. (2012). Thinking critically about critical thinking. *Educational Philosophy and Theory, 44*(5), 464–479. https://doi.org/10.1111/j.1469-5812.2010.00673.x

Palinkas, L. A., & Soydan, H. (2012). New horizons of translational research and research translation in social work. *Research on Social Work Practice, 22*(1), 85–92. https://doi.org/10.1177/1049731511408738

Patton, M. Q. (1999). Enhancing the quality and credibility of qualitative analysis. *Health Services Research, 34*(5 Pt. 2), 1189–1208. https://www.ncbi.nlm.nih.gov/pmc/articles/PMC1089059/

Pfeffer, J., & Sutton, R. (2006). Hard facts, dangerous half-truths, and total nonsense profiting from evidence-based management. *Strategy & Leadership, 34*, 35–42. https://doi.org/10.1108/10878570610652617

Potworowski, G., & Green, L. A. (2011). Assessing the uptake of evidence-based management: A systems approach. *Industrial and Organizational Psychology, 4*(1), 54–56. https://doi.org/10.1111/j.1754-9434.2010.01295.x

Rousseau, D. M. (2006). 2005 Presidential address: Is there such a thing as "evidence-based management"? *The Academy of Management Review, 31*(2), 256–269. https://doi.org/10.2307/20159200

Rousseau, D. M. (Ed.). (2012). *The Oxford handbook of evidence-based management*. Oxford University Press.

Rousseau, D. M. (2020). The realist rationality of evidence-based management. *Academy of Management Learning & Education, 19*(3), 415–424. https://doi.org/10.5465/amle.2020.0050

Rousseau, D. M., & Gunia, B. C. (2016). Evidence-based practice: The psychology of EBP implementation. *Annual Review of Psychology, 67*(1), 667–692. https://doi.org/10.1146/annurev-psych-122414-033336

Rousseau, D. M., & Mccarthy, S. (2007). Educating managers from an evidence-based perspective. *Academy of Management Learning & Education, 6*(1), 84–101. http://www.jstor.org/stable/40214519

Rousseau, D. M., & ten Have, S. (2022). Evidence-based change management. *Organizational Dynamics, 51*(3), 1–13. https://doi.org/10.1016/j.orgdyn.2022.100899

Sackett, D. L., Rosenberg, W. M. C., Gray, J. A. M., Haynes, R. B., & Richardson, W. S. (1996). Evidence based medicine: What it is and what it isn't. *BMJ, 312*(7023), 71–72. https://doi.org/10.1136/bmj.312.7023.71

Schraw, G., Crippen, K. J., & Hartley, K. (2006). Promoting self-regulation in science education: Metacognition as part of a broader perspective on learning. *Research in Science Education, 36*(1), 111–139. https://doi.org/10.1007/s11165-005-3917-8

Speicher-Bocija, J., & Adams, R. (2012). Designing strategies for the implementation of EBMgt among senior management, middle management, and supervisors. In D. M. Rousseau (Ed.), *Oxford handbooks online* (pp. 293–306). Oxford University Press. https://doi.org/10.1093/oxfordhb/9780199763986.013.0017

Spray, E., Scevak, J., & Cantwell, R. (2013). Personal epistemological and metacognitive awareness in first year preservice education students. *Australian Journal of Educational and Developmental Psychology, 13*, 44–57.

Spring, B. (2007). Evidence-based practice in clinical psychology: What it is, why it matters; what you need to know. *Journal of Clinical Psychology, 63*(7), 611–631. https://doi.org/10.1002/jclp.20373

Strauss, S. E., Richardson, W. S., Glasziou, P., & Haynes, R. B. (2005). *Evidence-based medicine: How to practice and teach EBM* (3rd ed). Elsevier Churchill Livingstone.

Tannenbaum, S. I., & Cerasoli, C. P. (2013). Do team and individual debriefs enhance performance? A Meta-Analysis: *Human Factors, 55*(1), 231–245. https://doi.org/10.1177/0018720812448394

Tetlock, P., & Mitchell, G. (2009). Implicit bias and accountability systems: What must organizations do to prevent discrimination? *Research in Organizational Behavior, 29*, 3–38. https://doi.org/10.1016/j.riob.2009.10.002

Tetlock, P. E. (1983). Accountability and the perseverance of first impressions. *Social Psychology Quarterly, 46*(4), 285. https://doi.org/10.2307/3033716

Tetlock, P. E., & Gardner, D. (2015). *Superforecasting: The art and science of prediction*. Crown.

Tourish, D. (2013). "Evidence based management," or "evidence oriented organizing"? A critical realist perspective. *Organization, 20*(2), 173–192. https://doi.org/10.1177/1350508411435281

Yaniv, I., & Choshen-Hillel, S. (2012). Exploiting the wisdom of others to make better decisions: Suspending judgment reduces egocentrism and increases accuracy. *Journal of Behavioral Decision Making, 25*(5), 427–434. https://doi.org/10.1002/bdm.740

Alessandra Capezio and Patrick L'Espoir Decosta

ETHICS IN WORK AND ORGANIZATIONAL PSYCHOLOGY

INTRODUCTION

Ethical issues in work and organizational psychology (WOP) naturally involve the interconnection of two domains of knowledge and practice. The first domain, ethics, has to do with notions of right and wrong or good and evil (or bad), and three normative frameworks have come to dominate the ways in which those terms are defined, each with different implications concerning the sort of *ethical reasoning* called for. It is important to note at the outset that those notions of right and wrong, and so forth, incorporate human values because they play a vital role in shaping ethical thought, emotions, and behavior. The second domain, work and organizational psychology, concerns the study of human behavior in work settings and other social organizations, and the effective application of the knowledge gained to enhance the functioning of the organizations and the well-being of the people within (and sometimes other stakeholders, as well). The conventional understanding of that juxtaposition concerns the propriety or morality by which research ("the study of human behavior") and practice ("the effective application of the knowledge gained") are conducted—the notion of doing good (or doing it right), while doing it well (i.e., competently). A less conventional understanding, emphasizing the values aspect, rather than focusing on only the ethics of how the profession goes about doing what it does (ethics *in* work and organizational psychology), also considers the moral and social bases that justify the profession's work and existence (the ethics *of* work and organizational psychology) (Lefkowitz, 1990, 2005, 2023).

CONCEPTUAL FOUNDATIONS

To have confidence in one's abilities to anticipate and, if necessary, understand and resolve unexpected ethical situations, one should be familiar with the conceptual building blocks of moral philosophy and moral psychology. They provide us with the tools necessary to accomplish good ethical reasoning or problem-solving. The objective is to be flexible in this domain. There is no other tenable option—it is not possible to memorize a near-infinite list of ethical "dos and don'ts," nor can one count on always finding one's current ethical challenge in some extant code or case book. Those who believe that reactions to moral transgressions are immediate and intuitive, not reasoned, have little to offer with respect to solving ethical problems (cf. Haidt, 2001). A learning specialist might view the objective in terms of *stimulus generalization* and *response generalization*—learning to recognize the nature of the many situations in which ethical threats or temptations can be manifest and for which ethical reasoning is appropriate, while also learning a repertoire of adaptive responses.

DEFINITIONAL AND META-ISSUES

What is an Ethical Situation or Problem? First, what makes anything a problem? Generally, it is a situation in which one must make a decision; one may have to find or choose among options. Often, all the alternatives are not known, nor are the outcome(s) of each. What makes a problem *ethical* in nature is that the situation invokes some ethical dimensions or principles such as truth-telling. Lastly, it wouldn't be a "problem" if it didn't have some genuine consequences for some. Therefore, "an ethical situation is taken to be essentially one in which *ethical dimensions* are relevant and deserve consideration in making some choice that will have significant impact on others" (Wittmer, 2001, p. 483, emphasis added). As presented below, it is fruitful to focus on the concept of an *ethical dilemma*.

What Are Those Ethical Dimensions? It depends on who's cutting the pie. Some believe that one or another version of "the golden rule," which exists in many cultural forms, is sufficient by itself. A common schema contains two broad meta-dimensions: *justice* (issues of fairness, equity, equality, etc.) and *welfare* or *an ethics of care* (beneficence, prosociality, harm avoidance, etc.). A common formulation is a domain of five ethical principles that is like the group of five contained in the *Ethical Code of the American Psychological Association* (American Psychological Association, 2017; hereafter, APA Code); the group of four in the *Canadian Psychological Association Code of Ethics for Psychologists* (Canadian Psychological Association, 2017; hereafter, CPA Code), or the *Universal Declaration of Ethical Principles for Psychologists* (Assembly of the International Union of Psychological Science, 2008; hereafter, Universal Declaration); or the three principles in the Academy of Management Code of Ethics (Academy of Management, n.d.). They are as follows:

Respect for People. Behavior that reflects the rights of all persons to be treated with respect and dignity, and to be allowed their rights to privacy, confidentiality, autonomy, and self-determination. It is one of the most widely espoused principles in Western ethical thought. (In eastern moral philosophies it is generally framed in a communitarian context—one's rights as a member of a collectivity.) These rights are to be considered *universalizable* (see "Universalizability" below).

Fairness and Justice. The reader is no doubt familiar with notions of distributive, procedural, and interactional justice. Their psychological meanings are probably more clearly defined than the ethical principle, which may vary as a function of personal, social, and cultural values and the philosophical lens one uses to view it. For example, in Western free-market economies the criterion of fairness is *equity*; but in the public domain of those same nations such as the courts, *equality* is more often appropriate. Fairness may refer to a person having an appropriate balance of rights versus duties, or an identified group's relative share of societal benefits and burdens. At the group or societal level of analysis, the term *social justice* or *economic justice* is often used.

Caring—Beneficence. The empathy-based origin of the "ethics of care" is in keeping with the traditional service ideal in the professions (Kimball, 1992): for example, "providers of I-O psychological services are guided primarily by the principle of promoting human welfare" (American Psychological Association, 1981, p. 668). Therefore, it is especially appropriate in relation to those for whom one has a special obligation or responsibility or who help further one's own interests (e.g., one's subordinate employees, students, clients, research participants). It is also driven by the principle of *universalism* (see "Universalism").

Caring—Nonmaleficence. Refraining from causing unjustifiable harm or preventing such if one can do so, is the ethical principle about which there is the most uniform agreement among moral philosophers. (Recall Hippocrates' "first, do no harm.") Accordingly, it is given great deference in the APA Code (2017): "Psychologists strive to benefit those with whom they work and take care to do no harm.... When conflicts occur among psychologists' obligations or concerns, they attempt to resolve these conflicts in a responsible fashion that avoids or minimizes harm" (Principle A). (Also cf. "Universalism".)

Moral Virtue or Character. The APA and CPA codes include in their lists of ethical principles attributes such as fidelity, integrity in relationships, scientific integrity, and trust. But there are numerous other virtues that make it onto other lists. For example, one popular ethics text offers a partial list of two dozen virtues (Rachels & Rachels, 2015). Consequently, it seems preferable to emphasize a broader perspective connoted by *moral character*. That includes traditional virtues like honesty, trustworthiness, and integrity, as well as other attributes studied by moral psychologists such as moral sensitivity (Rest, 1994), moral motivation (Stocker, 1976), moral emotions (Thompson, 2009), and self-sanctions (Bandura, 1991). Conceptions of moral virtue or character generally go beyond the specification of such behavioral traits as these to emphasize that character includes the moral motivations that underlie those sorts of actions.

Additional Guidelines

Universalism. A very old debate in Western moral philosophy concerns the metatheoretical issue of whose interests count in determining what is the right thing to do—just one's own or others' as well (*ethical egoism* vs. *universalism*).[1] Most contemporary moral philosophers seem to be in accord with Singer (1995): "Self-interested acts must be shown to be compatible with more broadly based ethical principles if they are to be ethically defensible, because the notion of ethics carries with it the idea of something bigger than the individual" (p. 10). Based on all the foregoing ethical principles, universalism decrees that no one's interests (including one's own) are a priori due greater consideration than anyone else's. The conditional phrase is important because there may be situations in which some people are owed special consideration because of prior commitments, obligations, duties, or other legitimate circumstances. The reader may recognize the *multiple-stakeholder* approach in management as an application of the universalist position.

    Although a universalist approach to the principle of beneficence is the default option—we should try to do well by everyone—the principle is opposed empirically by the greater care and concern most people naturally have for their family members, friends, colleagues, neighbors, and compatriots, in comparison with strangers, foreigners, and so on. Most people would understand your expressions of greater concern for those close to you. However, there are circumstances in which one would be expected to disregard those personal feelings—for example, in one's formal role as a supervisor in which such behavior is likely to be viewed as "favoritism." In contrast, universalism applied to the principle of nonmaleficence is generally viewed as more unequivocal—there is rarely a justifiable reason for causing gratuitous harm.

Universalizability. In ethics, *universalizability* is the equivalent of the bromide "what's good for the goose is good for the gander." There should be consistency in what is considered ethical. I cannot expect someone to accept my advice regarding what to do in response to an ethical dilemma if I would not do the same in that situation.

Ethical Reasoning. An ancient meta-ethical dispute in moral philosophy concerns the very nature of ethics and morality. One side, *subjectivism*, consists of what modern psychologists would call a phenomenological perspective. We each experience the world through our separate senses and process those experiences through our separate nervous systems and cognitive processes so there is no objectively verifiable truth—and that includes ethics. Hence, we have *ethical relativism*—our moral principles and values are reflections of our subjective feelings—and by extension at the societal level, *cultural relativism*. In contrast, an *objectivist* perspective (sometimes called *moral realism*) holds that what is morally correct exists as a body of "moral facts" that are at least potentially knowable and verifiable, as are empirical facts. Different objectivist theories involve different bases of such "knowing"—for example, natural law theory, which focuses on what is "natural" for human beings, whether from a religious point of view or evolutionary psychology.

As is often the case, both positions are open to numerous serious criticisms—especially in their extreme versions. But the issue doesn't have to be structured as a dichotomous choice. A popular philosophy text observes "This overlooks a third possibility. People have not only feelings but reason, and that makes a big difference. It may be that . . . moral truths are matters of reason; a moral judgment is true if it is backed by better reasons than the alternatives" (Rachels & Rachels, 2015, p. 41). Supporting moral judgments and actions with good reasons, explaining why those reasons are important, and illustrating that alternative possibilities are not as good, is as close to "proof" as one gets in ethics. That is why ethical reasoning or problem-solving is critical and why this article ends with an attempt to facilitate such.

NORMATIVE ETHICAL MODELS

There are three dominant Western philosophical traditions concerning the way in which right and wrong is determined, with quite a variety of normative theories within each: *deontology, consequentialism* or *utilitarianism*, and *virtue* (or *aretaic*) *theory*.

Deontological Approaches. The origins of the word are from the Greek *deon*, meaning duty, and deontological theories are those in which, according to the substance of each, an action is considered intrinsically right or wrong, irrespective of circumstances.

Deontological ethics emphasizes rights, duties, responsibilities, and justice. Examples include Immanuel Kant and the categorical imperative, Thomas Hobbes or John Rawls and the social contract, John Locke and natural rights theory, and G. W. F. Hegel and the societal process of self-realization.. Traditional deontological positions are absolutist—for example, it is wrong to lie, period; no exceptions—and usually framed in terms of which actions are *permissible* and which are *impermissible*.

The absolutist position is referred to as *rule*-deontology, and it runs into some well-known problems such as when two or more absolute principles conflict—for example, always tell the truth; always respect other people's dignity; never cause harm. In some instances, the best one might hope for is two out of three. To deal with those situations, one device has been to rank-order or prioritize principles as a means of facilitating an ethical choice, which is what is done in the CPA Code (2017): "[T]he four principles have been ordered according to the weight each generally should be given when they conflict" (p. 4). In order, the four are respect for the dignity of persons and peoples, responsible caring, integrity in relationships, and responsibility to society. But that approach moves a step away from rule-based ethics toward a more *act*-deontological position in which following the rule(s) may be contingent on the circumstances of the situation or ethical problem. In the absence of such formal prioritization, it is often the case that the actor facing an ethical difficulty will implicitly decide which among several permissible actions to execute, based on the anticipated degree of benefit or harm likely from each. If so, that has moved them out of the principled deontological camp and into the logic of consequentialism.

Teleological (Consequentialist or Utilitarian) Approaches.   Unlike deontology, teleological theories do not define right and wrong directly, but indirectly in terms of benefits and harms. The correct ethical choice, what is right, is that which produces the greatest overall good or the least overall harm (an analysis of *utility*), taking account of the consequences for all those affected (cf. *universalism*, above). Therefore, another distinction is that whereas deontology tells us which actions are permissible, consequentialism directs us to the one most ethically justified option as an imperative (hypothetically, at least). The utilitarianism of Jeremy Bentham, John Stuart Mill, and later, G. E. Moore, set out to rid ethics of abstract moral rules and put it on an empirical footing. For Bentham, the criteria were pleasure and pain (or happiness and unhappiness). Mill and Moore expanded that hedonistic perspective to include higher-order pleasures such as aesthetic beauty, the acquisition of knowledge, loving relationships, happiness, and so forth. But the key point was that the dimensions of experience could and would be specified and measured quantitatively to assess the overall utility of each option (the so-called *hedonic calculus*).

The Achilles heel of utilitarianism is the need to assess *all* the positive and negative aspects of *each* of the ethical choices with which one is confronted (assuming they can even all be specified) to perform the analysis needed to ascertain the most ethically justified option (the most utile). Hypothetically this calculation is to be done in each instance, meaning that this is an *act*-utilitarian model. But Mill recognized that this would often be unlikely, if not impossible, so he considered *secondary principles*—generalizations and extrapolations regarding the relative benefits to society of various kinds of actions, so that specific calculations don't have to be made in each instance—moving toward a *rule*-utilitarian posture. For example, over eons almost all societies have learned that telling the truth and being respectful to one another are generally beneficial and being deceitful is generally harmful; we don't have to work it out in each situation. Many utilitarian calculations are implicit and somewhat intuitive. But some critics contend that that's not really utilitarianism. Another frequent solution to the operational difficulties of utilitarianism, frequently used in modern political economy, is *preference utilitarianism* in which the a priori definition of goods is not necessary; the relative anticipated satisfaction of each person's legitimate preferences is the unit of analysis in the utility analysis.

Virtue (Aretaic) Theory. Critics have observed that both the deontological and consequentialist positions have weaknesses—and in fact become less distinguishable from each other when, in response to theoretical difficulties, act-deontological and rule-utilitarian versions of each are necessary. Anscombe (1958) is credited with reintroducing the importance of virtue theory as a response to the criticism of both deontological and consequentialist perspectives as having overlooked the person in their focus on abstract rules and theoretical analyses. "It is a deep fault of non-virtue theories that they pay little or no attention to the areas of life which form character" (Pence, 1993, p. 257). Aretaic theory shifts the essential ethical question from "what is the right thing to do?" to "what is the right kind of person to be?" or "what does it mean to be good?" We have moved into the aspect of personality referred to as character and the portion of character that is moral in nature. Mere "personal virtues" such as industriousness, thrift, perseverance, or sobriety may be considered virtuous because they are valuable and socially desirable attributes—but primarily for their possessor. The moral virtues such as honesty, integrity, or generosity are in the universalist tradition. But unlike consequentialism and deontology, which focus on actions, virtue theory emphasizes that "virtuous people are therefore defined not just by their deeds, but also by their inner life.... They see what's important, know what is right and why it is right, and want to do things because they are right" (Shafer-Landau, 2015, p. 261).

Notions of virtue have been applied fruitfully to business and management (Audi, 2012; Sadler-Smith, 2013; Sison et al., 2012), positive psychology (Alzola, 2015), and leadership (Kilburg, 2012), as well as to organizational levels of analysis (Chun, 2010; Moore, 2008). Nevertheless, like the two normative models considered previously, it has its theoretical problems and critics. There is a lack of consensus regarding the definition of virtue and how many of them there might be. Virtue theory also may go too far in emphasizing moral character to the exclusion of situational and contextual influences on ethical behavior (e.g., *organizational ethical climate*). A most important issue is whether virtue theory can stand on its own without the principled rules and reasoning it rejects. How does one know *what to do* to be virtuous?

Accepting All Three Normative Perspectives. As noted briefly in the previous paragraph, deontological, consequentialist, and virtue theory approaches all have their critics, theoretical weaknesses, and some operational difficulties. It is also evident that they each have nevertheless managed to make useful contributions to our understanding of moral action. Therefore, it would seem prudent to accept principled expressions of rights, duties, and justice and the analysis of foreseen consequences, as well as expressions of virtuous character, as legitimate resources in coping with ethical challenges. "Moral reasons can include both the duty to act *and* the consequences expected from the act *as well as* the belief that so acting is characteristic of the kind of person one wants to be" (Whetstone, 2001, p. 102, emphasis in original). Moreover, it has been my experience that some ethical challenges are framed more aptly in one or another of the three approaches, suggesting an advantage to acquiring familiarity with all.

THE ROLE OF VALUES

Approximately 15 years ago I was asked to make a presentation on the topic "In Order to Prosper, Industrial-Organizational Psychology Should Improve Its Ethics." It became apparent to me that that presented a problem. To begin with, the requested title seemed to suggest or assume that the ethical behavior of industrial-organizational psychologists *needed* improving! I did not know that to be so—not from personal observation and conversations with colleagues, nor from any empirical investigations; I was not aware of any such survey or even systematic anecdotal data. What to do? Well, I had already become convinced of the importance of values in shaping professional practice and even research (Lefkowitz, 1990, 2005), so I requested a change in topic and made the presentation about professional values (Lefkowitz, 2008). Values issues justifiably play a prominent role in a consideration of professional ethics.

Values are as important as ethics because they shape the "domain of moral action" (Lefkowitz, 2017, 2023) in which ethical principles and standards are interpreted and followed, and they are often contentious.[2] For example, the Preamble of the APA Code (2017) directs psychologists to use our knowledge "to improve the condition of individuals, organizations and society," but it doesn't specify *which* individuals, organizations, or segments of society—nor what to do when the interests of some of those conflict.[3] Principle A of the APA code reads, in part, that "[p]sychologists strive to benefit those with whom they work... [and] seek to safeguard the welfare and rights of those with whom they interact professionally and other affected persons." Principle B: "Psychologists establish relationships of trust with those with whom they work." And Principle E: "Psychologists respect the dignity and worth of all people, and the rights of individuals to privacy, confidentiality, and self-determination."

It is one's values that tend to shape whom each one of us includes as deserving our beneficence and trustworthiness, and whose welfare and rights we safeguard—including the right to self-determination. For example, do these ethical principles mean that we have an obligation to not aid and abet an organization's efforts to stymie an employee drive for union representation? Might it even mean that we have an affirmative duty to further the workers' efforts to enhance their well-being and sense of dignity and self-determination? Nor do any explicit value statements or implicit values of work and organizational psychology *qua* profession envision such ambiguities (cf. Lefkowitz & Lowman, 2017). For example, one of the expressed values of the Society for Industrial and Organizational Psychology (SIOP) in the United States is to "inspire individual and organizational health, well-being, and effectiveness" (SIOP 2021). Questions naturally arise: What if a policy designed to enhance organizational effectiveness is detrimental to employee well-being? Does hindering union representation fulfill that core value, or does furthering it do so? Might the answer be contingent on specifics of the situation? If so, what aspects? And is there an a priori default position? In fact, the long-noted dominant organizational perspective and managerialist bias of work and organizational psychology (Baritz,

1960; Katzell & Austin, 1992; Kornhauser, 1947; Lefkowitz, 2005, 2008; Roback, 1917) may put most work and organizational psychologist (WOP) practitioners on the side of not promoting union representation, thus thwarting those workers' rights to self-determination.

As another illustration, developing a valid employee selection procedure and implementing a high cutoff score ordinarily benefits the organization, but produces a higher proportion of qualified applicants who are inappropriately rejected ("false rejects") than those who are not qualified and so are rejected appropriately ("true rejects"). This is due to the imperfect nature of our (albeit professionally validated) procedures. Do we have any ethical responsibilities to those qualified stakeholder-applicants who nevertheless have been denied employment? One's answer to that not-so-hypothetical question depends largely on one's values concerning such matters as the extent of the organization's societal responsibilities, one's self-perceived obligations and professional identity as a WOP, and who one believes qualifies as a company stakeholder. To some this might seem to be an ethical issue. Yet neither the psychologist who responds "yes" nor one who responds "no" to the question posed in the previous paragraph (regarding promoting unionization) can unambiguously be characterized as unethical despite their divergent values positions—although they might each mistakenly perceive the other as such. That is how values issues play an important, sometimes contentious, and often unacknowledged role in ethical deliberations. Following is a proposed statement of values for the field that is responsive to the issues raised (cf. Lefkowitz, 2016, 2017):

Along with improving the effective functioning of organizations, a fundamental objective of research and practice in work and organizational psychology should be to assure that organizations are safe, just, healthy, challenging, and fulfilling places in which to work. Moreover, there is no inherent conflict between those objectives and improving organizational effectiveness. The two are often interdependent. However, when it is anticipated that actions undertaken to improve organizational effectiveness will adversely impact the well-being of employees or other organizational stakeholders, the appropriate role of the work and organizational psychologist is to challenge the morality, wisdom, and necessity of those actions and, if necessary, to attenuate their adverse consequences to the extent feasible.

A CENTRAL CONCEPT: ETHICAL DILEMMAS

Ethical principles such as those contained in the APA Code (2017), CPA Code (2017), and Universal Declaration (2008) are general, abstract, and, some would say, vague. They are, in fact, acknowledged to be "*general* principles" and "*aspirational* goals," representing the "highest *ideals* of psychology" (APA, 2017, p. 2, emphases added). As such, although they provide valuable guidance, they are of limited utility in helping one respond specifically to the vast variety of potential ethical challenges. That is why the bulk of the APA Code consists of 89 more specific standards that are descriptive and meant to be enforceable.

But no code can anticipate all possible challenges—not for a field as diverse as psychology (the APA has 56 divisions)—nor even for a single field such as work and organizational psychology. And if, as a social scientist or an ethicist, one is interested in the generalizability of professional ethics, there is an additional problem. Because of the obvious differences in role demands, responsibilities, work knowledge and functions, social relations, and contextual factors among different professions, the manifest ethical problems in each are very different; thus, different fields (and to some extent, even subfields) produce their own separate sets of ethical considerations. The lack of commensurability across professions is one of the reasons for a dearth of comparative ethics studies, and why the benefits of applied experience remain isolated in separate professional "silos." A similar phenomenon occurs even within fields, precluding meaningful longitudinal comparisons as the manifest ethical problems change over time because of technological, political, legal, or social advances (Lefkowitz, 2006).

A potential solution to the above difficulties was advanced and tested empirically in the field of work and organizational psychology, employing the construct of *ethical dilemmas* (Lefkowitz, 2021), focusing on the relatively "content-free" *form* or *structure* of the dilemma. McConnell (2018) noted that "debates about moral dilemmas have been extensive during the last six decades. These debates go to the heart of moral theory" (§10). As defined earlier, an ethical situation is one in which ethical dimensions are relevant in making some choice that will have significant impact on others. A dilemma is defined as "a usually undesirable or unpleasant choice. . . . What is distressing or painful about a dilemma is having to make a choice one does not want to make" (Merriam-Webster Unabridged Dictionary, 2016). McConnell (2018) explains that often "the agent is required to do each of two (or more) actions; the agent can do each of the actions, but the agent cannot do both (or all) of the actions. The agent thus seems condemned to moral failure . . ." (§2). Therefore, one can construe *unethical behavior* as the actor's failure to successfully resolve an ethical dilemma with which they were faced. In other words, we can presume that the person experiencing such a predicament is motivated to some degree by ethical (justice, caring, virtuous) motives to "do the right thing," hence the dilemma and hence the "failure." According to Lefkowitz (2021), "One might succumb due to the greater salience of egoistic asocial motives, external pressures, being prevented by circumstances from acting ethically, and/or other situational impediments" (p. 303).

But what about so-called "intentional unethical behavior"? Such intentional behavior is generally well-planned, persistent, and committed with little or no ambivalence concerning right and wrong (although there may be ambivalence regarding the consequences of getting caught). Such actions, in comparison with unethical failures, are better conceived as *corruption*, about which there has been considerable definitional ambiguity (Ashforth et al., 2008; Dion, 2010; Lefkowitz, 2009). The senior managers at Volkswagen who schemed, implemented, and persisted in operating the diesel exhaust emissions subterfuge were not (merely) being unethical; they were corrupt. In contrast, it is likely that at least some of the mid-level engineers and technicians who were directed by their bosses to carry out the subterfuge did experience ethical dilemmas. It seems like an inadequate description of the Ponzi schemer Bernard Madoff to think of him as (merely) unethical. On the other hand, corrupt acts can vary in degree—such as (merely) "borrowing" a small amount of office supplies from work to take home.

Unethical behavior, as defined above, can also be differentiated from (mere) *rudeness* or *incivility*. The distinction is that the former involves potential conflict and violations of moral norms or ethical principles (McConnell, 2018; Prinz, 2008). The latter concerns the violation of non-moral *social norms* of conventional behavior (Prinz & Nichols, 2010); that is also commensurate with how the terms are used by scholars in that area (Cortina et al., 2017).

Admittedly, however, the distinction may be difficult to make in practice: "Imagine that you are alone in an elevator, late for an appointment, impatiently waiting for the doors to close; just as the doors start to shut someone comes running down the hallway breathlessly shouting, 'hold the elevator, please, hold the door!'" (Lefkowitz, 2021, p. 302). This may be a dilemma (whether to be rude or late), but most people probably would not consider it a *moral* or *ethical* dilemma. The boundary between unethical and rude behavior can be difficult to discern.

Forms of Ethical Dilemmas. There is a conceptual "gap" between the theoretical level of general, abstract, idealistic, often ambiguous ethical principles, and the idiosyncratic near-infinite variety of usually domain-specific, manifest ethical situations, problems, or dilemmas. Using 292 ethical incidents reported by a sample of 228 professional work and organizational psychologists in a Society for Industrial and Organizational Psychology (SIOP)–sponsored ethics survey in 2009, it was demonstrated that a taxonomy of five paradigmatic, relatively content-free *forms* or *structures* of ethical dilemmas, could be differentiated reliably to fill that gap (Lefkowitz, 2021). The forms of dilemmas are defined more precisely than the abstract principles and yet are not particularistic and domain-specific as are the overt behavioral ethical situations. As such, they "provide a basis for meaningful analyses of ethical experiences across domains (of professions, organizations, demographic groups, age cohorts, etc.), even though the overt features of those experiences may have nothing in common, and/or over time—during which technological advances, social policies, and other changes give rise to new manifest ethical issues" (p. 303).

The five forms are: (a) the opportunity to prevent harm, (b) temptation, (c) role conflict, (d) values conflict, and (e) coercion. They are defined in Table 1, along with the two other kinds of misbehavior: *incivility* or *rudeness*, and *corruption*, which constitute behavioral boundary conditions for the ethical dilemmas. The forms of dilemma are not mutually exclusive—that is, a situation may be comprised of elements of two or more. An opportunity was afforded by SIOP to repeat the ethics survey (with some modifications) 10 years after the initial data were collected, and both waves of data were reported in Lefkowitz and Watts (2022). Table 2 presents some verbatim examples of the incidents reported by that second sample, categorized according to type of misbehavior, and segmented according to primary position of the respondent—practitioner or academic.

SOME ETHICS SURVEY DATA FROM WORK AND ORGANIZATIONAL PSYCHOLOGY

The two surveys noted above appear to be the only systematic empirical data concerning ethical incidents experienced in the field of work and organizational psychology.[4] In over half the incidents reported, the respondent was the person faced with the ethical issue, as opposed to occupying some other role or merely being an observer. Despite some differences in administration and scoring procedures in 2009 and 2019, it was observed that "there were remarkable consistencies across the ten-year span in the relative incidence of ethical challenges with respect to the work activity areas in which they arise, as well as the particular paradigmatic forms of ethical dilemmas, other misbehaviors [i.e., incivility and corruption], and HR [human resources]/managerial issues represented" (Lefkowitz & Watts, 2022, p. 1797). These are brief highlights:

ETHICS IN WORK AND ORGANIZATIONAL PSYCHOLOGY • **59**

Table 1. Five Structural Forms of Ethical Dilemma and Other Misbehavior

Form	Definition
Ethical dilemmas	
I. Opportunity to prevent harm	Awareness, anticipation or foreknowledge of someone or some entity (e.g., the organization) to be harmed or wronged by another or by circumstances.
II. Temptation	Contemplating (or taking) an action in accord with some self-serving motive, goal, or ambition that would be deceitful, unjust, or potentially harmful to another or to the organization; or would be knowingly inappropriate (such as not professionally competent or in violation of accepted standards/rules).
III. Role conflict	Having competing legitimate obligations or responsibilities (sometimes to two or more persons or other entities) such that fulfilling one entails failing to meet the other.
IV. Values conflict	Facing equally (or nearly equally) important but conflicting personal values that have been placed in opposition. Expressing one entails denying the other(s) expression.
V. Coercion	Being subject to external pressures to violate one's ethical or professional standards or legal requirements.
Incivility or rude behavior	Violation of conventional norms and expectations, resulting in some harm, disrespect, or insult to others, but not violating moral principles.
Corruption	Intentional, voluntary acts of misbehavior, misrepresentation, and deviant or counterproductive workplace behavior; not abiding by accepted norms or commitments made; or corruption directed against individuals or the organization for personal or organizational gain.

Source: Reproduced from Lefkowitz, J. (2021). Used with permission.

Table 2. Examples of Academic and Practitioner Ethical Situations

Form of dilemma or misbehavior	Academic incidents	Practitioner incidents
Opportunity to prevent harm	A fellow faculty member was asking inappropriately personal questions during faculty search interviews (e.g., what does your father do?) and making inappropriate comments to minority faculty (e.g., you won't just be a token Black faculty member). Her behaviors were reported to the department chair. For a while, she could not participate in interviews at all. Later she was permitted to only when there were other faculty members present. She filed a grievance, but the sanctions held.	Sent out survey to employees with a confidentiality statement around how the data would be used, who would see it and who would have access to it. Senior leader wanted to use the data to identify a group for a follow-up survey even though this what [sic] not how we said the data would be used. Someone else made decision to use the data.

(Continued)

Table 2. Continued

Form of dilemma or misbehavior	Academic incidents	Practitioner incidents
Temptation	We conducted a study and did not find any results. We looked for results in other parts of the study and found something interesting. My colleague wanted to publish this study, but I thought it slightly unethical as we had been "fishing" (though we had a good theoretical explanation for what we found and could base it in theory). I suggested to conduct at least one other study to see if the results hold and are thus not arbitrary. My colleague initially wasn't impressed, but we conducted more studies with better measures and the results held and everyone was happy.	Data had been coded wrong by mistake for a job analysis survey. I discovered my own mistake only after the review of the survey with the client. It affected a portion of the decisions made. If I kept quiet, no one would know. I told my supervisor, and a new meeting was scheduled to go over that portion of the survey.
Role conflict	A new faculty member needed a place to stay for a few days and asked a student to provide housing and transportation. This was inappropriate because the student felt he/she could not decline the request. I am not sure it was resolved at all, the event happened and resulted in tension afterwards.	There was a perceived conflict of interest between a manager and a supplier, where the two had a declared friendship. A third party raised concerns regarding the evaluation of the supplier and awarding of work. Unbeknown to the third party the manager and his immediate directors had already ensured that the supplier reported to and was evaluated by an unconnected party.
Values conflict	Teach a stats class. The textbook was available for free online, so I didn't have the students buy it. I'm basically violating copyright.	Improper use of measurement/ predictive modelling, resulting in recommending people who will be worse at the job. IO team raised that it was a problem and argued our stance. We were told that this is a value issue and that we will be continuing to build models that suggest clients should hire less intelligent people. No, the issue was not resolved satisfactorily
Coercion	Before I received tenure, the chair of my tenure committee stopped by my office one day to talk. During this conversation he brought up his role and that the committee largely felt that I was on track towards tenure. He then mentioned that he would appreciate being added to one of the papers that I was planning to submit as a co-author and implied that this could help with his support through my tenure review process. He asked me to think about it and to let him know if	When conducting a survey data collection, one of the manager level employees wanted to check each survey and require his subordinates to re-take the survey if they did not pass the attention check questions. I thanked him for supporting the survey but let him know that we couldn't require participants to take the survey (at all) or re-take them.

Table 2. Continued

Form of dilemma or misbehavior	Academic incidents	Practitioner incidents
	that was something that I would be willing to do and left. Following the conversation, I spoke with my department chair to let them know what had happened. I let them know that I felt I was meeting all of the tenure requirements at our university and that I did not plan to respond. As such, I wanted to inform them in case this became an issue. I didn't choose to otherwise report this individual or take action to report them but wanted to make sure that my decision to not agree to their request would [sic] lead to retribution. I never followed back up with them; this individual did a softer ask at a later time and I made it clear that I would be happy to potentially collaborate if they had a project that they felt I could contribute to, but that I would not feel comfortable simply adding their name to a paper that I was submitting (and I chose not to otherwise invite them to work on any of my current projects).	
Incivility or rudeness	Graduate student informed her advisor, in the presence of another faculty member, that she thought the advisor was engaging in "microaggressions." The advisor and other faculty member listened to the student's concerns and praised her for speaking up. The advisor met with the student afterwards and apologized for any actions that were perceived to be microaggressive, or otherwise hurtful. The advisor and student later created a mentoring compact. The issue was resolved satisfactorily.	A leader made a joke pertaining to the perils of hiring women (e.g., that they take extended parental leave). The woman who prompted the joke was a mid-level subordinate. She spoke with him several days later and expressed why jokes like his could be harmful. He apologized and has since made an effort to be more sensitive regarding gender issues.
Corruption	I alerted editors of numerous top IO journals to apparent data and results fabrication. Some acted appropriately but other [sic] acted completely unethically. Some of these admitted that the data appeared to be fabricated but said that they could not act out of fear of being sued by the apparent perpetrators. Others told me that the practice of fabrication was so widespread that it would be unfair to single out these particular individuals. One editor informed the perpetrator that I had contacted the journal to express my concerns, resulting in me getting threatening letters and threats to my personal safety.	A senior HR person at [company name omitted for anonymity] took our proposal for a project and sent it to her husband at [company name omitted for anonymity], who copied our proposal, resubmitted it, and got the project. Our ideas, they got the business.

Reproduced from Lefkowitz and Watts (2022). Used with permission, and edited lightly for punctuation and spelling.

- The most frequently experienced types of misbehavior across both cohorts were the ethical dilemmas of coercion and role conflict, and corruption. Someone's corrupt behavior may lead to an ethical dilemma for another (any of the five forms, depending on circumstances and the role relationship of the two people).
- The managerial/HR issues concerning confidentiality, honesty and integrity, obligation to profession and colleagues, and conflicts of interest were the most cited. Moreover, that held for each of 20 subgroups examined.
- Incidents concerning racial discrimination or sexual harassment were infrequent at both time periods.
- From among 13 areas of work activity considered, ethical incidents were reported most frequently for individual assessment/assessment centers, academic research/publication, and consulting issues concerning the client.
- Only about one-third of the respondents across both cohorts considered the incident reported to have had a positive outcome—that is, a satisfactory or mostly satisfactory resolution—although the incidence was significantly higher in 2019.

MULTIPLE WORK ROLES

Most work and organizational psychologists occupy primary or secondary work roles as (a) members of an academic faculty as instructors and advisors of undergraduate and graduate students, generally in university departments of psychology or schools of business; (b) researchers in an academic or applied organizational setting; (c) applied practitioners from the position of an "in-house" employee of the organization in some area of HR, or as an external consultant; and (d) administrator, manager, or supervisor in a corporate, academic, governmental, research, consulting, or other type of organization. The different duties and responsibilities in each venue give rise to different potential ethical challenges, although there are commonalities such as the obligation to practice only within one's areas of competence (cf. APA Code, 2017, Standard 2.01).[5]

THE WORK AND ORGANIZATIONAL PSYCHOLOGIST AS EDUCATOR

The APA Code (2017) contains an entire set of seven enforceable standards concerning education and training applicable to those of us involved in the education of undergraduate or graduate students, in addition to more generic standards that also pertain, such as aspects of human relations and privacy and confidentiality. The education standards include such admonitions as ensuring that our courses and programs provide appropriate materials and experiences, live up to our claims, and that our descriptions of course content and program requirements are accurate.

Authors such as Macrina (2014), Sales and Folkman (2000), and Shamoo and Resnick (2009) have elucidated many ethical issues concerning *professional relations* among researchers, collaborators, colleagues, and advisees, as well as journal editors and reviewers. In general, the usual principles of honesty, trust, fairness, respect, and nonmaleficence pertain. Common issues that arise include the appropriate allocation of authorship on publications; impartiality and respectfulness in peer reviews; and sensitivity and fairness in mentoring and advisee relationships (which also occur in the researcher, practitioner, and manager roles).

Lefkowitz (2005, 2014) suggested that values issues should be an explicit part of the graduate curriculum, and emphasized educating our students for "science, practice and social responsibility," focusing on the *informal curriculum* and *hidden curriculum*:

> To what extent do graduate programs, individual faculty members, internship supervisors, and research mentors explicitly engage with students on such topics as the underlying goals and values of the profession, how those values articulate with others, professional values in general, institutional values of the organizations we serve and how those relate to more broadly based societal concerns, or real-world dilemmas associated with potential conflicts between one's personal values and those of the organization? (Lefkowitz, 2014, pp. 40–41)

THE WORK AND ORGANIZATIONAL PSYCHOLOGIST AS RESEARCHER

The *responsible conduct of research* (RCR) refers to "conducting research in ways that fulfill the professional responsibilities of researchers, as defined by their professional organizations, the institutions for which they work and, when relevant, the government and public" (Steneck, 2006, p. 55). One aspect of that, *research ethics*, concerns the proper treatment of research participants (Lefkowitz, 2007a).[6] Preliminary federal regulations were published in 1974, with subsequent versions resulting in the "final rule" codified and updated in the *Federal Register* as 45 CFR Part 46, effective January 21, 2019 (U.S. Department of Health and Human Services, 2019). Aside from official directives such as the specific regulations from the U.S. Department of Health and Human Services, there are two related, ethically relevant but rarely acknowledged meta-issues to be noted: the social nature of research activities and the issue of "who benefits?"

The Social Nature of Research: Who Benefits?   Some years ago, Orne (1962) first called attention to the nature of the psychological experiment as a social relationship in which "the roles of subject and experimenter are well understood and carry with them well-defined mutual role expectations" (p. 777) that include the participants' willingness to comply with a very wide range of actions on request.[7] Kelman (1972) went on to elaborate the power imbalance between the researchers and sponsors of research vis-à-vis the subjects, and viewed the illegitimate use of that differential power as the cause of many problematic ethical issues in research. The subordinate status of research participants is partly why there is so much social science research with children and the aged, poor, infirmed, addicted, hospitalized, and incarcerated; college freshmen and sophomore members of a subject pool (rather than seniors); military personnel (enlisted ranks more than officers); and hourly employees and low- and mid-level managers (rather than corporate executives).

An aspect of the above, which encompasses work and organizational psychology, is that "the overriding issue that ought to influence our ethical deliberations is the simple realization that our research is not usually aimed at benefitting directly the people who participate in it as subjects" (Lefkowitz, 2017, p. 400). That holds even though it is true that the results of applied organizational research interventions may have direct benefits for employee-participants, and some may benefit indirectly from organizational improvements prompted by the findings. Nevertheless, most work and organizational psychologists' research is driven by organizational objectives or problems defined by those high in the organization's structure, and/or by the theoretical interests and curiosity of the researchers. The participants, college students, or even employees are usually not expected to benefit—as with the validation sample in employee selection research for example. A relevant attitude for us to adopt, therefore, is that "[r]esearch subjects trust the researcher to treat them with dignity and respect, to protect their well-being, and to safeguard them from potential dangers or risks of harm" (Kimmel, 2007, p. xx).

Scientific Integrity. The other aspect of RCR is the *ethics of science*, or scientific integrity—protecting the integrity and reputation of the scientific enterprise. This is an enormous area of concern and study (cf. Macrina, 2014), too large to do more than barely summarize here. It was observed by MacCoun (1998) that there has been "an erosion in the perceived legitimacy of science" in general (p. 259), as well as psychology (Ferguson, 2015; Lilienfeld, 2012).

Accordingly, the federal government's Office of Research Integrity is concerned primarily with research misconduct: *fabrication* or *falsification* of data and *plagiarism*, as defined in Table 3. "Fabrication and falsification obviously can have significant impacts on research. A researcher who intentionally publishes fabricated or falsified research results clearly undermines the reliability of the research record and of all decisions and/or relationships based on that research" (Steneck, 2006, p. 62). The scientific establishment is also concerned with the possible widespread incidence of somewhat less serious "questionable research practices" (QRPs) (Committee on Science, Engineering and Public Policy, 1992; Steneck, 2006; Sterba, 2006). Steneck discusses a range of QRPs that have been revealed in surveys, and Wasserman's (2013) ameliorative recommendations in this regard assume that QRPs are often the result of incompetence, carelessness, inadequate supervision, or a work environment that does not support ethical conduct.

THE WORK AND ORGANIZATIONAL PSYCHOLOGIST AS PRACTITIONER

As just discussed, work and organizational psychology research is not often aimed at benefitting directly the participants needed for its implementation. Thus, practitioners have reason to be grateful to them. Similarly, our "client" is most often the organization or a unit thereof, represented by a key manager or gatekeeper, whereas most, perhaps all, of those with whom we work are other employees (Lefkowitz, 2007b). This is largely commensurate with training to work with/for organizations, not individuals. But it opens the possibility of encountering situations in which the interests of the organization do not correspond with or may even run counter to the interests of employees with whom one is working. Earlier in the chapter it was noted that the Preamble of the APA Code (2017) tells psychologists to use knowledge gained "to improve the condition of individuals, organizations and society"—that is, all three. Sometimes those interests are not isomorphic.

Table 3. The Federal Government's Definition of Research Misconduct and Requisite Evidence

Research Misconduct Defined

Research misconduct is defined as fabrication, falsification, or plagiarism in proposing, performing, or reviewing research, or in reporting research results.

Research, as used herein, includes all basic, applied, and demonstration research in all fields of science, engineering, and mathematics. This includes, but is not limited to, research in economics, education, linguistics, medicine, psychology, social sciences, statistics, and research involving human subjects or animals.

Fabrication is making up data or results and recording or reporting them.

Falsification is manipulating research materials, equipment, or processes, or changing or omitting data or results such that the research is not accurately represented in the research record.

The research record is the record of data or results that embody the facts resulting from scientific inquiry, and includes, but is not limited to, research proposals, laboratory records, both physical and electronic, progress reports, abstracts, theses, oral presentations, internal repots, and journal articles.

Plagiarism is the appropriation of another person's ideas, processes, results, or words without giving appropriate credit. Research misconduct does not include honest error or differences of opinion.

Findings of Research Misconduct

A finding of research misconduct requires that there be a significant departure from accepted practices of the relevant research community; the misconduct be committed intentionally, or knowingly, or recklessly; and the allegation be proven by a preponderance of evidence.

Source: Office of Research Integrity. Federal research misconduct policy (https://ori.hhs.gov/federal-research-misconduct-policy) (2000). *Federal Register*, 65(235), 76260–76264. Reproduced with permission from Lefkowitz (2017).

The APA (2017) Ethics Code contains several enforceable standards specifically pertaining to those who work with organizations as opposed to individuals, and which suggest an approach. For example:

> 1.03. Conflicts Between Ethics and Organizational Demands. If psychologists' ethical responsibilities conflict with law, regulations, or other governing legal authority, psychologists clarify the nature of the conflict, make known their commitment to the Ethics Code, and take reasonable steps to resolve the conflict consistent with the General Principles and Ethical Standards of the Ethics Code. Under no circumstances may this standard be used to justify or defend violating human rights.

Other standards include 3.04, Avoiding Harm, which includes a concern for "organizational clients"; 3.11, Psychological Services Delivered to or Through Organizations, which emphasizes the extent of information that should be provided to a potential client up-front, such as the nature and objectives of the services, which of the individuals are clients, who will have access to the information, the limits of confidentiality, and so forth; and 8.05, Dispensing With Informed Consent for Research, which is permitted in "the study of factors related to job or organization effectiveness conducted in organizational settings for which there is no risk to participants' employability, and confidentiality is protected." It is the opinion of many practitioners (with whom I agree) that, notwithstanding Standard 8.05, we—as well as our organizational clients—are best served by proceeding on the assumption that every formal project that requires the participation of employees should be framed as voluntary and requiring informed consent, even if only informal (unless there is a good reason otherwise, such as the inability to guarantee anonymity or confidentiality in circumstances for which that would be problematic).

THE WORK AND ORGANIZATIONAL PSYCHOLOGIST AS ADMINISTRATOR

At some point, usually mid-career or later, some work and organizational psychologists (WOPs) take on considerable managerial responsibilities. Most frequently this is within a large human resources department in the private or public sector; as a principal or partner in a consulting organization; or as an educational administrator (such as department or program head, dean, head of an institute, or even college president). The person may maintain some responsibilities as a professional psychologist as well.

An important realization is that their sphere of legitimate influence and authority over others is likely to have increased, including the supervision of younger early-career-stage professionals. Accordingly, they are now more likely to be looked to by subordinates as a role model for appropriate attitudes, values, and professionalism within the organization, and seen externally as representing the organization; they may even have the authority to recommend or approve personnel actions (job assignments, promotion, salary increases). With such power comes increased responsibility for its just exercise, such as is noted in the APA Ethics Code's admonition against the exploitation of persons over which the psychologist has authority (Standard 3.08. Exploitative Relationships). WOPs are cognizant of the evidence that "emphasize[s] the salience of managerial leadership in the development, communication and effectiveness of an organization's goals, policies, practices, and expectations regarding morally relevant matters" (Lefkowitz, 2009, p. 78).

MAKING ETHICAL DECISIONS

How do people go about solving ethical dilemmas? How *should* one attempt to do so? An earlier summary offered five (overlapping) possibilities: "the legalistic approach, the cookbook approach to ethical codes, exercising one's virtues, the intuitive approach, and ethical reasoning" (Lefkowitz, 2011).

The Legalistic Approach. A rather myopic approach to morality is to view it as limited to the society's codified laws. This has the advantage of relative clarity and precision—although we know that legal interpretations do vary. A famous example is the economist Milton Friedman's (1970) argument against any form of voluntary socially responsible behavior on the part of a corporation. It was his view that because such acts are not required legally, they are immoral (spending resources that justly should go to shareholders, employees, or to consumers in the form of lower prices). However, not all corporations agree (B Corporation, 2015).

A theoretical drawback of the approach is that much of the law is limited to what is proscribed; less to what is prescribed. Consequently, it largely fails to account for the proactive, prosocial, beneficent, or justice- or virtue-based aspects of morality. A more reasonable approach is Carroll's (1991) scheme that includes four general obligations of organizations—their economic (profit-making), legal, ethical (acting within societal norms), and discretionary (promoting society's welfare) responsibilities. Another inherent limitation is that laws frequently lag behind a society's changing social and moral norms. For example, prior to the 1964 Civil Rights Act in the United States, many work and organizational psychologists implemented employee selection measures that inappropriately screened out some ethnic minorities despite the absence of demonstrated *job-relatedness* or *validation*. That was not "best practices," even at the time, but it was legal.

The Cookbook Approach. If one is fortunate, the problem under deliberation might be found in an ethical code or case book (e.g., Lowman et al., 2006) or other existing source so that a "recipe" for solution is available. That is one of the reasons to be familiar with such sources (see Stage I of "Ethical Reasoning"). But there are obvious finite limitations to the number of situations that might be represented in those sources, and the extent to which they could represent any given situation in all its particulars.

Being Virtuous. Simply deciding to be virtuous certainly sounds apt, except that there are several substantial limitations in the approach (cf. Pence, 1993; Rachels & Rachels, 2015). There is no uniform agreement on what qualifies as a virtue; many lists, of greatly varying lengths, exist. Even unambiguous virtues such as "honesty" fail to be operationalized so that one knows unambiguously how to be honest in the particular situation; and the problem of what to do when virtues apparently conflict (e.g., tell the truth versus do not cause harm) remains thorny, and might be different in different circumstances (e.g., whether the other person is a family member, acquaintance, or work colleague).

The Intuitive Approach. During the past 20 years or so the field of *moral psychology* has grown, including aspects of evolutionary psychology and neurocognitive psychology, emphasizing the role of inborn emotional responses to morally challenging situations (Alfano, 2016; Doris et al., 2010). For example, modern evolutionary theory accommodates well the propensity to develop prosocial, altruistic behavior as a consequence of both mindless automatic information processing as well as by controlled rational deliberation guided by conscious moral standards (Krebs, 2008); areas of the brain involved in one or another sorts of activities are activated in response to different kinds of moral dilemmas (Greene et al., 2001); both automatic and controlled processes have been applied to the study of ethical decision-making in the business context (Reynolds, 2006); some morally relevant situations elicit immediate emotional reactions that are experienced as automatic moral judgments that precede whatever rational deliberations might follow (Haidt, 2001; Haidt & Kesebir, 2010); and, similarly, emotional reactions to moral value statements that disagree with one's personal values occur very quickly—prior to evaluative processing (Van Berkum et al., 2009).

But however valuable this growing body of research proves to be in furthering our understanding of the evolutionary and developmental history of moral behavior, it currently offers little for those seeking guidance in how to respond appropriately to difficult ethical challenges. That is, even in those instances in which one might experience an immediate involuntary noxious reaction to a morally taboo situation so that one might be motivated to do something (e.g., being pressured to violate the confidentiality promised to survey respondents), what to do and how to arrive at that decision remain to be worked out.

Ethical Reasoning.   Even if for no other reason than the notable limitations of the other four approaches, a process of decision-making, problem-solving, or *right-reasoning* (Rachels & Rachels, 2015) seems to be necessary. But first, it is advisable to recognize the value of anticipating ethical problems before they arise so they might be prevented, avoided, or dealt with more easily.

Stage I. Practicing "Moral Hygiene."   To draw an analogy from the field of public health, "if moral problem solving represents the 'treatment' for a dilemma, this stage consists of maintaining good 'moral hygiene'" (Lefkowitz, 2017, p. 491). There are several features:

- Be familiar with the applicable ethics codes such as those of the American Psychological Association (2017), the Canadian Psychological Association (2017), the Academy of Management (n.d.), the Society for Human Resource Management (2014), and the International Task Force on Assessment Center Guidelines (2015).
- Know the applicable national and local laws and regulations.
- Be familiar with the policies, regulations, norms, expectations, and any ethics codes of the institution(s) in or with which you work.
- Engage in continuing education activities in professional ethics and other areas maintaining your competence.
- Try to be sensitive to identifying when there is a potential ethical problem by maintaining a mindset of *ethical watchfulness* (Pryor, 1989).
- Learn a method for analyzing ethical obligations in often complex situations (such as that presented immediately below, in "Stage II").

Stage II. Ethical Decision-Making.   Several ethical decision-making models have been proposed over the years, and a representative distillation of them has been presented previously (Lefkowitz, 2011, 2017). Very similar models have been proposed even more recently (e.g., Banks et al., 2022; Ethics and Compliance Initiative, n.d.). Banks et al. (2022) illustrate their model via presentation of five ethical situations. For didactic purposes, Lefkowitz's model consists of 11 discrete steps seriatim within four broad phases of analysis. But Ladenson's wry comment should be taken to heart: "in the case of any approach that analyzes the ethical decision-making process primarily in terms of a determinate, well-defined, and ordered sequence of steps, there is a near total lack of fit between subject matter and method" (cited in Gellermann et al., 1990, p. 90). Therefore,

> The "steps" in the decision-aid should not be viewed literally, to be taken seriatim—or, that the prior one must be "completed" before you can engage the next—or, for that matter, that all of them need occur in every situation. For example, it may seem that at the time one becomes cognizant of a dilemma to be dealt with, one has already implicitly

taken several of the "steps" (e.g., implicitly acquired much relevant information). It is not even unusual to begin thinking (perhaps prematurely) of solutions before one has fully articulated the issues. The "steps" should be thought of as highlighting more or less seamless points of an iterative process, as opposed to a discrete linear sequence. (Lefkowitz, 2017, p. 504)

The decision-making model is enumerated in the following sections.

Problem Identification

1. *Is the problem an ethical one?* Are ethical principles at stake? Will the alternative choices likely affect the welfare of others?
2. *Assess the structure and complexity of the problem.* Are there key issues and stakeholders you can identify? Might there be more than one of the five paradigmatic forms of ethical dilemmas involved (see Table 1)? Are there personal consequences for you?

Initial Information Gathering

3. *Get the facts.* Can you be certain of the facts underlying the situation—as distinct from assumptions and conjecture—regarding the causes and nature of the problem, as well as the anticipated consequences?
4. *Assess the seriousness of the problem.* Is physical, economic, or emotional harm to someone a possibility? If so, how many people might be so affected? What is your relationship to them; and is that a factor in the situation? Are you under time pressure to act, or can you be more deliberative?

Problem Analysis and Choice

5. *Restate the problem in ethical terms.* Based on the preceding steps, can you state the problem clearly in ethical terms? What specifically is causing the conflict? What are the ethical stakes at risk?
6. *Is there a readily available solution?* Sometimes the appropriate action will be "self-evident" to you even if distasteful in some respects. Might a compromise be possible (e.g., by accepting one moral value as outranking others with which it conflicts)? Might your advance preparation have revealed a published solution in some professional documentation? Do your colleagues or other trusted confidantes agree on the appropriate action?
7. *Acknowledge your own values and self-serving biases, as well as any external pressure.* Are there internal or extrinsic forces that might distort the quality of your ethical judgement (cf. Bazerman & Tenbrunsel, 2011)? Would you be able to acknowledge their potential role in providing a post hoc "values justification"—that is, rationalization—for a self-serving choice? Introspect: What do you know about yourself that might limit or distort your perspective?
8. *Enumerate all options and their consequences.* A "brainstorming" approach, attempting to identify all alternatives no matter how unlikely, is often useful. Similarly, try to anticipate the implications of each option for all stakeholders.
9. *Evaluate and choose.* The guiding principles for right-reasoning are universalism (appropriate consideration of the interests of all stakeholders) and universalizability (you would

accept others making the same choice as you have, and vice versa). So you are satisfied that the arguments favoring your choice are better than those supporting other options, and you are satisfied that self-interest has not played a major role in your decision.

Following Through

10. *Implement the choice.* If circumstances permit, are you willing to share your tentative decision with those affected? Is there something you missed? Be mindful that implementing a solution, especially in complex organizations, may be more difficult and require a different skill set than the ethical decision-making per se. So plan carefully; your good intentions may not be the primary determinants of actions taken.
11. *Evaluation and review.* Are the consequences as you expected? If no, why not? Did you misread the situation? To what extent has the initial problem been resolved? Might the "solution" have caused new problems that must be addressed? If so, have you acknowledged your responsibility? Note what have you learned that will be useful next time.

Given the findings of the ethics surveys reviewed above in which only about one-third of the respondents considered the ethical incident they reported to have been resolved relatively satisfactorily, it is probably unreasonable to expect that one can achieve an entirely positive outcome for every ethical dilemma. But producing increasingly skilled efforts to do so should be the objective.

REFERENCES

Academy of Management. (n.d.). *Academy of Management code of ethics.* Academy of Management code of ethics.

Alfano, M. (2016). *Moral psychology: An introduction.* Polity Press.

Alzola, M. (2015). Virtuous persons and virtuous actions in business ethics and organizational research. *Business Ethics Quarterly, 25*(3), 287–318.

American Psychological Association. (2017). *Ethical principles of psychologists and code of conduct.* American Psychological Association.

American Psychological Association, Committee on Standards for Providers of Psychological Services. (1981). Specialty guidelines for the delivery of services by industrial/organizational psychologists. *American Psychologist, 36*(6), 664–669.

Anscombe, G. E. M. (1958). Modern moral philosophy. *Philosophy, 33,* 1–19.

Aristotle. (2004). *The Nicomachean ethics.* Penguin Books. (Original work published 1953)

Ashforth, B. E., Gioia, D. A., Robinson, L. L., & TreviZo, L. K. (2008). Introduction to special topic forum: Re-viewing organizational corruption. *Academy of Management Review, 33*(3), 670–684.

Assembly of the International Union of Psychological Science. (2008). *Universal declaration of ethical principles for psychologists.* International Union of Psychological Science.

Audi, R. (2012). Virtue ethics as a resource in business. *Business Ethics Quarterly, 22*(2), 273–291.

B Corporation. (2015). *Make business a force for good.* http://www.bcorporation.net/

Bandura, A. (1991). Social cognitive theory of moral thought and action. In W. M. Kurtines & J. L. Gewirtz (Eds.), *Handbook of moral behavior and development: Vol. 1. Theory* (pp. 45–103). Lawrence Erlbaum Associates.

Banks, G. C., Knapp, D. J., Lin, L., Sanders, C. S., & Grand, J. A. (2022). Ethical decision-making in the 21st century: A useful framework for industrial-organizational psychologists. *Industrial and Organizational Psychology, 15*(2), 220–235.

Baritz, L. (1960). *The servants of power: A history of social science in American industry.* Greenwoods.

Bazerman, M. H., & Tenbrunsel, A. E. (2011). *Blind spots: Why we fail to do what's right and what to do about it.* Princeton University Press.

Canadian Psychological Association. (2017). *Canadian code of ethics for psychologists* (4th ed.).

Carroll, A. B. (1991). CSP measurement: A commentary for methods for evaluating an elusive construct. In J. E. Post (Ed.), *Research in corporate social performance and policy* (Vol. 12, pp. 385–401). JAI.

Chun, R. (2010). Organizational virtue, CSR, and performance. In M. Schminke (Ed.), *Managerial ethics: Managing the psychology of morality.* Routledge.

Committee on Science, Engineering and Public Policy (U.S.). Panel on Scientific Responsibility and the Conduct of Research. (1992). Responsible science: Ensuring the integrity of the research process. National Academy Press.

Cortina, L. M., Kabat-Farr, D., Magley, V. J., & Nelson, K. (2017). Researching rudeness: The past, present, and future of the science of incivility. *Journal of Occupational Health Psychology, 22*(3), 299–313.

Dion, M. (2010). What is corruption corrupting? A philosophical viewpoint. *Journal of Money Laundering Control, 13*(1), 45–54.

Doris, J. M., & the Moral Psychology Research Group. (2010). *The moral psychology handbook.* Oxford University Press.

Ethics and Compliance Initiative. (n.d.). *The PLUS ethical decision-making model.* https://www.ethics.org /resources/free-toolkit/decision-making-model/

Ferguson, C. J. (2015). "Everybody knows psychology is not a real science": Public perceptions of psychology and how we can improve our relationship with policymakers, the scientific community, and the general public. *American Psychologist, 70*(6), 527–542.

Friedman, M. (1970, September 13). The social responsibility of business is to increase its profits. *The New York Times* (pp. 32–33, 122, 124, 126).

Gellermann, W., Frankel, M. S., & Ladenson, R. F. (1990). *Values and ethics in organization and human systems development: Responding to dilemmas in professional life.* Jossey-Bass.

Greene, J. D., Sommerville, R. B., Nystrom, L. E., Darley, J. M., & Cohen, J. D. (2001). An fMRI investigation of emotional engagement in moral judgment. *Science, 293*(5537), 2105–2108.

Haidt, J. (2001). The emotional dog and its rational tail: A social intuitionist approach to moral judgment. *Psychological Review, 108*, 814–834.

Haidt, J., & Kesebir, S. (2010). Morality. In S. Fiske, D. Gilbert, & G. Lindzy (Eds.), *Handbook of social psychology* (5th ed., Vol. 2, pp. 797–832). Wiley.

International Task Force on Assessment Center Guidelines. (2015). Guidelines and ethical considerations for assessment center operations. *Journal of Management, 41*(4), 1244–1273.

Katzell, R. A., & Austin, J. T. (1992). From then to now: The development of industrial-organizational psychology in the United States. *Journal of Applied Psychology, 77*(6), 803–835.

Kelman, H. C. (1972). The rights of the subject in social research: An analysis in terms of relative power and legitimacy. *American Psychologist, 27*(11), 989–1016.

Kilburg, R. R. (2012). *Virtuous leaders: Strategy, character, and influence in the 21st century.* American Psychological Association.

Kimball, B. A. (1992). *The "true professional ideal" in America.* Blackwell.

Kimmel, A. J. (2007). *Ethical issues in behavioral research: Basic and applied perspectives* (2nd ed.). Blackwell.

Kornhauser, A. (1947). Industrial psychology as management technique and as social science. *American Psychologist, 2*(7), 224–229.

Krebs, D. L. (2008). Morality: An evolutionary account. *Perspectives on Psychological Science, 3*(3), 149–172.

Lefkowitz, J. (1990). The scientist-practitioner model is not enough. *The Industrial-Organizational Psychologist, 28*(1), 47–52.

Lefkowitz, J. (2005). The values of industrial-organizational psychology: Who are we? *The Industrial-Organizational Psychologist, 43*(2), 13–20.

Lefkowitz, J. (2006). The constancy of ethics amidst the changing world of work. *Human Resource Management Review, 16*(2), 245–268.

Lefkowitz, J. (2007a). Ethics in industrial-organizational psychology research. In S. Rogelberg (Ed.), *The encyclopedia of industrial and organizational psychology* (Vol. 1, pp. 218–222). SAGE.

Lefkowitz, J. (2007b). Ethics in industrial-organizational psychology practice. In S. Rogelberg (Ed.), *The encyclopedia of industrial and organizational psychology* (Vol. 1, pp. 215–218). SAGE.

Lefkowitz, J. (2008). To prosper, organizational psychology should . . . expand its values to match the quality of its ethics. *Journal of Organizational Behavior, 29*(4), 439–453.

Lefkowitz, J. (2009). Individual and organizational antecedents of misconduct in organizations: What do we [believe that we] know, and on what bases do we [believe that we] know it? In C. Cooper & R. Burke (Eds.), *Research companion to crime and corruption in organizations* (pp. 60–91). Edward Elgar.

Lefkowitz, J. (2011). Ethics in industrial-organizational psychology. In S. Knapp, L. VandeCreek, M. Gottlieb, & M. Handelsman (Eds.), *APA handbook of ethics in psychology* (Vol. 2). American Psychological Association.

Lefkowitz, J. (2014). Educating I–O psychologists for science, practice, and social responsibility. *Industrial and Organizational Psychology, 7*(1), 41–46.

Lefkowitz, J. (2016). News flash! Work psychology discovers workers! *Industrial and Organizational Psychology, 9*(1), 137–144.

Lefkowitz, J. (2017). *Ethics and values in industrial–organizational psychology* (2nd ed.). Routledge/Taylor & Francis.

Lefkowitz, J. (2021). Forms of ethical dilemmas in industrial-organizational psychology. *Industrial and Organizational Psychology: Perspectives on Science and Practice, 14*(3), 297–319.

Lefkowitz, J. (2023). *Values and ethics for industrial–organizational psychology* (3rd ed.). Routledge/Taylor & Francis.

Lefkowitz, J., & Lowman, R.L. (2017). Ethics of employee selection. In J. L. Farr & N. T. Tippins (Eds.), *Handbook of employee selection* (2nd ed., pp. 575–598). Routledge/Taylor & Francis.

Lefkowitz, J., & Watts, L. (2022). Ethical incidents reported by industrial-organizational psychologists: A ten-year follow-up. *Journal of Applied Psychology, 107*(10), 1781–1803. https://doi.org/10.1037/apl0000946

Lilienfeld, S. O. (2012). Public skepticism of psychology: Why many people perceive the study of human behavior as unscientific. *American Psychologist, 67*(2), 111–129.

Lowman, R. L., Lefkowitz, J., McIntyre, R., & Tippins, N. (Eds.). (2006). *The ethical practice of psychology in organizations* (2nd ed.). American Psychological Association.

MacCoun, R. J. (1998). Biases in the interpretation and use of research results. *Annual Review of Psychology, 49*, 259–287.

Macrina, F. L. (2014). *Scientific integrity: Text and cases in responsible conduct of research* (4th ed.). ASM Press.

McConnell, T. (2018). Moral dilemmas. In E. N. Zalta (Ed.), *The Stanford encyclopedia of philosophy* (Fall 2018 ed.). Metaphysics Research Lab, Center for the Study of Language, and Information, Stanford University. https://plato.stanford.edu/entries/moral-dilemmas/

Merriam-Webster Unabridged Dictionary. (2016). *Dilemma.* http://www.merriam-webster.com/dictionary/dilemma

Milgram, S. (1963). Behavioral study of obedience. *Journal of Abnormal and Social Psychology, 67*(4), 371–378.

Milgram, S. (1974). *Obedience to authority*. Harper & Row.

Moore, G. (2008). Re-imagining the morality of management: A modern virtue ethics approach. *Business Ethics Quarterly, 18*(4), 483–511.

Office of Research Integrity. Federal research misconduct policy (2000). *Federal Register, 65*(235), 76260–76264.

Orne, M. T. (1962). On the social psychology of the psychological experiment: With particular reference to demand characteristics and their implications. *American Psychologist, 17*(11), 776–783.

Pence, G. (1993). Virtue theory. In P. Singer (Ed.), *A companion to ethics* (pp. 249–258). Blackwell.

Prinz, J. J. (2008). Is morality innate? In W. Sinnott-Armstrong (Ed.), *Moral psychology: Vol. I. The evolution of morality: Innateness and adaptation* (pp. 367–406). Massachusetts Institute of Technology Press.

Prinz, J. J., & Nichols, S. (2010). Moral emotions. In J. M. Doris & the Moral Psychology Research Group, *The moral psychology handbook* (pp. 111–146). Oxford University Press.

Pryor, R. G. L. (1989). Conflicting responsibilities: A case study of an ethical dilemma for psychologists working in organizations. *Australian Psychologist, 24*(2), 293–305.

Rachels, J., & Rachels, S. (2015). *The elements of moral philosophy* (8th ed.). McGraw-Hill.

Rest, J. R. (1994). Background: Theory and research. In J. R. Rest & D. Narvaez (Eds.), *Moral development in the professions* (pp. 1–26). Lawrence Erlbaum Associates.

Reynolds, S. J. (2006). A neurocognitive model of the ethical decision-making process: Implications for study and practice. *Journal of Applied Psychology, 91*(4), 737–748.

Roback, A. A. (1917). The moral issues involved in applied psychology. *Journal of Applied Psychology, 1*(3), 232–243.

Sadler-Smith, E. (2013). Toward organizational environmental virtuousness. *The Journal of Applied Behavioral Science, 49*(1), 123–148.

Sales, B. D., & Folkman, S. (Eds.). (2000). *Ethics in research with human participants*. American Psychological Association.

Shafer-Landau, R. (2015). *The fundamentals of ethics* (3rd ed.). Oxford University Press.

Shamoo, A. E., & Resnik, D. B. (2009). *Responsible conduct of research* (2nd ed.). Oxford University Press.

Singer, P. (1995). *Practical ethics* (2nd ed.). Cambridge University Press.

Sison, A. J. G., Hartman, E. M., & Fontrodona, J. (2012). Reviving tradition: Virtue and the common good in business and management. *Business Ethics Quarterly, 22*(2), 207–210.

Society for Human Resource Management. (2014). *Code of ethics*. https://www.shrm.org/about-shrm/pages/code-of-ethics.aspx

Society for Industrial and Organizational Psychology. (2021). *SIOP vision, mission, values, and goals*. https://www.siop.org/About-SIOP/Mission

Steneck, N. H. (2006). Fostering integrity in research: Definitions, current knowledge, and future directions. *Science and Engineering Ethics, 12*(1), 53–74.

Sterba, S. K. (2006). Misconduct in the analysis and reporting of data: Bridging methodological and ethical agendas for change. *Ethics & Behavior, 16*(4), 305–318.

Stocker, M. (1976). The schizophrenia of modern ethical theories. *The Journal of Philosophy, 73*(14), 453–466.

Thompson, R. A. (2009). Early foundations: Conscience and the development of moral character. In D. Narvaez & D. K. Lapsley (Eds.), *Personality, identity, and character: Explorations in moral psychology* (pp. 159–184). Cambridge University Press.

U.S. Department of Health and Human Services. (2019). Subpart A of 45 CFR Part 46: *Basic HHS policy for protection of human subjects*. As revised Jan. 19, 2017, and amended on Jan. 22, 2018 and June 19, 2018. (Effective Jan. 21, 2019.)

Van Berkum, J. J. A., Holleman, B., Niewland, M., Otten, M., & Murre, J. (2009). Right or wrong? The brain's fast response to morally objectionable statements. *Psychological Science, 20*(9), 1092–1099.

Wasserman, R. (2013). Ethical issues and guidelines for conducting data analysis in psychological research. *Ethics & Behavior, 23*(1), 3–15.

Whetstone, J. T. (2001). How virtue fits within business ethics. *Journal of Business Ethics, 33*, 101–114.

Wittmer, D. P. (2001). Ethical decision-making. In T. L. Cooper (Ed.), *Handbook of administrative ethics* (2nd ed., pp. 481–507). Marcel Dekker.

NOTES

1. Although Aristotle (1953) was an ethical egoist (the criterion of a good life is one's own flourishing), he finessed the issue by observing that doing good for others, altruism, is personally pleasing/fulfilling, hence there is no conflict.
2. Values can be defined as "relatively stable cognitive representations of what the person believes are desirable standards of conduct or generalized end states. They have affective and evaluative components in that they are experienced in terms of their relative importance in the person's ideal self-concept; they have a motivational component in that they serve to initiate and guide people's evaluations, choices, and actions" (Lefkowitz, 2017, p. 190).
3. See section on "The Work and Organizational Psychologist as Practitioner" for more on this issue.
4. Details of the survey procedures and methodology are presented in the source citations.
5. The five structural forms of ethical dilemmas are descriptors designed to be applicable and commensurable across multiple work domains.
6. As distinct from the *ethics of science*, which has to do with the protection of the integrity of the scientific enterprise.
7. This willingness was exploited in a famous and ethically dubious series of experiments (Milgram, 1963, 1974).

Joel Lefkowitz

Main Theories
and Approaches

THE SOCIOTECHNICAL APPROACH TO WORK ORGANIZATION

INTRODUCTION

Simply described, the sociotechnical approach proposes that the organization of work should seek the joint optimization of the social and the technical systems in the workplace to the mutual benefit of both the employer and employees. Within a wider interdisciplinary framework, it offers the potential to apply a set of psychological principles to the organization of work. The idea of a sociotechnical approach to the organization of work first emerged in the 1950s and was extensively elaborated and applied in organizations in the following decades. However, academic evaluations revealed mixed results, including an overemphasis on the social at the expense of the technical system, leading to a number of adaptations that have been applied in contemporary organizations and are described in the section "Shifting the Focus: Giving Primacy to the Technical System." This review analyzes the nature, impact, evolution, and continuing viability of the sociotechnical systems approach as well as the challenges of introducing what can be viewed as quite radical changes in ways of working into complex organizational systems.

THE ORIGINS OF THE SOCIOTECHNICAL APPROACH

The Coal Mining Study Reported by Trist and Bamforth (1951). The idea of a sociotechnical approach to work organization can be traced to an article by Trist and Bamforth (1951) published in the journal *Human Relations*. This reported a study in the U.K. coal mining industry where a new and more efficient approach to extracting coal, the so-called longwall method, was replacing the traditional hand-got, small group-based approach. This reflected a significant technological advance and promised considerable improvements in productivity as well as opportunities for closer supervisory monitoring of work. However, this resulted in dissatisfaction among the miners because it had considerably narrowed roles and broken up the established work groups. In the context of the dangerous work at the coalface, these groups had consisted of workers who trusted each other and could be relied on to ensure safety and support. Alongside this, there was increased absenteeism, labor turnover, and industrial unrest and a failure to make the anticipated productivity gains. The researchers found one mine in the coalfield where a different approach had been adopted, which they termed the composite longwall system. This retained the intact work groups and many of the individual skills and provided the groups with considerable autonomy. While this did not appear to reflect the most efficient use of the technology, it resulted in higher worker satisfaction, better health indicators in a context where stress and ill health was a chronic problem among miners, and improvements in productivity. It is therefore an example of mutual gains for both management and workers.

Trist, Bamforth, and their colleagues at the Tavistock Institute of Human Relations drew several lessons from this study. First, they noted that organizations comprised both technical and social systems and that maximizing the technical system while ignoring the social system resulted in costs that were likely to limit any gains that the technical system offered. What was therefore required was an approach that optimized both the technical and the social system, namely a sociotechnical system. As Trist and Bamforth (1951, p. 38) put it, organizations should provide "responsible autonomy to primary groups throughout the system and ensuring that each of these groups has a satisfying sub-whole as its work task and some scope for flexibility in work pace." In short, sociotechnical work organization challenged technological determinism by requiring consideration of both the demands of technology and attention to social factors such as the division of labor, skill utilization, and responsible worker autonomy, with the work group as a primary unit of analysis.

The Background to the Emergence of Sociotechnical Work Organization. To understand why the sociotechnical concept seemed novel at the time, it is helpful to consider the wider context. Within industry, scientific management, advanced by Taylor, held sway (Taylor, 1947). This proposed that productivity gains could be achieved by advances in technology allied to simplification of work and by the organization of work to ensure that workers were subjugated to the demands of the technology. Techniques such as time and motion study were introduced with the aim of ensuring "a fair day's work" for "a fair day's pay" based on a careful analysis of the work of a "first class man." The aim was to arrive at the most efficient division of labor and organization of work. It was assumed that workers were extrinsically motivated and that financial incentives would therefore provide the best form of motivation to ensure high performance. The role of supervisors was to monitor performance. Taylor's assumption was that this would result in a fair effort-reward bargain. However, views about fairness differed and use of financial incentives often provided workers with the control to determine output leading to the potential for restriction of output and other forms of industrial conflict in an attempt to negotiate a better rate for the job. Accounts emerged of a range of ways in which workers controlled output and used group pressures to ensure a degree of work-group conformity (Lupton, 1963; Roy, 1952; Whyte, 1955), challenging the efficacy of the scientific management approach.

In parallel with, and partly in reaction to the application of scientific management, psychologists and other social scientists developed an alternative view of work organization with what came to be known at the human relations movement. They emphasized the importance of the social system as the major influence on workers' behavior, producing evidence to show that a supportive social system resulted in superior performance to the approach associated with scientific management. Most notably, the Hawthorne Studies (Roethlisberger & Dickson, 1939) appeared to demonstrate that the work group had a major influence on individual worker performance, confirming the role of the group as a key unit of analysis that could influence increases in performance but also restriction of output. An influential experiment by Lewin et al. (1939) revealed the benefits of participative leadership, while Coch and French (1948) reported that group participation could help to overcome resistance to change. However, these studies were not without their critics. For example, a follow-up study by French et al. (1960) in a Norwegian factory failed to replicate the original study by Coch and French, partly because it went against the grain of traditional negotiations with unions about change that were perceived as more likely to ensure protection of pay levels. Perhaps more tellingly, a study by Strauss, reported in Whyte (1955) provides an account of how a group involved in paint spraying of dolls were given the autonomy to determine the speed of their production line. Soon their productivity soared and they were earning more than skilled workers. However, they were part of a larger production line and created problems for those who came before and after them in the production process to such an extent that the experiment was abandoned. As a result, 75% of the group left the company within a month. The important lesson is that group autonomy must be viewed within the context of the wider production and social system. This is one of the central tenets of the sociotechnical systems approach.

THE EVOLUTION OF THE SOCIOTECHNICAL APPROACH

A group of social scientists, mainly based at the Tavistock Institute of Human Relations in London, was largely responsible for the development and initial application of the sociotechnical systems approach. They developed a number of general principles that informed the approach and a set of more specific guidelines and assumptions on which to base interventions in organizations.

The General Principles of Sociotechnical Work Organization

The principle of organizational choice.   This challenges technological determinism and argues that there is always a choice of design of work arrangements. This principle is elaborated by Trist et al. (1963) in their book *Organizational Choice*. There had been some consideration about whether greater weight should be given to the economic system but this was dropped on the grounds that it was not central to the organization of work. The core choice therefore centered around the relationship between the technical and the social system reflecting the view that work systems should be designed to achieve both high performance and high worker well-being.

Organizations as open systems.   Advocates of the sociotechnical approach were influenced by the work of Von Bertalanffy (1950) who proposed an open system in the analysis of physics and biology. Adapting this to the organizational context, organizations were viewed as systems with inputs, processes, and outputs. The significance of this was that changes to external circumstances would be likely to influence internal processes (Emery & Trist, 1965). It was therefore inappropriate to view the organization and its internal systems as closed or independent. It also meant that organizations needed to be adaptable since neither the technological nor the social system were immutable.

The principle of joint optimization.   While organizations operate in open systems with a range of external and internal influences requiring adaptability and scope for organizational choice, a major goal for achieving the best outcomes is to ensure optimization of both the technical and the social systems. This may mean that neither receives primacy and that some compromises have to be made based on the assumption that the benefits of joint optimization outweigh the costs of giving primacy to one system, usually the technical system, at the expense of the other.

Work groups as the primary unit of analysis.   While it was accepted that analysis could be conducted at a number of different levels within an organizational system, it was proposed the key level of analysis was the work group subsystem where the main interface between the technical and social systems was likely to occur. One telling example of this was provided in a series of studies in Norway by Emery and Thorsrud (1976). Their initial investigation of the appointment of worker representatives to boards of companies (Emery & Thorsrud, 1969) found that this had little or no impact on the experience of workers on the shop floor justifying their shift in focus to the work group and work unit.

Action research and participation.   Researchers at the Tavistock Institute had been heavily influenced by the work of Lewin (1947) who had conducted experiments showing how social groups could influence behavior through what was described as action research. Specifically, he had shown how eating habits could be changed through behavioral commitment and how leadership could influence group behavior. The study of Coch and French (1948) had appeared to show how group participation could help to overcome resistance to change. The lessons that were taken from these studies were that the role of a change agent could facilitate change and that ownership of change by a group could be a powerful way of generating commitment to new ways of working.

Principles of Sociotechnical Design of Jobs and Work Units.   Drawing on the experience gained from early studies of sociotechnical design and other studies conducted by the Tavistock Institute, Emery set out more specific principles for the design of jobs and work groups (Emery & Thorsrud, 1976). These started from the premise that workers had certain "needs" that should be met at work to avoid alienation and provide scope for fulfilling work. These consisted of:

- The need for a job to be reasonably demanding/challenging.
- The need to learn and go on learning on the job.
- The need for some area of decision-making.
- The need for a minimal degree of helpfulness and recognition.
- The need to be able to relate work to social life.
- The need to feel the job leads to some sort of desirable future.

While this is a plausible list and provides some potentially useful guidelines, it does not reflect any established notion of psychological needs. An important feature of the list is the emphasis on an optimal amount of responsibility, decision-making, and so on; not too much and not too little. There are parallels here with the job demands–resources models of Karasek (1979) and Bakker and Demerouti (2017) in seeking to find a balance and at the same time account for individual differences and competences.

The set of needs were translated by Emery and Thorsrud (1976) into specific principles for work design. First, with respect to individual jobs:

- There should be an optimum variety of tasks.
- There should be a pattern of tasks that provides a sense of a meaningful whole.
- There should be an optimum length of a work cycle.
- Workers should have some scope to determine the quantity and quality of the work.
- The job should include and carry some responsibility for preparatory and boundary tasks.
- The tasks and the job should command some respect in the community.
- The job should make some perceptible contribution to the utility of the product for the consumer.

Again, the emphasis is on an optimum level of activity rather than any risk of overreaching through levels of variety or responsibility that could lead to excessive demand. Since the major interest lay in the group as a central unit within the social system, the job design principles were extended to the design of activities for what Trist and others described as primary work groups and came to be known as autonomous work groups. In practice, advocates acknowledged that almost no work groups were entirely autonomous so that the more correct term was a semiautonomous work group. The principles set out by Emery and Thorsrud (1976) for their design included:

- There should be provision for "interlocking" tasks, job rotation, and physical proximity where there is a necessary interdependence of jobs, where individual jobs entail a relatively high degree of stress, and where individual jobs don't make a discernible contribution to the end product.
- Groups should, as an extension of the principle for individual job design, have an overall task that makes an identifiable contribution, have scope for setting standards and receiving feedback on results, allocate roles within the group, and have some control over boundary tasks. At the heart of the concept of the autonomous work group is therefore the concept of self-regulation by the group members.

Cherns (1976, 1987) set out an overlapping set of sociotechnical principles for work design that address concerns primarily at the organizational level. His 1987 paper was a development and essentially a clarification and extension of his earlier paper based on experience in the intervening decade. His principles included:

- Compatibility of design with the aims of the system.
- Minimal critical specification to allow scope for adaptation and learning.
- Variance control as close as possible to the potential source of the variance.
- Appropriate boundary location. This calls for the establishment of boundaries between work groups and between groups and management as well as boundary management. This could be a role for members of the group within the boundary or a role for supervisors at the boundary.
- Information flow to ensure that relevant information reaches those who need it.
- Support congruence to ensure that other organizational systems and notably human resource systems, such as rewards, are compatible with the organization design.
- Power and authority should operate to ensure that there is access to, and responsibility for materials, resources, and performance at the appropriate level and in the appropriate units or groups in the organization.
- Incompletion, which can be coupled with a new 1987 principle of transitional organizations, to reflect a view that design of organizations is a continuous process.
- A concern for quality of working life as one of the goals of the system.

This set of principles goes well beyond what might be viewed as the territory of sociotechnical systems. Indeed, it is directed in part at consultants and change agents drawing on Cherns's own experience and that of others such as Davis (1977), an engineer who developed an interest in sociotechnical principles.

It can be seen from analysis of these lists of principles for sociotechnical design set out by its advocates that they are fluid and dynamic and reflect experience as action researchers who have engaged in consultancy to contribute to both the design and evaluation of sociotechnical systems at different levels within organizations. The different experiences result in varying emphases which from time to time have been drawn together, more particularly by the team of Tavistock action researchers (Trist et al., 1963; Trist et al., 1993). Over time, different action researchers have extensively adapted or extended the sociotechnical principles to meet different conditions.

Having set out the rather disparate principles for sociotechnical design, the next section reviews its impact, first at the workplace level and then at the organizational level.

OUTCOMES OF THE SOCIOTECHNICAL DESIGN OF WORKPLACES AND ORGANIZATIONS

It is difficult to provide a systematic evaluation of sociotechnical interventions due to the variety of contexts, interventions, and measures. Since many of the widely known interventions are presented as extended case studies, this section will describe and evaluate some of these "demonstration" examples before drawing together the lessons that emerge.

The Coal Mining Studies. The original coal mining studies in the Yorkshire coalfield (Trist & Bamforth, 1951) that had led to the idea of a sociotechnical system with autonomous work groups were followed up when more examples were found of similar work arrangements in other U.K. mines which are described in Trist et al. (1963) and summarized in Trist (1993). In the Nottingham coalfield, partly at the initiative of a local area manager, autonomous work groups of 20 to 25 miners carried out all the tasks on a shift. All were multiskilled and all received the same pay. Trist reports that "productivity and work satisfaction were unusually and consistently high" (1993, p. 44). Steps were taken to extend the approach to other mines in the area. In the Durham coalfield, an example of large autonomous work groups was found. Over a 4-year project, a complete colliery changed to the "composite" form of group working. Evaluations revealed that output was 25% higher with lower costs compared with conventional methods, while accidents, sickness, and absenteeism were halved (Trist et al., 1963). It was also possible to reduce layers of management, reflecting the system-wide implications. Despite the acknowledged success of autonomous group working in each of the mining studies, the researchers encountered what was to become a familiar problem. In both cases, the Divisional Boards blocked further development, partly, it was argued, because of fear of giving too much autonomy to miners and partly because of their belief that technology should have primacy. Following the Durham research, both the National Coal Board and the National Union of Miners, while acknowledging the success of autonomous group working, were giving priority to negotiations over pit closures and neither wanted to take the approach further.

Some years later, Trist participated in a study exploring the possibility of introducing autonomous group working in an American mine (Trist et al., 1977). The union, which had concerns about safety in the mine, supported an experiment to introduce autonomous work groups, and top management was also enthusiastic. The action research project involved extensive preparatory processes, two experimental autonomous work groups, and control groups. The evaluation showed that the first autonomous work group in particular was successful in achieving comparatively fewer safety violations and accidents, somewhat lower absence, lower maintenance costs, and higher productivity. Members of the group reported higher autonomy and decision latitude, a reduction in pressure from management, and generally less stress and tiredness at the end of the working day, all reflecting improvement in their quality of working life. Despite these indications of success, when it was proposed to extend autonomous group work to the entire mine, this was narrowly voted down by the local union members. In the following months the autonomous work groups disintegrated and the mine experienced several short strikes. The subsequent evaluation identified a number of reasons for this negative outcome. First, there was relatively low trust in management's aims allied to suspicion that autonomous work groups would be used to derecognize the union. Second, there was jealousy of the privileges accorded in particular to the first group members who were able, for example, to attend meetings outside the mine. Third, there was resentment among experienced miners when newcomers were drafted into the second autonomous work group and received higher pay than their experienced colleagues elsewhere in the mine. Finally, there was opposition from middle management who perceived the innovations as a threat to their role and status. The lessons from this study concern the importance of being sensitive to, and taking account of the wider systems implications including traditional status hierarchies, issues of perceived fairness, and the history of labor relations.

The Ahmedabad Experiment. Rice (1953, 1955, 1963), another member of the Tavistock Institute of Human Relations, was invited to visit the Calico Mills in Ahmedabad, India, where he raised the idea of a sociotechnical approach, and specifically the possibility that a group of workers should become responsible for the whole process for a sizeable set of looms in the automatic loom shed. The workers themselves developed the approach which was successfully implemented with management support and subsequently transferred to other loom sheds in the large 9,000-worker plant. The application of autonomous group working resulted in higher productivity and higher worker satisfaction as well as significant gains in efficiency and reduced maintenance costs. It should be noted that there were also increases in basic pay and financial incentives which one critical reviewer suggested could account for the performance gains (Roy, 1969).

Miller (1975) conducted a follow-up 15 years later. He found that workers in the original experimental shed had continued to operate as an autonomous work group throughout the period producing high performance and displaying a strong group identity and high morale. However, the workers in the other sheds had largely reverted to the original work system. Miller offers a number of explanations for this. First, he notes that the original experimental site had retained many of the original group members whereas the others had experienced high turnover drawing in new workers who were not familiar with group working. Second, the experimental group had continued to undertake the same kinds of weaving and yarn whereas other groups had seen constant changes in line with changes in fashion. Third, as the business entered new markets, there were demands for higher efficiency along with regular changes in market requirements. One consequence was that financial incentives were geared more strongly to output at the expense of good maintenance creating a vicious circle as machines broke down more often resulting in extra pressure, which management sought to control. Finally, and linked to these pressures, boundary management, which was an essential feature of autonomous work groups, was neglected at all levels within the organization, partly reflecting a loss of interest among senior management in autonomous group working. These points illustrate the importance of an open systems perspective and the comparison between the calm environment for the sustained success of the experimental group and the turbulent environment that led to the gradual collapse of group working at the other sites.

The Norwegian Studies. A set of Norwegian studies applied a sociotechnical systems approach with the broad aim of extending industrial democracy on the shop floor. They were intended to provide demonstration cases for possible wider national application and the program of action research had support at the national level from business and unions. They followed the evidence that appointing worker directors to company boards had no perceptible impact on industrial democracy for workers on the ground (Emery & Thorsrud, 1969). As a result, an action research approach based on sociotechnical principles, with considerable involvement at the local level, including workers' representatives, was adopted. Four organizations provided the experimental context. The sociotechnical principles outlined by Emery and Thorsrud (1976) were applied with a core focus on identifying the tasks for autonomous groups, including management of variances, developing systems of self-regulation and managing boundary conditions.

The first study in the wire-drawing department of the metal manufacturing company, Christiania Spigerverk, was not a success. A change from one worker to one machine to a group of workers looking after a set of machines was proposed but a number of workers were reluctant to take part in the study, viewing it as something being imposed on them. Group working was eventually agreed and productivity rose by 20%. However, this also meant an increase in the agreed bonus, which caused dissatisfaction elsewhere in the plant. Therefore, although workers directly involved were happy with the new arrangements, management felt unable to extend group working throughout the plant and the experimental group returned to the old ways of working. This highlights once again the systems implications and the importance of gaining commitment at all levels in the organization to support the changes. In this case, relevant features of the wider system include industrial relations and rewards, job security, and the levels of trust between workers, management, and sometimes between workers and their union, as well as suspicion of the role of the researchers. These lessons were taken forward into the three subsequent studies.

The second field experiment involved a 30-worker section of the Hunsfos paper mill. The research team designed a group scheme involving greater local decision-making, training to upgrade skills and enable workers to undertake all the tasks in the section, greater internal communication and information provision, and a move from a complex individual reward system to a local departmental bonus scheme. Once again, the core principle was to create autonomous group working by a self-managed team. Following initial skepticism among some workers, partly reflecting concerns about the role of the researchers, implementation occurred once a local action committee was formed to take the project forward. The result was an improvement in quality and output levels and enthusiasm among the workers to continue working under the new system. The experiment had the strong support of the local union and management and over a number of years the sociotechnical approach spread successfully throughout the plant.

A third study was conducted at Nobo in a new department of 30 workers manufacturing electric panel heaters. The work was largely unskilled and organized along scientific management principles with piece-rate payment. Management invited the researchers to set up a sociotechnical system of working. Training enabled workers to become skilled to undertake several tasks, coordination roles were established, and some support tasks were incorporated enabling autonomous group working. Piecework was replaced by fixed basic pay plus a group bonus. After 10 weeks, productivity had increased by 20% and continued to rise further. Most workers were happy with the new system of group working and it spread successfully to the rest of the 100-worker site.

The final study took place at the Norsk Hydro fertilizer company. The impetus for the experiment lay in the challenging financial circumstances the company faced and the poor industrial relations at the plant. Initial discussions centered on pay and job security, both of which had to be resolved before any progress on the design of work was possible. A new pay scheme linking payment to the acquisition of skills provided an incentive for team members to become multiskilled. The multiskilling enabled job rotation and incorporation of many maintenance tasks facilitating the development of small autonomous work groups. A group bonus was linked to quantity and quality of output. The outcome was judged to be a success and the sociotechnical principles were then applied to the design of a new plant. The initial proposal, based on traditional scientific management lines, had been for a workforce of 94 undertaking a range of specialist tasks. The new proposal suggested that 56 workers would be sufficient, and 60 were eventually agreed. The new plant was successfully set up based on the sociotechnical design principles resulting in high levels of output and high worker satisfaction. This project was viewed as a success and it was agreed to diffuse the approach throughout the organization. But a range of external factors limited progress. These included changes in markets and in strategic priorities as well as the considerable complexity of trying to bring about this type of change in one of the largest companies in Norway.

These Norwegian examples indicate that the challenge lies not so much in the application of sociotechnical principles for the design of autonomous group working but in gaining commitment to change, in creating and sustaining ownership of the new system of working, in building in resilience when external factors present possible threats, and in achieving diffusion to other sites. In all this, the role of external consultants and researchers is considered essential in facilitating change through their action research activity but also potentially problematic if they are perceived as a threat or if they become too central to the success of the whole exercise.

Assumptions about potential diffusion of the lessons from these field experiments was a central feature of support for them at the national level. The broad aim was to use these demonstration cases as examples to spread the application of industrial democracy and sociotechnical work organization throughout Norwegian industry. It largely failed in this endeavor. As Bolweg (1976) notes, despite considerable efforts by the joint union and management national-level Cooperation Council, only 32 companies tried to introduce changes along the lines suggested and only five managed to produce sustained change. Bolweg describes one of these, Norsk Medisinaldepot, which was particularly successful, but it was very much the exception to the rule. In a balanced assessment, Qvale (1976), who was involved in some of the projects, concludes that as demonstration cases to promote industrial democracy on the shop floor they were a modest success but as the basis for diffusion they were a failure.

Shell's New Philosophy of Management. In 1965, the top management at Shell Refining Company in the United Kingdom, part of the larger Shell Group, agreed to develop a new philosophy of management designed to address a range of industrial relations problems and, on a larger scale, help it to cope with an increasingly uncertain external environment. They invited social scientists from the Tavistock Institute to assist with this process. Emery and Trist (1965) had just published what came to be regarded as a major statement about the need to adopt an open systems approach to the analysis of organizations. They argued that management faced increasing challenges from a turbulent and uncertain external environment which lay largely beyond their control. This required organizational structures that were flexible and adaptable which in turn depended on the commitment of employees at all levels within the organization. The idea of the new philosophy of management was to set out agreed principles on which this might be achieved. The subsequent stage was to put it into practice applying sociotechnical principles of work design.

Hill (1971), the main internal Shell consultant involved in the project, has provided an account of the development and implementation of the new philosophy. A document was initially drafted with the help of Tavistock social scientists and over a period of 4 years, extensively communicated through a series of workshops to management and employees throughout the organization. At the Stanlow Refinery, where the local manager was enthusiastic about the new philosophy, three "demonstration" projects in work redesign were introduced, but none survived. A later project, drawing on the lessons from these early projects, used sociotechnical principles in the microwax department with greater success resulting in higher productivity and lower absence (Burden, 1975). The philosophy also influenced a more positive industrial relations climate, reflected in a sequence of productivity deals, and influenced decisions about the organization of work based on sociotechnical principles at a new Teesside refinery (Hill, 1971). A highly critical account of the application of the philosophy by Blackler and Brown (1980) challenged the wider commitment to the philosophy within the company, suggesting that many of the initiatives lost their impetus over time while those that did get successfully implemented depended on the enthusiasm of local managers rather than any wider commitment to the philosophy. Despite this critical analysis, this company-wide initiative to apply sociotechnical principles provides an interesting case study of the potential for their application at this level which has some similarities to the Norwegian Norsk Hydro example. One indication of its impact is that the approach was subsequently adopted within some success at Shell plants in Canada and Australia (Trist, 1981).

The Sheffield Studies. Although the various case studies largely inspired by researchers from the Tavistock Institute have been widely cited and highly influential in promoting interest in the concepts of sociotechnical systems, autonomous work groups, and in the wider quality of working life, they lack the kind of evaluative rigor that is normally associated with research in the field of work and organizational psychology (Cummings et al., 1977; Lawler, 1977). Researchers at the Sheffield University Institute of Work Psychology sought to remedy this. Their first study evaluated the introduction of autonomous work groups in an established confectionary factory (Wall & Clegg, 1981). Workers in sections manufacturing and packing boiled sweets reported low levels of satisfaction, mental health, and performance. Following extensive diagnosis, a reorganization removed the physical separation of the two sections and instead created two groups responsible for all processes. This involved the removal of supervisors and a chargehand. Data collected prior to the change, and 6 and 18 months afterward revealed perceived increases in work group identity and autonomy and increases in intrinsic motivation and performance between the pre- and postchange periods, which were maintained at Time 3. Job satisfaction and mental health also improved, although the larger changes occurred between Times 2 and 3. Labor turnover reduced significantly compared with other sections of the plant. This study is therefore evidence of the successful application of autonomous work groups although it had some unanticipated systems implications. Engineering staff, and in particular maintenance workers, were put under pressure to improve the reliability of the machinery and, as production increased, marketing staff were under pressure to sell more sweets.

The next Sheffield study was a more ambitious quasi-experimental evaluation of the introduction of autonomous group working at a new confectionary manufacturing plant where the sociotechnical system was designed with the help of a Tavistock Institute consultant (Wall et al., 1986). The impact was monitored over 3 years and compared with a traditionally organized plant with extensive data collected at three time points. The results were very mixed.

They revealed that perceptions of autonomy among members of autonomous work groups were high and there was an increase over time and by comparison with the other plant in both intrinsic and extrinsic satisfaction. However, there was no increase in intrinsic motivation or in well-being and there was higher labor turnover and more cases of dismissal under conditions of autonomous group working. It took almost 2 years to reach production targets, after which production levels were maintained. One indirect benefit was that labor costs were reduced by the absence of supervisors. While the authors offer plausible explanations for the higher labor turnover (a tighter local labor market) and the poorer disciplinary record (the work groups were reluctant to act against poor team-member behavior until it was too late and management had to step in) the overall results of this methodologically more rigorous study raise questions about the efficacy of autonomous work groups in relatively routine production contexts.

A Preliminary Assessment. The well-known examples of the application of the aforementioned sociotechnical systems approach had a considerable impact on the social sciences and on wider debates on the quality of working life (see, for example, Davis & Cherns, 1975). They stimulated a considerable number of studies in North America and Europe that purported to be influenced by sociotechnical systems thinking. By 1982, Pasmore et al. (1982) were able to review 134 "experiments." They reported that 53% involved autonomous work groups but only 16% involved technological change. Authors claimed that most of the studies were successful with 60% reporting productivity increases, 54% reporting more positive attitudes, and 27% reporting cost savings. Changes involving the technical system were the least likely to report productivity increases. Pasmore et al. noted that there was a clear bias toward reporting positive results and an often poor research design. This point is reinforced in a review by Cummings et al. (1977) who, using stricter criteria for inclusion, reviewed 58 experiments in work redesign. They note that while most studies report positive results, most also have serious design limitations such as lack of control groups or appropriate statistical tests, questionable measures, and a tendency to select what were identified as positive groups for study. They outline 10 steps to ensure future high-quality research. Finally, Kelly (1978) has provided a highly critical review of the main sociotechnical case studies, concluding that they allowed only a limited degree of autonomy, failed to address joint optimization effectively, and underplayed the role of financial incentives. However, he does acknowledge that there is evidence for the benefits of autonomous work groups. Pasmore et al. (1982) conclude that "the success of the interventions may have more to do with changes in the social system and in the qualifications of personnel than with joint optimization of social *and* technical systems" (p. 1195). This raises the important question of whether psychologists and other social scientists are best placed to introduce a sociotechnical system without the active collaboration of engineers or other technology experts.

The previous section has described and evaluated some of the best-known examples of the application of the sociotechnical systems approach to the redesign of work. It is notable that most of these studies took place over three decades following the seminal paper by Trist and Bamforth (1951). They have stimulated the large body of research reviewed by Pasmore et al. (1982) and Cummings et al. (1977). Trist et al. (1993) brought together many of the most important publications addressing sociotechnical systems theory and practice and offered another opportunity to evaluate its impact. The book received two full and contrasting reviews in *Human Relations*. Pasmore (1995), while acknowledging some of the challenges, describes sociotechnical systems as "a paradigm which had a greater impact on the 'practical affairs of man' than almost any other in the social sciences" (p. 15) and suggests that "clearly, sociotechnical systems theory remains as valid today as it was in the 1950s" (p. 15). The second review by Scarborough (1995) is much more critical. He raises many familiar concerns such as the neglect of power and politics, the validity of the systems concept of organizations, the dominance of action research at the expense of rigorous research and theory development, and the ambiguity of some of the language. Indeed, he characterizes sociotechnical thinking as "a kind of intellectual Esperanto: a language championed by a brave and enthusiastic few, but actually spoken by no one else" (p. 32). More broadly, he believes that "as an intellectual project [sociotechnical analysis] seems at best stalled, at worst moribund" (p. 24).

Both reviews overstate their case. Pasmore overstates the influence and robustness of the sociotechnical systems approach while Scarborough is too negative. The impact of the approach and its link to concepts of industrial democracy and quality of working life owe much to the spirit of the times. There were extensive debates about alienation, rising expectations among an increasingly well-educated workforce, and associated concerns about low motivation and poor productivity (Work in America 1973; Walton, 1982). By the mid-1970s some of these concerns had been superseded in the eyes of managers by the first oil crisis and its consequences. A notable feature of the main examples provided above is that they all involved social scientists from the Tavistock Institute of Human Relations. They also involved a form of action research with a strong "normative re-educative" (Bennis et al., 1961) component and tended to depend on support from local champions. When the social scientists left and the champions moved on, the chances of sustainability declined, though there were exceptions to this, notably in the initial experimental plant at Ahmedabad.

Since the 1980s, research by work and organizational psychologists using the sociotechnical systems paradigm has greatly declined. Nevertheless, relevant insights that draw on the sociotechnical approach have appeared from time to time. For example, an important feature of sociotechnical analysis concerns variances and the argument that these should be handled at the point where they arise. Wall et al. (2002) proposed a contingency approach suggesting that workgroup autonomy is most effective under conditions of uncertainty. Griffin et al. (2007) define uncertainty as a contextual variable reflected in lack of predictability about the inputs, processes, and outputs. Cordery et al. (2010) tested the proposition in Australia with 17 wastewater treatment teams that faced different levels of complexity and uncertainty in their work. Prior to any changes, greater uncertainty was associated with poorer performance. However, after autonomous group working was introduced, uncertainty was associated with higher performance, a result partly attributed to the ability of the team to deal with variances on the spot rather than referring them up the hierarchy. While the focus on uncertainty and variances may help some of the different results of studies of autonomous team working, it is notable that the Cordery et al. study altered the social system rather than the technical system. As the cited reviews have noted, while these studies have merit as examples of work redesign, the neglect of the technical system is a common limitation in tests of the sociotechnical approach. The next section therefore turns to look at research that gives greater primacy to the technical system. One consequence is that the contribution from work and organizational psychology is less central.

SHIFTING THE FOCUS: GIVING PRIMACY TO THE TECHNICAL SYSTEM

The relative weakness of the technical dimension in much of the initial application of socio-technical systems is perhaps not surprising when the changes and their evaluation are led by psychologists and other social scientists who are more familiar with analysis of the social system. Arguably, if joint optimization of social and technical systems is to be achieved, production engineers are an important constituency to win over to the concept. An early example is Davis, an engineer by training, who had recognized that technological determinism made assumptions about workers that accorded them a minimal role in organizations, with consequent dysfunctions (Davis et al., 1955). He went on to champion use of sociotechnical systems design to promote the quality of working life (Davis, 1977; Davis & Cherns, 1975). An engineering perspective has subsequently played a prominent role in the application of a sociotechnical approach although the terminology sometimes differs.

The Case of Volvo.   Engineers had a central role in one of the most famous examples of a new approach to the design of work provided by Volvo, the Swedish car manufacturing company. In the 1960s and 1970s, they faced the challenges of high absenteeism and labor turnover among workers engaged in routine production work. Following some initial activities in existing plants to increase worker participation and adapting the technology to provide more variety and autonomy for production workers, it was accepted that the existing technology limited the scope for radical redesign of work. Supported by the company president, Gyllenhammar, Volvo adopted a radical approach to the manufacture of vehicles at the new Kalmar plant. Instead of the traditional moving assembly line, what they sought to achieve, in the words of Gyllenhammar was

> a manufacturing facility which, without any sacrifice of efficiency or profitability, will give employees the opportunity to work in groups, to communicate freely with each other, to shift between jobs, to feel genuine identification with the product and a responsibility for quality, and to influence their working environment. (Lindholm & Norstedt, 1975, p. 63)

Groups of 15 to 20 worked on sections of a car such as the chassis, the engine, and the gearbox. The new plant was radically designed to provide cells for small work groups although it still required a final production system where groups had responsibility for sub-sections such as the electrics or the steering mechanism. A docking system provided buffers that removed the pressures of conventional assembly. While subsections of the assembly typically took 3 minutes, it was possible for a worker to learn how to do all the elements and therefore assemble the entire subsection of a vehicle over 30 minutes. Therefore, without using the language of sociotechnical systems, the Kalmar factory provides an example of how innovative production engineering can promote the quality of work and address concerns about worker dissatisfaction. In an initial evaluation, Lindholm and Norstedt claimed that the Kalmar factory achieved standard production efficiency targets within 6 months of its opening in 1974 while also providing high levels of job satisfaction.

Volvo took the concept of autonomous group working a step further at the Uddevalla car plant (Sandberg, 1995). Its distinctive feature was that workers had the ability to complete all elements in the manufacture of a car. The cycle times which in traditional car plants might be 1 or 2 minutes were between 1 and 3½ hours. Typically, a group of nine workers would assemble a complete car. There was flexibility to work either in a small group or individually. For this to be successful, a key element was continuous learning at the individual level and also at the plant level. As workers became familiar with the process, production speeded up and quality improved. Reviews suggested that production levels were comparable with the main traditionally organized Volvo plant at Torslanda, Gothenburg. However just as production reached high levels, Volvo took the decision to close the plant in 1993, 4 years after it opened. One year later they also closed Kalmar. A number of external factors accounted for this including rising unemployment in Sweden, which had become a focus of trade union attention, and a decline in the market for Volvo cars. The company, now under a new president, decided it was simpler to shut these smaller plants than the large traditional plant. While those involved in the Volvo experience did not describe these initiatives in sociotechnical terms, they were, for all intents and purposes, examples of plant-level sociotechnical design and operation. Indeed, Buchanan (1997, p. 89) noted "Volvo's retreat was thus damaging to the sociotechnical systems movement in that it had become an exemplar for organisations in many other sectors." Despite some further initiatives in work design in the auto industry such as General Motors' Saturn plant, the analysis by Womack et al. (1990) of lean production at Toyota reflected a resurgence of technological determinism and the decline of sociotechnical experimentation in the industry.

The Dutch Approach.   In parallel with developments in Scandinavia, other European countries such as Germany and Italy had begun to support activities in work redesign that were heavily influenced by the sociotechnical systems approach. It is probably in the Netherlands that the most distinctive developments occurred. In the 1970s, Philips had begun a series of experiments in what they termed "work restructuring," which bore similarities to sociotechnical design. While these had some success, they often failed to diffuse beyond the context in which they had taken place. Influenced by this experience as well as by the Norwegian emphasis on industrial democracy and the Swedish use of production engineering expertise, Dutch researchers developed their own adapted version of a sociotechnical systems application (de Sitter et al., 1997). They suggest it "can be viewed as a Dutch variant of sociotechnical systems design" (de Sitter et al., 1997, p. 497). At the same time, they are critical of certain features of sociotechnical systems analysis including what they view as an artificial and in practice unsustainable distinction between social and technical systems and an oversimplification of the concept of joint optimization that lacked guidance on how this can be achieved. They are also critical of the use of outside experts at the expense of embedded local knowledge. They suggest this partly accounts for the lack of diffusion of the sociotechnical projects both within and across organizations, a point also emphasized by Pava (1986) and Engelstad and Gustavsen (1993). The Dutch contribution is the concept of "Integral Organizational Renewal" (IOR) subsequently also labeled "modern sociotechnical thinking" (Kopp et al., 2019).

IOR is described as "a systematic approach to design which supports improvements in both the quality of work and what is called 'the quality of the organization' (i.e., its ability to deal with a complex and continuously changing environment)," (de Sitter et al., 1997, p. 498). In acknowledging the importance of the environment, they are supporting the analysis of open systems by Emery and Trist (1965) that highlighted the need to design organizations that can cope with a turbulent and uncertain external environment. A core feature of IOR is its emphasis on the organization as the key unit of analysis and the principle that organizations can be simple, but jobs are complex. There are a set of design principles such as a focus on integral design, on understanding controllability, on control structures, and on structural parameters that add up to a potentially complex set of requirements. Central to the approach is a participative strategy of change where experts aid in the process including providing intensive training in design so that the workforce, both workers and managers, can own the design with a principle of organizing a structure from the bottom up in a way that maximizes the quality of work as well as meeting the technical requirements for organizational design. Combined with the need for support from senior management and works councils, the aim is to embed an organizational design that can respond to external uncertainties, enhance productivity and also ensure the quality of work. Activities reflecting this approach have been coordinated through The Netherlands Institute for the Improvement of the Quality of Work and Organization (NKWO) and de Sitter et al. (1997) describe examples of its application across a range of contexts. Nevertheless, despite the greater focus of this approach on managerial priorities, Kopp et al. (2019) acknowledge that there are still only relatively limited examples of its application.

The Dutch approach with its greater focus on technology nevertheless retains a strong emphasis on participation. This is based on the view that changes in work organization are unlikely to be effective if they are imposed. Instead they have to be "owned" by those who are going to experience them. At the same time, they accept that if there is to be a fully open system with its variety of internal and external influences, there will be limits to the extent of employee participation. They therefore believe that their approach to sociotechnical systems design is incompatible with other approaches that give primacy of industrial democracy, as was the case in Norway, or to quality of working life, with its tendency to emphasize the social system (Davis & Cherns, 1975). This is not to claim that these alternatives are not legitimate goals, but more to argue that they are not compatible with some of the core features of sociotechnical systems design.

Information Systems and Ergonomics. There has been a longstanding interest in sociotechnical systems among researchers in the fields of information and computer technologies and ergonomics. This is important because much of the reported research has addressed production technologies while most employment in advanced economies is found in the service sector. Mumford (2006) pioneered an interest in the application of sociotechnical thinking to information systems and it is implicit in the work of Checkland (1981) on soft systems. Eason (2007) illustrates an application of sociotechnical systems thinking to the analysis of the U.K. National Health Service Information Technology Program.

Ergonomists, with their longstanding interest in human factors, have much to contribute to work design and Clegg (2000), adopting an ergonomic perspective, endorsed the view that there was a need to rethink sociotechnical analysis for an era of information and communication technologies and the resultant new forms of work organization. He argued that new technologies had often failed to advance productivity because they had neglected the social system. He wanted to see social scientists, including ergonomists, involved in the design of new technologies and outlined a set of principles and processes to achieve this. Subsequently, Baxter and Somerville (2011), for example, have argued the case for building sociotechnical analysis into design methods for systems engineering.

CONCLUSIONS AND THE FUTURE OF SOCIOTECHNICAL SYSTEMS DESIGN

Much of this article may have the appearance of a historical review. Sociotechnical systems analysis was developed by psychologists and other social scientists at the Tavistock Institute of Human Relations in London during the 1950s and stimulated extensive research by social scientists around the world over 3 decades. The evidence about its impact is very mixed. There are examples of successful applications but also many illustrations of the limitations imposed by wider systems constraints. These attest to the difficulties of bringing about organizational change when commitment to the change is highly conditional and often temporary. Over the years, the contribution of organizational psychologists to work redesign has continued, including some interest in autonomous work groups, while largely neglecting the technical system. The article by Van den Broeck and Parker (2017) provides a comprehensive overview of work redesign research. It has been largely left to engineers and interdisciplinary teams to pursue innovations in the organization of work that give full weight to the technical system within what might be described as a technical-social systems framework.

Looking forward, it is premature to write off the potential contribution of organizational psychologists to sociotechnical analysis and work design. Growing concern about the impact of "Industry 4" (Frey & Osborne, 2017), the era of artificial intelligence (AI), smart factories, robotics, and extensive digitization has led to calls for the incorporation of sociotechnical systems thinking into workplace design (Kopp et al., 2019). They note that in Germany, "Work 4.0" is set alongside "Industry 4.0" to offer "a broader perspective on digital transformation as an enabler for people-centred new work designs" (p. 293) based largely on sociotechnical principles. Bednar and Welch (2020) have also highlighted the risks of neglecting the social system in "Industry 4.0." Instead they advocate the rapid introduction of "Industry 5.0," which recognizes the need to design sociotechnical systems that optimize the interests of both the technology and those employees who have to work with it. It is notable that the European Community has initiated "EUWIN," the European Workplace Innovation Network, with the aim of simultaneously improving both productivity and well-being in the context of "Industry 4." The relationship between new digital technologies and worker well-being offers a fertile focus of research by work and organizational psychologists. Indeed, Parker and Grote (2020) argue that in the digital age work design matters more than ever and psychologists with their expertise in this field should be making an important contribution. They outline some research priorities including working proactively alongside technologists to influence the design of work, highlighting in particular the importance of workers autonomy and local variance control. They also suggest the need to be involved in the education of technologists to highlight the importance of work design as well as the need to ensure that workers are educated to recognize the importance of adaptability, proactivity, and the need to engage in continuous development. Organizational psychologists should become involved in intervention studies to test some of the relevant approaches to sociotechnical design of work places (e.g., Clegg, 2000; Waterson et al., 2002). Finally, Parker and Grote (2020) recognize the need to reemphasize sociotechnical systems thinking as a major analytic framework.

Developments in sociotechnical analysis are extending beyond the workplace. One of the interesting contemporary applications of sociotechnical systems thinking can be found in policy analysis applied to complex problems. These include management of transitions such as the introduction of Industry 4 technologies but also the challenge of climate change. The core argument of policy analysts such as Geels (2004, 2018) and Edmondson et al. (2019) is that sustainable transitions require analysis of both the social and the technical systems and their interaction. For Geels (2004, p. 900) sociotechnical systems are "linkages between elements necessary to fulfil societal functions" including energy, transport, housing, food production, and consumption. Like the initial sociotechnical thinking, the core point is that technological determinism and advances in technology are not enough to ensure that change brings societal benefits and therefore change requires analysis of complex, open, dynamic, multilevel systems in which change is only likely to be effective if "the social" can be effectively engaged in the process. A somewhat similar view is taken by Davis et al. (2014) who acknowledge the potential of sociotechnical systems thinking if it can move beyond its focus on traditional notions of technology to a wider focus on complex systems. They illustrate its potential with an analysis of a crowd disaster at a football match (Challenger & Clegg, 2011).

At the start of the 1980s, Emery (1982), one of the main pioneers of sociotechnical analysis was also one of the first to identify the declining interest in its application. He used the idea of Kondratieff cycles to argue that interest would wax and wane over the long term according to wider contextual circumstances such as the economic changes precipitated by the oil crisis of the 1970s. A glance at Google Scholar reveals that the concept of sociotechnical systems analysis remains alive and well. The promise and the threat of Industry 4 for societal and individual well-being suggests that there is still a major role for work and organizational psychologists to play in exploring the interplay between social and technical systems at work and in society more widely.

FURTHER READING

Boos, D., Grote, G., & Guenter, H. (2013). A toolbox for managing organisational issues in the early stage of development of a ubiquitous computing application. *Personal and Ubiquitous Computing, 17*, 1261–1279.

Cohen-Rosenthal, E. (1997). Sociotechnical systems and unions: Nicety of necessity? *Human Relations, 50*(5), 585–604.

Dankbaar, B. (1997). Lean production: Denial, confirmation or extension of socio-technical systems design? *Human Relations, 50*, 567–583.

Grote, G., Ryser, C., Wafler, T., Windischer, A., & Weik, S. (2000). KOMPASS: A method for complementary function allocation in automated work systems. *International Journal of Human-Computer Studies, 52*, 267–287.

Herbst, P. (1976). *Alternatives to hierarchies.* Martinus Nijhoff.

Parker, S., & Jorritsma, K. (2021). Good work design for all: Multiple pathways to making a difference. *European Journal of Work and Organizational Psychology, 30* (3), 456–468.

Pearson, C. (1992). Autonomous work groups: An evaluation at an industrial site. *Human Relations, 45*(9), 905–936.

Van Eijnatten, F., & Van der Zwann, H. (1998). The Dutch IOR approach to organizational design: An alternative to business process reengineering? *Human Relations, 51*(3), 289–318.

REFERENCES

Bakker, A., & Demerouti, E. (2017). Job demands–resources theory: Taking stock and looking forward. *Journal of Occupational Health Psychology, 22*(3), 273–285.

Baxter, G., & Somerville, I. (2011). Socio-technical systems: From design methods to systems engineering. *Interacting with Computers, 23*, 4–17.

Bednar, P., & Welch, C. (2020). Socio-technical perspectives on smart working: Creating meaningful and sustainable systems. *Information Systems Frontiers, 22*, 281–298.

Bennis, W., Benne, K., & Chin, R. (Eds.). (1961). *The planning of change: Readings in applied behavioral sciences.* Holt, Rinehart & Winston.

Blackler, F., & Brown, C. (1980). *Whatever happened to Shell's new philosophy of management?* Saxon House.

Bolweg, J. (1976). *Job design and industrial democracy.* Martinus Nijhoff.

Buchanan, D. (1997). Review of Sandberg (ed.) op cit. *Human Resource Management Journal, 7*(4), 89.

Burden, D. (1975). Participative management as a basis for improved quality of jobs: The case of the micro-wax department Shell UK Ltd. In L. Davis & A. Cherns (Eds.), *The quality of working life* (Vol II, pp. 201–215). Free Press.

Challenger, R., & Clegg, C. (2011). Crowd disasters: A socio-technical systems perspective. *Contemporary Social Science, 6*, 343–360.

Checkland, P. (1981). *Systems thinking, systems practice.* Wiley.

Cherns, A. (1976). The principles of socio-technical design. *Human Relations, 29*(8), 783–792.

Cherns, A. (1987). Principles of socio-technical design revisited. *Human Relations, 40*(3), 153–1602.

Clegg, C. (2000). Sociotechnical principles for system design. *Applied Ergonomics, 31*(5), 463–477.

Coch, L., & French, J. (1948). Overcoming resistance to change. *Human Relations, 1*, 512–532.

Cordery, J., Morrison, D., Wright, B., & Wall, T. (2010). The impact of autonomy and task uncertainty on team performance: A longitudinal field study. *Journal of Organizational Behavior, 31*, 240–258.

Cummings, T., Molloy, E., & Glen, R. (1977). A methodological critique. *Human Relations, 30*(8), 675–708.

Davis, L. (1977). Evolving alternative organizational designs: Their socio-technical bases. *Human Relations, 30*(3), 261–273.

Davis, L., Canter, R., & Hoffman, J. (1955). Current job design criteria. *Journal of Industrial Engineering, 6*, 5–11.

Davis, L., & Cherns, A. (Eds.). (1975). *The quality of working life* (Vol 1). The Free Press.

Davis, M., Challenger, R., Jayewardene, D., & Clegg, C. (2014). Advancing sociotechnical systems thinking: A call for bravery. *Applied Ergonomics, 45*(2), 171–180.

De Sitter, U., Den Hartog, F., & Dankbaar, B. (1997). From complex organizations with simple jobs to simple organizations with complex jobs. *Human Relations, 50*(5), 497–534.

Eason, K. (2007). Local sociotechnical systems development in the NHS National Programme for Information Technology. *Journal of Information Technology, 22*, 257–264.

Edmondson, D., Kern, F., & Rogge, K. (2019). The co-evolution of policy mixes and socio-technical systems: Towards a conceptual framework of policy mix feedback in sustainable transitions. *Research Policy, 48*(10), 103555.

Emery, F. (1982). Sociotechnical foundations for a new social order? *Human Relations, 35*(12), 1095–1122.

Emery, F., & Thorsrud, E. (1969). *Form and content in industrial democracy.* Tavistock Publications.

Emery, F., & Thorsrud, E. (1976). *Democracy at work.* Martinus Nijhoff.

Emery, F., & Trist, E. (1965). The causal texture of organizational environments. *Human Relations, 18*(1), 21–32.

Engelstad, P., & Gustavsen, B. (1993). Swedish network development for implementing national work reform. *Human Relations, 46*(2), 219–248.

French, J., Israel, J., & As, D. (1960). An experiment on participation in a Norwegian factory. *Human Relations, 13*(1), 3–19.

Frey, C., & Osborne, M. (2017). The future of employment: How susceptible are jobs to computerisation? *Technological Forecasting and Social Change, 114*, 254–280.

Geels, F. (2004). From sectoral systems of innovation to socio-technical systems: Insights about dynamics and change from sociology and institutional theory. *Policy, 36*(6–7), 897–920.

Geels, F. (2018). Disruption and low carbon systems transformation: Progress and new challenges in socio-technical transitions research and the multi-level perspective. *Energy Research and Social Science, 37*, 224–231.

Griffin, M., Neal, A., & Parker, S. (2007). A new model of work role performance: Positive behaviour in uncertain and interdependent contexts. *Academy of Management Journal, 50*(2), 327–347.

Hill, P. (1971). *Towards a new philosophy of management*. Gower Press.

Karasek, R. (1979). Job demands, job decision latitude, and mental strain: Implications for job redesign. *Administrative Sciences Quarterly, 24*(2), 285–308.

Kelly, J. (1978). A re-appraisal of sociotechnical systems theory. *Human Relations, 31*(12), 1069–1099.

Kopp, R., Dhondt, S., Hirsch-Kreinsen, H., Kohlgruber, M., & Preenen, P. (2019). Sociotechnical perspectives on digitalisation and Industry 4.0. *International Journal of Technology Transfer and Commercialisation, 16*(3), 290–309.

Lawler, E. (1977). Adaptive experiments: An approach to organizational behaviour research. *Academy of Management Review, 2*(4), 576–585.

Lewin, K. (1947). Frontiers of groups dynamics. *Human Relations, 1*(5), 5–41.

Lewin, K., Lippitt, R., & White, R. (1939). Patterns of aggressive behaviour in experimentally induced social climates. *Journal of Social Psychology, 10*, 271–299.

Lindholm, R., & Norstedt, J. (1975). *The Volvo report*. Swedish Employers' Federation.

Lupton, T. (1963). *On the shop floor*. Pergamon Press.

Miller, E. (1975). Socio-technical systems in weaving, 1953–1970: A follow-up study. *Human Relations, 28*(4), 349–386.

Mumford, E. (2006). The story of socio-technical design and reflections on its successes, failures and potential. *Information Systems Journal, 16*, 317–342.

Parker, S., & Grote, G. (2020). Automation, algorithms and beyond: Why work design matters more than ever in a digital world. *Applied Psychology: An International Review*. https://doi.org/10.1111/apps.12241

Pasmore, W. (1995). Social science transformed: The socio-technical perspective. *Human Relations, 48*(1), 1–21.

Pasmore, W., Francis, C., Haldeman, J., & Shani, A. (1982). Sociotechnical systems: A North-American reflection of empirical studies of the seventies. *Human Relations, 35*(12), 1179–1204.

Pava, C. (1986). Redesigning sociotechnical systems design: Concepts and methods for the 1990s. *Journal of Applied Behavioral Science, 22*(3), 201–221.

Qvale, T. (1976). A Norwegian strategy for democratization of industry. *Human Relations, 29*(5), 453–469.

Rice, A. K. (1953). Productivity and social organization in an Indian weaving shed: An examination of the socio-technical system of an experimental automatic loomshed. *Human Relations, 6*(94), 297–329.

Rice, A. K. (1955). Productivity and organization in an Indian weaving mill: A follow-up study of the experimental reorganization of automatic weaving. *Human Relations, 8*(4), 399–428.

Rice, A. K. (1963). *The enterprise and its environment*. Tavistock.

Roethlisberger, F., & Dickson, W. (1939). *Management and the worker*. Harvard University Press.

Roy, D. (1952). Quota restriction and gold-bricking in a machine shop. *American Journal of Sociology, 57*(5), 427–442.

Roy, S. K. (1969). A re-examination of the methodology of A.K. Rice's India textile mill work reorganisation. *Indian Journal of Industrial Relations, 5*, 170–191.

Sandberg, A. (Ed.). (1995). *Enriching production: Perspectives on Volvo's Uddevalla plant as an alternative to lean production*. Ashgate.

Scarborough, H. (1995). The social engagement of social science: A Tavistock anthology. *Human Relations, 48*(1), 22–33.

Taylor, F. (1947). *Scientific management*. Harper.

Trist, E. (1993). Introduction to Volume 11: Origins of the concept. In E. Trist, H. Murray, & B. Trist (Eds.), *The social engagement of social science: A Tavistock anthology: Volume 11: The socio-technical approach* (pp. 36–60). Pennsylvania University Press.

Trist, E. (1981). *The evolution of socio-technical systems*. Ontario Ministry of Labour.

Trist, E., & Bamforth, K. (1951). Some social and psychological consequences of the longwall method of coal getting. *Human Relations, 4*(1), 3–38.

Trist, E., Higgin, G., Murray, H., & Pollock, A. (1963). *Organizational choice*. Tavistock Publications.

Trist, E., Murray, H., & B. Trist (Eds.) (1993). *The social engagement of social science: A Tavistock anthology: Vol.11: The socio-technical perspective*. University of Philadelphia Press.

Trist, E. Susman, G., & Brown, G. (1977). An experiment in autonomous group working in an American underground mine. *Human Relations, 30*(3), 201–236.

Van den Broeck, A., & Parker, S. (2017). Job and work design. In *Oxford research encyclopedias: Psychology*. Oxford University Press.

Von Bertalanffy, L. (1950). An outline of general system theory. *British Journal for the Philosophy of Science, 1*, 134–165.

Wall, T., & Clegg, C. (1981). A longitudinal study of group work redesign. *Journal of Organizational Behavior, 2*(1), 31–49.

Wall, T., Cordery, J., & Clegg, C. (2002). Empowerment, performance and organizational uncertainty: A theoretical integration. *Applied Psychology: An International Review, 51*(1), 146–149.

Wall, T., Kemp, N., Jackson, P., & Clegg, C. (1986). Outcomes of autonomous work groups: A long-term field experiment. *Academy of Management Journal, 29*(2), 280–304.

Walton, R. (1982). Social choice in the development of advanced information technology. *Human Relations, 35*(12), 1073–1084.

Waterson, P., Older Gray, M., & Clegg, C. (2002). A sociotechnical method for designing work systems. *Human Factors, 44*(3), 376–391.

Whyte, W. (1955). *Money and motivation: An analysis of incentives in industry*. Harper and Bros.

Womack, J., Jones, D., & Roos, D. (1990). *The machine that changed the world*. Simon & Schuster.

Work in America. (1973). *Work in America*. MIT Press.

David E. Guest

ACTION REGULATION THEORY

INTRODUCTION

Action regulation theory is a metatheory on the psychological regulation of goal-directed behavior in the work context (Frese & Zapf, 1994; Hacker, 1971, 1998). It describes and explains cognitive and behavioral processes during work-related action sequences and the effects of work design and tasks on individual workers. As a metatheoretical framework, action regulation theory allows integrating midrange theories that focus on human action

(Frese, 2006). Over the past decades, action regulation theory has become an important basic theory in applied psychology, particularly in the field of industrial, work, and organizational psychology (Frese, Rank, & Zacher, 2017; Hacker, 2003; Zacher & Frese, 2018). This article first provides a brief historical overview of the development of action regulation theory. Second, the most important concepts of the theory are defined and explained, including actions and central characteristics of actions, the sequential and hierarchical structure of action regulation, the concept of complete tasks and actions, the action-oriented mental model, and different foci of action regulation. Finally, theoretical and practical implications of action regulation theory for the design of work tasks, worker stress and well-being, as well as positive psychological development and successful aging in the work context are outlined.

BRIEF HISTORICAL OVERVIEW

Action regulation theory was developed in the 1960s and 1970s in response to the dominant paradigm of behaviorism, which focused primarily on observed behavior as a reaction to environmental stimuli and neglected cognitive processes residing in the "black box." In the United States, Miller, Galanter, and Pribram (1960) published an influential book *Plans and the Structure of Behavior*, in which they examined the cognitive underpinnings of complex actions. Additionally, research on cognitive and human factors in countries of the former Soviet Union, particularly Russia and Poland, had an influence on the development of action regulation theory (Leontjev, 1978; Tomaszewski, 1978). In Germany, Hacker (1971) published the seminal book *General Work and Engineering Psychology* in which he laid out the fundamental concepts and tenets of action regulation theory (Hacker updated and extended the book several times, see Hacker, 1998; Hacker & Sachse, 2014, for more recent versions). Hacker's (1971) work had a significant influence on work psychology research in German-speaking countries over the following decades.

In the 1980s and 1990s, Frese and colleagues introduced action regulation theory as a "German approach to work psychology" to a broader international audience (Frese & Sabini, 1985; Frese & Zapf, 1994). Since then, action regulation theory has been used to investigate numerous topics in industrial, work, and organizational psychology (see Zacher & Frese, 2018, for a comprehensive review of these applied topics), including team work (von Cranach, 1996); proactive work behavior (Frese & Fay, 2001); emotions, stress, and well-being (Zapf, 2002); entrepreneurship (Frese, 2009); errors in organizations (Hofmann & Frese, 2011); career development (Raabe, Frese, & Beehr, 2007); and successful aging at work (Zacher, Hacker, & Frese, 2016). Action regulation theory is distinct from, but shares some concepts and propositions with, other cognitive-behavioral theories, including control theory (Carver & Scheier, 1982) and goal setting theory (Locke & Latham, 1990, 2002; Zacher & Frese, 2018, provide a more detailed comparison of the theories).

Recent research in the area of self-regulation (a field closely related to action regulation theory) has focused increasingly on the dynamic process of action regulation (Lord, Diefendorff, Schmidt, & Hall, 2010; Neal, Ballard, & Vancouver, 2017). While people strive to attain desired outcomes (i.e., "approach goals") and prevent undesired outcomes (i.e., "avoidance goals"), they often have to flexibly manage multiple competing demands on their time and personal resources (Neal et al., 2017). For instance, people have to make decisions on which goals or tasks they are able and want to pursue; they have to invest their physical, cognitive, and emotional energies to complete their tasks; and they might have to make changes to or disengage from certain goals and tasks based on the availability of personal and external resources and constraints.

ACTION AND CENTRAL CHARACTERISTICS OF ACTION

Action is defined as goal-directed behavior (Hacker, 1985). More specifically, Hacker (1985) characterizes an action as the smallest psychologically relevant or self-contained (in terms of content and time) unit of behavior. Goals are mentally anticipated and desired results of action that have a motivational influence, because they set ideal standards for behavior and can "pull" behavior (Austin & Vancouver, 1996; Locke & Latham, 1990). To initiate an action, people first need to anticipate an ideal state (i.e., goal) and recognize a discrepancy between this ideal state and their current state or outcomes. With regard to the notion of discrepancy reduction, action regulation theory partially overlaps with propositions of control theory (Carver & Scheier, 1982; Lord & Levy, 1994). However, action regulation theory goes beyond control theory in that it assumes humans as active agents that set themselves more challenging goals and higher standards over time and with increased experience (Zacher & Frese, 2018). A goal is achieved through action and the results of action. The action is completed when the relevant goal has been attained and a discrepancy between the ideal state and the current state does not exist anymore.

While not all goals are conscious and not all actions are consciously regulated, a defining feature of an action is that its goal could principally be brought to conscious awareness (Hacker, 1998; Locke & Latham, 2013). Furthermore, action regulation theory assumes that actions are closely linked to and embedded in the objective (i.e., material, social, societal) environment. On the one hand, the environment can trigger and shape actions (e.g., effects of organizational culture on individual behavior; Schneider, Ehrhart, & Macey, 2013); on the other hand, actions can also shape the environment consistent with a person's goals (e.g., job crafting; Rudolph, Katz, Lavigne, & Zacher, 2017; Wrzesniewski & Dutton, 2001). Action regulation theory assumes that, through their actions, reactions, and interactions with the environment, workers adapt and improve their cognitive representation of the environment (Frese & Sabini, 1985). Thus, action regulation theory proposes that actions contribute to the development of the human psychological system (e.g., action errors are considered learning devices that help improve a concept of reality; Frese & Keith, 2015). In contrast to behaviorist theories, cognitive processes such as goal development, planning, and feedback processing play an important role in action regulation theory. At the same time, the theory differs from purely cognitive and information processing theories in that the links between cognitive processes, behavior, and the objective environment and objective outcomes of action play an important role.

SEQUENTIAL-HIERARCHICAL STRUCTURE OF ACTION REGULATION

Sequential Structure of Action Regulation. Action regulation theory assumes that people's actions unfold across five cyclical phases: goal development and selection, orientation or mapping the environment, plan development and selection (planning), monitoring of execution, and feedback processing (Frese & Zapf, 1994). The first three phases develop or retrieve information necessary for action regulation. The following phases implement the action plans and collect action-relevant feedback. Feedback processing, in turn, may inform continued goal development, selection, or disengagement. It is important to note that this idealized action regulation sequence does not have to be followed in a rigid way. For instance, sometimes it may be necessary to skip certain steps (e.g., develop a plan without searching for goal-relevant information), repeat steps (e.g., develop a new goal if the former goal turns out to be difficult or impossible to achieve), or go back and forth between steps (Frese & Zapf, 1994).

In the first action regulation phase, workers develop and select goals that they intend to pursue. Goals can be either internally generated (i.e., self-set) based on broader values, motives, and expectations (DeShon & Gillespie, 2005) or assigned by others (e.g., supervisor, organizational management). If assigned by others in the form of work tasks, individuals have to redefine these tasks and turn them into personal goals (Hackman, 1970). The success of this redefinitions process is dependent on various individual (e.g., experience) and contextual (e.g., clarity of task) factors. Goals can be either consciously or subconsciously represented (Bargh & Barndollar, 1996; Latham & Piccolo, 2012). Regarding the latter, it is possible that organizational environments trigger actions subconsciously. Moreover, goals can range from short-term goals (e.g., work goal for this afternoon) to longer-term goals (e.g., life goals). People differ in their characteristic way of developing and pursuing goals (Frese, Stewart, & Hannover, 1987). In addition, research has shown that certain goal orientations (e.g., approach or avoidance goals) can be primed in experimental studies (Ballard, Yeo, Neal, & Farrell, 2016).

Goals are hierarchically structured (Volpert, 1982). Thus, the attainment of lower-order goals may contribute to higher-order goals, and higher-order goals can help establish continuity among lower-order goals. Each goal can have multiple subgoals, sub-subgoals, and so forth; and each goal is linked to a cyclical action unit with the five action regulation phases. For instance, the goal of publishing a scientific manuscript entails several subgoals (e.g., finding collaborators, literature search, carrying out a study, drafting the different sections). At the same time, publishing a manuscript can be a subgoal of the higher-order goal of getting promoted. The more lower-order goals exist, the more orientation, planning, monitoring, and feedback processing are necessary. Research on goals has shown that the nature of goals and coordination of multiple goals is linked to the efficiency and effectiveness of action regulation. For instance, research on goal setting theory has consistently shown that specific and challenging goals have the strongest effects on performance, if goals are realistic, accepted, and feedback is provided (Locke & Latham, 2002). In contrast, vague goals (e.g., "do your best"), too easy or too difficult goals, and multiple competing or contradictory goals typically lead to poorer performance.

Conceptual and empirical research on multiple goal pursuit is a relatively new development in the area of self-regulation (Neal et al., 2017; Sun & Frese, 2013; Unsworth, Yeo, & Beck, 2014; Vancouver, Weinhardt, & Schmidt, 2010). Researchers in this area are interested in why and when people prioritize some goals over others. For instance, in a conceptual paper, Unsworth et al. (2014) derived a set of six principles of multiple goal pursuit, which refer to goal structure and activation, goal alignment, goal-based informational and affective value, goal-performance discrepancies, expectancy, and goal shielding. In an experimental study, Ballard et al. (2016) investigated why people depart from optimality when pursuing multiple goals. They found that people are more risk averse when they pursue multiple "approach goals" (i.e., attaining desired outcomes). In contrast, people are more risk seeking when they pursue multiple "avoidance goals" (i.e., avoiding undesired outcomes). The second action regulation phase, mapping the environment or orientation, involves that individuals search for goal-relevant information in their memory as well as in the objective physical and social environment (Frese & Zapf, 1994). The process of searching for information can be more or less active, ranging from deliberate and conscious efforts to an unconscious and intuitive understanding of situations. The retrieval, recognition, and understanding of relevant information depend on both individual (e.g., experience with a task) and contextual factors (e.g., transparency of signals). Based on the information retrieved from memory or obtained from environmental signals, individuals regulate their actions. Action-relevant information includes previous experiences and expertise, possible execution opportunities and constraints, availability of relevant tools and methods, and important boundary conditions for goal attainment. This information enables individuals to make predictions about the likelihood of successful goal attainment. Moreover, it can help them coordinate individuals' actions with those of supervisors and colleagues (Hacker, 2003). If workers develop adequate, action-relevant mental representations of their tasks, goals, and associated boundary conditions, the action process becomes more efficient and effective. In contrast, when individuals do not retrieve information accurately or too slowly, their information search does not lead to relevant action, or information is processed in a biased way, their performance may suffer.

The third phase, planning, consists of plan development and selection. Plans have been described as bridges between thoughts and actions (Miller et al., 1960). They are mental simulations of the behavioral steps (also called transformations or operations) that are necessary to attain a goal and can be more or less detailed and complex. A list of subgoals constitutes a simple plan (Locke & Latham, 2002). Moreover, the planning process may involve the development of one or more backup plans that can be put in place in case an initial plan fails or is increasingly considered to be less likely successful (Napolitano & Freund, 2016). Generally, detailed planning is considered an effective strategy in the work context. However, when detailed plans are followed in an overly rigid manner, they can become ineffective when goals are complex and when situational requirements change (Baker & Nelson, 2005). Plans are also inefficient when planning entails the disproportionate investment of cognitive effort (Mumford, Mecca, & Watts, 2015). Action regulation theory suggests that so-called best-workers or super-workers develop more elaborate and proactive task-oriented plans that allow them to better deal with errors, interruptions, and other challenging work situations (Frese & Zapf, 1994).

The fourth phase, monitoring of execution, involves comparisons between goals, associated plans, and the actual execution of goal-directed behavior. This comparison draws heavily on individuals' working memory capacity and general mental ability. Moreover, during the execution of behavior, workers may be required to deal with unexpected barriers and constraints (or new opportunities), adapt their goals and plans accordingly, and coordinate action efficiently with regard to the limited time and resources available (Frese & Zapf, 1994). Efficient and effective action regulation may be impaired by the intrusion of distracting thoughts, cognitive overload, and attention problems that reduce the accuracy of plan execution.

Finally, the last step of the cyclical action sequence entails that individuals process feedback that may signal to them that the goal has been attained or not, and that the goal may need to be revised or dropped (i.e., goal disengagement; Haase, Heckhausen, & Wrosch, 2013). Feedback can be internally or externally generated and provides workers with goal-relevant information (e.g., discrepancy between ideal and current state, or progress made). Feedback can be more or less detailed and timely, and it can be either positive or negative. Similar to behavioristic and social-cognitive theories (Bandura, 2001), action regulation theory suggests that positive feedback is beneficial in terms of maintaining or repeating behavior. In contrast, the theory proposes that negative feedback is a useful device to stimulate and facilitate learning, innovation, and personal development, as long as it is task related and provides clear information (Frese & Keith, 2015; Kluger & DeNisi, 1996). Feedback processing may occur during and after the execution of behavior. Anticipated feedback (i.e., feedforward, or people's ideas and expectations regarding the feedback they likely would receive) and the feedback received during action execution are most important for efficient action regulation, because these forms of feedback can lead to immediate corrections of faulty actions (Hacker, 1998).

Hierarchical Structure of Action Regulation. In addition to the sequential process of action regulation, action regulation theory proposes that action is regulated on different mental levels. For instance, Hacker (1971) originally proposed three distinct yet interconnected levels, whereas Frese and Zapf (1994) described four levels of action regulation: the sensorimotor or skill level, the level of flexible action patterns, the intellectual or conscious level, and the level of metacognitive heuristics. These levels can be arranged along a dimension ranging from unconscious and automatized control of actions to conscious intellectual processes, and on another dimension ranging from muscular action to thought processes (Frese & Zapf, 1994). Action regulation at lower levels in the hierarchy is more situation specific, requires less cognitive effort, and movements are more elegant and parsimonious.

The hierarchical organization of these levels implies that action sequences on lower levels can be triggered and regulated by higher levels. For instance, the sequence of observable behaviors at the lowest level (e.g., cutting vegetables in the kitchen) follows from a higher-order goal and planning (e.g., preparing a meal). These hierarchies are relatively weak, however, such that higher levels do not completely determine action regulation on lower levels, and results obtained at lower levels may lead to changes at higher levels (e.g., cutting one's finger leads to a change in goals; Frese & Zapf, 1994; Hacker, 2003). In addition, over time and with experience, action regulation can be "shifted" from one level to another. For instance, when actions are automatized with practice in a redundant environment (e.g., operating a truck), they are shifted to the lower sensorimotor level or level of flexible action patterns that do not require attention and cognitive effort (Lord & Levy, 1994). In contrast, when actions need to be better understood or problems need to be solved (e.g., after an error has occurred), action regulation can be shifted to higher intellectual levels that require conscious attention and concentration.

At the sensorimotor or skill level, highly automatized movement patterns and cognitive routines are regulated (e.g., typing on a keyboard, driving a car). These processes are not associated with independent and conscious goals but are usually triggered by regulation processes at higher levels. However, consciously changing or interrupting these automatized action programs requires cognitive effort. Feedback at this level involves automatically generated kinesthetic and proprioceptive signals regarding motor movement coordination.

The level of flexible action patterns entails action regulation based on automatized schemata or scripts that can be either conscious or semiconscious (e.g., performing a routine medical checkup, serving a customer). At this level, workers process information from the environment according to well-established rules. Flexible action patterns can be activated from memory based on only a few signals from the environment, and they are then typically carried out as a whole without the investment of much cognitive effort. Moreover, the action programs can be flexibly adapted to specific situations (e.g., different patients or customers).

At the intellectual level, employees consciously regulate new or complex actions. This entails the development and selection of new and challenging goals and detailed action plans. Feedback processing at this level requires the analysis and evaluation of novel and complex information. While action regulation at the intellectual level requires attention and cognitive effort, it can be routinized through practice and shifted to lower levels of action regulation.

Finally, the level of metacognitive heuristics (which was not explicitly included in Hacker's original work of 1998) involves the use of more abstract, less task-oriented templates, strategies, and heuristics to guide action regulation (Frese & Zapf, 1994). These metacognitive heuristics enable individuals to solve similar problems in an efficient and effective way. For example, workers could use selection, optimization, and compensation strategies to deal successfully with high job demands and limited job resources, and to invest their personal resources optimally (Baltes & Baltes, 1990; Moghimi, Zacher, Scheibe, & Von Yperen, 2017).

COMPLETE TASKS AND ACTION

A core concept in action regulation theory is the notion of complete (versus partial or fragmented) tasks and actions. Complete tasks and action entail that workers regulate their actions across all five phases of the action regulation sequence as well as at different and alternating mental levels of action regulation (a related concept in job characteristics theory is "task identity"; Hackman & Oldham, 1976). For example, instead of merely executing behavior, workers are also involved in preparatory activities (i.e., goal and plan development and selection, requesting and retrieving relevant information) as well as feedback processing (Hacker, 1986). With regard to the hierarchical structure, complete tasks and actions require action regulation on the sensorimotor level, the level of flexible action patterns, the intellectual level, and the metacognitive heuristics level. As complete tasks require high levels of decision-making, responsibility, and learning, they are more likely to contribute to worker health, well-being, and positive development in the work context (Hacker, 1986; Hackman & Oldham, 1976).

ACTION-ORIENTED MENTAL MODEL AND FOCI OF ACTION REGULATION

Over time and with increased experience, workers develop action-oriented mental models that include cognitive representations of the input conditions, goals, plans, results of action, and knowledge about boundary conditions of action at different levels of the action regulation hierarchy (Frese & Zapf, 1994; Hacker, 1985). An action-oriented mental model contains unconscious movement schemata, routinized yet flexible action schemata, representations of complex and conscious intellectual processes, and generalized metaplans and heuristics. These elements across the four levels of action regulation constitute the knowledge base of action regulation. Action-oriented mental models guide workers until the action sequence is completed. The accuracy and level of detail of action-oriented mental models determines the efficiency and effectiveness of action regulation (Frese & Zapf, 1994).

Three different foci can be in the foreground of action regulation (Frese, 2007; Zacher & Frese, 2018). A focus on the task entails that workers analyze the task content (e.g., redundancy of elements) and context (e.g., opportunities to perform). A strong task focus links task-related goals with relevant plans and behavior, as well as task-relevant feedback. Therefore, a strong task focus is associated with high efficiency and effectiveness of action regulation.

A focus on the social context of action regulation involves that workers consider how other people or groups may influence the processes of goal development and selection, mapping the environment, planning, monitoring of execution, and feedback processing. A focus on the social context can facilitate or constrain the efficiency and effectiveness of action regulation, depending on the nature and importance of social relationships. For instance, research on self-monitoring (Snyder, 1974) has suggested that a social focus during action regulation can improve task performance, whereas research on emotion work, particularly emotional demands and dissonance, suggests negative effects of a social focus during action regulation (Zapf, 2002).

Finally, a focus on the self during action regulation means that workers concentrate on the implications of their actions on the self (e.g., emotions, self-beliefs). Research suggests that self-regulatory processes can have positive effects on work outcomes (Latham & Locke, 2007). At the same time, a self-focus may distract from the task at hand and thus have a disruptive function during action regulation (Kluger & DeNisi, 1996; Sonnentag, 1998).

THEORETICAL AND PRACTICAL IMPLICATIONS OF ACTION REGULATION THEORY

Action regulation theorists have suggested that actions in the context of monotonous work tasks can lead to impaired health and well-being (Hacker & Richter, 1984). At the same time, researchers have acknowledged that actions can be important contributors to "personality development," which is conceived broadly to include not only changes in narrow personality traits, but also positive changes in knowledge, skills, abilities, and other factors such as self-efficacy beliefs and control orientations (Bandura, 1986; Leontjev, 1978). Accordingly, action regulation theory has several important implications for work design and individual workers (Frese & Zapf, 1994; Hacker, 2003). In the following, we focus on theoretical and practical implications for work design, strain and well-being, learning and development, and successful aging at work (for additional implications, see Frese & Zapf, 1994; Zacher & Frese, 2018).

First, the complexity and completeness of tasks (i.e., level of task-related challenge) determines the extent to which action regulation contributes to positive personality development. Complete tasks enable workers to experience different phases of action regulation and to regulate actions at different mental levels. Thus, complete tasks can help improve competencies and motivate workers (Frese & Zapf, 1994; Hackman & Oldham, 1976). In contrast, partial or fragmented tasks are problematic because they do not allow workers to make use of different skills and abilities, which can lead to losses in competencies and feelings of boredom and demotivation over time (cf. "use-it-or-lose-it hypothesis"; Salthouse, 2006).

Second, the design of work tasks also has implications for workers' experienced strain and well-being. Action regulation theorists have argued that to reduce strain and improve well-being, work needs to be designed such that it provides workers with challenging tasks (i.e., regulation requirements) and control (i.e., regulation possibilities), as well as reduced stressors in the work environment (i.e., regulation problems; Zapf, 2002). Action regulation theorists further distinguish between three broad categories of work-related stressors that lead to action regulation problems (Frese & Zapf, 1994). Regulation obstacles are events or conditions that make it difficult or impossible to attain a goal (e.g., interruptions, lack of information or equipment). Regulation uncertainty may be due to a lack of knowledge or available information on how to attain a goal, which plan is most likely to be successful, and whether feedback is useful. Finally, overtaxing regulation describes a situation in which work demands are too high (e.g., time pressure) or signals are too intense (e.g., information overload), disrupt the action sequence, and cause strain and lower well-being (Frese & Zapf, 1994).

Third, action regulation theory further has implications for learning and training in work and organizational contexts (Frese & Keith, 2015). Learning and training lead to improved and more differentiated action-oriented mental models, which are important prerequisites for efficient and effective work behavior. So-called superworkers have superior knowledge and skills, a deeper understanding of tasks, use more active and long-term strategies, and structure their work situations so that they receive useful feedback. In addition, superworkers are more sensitive to relevant signals from the environment and perceive signals, differences between signals, and errors more accurately (Hacker, 1985). At the beginning of learning processes, actions are regulated on the conscious intellectual level. Over time and with practice in redundant work environments, action regulation shifts to lower levels for more automatized processing and routinized actions. Establishing action regulation routines allows for additional cognitive operations to be performed at higher levels (e.g., creative thinking), because automatized operations do not require a lot of attention (Gielnik, Frese, & Stark, 2015; Ohly, Sonnentag, & Pluntke, 2006). Action regulation theory has been used to develop training programs in the domains of leadership (Frese, Beimel, & Schoenborn, 2003) and entrepreneurship (Gielnik, Frese, Kahara-Kawuki, et al., 2015; Glaub, Frese, Fischer, & Hoppe, 2014). This research has shown that efficient and effective action regulation contributes importantly to leadership success and the startup of new businesses.

Finally, researchers have integrated action regulation and life-span developmental theories to better understand and derive implications for successful aging at work (Frese & Stewart, 1984; Zacher, 2015; Zacher et al., 2016). For instance, in their "action regulation across the adult lifespan" (ARAL) metatheoretical framework comprising 35 testable research propositions, Zacher and colleagues (2016) analyzed workers' action regulation from a life-span developmental perspective to explain the effects of age-related changes in cognitive abilities (i.e., fluid and crystallized intelligence), personality, socioemotional goal priorities, and contextual factors on the regulation of action across different phases and levels. Furthermore, these researchers analyzed aging and development in the work context from an action regulation theory perspective. To this end, they explained how workers' action regulation may impact their developmental outcomes, including age-related changes in cognitive abilities and personality characteristics. For example, based on the use-it-or-lose-it hypothesis from the life-span developmental literature (Salthouse, 2006), they suggested that complete tasks and actions may help older workers maintain cognitive abilities and openness to experience with increasing age. Zacher and colleagues (2016) further integrated concepts from action regulation theory with life-span theories of motivation, including the model of selection, optimization, and compensation (Baltes & Baltes, 1990) and the motivational theory of life-span development (Heckhausen, Wrosch, & Schulz, 2010), as well as theories on socioemotional experience, including socioemotional selectivity theory (Carstensen, Isaacowitz, & Charles, 1999) and the strength and vulnerability integration model (Charles, 2010).

CONCLUSION

This article reviewed the history, basic concepts and tenets, and theoretical and practical implications of action regulation theory. Developed in the 1960s and 1970s, action regulation theory is an important basic theory for applied psychology, and particularly industrial, work, and organizational psychology. The theory provides an integrative framework that describes and explains the sequence and structure of action regulation, as well as the notion of complete tasks and actions. Moreover, the theory examines the role of action-oriented mental models and different foci of action regulation (on the task, social context, or self) in work and organizational contexts. Action regulation theory has important implications for work design, worker stress and well-being, and learning, as well as positive development and successful aging in the work context.

REFERENCES

Austin, J. T., & Vancouver, J. B. (1996). Goal constructs in psychology: Structure, process, and content. *Psychological Bulletin, 120,* 338–375. http://dx.doi.org/10.1037/0033-2909.120.3.338

Baker, T., & Nelson, R. E. (2005). Creating something from nothing: Resource construction through entrepreneurial bricolage. *Administrative Science Quarterly, 50,* 329–366. http://dx.doi.org/10.2189/asqu.2005.50.3.329

Ballard, T., Yeo, G., Neal, A., & Farrell, S. (2016). Departures from optimality when pursuing multiple approach or avoidance goals. *Journal of Applied Psychology, 101,* 1056–1066. http://dx.doi.org/10.1037/apl0000082

Baltes, P. B., & Baltes, M. M. (1990). Psychological perspectives on successful aging: The model of selective optimization with compensation. In P. B. Baltes & M. M. Baltes (Eds.), *Successful aging: Perspectives from the behavioral sciences* (pp. 1–34). New York: Cambridge University Press.

Bandura, A. (1986). *Social foundations of thought and action: A social cognitive theory.* Englewood Cliffs, NJ: Prentice-Hall.

Bandura, A. (2001). Social cognitive theory: An agentic perspective. *Annual Review of Psychology, 52,* 1–26. http://dx.doi.org/10.1146/annurev.psych.52.1.1

Bargh, J. A., & Barndollar, K. (1996). Automaticity in action: The unconscious as repository of chronic goals and motives. In P. M. Gollwitzer & J. A. Bargh (Eds.), *The psychology of action: Linking cognition and motivation to behavior* (pp. 457–481). New York: Guilford.

Carstensen, L. L., Isaacowitz, D. M., & Charles, S. T. (1999). Taking time seriously: A theory of socioemotional selectivity. *American Psychologist, 54*(3), 165–181. http://dx.doi.org/10.1037/0003-066X.54.3.165

Carver, C. S., & Scheier, M. F. (1982). Control theory: A useful conceptual framework for personality-social, clinical, and health psychology. *Psychological Bulletin, 92,* 111–135. http://dx.doi.org/10.1037/0033-2909.92.1.111

Charles, S. T. (2010). Strength and vulnerability integration: A model of emotional well-being across adulthood. *Psychological Bulletin, 136*(6), 1068–1091. http://dx.doi.org/10.1037/a0021232

von Cranach, M. (1996). Toward a theory of the acting group. In E. Witte & J. H. Davis (Eds.), *Understanding group behavior: Small group processes and interpersonal relations* (pp. 147–187). Hillsdale, NJ: Lawrence Erlbaum.

DeShon, R. P., & Gillespie, J. Z. (2005). A motivated action theory account of goal orientation. *Journal of Applied Psychology, 90,* 1096–1127. http://dx.doi.org/10.1037/0021-9010.90.6.1096

Frese, M. (2006). Grand theories and mid-range theories: Cultural effects on theorizing and the attempt to understand active approaches to work. In K. G. Smith & M. A. Hitt (Eds.), *Great minds in management: The process of theory development* (pp. 84–108). Oxford: Oxford University Press.

Frese, M. (2007). The psychological actions and entrepreneurial success: An action theory approach. In J. R. Baum, M. Frese, & R. A. Baron (Eds.), *The psychology of entrepreneurship* (pp. 151–188). Mahwah, NJ: Lawrence Erlbaum.

Frese, M. (2009). Towards a psychology of entrepreneurship: An action theory perspective. *Foundations and Trends in Entrepreneurship, 5*(6), 435–494. http://dx.doi.org/10.1561/0300000028

Frese, M., Beimel, S., & Schoenborn, S. (2003). Action training for charismatic leadership: Two evaluations of studies of a commercial training module on inspirational communication of a vision. *Personnel Psychology, 56*(3), 671–698. http://dx.doi.org/10.1111/j.1744-6570.2003.tb00754.x

Frese, M., & Fay, D. (2001). Personal initiative: An active performance concept for work in the 21st century. *Research in Organizational Behavior, 23,* 133–187. http://dx.doi.org/10.1016/S0191-3085(01)23005-6

Frese, M., & Keith, N. (2015). Action errors, error management and learning in organizations. *Annual Review of Psychology, 66,* 661–687. http://dx.doi.org/10.1146/annurev-psych-010814-015205

Frese, M., Rank, J., & Zacher, H. (2017). Action regulation theory. In S. G. Rogelberg (Ed.), *The SAGE encyclopedia of industrial and organizational psychology* (2d ed., Vol. 1, pp. 13–15). Thousand Oaks, CA: SAGE.

Frese, M., & Sabini, J. (Eds.). (1985). *Goal directed behavior: The concept of action in psychology.* Hillsdale, NJ: Lawrence Erlbaum.

Frese, M., & Stewart, J. (1984). Skill learning as a concept in life-span developmental psychology: An action theoretic analysis. *Human Development, 27,* 145–162. http://dx.doi.org/10.1159/000272909

Frese, M., Stewart, J., & Hannover, B. (1987). Goal-orientation and planfulness: Action styles as personality concepts. *Journal of Personality and Social Psychology, 52,* 1182–1194. http://dx.doi.org/10.1037/0022-3514.52.6.1182

Frese, M., & Zapf, D. (1994). Action as the core of work psychology: A German approach. In H. C. Triandis, M. D. Dunnette, & L. Hough (Eds.), *Handbook of industrial and organizational psychology* (Vol. 4, pp. 271–340). Palo Alto, CA: Consulting Psychologists Press.

Gielnik, M. M., Frese, M., Kahara-Kawuki, A., Katono, I., Kyejjusa, S., Munene, J., . . . Dlugosch, T. (2015). Action and action regulation in entrepreneurship: Evaluating a student training for promoting entrepreneurship. *Academy of Management Learning & Education, 14*(1), 69–94. http://dx.doi.org/10.5465/amle.2012.0107

Gielnik, M. M., Frese, M., & Stark, M. S. (2015). Planning and entrepreneurship. In M. D. Mumford & M. Frese (Eds.), *The psychology of planning* (pp. 289–311). New York: Routledge.

Glaub, M. E., Frese, M., Fischer, S., & Hoppe, M. (2014). Increasing personal initiative in small business managers or owners leads to entrepreneurial success: A theory-based controlled randomized field intervention for evidence-based management. *Academy of Management Learning & Education, 13*(3), 354–379. http://dx.doi.org/10.5465/amle.2013.0234

Haase, C. M., Heckhausen, J., & Wrosch, C. (2013). Developmental regulation across the life span: Toward a new synthesis. *Developmental Psychology, 49*(5), 964–972. http://dx.doi.org/10.1037/a0029231

Hacker, W. (1971). *Allgemeine Arbeits- und Ingenieurpsychologie* [General work and engineering psychology]. Berlin: Deutscher Verlag der Wissenschaften.

Hacker, W. (1985). Activity: A fruitful concept in industrial psychology. In M. Frese & J. Sabini (Eds.), *Goal directed behavior: The concept of action in psychology* (pp. 262–284). Hillsdale, NJ: Lawrence Erlbaum.

Hacker, W. (1986). Complete vs. incomplete working tasks—a concept and its verification. In G. Debus & W. Schroiff (Eds.), *The psychology of work organization* (pp. 23–36). Amsterdam: Elsevier.

Hacker, W. (1998). *Allgemeine Arbeitspsychologie: Psychische Regulation von Arbeitstätigkeiten* [General work psychology: Mental regulation of work tasks]. Bern, Switzerland: Huber.

Hacker, W. (2003). Action regulation theory: A practical tool for the design of modern work processes? *European Journal of Work and Organizational Psychology, 12,* 105–130. http://dx.doi.org/10.1080/13594320344000075

Hacker, W., & Richter, P. (1984). *Psychische Fehlbeanspruchung: Psychische Ermüdung, Monotonie, Sättigung und Streß* [Mental strain: Mental fatigue, monotony, repletion, and stress]. Berlin: Springer.

Hacker, W., & Sachse, P. (2014). *Allgemeine Arbeitspsychologie: Psychische Regulation von Tätigkeiten* [General work psychology: Mental regulation of tasks]. Göttingen, Germany: Hogrefe.

Hackman, J. R. (1970). Tasks and task performance in research on stress. In J. E. McGrath (Ed.), *Social and psychological factors in stress* (pp. 202–237). New York: Holt, Rinehart & Winston.

Hackman, J. R., & Oldham, G. R. (1976). Motivation through the design of work: Test of a theory. *Organizational Behavior and Human Performance, 16,* 250–279. http://dx.doi.org/10.1016/0030-5073(76)90016-7

Heckhausen, J., Wrosch, C., & Schulz, R. (2010). A motivational theory of life-span development. *Psychological Review, 117*(1), 32–60. http://dx.doi.org/10.1037/a0017668

Hofmann, D. A., & Frese, M. (Eds.). (2011). *Errors in organizations.* New York: Taylor & Francis.

Kluger, A. N., & DeNisi, A. (1996). The effects of feedback interventions on performance: A historical review, a meta-analysis, and a preliminary feedback intervention theory. *Psychological Bulletin, 119,* 254–284. http://dx.doi.org/10.1037/0033-2909.119.2.254

Latham, G. P., & Locke, E. A. (2007). New developments in and directions for goal-setting research. *European Psychologist, 12,* 290–300. http://dx.doi.org/10.1027/1016-9040.12.4.290

Latham, G. P., & Piccolo, R. F. (2012). The effect of context-specific versus nonspecific subconscious goals on employee performance. *Human Resource Management, 515,* 511–524. http://dx.doi.org/10.1002/hrm.21486

Leontjev, A. N. (1978). *Activity, consciousness, and personality.* Englewood Cliffs, NJ: Prentice-Hall.

Locke, E. A., & Latham, G. P. (1990). *A theory of goal setting and task performance.* Englewood Cliffs, NJ: Prentice-Hall.

Locke, E. A., & Latham, G. P. (2002). Building a practically useful theory of goal and task motivation. *American Psychologist, 57,* 705–717. http://dx.doi.org/10.1037/0003-066X.57.9.705

Locke, E. A., & Latham, G. P. (Eds.). (2013). *New developments in goal setting and task performance.* New York: Routledge.

Lord, R. G., Diefendorff, J. M., Schmidt, A. M., & Hall, R. J. (2010). Self-regulation at work. *Annual Review of Psychology, 61,* 543–568. http://dx.doi.org/10.1146/annurev.psych.093008.100314

Lord, R. G., & Levy, P. E. (1994). Moving from cognition to action: A control theory perspective. *Applied Psychology: An International Review, 43,* 335–366. http://dx.doi.org/10.1111/j.1464-0597.1994.tb00828.x

Miller, G. A., Galanter, E., & Pribram, K. H. (1960). *Plans and the structure of behavior.* New York: Henry Holt.

Moghimi, D., Zacher, H., Scheibe, S., & Von Yperen, N. W. (2017). The selection, optimization, and compensation model in the work context: A systematic review and meta-analysis of two decades of research. *Journal of Organizational Behavior, 38*(2), 247–275. http://dx.doi.org/10.1002/job.2108

Mumford, M. D., Mecca, J. T., & Watts, L. L. (2015). Planning processes: Relevant cognitive operations. In M. D. Mumford & M. Frese (Eds.), *Organizational planning: The psychology of performance* (pp. 9–30). New York: Routledge, Taylor & Francis.

Napolitano, C. M., & Freund, A. M. (2016). On the use and utility of backup plans. *Perspectives on Psychological Science, 11*(1), 56–73. http://dx.doi.org/10.1177/1745691615596991

Neal, A., Ballard, T., & Vancouver, J. B. (2017). Dynamic self-regulation and multiple-goal pursuit. *Annual Review of Organizational Psychology and Organizational Behavior, 4*, 401–423. http://dx.doi.org/10.1146/annurev-orgpsych-032516-113156

Ohly, S., Sonnentag, S., & Pluntke, F. (2006). Routinization, work characteristics and their relationships with creative and proactive behaviors. *Journal of Organizational Behavior, 27*, 257–279. http://dx.doi.org/10.1002/job.376

Raabe, B., Frese, M., & Beehr, T. A. (2007). Action regulation theory and career self-management. *Journal of Vocational Behavior, 70*, 297–311. http://dx.doi.org/10.1016/j.jvb.2006.10.005

Rudolph, C. W., Katz, I. M., Lavigne, K. N., & Zacher, H. (2017). Job crafting: A meta-analysis of relationships with individual differences, job characteristics, and work outcomes. *Journal of Vocational Behavior, 102*, 112–138. http://dx.doi.org/2010.1016/j.jvb.2017.05.008

Salthouse, T. A. (2006). Mental exercise and mental aging: Evaluating the validity of the "use it or lose it" hypothesis. *Perspectives on Psychological Science, 1*, 68–87. http://dx.doi.org/10.1111/j.1745-6916.2006.00005.x

Schneider, B., Ehrhart, M. G., & Macey, W. H. (2013). Organizational climate and culture. *Annual Review of Psychology, 64*, 361–388. http://dx.doi.org/10.1146/annurev-psych-113011-143809

Snyder, M. (1974). Self-monitoring of expressive behavior. *Journal of Personality and Social Psychology, 30*(4), 526–537. http://dx.doi.org/10.1037/h0037039

Sonnentag, S. (1998). Expertise in professional software design: A process study. *Journal of Applied Psychology, 83*, 703–715. http://dx.doi.org/10.1037/0021-9010.83.5.703

Sun, S., & Frese, M. (2013). Multiple goal pursuit. In E. A. Locke & G. P. Latham (Eds.), *New developments in goal setting and task performance* (pp. 177–194). New York: Routledge.

Tomaszewski, T. (1978). *Tätigkeit und Bewusstsein: Beiträge zur Einführung in die polnische Tätigkeitspsychologie* [Activity and consciousness: Contributions to an introduction of Polish psychology of activity]. Basel, Switzerland: Beltz.

Unsworth, K., Yeo, G., & Beck, J. (2014). Multiple goals: A review and derivation of general principles. *Journal of Organizational Behavior, 35*(8), 1064–1078. http://dx.doi.org/10.1002/job.1963

Vancouver, J. B., Weinhardt, J. M., & Schmidt, A. M. (2010). A formal, computational theory of multiple-goal pursuit: Integrating goal-choice and goal-striving processes. *Journal of Applied Psychology, 95*, 985–1008.

Volpert, W. (1982). The model of the hierarchical-sequential organization of action. In W. Hacker, W. Volpert, & M. V. Cranach (Eds.), *Cognitive and motivational aspects of action* (pp. 35–51). Berlin: Hüthig Verlagsgemeinschaft.

Wrzesniewski, A., & Dutton, J. E. (2001). Crafting a job: Revisioning employees as active crafters of their work. *Academy of Management Review, 26*(2), 179–201. http://dx.doi.org/10.5465/AMR.2001.4378011

Zacher, H. (2015). Successful aging at work. *Work, Aging and Retirement, 1*(1), 4–25. http://dx.doi.org/10.1093/workar/wau006

Zacher, H., & Frese, M. (2018). Action regulation theory: Foundations, current knowledge, and future directions. In D. S. Ones, N. R. Anderson, C. Viswesvaran, & H. K. Sinangil (Eds.), *The SAGE handbook of industrial, work and organizational psychology* (2d ed., Vol. 2, pp. 80–102). Thousand Oaks, CA: SAGE.

Zacher, H., Hacker, W., & Frese, M. (2016). Action regulation across the adult lifespan (ARAL): A meta-theory of work and aging. *Work, Aging and Retirement, 2*(3), 286–306. http://dx.doi.org/10.1093/workar/waw015

Zapf, D. (2002). Emotion work and psychological well-being: A review of the literature and some conceptual considerations. *Human Resource Management Review, 12*, 237–268. http://dx.doi.org/10.1016/S1053-4822(02)00048-7

Hannes Zacher

GOAL SETTING THEORY: CAUSAL RELATIONSHIPS, MEDIATORS, AND MODERATORS

Theories in psychology enable predicting, explaining, and influencing behavior. To qualify as a theory, causal relationships must be specified, mediators that explain the causal relationships must be identified, and the boundary conditions within which the theory is applicable must be known. Locke and Latham's (1990, 2002, 2013; Latham & Locke, 2007, in press) goal setting theory of motivation satisfies these three criteria. This article explains the theory, describing the inductive method used to develop that theory, examples of experiments supporting the theory, the perils in ignoring the theory's moderator variables, the various ways of setting goals, and the economic benefits of setting specific, high goals. It concludes with a discussion of goals that are primed in the subconscious.

GOAL SETTING THEORY

With regard to causal relationships, goal setting theory makes three assertions. First, specific, high goals lead to higher performance than setting no goals or even a vague goal such as the exhortation to "do your best." Second, the higher the goal, the higher an individual's performance. Third, such variables as feedback or knowledge of one's results, participation in the making of decisions, or competition with others have little or no effect on a person's behavior unless they lead to the setting of a goal that is both specific and difficult.

The mediators that explain why specific, high goals increase an individual's performance are four-fold. First, consistent with the definition of motivation, a specific goal involves the *choice* to take action to pursue X to the exclusion of other factors. Thus a goal that is specific enables people to focus, to have a purpose in what they do rather than to meander relatively aimlessly. Second, a goal that is difficult as well as specific engenders *effort*, a second cornerstone of motivation. Hence, the higher a specific goal, the more effort that is expended. The third mediator is *persistence*. When a goal that is chosen is specific rather than vague, and difficult rather than easy, people persist in their pursuit of the goal until it is attained. The problem with a vague goal is that it allows multiple interpretations as to whether the goal is attained (e.g., my goal is to lose weight). Thus people may pat themselves on the back undeservedly. A specific goal makes explicit the desired level of performance and hence whether it has been attained (e.g., my goal is to lose 15 pounds). Persistence is a third cornerstone of motivation (Latham, 2012). A fourth mediator is relatively cognitive in nature. Setting a specific, high goal cues an individual's extant *strategies* necessary to attain it.

Moderator variables specify the boundary conditions within which the above assertions are applicable. A specific, high goal leads to higher performance than an easier goal, a vague goal, or no goal only under four conditions. First, the person must have the *ability* to attain a high goal or the person is unlikely to commit to attaining it. *Goal commitment* is a second, and arguably the most important, moderator variable. If an individual is not committed to goal attainment, by definition that individual does not have a goal. Third, people must receive *feedback* on their performance in relation to the goal they are striving to attain. In the absence of feedback, people lack the information necessary to ascertain whether they should adhere to or change their strategy, a mediator in goal setting theory, for goal attainment.[1] Finally, the requisite *resources* must be available for goal attainment. Situational constraints can mitigate ability for and commitment to goal attainment, no matter how difficult or easy the goal may be.

INDUCTION

Many, if not most, theories in psychology are developed through deduction. The authors of a deductive theory typically begin with plausible statements based on their observations. They then make predictions regarding the relationships between variables, they offer an explanation for the alleged relationships (i.e., mediators), and they state the conditions (e.g., boundary/moderators) under which the relationships should occur. Finally, empirical experiments are conducted to test the predicted causal relationships, mediators, and moderators that the theorist expects to observe. An example of a deductively derived theory in organizational psychology is Vroom's (1964) expectancy theory.[2]

A major limitation of developing a theory through deduction is that it can lead to what Kahneman (2011, p. 211), the Nobel Prize–winning psychologist, labeled as theory-induced blindness: "Once you have scripted a theory and used it as a tool in your thinking, it is extraordinarily difficult to notice its flaws. If you come upon an observation that does not seem to fit the model, you assume that it must be a perfectly good explanation that you are somehow missing. You give the thought the benefit of the doubt, trusting the community of experts who have accepted it."

The alternative to deductively developing a theory is to do so inductively. The primary difference between deduction and induction is the time-period or sequential order for conducting empirical experiments. As noted above, the deductive method involves the specification of causal variables, its mediators and moderators, before rather than after conducting empirical experiments to determine whether the deductions can be supported by scientifically obtained evidence. The inductive method requires conducting experiments, accumulating knowledge from these experiments, and then and only then developing a theory.

Empirical research was conducted inductively from the 1960s through the 1980s in both laboratory and field settings before the theory of goal setting was formally developed (Locke & Latham, 1990). The theory is based on nearly 400 studies involving close to 40,000 participants from eight different countries who performed one or more of 88 different tasks. The time span of these tasks ranged from 1 minute to 3 years. A decade later more than 1,000 studies had been conducted (Mitchell & Daniels, 2003). These studies show that goal setting theory is not only applicable to the motivation of an individual, it is applicable to groups/teams (Kramer, Thayer, & Salas, 2013), departments (Porter & Latham, 2013), and organizations as well (Pritchard et al., 2013; Saari, 2013).

The time span showing the beneficial relationship of goal setting to performance has been shown to be considerably longer than 3 years. A goal for job promotion at AT&T correlated positively with actual job promotion 25 years later (Howard, 2013).

EMPIRICAL RESEARCH

Field experiments have been conducted with pulpwood crews in the southeastern United States. They were matched on such variables as crew size, type of terrain where they were cutting trees, and the level of mechanization they owned to cut the trees. Then they were randomly assigned to the experimental or control condition. The crews that were assigned a specific, high weekly goal to attain had significantly higher productivity the very first week of the 3-month experiment than the crews in the control condition who were urged to do their best. "To do one's best" was not a meaningless exhortation because all the crews were paid on a piece-rate basis. Yet those with a specific, high goal not only had higher productivity (cords per employee hour) throughout the experiment, they also had higher job attendance than those who were urged to do their best. People were now eagerly coming to work because their job, previously viewed by them as tedious, was now viewed as meaningful. The performance goal became a self-evaluative standard for comparing their current performance with their previous performance. The goal also allowed the employees to assess their personal effectiveness relative to others. Thus, the goal setting initiative engendered competition among the crews, competition that could just as easily have occurred, but did not occur, among the crews in the control condition who had been urged to do their best (Latham & Kinne, 1974).

The wood supply of pulp and paper companies sometimes exceeds their processing capacity. Consequently, the companies impose a wood quota where they restrict the number of days they will buy wood to 3 rather than 5. Independently owned logging crews were found to perceive this restriction as a challenging goal. That is, they made the *choice* to exert the *effort* necessary and to *persist* in doing so until they harvested as many trees in 3 days as they normally did in 5 (Latham & Locke, 1975).

The beneficial effect of goal setting on job performance has also been shown with high-level employees, namely, engineers and scientists with masters and doctoral degrees in an R&D department (Latham, Mitchell, & Dossett, 1978). There were 10 conditions. Employees (1) were assigned a goal, (2) participated in setting the goal, or (3) were urged to do their best. This latter condition was highly relevant for these employees because an ad hoc task force of line managers was examining ways for the company to reduce costs. Rumors abounded that R&D was likely to be reduced in both funding and manpower. The employees in these three goal conditions received feedback in the form of (1) praise, (2) public recognition, or (3) a monetary bonus. This 3×3 experimental design yielded nine conditions. A 10th condition was a true control group consisting of engineers/scientists who were not aware that they were involved in this field experiment.

Consistent with the predictions of goal setting theory, the employees in the do-your-best conditions performed no better than the employees in the control condition, even though those in the control condition did not receive performance feedback in the form of praise, public recognition, or a monetary bonus. Remember, the theory states and research shows that feedback only affects performance positively if it leads to the setting of a specific, high goal.

Consistent with goal setting theory, those engineers/scientists whose goals had been assigned to them performed better than those in the do-best and control conditions. But, the highest performing employees were those who had participated in the goal setting process even though their goal commitment was not significantly higher than their peers with assigned goals. The reason for the higher performance is explained by the theory—they set higher goals. The theory states that the higher the goal, the higher the performance, given the presence of the four moderators.

In all of these studies, money was not necessary for goal commitment. When money is tied to goal setting, it should not be tied to only goal attainment but rather to the attainment of subgoals as well as the final goal.

PERILS IN IGNORING MODERATORS

Ignoring the moderators in goal setting theory is done at one's peril.

Feedback. In a dynamic environment where what is true in one time period is no longer true at a later point in time, blindly adhering to a strategy for goal attainment will likely prove to be costly. In such circumstances, proximal goals (i.e., subgoals) should be set. Proximal goals are advantageous for two reasons. First, they are motivational for maintaining focus, effort, and persistence until the distal goal is attained. Second, and arguably more important in a dynamic setting, is the informative nature of proximal goals. They provide *feedback* as to whether the strategy for attaining the distal goal requires modification (Seijts & Latham, 2001).

Ability. A series of laboratory experiments show that setting performance goals that only 10% of participants can attain sometimes leads to unethical behavior, as defined by overstating one's performance. What is fascinating is that the exaggeration is only done by people who are close to attaining the goal, especially people who in addition receive a monetary bonus for goal attainment. An even more fascinating finding is that people who exaggerated their performance regarding goal attainment did not take the money even though the experiment was designed to allow them to do so (Schweitzer, Ordonez, & Douma, 2004).

Ordonez and colleagues (2009) concluded from their laboratory findings that performance goals should not be set in the workplace. There are at least two problems with their conclusion. First, by setting goals that only 10% of the participants could attain, they failed to take into account one of the theory's moderator variables, ability. They did so based on Appendix C of Locke and Latham's (1990) book, where this level of difficulty is recommended solely for laboratory settings to ensure variance in the participants' performance.[3] Second, Ordonez and colleagues failed to realize that the goals set in field settings reflect the values of the leaders and an organization's culture. Goal setting is both a theory and a technique for increasing performance. As is any technique, goal setting is subject to misuse. Nevertheless, few if any historians blame goal setting for Hitler's egregious behavior leading to the Holocaust. Rather, they blame his values and the Nazi culture. Few if any management scholars blame goal setting for market penetration into legitimate businesses by the Mafia. Instead, they blame the values of the Mafia leaders and the Mafia culture. Similarly, few if any people in the judiciary blame goal setting for the illegal behavior that took place in the undoing of Enron. The fault has been attributed to the company's leaders and the values they inculcated throughout the organization.

In the field of education, there are students who set a specific high goal for the grade they want to attain and then cheat to ensure that they attain it. This is particularly true for some students who aspire to attain high grades in order to get into medical school, law school, or any of the graduate departments (e.g., psychology) where the number of acceptances relative to the number of applicants is small. Yet few people argue for the abolishment of grades because they sometimes lead to unethical behavior on the part of students whose values allow them license to engage in it.

As is the case in any endeavor where there are standards, there will likely be people who will lie about or cheat on ways to ensure their attainment. To paraphrase Shakespeare, the fault is not in the goals but in ourselves, that is, the values we hold while pursuing them (Latham & Locke, 2009). In short, goal setting theory provides an excellent framework for managers and employees to increase their performance. Yet as is the case with any scientific theory and/or technique, there is no foolproof way of ensuring that it will not be misused.

Situational Resources.　During a downturn in the economy, senior management may set performance goals that are perceived by supervisors as too high for them to attain. A correlational study revealed that when supervisors see the goal as exceeding their ability to attain it, when in addition they believe they lack the resources to attain it, they experience "hindrance stress." This in turn has been shown to correlate with their subsequent abuse of their subordinates (Mawritz, Folger, & Latham, 2014). This correlational finding is consistent with a seminal experiment conducted years ago that showed that frustration leads to aggression (Dollard, Doob, Miller, Mowrer, & Sears, 1939). Hence the importance of taking into account a person's or team's resources when setting a goal.

Learning Goals.　There are occasions when an individual lacks the ability to attain a performance goal (e.g., generate X new revenue streams; develop Y products that will not be easily copied by competitors) regardless of its specificity or level of difficulty. People may simply lack knowledge of the strategies necessary for goal attainment. When this is the case, urging people to do their best typically leads to higher performance than a specific, high performance goal. This is because the latter often increases anxiety that in turn yields to a mindless scramble to find solutions (Mone & Shalley, 1995). The solution is to set a specific, challenging learning goal. A learning goal shifts attention from the desired performance level to be attained to the discovery of X processes, procedures, systems, or strategies. Laboratory experiments show consistently that a specific, high learning goal leads to higher performance than urging people to do their best (e.g., Latham, Seijts, & Crim, 2008). A field study revealed that during a turbulent economic cycle, only learning goals correlated positively with a department's performance (Porter & Latham, 2013).

GOAL SETTING METHOD

Goal setting theory is silent about the optimum method for setting the goal. Programmatic research involving at least 11 experiments revealed that an assigned goal is as effective a method for increasing task performance as a goal that is set participatively between the employee and the supervisor. However, there are a number of caveats regarding this conclusion. First, the statement is correct as long as there are no significant differences in the level of goal difficulty between the two goal setting methods (Latham & Saari, 1979a). If the assigned goal is significantly higher than the goal the employee was involved in choosing, consistent with goal setting theory, the higher goal leads to higher performance (Latham, Steele, & Saari, 1982).

Second, a rationale must accompany an assigned goal; a goal that is assigned curtly is unlikely to increase an individual's performance (Latham, Erez, & Locke, 1988).

Latham and Steele (1983) manipulated independently participative decision-making (PDM) on task strategy versus assigned, PDM, and do-best goals. The results revealed that only setting a specific high goal increased performance. PDM had no effect. However, another caveat is in order. In all the field and laboratory experiments conducted by Latham, the supervisor/experimenter who assigned the goal did so in a supportive manner in interacting with the employee/participant. In the one laboratory experiment where the experimenter deliberately behaved in a nonsupportive manner, the participants set significantly lower goals than those who had been randomly assigned to the supportive condition (Latham & Saari, 1979b).

These findings are consistent with Dember (1974), who, after reviewing the literature on motivation, concluded that in the right setting, being told to do something is tantamount to being motivated to do it. It seems that instructions that are deemed appropriate by an individual take on the formation of powerful internally generated drives. Similarly, Salancik and Pfeffer (1977) concluded that the assignment of a goal implies to an individual that she or he is capable of attaining it. A meta-analysis by Wagner and Gooding (1987) of the research on this topic revealed no noteworthy relationship between participation in decision-making and either job performance or job satisfaction.

Subsequent research has shown that researchers were going down the wrong path in their attempts to show the beneficial effect of an individual's participation in deciding on the goal that should be set. When there is a beneficial effect for PDM, the effect is primarily cognitive rather than motivational. When the task is complex, participants ask more questions than do those who are assigned goals. The information gleaned from these questions improve their performance (Latham & Saari, 1979b). Moreover, participation in decision-making can lead to the development of an effective strategy for attaining the goal; this in turn increases a participant's self-efficacy that the goal is attainable. Strategy and self-efficacy have been shown to have a reciprocal effect on one another, and both have been shown to mediate the PDM–performance relationship (Latham, Winters, & Locke, 1994). Self-efficacy is defined as one's belief or confidence that the goal is attainable. Self-efficacy influences goal choice and goal commitment (Bandura, 2013). That is, people with high self-efficacy choose and commit to high goals. They are resilient in the face of goal setbacks. People with low self-efficacy quickly abandon the goal when they experience difficulties in goal pursuit.

With regard to self-set goals, an experiment conducted in a government agency showed that goal difficulty level, goal acceptance, goal attainment, and task performance were as effective as goals that were assigned or set in a participatory manner (Latham & Marshall, 1982). In summary, from a motivational standpoint, one method of goal setting is not necessarily more effective than another. From a motivational standpoint, the critical factor for increasing performance is the level of difficulty of the goal that is set.

There are contexts where only self-set goals are appropriate, especially off-the-job settings. Frayne and Latham (1987) successfully taught a self-management program to unionized state government employees whose job attendance was low. The core of the program was goal setting and its moderator, feedback, regarding weekly/monthly job attendance. Millman and Latham (2001) taught displaced managers who had been out of work for 13 months to set a goal for re-employment and to use verbal self-guidance to increase self-efficacy for goal attainment, namely, re-employment. Similarly, Latham and Budworth (2006) used this approach for enabling Native North Americans to obtain employment, as did Yanar, Budworth, and Latham (2009) for enabling women in Turkey over the age of 40 to attain their goal of becoming re-employed.

ECONOMIC BENEFITS

Latham and Baldes (1975) reported that goal setting regarding loading trucks to their maximum legal weight saved a forest-product company a quarter of a million dollars over 9 months. Schmidt (2013) used utility analysis procedures to estimate the economic value of goal setting to employers in today's dollars. Specifically, he examined the difference between do-your-best or no-goal conditions and specific, difficult goals. The dollar value figures indicate the increase in revenue from improved performance. His sample is based on four meta-analyses of goal setting experiments. These four meta-analyses included 19,839 data points. The results revealed that the average increase in employee output per year as a result of a goal setting intervention is $9,200. A goal setting intervention that lasts for 5 years, involving only 35 employees, costing $200 per employee, yields an organization $1,603,000 due to the increase in production. The percentage increase in employee output is 9.2%.

PRIMING GOALS IN THE SUBCONSCIOUS

In suggesting directions for future research on motivation, Locke and Latham (2004) pointed to a limitation of goal setting theory, namely that it is a cognitive theory that ignores the subconscious. This is a limitation because cognitive resources are limited (Miller, 1956). In contrast to consciousness, the subconscious is a vast reservoir of information (Vorhauser-Smith, 2011).

Bargh's (1990) automaticity model focuses on goals that are primed in the subconscious. As is the case with goal setting theory, the model asserts that a goal is a mental representation of a desired state that is pursued through action. The goal can be primed in the subconscious in one of two ways, subliminally or supraliminally. The model further asserts that an external stimulus in the environment can passively, subtly, and unobtrusively activate a goal. If the priming is done subliminally, the stimulus is presented below focal awareness; if the priming is done supraliminally, the individual is aware of the stimulus yet is unaware of its influence on subsequent behavior. In short, the model states that a primed goal guides behavior in the absence of conscious intention. In agreement with goal setting theory, this occurs only if the goal is important to the person.

After reviewing the literature in social psychology on primed goals, Latham, Stajkovic, and Locke (2010) concluded that this methodology should be examined with regard to organizational behavior. A laboratory experiment involving brainstorming had revealed that making sentences from scrambled achievement-related words (e.g., win) led to higher performance than making sentences from scrambled neutral words (e.g., tree) (Stajkovic, Locke, & Blair, 2006).

Most social psychology experiments on primed goals involve the presentation of the prime and the measurement of the dependent variable seconds/minutes later (e.g., length of time to walk from a laboratory to an elevator). Thus a field experiment was conducted in a call center to determine whether laboratory findings on primed goals generalize to work settings.[4] As was the case in the preceding laboratory experiment, a supraliminal prime was used to prime the goal for achievement, namely a photograph of a woman winning a race. At the end of the work shift, the employees with the primed goal raised significantly more money from donors than did those in the control group (Shantz & Latham, 2009). These results were replicated in two additional call centers (Shantz & Latham, 2011). Of further practical significance was the finding that the two goals, consciously set and primed, led to higher productivity than either goal alone (Shantz & Latham, 2009).

Consistent with goal setting theory, Latham and Piccolo (2012) hypothesized that a context-specific goal that is primed leads to higher performance than a more general goal. The results from a fourth call center supported this hypothesis. The employees who were primed with a photograph of call center employees in the workplace raised 16% more money than those who were primed with the photograph of the racer, and 85% more money than the employees in the control group. Those employees who were primed with the racer raised 60% more money than those in the control condition. Of further practical significance is the finding that these results were obtained on the first day and lasted throughout the 4-day work week.

What remains to be explored is the time length with which a primed goal influences behavior and the frequency with which the prime should be changed to maintain high performance. The effect of a consciously set specific, high goal on an employee's behavior has been shown to last for months, if not years (e.g., Latham & Baldes, 1975; Howard, 2013).

CONCLUSION

Goal setting theory is among the most valid and useful theories of motivation of organizational behavior (Lee & Earley, 1992; Miner, 2003; Pinder, 1998). The theory is straightforward: set a specific, high goal and the result will be high performance. This is because the specific goal that is *chosen* focuses an individual's attention on goal-relevant activities. Individuals exert far more *effort* for a higher goal than they do for an easier one, and they *persist* in doing so until the goal is attained. However, the beneficial effect of the goal–performance relationship only occurs if the person has the *ability* to attain the goal, is *committed* to goal attainment, receives *feedback* on goal pursuit, and has the requisite *resources* to pursue and attain the goal. Dysfunctional behavior is likely to occur if the theory's moderator variables are ignored.

The theory was developed through induction rather than deduction. Thus it is an open rather than a closed theory; that is, goal setting theory is open to modification through findings from subsequent research (e.g., the discovery of the necessity for setting learning rather than performance goals). A new research frontier is the exploration of the effect of primed goals on organizational behavior and the extent to which their effects on performance are similar to or differ from the effects that have been found with goals that are consciously set.

REFERENCES

Bandura, A. (2013). The role of self-efficacy in goal based motivation. In E. A. Locke & G. P. Latham (Eds.), *New developments in goal and task performance* (pp. 51–64). New York: Routledge.

Bargh, J. A. (1990). Auto-motives: Preconscious determinants of thought and behaviour. Multiple affects from multiple stages. In E. T. Higgins & R. M. Sorrentino (Eds.), *Handbook of motivation and cognition: Foundations of social behaviour* (Vol. 2, pp. 93–130). New York: Guilford Press.

Dember, W. N. (1974). Motivation and the cognitive revolution. *American Psychologist, 29*(3), 161–168.

Dollard, J., Doob, L. W., Miller, N. E., Mowrer, O. H., & Sears, R. R. (1939). *Frustration and aggression.* New Haven, CT: Yale University Freer.

Frayne, C. A., & Latham, G. P. (1987). The application of social learning theory to employee self management of attendance. *Journal of Applied Psychology, 72,* 387–392.

Howard, A. (2013). The predictive validity of conscious and subconscious motives on career advancement. In E. A. Locke & G. P. Latham (Eds.), *New developments in goal setting and task performance.* New York: Routledge.

Kahneman, D. (2011). *Thinking, fast and slow.* New York: Farrar, Straus, and Giroux.

Kramer, W. S., Thayer, A. L., & Salas, E. (2013). Goal setting in teams. In E. A. Locke & G. P. Latham (Eds.), *New developments in goal setting and task performance.* New York: Routledge.

Latham, G. P. (2012). *Work motivation: History, theory, research and practice.* Thousand Oaks, CA: SAGE.

Latham, G. P., & Baldes, J. J. (1975). The "practical significance" of Locke's theory of goal setting. *Journal of Applied Psychology, 60,* 122–124.

Latham, G. P., & Budworth, M. H. (2006). The effect of training in verbal self-guidance on the self-efficacy and performance of Native North Americans in the selection interview. *Journal of Vocational Behavior, 68,* 516–523.

Latham, G. P., Erez, M., & Locke, E. A. (1988). Resolving scientific disputes by the joint design of crucial experiments by the antagonists: Application of the Erez-Latham dispute regarding participation in goal setting. *Journal of Applied Psychology Monograph, 73,* 753–772.

Latham, G. P., & Kinne, S. B. (1974). Improving job performance through training in goal setting. *Journal of Applied Psychology, 59,* 187–191.

Latham, G. P., & Lee, T. W. (1986). Goal setting. In E.A. Locke (Ed.), *Generalizing from laboratory to field settings: Research findings for industrial-organizational psychology, organizational behavior, and human resource management,* (pp. 101–117). Lexington, MA: Heath Lexington.

Latham, G. P., & Locke, E. A. (1975). Increasing productivity with decreasing time limits: A field replication of Parkinson's law. *Journal of Applied Psychology, 60,* 524–526.

Latham, G. P., & Locke, E. A. (2007). New developments in and directions for goal-setting research. *European Psychologist, 12*(4), 290–300.

Latham, G. P., & Locke, E. A. (2009). Science and ethics: What should count as evidence against the use of goal setting? *Academy of Management Perspectives, 23,* 83–91.

Latham, G. P., & Locke, E. A. (in press). Goal setting theory: Controversies and resolutions. In D. Ones, N. Anderson, C. Viswesvaran, & H. Sinangil (Eds.), *Handbook of industrial, work & organizational psychology.* Vol. 1. Thousand Oaks, CA:SAGE.

Latham, G. P., & Marshall, H. A. (1982). The effects of self set, participatively set, and assigned goals on the performance of government employees. *Personnel Psychology, 35,* 399–404.

Latham, G. P., Mitchell, T. R., & Dossett, D. L. (1978). The importance of participative goal setting and anticipated rewards on goal difficulty and job performance. *Journal of Applied Psychology, 63,* 163–171.

Latham, G. P., & Piccolo, R. F. (2012). The effect of context specific versus non-specific subconscious goals on employee performance. *Human Resource Management, 51,* 535–538.

Latham, G. P., & Saari, L. M. (1979a). The effects of holding goal difficulty constant on assigned and participatively set goals. *Academy of Management Journal, 22,* 163–168.

Latham, G. P., & Saari, L. M. (1979b). The importance of supportive relationships in goal setting. *Journal of Applied Psychology, 64,* 151–156.

Latham, G. P., Seijts, H., & Crim, D. (2008). The effects of learning goal difficulty level and cognitive ability on strategies and performance. *Canadian Journal of Behavioural Science, 40*, 220–229.

Latham, G. P., Stajkovic, A., & Locke, E. A. (2010). The relevance and viability of subconscious goals in the workplace. *Journal of Management, 36*, 234–255.

Latham, G. P., & Steele, T. P. (1983). The motivational effects of participation versus goal setting on performance. *Academy of Management Journal, 26*, 406–417.

Latham, G. P., Steele, T. P., & Saari, L. M. (1982). The effects of participation and goal difficulty on performance. *Personnel Psychology, 35*, 677–686.

Latham, G. P., Winters, D. C., & Locke, E. A. (1994). Cognitive and motivational effects of participation: A mediator study. *Journal of Organizational Behavior, 15*, 49–63.

Lee, C., & Earley, P. C. (1992). Comparative peer evaluations of organizational behavior thoeries. *Organizational Development Journal, 10*, 37–42.

Locke, E. A., & Latham, G. P. (1990). *A theory of goal setting and task performance.* Englewood Cliffs, NJ: Prentice Hall.

Locke E. A., & Latham, G. P. (2002). Building a practically useful theory of goal setting and task motivation: A 35-year odyssey. *American Psychologist, 57*, 705–717.

Locke E. A., & Latham, G. P. (2004). What should we do about motivation theory? Six recommendations for the twenty-first century. *Academy of Management Review, 29*, 388–403.

Locke E. A., & Latham, G. P. (2013). *New developments in goal setting and task performance.* New York: Routledge.

Mawritz, M., Folger, R., & Latham, G. P. (2014). Supervisors' exceedingly difficult goals and abusive supervision: The mediating effects of hindrance stress, anger, and anxiety. *Journal of Organizational Behavior, 35*, 358–372.

Mealiea, L. W., & Latham, G. P. (1996). *Skills for managerial success: Theory, experience, and practice.* Chicago: Irwin.

Miller, G. A. (1956). The magical number seven, plus or minus two: Some limits on our capacity for processing information. *Psychological Review, 63*(2), 81–97.

Millman, Z., & Latham, G. P. (2001). Increasing re-employment through training in verbal self-guidance. In M. Erez, U. Kleinbeck, & H. K. Thierry (Eds.), *Work motivation in the context of a globalizing economy.* London: Lawrence Erlbaum.

Miner, J. B. (2003). The rated importance, scientific validity, and practical usefulness of organizational behaviour theories: A quantitative review. *Academy of Management Learning and Education, 2*(3), 250–268.

Mitchell, T. R., & Daniels, D. (2003). Motivation. In W. C. Borman, D. R. Ilgen, & R. J. Klimoski (Eds.), *Comprehensive handbook of psychology: Industrial organizational psychology* (Vol. 12, pp. 225–254). New York: Wiley.

Mone, M. A., & Shalley, C. E. (1995). Effects of task complexity and goal specificity on change in strategy and performance over time. *Human Performance, 8*, 243–262.

Ordonez, L., Schweitzer, M. E., Galinsky, A., & Bazerman, M. (2009). Goals gone wild: How goals systematically harm individuals and organizations. *Academy of Management Perspectives, 23*, 6–16.

Pinder, C. C. (1998). *Work motivation. Theory, issues, and applications.* Upper Saddle River, NJ: Prentice-Hall.

Porter, R. L., & Latham, G. P. (2013). The effect of employee learning goals and goal commitment on departmental performance. *Journal of Leadership and Organizational Studies, 20*, 62–68.

Pritchard, R. D., Young, B. L., Koenig, N., Schmerling, D., & Dixon, N. W. (2013). Long-term effects of goal setting on performance with the productivity measurement and enhancement system (ProMES). In E. A. Locke & G. P. Latham (Eds.), *New developments in goal setting and task performance* (pp. 233–245) New York: Routledge.

Saari, L. M. (2013). Goal setting and organizational transformation. In E. A. Locke & G. P. Latham (Eds.), *New developments in goal setting and task performance* (pp. 233–245). New York: Routledge.

Salancik, G. R., & Pfeffer, J. (1977). Who gets power—and how they hold on to it: A strategic-contingency model of power. *Organizational Dynamics, 5*(3), 2–21.

Schmidt, F. L. (2013). The economic value of goal setting to employers. In E. A. Locke & G. P. Latham (Eds.), *New developments in goal setting and task performance* (pp. 16–20). New York: Routledge.

Schweitzer, M. E., Ordóñez, L., & Douma, B. (2004). The role of goal setting in motivating unethical behavior. *Academy of Management Journal, 47*, 422–432.

Seijts, G. H., & Latham, G. P. (2001). The effect of learning, outcome, and proximal goals on a moderately complex task. *Journal of Organizational Behaviour, 22*, 291–307.

Shantz, A., & Latham, G. P. (2009). An exploratory field experiment of the effect of subconscious and conscious goals on employee performance. *Organizational Behavior and Human Decision Processes, 109*, 9–17.

Shantz, A., & Latham, G. P. (2011). The effect of primed goals on employee performance: Implications for human resource management. *Human Resource Management, 50*, 289–299.

Stajkovic, A. D., Locke, E. A., & Blair, E. S. (2006). A first examination of the relationships between primed subconscious goals, assigned conscious goals, and task performance. *Journal of Applied Psychology, 91*(5), 1172–1180.

Vorhauser-Smith, S. (2011). The neuroscience of talent management. *Employment Relations Today, 28*, 17–22.

Vroom, V. H. (1964). *Work motivation.* New York: John Wiley.

Vroom, V. H. (2015). In the origins of expectancy theory. In K. G. Smith & M. A. Hitt (Eds.), *The process of theory development* (pp. 239–258). Oxford: Oxford University Press.

Wagner, J. A., III, & Gooding, R. Z. (1987). Shared influence and organizational behavior: A meta-analysis of situational variables expected to moderate participation-outcome relationships. *Academy of Management Journal, 30*, 524–541.

Wood, R. E., Whelan, J., Sojo, V., & Wong M. (2013). Goals, goal orientations, strategies, and performance. In E. A. Locke & G. P. Latham (Eds.), *New developments in goal setting and task performance.* New York: Routledge.

Yanar, B., Budworth, M. H., & Latham, G. P. (2009). The effect of verbal self-guidance training for overcoming employment barriers: A study of Turkish women. *Applied Psychology: An International Review, 58*, 586–601.

NOTES

1. Wood et al. (2013) found that strategy can also moderate, in addition to mediate, the goal–performance relationship.

2. Interestingly, Vroom himself never conducted an empirical experiment to test any aspect of his theory (Vroom, 2015).

3. To the author's knowledge, no field experiment has set goals that only 10% of the participants could attain. Most practitioners adopt the heuristic explained by Mealiea and Latham (1996), namely, SMART—that is, a goal should be specific, measurable, attainable, relevant, and have a time frame for its attainment.

4. Findings from laboratory settings regarding consciously set specific, high goals do have external validity for the workplace (Latham & Lee, 1986).

Gary P. Latham

SELF-DETERMINATION THEORY AND ITS RELATION TO ORGANIZATIONS

SELF-DETERMINATION THEORY

Self-determination theory (SDT) (Deci & Ryan, 2000; Ryan & Deci, 2017) is a theory of basic psychological needs in mclness. It has become a very prominent approach to human motivation around the world, and it has been applied in many domains of life, including the workplace and other types of organizations. The theory is built upon an organismic-dialectical metatheory in that it assumes humans are active organisms striving for growth through integration of both internal and external psychological material. It further recognizes that the surrounding social environments either support or thwart this natural tendency. Hence, SDT is a motivational theory that examines the interaction of our inherent developmental tendencies with our external environments.

SDT is concerned primarily with the quality or type of motivation and with a set of psychological needs. Specifically, SDT distinguishes between autonomous motivation and controlled motivation. When autonomously motivated, people engage in activities with a full sense of willingness, volition, and choice. By contrast, when controlled, people engage in activities with a sense of coercion, pressure, and demand. Considerable SDT research has examined the different consequences of autonomous versus controlled motivations. In addition to the differentiation of the types (i.e., qualities) of motivation, SDT has specified three basic and universal psychological needs—the needs for competence, autonomy, and relatedness. Satisfaction of the inherent needs have proven essential nutrients for optimal motivation, functioning, and health.

SDT, as a macrotheory, has been formulated in terms of a set of six mini-theories, each of which addresses different aspects of motivation. The distinction between autonomous and controlled motivation plays a key role in each of the mini-theories, as do the basic needs for competence, autonomy, and relatedness.

Cognitive Evaluation Theory. The first of the SDT mini-theories was cognitive evaluation theory (CET) (Deci & Ryan, 1980). It concerns how factors in social environments affect intrinsic motivation—the prototype of autonomous motivation (Deci, 1975). When intrinsically motivated for an activity, people engage in it because they find it interesting and enjoyable, and while doing it they experience satisfaction of the three basic psychological needs. Research has shown that factors that frustrate the basic needs for competence or autonomy tend to diminish intrinsic motivation, whereas factors that support those needs tend to enhance intrinsic motivation. Factors that support the needs are referred to as *informational* and those that thwart them are referred to as *controlling*.

The first studies focused on the effects of rewards, where it was found that certain types of rewards, such as performance-contingent rewards, were likely to be perceived as controlling and thus to diminish intrinsic motivation. Other rewards, such as positive feedback, were more readily perceived as informational and thus contributed to supporting competence and enhancing intrinsic motivation. Although controversial at the time, a meta-analysis by Deci,

Koestner, and Ryan (1999) confirmed the distinction between informational and controlling rewards and also neuropsychological research lends support (e.g., Di Domenico & Ryan, 2017). This distinction between informational and controlling environments, or as it has later been termed, the distinction between need-supportive and need-thwarting contexts, broadened the investigations of social contexts on motivational processes across a broad range of life's domains.

Organismic Integration Theory. The second mini-theory was organismic integration theory (OIT) (Ryan, Connell, & Deci, 1985). It is concerned with the internalization and integration of extrinsic motivation. Because many activities are not interesting, and therefore not intrinsically motivated, extrinsic contingencies are often required as a source of motivation. OIT suggested that extrinsic motivation can vary in its degree of control versus autonomy as a function of the degree to which the motivation is internalized. Specifically, OIT proposes that there are four types of extrinsic motivation or regulation depending on their degree of internalization and integration. *External regulation* involves being regulated by controlling external reward-and-punishment contingencies, including both material and social factors. It is the least autonomous type of extrinsic motivation. *Introjected regulation* refers to behavior being regulated by internal, controlling contingencies such as contingent self-esteem or the avoidance of shame and guilt. Introjection is a partial internalization and is the second least autonomous type of extrinsic motivation. A more autonomous type of extrinsic motivation is referred to as *identified regulation* and results from a fuller internalization of the personal importance and value of the behavior. Finally, *integrated regulation* is behavior that has been fully assimilated and has become part of the person's sense of true or integrated self. It is the most autonomous type of extrinsic motivation.

Autonomous motivation, which was introduced earlier, comprises intrinsic motivation and fully internalized extrinsic motivation, whereas controlled motivation comprises external and introjected regulations. In addition, in SDT, the concept of amotivation refers to the lack of intention and motivation, and of course it is wholly non-autonomous.

Causality Orientations Theory. The third SDT mini-theory concerns individual differences or personality factors in motivational orientations. Whereas CET and OIT are concerned with how social contexts affect the state levels of motivations, and, in turn, performance and wellness outcomes, causality orientations theory (COT) (Deci & Ryan, 1985) addresses how enduring individual differences in people's motivational orientations affect their outcomes. There are three causality orientations—autonomous, controlled, and impersonal. *Autonomy orientation* refers to viewing one's surroundings as informational and being focused on interest and opportunities for growth. *Controlled orientation* refers to viewing contexts as controlling where external contingencies and power structures guide behavior. Impersonal orientation relates to amotivation and lack of intentional action where performance anxieties and avoidance of failures pertain. According to the theory, everyone has each of those three orientations to some degree as personal characteristics. Thus, people vary in the strength of each of the orientations, and it is the strength of those orientations that predict outcomes. Thus, a person is not characterized as one of the three types of people, although the person may have one of the orientations that is considerably stronger than the other two.

Basic Psychological Needs Theory. Research on CET, OIT, and COT made it very clear that the basic psychological needs for competence autonomy and relatedness play an important part in the quality of peoples' motivation and wellness. This prompted a clear definition of basic psychological needs and the formulation of the fourth mini-theory—namely, basic psychological needs theory (BPNT) (Ryan, 1995). Whereas some theories use the term "needs" to refer to what people desire, BPNT emphasizes that the basic psychological needs are essential nutrients for integrity, high quality motivation, and well-being. While many basic psychological needs have been suggested, there are currently three that satisfy the definition of a basic need within the SDT framework—competence, autonomy, and relatedness. The need for *competence* refers to the feeling of being effective in one's interactions with the environment and experiencing opportunities to both express and exercise one's capacities; the need for *autonomy* concerns the feeling of choice and concurrence with one's own actions; and the need for *relatedness* concerns the feeling of belonging and connection with others such that one is cared for by others and cares for those others. The three basic psychological needs are considered universal as they apply across gender, age, and cultures in being essential for well-being. Furthermore, integration, as described in relation to OIT, is assumed to be a natural process, but a process that requires nutrients. The three basic psychological needs, when satisfied, act as the nutrients through which social environments and causality orientations are manifest in high quality motivation.

Goal Contents Theory. Subsequent research showed that the basic needs were differentially afforded or crowded out by different lifestyles and the aspirations that prompt them. Specifically, the aspirations for accumulating wealth, becoming famous, and looking attractive were found to form one factor, whereas the aspirations for experiencing personal growth, forming close affiliations, contributing to one's community, and being physically fit formed a second factor. The first factor was termed *extrinsic aspirations*, whereas the second was termed *intrinsic aspirations*. That set the stage for the formulation of goal contents theory (GCT) (Kasser & Ryan, 1996). GCT is concerned with the distinction between extrinsic and intrinsic aspirations or life goals as it became apparent that these not only shaped peoples' attitudes and behaviors differently, but also that the pursuit and attainment of the extrinsic life goals were associated with need frustration and ill-being, whereas the pursuit and attainment of intrinsic life goals were associated with need satisfaction and well-being.

Relationships Motivation Theory. The last mini-theory, relationships motivation theory (RMT) (Deci & Ryan, 2014), was formulated on the basis of empirical research about the dynamics of close personal relationships. Evidence indicates that high-quality relationships are strongly related to need satisfaction and autonomous motivation within the relationship, whereas lower quality relationships are related to need frustration and controlled motivation within the relationship. Because close personal relationships are not crucial to the workplace, this mini-theory will receive relatively little attention in what follows.

SDT AS A LENS FOR THE STUDY OF MOTIVATIONAL PROCESSES AT WORK

Research has used the motivational concepts within SDT's mini-theories to explain phenomena across various areas of psychology and several applied domains, including the organizational domain. In 2005, Gagné and Deci (2005) published a review article summarizing the early SDT organizational studies. Following this, a burgeoning literature has developed, and this was summarized in an article by Deci, Olafsen, and Ryan (2017). That article pointed to more than 200 contributions, and since then the literature has increased further.

At the core, this body of research has attempted to identify, examine, and explain antecedents and outcomes of motivational processes described across the mini-theories of SDT. Deci et al. (2017), after reviewing the research, presented a basic SDT model in the workplace (see Figure 1). The model consists of two main categories of independent variables, namely social contexts and individual differences. Specifically, studies have sought to identify workplace factors as contextual variables of importance for motivational processes as described in CET. Furthermore, causality orientations, described in COT, and aspirations, described in GCT, have also been examined to account for individual differences in motivational processes at work, albeit to a much lesser extent than the contextual variables.

These two sets of independent variables have been shown to predict performance and wellness outcomes, often with satisfaction versus frustration of the basic psychological needs and/or autonomous versus controlled work motivation appearing as mediators in the model, in accordance with BPNT and OIT respectively. Typically, studies include either the basic needs or types of motivation, although some include both. A meta-analysis by Van den Broeck, Ferris, Chang, and Rosen (2016) displayed the associations between these SDT concepts. In this analysis, each of the basic needs was negatively related to amotivation. The satisfaction of the need for autonomy and competence demonstrated negative and significant relations with external motivation, whereas the need for relatedness was unrelated to external motivation. Each basic need had positive significant relations with introjected, identified, and intrinsic motivation. Further, in a longitudinal analysis, Olafsen, Deci, and Halvari (2018) found that the social context represented by managerial need support was associated with need satisfaction and, in turn, with autonomous work motivation. Importantly, in this study, the authors did not find the reverse link for the needs and motivations, hence the order of the variables in the model was unidirectional. Another thing that is important to note, is that research employing SDT to study organizational questions has for the most part emphasized the bright motivational process (i.e., need satisfaction and autonomous motivation), while the dark side of these motivational processes (i.e., need frustration and controlled motivation) was set on the research agenda in the first part of the 2010s (Gillet, Fouquereau, Forest, Brunault, & Colombat, 2012).

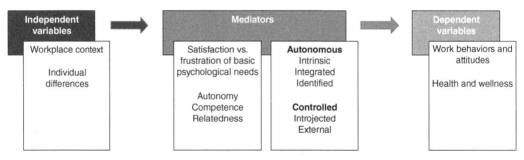

Figure 1. The basic SDT model in the workplace.
Source: Reprinted with permission from Deci et al., 2017.

Finally, the basic SDT model in the workplace consists of two main categories of work outcomes, namely work behaviors and attitudes, and health and wellness. In this body of research, the importance of basic psychological needs satisfaction and the autonomous forms of motivation for employees' work behavior, work attitudes, and general wellness have become evident. On the other hand, frustration of basic psychological needs and controlled motivation may have detrimental effects on these diverse outcomes. In the following, this model is highlighted through a review of the literature.

RESEARCH ON THE BASIC SDT MODEL IN THE WORKPLACE

Researchers on SDT in work organizations have done an outstanding job of identifying antecedents and outcomes of satisfaction and frustration of the basic needs as well as quality of work motivation across cultures, industries, and occupations. The following literature review of SDT research in work organizations will present core SDT articles and various other studies although it will not be possible to review them all given their quantity.

Antecedents of the Basic SDT Model in the Work Domain—Social-Contextual Climate and Individual Differences.
A large part of the literature on SDT in work organizations pertains to social-contextual variables that promote need satisfaction and optimal motivation at work according to the basic SDT model in the workplace. Three broad categories of such social-contextual factors stand out in the literature and are reviewed here, namely, interpersonal climate, job design, and compensation. In addition, studies pertaining to individual differences variables are reviewed.

Interpersonal Climate.   Although also other aspects of the social climate have also been investigated, much of the research on the interpersonal climate at work involves how different types of leadership either support or thwart the basic psychological needs and promote different kinds of motivation. Need support refers to understanding and acknowledging others' perspectives, providing them meaningful information, offering opportunities for choice, and encouraging self-initiation (Deci et al., 2017). By contrast, a controlling or need-thwarting style describes a manager imposing external constraints on behavior in order to make others produce specific outcomes by being demanding, rigid, inflexible, and pressuring.

As mentioned, in studies within the work domain, need support has typically been studied through employees' perceptions of their immediate managers (Baard, Deci, & Ryan, 2004; Olafsen, Halvari, Forest, & Deci, 2015), but a few studies have explored need support from other levels in the organization, such as colleagues (Jungert, Koestner, Houlfort, & Schattke, 2013; Moreau & Mageau, 2012). These and other studies have shown the importance of need support for satisfaction of employees' basic psychological needs (Baard et al., 2004; Olafsen et al., 2015; Olafsen et al., 2018) and autonomous work motivation (Williams et al., 2014). In addition, studies have shown direct implications of managerial need support on work behavior, work attitudes, and employee well-being (e.g., Kanat-Maymon, Mor, Gottlieb, & Shoshani, 2017; Williams et al., 2014).

The large literature on the importance of managerial need support for employee need satisfaction, work motivation, and work functioning was summarized in a meta-analysis by Slemp,

Kern, Patrick, and Ryan (2018). The meta-analysis focused on managerial need support in 83 unique samples of participants, and the findings showed that managerial need support was positively related to employees' basic need satisfaction and autonomous motivation. Additional results showed positive relations of need support to general well-being, job satisfaction, and work performance. The meta-analysis also showed evidence of a path model similar to the SDT work model discussed above. In sum the meta-analysis concluded that need support is "a leadership approach that is consistent with self-determination and optimal functioning in work settings" (Slemp et al., 2018, p. 706).

Fortunately, studies have shown that need support can be learned by managers and others. The first SDT intervention study in work organizations involved training managers, and results revealed that managers who received the training became more need-supportive and this had a positive effect on employees' satisfaction and trust (Deci, Connell, & Ryan, 1989). Similar results were found by Hardré and Reeve (2009), who showed that trained managers became more need-supportive and that the employees of the trained managers were more autonomously motivated and displayed higher levels of work engagement.

Leadership. Not only does need support, per se, as specified by SDT, promote high-quality motivational process at work, but some distinct leadership approaches bear clear similarities to the SDT need-supportive managerial style. For instance, transformational leadership (Bass & Avolio, 1995) has clear similarities to the need-supportive approach of SDT and promotes need satisfaction (Hetland, Hetland, Andreassen, Pallesen, & Notelaers, 2011) and autonomous motivation (Conchie, 2013; Gagné, Morin, et al., 2019). By contrast, transactional leadership, which emphasizes the exchange process through contingent rewards as well as corrective and monitoring behavior, has been linked to lower satisfaction of the basic psychological needs (Hetland et al., 2011) and to controlled motivation (Gagné, Morin, et al., 2019). Also, other leadership theories have been linked to the basic SDT model in the workplace. For instance, Trépanier, Boudrias, and Peterson (2019) showed how destructive leadership represented by tyrannical and laissez-faire management frustrated nurses' basic psychological needs, leading to controlled work motivation and impaired health.

Other Aspects of Social Climate. In addition to leadership approaches that have received considerable attention, other aspects of the social climate have also been investigated. For instance, perceptions of organizational support (Van den Broeck et al., 2016), quality of relationships (Trépanier, Fernet, & Austin, 2012), and communication quality (Nukta, Haueis, Spitzer, & Hille, 2011) have been related positively to the positive motivational mechanisms within SDT. On the other hand, climates characterized by conflict (Hon, 2012), harassment (Trépanier, Fernet, & Austin, 2013b), and bullying (Trépanier, Fernet, & Austin, 2015) have shown negative implications.

Job and Organizational Characteristics. Besides the clear relations of social climates to motivational processes, a fairly large literature has also examined the relations of job or organizational characteristics to motivational processes. In particular, studies of the job demands-resources (JD-R) model (Bakker & Demerouti, 2007) will be reviewed. The JD-R model proposes two broad categories of work characteristics, namely, job demands and job resources. Job demands are typically the work characteristics that require sustained mental and/or physical effort from employees and may thus be energy depleting with its associated physiological and psychological costs. Job resources are those characteristics of work that have a motivational potential by promoting development and goal achievement.

To unravel the underlying mechanisms of how such broad categories of work characteristics have these consequences, studies have made use of SDT. In particular, SDT has accounted empirically for the underlying processes by taking into account the basic psychological needs and type of work motivation. In particular, the motivational process of job resources can be explained by their contribution to the satisfaction of the basic psychological needs and, in turn, the internalization of work activities. The energetic process of job demands, on the other hand, can be explained by their negative impact on the basic need, leading to less internalization. One of the first studies on these relations was by Van den Broeck, Vansteenkiste, De Witte, and Lens (2008), who showed how basic psychological need satisfaction accounted for the psychological mechanism relating job resources to vigor and job demands to exhaustion. Subsequent research has expanded these findings to account for the full SDT model, where both basic psychological needs and type of work motivation have accounted for these underlying processes (Olafsen & Halvari, 2017; Trépanier, Forest, Fernet, & Austin, 2015). Furthermore, studies have shown that job challenge demands and job hindrance demands are differentially related to work outcomes because of their differential relation to basic psychological need satisfaction and quality of motivation. In the meta-analysis by Van den Broeck et al. (2016), results indeed showed that although job resources were consistently predictive of satisfaction of the three basic psychological needs, job demands had mixed relations to satisfaction of these needs. Adding to this, Olafsen and Frølund (2018) showed how job challenges related positively to satisfaction of competence and autonomy, and in turn autonomous work motivation in predicting vitality, whereas job hindrances were negatively related to satisfaction of the basic psychological needs for autonomy, competence, and relatedness.

Compensation. Because of the crucial function of compensation in work organizations, the debate about its effects has been heated. In particular, the discussion has revolved around issues such as contingent rewards, justice perceptions, and money motives. The SDT-based literature on compensation in the work context is reviewed next.

Contingent Pay. Based on CET research, SDT postulates that contingent rewards create pressure toward control and are thus potentially harmful for need satisfaction and autonomous motivation. This postulate was supported in a large meta-analysis of 128 experiments on reward effects (Deci et al., 1999). A meta-analysis by Cerasoli, Nicklin, and Ford (2014) reached the same conclusions. In particular, Cerasoli et al. (2014) found that intrinsic motivation had a weaker effect on performance when incentives were performance contingent and a stronger relation when the incentives were not directly performance contingent. Furthermore, the meta-analysis showed that intrinsic motivation predicted performance quality, whereas extrinsic incentives were more strongly related to performance quantity.

Field studies have also supported these findings. Kuvaas, Buch, Gagné, Dysvik, and Forest (2016) showed that employees receiving pay-for-performance on a yearly basis reported less autonomous work motivation and more controlled work motivation. Although controlled work motivation related positively to work effort in this study, autonomous motivation was more strongly related to this performance measure. Moreover, Kuvaas et al. (2017) found that when testing the unique relation between intrinsic and extrinsic motivation on employee outcomes, intrinsic work motivation related positively to supervisor-rated performance, whereas extrinsic motivation—measured as the importance of compensation for work effort—related negatively to such performance. This latter publication also showed a negative correlation between intrinsic and extrinsic motivation across the two included studies. A diary study by Hewett and Conway (2015) showed that contingent verbal rewards were positively associated with introjected and external regulations, and for complex tasks, highly salient verbal rewards were also negatively associated with identified regulation as well as intrinsic motivation, showing the undermining effect of salient rewards on autonomous work motivation for heuristic task as suggested by earlier SDT research. In sum, these findings seem to indicate that pay-for-performance approaches tend not to be compatible with high-quality performance because of their implications on quality of motivation.

Research on compensation does suggests that there exist some moderators on the effects of monetary rewards on motivation and other types of functioning. In a series of studies by Thibault Landry and colleagues, the functional meaning of rewards was examined. In both field and experimental studies, it has been shown that monetary rewards perceived as informational led to healthier forms of motivation, greater psychological health, and better overall work intentions than did cash rewards perceived as controlling, because informational rewards are conducive to greater basic psychological need satisfaction (e.g., Thibault Landry, Forest, Zigarmi, Houson, & Boucher, 2017; Thibault Landry, Zhang, Papachristopoulos, & Forest, 2019). These and other findings suggest that rewards can have a distinct effect on individuals' motivation and performance depending on whether they take on a need-supportive or controlling meaning.

Justice has also been suggested as a factor of importance when evaluating reward effects. For instance, in a study by Thibault Landry, Gagné, et al. (2017), it was shown that when bonuses were fairly distributed, using financial incentives made employees feel more competent and autonomous, which in turn fostered greater autonomous motivation and lower controlled motivation, and better work performance. Related, Hewett and Leroy (2019) found that higher bonuses associated with higher levels of perceived manager discretion in incentive allocation enhanced procedural fairness, but those based on lower discretion did not. Further, bonuses enhanced intrinsic motivation indirectly through procedural fairness, but only when employees perceived their bonuses to be based on higher levels of perceived manager discretion.

In sum, this stream of research pertaining to contingent pay shows that it can play an undermining role on employees' autonomous work motivation by frustrating basic psychological needs. However, this research also shows that financial incentives are contextual, and when managed in an informational, need-supportive way, these detrimental effects may disappear.

Non-Contingent Pay. From a SDT perspective, the role of non-contingent pay for employee motivation, performance, and well-being is less clear. Some studies have reported a positive relation between pay level and intrinsic and autonomous work motivation (e.g., Kuvaas et al., 2016), whereas others have not found a positive relation between pay level and need satisfaction, and, subsequently, intrinsic work motivation (Olafsen et al., 2015). Regardless of amount, fairness perceptions of also non-contingent compensation seem relevant to need satisfaction and work motivation. In Olafsen et al. (2015), procedural pay justice was positively related to intrinsic motivation through satisfying employees' basic psychological needs. The same study showed that when managerial need support was low, distributive justice had a significantly positive relation to employee need satisfaction, suggesting that money may be more important when the environment is non-supportive. Furthermore, Hartmann and Slapničar (2012) found that the relation between pay justice and intrinsic work motivation was moderated by pay transparency in that procedural justice was a better predictor of intrinsic motivation when pay transparency was low, and that distributive justice was a better predictor of intrinsic motivation when pay transparency was high.

From the discussion regarding compensation, there are many aspects to take into account in assessing its motivating potential. As will be seen later, a number of studies point to autonomous work motivation as a sustainable type of motivation that creates positive consequences both for employees and organizations. To foster this type of motivation, it may be that paying the employees a fair wage level, in a way such that the pay is need-supportive, will yield the most positive results.

Employee Orientations and Aspirations.   Within the work literature, individual differences as proposed by COT and GCT have received far less attention than social-contextual variables. In terms of causality orientations, Baard et al. (2004) found that both managerial need support and employees' autonomy orientation were linked to satisfaction of the basic psychological needs, and Lam and Gurland (2008) reported a positive association between employees' autonomy orientation and self-determined motivation, and a negative association between employees' control orientation and self-determined motivation. In a series of studies, Liu and colleagues studied autonomous causality orientations as they related to various work outcomes. For instance, Liu and Fu (2011) showed that autonomy orientation related positively to personal learning, job involvement, and organizational citizenship behavior, and Liu, Zhang, Wang, and Lee (2011) found that autonomy orientation was positively related to psychological empowerment and negatively related to voluntary turnover. As seen from this review of the literature, studies have focused on autonomy orientation at work and have done little with controlled and impersonal orientations.

One of the first studies pertaining to aspirations based on GCT was by Vansteenkiste et al. (2007), who assessed employees' extrinsic and intrinsic life goals as they related to their well-being. The results showed that employees who held high extrinsic life goals were less satisfied with their jobs and less happy with their lives because holding an extrinsic relative to an intrinsic orientation thwarted satisfaction of the basic needs at work. Further, Jambrak, Deane, and Williams (2014) found that holding extrinsic work values related to burnout, whereas intrinsic work values predicted less intention of leaving the organization, and Roche and Haar (2013) showed that intrinsic aspirations were linked to higher levels of organizational citizenship behavior. Related to money, Thibault Landry et al. (2016) showed how people's motives for pursuing money related to well-being through satisfaction and frustration of the basic psychological needs. Further, a study by Zhang, Zhang, Forest, and Chen (2019) showed that perceptions of managerial need support promoted intrinsic goals by satisfying employees' basic psychological needs, whereas controlling environments promoted extrinsic goals by frustrating the basic psychological needs. In sum, this line of research clearly suggests that, in line with GCT, employees' work aspirations can be predictive of, as well as predicted by, the basic SDT model in the workplace. Intrinsic goals or aspirations are linked to the bright path of motivation, whereas extrinsic goals belong to the dark path in the model.

Outcomes of the Basic SDT Model in the Workplace. Both the basic psychological needs and quality of work motivation have received attention in the literature for predicting various work outcomes. This literature typically focused on the bright path of the basic SDT model in the workplace in terms of showing conditions and processes that foster healthy development and functioning by satisfying the basic psychological needs and promoting autonomous work motivation. More recently, research has also taken interest in the dark path of this model by looking at basic psychological need frustration and, to some extent, controlled work motivation as distinct mechanisms that explain cognitive, affective, and behavioral patterns in predicting the non-optimal or darker sides of human functioning. This has been an important extension as need frustration cannot be viewed simply as a low level of need satisfaction, and controlled motivation cannot be viewed simply as a low level of autonomous motivation. By considering both paths, research has been able to explain how these processes lead to effective functioning and well-being in contrast to compromised functioning and ill-being. This section is structured into work behavior, work attitudes, and wellness as broad categories of outcomes of the SDT workplace model.

Work Behavior. Organizations are, of course, very much concerned with the performance of their employees. Based on our screening of the literature, several studies have shown autonomous work motivation as being the optimal type of work motivation for high-quality performance. In studies by Trépanier, Forest, et al. (2015) and Sandrin, Gillet, Fernet, Leloup, and Depin-Rouault (2019), autonomous work motivation was positively associated while controlled work motivation was negatively associated with self-reported work performance. Studies also support such relations based on more objective performance measures such as supervisor-rated work performance (Kuvaas, Buch, Weibel, Dysvik, & Nerstad, 2017) and supervisor-rated creative performance among employees (e.g., Grant & Berry, 2011; Hon, 2012).

Several of the studies supporting the relation between autonomous motivation and work performance (or the negative association between controlled work motivation and work performance) have predicted the motivational concept from the basic psychological needs, and have also demonstrated indirect links between basic psychological need satisfaction and work performance (e.g., Olafsen & Halvari, 2017). There has also been support for direct relations between satisfaction of the basic psychological needs at work and work performance (e.g., Baard et al., 2004; Greguras & Diefendorff, 2009). A diary study by De Gieter, Hofmans, and Bakker (2018) showed that satisfaction of the needs for autonomy and competence predicted self-reported performance over 10 consecutive working days. The meta-analytic findings in Van den Broeck et al. (2016) demonstrated that each of the basic needs had positive relations with the different performance measures.

Not only has performance been studied as an important work behavior outcome of the SDT workplace model, but a large body of literature pertains to the implications of quality of work motivation in relation to organizational citizenship behavior (Güntert, 2015), knowledge sharing behavior (Gagné, Tian, et al., 2019), organizational deviance (Bureau et al., 2018), absence (Austin, Fernet, Trépanier, & Lavoie-Tremblay, 2020), and a variety of other organizational behavior variables. Further, although indicated as an antecedent in the SDT workplace model, need-supportive behavior can also be promoted through the bright side of the motivational process. For instance, Robertson and Jones (2013) found that teachers' self-determined motivation was related to their level of need support, and Trépanier et al. (2012) showed how managers' autonomous motivation, and self-efficacy, were positively associated with their perception of their own transformational leadership behaviors.

As for the basic psychological needs, need satisfaction has been directly related to a decrease in deviant behavior in the organization (Lian, Lance Ferris, & Brown, 2012), greater learning (Nukta et al., 2011), and more organizational citizenship behavior (Chiniara & Bentein, 2015). In the meta-analysis by Van den Broeck et al. (2016), satisfaction of each of the basic psychological needs was negatively related to deviance, whereas only satisfaction of the needs for autonomy and relatedness predicted absenteeism. On the other hand, frustration of the basic psychological needs has been associated with higher levels of counterproductive work behavior (Van den Broeck et al., 2014).

Work Attitudes. The basic SDT model in the workplace has also been shown to display variation in employee's work attitudes. Basic psychological need satisfaction has, for instance, been directly related to a decrease in turnover intention (Trépanier, Fernet, et al., 2015) and an increase in positive work attitudes such as affective organizational commitment (e.g., Marescaux, De Winne, & Sels, 2013). Further, Van den Broeck et al. (2016) found that each of the basic needs was positively related to job satisfaction and affective commitment, and negatively related to turnover intentions. Contrary, frustration of the basic psychological needs has been related to increased turnover intention (Gillet, Forest, Benabou, & Bentein, 2015).

Regarding quality of motivation, autonomous work motivation has, for instance, been linked to increased work satisfaction (Gillet, Fouquereau, Lafrenière, & Huyghebaert, 2016) as well as occupational and organizational affective commitment (Fernet, Trépanier, Demers, & Austin, 2017), while decreased intention to quit (Austin et al., 2020). Conversely, controlled work motivation has related positively to both occupational and organizational continuance commitment (Fernet, Trépanier, et al., 2017) as well as normative organizational commitment (Gagné, Chemolli, Forest, & Koestner, 2008), while negatively to work satisfaction (Gillet et al., 2016).

Worker Well-Being and Functioning. According to SDT, satisfaction of the three basic psychological needs is essential to facilitate optimal workplace functioning. Research has linked basic need satisfaction to higher work engagement (e.g., Deci et al., 2001), psychological adjustment (Baard et al., 2004), happiness (Gillet et al., 2012), vitality (Vansteenkiste et al., 2007), and mindfulness (Olafsen, 2017) as well as less burnout (e.g., Fernet, Austin, Trépanier, & Dussault, 2013), anxiety (Deci et al., 2001), depressive symptoms (Thibault Landry et al., 2016), and distress (Boudrias et al., 2011). In the meta-analysis by Van den Broeck et al. (2016), satisfaction of each basic need demonstrated significant relations with indicators of well-being. That is, the relations were positive for positive affect, engagement, general well-being, and life satisfaction; and negative for negative affect, strain, and burnout.

In contrast to need satisfaction, need frustration has more recently been given increased attention in the work literature. For instance, Olafsen, Niemiec, Halvari, Deci, and Williams

(2017) showed in a longitudinal analysis that there is a dark path of motivational processes in which frustration of the basic psychological needs related to increased work stress, which in turn was associated with higher levels of somatic symptom burden, emotional exhaustion, and turnover intentions among employees. Other studies have shown that frustration of the basic psychological needs is negatively related to happiness (Gillet et al., 2012), self-realization (Gillet et al., 2012), and vigor (Vander Elst, Van den Broeck, De Witte, & De Cuyper, 2012), and is positively related to work–home conflict (Huyghebaert, Gillet, Fernet, Lahiani, & Fouquereau, 2018), distress and depression (Rouse et al., 2019), and burnout in general (Huyghebaert et al., 2018). In sum, empirical studies suggest that need satisfaction is positively related to employee well-being and occupational health, and frustration of employees' basic psychological needs has a detrimental effect on well-being and occupational health. This goes to show that need frustration is a better explanation of individuals' ill-being and sub-optimal functioning.

Research has also demonstrated the implications of quality of motivation in relation to workers' well-being and functioning. Several studies have reported a negative association between autonomous work motivation and indicators of ill-being such as perceived stress (Sandrin et al., 2019), burnout (Fernet, Chanal, & Guay, 2017), anxiety (Gillet, Fouquereau, Lafrenière, & Huyghebaert, 2016), and somatic symptoms (Williams et al., 2014), and a positive association has been found between autonomous work motivation and engagement (Austin, Fernet, Trépanier, & Lavoie-Tremblay, 2020), vitality (Graves & Luciano, 2013), and perceived health (Sandrin et al., 2019). On the other hand, controlled forms of work motivation have been associated with increased work stress (Sandrin et al., 2019), burnout (Fernet, Chanal, et al., 2017), and anxiety (Gillet et al., 2016), but a decrease in perceived health (Sandrin et al., 2019).

Moreover, studies have shown that satisfaction (or frustration) of basic psychological needs as well as type of motivational regulation can moderate the implications of social-contextual factors on well-being-related outcomes in the work domain. For instance, Trépanier, Fernet, and Austin (2013a) found that employees high in autonomous work motivation experienced less psychological distress in the presence of job demands. In sum, this body of research clearly goes to show that while basic psychological need satisfaction and autonomous work motivation is linked to better mental and physical health, basic psychological need frustration and controlled work motivation are more likely to promote ill-being.

Advancements of SDT Research in the Workplace.
With the rapidly increasing literature on SDT in the work domain, new and advanced approaches to the study of work motivation based on this theoretical framework have emerged. Some of these important advancements to the field are reviewed in the following.

Person-Centered Approaches.
In addition to the many variable-centered studies reviewed above, person-centered studies have started to emerge in the field of SDT in work organizations. Most of these studies have used person-centered approaches to understand how patterns of motivational regulations relate to various predictors and outcomes. Specifically, as it is assumed that people can have varying levels of the different types of motivational regulations, it becomes interesting to understand how different combinations or patterns of

motivations relate to organizational factors. These studies of motivational profiles reveal distinct clusters of motivation and in turn show that these clusters are differentially related to various predictors and outcomes (e.g., Howard, Gagné, Morin, & Van den Broeck, 2016; Van den Broeck, Lens, De Witte, & Van Coillie, 2013). Most results point to four common profiles represented by high autonomy, high motivation, high controlled motivation, and low motivation. Further, results from these studies support the variable-centered studies in suggesting that autonomous forms of motivation are far more important in promoting positive workplace outcomes than more controlling forms. However, it also seems that as long as the profile contains high levels of autonomous forms of motivation, controlled motivation does provide negative implications. As such, employees higher in both forms are not at jeopardy, but the amount of controlled motivation does not give any benefits either. These results seem to hint at a relatively powerful impact of autonomous motivation, which is consistent with the qualitative (as opposed to the quantitative) view on motivation. A study also investigated transitions between profile membership over time by examining temporal stability and change in employees' work motivation profiles (Fernet et al., 2019). In this study, the motivational profiles were entirely stable at the within-sample level, whereas within-person changes in profile membership occurred for 30–40% of employees.

Although the person-centered approaches for the most part have taken an interest in motivational profiles, studies have also started using the basic psychological needs as the basis for the study of profiles. Gillet, Morin, Choisay, and Fouquereau (2019) discovered four different profiles of basic psychological need satisfaction at work. The profile that characterized most employees revealed higher global levels of need satisfaction and a balance in the specific levels of autonomy, competence, and relatedness satisfaction (profile 1). The remaining profiles were characterized by moderately low to very low global levels of need satisfaction and a strong imbalance in the degree of satisfaction of each specific need. Job demand predicted a decrease, and job resources predicted an increase in likelihood of membership in profile 1. Furthermore, the lowest levels of physical fatigue were observed in the balanced profile, demonstrating the key role of employees' need satisfaction balance in the prediction of work outcomes. In another study, Rouse et al. (2019) identified five profiles based on measures of both need satisfaction and need frustration that became progressively less adaptive. Results further revealed that, based on measures of stress, depression, anxiety, and life satisfaction, the two first profiles were the most adaptive by experiencing the fewest symptoms of the indicators of ill-being and the highest levels of life satisfaction. By contrast, the two last profiles experienced the worst levels of dysfunction.

Longitudinal Approaches. Because the benefit of SDT is providing the underlying mechanisms linking workplace factors to work outcomes through basic psychological needs and/or quality of motivation, longitudinal studies are beneficial to reveal the temporal sequence of these motivational processes as they unfold at work. Research designs enabling the study of the development and change seem especially relevant for questions related to occupational health and work-related correlates. Luckily, the literature of SDT in the workplace has increasingly moved in the direction of longitudinal study designs with two or more measurement points. The majority of these studies are typically panel studies with the aim of describing and understanding developmental processes between focal variables within the basic SDT model in the workplace. For instance, in the study by Olafsen et al. (2018) mentioned above, the temporal associations among need support, need satisfaction, and autonomous work motivation were in focus, where the analyses over four measurement points were able to provide support for the sequence from need support to need satisfaction to autonomous work motivation in the basic SDT model in the workplace, as it is displayed in Figure 1. Furthermore, Austin et al. (2020) showed the path from fatigue to autonomous and controlled work motivation, and, in turn, affective, attitudinal, and behavioral work outcomes in a two-wave longitudinal study over 12 months, and Huyghebaert et al. (2018) showed how psychological safety climate had a negative association with burnout 3 months later through its negative relation with need frustration. These studies are examples of support of the intervening roles of the basic psychological needs and quality of work motivation within SDT and how they can be used to study how and why workplace factors give implications for employee behavior, attitudes, and well-being.

Another form of longitudinal research that has entered the SDT literature in the work domain is diary studies. Although most studies of SDT in the work domain have examined the motivational process as they occur across individuals (between-person level), a few diary studies have been used to examine these processes as they occur within individuals (within-person level). This is important as the relations in question may not only differ across individuals but also vary within employees over time. Furthermore, whereas between-person effects are best suited for large, more lasting associations observed among employees, within-person effects typically focus on short-term changes. For instance, there is reason to believe that specific need satisfaction levels can vary in the short term within the context of work, and daily diary designs can offer great insight into the antecedents and processes of these processes. Consequently, the few diary studies in this field of research have sought to identify short-term, within-person processes occurring among work factors, important SDT variables, and work outcomes. For instance, in a study already mentioned above, De Gieter et al. (2018) demonstrated that the within-person relations between job resources, challenge and hindrance demands, and strain were mediated by autonomy need satisfaction, whereas the relations between job resources and hindrance demands, and performance were mediated by both competence and autonomy need satisfaction. In another study, Reizer, Brender-Ilan, and Sheaffer (2019) increased insight into the short-term dynamic fluctuations of the motivation–performance link in the workplace by showing the mediating role of daily positive and negative emotions and daily job satisfaction.

General Methodology. Deci et al. (2017) noted that the literature on SDT in work organizations to a great extent has made use of correlational cross-sectional designs. This limitation has since been alleviated by a number of new studies utilizing more rigorous research designs, most notably the already mentioned advanced longitudinal studies (e.g, Fernet et al., 2019; Olafsen, 2017; Olafsen et al., 2018), but also multilevel studies (e.g., Gagné, Morin, et al., 2019) and meta-analyses (Slemp et al., 2018; Van den Broeck et al., 2016), providing more confidence and nuance in the previous established antecedents and outcomes of the basic SDT model in the workplace. The field has also seen some recent interventions studies (e.g., Jungert, Van den Broeck, Schreurs, & Osterman, 2018; Lundmark, von Thiele Schwarz, Hasson, Stenling, & Tafvelin, 2018) that are focused on training in the concept of need support to increase need satisfaction and/or autonomous motivation. Such interventions are desirable, as experimental methods are in need to draw causal conclusions on the associations displayed in the basic SDT model in the workplace. With the many correlational studies that have gained insight into the various antecedents of this model, it is important to target these factors in interventions aimed at improving employee well-being (or decreasing ill-being), performance, and other desirable behaviors and attitudes within the workplace. Conducting intervention studies focusing on a broader spectrum of environmental factors seems like a fruitful next step within this field of research. Finally, going into the 2020s, this field of research has several meta-analyses, and to complete the circle, meta-analytic findings of motivational regulations in this literature seems like the next step forward.

CONCLUSION

As the review of the status of SDT studies in the work domain demonstrates, a substantial body of literature contributes to our understanding of different phenomena within SDT in work organizations and organizational psychology in general. Together they go in the direction of supporting the theoretical postulations made by the SDT framework and the mini-theories in relation to the basic SDT model in the workplace: the social-contextual environment has important implications for the basic psychological needs, intrinsic motivation, and internalization of extrinsic motivation. The basic psychological needs provide the energy through which internalization occurs and explain how our immediate (and past) environments give implications for our work behavior, functioning, and health.

REFERENCES

Austin, S., Fernet, C., Trépanier, S.-G., & Lavoie-Tremblay, M. (2020). Fatigue in new registered nurses: A 12-month cross-lagged analysis of its association with work motivation, engagement, sickness absence, and turnover intention. *Journal of Nursing Management, 28*(3), 606–614.

Baard, P. P., Deci, E. L., & Ryan, R. M. (2004). Intrinsic need satisfaction: A motivational basis of performance and well-being in two work settings. *Journal of Applied Social Psychology, 34*(10), 2045–2068.

Bakker, A. B., & Demerouti, E. (2007). The job demands-resources model: State of the art. *Journal of Managerial Psychology, 22*(3), 309–328.

Bass, B. M., & Avolio, B. J. (1995). *Transformational leadership development: Manual for the Multifactor Leadership Questionnaire.* Palo Alto, CA: Consulting Psychologists Press.

Boudrias, J. S., Desrumaux, P., Gaudreau, P., Nelson, K., Brunet, L., & Savoie, A. (2011). Modeling the experience of psychological health at work: The role of personal resources, social-organizational resources, and job demands. *International Journal of Stress Management, 18*(4), 372–395.

Bureau, J. S., Mageau, G. A., Morin, A. J., Gagné, M., Forest, J., Papachristopoulos, K., . . . Parenteau, C. (2018). Promoting autonomy to reduce employee deviance: The mediating role of identified motivation. *International Journal of Business and Management, 13*(5), 61–74.

Cerasoli, C. P., Nicklin, J. M., & Ford, M. T. (2014). Intrinsic motivation and extrinsic incentives jointly predict performance: A 40-year meta-analysis. *Psychological Bulletin, 140*(4), 980–1008.

Chiniara, M., & Bentein, K. (2015). Linking servant leadership to individual performance: Differentiating the mediating role of autonomy, competence and relatedness need satisfaction. *Leadership Quarterly, 27*(1), 124–141.

Conchie, S. M. (2013). Transformational leadership, intrinsic motivation, and trust: A moderated-mediated model of workplace safety. *Journal of Occupational Health Psychology, 18*(2), 198–210.

De Gieter, S., Hofmans, J., & Bakker, A. B. (2018). Need satisfaction at work, job strain, and performance: A diary study. *Journal of Occupational Health Psychology*, 23(3), 361–372.

Deci, E.L. (1975). *Intrinsic motivation*. New York, NY: Plenum Press.

Deci, E. L., Connell, J. P., & Ryan, R. M. (1989). Self-determination in a work-organization. *Journal of Applied Psychology*, 74(4), 580–590.

Deci, E. L., Koestner, R., & Ryan, R. M. (1999). A meta-analytic review of experiments examining the effects of extrinsic rewards on intrinsic motivation. *Psychological Bulletin*, 125(6), 627–668.

Deci, E. L., Olafsen, A. H., & Ryan, R. M. (2017). Self-determination theory in work organizations: State of the science. *Annual Review of Organizational Psychology and Organizational Behavior*, 4(1), 19–43.

Deci, E. L., & Ryan, R. M. (1980). *The empirical exploration of intrinsic motivational processes* (Vol. 13). New York, NY: Academic Press.

Deci, E. L., & Ryan, R. M. (1985). The general causality orientations scale—self-determination in personality. *Journal of Research in Personality*, 19(2), 109–134.

Deci, E. L., & Ryan, R. M. (2000). The "what" and "why" of goal pursuits: Human needs and the self-determination of behavior. *Psychological Inquiry*, 11(4), 227–268.

Deci, E. L., & Ryan, R. M. (2014). Autonomy and need satisfaction in close relationships: Relationships motivation theory. In N. Weinstein (Ed.), *Human motivation and interpersonal relationships: Theory, research, and applications* (pp. 53–73). Dordrecht, Netherlands: Springer Netherlands.

Deci, E. L., Ryan, R. M., Gagné, M., Leone, D. R., Usunov, J., & Kornazheva, B. P. (2001). Need satisfaction, motivation, and well-being in the work organizations of a former eastern bloc country: A cross-cultural study of self-determination. *Personality and Social Psychology Bulletin*, 27(8), 930–942.

Di Domenico, S. I., & Ryan, R. M. (2017). The emerging neuroscience of intrinsic motivation: A new frontier in self-determination research. *Frontiers in Human Neuroscience*, 11(145). https://dx.doi.org/10.3389/fnhum.2017.00145

Fernet, C., Austin, S., Trépanier, S. G., & Dussault, M. (2013). How do job characteristics contribute to burnout? Exploring the distinct mediating roles of perceived autonomy, competence, and relatedness. *European Journal of Work and Organizational Psychology*, 22(2), 123–137.

Fernet, C., Chanal, J., & Guay, F. (2017). What fuels the fire: Job- or task-specific motivation (or both)? On the hierarchical and multidimensional nature of teacher motivation in relation to job burnout. *Work and Stress*, 31(2), 145–163.

Fernet, C., Litalien, D., Morin, A. J. S., Austin, S., Gagné, M., Lavoie-Tremblay, M., & Forest, J. (2019). On the temporal stability of self-determined work motivation profiles: A latent transition analysis. *European Journal of Work and Organizational Psychology*, 29(1), 49–63.

Fernet, C., Trépanier, S.-G., Demers, M., & Austin, S. (2017). Motivational pathways of occupational and organizational turnover intention among newly registered nurses in Canada. *Nursing Outlook*, 65(4), 444–454.

Gagné, M., Chemolli, E., Forest, J., & Koestner, R. (2008). A temporal analysis of the relation between organisational commitment and work motivation. *Psychologica Belgica*, 48(2–3), 219–241.

Gagné, M., & Deci, E. L. (2005). Self-determination theory and work motivation. *Journal of Organizational Behavior*, 26(4), 331–362.

Gagné, M., Morin, A. J. S., Schabram, K., Wang, Z.N., Chemolli, E., & Briand, M. (2019, August 27). Uncovering relations between leadership perceptions and motivation under different organizational contexts: A multilevel cross-lagged analysis. *Journal of Business and Psychology*. http://dx.doi.org/10.1007/s10869-019-09649-4

Gagné, M., Tian, A. W., Soo, C., Zhang, B., Ho, K. S. B., & Hosszu, K. (2019). Different motivations for knowledge sharing and hiding: The role of motivating work design. *Journal of Organizational Behavior*, 40(7), 783–799.

Gillet, N., Forest, J., Benabou, C., & Bentein, K. (2015). The effects of organizational factors, psychological need satisfaction and thwarting, and affective commitment on workers' well-being and turnover intentions. *Le Travail Humain*, *78*(2), 119–140.

Gillet, N., Fouquereau, E., Forest, J., Brunault, P., & Colombat, P. (2012). The impact of organizational factors on psychological needs and their relations with well-being. *Journal of Business and Psychology*, *27*(4), 437–450.

Gillet, N., Fouquereau, E., Lafrenière, M.-A. K., & Huyghebaert, T. (2016). Examining the roles of work autonomous and controlled motivations on satisfaction and anxiety as a function of role ambiguity. *Journal of Psychology*, *150*(5), 644–665.

Gillet, N., Morin, A. J. S., Choisay, F., & Fouquereau, E. (2019). A person-centered representation of basic need satisfaction balance at work. *Journal of Personnel Psychology*, *18*(3), 113–128.

Grant, A. M., & Berry, J. W. (2011). The necessity of others is the mother of invention: Intrinsic and prosocial motivations, perspective taking, and creativity. *Academy of Management Journal*, *54*(1), 73–96.

Graves, L. M., & Luciano, M. M. (2013). Self-determination at work: Understanding the role of leader-member exchange. *Motivation and Emotion*, *37*(3), 518–536.

Greguras, G. J., & Diefendorff, J. M. (2009). Different fits satisfy different needs: Linking person-environment fit to employee commitment and performance using self-determination theory. *Journal of Applied Psychology*, *94*(2), 465–477.

Güntert, S. (2015). The impact of work design, autonomy support, and strategy on employee outcomes: A differentiated perspective on self-determination at work. *Motivation and Emotion*, *39*(1), 74–87.

Hardré, P. L., & Reeve, J. (2009). Training corporate managers to adopt a more autonomy-supportive motivating style toward employees: An intervention study. *International Journal of Training and Development*, *13*(3), 165–184.

Hartmann, F., & Slapničar, S. (2012). Pay fairness and intrinsic motivation: The role of pay transparency. *International Journal of Human Resource Management*, *23*(20), 4283–4300.

Hetland, H., Hetland, J., Andreassen, C. S., Pallesen, S., & Notelaers, G. (2011). Leadership and fulfillment of the three basic psychological needs at work. *Career Development International*, *16*(5), 507–523.

Hewett, R., & Conway, N. (2015). The undermining effect revisited: The salience of everyday verbal rewards and self-determined motivation. *Journal of Organizational Behavior*, *37*(3), 436–455.

Hewett, R., & Leroy, H. (2019). Well it's only fair: How perceptions of manager discretion in bonus allocation affect intrinsic motivation. *Journal of Management Studies*, *56*(6), 1105–1137.

Hon, A. H. Y. (2012). Shaping environments conductive to creativity: The role of intrinsic motivation. *Cornell Hospitality Quarterly*, *53*(1), 53–64.

Howard, J., Gagné, M., Morin, A. J., & Van den Broeck, A. (2016). Motivation profiles at work: A self-determination theory approach. *Journal of Vocational Behavior*, *95–96*, 74–89.

Huyghebaert, T., Gillet, N., Fernet, C., Lahiani, F.-J., & Fouquereau, E. (2018). Leveraging psychosocial safety climate to prevent ill-being: The mediating role of psychological need thwarting. *Journal of Vocational Behavior*, *107*, 111–125.

Jambrak, J., Deane, F. P., & Williams, V. (2014). Value motivations predict burnout and intentions to leave among mental health professionals. *Journal of Mental Health*, *23*(3), 120–124.

Jungert, T., Koestner, R. F., Houlfort, N., & Schattke, K. (2013). Distinguishing source of autonomy support in relation to workers' motivation and self-efficacy. *Journal of Social Psychology*, *153*(6), 651–666.

Jungert, T., Van den Broeck, A., Schreurs, B., & Osterman, U. (2018). How colleagues can support each other's needs and motivation: An intervention on employee work motivation. *Applied Psychology*, *67*(1), 3–29.

Kanat-Maymon, Y., Mor, Y., Gottlieb, E., & Shoshani, A. (2017). Supervisor motivating styles and legitimacy: Moderation and mediation models. *Journal of Managerial Psychology*, *32*(8), 561–580.

Kasser, T., & Ryan, R. M. (1996). Further examining the American dream: Differential correlates of intrinsic and extrinsic goals. *Personality and Social Psychology Bulletin, 22*(3), 280–287.

Kuvaas, B., Buch, R., Gagné, M., Dysvik, A., & Forest, J. (2016). Do you get what you pay for? Sales incentives and implications for motivation and changes in turnover intention and work effort. *Motivation and Emotion, 40*(5), 667–680.

Kuvaas, B., Buch, R., Weibel, A., Dysvik, A., & Nerstad, C. G. L. (2017). Do intrinsic and extrinsic motivation relate differently to employee outcomes? *Journal of Economic Psychology, 61*, 244–258.

Lam, C. F., & Gurland, S. T. (2008). Self-determined work motivation predicts job outcomes, but what predicts self-determined work motivation? *Journal of Research in Personality, 42*(4), 1109–1115.

Lian, H., Lance Ferris, D., & Brown, D. J. (2012). Does taking the good with the bad make things worse? How abusive supervision and leader–member exchange interact to impact need satisfaction and organizational deviance. *Organizational Behavior and Human Decision Processes, 117*(1), 41–52.

Liu, D., & Fu, P.-P. (2011). Motivating proteges' personal learning in teams: A multilevel investigation of autonomy support and autonomy orientation. *Journal of Applied Psychology, 96*(6), 1195.

Liu, D., Zhang, S., Wang, L., & Lee, T.W. (2011). The effects of autonomy and empowerment on employee turnover: Test of a multilevel model in teams. *Journal of Applied Psychology, 96*(6), 1305.

Lundmark, R., von Thiele Schwarz, U., Hasson, H., Stenling, A., & Tafvelin, S. (2018). Making it fit: Associations of line managers' behaviours with the outcomes of an organizational-level intervention. *Stress and Health, 34*(1), 163–174.

Marescaux, E., De Winne, S., & Sels, L. (2013). HR practices and affective organisational commitment: (When) does HR differentiation pay off? *Human Resource Management Journal, 23*(4), 329–345.

Moreau, E., & Mageau, G. (2012). The importance of perceived autonomy support for the psychological health and work satisfaction of health professionals: Not only supervisors count, colleagues too! *Motivation and Emotion, 36*(3), 268–286.

Nukta, A., Haueis, M., Spitzer, M., & Hille, K. (2011). Designing learning environments in assembly lines through self-determination. *Procedia-Social and Behavioral Sciences, 29*, 752–757.

Olafsen, A. H. (2017). The implications of need-satisfying work climates on state mindfulness in a longitudinal analysis of work outcomes. *Motivation and Emotion, 41*(1), 22–37.

Olafsen, A. H., Deci, E. L., & Halvari, H. (2018). Basic psychological needs and work motivation: A longitudinal test of directionality. *Motivation and Emotion, 42*(2), 178–189.

Olafsen, A. H., & Frølund, C. W. (2018). Challenge accepted! Distinguishing between challenge- and hindrance demands. *Journal of Managerial Psychology, 33*(4/5), 345–357.

Olafsen, A. H., & Halvari, H. (2017). Motivational mechanisms in the relation between job characteristics and employee functioning. *Spanish Journal of Psychology, 20*, E38. http://dx.doi.org/10.1017/sjp.2017.34

Olafsen, A. H., Halvari, H., Forest, J., & Deci, E. L. (2015). Show them the money? The role of pay, managerial need support, and justice in a self-determination theory model of intrinsic work motivation. *Scandinavian Journal of Psychology, 56*(4), 447–457.

Olafsen, A. H., Niemiec, C. P., Halvari, H., Deci, E. L., & Williams, G. C. (2017). On the dark side of work: A longitudinal analysis using self-determination theory. *European Journal of Work & Organizational Psychology, 26*(2), 275–285.

Reizer, A., Brender-Ilan, Y., & Sheaffer, Z. (2019). Employee motivation, emotions, and performance: A longitudinal diary study. *Journal of Managerial Psychology, 34*(6), 415–428.

Robertson, L., & Jones, M. G. (2013). Chinese and US middle-school science teachers' autonomy, motivation, and instructional practices. *International Journal of Science Education, 35*(9), 1454–1489.

Roche, M., & Haar, J. M. (2013). A metamodel approach towards self-determination theory: A study of New Zealand managers' organisational citizenship behaviours. *International Journal of Human Resource Management, 24*(18), 3397–3417.

Rouse, P. C., Turner, P. J. F., Siddall, A. G., Schmid, J., Standage, M., & Bilzon, J. L. J. (2019). The interplay between psychological need satisfaction and psychological need frustration within a work context: A variable and person-oriented approach. *Motivation and Emotion, 44*, 176–199.

Ryan, R. M. (1995). Psychological needs and the facilitation of integrative processes. *Journal of Personality, 63*(3), 397–427.

Ryan, R. M., Connell, J. P., & Deci, E. L. (1985). A motivational analysis of self-determination and self-regulation in education. 2, 13–51. In C. Ames & E. E. Ames (Eds.), *Research on motivation in education: The classroom milieu* (pp. 13–51). New York, NY: Academic Press.

Ryan, R. M., & Deci, E. L. (2017). *Self-determination theory: Autonomy and basic psychological needs in human motivation, social development, and wellness.* New York, NY: Guilford.

Sandrin, É., Gillet, N., Fernet, C., Leloup, M., & Depin-Rouault, C. (2019). Effects of motivation and workload on firefighters' perceived health, stress, and performance. *Stress and Health, 35*(4), 447–456.

Slemp, G. R., Kern, M. L., Patrick, K. J., & Ryan, R. M. (2018). Leader autonomy support in the workplace: A meta-analytic review. *Motivation and Emotion, 42*(5), 706–724.

Thibault Landry, A., Forest, J., Zigarmi, D., Houson, D., & Boucher, É. (2017). The carrot or the stick? Investigating the functional meaning of cash rewards and their motivational power according to self-determination theory. *Compensation and Benefits Review, 49*(1), 9–25.

Thibault Landry, A., Gagné, M., Forest, J., Guerrero, S., Séguin, M., & Papachristopoulos, K. (2017). The relation between financial incentives, motivation, and performance: An integrative SDT-based investigation. *Journal of Personnel Psychology, 16*(2), 61–76.

Thibault Landry, A., Kindlein, J., Trépanier, S. G., Forest, J., Zigarmi, D., Houson, D., & Brodbeck, F. C. (2016). Why individuals want money is what matters: Using self-determination theory to explain the differential relationship between motives for making money and employee psychological health. *Motivation and Emotion, 40*(2), 226–242.

Thibault Landry, A., Zhang, Y., Papachristopoulos, K., & Forest, J. (2019). Applying self-determination theory to understand the motivational impact of cash rewards: New evidence from lab experiments. *International Journal of Psychology, 55*(3), 487–498.

Trépanier, S.-G., Boudrias , V., & Peterson, C. (2019). Linking destructive forms of leadership to employee health. *Leadership & Organization Development Journal, 40*(7), 803–814.

Trépanier, S. G., Fernet, C., & Austin, S. (2012). Social and motivational antecedents of perceptions of transformational leadership: A self-determination theory perspective. *Canadian Journal of Behavioural Science/Revue Canadienne des sciences du comportement, 44*(4), 272–277.

Trépanier, S. G., Fernet, C., & Austin, S. (2013a). The moderating role of autonomous motivation in the job demands-strain relation: A two sample study. *Motivation and Emotion, 37*(1), 93–105.

Trépanier, S. G., Fernet, C., & Austin, S. (2013b). Workplace psychological harassment in Canadian nurses: A descriptive study. *Journal of Health Psychology, 18*(3), 383–396.

Trépanier, S. G., Fernet, C., & Austin, S. (2015). A longitudinal investigation of workplace bullying, basic need satisfaction, and employee functioning. *Journal of Occupational Health Psychology, 20*(1), 105–116.

Trépanier, S. G., Forest, J., Fernet, C., & Austin, S. (2015). On the psychological and motivational processes linking job characteristics to employee functioning: Insights from self-determination theory. *Work and Stress, 29*(3), 286–305.

Van den Broeck, A., Ferris, D. L., Chang, C.-H., & Rosen, C.C. (2016). A review of self-determination theory's basic psychological needs at work. *Journal of Management Accounting Research, 42*(5), 1195–1229.

Van den Broeck, A., Lens, W., De Witte, H., & Van Coillie, H. (2013). Unraveling the importance of the quantity and the quality of workers' motivation for well-being: A person-centered perspective. *Journal of Vocational Behavior, 82*(1), 69–78.

Van den Broeck, A., Sulea, C., Vander Elst, T., Fischmann, G., Iliescu, D., & De Witte, H. (2014). The mediating role of psychological needs in the relation between qualitative job insecurity and counterproductive work behavior. *Career Development International*, 19(5), 526–547.

Van den Broeck, A., Vansteenkiste, M., De Witte, H., & Lens, W. (2008). Explaining the relationships between job characteristics, burnout, and engagement: The role of basic psychological need satisfaction. *Work and Stress*, 22(3), 277–294.

Vander Elst, T., Van den Broeck, A., De Witte, H., & De Cuyper, N. (2012). The mediating role of frustration of psychological needs in the relationship between job insecurity and work-related well-being. *Work and Stress*, 26(3), 252–271.

Vansteenkiste, M., Neyrinck, B., Niemiec, C. P., Soenens, B., De Witte, H., & Van den Broeck, A. (2007). On the relations among work value orientations, psychological need satisfaction and job outcomes: A self-determination theory approach. *Journal of Occupational and Organizational Psychology*, 80(2), 251–277.

Williams, G. C., Halvari, H., Niemiec, C. P., Sørebø, Ø., Olafsen, A. H., & Westbye, C. (2014). Managerial support for basic psychological needs, somatic symptom burden and work-related correlates: A self-determination theory perspective. *Work and Stress*, 28(4), 404–419.

Zhang, Y., Zhang, J., Forest, J., & Chen, Z. (2019). A dynamic computational model of employees goal transformation: Using self-determination theory. *Motivation and Emotion*, 43(3), 447–460.

Anja H. Olafsen and Edward L. Deci

INDIVIDUAL DIFFERENCES IN THE VITAMIN MODEL OF WELL-BEING

Well-being—one's own or that of other people—is of concern to almost everyone. Among well-being perspectives, the Vitamin Model has been widely applied to characteristics and experiences in jobs, unemployment, and retirement (see Warr, 1987, 2007, 2019, 2020). This article develops the model from earlier accounts of in-general processes to explore differences between individual people.

The Vitamin Model seeks to be distinctive in four respects. First, it takes a broad perspective, bringing together themes from several other frameworks and covering sources of well-being from within people themselves as well as from the environment. It distinguishes between three levels of scope, considering separately well-being in a person's life as a whole (through life satisfaction and other global indicators), well-being in specific contexts (in family life, in a job, during unemployment, and so on), and well-being that is focused on specific elements in a particular context (e.g., feelings about your boss or salary). These three levels of scope can be described respectively as "context-free," "domain-specific," and "feature-specific." Note that experiences of global or context-free well-being are crucially dependent on typical feelings at the more restricted levels—domain-specific or feature-specific. The Vitamin Model is distinctive in emphasizing feature-specific well-being as well as more global forms.

Second, the Vitamin Model extends beyond merely a negative perspective and can be applied to activities and processes that are positive, as well as those that are stressful. Many psychological approaches to well-being are focused intentionally and entirely on threatening aspects of a person's environment. Such negative emphases are important for their potential to remedy harmful conditions, but they necessarily cut out huge sections of experience and exclude more positive ways of thinking.[1]

Third, the model does not follow the currently common practice of being framed in terms of a small number of environmental categories, such as "resources," "demands," or "stressors" as a group. Instead, different features are recognized to operate in different ways and are treated separately, each with its own origins and consequences (see Halbesleben et al., 2014).

A fourth notable aspect of the Vitamin Model is its divergence from the standard assumption that features in the environment are consistently either positive (e.g., always a desirable resource) or negative (e.g., always a harmful stressor). Instead, it is argued that important inputs can be either affectively positive or negative depending on their level. The notion that different forms of the same feature can be evaluated in contrasting ways leads in turn to an emphasis on stimulus–outcome relationships, which are nonlinear rather than linear as is generally presumed. That point is developed later.

This article focuses on differences between people. As a preliminary, the Vitamin Model's primary sources of well-being in the environment need to be spelled out, and then two sections will address primary forms of variation between people. Initially, long-standing influences from within the individual are introduced as "generic," and then forms of "emotion regulation" are considered through short-term perspectives on a particular situation.

"Well-being" is sometimes treated as equivalent to "happiness." However, well-being is a more wide-ranging construct, extending beyond the feelings and thoughts of happiness to also cover states of, for instance, physical well-being, social well-being, or financial well-being. Happiness is better viewed more narrowly as psychological, affective, or subjective well-being, with happiness considered as a subset of the wider notion of well-being (see Diener et al., 1999).

We should distinguish between well-being themes that are "hedonic" and those concerned with "flourishing." The term *hedonic* derives from the Greek word for pleasure (*hēdon*), and a hedonic perspective on happiness is in terms of different feelings of pleasure or displeasure. "Flourishing" well-being, a concept developed from writings about *eudaimonia* by Aristotle (384–322 BC) and other ancient Greek philosophers, is more concerned with personal development and aspects of "a good life." Eudaemonic well-being has less often been investigated, and the construct remains imprecisely defined (see, for instance, Warr, 2019). This article focuses on individual differences in hedonic well-being.[2]

This form of well-being has often been studied through positive or negative feelings. However, in addition to their positive or negative direction, feelings also vary in their activation or arousal—a person's "state of readiness for action or energy expenditure" (Russell, 2003, p. 156). We should thus distinguish between levels of activation as well as of valence. For example, joyful well-being is activated and has positive valence, whereas relaxed well-being is also positive but with reduced activation.

Well-being feelings are sometimes mixed together in an overall experience that is ambivalent—combining positive and negative affects when a person feels both good and bad about life in general or about a domain or feature. Ambivalence can arise from varying reactions to different aspects of the situation, or it can occur sequentially across time. For instance, it is often the case that goal achievement depends on previous success in overcoming obstacles; in that case, a person has to experience negative well-being before feeling more positive.

Domain-specific well-being in job situations has been measured positively as job satisfaction, job engagement, job involvement, and life satisfaction, and negatively as job dissatisfaction, burnout, or strain. For example, job satisfaction has been recorded through responses to statements like "I find real enjoyment in my work" (Brayfield & Rothe, 1951), and the Utrecht

142 • INDIVIDUAL DIFFERENCES IN THE VITAMIN MODEL OF WELL-BEING

Work Engagement Scale (with items more activated than those tapping satisfaction) contains "At my work, I feel bursting with energy" (see Schaufeli et al., 2006). Feelings within each of the valence-and-activation quadrants have been recorded directly by the Multi-Affect Inventory (see Warr et al., in press).

SOURCES OF WELL-BEING FROM THE ENVIRONMENT

Table 1 summarizes 12 aspects of the social and physical world that have been found in many studies to be associated with well-being (see Crawford et al., 2010; Humphrey et al., 2007; Luchman & Gonzáles-Morales, 2013) and that are central to the Vitamin Model (see Warr, 1987, 2007, 2020). The table is constructed so that well-being in any life context can

Table 1. Principal Environmental Features in the Vitamin Model, and Some Themes Studied in Job Settings

Environmental Feature (E)	Themes Studied in Job Settings
E1. Opportunity for personal control	Autonomy, discretion, decision latitude, personal influence, participation (AD)
E2. Opportunity for skill use and acquisition	Potential for applying and developing expertise (AD)
E3. Externally generated goals	Workload, external demands, challenge, underload and overload, competition from others, task identity, role conflict, work–home conflict, required emotional labor (AD)
E4. Variety	Variation in task content and social contact, varied work location (AD)
E5. Environmental clarity	Clear task requirements, role clarity, predictable outcomes of action, task feedback, low future ambiguity (AD)
E6. Contact with others	Quality of relationships, amount of social contact, interdependence with others, team working (AD)
E7. Availability of money	Income or pay level (CE)
E8. Physical security	Working conditions, degree of hazard, quality of equipment (CE)
E9. Valued social position	Significance of a role or of certain components, position in valued groups, contribution to society (CE)
E10. Supportive supervision	Fair treatment by supervisor and other bosses, concern for one's welfare, effective supervisory behavior (CE)
E11. Career outlook	Job security, the opportunity to gain promotion or to move to other roles (CE)
E12. Equity	Justice within one's organization, fairness in the organization's relations with society (CE)

Note: AD = additional decrement; CE = constant effect; see text.

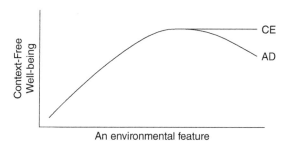

Figure 1. The vitamin analogy: Proposed additional decrement (AD) and constant effect (CE) relationships between environmental features and context-free well-being.

depend on the first nine aspects. Thus, the opportunity for some personal control (E1) is essential in any setting for goal achievement and for permitting a sense of personal agency. Similarly, environmental clarity (E5) is essential to allow predictions and planning and to reduce anxiety about the future, which otherwise would remain unpredictable. And demands from the environment (E3) need to be moderate to prevent both underload and overload.

In addition to these everywhere-important features (E1 to E9), other influential aspects of the environment are specific to particular domains. In respect specifically of jobs, the Vitamin Model identifies E10 to E12 as important beyond the first nine. Thus, central to workers' feelings about their job are aspects of supervisory consideration and initiating structure (environmental characteristic E10; see Judge et al., 2004). The vitamin framework thus expects in particular domains that additional aspects of the environment are influential beyond the everywhere-important first nine.

The impact of these environmental features or their principal components has been demonstrated by research in many countries, almost always envisaging a linear relationship between levels of well-being and the feature. However, it is more likely that the level of an environmental feature is associated with well-being in a nonlinear fashion, specifically in patterns analogous to the effect of vitamins on bodily condition. Vitamins are important for physical health up to, but not beyond, a certain level. At low levels of intake, vitamin deficiency gives rise to physical impairment and ill health, but after a moderate intake has been reached (the "recommended daily allowance"), there is usually no benefit from additional quantities. By analogy, it may be that the absence or near-absence of an environmental feature in Table 1 leads to negative psychological states, but that the presence of that feature above a certain level does not further improve well-being.

In addition, some vitamins become harmful in large quantities, so that the association between increased vitamin intake and physical health becomes negative above moderate amounts. This pattern may also occur for some features of an environment, particularly with respect to context-free happiness rather than a more restricted form of well-being; many environmental features are positively evaluated until moderately high levels are reached. That possibility ("too much of a good thing") is illustrated in Figure 1, where low values of the 12 environmental features are depicted as particularly harmful to well-being. A second, smaller decrement is proposed- at particularly high values for certain environmental features labeled "AD" rather than "CE."

Those two labels are also based on abbreviations in the vitamin analogy. Vitamins A and D are toxic at very high levels, and AD in Figure 1 may be read as an "additional decrement." However, other vitamins appear to have no harmful consequences at very high intakes: for those vitamins, a deficiency causes ill health but increasingly large doses beyond a moderate amount are likely to have a constant effect. Vitamins C and E appear to be of that kind, and the abbreviation CE in Figure 1 and Table 1 reflects that pattern. In the Vitamin Model, CE indicates "constant effect" rather than "additional decrement."

The model thus argues that 12 features from the environment have a primary influence on job well-being. Table 1 suggests that six may be viewed as similar to vitamins A and D, and that in job settings the other six instead parallel vitamins C and E. Proposed AD features (with an additional decrement in well-being at very high levels) are E1 to E6 in Table 1: opportunity for personal control, opportunity for skill use and acquisition, externally generated goals, variety, environmental clarity, and contact with others. The CE features in job settings (thought to have an average constant effect beyond moderate levels) are E7 to E9: availability of money, physical security, and valued social position. In addition, within the domain of paid work, E10 to E12—supportive supervision, career outlook, and equity—are also likely to take the CE form (see Warr, 2007, 2019).

Why should AD features of the environment (E1 to E6), desirable up to moderate levels, become harmful when extremely high? The curvilinear pattern seems likely for both intrinsic reasons and because of associated effects from other features. Very high levels of environmental characteristics can become punishing in themselves, and several are likely also to be accompanied by extremely high levels of other features that themselves yield an additional decrement.

Thus, features identified as "opportunities" (for control and for skill use; E1 and E2) are expected to yield decrements in well-being at the extreme right-hand side of Figure 1 as an opportunity becomes a "requirement" at very high levels; behavior is then constrained and coerced rather than being encouraged or facilitated. For example, environments that call for unremitting control (an extremely high level of E1) through personal decision-making and sustained individual responsibility, or that demand continuous use of extremely complex skills (E2), can generate overload as the very high imposed requirements exceed capability (see Burger, 1989). In part, the problems of excessive control arise from an associated shift to a particularly high level of another goal-related aspect (E3): when imposed demands become extremely numerous and/or difficult, multiple requirements may also become internally contradictory (see Warr, 2007, Chapter 6).

Extremely high levels of the fourth environmental feature in Table 1, variety (E4), require a person to constantly switch attention and activity, with resulting low concentration and limited attainment of single goals. Conflict between mutually inconsistent goals is often present (an aspect of E3), and extreme goal diversity may prevent the sustained use of skills (E2). Environmental clarity (E5) also appears to be of the additional decrement kind. At extremely high clarity, events are entirely predictable and never novel, and a fixed set of role requirements permits no new experiences. Such settings prevent any risk-taking, contain little potential for skill development, and provide no opportunity to expand one's control over the environment.

A similar downturn in well-being is expected at very high levels of contact with other people (E6). Extremely high levels of social input can impair well-being through absence of privacy and overcrowding and/or through a lack of personal control, frequent interruptions, and the prevention of valued activities because of other people's continuing demands (see Deelstra et al., 2003). Behavioral constraints and physical structures to prevent excessive social contact have been created in cultures of all kinds.

In overview, the model's all-person account of environmental sources of high or low well-being assumes that the first six features in Table 1 are of the additional decrement kind, with their positive association with well-being being reversed at very high levels. Harmful effects at very high levels are likely to be less severe than at very low levels, since even extremely high levels provide some of the benefits supplied in the moderate range, and very low levels of a feature (at the left of Figure 1) are particularly negative for the person.

The average single-variable pattern in Figure 1 is likely to differ according to the scope of well-being in question—context-free, domain-specific, or feature-specific. The relationship between *context-free* feelings and an environmental feature is simultaneously determined by a wide range of features, so that a variety of aspects from within social, family, and job domains cumulatively bear upon context-free happiness in different ways for different people, with varying impact on context-free feelings. Thus, average context-free well-being has been created from features across a range of life domains.

However, more focused forms of well-being (such as job satisfaction rather than satisfaction with one's life as a whole) are less subject to a wide variety of influences, and the average mid-range plateau in Figure 1 is likely to be progressively shorter as consideration moves from context-free through *domain-specific* well-being to *feature-specific* well-being, with correlations at the most focused level expected to be most linear (see Warr, 2007, Chapter 4).

In addition to the well-being influence of single job features, specific combinations can collectively have different impacts on well-being. It is now necessary to identify and explore principal groups of environmental influences, including those that are primary within jobs. How do particular syndromes from the environment combine together to influence well-being to a greater or lesser extent? In particular combinations, external features are likely to have a disproportionate impact on well-being.

In all cases, we should recognize that increased well-being depends in part on being lucky—with a fortuitous combination of happenings in our world that encourages positive or negative feelings. In respect to jobs, were you coincidentally in the right place at the right time? More generally, were you lucky enough to be born with the right genes? Did the many people you met turn out to include a future partner?[3]

The Vitamin Model also proposes that levels of the other six features in Table 1 (E7 to E12) make no difference across their higher range, exhibiting a constant effect in that range (CE in Figure 1 and Table 1). Extremely high levels of these features may be linked to well-being for particular individuals, but, on average across people, additional increases in the moderate-to-high range are not expected to influence well-being.

Given that feelings are inherently limited in their intensity, some nonlinearity is logically necessary; it is not possible for well-being to continue to increase at the same rate without limit. Thus nonlinear relationships should be considered logically necessary, but it should be recognized that they may or may not be demonstrated in a particular investigation. Empirical studies differ in their potential to display this logical necessity; AD or CE relationships are in general necessary, but in particular investigations they are not always apparent.

Only a tiny proportion of studies have examined possible departures from linearity, and many of those are not suitable for the task. In a large number of publications, environmental (e.g., job) scores are restricted in range and fail to extend across the breadth of possibilities in Figure 1, from very low to very high inputs. Furthermore, some research has intentionally focused on only a limited section of high or low scores (only underload or only overload, for example).

Empirical evidence to assess the relationships shown in Figure 1 is thus both scarce and often methodologically inadequate. However, additional decrements (as proposed for the first six "vitamins"), have been observed in several studies of job-related well-being. With respect to E1 (opportunity for personal control), Baltes et al. (2002) recorded an AD pattern for job satisfaction. The negative impact of very difficult decisions was demonstrated by Anderson (2003), and a leveling off beyond medium levels was present in studies by Stiglbauer and Kovacs (2018) and those reviewed by Warr (2007). Research extending across a broad range of E2 (opportunity for skill use and acquisition) is not available in job settings but overlaps of that feature with the curvilinear E1 and E3 suggest that a similar pattern is present.[4]

For externally generated goals (E3), occupational research restricted to merely low or high demands has shown that well-being is, as expected, correlated in opposite directions at the two ends of the horizontal axis in Figure 1. Both an absence of demands and excessive demand are undesirable (see reviews by Warr, 1987, Chapter 7, and Warr, 2007, Chapter 6). Across a wide range of workload, AD patterns have been demonstrated in jobs by, for instance, Karasek (1979) and Warr (1990).

For role clarity (an aspect of E5), significant nonlinearity with a decrement at highest levels was observed in job settings by Baltes et al. (2002). With respect to social contact (E6), research has examined both quantity and quality of interaction. In terms of quantity, very low social density can yield feelings of personal isolation and loneliness, and studies of open-plan offices have revealed that very high levels of input from other people are undesirable in work settings (see Brennan et al., 2002). An experiment by Deelstra et al. (2003) arranged for workers in a laboratory setting to receive instrumental assistance from a coworker, who was in fact a confederate of the investigators. Extremely large amounts of social support of this kind led to a downturn in affect, as in Figure 1. That pattern has also been found in an organizational sample by De Jonge et al. (2000).

The association between income (E7) and context-free happiness has frequently been shown to level off after moderate incomes. For individuals in poverty, a standard increment in income yields a substantial increase in well-being, but for wealthy people that same increment yields a smaller or no benefit. This CE pattern has been found in comparisons between individuals within a single country (see Diener et al., 1993) and in terms of average incomes for entire nations (see Diener & Seligman, 2004; Jebb et al., 2018). In research on variation in considerate supervisor behavior (E10), nonlinearity at the work-group level (rather than with respect to individuals themselves) was observed by Fleishman and Harris (1962) in a study of subordinates' grievances and turnover. For equity (E12), Schaufeli's (2006) review identified nonlinear patterns in several occupational studies.

In summary, nonlinear relations between the job features in Table 1 and well-being are logically necessary. However, demonstrating the presence of that logical necessity requires appropriately designed research, and empirical studies are not always suitable for the purpose.

Nevertheless, several publications have reported an AD inverted-U with respect to features E1 to E6 and a CE pattern with respect to features E7 to E12.

DIFFERENCES BETWEEN PEOPLE

A person's well-being derives from a combination of factors in the environment and from the person. Both sources are in general influential, but in varying proportions across different settings. The relative joint impacts of environmental and personal variables are in principle described in Figure 2. Toward the right of the figure, situational conditions and events make an increasingly large contribution to well-being, and toward the left, personal variables have a progressively greater impact. The present section focuses on contributions from people themselves.

The next two sections examine mental processes and behaviors that can determine well-being in addition to the environmental features discussed so far. First, the discussion turns to personal variables that have an overarching impact across situations and times, and these variables are described as "generic." Then, thoughts and behaviors that are specific to a particular situation are described within a framework of "emotion regulation."

Generic Personal Characteristics.
Among generic personal variables, seven are especially important for differences between people in their well-being.

Inherited Differences. There is no doubt from studies of twins that a person's level of well-being is substantially inherited. Twins from a single fertilized egg (monozygotic twins) are genetically almost identical, but dizygotic/nonidentical twins (from two eggs) share about 50% of their genes—just like other pairs of siblings. By comparing pairs of each kind of twin reared together against those reared apart (and thus with varied environments), researchers have estimated the relative contribution of genetic and environmental factors. Their studies have suggested that up to 40% of well-being differences are determined by inheritance (see Bartels, 2015; Nes & Røysamb, 2017).

As with other genetic influences, the inheritance of well-being develops through continuing interplay between genetic and environmental variables. For example, people are likely to strengthen inherited preferences by entering or leaving particular situations or by responding to social norms. In the latter respect, boys and girls are socialized to express and experience

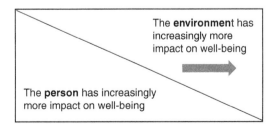

Figure 2. In-principle gradations of personal versus environmental variables' impact on well-being. Toward the left of the diagram, personal variables become increasingly influential, and toward the right, environmental features have an increasing impact on well-being.

emotions in different ways, with adults ascribing more "female" expectations to babies they believe to be girls (see Brody, 2000).

Affective Disposition. Inherited feelings are part of a personal baseline of positivity or negativity, sometimes described as a person's "affective disposition." This can ensure that well-being is typically experienced as generally positive or negative, so that a person in general tends to be relatively cheerful or relatively gloomy.[5]

People are often uncertain about their feelings, and their affective disposition can lead them to have better or worse well-being than might otherwise be the case. For example, when people are unsure how to feel, a positive disposition might lead them to place less weight on (or ignore) the negative aspects of a situation, perhaps emphasizing current features that are attractive. Furthermore, a person who is uncertain about his or her level of well-being is especially likely to be influenced by reactions to some other issue or topic. For example, well-being that is unclear with respect to one's health (a feature-specific form of well-being) can be greatly influenced by successful progress toward a goal in nonhealth areas.

Affective disposition has sometimes been measured through the Neutral Objects Satisfaction Questionnaire (see Eschleman & Bowling, 2011; Weitz, 1952), which asks for "satisfied," "dissatisfied," or "neutral" responses to 25 features thought to be on average affectively neutral, such as 8½″ × 11″ paper, your telephone number, your first name, and the way people drive. Measured in that way, a disposition to view the world in affectively more negative, rather than more positive, terms is known to be associated with context-free anxiety, depression, and low global happiness (see Judge & Locke, 1993). And among employee samples, a significant association with affective disposition has been reported for several indicators of job satisfaction, both at a single time and across several years (see Eschleman & Bowling, 2011; Judge & Hulin, 1993).

A person's affective disposition is likely in part to be inherited and has been underemphasized in the literature. As a source of individual difference, this variable now deserves additional investigation.

Age. Intergroup comparisons have often revealed an association between age and well-being—in a U-shaped rather than a straight-line pattern. Between the age of around 20 and the decades between 30 and 50, progressively lower hedonic well-being occurs in comparisons between different ages, but after the middle years, the between-group trend is reversed, so that average well-being becomes steadily higher until it levels off at about age 70 (see Steptoe et al., 2015). In Western societies, this nonlinear pattern has also been shown for job satisfaction (see Clark et al., 1996) and for job stress (see Birdi et al., 1995) and is probably susceptible within an age group to gender and other factors discussed in this section.

Gender. On average, men and women describe similar levels of positive affect, but studies have shown that women are more likely than men to report being upset about their situation or themselves. They tend to focus more on troublesome aspects of their world and themselves and to report more negative experiences (see Nolen-Hoeksema & Rusting, 1999; Rosenfield & Mouzon, 2013). In part, this gender difference is likely to derive from differences in normative display rules between men and women, outlined above in the section on genetic differences.

Value Priorities. Also important for subjective well-being are value priorities. Values make us more sensitive or less sensitive to different stimuli, encourage entry into and departure from particular situations, and modify the allocation of effort. In some cases values have a moral, religious, or social content, but they often represent individual preferences—what a person likes and dislikes. Values range from short-term preferences, which can vary from time to time, to longer-term orientations, perhaps within a personality trait. In all cases, values are made up of preferences; people differ in finding some themes more personally important than others. As a result, particular features can be valued in different ways by different people or by the same person at different times.

In general, if an environmental feature matters to a person, its presence or absence more strongly determines that person's feelings. A great deal of research has confirmed that correlations between a job feature and job satisfaction are larger for people who more strongly value the presence of that feature. As a result, different people (with different preferences) can sometimes feel differently about the same environmental feature; its presence or absence influences well-being more when it is more strongly valued (see Loher et al., 1985; Warr & Inceoglu, 2015).

This general finding has much in common with notions of "person–environment fit." Closer congruence between a job-holder's preference and role characteristics has frequently been found to be important to well-being. In an initial investigation, French et al. (1982) studied the perceived discrepancy between current job features and how much a person "would like" in each case.[6] They found significant associations between job strain and the magnitude of mismatches between job features and preferences. Subsequent research has often confirmed that poor fit is associated with lower job well-being (see Kristoff-Brown et al., 2005; Oh et al., 2013; Ostroff & Judge, 2007).

However, simple difference scores between perceived actual and desired levels of a job or other feature are subject to several confounding influences (see Cronbach & Furby, 1970; Edwards, 2001, 2013; Edwards & Van Harrison, 1993), and the replacement of difference scores by polynomial equations can often be less user-friendly than difference scores alone. Nevertheless, the general theme that congruence between job supplies and job values is linked to well-being has been widely supported in analyses that extend beyond simple difference scores on their own (see Edwards & Cable, 2009; Warr & Inceoglu, 2012). Not having what you want is associated with low well-being.

Personality Traits. Well-being levels are also linked to some traits of personality. In particular, high scorers on scales of neuroticism have significantly lower well-being than less-high neuroticism scorers (see DeNeve & Cooper, 1998; Judge et al., 2002), in part because of overlap between wording in the two kinds of measure (see Steel et al., 2008). Conceptual overlap between negative affective disposition (above) and neuroticism is also likely, but that possibility has yet to be investigated.

In respect to other personality traits, significant positive associations have been reported between measures of well-being and scales of extraversion and conscientiousness (see Grant & Langan-Fox, 2007; Judge et al., 2002). Additionally, trait optimism (dispositionally expecting good outcomes even when circumstances are difficult) and trait proactivity (showing initiative, making suggestions, etc.) have been shown to be significantly associated with aspects of well-being (Carver et al., 2010; Tornau & Frese, 2013).

Statements about personality trait may concern one or more of affect (A), behavior (B), cognition (C), and desire (D; see Thapa et al., 2020; Wilt & Revelle, 2015). "Affect" refers to moods, emotions, feelings, preferences, and other valenced constructs; "behavior" in this context concerns observable trait-related actions; and "cognition" refers to thoughts and other mental activity associated with the trait. Dispositional "desires" combine with situational characteristics to yield habitual behaviors or thoughts. Mischel and Shoda (1995) examined *if . . . then* routines in particular types of situation: *if* a situation is of a certain kind, *then* a particular trait is likely to be reflected in a specific behavior or thought. Traits should be viewed as habitual applications of such *if . . . then* routines, recognizing that routines can be habits of thought as well as of behavior (see Warr, in press).

There is growing evidence that environmental features can have a stronger or weaker association with well-being depending on the strength of a person's preference for that feature—a moderating pattern described earlier with respect to values. In research into the moderating influence of values described as needs, Vroom (1959) found that the well-being gain from employee participation was greatest among workers with a conceptually linked high need for independence. And studies by Kahn et al. (1964) and Keenan and McBain (1979) both showed that the correlation between role ambiguity and low job well-being was greater for workers with a high, rather than low, need for structured cognition.

Similar moderation by personality of the association between a feature and well-being has been reported by Rogelberg et al. (2006, with respect to accomplishment striving and meeting attendance), Bond et al. (2008, studying psychological flexibility and psychological distress), Rego et al. (2009, with respect to need for belonging and the spirit of camaraderie), and Van Doorn and Hülsheger (2015, examining psychological distress and core self-evaluations). In summary, several personality traits can moderate the well-being impact of potential causes in the environment.

Degree of Adaptation. Well-being is also dependent on a person's degree of adaptation, as feelings in response to a constant or repeated stimulus become less pronounced across time. In Frijda's (1988) terms, "continued pleasures wear off; continued hardships lose their poignancy." Adaptation can occur in simple cases within minutes, but regression toward a previous level of well-being can also extend across months.

For example, a review of 313 longitudinal samples (Luhmann et al., 2012) illustrated positive or negative changes in well-being after marriage, divorce, bereavement, childbirth, unemployment, re-employment, and retirement, but also demonstrated a clear impact of adaptation across time. Although the studied events were initially unpleasant or welcome as expected (for instance, marriage was followed by a "honeymoon effect"), well-being was found to stabilize in the subsequent months or years and sometimes to shift back toward previous levels.

Adaptation of well-being also occurs in a job. Griffin (1988, 1991) reported that organizational changes to improve job satisfaction in two different studies had an initially positive impact, but satisfaction returned to its original level after 2 or 3 years. Furthermore, Boswell et al. (2005) found that job satisfaction increased immediately after managers' self-chosen moves into a new position, but it declined significantly in subsequent years as they became adapted to their new role.

Findings about adaptation have suggested the presence of a personal set point, described as an "equilibrium state" of well-being by Headey and Wearing (1992). More likely than a single equilibrium state is a recurring *range* of well-being as people adapt over time to positive or negative inputs from the environment (see Cummins et al., 2014).[7]

Emotion Regulation. Differences between individuals in their well-being are also brought about by different interpretations of a particular situation, sometimes examined in a framework of "emotion regulation." As described by Gross (1998, p. 275), "emotion regulation refers to the processes by which individuals influence which emotions they have, when they have them, and how they experience and express those emotions. Emotion regulatory processes may be automatic or controlled, conscious or unconscious, and may have their effects at one or more points in the emotion generative process."[8] In addition to occurring in isolation, specific emotion regulation activities are likely to be repeated and to develop into habitual routines.

Gross's perspective on emotion regulation extends across five stages in which well-being might be affected by people themselves: situation selection, situation modification, attention deployment, reappraisal, and behavioral adjustment. Each of those needs to be included among the contributors to a person's well-being.[9]

Situation Selection and Situation Modification. It is obvious that well-being can be greatly influenced by choosing which situations to enter or leave or by making changes to a current situation. As is true for other processes in this section, decisions about which settings to enter, leave, or modify can derive from internal ("controlled") variables or from external sources (other people or circumstances). In most cases, a combination of internal and external sources is to be expected, as in Figure 2.

Occupational research into the personal modification of job situations has focused on "job crafting"—the ways in which workers adjust their work demands or social interactions to decrease negative experiences and to increase positive ones. Unsurprisingly, workers who report this kind of process are likely also to experience better well-being in terms of job satisfaction and job engagement—they have shaped their activities for their benefit (see Rudolph et al., 2017).

Attention Deployment. Well-being can also be influenced by how people allocate attention, directing their thoughts to one particular target rather than to others. We can often adjust an experience by shifting our mental focus to alternative themes. The "power of positive thinking," "accentuating the positive," and "looking on the bright side" have regularly been advocated in popular culture.

Experimental studies comparing the subjective well-being of people who have been asked to think and/or behave in different ways have pointed to the beneficial impact of certain kinds of mental focus. For instance, research participants were asked to think about and write down five things for which they were grateful, and then their well-being was compared to that of a group undertaking different activities. Emphasizing or expressing one's gratitude was found to increase subjective well-being, as were instructions to reflect on positive experiences, to practice optimism, or to express forgiveness (see Clauss et al., 2018; Lyubomirsky & Layous, 2013).

For example, Chancellor et al. (2015) asked employees to write for 10 minutes about three things that went well in their job in the previous week. In comparison to a control group who spent 10 minutes describing their last week's activities, those recalling positive work events became generally more happy across time. Another within-organization comparison involved quiet contemplation with warm feelings directed toward other people (Frederickson et al., 2008). In comparison to a control group, participating workers were found to have clear benefits in terms of positive emotions, psychological well-being, and life satisfaction.

Processes of attention-deployment also illustrate Frijda's (1988) law of comparative feeling—"the intensity of emotion depends on the relationship between an event and some frame of reference against which the event is evaluated." A principal form of this is in terms of mental comparison between a current situation and those in the past or in a potential future—thinking how things are getting better or getting worse or are likely to get better or to get worse. If you are able to focus attention on previous improvements or on probable future improvements, you are likely to feel more positive about an unpleasant situation. Conversely, when you think about how things are getting worse or are likely to remain bad, you will probably experience reduced well-being (Emmons, 1986; Roese, 1997), often in part through anticipatory worry about future problems (see Meurs & Perrewé, 2011). A key point is that well-being is determined not only by a current situation, but also by a person's mental comparisons with how things used to be and how they are expected to be in the future.

Two other mental comparisons are also important for well-being—against the frame of reference provided by other people and by other situations. These have both been viewed as either "upward" or "downward." Emotion regulation by upward comparison with other people involves mentally comparing oneself, often unfavorably, to individuals who are in a better situation; upward comparisons of that kind tend to reduce a person's well-being. On the other hand, downward social comparisons, against people who are worse off in the compared respect, tend to encourage better well-being (see Wheeler, 2000).

In addition to comparing yourself to other people, mental comparisons to other situations can contribute to differences in well-being. Among these counterfactual conditionals, upward thoughts (reflecting how things might have developed more favorably) are known to depress subjective well-being, whereas downward comparisons (considering how matters could have turned out worse than they are) can evoke more positive feelings.

These comparisons have been illustrated in a study of Olympic medalists. Runners who received silver medals for achieving second place were judged from videotapes to be less happy with their position than were bronze medalists in third place. Many second-place winners appeared to base their less positive feelings in part on upward counterfactual comparisons ("I couldn't be the best"), whereas athletes in third place were more likely to make downward comparisons, being happy to have reached a medal position ("I did better than almost everyone"; Medvec et al., 1995).

This pattern was confirmed in a second sample of Olympic athletes by McGraw et al. (2005), who additionally emphasized mental comparisons against prior expectations. Medal winners with lower published expectations reported more positive well-being than others with higher expectations, and high expectations (such as anticipation of a winners' medal) appeared to make objectively better outcomes seem worse. In general, people compare their achievements against what they expect, and well-being depends in part on prior expectation (Shepperd & McNulty, 2002).

Reappraisal. Emotion regulation also ranges across additional ways in which people adjust how they think about a situation. Particularly important is the degree to which they can identify positive meanings, perhaps after the event. Different people in the same job or other situation can vary in how far they perceive required actions as personally meaningful and rewarding, leading to differences in their well-being.

Another form of reappraisal has been described as "acceptance"—recognizing the negative aspects of a fact but mentally setting aside associated negative feelings (see Bond & Bunce, 2003; Kuba & Scheibe, 2017). Low well-being after an unpleasant event can be improved by mentally uncoupling one's negative feelings from the recognition that an unpleasant fact had occurred. In that way, job satisfaction and global well-being are more positive among workers who score higher on acceptance thinking (Bond & Bunce, 2003), and a day's negative events tend to be less disturbing to workers who accept the events without also experiencing linked negative affect (Kuba & Scheibe, 2017).[10] Furthermore, training in acceptance thought and behavior has been shown to reduce workers' perceived stress and burnout (Hofer et al., 2018). As with other forms of emotion regulation, the same situation can influence well-being to different degrees depending on a person's mental processes.

Subsequent Behavior. The final element of Gross's framework of emotion regulation concerns how people behave in response to what has happened. For example, a person with low well-being might aim to improve feelings through alcohol, exercise, meditation, or drugs. Occupational researchers in this area have concentrated on "expressive suppression"—adjusting behavior to distort how you feel. Processes of that kind have been studied in work with a strong emphasis on service relationships, such as waiting on customers in a restaurant or handling inquiries in a telephone call center. These workers are often expected to conceal their negative feelings about rude or aggressive customers and to behave as if an offensive customer has behaved in an acceptable fashion. That form of emotional suppression has been found to be linked with psychological strain, emotional exhaustion, low job satisfaction, and similar forms of low well-being (Grandey, 2015; Hülsheger & Schewe, 2011).

In summary, experiences of well-being are often influenced by situation-specific forms of emotion regulation. Single instances of regulation can be undertaken explicitly and with an intention to increase well-being, or emotion regulation can be included in mental and behavioral routines that have become established through repetition as personal habits.[11]

CONCLUDING REMARKS ABOUT PERSONAL INFLUENCES ON WELL-BEING

Self-generated well-being differences between people arise in two ways—from long-standing factors within a person (inheritance, age, gender, values, traits, etc.) and through mental or behavioral shifts in the way a particular situation is perceived (see, for instance, Warr, 2019). Some frequently repeated adjustments of the latter kind can become personal values or traits in the former category, and interdependence between the two kinds of source requires further investigation.

Also deserving additional research are processes of emotional ambivalence—when positive and negative feelings occur together. Mixed feelings of that kind occur in two ways, each with its own conceptual and empirical challenges. Ambivalence can arise concurrently, when contrasted feelings arise from different aspects of a situation, and ambivalence that is sequential occurs, for instance, when a person works through negative situations before attaining well-being in some form. We need more sophisticated conceptual analyses of these two episodes in work and other settings, together with more rigorous longitudinal investigations (see Berrios et al., 2015; Hershfield et al., 2013). Progress in understanding ambivalence is likely also to require approaches that are more qualitative than our field's conventional emphasis on quantitative designs.

REFERENCES

Anderson, C. J. (2003). The psychology of doing nothing: Forms of decision avoidance result from reason and emotion. *Psychological Bulletin, 129*, 139–167.

Baltes, B. B., Bauer, C. C., Bajdo, L. M., & Parker, C. P. (2002). The use of multitrait-multimethod data for detecting nonlinear relationships: The case of psychological climate and job satisfaction. *Journal of Business and Psychology, 17*, 3–17.

Bartels, M. (2015). Genetics of wellbeing and its components satisfaction with life, happiness, and quality of life: A review and meta-analysis of heritability studies. *Behavior Genetics, 45*, 137–156.

Berrios, R., Totterdell, P., & Kellett, S. (2015). Investigating goal conflict as a source of mixed emotions. *Cognition and Emotion, 29*, 755–763.

Birdi, K., Warr. P. B., & Oswald, A. (1995). Age differences in three components of employee well-being. *Applied Psychology: An International Review, 44*, 345–373.

Bond, F. W., & Bunce, D. (2003). The role of acceptance and job control in mental health, job satisfaction, and work performance. *Journal of Applied Psychology, 88*, 1057–1067.

Bond, F. W., Flaxman, P. E., & Bunce, D. (2008). The influence of psychological flexibility on work design: Mediated moderation of a work reorganization intervention. *Journal of Applied Psychology, 95*, 645–653.

Boswell, W. R., Boudreau, J. W., & Tichy, J. (2005). The relationship between employee job change and job satisfaction: The honeymoon-hangover effect. *Journal of Applied Psychology, 90*, 882–892.

Brayfield, A. H., & Rothe, H. F. (1951). An index of job satisfaction. *Journal of Applied Psychology, 35*, 307–311.

Brennan, A., Chugh, J. S., & Kline, T. (2002). Traditional versus open office design: A longitudinal field study. *Environment and Behavior, 34*, 279–299.

Brody, L. R. (2000). The socialization of gender differences in emotional expression: Display rules, infant temperaments, and differentiation. In A. Fisher (Ed.), *Gender and emotion* (pp. 24–47). Cambridge University Press.

Burger, J. M. (1989). Negative reactions to increases in perceived personal control. *Journal of Personality and Social Psychology, 56*, 246–256.

Burke, M. J., Brief, A. P., George, J. M., Roberson, L., & Webster, J. (1989). Measuring affect at work: Confirmatory analyses of competing mood structures with conceptual linkage to cortical regulatory systems. *Journal of Personality and Social Psychology, 57*, 1091–1102.

Buruck, G., Dörfel, D., Kugler, J., & Brom, S. S. (2016). Enhancing well-being at work: The role of emotion regulation skills as personal resources. *Journal of Occupational Health Psychology, 21*, 480–493.

Buunk, B. P., Zurriaga, R., Peiró, J. M., Nauta, A., & Gonsalvez, I. (2005). Social comparisons at work as related to a comparative social climate and to individual differences in social comparison orientation. *Applied Psychology: An International Review, 54*, 61–80.

Carver, C. S., Scheier, M. F., & Segerstrom, S. C. (2010). Optimism. *Clinical Psychology Review, 30*, 879–889.

Chancellor, J., Layous, K., & Lyubomirsky, S. (2015). Recalling positive event at work makes employees feel happier, move more but interact less: A 6-week randomized controlled intervention at a Japanese workplace. *Journal of Happiness Studies, 16,* 871–887.

Christian, M. S., Garza, A. S., & Slaughter, J. E. (2011). Work engagement: A quantitative review and test of its relations with task and organizational performance. *Personnel Psychology, 64,* 89–166.

Clark, A. E., Oswald, A., & Warr, P. B. (1996). Is job satisfaction U-shaped in age? *Journal of Occupational and Organizational Psychology, 69,* 57–81.

Clauss, E., Hoppe, A., O'Shea, D., Gonzáles Morales, M. G., Steidle, A., & Michel, A. (2018). Promoting personal resources and reducing exhaustion through positive work reflection among caregivers. *Journal of Occupational Health Psychology, 23,* 127–140.

Crawford, E. R., LePine, J. A., & Rich, B. L. (2010). Linking job demands and resources to employee engagement and burnout: A theoretical extension and meta-analytic test. *Journal of Applied Psychology, 95,* 834–848.

Cronbach, L. J., & Furby, L. (1970). How should we measure "change"—Or should we? *Psychological Bulletin, 74,* 68–80.

Cummins, R. A., Li, N., Wooden, M., & Stokes, M. (2014). A demonstration of set-points for subjective wellbeing. *Journal of Happiness Studies, 15,* 183–206.

Deelstra, J. T., Peeters, M. C. W., Schaufeli, W. B., Stroebe, W., Zijlstra, F. R. H., & van Doornen, L. P. (2003). Receiving instrumental support at work: When help is not welcome. *Journal of Applied Psychology, 88,* 324–331.

De Jonge, J., Reuvers, M. M., Houtman, I. L. D., Bongers, P. M., & Kompier, M. A. J. (2000). Linear and non-linear relations between psychosocial job characteristics, subjective outcomes, and sickness absence: Baseline results from SMASH. *Journal of Occupational Health Psychology, 5,* 256–268.

DeNeve, K. M., & Cooper, H. (1998). The happy personality: A meta-analysis of 137 personality traits and subjective well-being. *Psychological Bulletin, 124,* 197–229.

Diener, E., Emmons, R. A., Larsen, R. J., & Griffin, S. (1985). The Satisfaction with Life Scale. *Journal of Personality Assessment, 49,* 71–75.

Diener, E., Kanazawa, S., Suh, E. M., & Oishi, S. (2015). Why people are in a generally good mood. *Personality and Social Psychology Review, 19,* 235–256.

Diener, E., & Seligman, M. E. P. (2004). Beyond money: Toward an economy of well-being. *Psychological Science in the Public Interest, 5,* 1–31.

Diener, E., Sandvik, E., Seidlitz, L., & Diener, M. (1993). The relationship between income and subjective well-being: Relative or absolute? *Social Indicators Research, 28,* 195–223.

Diener, E., Suh, E. M., Lucas, R. E., & Smith, H. L. (1999). Subjective well-being: Three decades of progress. *Psychological Bulletin, 125,* 276–302.

Edwards, J. R. (2001). Ten difference score myths. *Organizational Research Methods, 4,* 265–287.

Edwards, J. R. (2013). The study of congruence in organizational behavior research. Critique and a proposed alternative. *Organizational Behavior and Human Decision Processes, 58,* 51–100.

Edwards, J. R., & Cable, D. M. (2009). The value of value congruence. *Journal of Applied Psychology, 94,* 654–677.

Edwards, J. R., & Van Harrison, R. (1993). Job demands and worker health: Three-dimensional re-examination of the relationship between person-environment fit and strain. *Journal of Applied Psychology, 78,* 628–648.

Emmons, R. A. (1986). Personal strivings: An approach to personality and subjective well-being. *Journal of Personality and Social Psychology, 51,* 1058–1068.

Eschleman, K. J., & Bowling, N. A. (2011). A construct validation of the Neutral Objects Satisfaction Questionnaire. *Journal of Business and Psychology, 26,* 501–515.

Fleishman, E. A., & Harris, E. F. (1962). Patterns of leadership behavior related to employee grievances and turnover. *Personnel Psychology, 15*, 43–56.

Frederickson, B. L., Cohn, M. A., Coffey, K. A., Pek, J., & Finkel, S. M. (2008). Open hearts build lives: Positive emotions, induced through loving-kindness meditation, build consequential personal resources. *Journal of Personality and Social Psychology, 95*, 1045–1062.

French, J. R. P., Caplan, R. D., & Van Harrison, R. (1982). *The mechanisms of job stress and strain.* Wiley.

Frijda, N. H. (1988). The laws of emotion. *American Psychologist, 43*, 349–358.

Grandey, A. A. (2015). Smiling for a wage: What emotional labor teaches us about emotion regulation. *Psychological Inquiry, 26*, 54–60.

Grant, S., & Langan-Fox, J. (2007). Personality and the occupational stressor-strain relationship: The role of the Big Five. *Journal of Occupational Health Psychology, 12*, 20–33.

Grant, A. M., & Schwartz, B. (2011). Too much of a good thing: The challenge and opportunity of the inverted U. *Perspectives on Psychological Science, 6*, 61–76.

Griffin, R. W. (1988). Consequences of quality circles in an industrial setting: A longitudinal assessment. *Academy of Management Journal, 31*, 338–358.

Griffin, R. W. (1991). Effects of work redesign on employee perceptions, attitudes, and behaviors: A long-term investigation. *Academy of Management Journal, 34*, 425–435.

Gross, J. J. (1998). The emerging field of emotion regulation: An integrative review. *Review of General Psychology, 2*, 271–299.

Gross, J. J. (Ed.). (2014). *Handbook of emotion regulation* (2nd ed.). Guilford Press.

Gross, J. J. (2015). Emotion regulation: Current status and future perspectives. *Psychological Inquiry, 26*, 1–26.

Hakanen, J. J., Peeters, M. C. W., & Schaufeli, W. B. (2018). Different types of employee well-being across time and their relationships with job crafting. *Journal of Occupational Health Psychology, 23*, 289–301.

Halbesleben, J. R. B., Neveu, J.-P., Paustian-Underdahl, S. C., & Westman, M. (2014). Getting to the "COR": Understanding the role of resources in Conservation of Resources Theory. *Journal of Management, 40*, 1334–1364.

Headey, B., & Wearing, A. (1992). *Understanding happiness: A theory of subjective well-being.* Longman Cheshire.

Hershfield, H. E., Scheibe, S., Sims, T. L., & Carstensen, L. L. (2013). When feeling bad can be good: Mixed emotions benefit physical health across adulthood. *Social Psychological and Personality Science, 4*, 54–61.

Hofer, P. D., Waadt, M., Aschwanden, R., Milidou, M., Acker, J., Meyer, A. H., Lieb, R., & Gloster, A. T. (2018). Self-help for stress and burnout without therapist contact: An online randomised controlled trial. *Work & Stress, 32*, 189–208.

Hülsheger, U. R., & Schewe, A. F. (2011). On the costs and benefits of emotional labor: A meta-analysis of three decades of research. *Journal of Occupational Health Psychology, 16*, 361–389.

Humphrey, S. E., Nahrgang, J. D., & Morgeson, F. P. (2007). Integrating motivational, social, and contextual work design features: A meta-analytic summary and theoretical extension of the work design literature. *Journal of Applied Psychology, 92*, 1332–1356.

Jebb, A. J., Tay, L., Diener, E., & Oishi, S. (2018). Happiness, income satiation and turning points around the world. *Nature, Human Behaviour, 2*, 33–38.

Judge, T. A., Heller, D., & Mount, M. K. (2002). Five-factor model of personality and job satisfaction: A meta-analysis. *Journal of Applied Psychology, 87*, 530–541.

Judge, T. A., & Hulin, C. L. (1993). Job satisfaction as a reflection of disposition: A multiple source causal analysis. *Organizational Behavior and Human Decision Processes, 56*, 388–421.

Judge, T. A., & Locke, E. A. (1993). Effect of dysfunctional thought processes on subjective well-being and job satisfaction. *Journal of Applied Psychology, 78*, 473–490.

Judge, T. A., Piccolo, R. F., & Ilies, R. (2004). The forgotten ones? The validity of consideration and initiating structure in leadership research. *Journal of Applied Psychology, 89*, 36–51.

Kahn, R. L., Wolfe, D. M., Quinn, R. P., & Snoek, J. D. (1964). *Organizational stress: Studies in role conflict and ambiguity*. Wiley.

Karasek, R. A. (1979). Job demands, job decision latitude, and mental strain: Implications for job redesign. *Administrative Science Quarterly, 24*, 285–308.

Keenan, A. & McBain, G. D. M. (1979). Effects of type-A behaviour, intolerance of ambiguity, and locus of control on the relationship between role stress and work-related outcomes. *Journal of Occupational Psychology, 52*, 277–285.

Kristoff-Brown, A. L., Zimmerman, R. D., & Johnson, E. C. (2005). Consequences of individuals' fit at work: A meta-analysis of person-job, person-group, and person-supervisor fit. *Personnel Psychology, 58*, 281–342.

Kuba, K., & Scheibe, S. (2017). Let it be and keep on going! Acceptance and daily occupational well-being in relation to negative work events. *Journal of Occupational Health Psychology, 22*, 59–70.

Loher, B. T., Noe, R. A., Moeller, N. L., & Fitzgerald, M. P. (1985). A meta-analysis of the relation of job characteristics to job satisfaction. *Journal of Applied Psychology, 70*, 280–289.

Lucas, R. E., & Diener, E. (2015). Personality and subjective well-being: Current issues and controversies. In M. Mikulincer & P. R. Shaver (Eds.), *APA handbook of personality and social psychology* (pp. 577–599). American Psychological Association.

Luchman, J. N., & Gonzáles-Morales, M. G. (2013). Demands, control and support: A meta-analytic review of work characteristics interrelationships. *Journal of Occupational Health Psychology, 18*, 37–52.

Luhmann, M., Hofmann, W., Eid, M., & Lucas, R. E. (2012). Subjective well-being and adaptation to life events: A meta-analysis. *Journal of Personality and Social Psychology, 102*, 592–615.

Lyubomirsky, S., & Layous, K. (2013). How do simple positive activities increase well-being? *Current Directions in Psychological Science, 22*, 57–62.

McGraw, A. P., Mellers, B. A., & Tetlock, P. E. (2005). Expectations and emotions of Olympic athletes. *Journal of Experimental Social Psychology, 41*, 438–446.

Medvec, V. H., Madey, S. F., & Gilovich, T. (1995). When less is more: Counterfactual thinking and satisfaction among Olympic athletes. *Journal of Personality and Social Psychology, 69*, 603–610.

Meurs, J. A., & Perrewé, P. L. (2011). Cognitive activation theory of stress: An integrative theoretical approach to work stress. *Journal of Management, 37*, 1043–1068.

Miner, A. G., Glomb, T. M., & Hulin, C. (2005). Experience sampling mood and its correlates at work. *Journal of Occupational and Organizational Psychology, 78*, 171–193.

Mischel, W., & Shoda, Y. (1995). A cognitive-affective system theory of personality: Reconceptualizing situations, dispositions, dynamics, and invariance in personality structure. *Psychological Review, 102*, 246–268.

Nes, R. B., & Røysamb, E. (2017). Happiness in behaviour genetics: An update on heritability and changeability. *Journal of Happiness Studies, 18*, 1533–1552.

Nolen-Hoeksema, S., & Rusting, C. (1999). Gender differences in well-being. In D. Kahneman, E. Diener, & N. Schwarz (Eds.), *Well-being: The foundations of hedonic psychology* (pp. 330–350). Russell Sage Foundation.

Oh, I.-S., Guay, R. P., Kim, K., Harold, C. M., Lee, C.-G., Heo, J.-H., & Shin, K.-H. (2013). Fit happens globally: A meta-analytic comparison of the relationships of person–environment fit dimensions with work attitudes and performance across East Asia, Europe, and North America. *Personnel Psychology, 67*, 99–152.

Ostroff, C., & Judge, T. A. (2007). *Perspectives on organizational fit*. Lawrence Erlbaum.

Pavot, W., & Diener, E. (2008). The Satisfaction With Life Scale and the emerging construct of life satisfaction. *Journal of Positive Psychology, 3*, 137–152.

Pierce, J. R., & Aquinas, H. (2013). The too-much-of-a good-thing effect in management. *Journal of Management, 39*, 313–338.

Quoidbach, J., Mikolajczak, M., & Gross, J. J. (2015). Positive interventions: An emotion regulation perspective. *Psychological Bulletin, 141*, 655–693.

Rego, A., Souto, S., & Cunha, M. P. (2009). Does the need to belong moderate the relationship between perceptions of spirit of camaraderie and employees' happiness? *Journal of Occupational Health Psychology, 14*, 148–164.

Remington, N. A., Fabrigar, L. R., & Visser, P. S. (2000). Re-examining the circumplex model of affect. *Journal of Personality and Social Psychology, 79*, 286–300.

Roese, N. J. (1997). Counterfactual thinking. *Psychological Bulletin, 121*, 133–148.

Rogelberg, S. G., Leach, D. J., Warr, P. B., & Burnfield, J. (2006). "Not another meeting!" Are meeting time demands related to employee well-being? *Journal of Applied Psychology, 91*, 83–96.

Rosenfield, S., & Mouzon, D. (2013). Gender and mental health. In C. S. Aneshensel, J. C. Phelan, & A. Bierman (Eds.), *Handbook of the sociology of mental health* (pp. 277–296). Springer.

Rozin, P., & Royzman, E. B. (2001). Negativity bias, negativity dominance, and contagion. *Personality and Social Psychology Review, 5*, 296–320.

Rudolph, C. W., Katz, I. M., Lavigne, K. N., & Zacher, H. (2017). Job crafting: A meta-analysis of relationships with individual differences, job characteristics, and work outcomes. *Journal of Vocational Behavior, 102*, 112–138.

Russell, J. A. (1980). A circumplex model of affect. *Journal of Personality and Social Psychology, 39*, 1161–1178.

Russell, J. A. (2003). Core affect and the psychological construction of emotion. *Psychological Review, 110*, 145–172.

Ryff, C. D., & Singer, B. H. (2008). Know thyself and become what you are: A eudaimonic approach to psychological well-being. *Journal of Happiness Studies, 9*, 13–39.

Schaufeli, W. B. (2006). The balance of give and take: Toward a social exchange model of burnout. *Revue Internationale de Psychologie Sociale, 19*, 87–131.

Schaufeli, W. B., Bakker, A. B., & Salanova, M. (2006). The measurement of work engagement with a short questionnaire. *Educational and Psychological Measurement, 66*, 701–716.

Seligman, M. E. P. (2002). *Authentic happiness*. Free Press.

Shepperd, J. A., & McNulty, J. K. (2002). The affective consequences of expected and unexpected outcomes. *Psychological Science, 13*, 85–88.

Steel, P., Schmidt, J., & Schultz, J. (2008). Refining the relationship between personality and subjective well-being. *Psychological Bulletin, 134*, 138–161.

Steptoe, A., Deaton, A., & Stone, A. A. (2015). Subjective well-being, health, and ageing. *The Lancet, 385*, 640–648.

Stiglbauer, B., & Kovacs, C. (2018). The more, the better? Curvilinear effects of job autonomy on well-being from Vitamin Model and P-E fit perspectives. *Journal of Occupational Health Psychology, 23*, 520–536.

Thapa, S., Beck, E. D., & Tay, L. (2020). Personality affect construal theory. In L.-Q. Yang, R. Cropanzano, C. S. Daus, & V. Martinez-Tur (Eds.), *The Cambridge handbook of workplace affect*. Cambridge University Press.

Thoresen, C. J., Kaplan, S. A., Barsky, A. P., Warren, C. R., & de Chermont, K. (2003). The affective underpinnings of job perceptions and attitudes: A meta-analytic review and integration. *Psychological Bulletin, 129*, 914–945.

Tornau, K., & Frese, M. (2013). Construct clean-up in proactivity research: A meta-analysis on the nomological net of work-related proactivity and their incremental validities. *Applied Psychology, An International Review, 62*, 44–96.

Van Doorn, R. R. A., & Hülsheger, U. R. (2015). What makes employees resilient to job demands? The role of core self-evaluations in the relationship between job demands and strain reactions. *European Journal of Work and Organizational Psychology, 24*, 76–87.

Van Katwyk, P. T., Fox, S., Spector, P. E., & Kelloway, E. K. (2000). Using the Job-related Affective Well-being Scale (JAWS) to investigate affective responses to work stressors. *Journal of Occupational Health Psychology, 5*, 219–230.

Vroom, V. H. (1959). Some personality determinants of the effects of participation. *Journal of Abnormal and Social Psychology, 59*, 322–327.

Warr, P. B. (1987). *Work, unemployment, and mental health.* Clarendon Press.

Warr, P. B. (1990). The measurement of well-being and other aspects of mental health. *Journal of Occupational Psychology, 63*, 193–210.

Warr, P. B. (2007). *Work, happiness, and unhappiness.* Erlbaum.

Warr, P. B. (2019). *The psychology of happiness.* Routledge.

Warr, P. B. (2020). Happiness in its many forms. In L.-Q. Yang, R. Cropanzano, C. S. Daus, & V. Martinez-Tur (Eds.), *The Cambridge handbook of workplace affect.* Cambridge University Press.

Warr, P. B. (in press). Personality and habits. *The Psychologist.*

Warr, P. B., Bindl, U. K., Parker, S. K., & Inceoglu, I. (2014). Four-quadrant investigation of job-related affects and behaviours. *European Journal of Work and Organizational Psychology, 23*, 342–363.

Warr, P. B., & Inceoglu, I. (2012). Job engagement, job satisfaction, and contrasting associations with person-job fit. *Journal of Occupational Health Psychology, 17*, 129–138.

Warr, P. B., & Inceoglu, I. (2015). Job features, job values, and affective strength. *European Journal of Work and Organizational Psychology, 24*, 101–112.

Warr, P. B., & Nielsen, K. (2017). Wellbeing and work performance. In E. Diener, S. Oishi, bINDL, & L. Tay (Eds.), *E-handbook of wellbeing.* Noba Scholar (open access).

Warr, P. B., Sanchez-Cordoba, I., Taneva, S., Vera, M., Bindl, U., & Cifre, E. (in press). Reinforcement sensitivity theory, approach-affect and avoidance-affect. *Cognition and Emotion.*

Waterman, A. S. (2008). Reconsidering happiness: A eudaimonist's perspective. *Journal of Positive Psychology, 3*, 234–252.

Watson, D., Clark, L. A., & Tellegen, A. (1988). Development and validation of brief measures of positive and negative affect: The PANAS scales. *Journal of Personality and Social Psychology, 54*, 1063–1070.

Watson, D., & Tellegen, A. (1985). Toward a consensual structure of mood. *Psychological Bulletin, 98*, 219–235.

Watson, D., Wiese, D., Vaidya, J., & Tellegen, A. (1999). The two general activation systems of affect: Structural findings, evolutionary considerations, and psychobiological evidence. *Journal of Personality and Social Psychology, 76*, 820–838.

Weitz, J. (1952). A neglected concept in the study of job satisfaction. *Personnel Psychology, 5*, 201–205.

Wheeler, L. (2000). Individual differences in social comparison. In J. Suls & L. Wheeler (Eds.), *Handbook of social comparison: Theory and research* (pp. 141–158). Kluwer/Plenum.

Wilt, J., & Revelle, W. (2015). Affect, behaviour, cognition and desire in the Big Five: An analysis of item content and structure. *European Journal of Personality, 29*, 478–497.

Yik, M., Russell, J. A., & Steiger, J. H. (2011). A 12-point circumplex structure of core affect. *Emotion, 11*, 705–711.

Young, H. R., Glerum, D. R., Wang, W., & Joseph, D. L. (2018). Who are the most engaged at work? A meta-analysis of personality and employee engagement. *Journal of Organizational Behavior, 39*, 1330–1346.

Zelenski, J. M., Murphy, S. A., & Jenkins, D. A. (2008). The happy-productive worker hypothesis revisited. *Journal of Happiness Studies, 9*, 521–537.

NOTES

1. The valence of everyday feelings overall has been found to be positive rather than negative. See for example Diener et al. (2015) and Miner et al. (2005).
2. Flourishing well-being is explored, for instance, by Warr (2019).
3. Of course, one can influence the outcomes of luck, shaping a resulting situation in positive rather than negative ways.
4. A general account of curvilinearity has been provided by Grant and Schwartz (2011).

5. This process is sometimes described in terms of a glass being viewed either as half full or as half empty.
6. This form of person–environment match is sometimes described as "supplies–value" fit. Another kind of misfit has been viewed in terms of incongruence between the demands of a job and a worker's ability.
7. This set range may be partly inherited within a general affective disposition, considered earlier in the section.
8. See also Gross (2014, 2015) and Quoidbach et al. (2015).
9. Other models of emotion regulation (e.g., Buruck et al., 2016) also extend across several of the stages considered here.
10. Uncoupling negative affect from an associated unpleasant experience is likely also to be central to processes of adaptation.
11. In many respects, personality traits can be viewed as habitual routines (Warr, in press).

Peter Warr

A SELECTIVE REVIEW OF DEVELOPMENTS IN POSITIVE STUDIES OF WORK AND ORGANIZATIONS

OVERVIEW

In the 1990s, Martin Seligman helped establish positive psychology (Seligman & Csikszentmihalyi, 2000). It was described as a counterbalance to a perceived negative bias in psychology, which typically studied and treated illness, concentrating on how to move people from deficit states to normal functioning. In contrast, positive psychology promoted the development of strengths and practices that contribute to thriving and fulfillment (Donaldson et al., 2020). Positive psychology fostered a similar trend in management and organization studies, where scholars highlighted what they perceived as a problem-focused bias (Caza & Caza, 2008; Walsh, 2000). Scholars have argued that the "tyranny of negativity" (Youssef-Morgan & Luthans, 2013, p. 198) created the need to add a positive perspective in studying work and organizations (Roberts, 2006). As a result, several positivity-focused research programs were launched, such as positive organizational behavior (POB; Luthans, 2002) and positive organizational scholarship (POS; Cameron et al., 2003). In addition to these programs, increased attention was devoted to existing topics that had a positive orientation, such that organizational research was described as taking a "positive turn" at the start of the 21st century (Fineman, 2006, p. 270).

This article provides a brief introduction to some of the themes and questions raised in the first 20 years of explicitly positive-oriented organizational studies. In doing so, several simplifications are introduced. First, no distinction is made between the numerous branches of positive organizational studies (e.g., POB vs. POS), since they are highly compatible (Luthans & Avolio, 2009) and often not easily distinguished (Donaldson & Ko, 2010). Instead, the umbrella label of positive work and organization (PWO) studies (Warren et al., 2017) is used to encompass these domains. Second, for brevity, this article only considers what might be called "explicit" PWO developments. Before any formal declaration of PWO, there were many studies of seemingly positive organizational behaviors and outcomes, including appreciative inquiry (Cooperrider & Srivastava, 1987), empowerment (Spreitzer, 1996), corporate social responsibility (Cochran & Wood, 1984), and servant leadership (Greenleaf, 1998). These studies, and others like them, are beyond the scope of this article. Third, to maintain some distinction between PWO and positive psychology, this article does not address many relevant studies, despite their clear implications for organizational behavior, if those studies were not specifically focused on organizational domains (e.g., flow states, character strengths, core self-evaluations). There are already fine reviews of positive psychology available (e.g., Donaldson et al., 2020).

What then are PWO studies? This article follows the lead of Cameron and Spreitzer (2012), who suggest that PWO studies are defined by two qualities: their focus on processes and states that occur in association with organizations and their fit with one of four broad themes: a new way of looking at phenomena previously viewed as negative or harmful, directing attention to exceptionally positive outcomes, an affirmative bias directed toward fostering resourcefulness, or examining virtuousness and "the best of the human condition" (Cameron & Spreitzer, 2012, p. 3). Adopting this perspective, the article highlights some key lines of PWO research in six broad domains. It also notes important criticisms and unanswered questions that remain in PWO studies.

SELECTED DOMAINS OF POSITIVE STUDIES IN WORK AND ORGANIZATIONS

PWO findings and theory are discussed below in six domains: psychological capital, organizational virtue, positive relationships, leadership, outcomes, and practice.

Psychological Capital. Many positive individual qualities and virtues have been studied in organizations (e.g., Alzola, 2008; Wright & Goodstein, 2007). However, most such studies are best thought of as applications of positive psychology rather than uniquely PWO studies, and so are not addressed here. One important exception is psychological capital (PsyCap). PsyCap is an individual construct developed entirely in the PWO tradition, and explicitly focused on organizational contexts (Avey et al., 2011). Indeed, PsyCap may be the most focused and consistently developed area of study within PWO, with dozens of empirical studies conducted (see Kong et al., 2018). It is defined as a bundle of cognitive resources comprising efficacy (the confidence to undertake challenging tasks), optimism (the tendency to make positive attributions and expect success), hope (the ability to pursue goals and adjust as required to reach them), and resilience (the ability to persevere and recover from adversity; Luthans & Youssef-Morgan, 2017). PsyCap is a synergistic, composite characteristic, such that the four components are collectively more strongly associated with outcomes than the sum of the individual constituent parts (Luthans et al., 2007). In addition, PsyCap is described as "state-like" in that it can be intentionally developed but is not as variable as true state qualities like moods (Lupsa et al., 2020). Higher levels of PsyCap have been associated with many desirable outcomes, including organizational climate, justice, leadership, job satisfaction, commitment, and performance (Kong et al., 2018).

Organizational Virtue. Extending psychological studies of individual virtue, the study of organizational virtue posits that characteristics traditionally considered virtuous in individuals (e.g., courage, forgiveness, integrity) can also be features of collectives (Cameron et al., 2004).

Through attribution and institutionalization, the cultures, systems, and practices of organizations may take on virtuous qualities and facilitate virtuous action by members (Caza, 2015). Because organizations do not literally act for themselves, the expression of their virtue can take one of two forms: "virtue enabled by organizations" involves organizational practice fostering virtue among members, and "virtue in organizations" involves virtuous action taken by members as agents of the organization (Cameron et al., 2004, p. 768). Thus, an organization whose structure makes individual members more likely to notice the suffering of others, and more likely and able to act in response to that suffering is a more compassionate organization (Dutton et al., 2006). Organizational virtues have been studied in terms of specific qualities (e.g., forgiveness; Bright & Exline, 2012), and as composites of multiple virtues in the form of overall virtuousness (e.g., Rego et al., 2010). In both forms, organizational virtues have been linked to a variety of desirable outcomes, including resilience, improved performance, and reduced employee turnover (Cameron, 2020). These effects are explained through organizational virtue's ability to buffer members (protect against harmful forces) and amplify their work (facilitate effective action; Bright et al., 2006). One should note that most organizational virtue researchers stress that these processes and desirable effects are of secondary importance, emphasizing that virtue is its own reward and deserving of cultivation even if it does not lead to beneficial outcomes (e.g., Cameron et al., 2004; Dutton et al., 2006; Meyer, 2018; see also Roberts, 2020).

Positive Relationships.   Most studies of interactions at work tend to focus on exchange, assuming that interactants are motivated primarily by duty or desire for personal benefit (Spreitzer et al., 2019). In contrast, PWO research suggests viewing relationships as ends in themselves, particularly as sources of positive identity and thriving (both concepts are discussed in the "States and Outcomes" section). Moreover, since interactions are an inherent part of organizing, relationships will inevitably develop among members, making it valuable to understand what distinguishes beneficial ones. Studying relationships for their own sake has led PWO studies to highlight previously neglected elements, such as a connection's tensility (ability to withstand strain) and its emotional carrying capacity (quantity and constructiveness of emotional expression that the link between two people sustains; Dutton & Heaphy, 2003). These relationship qualities have been shown to foster safety, growth, and resilience (Stephens et al., 2013).

Indeed, consideration of emotion in interactions is an area where PWO studies have fostered many new developments, highlighting how emotional energy created between individuals is a key element of all communications (Quinn & Dutton, 2005). This emotional energy has been shown to be an important predictor of outcomes between individuals, in groups, and within organizations (Baker, 2019). For example, at the organizational level, emotional cultures characterized by companionate love (affection, compassion, caring, and tenderness) are associated with better outcomes for employees and clients (Barsade & O'Neill, 2014). Extending beyond traditional organizations, PWO scholars have also explored positive relational dynamics among distributed work teams (Lee et al., 2020), sense of community in co-working spaces (Garrett et al., 2017), and members of temporary teams (Livne-Tarandach & Jazaieri, 2020), as well as positive identity among gig workers (Petriglieri et al., 2019) and inmates (Rogers et al., 2017).

Leadership. Leadership, broadly defined, may have received the greatest amount of PWO research attention (Donaldson & Ko, 2010). Sometimes this work involves extending positive constructs to leadership contexts, such as the role of forgiveness in leadership (Cameron & Caza, 2002) or how leaders foster vigor among followers (Carmeli et al., 2009), but most often it consists of the study of one of the many positive leadership styles that have been proposed. These styles include authentic leadership (self-awareness, balanced processing, internalized moral perspective, and relational transparency; Gardner et al., 2011), ethical leadership (demonstration and promotion of normatively appropriate behavior; Bedi et al., 2016), spiritual leadership (creating a vision and culture supporting a sense of calling; Fry, 2003), leadership humility (self-transcendence reflected in self-knowledge, teachability, and appreciation of others' strengths; Wang et al., 2018), and many others (Mumford & Fried, 2014). These positive forms of leadership are typically presented as reactions to the failure of leadership implied by well-known corporate scandals (e.g., Enron, WorldCom, Lehman Brothers). Each style of positive leadership has been associated with a range of important outcomes, and has also influenced research in cognate disciplines. For example, authentic leadership has shaped research in fields such as sports (McDowell et al., 2018), healthcare (Baek et al., 2019), and education (Alazmi & Al-Mahdy, 2020).

States and Outcomes. In an apparent effort to address the PWO claim that prior research has had a bias toward negative phenomena (Cameron et al., 2003), many new outcomes have been proposed and examined. As noted previously, high-quality relationships and organizational virtuousness have been advanced as intrinsically valuable phenomena that should be better understood for their own sake. Attention has also been devoted to examining a variety of positive states and outcomes, both to highlight their relevance and to explain their origins. These efforts sometimes involved extending established concepts to a collective level of analysis. For example, the psychological construct of individual resilience has been extrapolated to the team and organizational levels, highlighting how groups differ in their ability to regain previous levels of function following stress, and may even have the potential to benefit and grow from the experience (Sutcliffe & Vogus, 2003). More frequently, though, PWO research has promulgated new constructs such as thriving (a subjective experience of vitality and forward momentum at work; Spreitzer et al., 2005) or positive work-identity (one's enriching self-definition based on professions, roles, memberships, or other work-related characteristics; Dutton et al., 2020).

Application and Practice. Consistent with the explicit PWO agenda of improving the human condition, considerable effort has been devoted to practical applications and organizational interventions. For example, a collected book of case studies (Hess & Cameron, 2006) highlights the success of positive practices in various organizations as role models for others on how to foster change (see also Cameron & Lavine, 2006). There is also a range of tools and activities designed to foster positive outcomes for individuals and groups, such as the Reflected Best-Self Exercise (Quinn et al., 2003), the Reciprocity Ring (Baker, 2007), and the Relational Coordination Collaborative (Hoffer Gittell, n.d.). To promote such exercises and to foster a community of practitioners, the University of Michigan's Center for Positive Organizations (http://www.positiveorgs.bus.umich.edu/) provides links to resources and syllabi, in addition to hosting talks and networking events.

In terms of the effectiveness of these efforts, a meta-analysis of PWO interventions at work found that positive activities do matter. Based on 52 effects, positive interventions were associated with increases in desirable outcomes, such as subjective feelings of well-being, and with decreases in undesirable outcomes, such as job stress (Donaldson et al., 2019). Interestingly, in that meta-analysis the effect sizes associated with reducing undesirable outcomes tended to be larger than those for increasing desirable ones. That is, it appears that PWO interventions do more to eliminate negative states than they do to enhance positive ones. This difference seems somewhat ironic, given that a foundational assumption of PWO studies is the qualitative difference between moving from deficit to normality versus moving from normal to flourishing. It is an issue that bears further investigation.

CONCERNS AND FUTURE DIRECTIONS

Given the depth of enthusiasm and breadth of attention that positive work and organization (PWO) studies have attracted (e.g., Glover, 2020; Business Roundtable (https://www.businessroundtable.org/); SET Management (https://www.setmanage.org/)), it is perhaps not surprising that a range of critiques and challenges have also arisen. Moreover, since PWO studies are explicitly attempting to introduce something new to research on management and organizations, it is inevitable that the work will take time to develop and require adjustments as it does so. This section considers three areas in which serious questions have been raised about PWO studies, and in which future development may be particularly useful.

Nature of Positive. The defining element of PWO—positivity—is not easily, or consistently, defined. The current lack, and potential impossibility (e.g., Cameron & Spreitzer, 2012), of a unifying definition of the positive aspect of PWO creates many challenges and much potential for misunderstanding. "Positive" behaviors may lead to negative results in organizations, and vice versa (Lee et al., 2003). For example, the presumably positive emotion of pride can produce both desirable (positive?) and undesirable (negative?) outcomes among employees (Verbeke et al., 2004). Likewise, shame, which is likely a negative state since those experiencing it report emotional pain, has been shown to foster relationships and virtue (Bagozzi, 2003), both of which have been identified as PWO outcomes. Of course, PWO scholars recognize such complexities, noting that positive outcomes may arise from both positive and negative phenomena (Kanov, 2021; Spreitzer et al., 2019). But admission of equivocality and equifinality does not eliminate the uncertainty. Unlike psychology, where established professional guidelines specify what constitutes normal, exceptional, and deficit states (American Psychiatric Association, 2013), there is no consensual definition in organization studies. To the extent that it is unclear or debatable what constitutes "positive" in organizations, then it is unclear what constitutes PWO.

There is a risk that labeling something positive will signify nothing more than approval by the person applying the label. If positivity is entirely context dependent, it seems to undermine the PWO goal of developing general theories of positive phenomena (Cameron et al., 2003). Unfortunately, the contingent nature of what constitutes positive is especially complex when focusing on organizations because they are inherently interdependent. There may be consensus that the welfare of one individual does not outweigh the welfare of their community (Seligman & Csikszentmihalyi, 2000), but less extreme cases of interdependence are not so clear. For example, is a group of workers who derive satisfaction and positive identity from resisting a management structure that they perceive as misguided (Learmonth & Humphreys, 2011) positive or negative?

Although PWO studies describe themselves as countering the tyranny of negativity (Youssef-Morgan & Luthans, 2013), they risk introducing a tyranny of their own. The foundational (Cameron et al., 2003) and continuing (Spreitzer et al., 2019) claim that there are inherent, universal human virtues and tendencies seems to conflict with the ideas of socialization and cultural contingency (Fineman, 2006). As well, an explicit focus on the positive may direct attention away from negative realities. Scholars of PWO have explicitly stated that denial of negative experiences is not a part of their goals (e.g., Cameron et al., 2003; Spreitzer et al., 2019), but it may nonetheless be a consequence of their actions. For example, there has been growing resistance to the popularization of resilience in American public education, because emphasizing student hardiness seems to blame students for not thriving amidst stress, deflecting attention and resources away from genuine environmental disadvantages that many poor-performing students face (Ris, 2016). Similarly, PWO's explicit focus on "human goodness" (Cameron et al., 2003) risks de-emphasizing non-human costs, such as ecological damage and habitat loss (Dyck & Caza, 2020). A clear and encompassing definition of "positive" seems to be a matter of challenge and potential development for PWO studies.

Another important aspect of any definition of positivity involves the issue of excess. Doubts have been raised whether more good things are always better. In particular, observers have challenged the PWO focus on positive phenomena by raising the question of whether there might sometimes be too much of a good thing. Grant and Schwartz (2011) suggest that the ideal state is an intermediate one between the vices of deficiency and excess; for example, too little courage is cowardice, too much is recklessness, and neither is desirable. The PWO scholars studying virtues have responded by suggesting that virtues cannot be excessive; for example, recklessness is not excess courage, but a misunderstanding of the true nature of courage (Cameron & Winn, 2012). As this disagreement highlights, the questions of how to define and measure organizational virtue are yet to be resolved (Meyer, 2018). It may be that these uncertainties arise from the more general PWO problem of distinguishing positive from negative.

Construct Clarity and Proliferation.　Debate about progress in social science research is so longstanding and widespread that it is itself a platitude, and the source of numerous clichés. For example, the idea of old wine in new bottles points to the recurrent concern that "new" ideas are merely disingenuous or naïve restatements of old ones (e.g., Friedman, 1991). The same doubts have been raised about the novelty of positive studies in general (Kristjansson, 2012), and PWO research in particular (George, 2004). Such concerns may be particularly acute in the case of PWO, since positive organizational researchers tend to stress that there is a fundamental, qualitative difference between positive and negative, such that they are wholly different phenomena, not just opposite ends of one continuum (Cameron, 2020; Spreitzer et al., 2005). In the same way that positive and negative emotions are distinct experiences (Kercher, 1992), positive organizational phenomena are asserted to be independent and unique, rather than merely the absence of corresponding negative phenomena. Taking this distinction as dogma may have caused PWO researchers to devote less attention than they otherwise might have to investigating the relationships among potentially convergent constructs.

Indeed, relatively little effort has been focused on distinguishing positive constructs from negative ones. Moreover, what evidence does exist tends to raise doubts about the qualitative distinction between positive and negative organizational phenomena. For example, meta-analysis suggests that burnout (a state of low energy and withdrawal resulting from job strain) and job engagement (a state of high energy and dedication regarding one's work) are not two distinct constructs, but rather are negative and positive opposites of a single attitude toward one's work (Cole et al., 2012). Since burnout and job engagement both predate the PWO movement, they fall outside the scope of this article; however, they seem to reflect negative and positive states in organizational life, so the fact of their interdependence suggests that positive may sometimes be no more than the lack of negative. Consistent with this reasoning, a meta-analysis of PWO interventions found that positive practices had their strongest effects on reducing negative outcomes, rather than fostering positive ones (Donaldson et al., 2019). At present, the relationship between positive and negative remains uncertain, as do the relationships among new positive constructs developed in reaction to existing negative ones.

In addition, there are outstanding questions about construct proliferation even within PWO studies. Positive leadership provides an illustrative example. There appears to be significant conceptual overlap among the positive leadership constructs, raising doubts about their distinctiveness and utility (Anderson & Sun, 2015). For example, almost all of the positive leadership styles include a significant moral component (Mumford & Fried, 2014). One empirical examination of this overlap (Hoch et al., 2018) suggests that there is little to distinguish positive leadership styles from each other. The ethical concerns that motivated positive leadership researchers are admirable, but one wonders if their enthusiasm influenced their scientific choices and clarity.

The risks of enthusiasm are likely not limited to leadership studies. The inherent appeal of being more positive, and the crusading zeal that it sometimes produces (Fineman, 2006), might be clouding some scholars' judgment. For example, in the initial years of PWO, the notion of the "positivity ratio" attracted great attention. It was claimed that there is a specific ratio (2.9013 positive to 1 negative) between positive and negative emotions that is required for one to flourish. However, the associated research has since been discredited and retracted (Brown et al., 2013). In fact, there have been a number of retractions of PWO research reports (e.g., Atwater et al., 2014), leading observers to wonder if PWO practice may reflect passion and hope more than evidence-based management (Alvesson & Einola, 2019; Baker, 2019).

Co-Optation or Misuse. Although the authors of positive studies often describe their work as different from "traditional" research because of their focus on thriving and other exceptional outcomes, the distinction is often not clear. For example, the foundational studies of organizational virtue linked them to increased organizational performance, and explicitly admitted that without that performance link, organizational virtue might not attract much attention (Cameron et al., 2004). Likewise, a primary rationale given for psychological capital's (PsyCap) value was its ability to provide a performance advantage in a world of "cutthroat competition" (Luthans & Youssef, 2007, p. 322). Indeed, an early review of the literature pointed out that studies of PWO constructs were frequently justified in terms of their performance benefits (Caza & Carroll, 2012). One might argue, as some PWO scholars have (e.g., Cameron, 2003), that it was required to initially ground positive studies in traditional "non-positive" organizational science in order to gain credibility and resources. Once a beachhead was established and the movement gathered momentum, it could shift focus and concentrate on its original mission of fostering flourishing instead of financial profit.

However, it is not clear that such a shift has occurred. In 2019, Spreitzer and colleagues summarized PWO by stating that

[O]rganizations are flourishing when individuals and teams (1) are experiencing positive emotions, (2) are fully engaged in their jobs, (3) have high quality connections with coworkers, bosses, and customers, (4) believe their work is meaningful and with purpose, and (5) when they achieve goals and exceed expectations. (p. 4)

The fifth outcome is entirely consistent with traditional organizational research and the prioritization of financial profit. The other four risk co-optation, in the sense that those outcomes could be used to pacify employees and thus prevent any challenge or meaningful change in how organizations are run (Dyck & Caza, 2020). Moreover, recent work drawing on PWO theory appears to be continuing to support traditional organizational goals, for example fostering organizational compassion to reduce turnover (Simpson et al., 2020), structuring tasks to promote prosocial action with the intent of improving service quality (Kang et al., 2020), and using job crafting to increase job performance (Dan et al., 2020).

Of course, studies such as these do not necessarily mean that PWO theory and practices are being used to manipulate workers in service of organizational gain. But that outcome is a potential risk. Areas of research outside the scope of PWO as reviewed here demonstrate the real dangers of co-optation. Consider the case of corporate social responsibility (CSR). As noted by Margolis and Walsh (2003), through 30 years of extensive research and growing practical interest, the focus stayed on the link between CSR and financial performance; beyond the potential profit gain, little attention was paid to how or why organizations might make a positive difference in the world. It seems worth asking whether PWO faces a similar risk.

CONCLUSION

Organizational studies experienced a positive turn at the start of the century. A great deal of attention and effort was devoted to countering the seemingly negative focus of prior research. Introducing a positive perspective led to many developments, including new constructs and a richer understanding of familiar ones. Much has been gained from the introduction of positive work and organization (PWO) studies, but much also remains to be done, particularly in terms of clarifying the nature of positivity and its relationship to existing research and theory.

FURTHER READING

Bernstein, S. D. (2003). Positive organizational scholarship: Meet the movement: An interview with Kim Cameron, Jane Dutton, and Robert Quinn. *Journal of Management Inquiry, 12*(3), 266–271.

Cameron, K. S., Dutton, J. E., & Quinn, R. E. (Eds.). (2003). *Positive organizational scholarship: Foundations of a new discipline.* Berrett-Koehler Publishers.

REFERENCES

Alazmi, A. A., & Al-Mahdy, Y. F. H. (2020). Principal authentic leadership and teacher engagement in Kuwait's educational reform context. *Educational Management Administration & Leadership.* https://doi.org/10.1177/1741143220957339

Alvesson, M., & Einola, K. (2019). Warning for excessive positivity: Authentic leadership and other traps in leadership studies. *Leadership Quarterly, 30*(4), 383–395. https://doi.org/10.1016/j.leaqua.2019.04.001

Alzola, M. (2008). Character and environment: The status of virtues in organizations. *Journal of Business Ethics, 78*(3), 343–357. https://doi.org/10.1007/s10551-006-9335-7

American Psychiatric Association. (2013). *Diagnostic and statistical manual of mental disorders (DSM-5).*

Anderson, M. H., & Sun, P. Y. T. (2015). Reviewing leadership styles: Overlaps and the need for a new "full-range" theory. *International Journal of Management Reviews, 19*(1), 76–96. https://doi.org/10.1111/ijmr.12082

Atwater, L. E., Mumford, M. D., Schriesheim, C. A., & Yammarino, F. J. (2014). Retraction of leadership articles: Causes and prevention. *Leadership Quarterly, 25*(6), 1174–1180. https://doi.org/10.1016/j.leaqua.2014.10.006

Avey, J. B., Reichard, R. J., Luthans, F., & Mhatre, K. H. (2011). Meta-analysis of the impact of positive psychological capital on employee attitudes, behaviors, and performance. *Human Resource Development Quarterly, 22,* 127–152. https://doi.org/10.1002/hrdq.20070

Baek, H., Han, K., & Ryu, E. (2019). Authentic leadership, job satisfaction and organizational commitment: The moderating effect of nurse tenure. *Journal of Nursing Management, 27*(8), 1655–1663. https://doi.org/10.1111/jonm.12853

Bagozzi, R. P. (2003). *Positive and negative emotions in organizations* (pp. 176–193). Berrett-Koehler Publishers.

Baker, W. E. (2007). *The Reciprocity Ring.* Center for Positive Organizational Scholarship, University of Michigan.

Baker, W. E. (2019). Emotional energy, relational energy, and organizational energy: Toward a multilevel model. *Annual Review of Organizational Psychology and Organizational Behavior, 6,* 373–395.

Barsade, S. G., & O'Neill, O. A. (2014). What's love got to do with it? A longitudinal study of the culture of companionate love and employee and client outcomes in a long-term care setting. *Administrative Science Quarterly, 59*(4), 551–598. https://doi.org/10.1177/0001839214538636

Bedi, A., Alpaslan, C. M., & Green, S. (2016). A meta-analytic review of ethical leadership outcomes and moderators. *Journal of Business Ethics, 139*(3), 517–536. https://doi.org/10.1007/s10551-015-2625-1

Bright, D., Cameron, K. S., & Caza, A. (2006). The amplifying and buffering effects of virtuousness in downsized organizations. *Journal of Business Ethics, 64,* 249–269.

Bright, D. S., & Exline, J. J. (2012). Forgiveness at four levels. In K. S. Cameron & G. M. Spreitzer (Eds.), *Oxford handbook of positive organizational scholarship* (pp. 244–259). Oxford University Press.

Brown, N. J. L., Sokal, A. D., & Friedman, H. L. (2013). The complex dynamics of wishful thinking: The critical positivity ratio. *American Psychologist, 68*(9), 801–813. https://doi.org/10.1037/a0032850

Cameron, K. S. (2003). Organizational virtuousness and performance. In K. S. Cameron, J. E. Dutton, & R. E. Quinn (Eds.), *Positive organizational scholarship: Foundations of a new discipline* (pp. 48–65). Berrett-Koehler Publishers.

Cameron, K. S. (2020). Effects of virtuous leadership on organizational performance. In S. I. Donaldson, M. Csikszentmihalyi, & J. Nakamura (Eds.), *Positive psychological science: Improving everyday life, well-being, work, education, and societies across the globe* (2nd ed., pp. 145–158). Routledge.

Cameron, K. S., Bright, D., & Caza, A. (2004). Exploring the relationships between organizational virtuousness and performance. *American Behavioral Scientist, 47*, 766–790.

Cameron, K. S., & Caza, A. (2002). Organizational and leadership virtues and the role of forgiveness. *Journal of Leadership & Organizational Studies, 9*, 33–48.

Cameron, K. S., & Lavine, M. (2006). *Making the impossible possible: Leading extraordinary performance—The Rocky Flats story.* Berrett-Koehler Publishers.

Cameron, K. S., & Spreitzer, G. M. (Eds.). (2012). *Oxford handbook of positive organizational scholarship.* Oxford University Press.

Cameron, K. S., & Winn, B. (2012). Virtuousness in organizations. In K. S. Cameron & G. M. Spreitzer (Eds.), *Oxford handbook of positive organizational scholarship* (pp. 231–243). Oxford University Press.

Carmeli, A., Ben-Hador, B., Waldman, D. A., & Rupp, D. E. (2009). How leaders cultivate social capital and nurture employee vigor: Implications for job performance. *Journal of Applied Psychology, 94*(6), 1553–1561.

Caza, A. (2015). Organizational virtue. In A. J. G. Sison (Ed.), *Handbook of virtue ethics in business and management* (pp. 1–9). Springer. https://doi.org/10.1007/978-94-007-6729-4_30-1

Caza, A., & Carroll, B. (2012). Critical theory and positive organizational scholarship. In K. S. Cameron & G. M. Spreitzer (Eds.), *Handbook of positive organizational scholarship* (pp. 965–978). Oxford University Press.

Caza, B. B., & Caza, A. (2008). Positive organizational scholarship—A critical theory perspective. *Journal of Management Inquiry, 17*, 21–33.

Cochran, P. L., & Wood, R. A. (1984). Corporate social responsibility and financial performance. *Academy of Management Journal, 27*(1), 42–56.

Cole, M. S., Walter, F., Bedeian, A. G., & O'Boyle, E. H. (2012). Job burnout and employee engagement: A meta-analytic examination of construct proliferation. *Journal of Management, 38*(5), 1550–1581. https://doi.org/10.1177/0149206311415252

Cooperrider, D. L., & Srivastva, S. (1987). A contemporary commentary on appreciative inquiry in organizational life. In R. Woodman & W. Pasmore (Eds.), *Research in organizational change and development* (Vol. 1, pp. 129–169). Emerald Group Publishing. https://doi.org/10.1108/S1475-9152(2013)0000004001

Dan, C.-I., Roşca, A. C., & Mateizer, A. (2020). Job crafting and performance in firefighters: The role of work meaning and work engagement. *Frontiers in Psychology, 11*(894). https://doi.org/10.3389/fpsyg.2020.00894

Donaldson, S. I., Csikszentmihalyi, M., & Nakamura, J. (Eds.). (2020). *Positive psychological science: Improving everyday life, well-being, work, education, and societies across the globe* (2nd ed.). Routledge.

Donaldson, S. I., & Ko, I. (2010). Positive organizational psychology, behavior, and scholarship: A review of the emerging literature and evidence base. *Journal of Positive Psychology, 5*(3), 177–191. https://doi.org/10.1080/17439761003790930

Donaldson, S. I., Lee, J. Y., & Donaldson, S. I. (2019). Evaluating positive psychology interventions at work: A systematic review and meta-analysis. *International Journal of Applied Positive Psychology, 4*(3), 113–134. https://doi.org/10.1007/s41042-019-00021-8

Dutton, J. E., & Heaphy, E. D. (2003). The power of high-quality connections. In K. S. Cameron, J. E. Dutton, & R. E. Quinn (Eds.), *Positive organizational scholarship: Foundations of a new discipline* (pp. 263–278). Berrett-Koehler Publishers.

Dutton, J. E., Roberts, L. M., & Bednar, J. S. (2020). Prosocial practices, positive identity, and flourishing at work. In S. I. Donaldson, M. Csikszentmihalyi, & J. Nakamura (Eds.), *Positive psychological science: Improving everyday life, well-being, work, education, and societies across the globe* (2nd ed., pp. 128–144). Routledge.

Dutton, J. E., Worline, M. C., Frost, P. J., & Lilius, J. (2006). Explaining compassion organizing. *Administrative Science Quarterly, 51*(1), 59–96. https://doi.org/10.2189/asqu.51.1.59

Dyck, B., & Caza, A. (2020). *Teaching multiple approaches to management to facilitate the educational aims of positive organizational scholarship and critical management studies* (University of Manitoba Working Paper). University of Manitoba.

Fineman, S. (2006). On being positive: Concerns and counterpoints. *Academy of Management Review, 31,* 270–291.

Friedman, M. (1991). Old wine in new bottles. *Economic Journal, 101*(404), 33–40.

Fry, L. W. (2003). Toward a theory of spiritual leadership. *Leadership Quarterly, 14*(6), 693–727. https://doi.org/10.1016/j.leaqua.2003.09.001

Gardner, W. L., Cogliser, C. C., Davis, K. M., & Dickens, M. P. (2011). Authentic leadership: A review of the literature and research agenda. *Leadership Quarterly, 22*(6), 1120–1145. https://doi.org/10.1016/j.leaqua.2011.09.007

Garrett, L. E., Spreitzer, G. M., & Bacevice, P. A. (2017). Co-constructing a sense of community at work: The emergence of community in coworking spaces. *Organization Studies, 38*(6), 821–842. https://doi.org/10.1177/0170840616685354

George, J. M. (2004). Book review of "Positive organizational scholarship: Foundations of a new discipline." *Administrative Science Quarterly, 49*(2), 325–330.

Glover, P. (2020, October 2). Seven steps to eliminating Theory X management for organizational success. *Forbes.* https://www.forbes.com/sites/forbescoachescouncil/2020/10/02/seven-steps-to-eliminating-theory-x-management-for-organizational-success/

Grant, A. M., & Schwartz, B. (2011). Too much of a good thing: The challenge and opportunity of the inverted U. *Perspectives on Psychological Science, 6*(1), 61–76. https://doi.org/10.1177/1745691610393523

Greenleaf, R. K. (1998). *The power of servant-leadership: Essays.* Berrett-Koehler Publishers.

Hess, E. D., & Cameron, K. S. (2006). *Leading with values: Positivity, virtue and high performance.* Cambridge University Press.

Hoch, J. E., Bommer, W. H., Dulebohn, J. H., & Wu, D. (2018). Do ethical, authentic, and servant leadership explain variance above and beyond transformational leadership? A meta-analysis. *Journal of Management, 44*(2), 501–529. https://doi.org/10.1177/0149206316665461

Hoffer Gittell, J. (n.d.). *Relational Coordination Collaborative.* Brandeis University. https://heller.brandeis.edu/relational-coordination

Kang, H. J. (Annette), Kim, W. G., Choi, H.-M., & Li, Y. (2020). How to fuel employees' prosocial behavior in the hotel service encounter. *International Journal of Hospitality Management, 84,* 102333. https://doi.org/10.1016/j.ijhm.2019.102333

Kanov, J. (2021). Why suffering matters! *Journal of Management Inquiry, 30*(1), 85–90. https://doi.org/10.1177/1056492620929766

Kercher, K. (1992). Assessing subjective well-being in the old-old: The PANAS as a measure of orthogonal dimensions of positive and negative affect. *Research on Aging, 14*(2), 131–168. https://doi.org/10.1177/0164027592142001

Kong, F., Tsai, C.-H., Tsai, F.-S., Huang, W., & De la Cruz, S. M. (2018). Psychological capital research: A meta-analysis and implications for management sustainability. *Sustainability, 10*(10), 3457. https://doi.org/10.3390/su10103457

Kristjansson, K. (2012). Positive psychology and positive education: Old wine in new bottles? *Educational Psychologist, 47*(2), 86–105. https://doi.org/10.1080/00461520.2011.610678

Learmonth, M., & Humphreys, M. (2011). Blind spots in Dutton, Roberts, and Bednar's "pathways for positive identity construction at work": "You've got to accentuate the positive, eliminate the negative." *Academy of Management Review, 36*(2), 424–427. https://doi.org/10.5465/amr.2010.0153

Lee, F., Caza, A., Edmondson, A. C., & Thomke, S. (2003). New knowledge creation in organizations. In K. S. Cameron, J. E. Dutton, & R. E. Quinn (Eds.), *Positive organizational scholarship: Foundations of a new discipline* (pp. 194–206). Berrett-Koehler Publishers.

Lee, M. Y., Mazmanian, M., & Perlow, L. (2020). Fostering positive relational dynamics: The power of spaces and interaction scripts. *Academy of Management Journal, 63*(1), 96–123. https://doi.org/10.5465/amj.2016.0685

Livne-Tarandach, R., & Jazaieri, H. (2020). Swift sense of community: Resourcing artifacts for rapid community emergence in a temporary organization. *Academy of Management Journal.* https://doi.org/10.5465/amj.2019.0410

Lupsa, D., Virga, D., Maricutoiu, L. P., & Rusu, A. (2020). Increasing psychological capital: A pre-registered meta-analysis of controlled interventions. *Applied Psychology, 69*(4), 1506–1556. https://doi.org/10.1111/apps.12219

Luthans, F. (2002). The need for and meaning of positive organizational behavior. *Journal of Organizational Behavior, 23*(6), 695–706. https://doi.org/10.1002/job.165

Luthans, F., & Avolio, B. J. (2009). Inquiry unplugged: Building on Hackman's potential perils of POB. *Journal of Organizational Behavior, 30*(2), 323–328.

Luthans, F., Avolio, B. J., Avey, J. B., & Norman, S. M. (2007). Positive psychological capital: Measurement and relationship with performance and satisfaction. *Personnel Psychology, 60,* 541–572.

Luthans, F., & Youssef, C. A. (2007). Emerging positive organizational behavior. *Journal of Management, 33*(3), 321–349.

Luthans, F., & Youssef-Morgan, C. M. (2017). Psychological capital: An evidence-based positive approach. *Annual Review of Organizational Psychology and Organizational Behavior, 4*(1), 339–366. https://doi.org/10.1146/annurev-orgpsych-032516-113324

Margolis, J. D., & Walsh, J. P. (2003). Misery loves companies: Rethinking social initiatives by business. *Administrative Science Quarterly, 48,* 268–305.

McDowell, J., Huang, Y.-K., & Caza, A. (2018). Does identity matter? An investigation of the effects of authentic leadership on student-athletes' psychological capital and engagement. *Journal of Sport Management, 32*(3), 227–242.

Meyer, M. (2018). The evolution and challenges of the concept of organizational virtuousness in positive organizational scholarship. *Journal of Business Ethics, 153*(1), 245–264. https://doi.org/10.1007/s10551-016-3388-z

Mumford, M. D., & Fried, Y. (2014). Give them what they want or give them what they need? Ideology in the study of leadership. *Journal of Organizational Behavior, 35*(5), 622–634. https://doi.org/10.1002/job.1921

Petriglieri, G., Ashford, S. J., & Wrzesniewski, A. (2019). Agony and ecstasy in the gig economy: Cultivating holding environments for precarious and personalized work identities. *Administrative Science Quarterly, 64*(1), 124–170. https://doi.org/10.1177/0001839218759646

Quinn, R. E., Dutton, J. E., Spreitzer, G. M., & Roberts, L. M. (2003). *Reflected Best Self Exercise.* [Personal development tool] Center for Positive Organizational Scholarship, University of Michigan.

Quinn, R. W., & Dutton, J. E. (2005). Coordination as energy-in-conversation. *Academy of Management Review, 30*(1), 36–57.

Rego, A., Ribeiro, N., & Cunha, M. P. (2010). Perceptions of organizational virtuousness and happiness as predictors of organizational citizenship behaviors. *Journal of Business Ethics, 93*(2), 215–235. https://doi.org/10.1007/s10551-009-0197-7

Ris, E. (2016, May 10). The problem with teaching "grit" to poor kids? They already have it. Here's what they really need. *The Washington Post.* https://www.washingtonpost.com/news/answer-sheet/wp/2016/05/10/the-problem-with-teaching-grit-to-poor-kids-they-already-have-it-heres-what-they-really-need/

Roberts, L. M. (2006). Shifting the lens on organizational life: The added value of positive scholarship—Response. *Academy of Management Review, 31,* 292–305.

Roberts, L. M. (2020, June 28). Move beyond the business case for diversity. *Bloomberg Opinion.* https://www.bloomberg.com/opinion/articles/2020-06-28/business-case-for-diversity-isn-t-enough-to-end-corporate-racism

Rogers, K. M., Corley, K. G., & Ashforth, B. E. (2017). Seeing more than orange: Organizational respect and positive identity transformation in a prison context. *Administrative Science Quarterly, 62*(2), 219–269. https://doi.org/10.1177/0001839216678842

Seligman, M. E. P., & Csikszentmihalyi, M. (2000). Positive psychology: An introduction. *American Psychologist, 55*, 5–14.

Simpson, A. V., Farr-Wharton, B., & Reddy, P. (2020). Cultivating organizational compassion in healthcare. *Journal of Management & Organization, 26*(3), 340–354. https://doi.org/10.1017/jmo.2019.54

Spreitzer, G. M. (1996). Social structural characteristics of psychological empowerment. *Academy of Management Journal, 39*(2), 483–504.

Spreitzer, G., Myers, C. G., Kopelman, S., & Mayer, D. (2019). The conceptual and empirical value of a positive lens: An invitation to organizational scholars to develop novel research questions. *Academy of Management Perspectives.* https://doi.org/10.5465/amp.2015.0056

Spreitzer, G., Sutcliffe, K., Dutton, J., Sonenshein, S., & Grant, A. M. (2005). A socially embedded model of thriving at work. *Organization Science, 16*(5), 537–549. https://doi.org/10.1287/orsc.1050.0153

Stephens, J. P., Heaphy, E. D., Carmeli, A., Spreitzer, G. M., & Dutton, J. E. (2013). Relationship quality and virtuousness emotional carrying capacity as a source of individual and team resilience. *Journal of Applied Behavioral Science, 49*(1), 13–41. https://doi.org/10.1177/0021886312471193

Sutcliffe, K. M., & Vogus, T. J. (2003). Organizing for resilience. In K. S. Cameron, J. E. Dutton, & R. E. Quinn (Eds.), *Positive organizational scholarship* (pp. 94–110). Berrett-Koehler Publishers.

Verbeke, W., Belschak, F., & Bagozzi, R. P. (2004). The adaptive consequences of pride in personal selling. *Academy of Marketing Science Journal, 32*(4), 386–402.

Walsh, J. P. (2000). Business must talk about its social role. In T. Dickson (Ed.), *Mastering strategy* (pp. 289–294). Prentice Hall.

Wang, L., Owens, B. P., Li, J. (Jason), & Shi, L. (2018). Exploring the affective impact, boundary conditions, and antecedents of leader humility. *Journal of Applied Psychology, 103*(9), 1019–1038. https://doi.org/10.1037/apl0000314

Warren, M. A., Donaldson, S. I., & Luthans, F. (2017). Taking positive psychology to the workplace: Positive organizational psychology, positive organizational behavior, and positive organizational scholarship. In M. A. Warren & S. I. Donaldson (Eds.), *Scientific advances in positive psychology* (pp. 195–227). Praeger.

Wright, T. A., & Goodstein, J. (2007). Character is not "dead" in management research: A review of individual character and organizational-level virtue. *Journal of Management, 33*, 928–958. https://doi.org/10.1177/0149206307307644

Youssef-Morgan, C. M., & Luthans, F. (2013). Positive leadership: Meaning and application across cultures. *Organizational Dynamics, 42*(3), 198–208. https://doi.org/10.1016/j.orgdyn.2013.06.005

Arran Caza

AN APPLIED APPROACH TO PSYCHOLOGY OF SUSTAINABILITY

INTRODUCTION

Contrary to Darwin's assumption that most adaptations are very context specific (Ermer, Cosmides, & Tooby, 2007; Price & Van Vugt, 2015), it appears that the evolution of the human neocortex has provided us with very broad adaptive capacities (Gottfredson, 1997). We have used our new brains—and the social structures we commonly form—to create artificial adaptations in the most extreme of physical environments, to rapidly manage exceptionally complex challenges, and to develop highly flexible systems that have revolutionized the relationship between living species and the broader natural environment. In terms of most criteria for adaptation, we have excelled wildly, enhancing individual survival and well-being to the point where we are at risk of outstripping the carrying capacity of our planet (never mind some specific ecological niche). We are a species run amok.

This ultimate "mismatch" between species adaptation and carrying capacity has led to massive extinctions of similarly successful organisms (e.g., parasitic organisms that overwhelm their hosts). But our adaptation has not been based on the sorts of fixed, highly predictable action patterns generally responsible for the success and demise of other species (Cialdini, 1988). Instead, this new form of adaptive system—flexible, broadly applicable, and rapid—poses a problem within a problem. Can we use our brains to solve the problems our brains have caused? Can we deliberately employ the same flexible adaptive systems (e.g., science) that have won us such evolutionary success to enhance our future survival beyond current planetary carrying capacity? Can we hope that our new adaptive abilities will help us to adjust for our massive organism-environment mismatch?

This article will follow a straightforward approach to answer this question. First, adaptation will be defined in terms of *mental* adaptations. It may seem obvious that human mental adaptations involve change. However, our ability to alter the direction and possibly the means of such change is central to solving this problem within a problem. So, rather than attending to outcomes in the physical environment that signal frightening changes (e.g., global warming, species extinction, toxic waste accumulation), there are several *psychological* outcomes that mediate between psychological processes and the daunting effects of our activities at broader (especially environmental) levels of analysis. These will be framed as five broad *psychological criteria* for adaptation that mediate between individual processes and environmental outcomes.

Second, this article will propose an applied approach, breaking somewhat from the traditional approaches taken by environmental and conservation psychology.

THE NEED FOR AN APPLIED PSYCHOLOGY OF SUSTAINABILITY

There are several reasons for taking an applied approach. One is that there is a very substantial scientific literature evaluating the efficacy of large, mainstream methods. Sadly, little of this work has addressed sustainability (Boiral, Paillé, & Raineri, 2015; Huffman & Klein, 2013; Ones & Dilchert, 2013), and few of these methods have found their way into traditional environmental and conservation psychology (Jones, 2015). Still, the most widely used methods in this literature have succeeded at effecting widespread psychological change of the sort that positively influences both individual and broader organizational and community well-being.

Another reason for focusing on applied research is that most of the large applied subfields of psychology have established ethical codes of practice. Much of the current psychological research on sustainability has been accomplished by university researchers, where methods for addressing psychological outcomes need only conform to ethical codes of research conduct—not ethical codes of practice. The scientist-practitioner model (see Hakel, 2013) is a widely accepted code of practice in the large applied sub-disciplines (i.e., clinical, counseling, industrial-organizational, and educational psychology). Among other ethical requirements, the scientist-practitioner model requires that psychologists base their practices on the best available science, that they maintain confidentiality, and that they consider the interests of multiple stakeholders as they assist clients with decision processes.

Third, and related to this, applied areas have existing client relationships that can serve as ready avenues for change. There are many promising approaches that are not found in the applied literature (e.g., Devine-Wright, 2011), but, for most of these, the social groups that are consistently involved are within a small academic community of interest. The larger applied areas are deeply embedded in social systems that can be highly influential for ethically crossing the levels of analysis needed to address the problem of sustainability (Jones, 2015). In particular, and in addition to the ethical codes that this embedding has spawned, scientist-practitioner research has done much to help understand the dynamics of stakeholder relationships essential to change. This relationship component of change is central to the methods described here.

Fourth, with a few exceptions, environmental and conservation psychology have contrived research from a fairly narrow academic perspective, with regard to both independent and dependent variables of interest (Giuliani & Scopelliti, 2009; Lévy-Leboyer, 1976; Schultz, 2014). Independent variables have been almost exclusively derived from basic research in the behaviorist perspective. This has followed appropriately from some of the earlier questions of traditional environmental psychology (Gifford, 2007a). But it is also an error of omission, missing questions that do not address individual behaviors in carefully defined stimulus environments. To emphasize this omission, mainstream environmental psychology has done almost no research to evaluate the many methods currently being used by practitioners to try to effect change (see Hattie, Marsh, Neill, & Richards, 1997 and Zelezny, 1999 for notable exceptions).

In terms of dependent variables, environmental psychology appears to have relied almost entirely on researchers themselves to define outcomes of interest (Matthies & Krömker, 2000; Steg & Vlek, 2009)—a decision that applied psychologists make on the basis of formal processes with clients (DuBois, Astakhova, & DuBois, 2013; Jones, 2015; Lévy-Leboyer, 1988; Ryan & Wilson, 2013). Not surprisingly, given the narrow focus on behaviorism, the dependent variable in the vast majority of published environmental psychology research is some collection of behaviors, with only secondary attention to the underlying patterns of such behaviors (see Karlin et al., 2014; Karlin, Zinger, & Ford, 2015; Osbaldiston & Schott, 2012). Attitude outcomes have also been explored at some length, but again defined by academic researchers, rather than by reference to potential clients in the field (see Schwartz, Bruine de Bruin, Fischhoff, & Lave, 2015; Gifford et al., 2009; Devine-Wright, 2011 for recent exceptions). The only outcome requested by clients in paradigmatic environmental psychology appears to be postoccupancy evaluation of the livability of a built environment (Bechtel, 1996).

It should not come as a surprise to environmental psychologists (Gifford, 2007b; Oskamp, 2007; Weber & Stern, 2011) that policy makers and the public have paid little attention to a body of research that pays little attention to the questions as they are framed by these same interested parties (Uiterkamp & Vlek, 2007). Environmental and conservation psychologists are on the lookout for opportunities to use behavior analysis and attitude measurement to influence outcomes that small academic research teams and architect clients have deemed important. Integrating an applied perspective would help to refocus our broad and formidable science on understanding the psychology of the large number of people and organizations who are directly involved in decisions affecting sustainability. Ultimately, this could lead to a much greater impact (Uiterkamp & Vlek, 2007; Weber & Stern, 2011).

Thus, rather than critiquing 40 years of attempts in basic research to change our impact on the environment (Schultz, 2014), this article uses the term *psychology of sustainability* to distinguish an applied field of science-based practice (Jones, 2015) from traditional environmental and conservation psychology. Given the urgency of the problems of sustainability, psychologists would do well to follow the lead of successful applied areas. If we start by framing problems using interested parties' definitions of them, then use prior research from many subdisciplines to arrive at approaches to these, our science is more likely to be accepted and used.

FUNDAMENTAL ASSUMPTIONS

There are several problems which, once addressed, may bring greater coherence to the psychology of sustainability. Conveniently, these problems can be addressed by some fundamental assumptions underlying the methods used in applied psychology.

First, we have yet to empirically establish links between many environmental behaviors, on one hand, and environmental outcomes, on the other (Boiral et al., 2015; Whitmarsh, 2009). Some of these links may seem obvious, as in the case where turning lights off when leaving a room reduces energy consumption. Other behaviors are linked more ambiguously with environmental outcomes, as in the case where recycling glass requires the expenditure of considerable additional fossil fuel for transport to recycling facilities. In the absence of such links between behaviors and outcomes, it is hard to decide which psychological variables (e.g., "pro-environmental behaviors") should be targeted to accomplish which environmental ends (Whitmarsh, 2009). Even more importantly, targeting scarce resources relies on a basis in the facts of a situation: Until we know some of the situational contingencies between behaviors and outcomes, it will be difficult to be efficient.

A fundamental assumption here is that linking human decisions with broader outcomes requires a *situationally specific* understanding of the decisions of people who are taking these decisions. The idea that there are general solutions that apply to all circumstances (Muchinsky & Raines, 2013) is still in the vocabulary of many practitioners and their clients—but not environmental psychologists. So, whenever possible, scientist-practitioners need empirical assessments of the situational system in which they are seeking to change human thinking and behavior. Gathering information about actors' situational perceptions and motives helps to narrow the field of likely means to effect change.

A second problem contributing to the apparent incoherence of current psychological research on sustainability is the same narrow behavioral definition of the outcomes of interest that was discussed in the previous section (Giuliani & Scopelliti, 2009; Steg & Vlek, 2009). Integrating behavioral definitions with other, more ambiguous and complex psychological constructs (including heuristic decision-making, individual differences, and cognitive learning) is an important challenge, since much of the applied research deals with these, rather than behaviors.

Applied researchers often deal with these other psychological variables by categorizing them logically and empirically. For example, the "Green Five" taxonomy (Ones & Dilchert, 2013) categorizes psychological variables using non-psychologist language (behavioral, cognitive, and social "actions"). Gattig and Hendrickx (2007) have developed a typology of risk perceptions that are relevant to policy decisions regarding sustainability. These may provide useful heuristics for practitioners who are talking with non-psychologists, as a means for categorizing, and to some extent directing, pro-environmental activities (Boiral et al., 2015).

However, there is, as yet, no scientific guide for interventions aimed at the problem within a problem posed here. Specifically, heuristic groupings have not yet accounted for other levels of analysis. Thus, a second assumption of the approach offered here is that effective action must link individual variables with criteria at broader *levels of analysis* (Gifford, 2007b). The broader levels of greatest importance appear to be organizational, community, and political levels, all of which will be addressed in this article.

Third, an important "next step" in applied psychology of sustainability is to organize effective processes through which psychological change can occur (Jones, 2015). Sustainable behaviors have been addressed using some of the variables found in major subfields, including clinical, industrial-organizational (I-O), and educational psychology. However, there have been few or no studies in other applied subfields, and the only organizing framework for the variables used has been these broad subfields themselves, and presumed "sustainability" outcomes. So, an article title may look something like "An I-O psychology perspective on sustainability," rather than "Developing relationships for sustainable organizational change."

One way to organize the variables linking individual with broader-level outcomes is through commonalities in the *processes* these subfields use for intervention. A third fundamental assumption here is based on such commonalities. Clinical, educational, and I-O psychologists rely heavily on the following ***common process***:

(1) arriving at a shared definition of desired outcomes among the primary parties to the professional relationship;
(2) systematic assessment methods (i.e., individual difference inventories, situation analyses) to gain an empirical understanding of the current status of stakeholders before change is initiated;
(3) inclusion of the interests of other key stakeholders in the decision process;
(4) feedback to decision makers (Jones, 2015).

This process also encompasses the codes of ethical conduct in the largest applied subfields of psychology. Stated broadly, this ethical process is essential to effective, lasting change. It may appear cumbersome, but is actually efficient in the long term.

FIVE PSYCHOLOGICAL CRITERIA FOR SUSTAINABILITY

Step one in this common process presents an enduring problem in applied psychology. For most, the issues around sustainability—both "pro" and "con"—are value-laden, however practically driven they may appear. This may be part of the reason that there is no scientific definition of the term *sustainability* itself; but it is certainly a major challenge to integrate multiple stakeholder criteria in practice. Called the "criterion problem" (Austin & Villanova, 1992), it has spawned a host of innovative and well-considered approaches to managing human behavior (e.g., Bartram, 2005).

The five criteria here provide a starting framework for this step in the intervention process. Specifically, they organize the long list of psychological criteria for sustainability according to an empirically driven *decision process* that is consistent with common science and practice. They also serve to clarify the intervention process for non-psychologist stakeholders, and make an essential first step toward understanding situational contingencies. Their primary purpose is to help scientist-practitioners to incorporate different stakeholder interests across levels of analysis in a particular situation.

In this vein, it bears repeating that an applied psychology of sustainability is not about changing external variables (e.g., carbon emissions, accumulation of toxic trash, etc.) directly, but rather about changing anthropocentric causes of these through managed, empirically driven, and ethically rational processes. In addition, an important lesson from successful applied psychological practice is that the relationship between client(s) and psychologist(s) is an essential focus of the change process. Stated more broadly, effective change relies on collective rather than individual action. This is implied in other pro-environmental taxonomies (e.g., Boiral et al., 2015; Ones & Dilchert, 2013), as is the ethical imperative of considering the interests of future human stakeholders in current collective decision processes.

Stated broadly, the five criteria are (1) discrepancy testing, (2) deliberative processing, (3) psychological change, (4) taking action, and (5) practicality. These will be elaborated in turn, using a "question and answer" format.

Criterion 1. When do people decide they have a problem and acknowledge it? Although many are convinced that humans are in serious danger of extinction as a result of our collective activity, there are also those who are unaware of the significance of anthropocentric environmental degradation, who deny it, or who discount its seriousness for various reasons. Perhaps because many researchers involved in the psychology of sustainability start with the assumption that there are important anthropocentric environmental problems (Swim et al., 2011), research regarding this criterion question has been scarce.

A simplistic answer to this question is just to try to increase awareness of environmental problems. In fact, sciences other than psychology have been widely quoted in the popular press about sustainability issues for many years, yet we seem to have made very modest progress toward positive change.

Fortunately, the concept of *discrepancy testing* provides some direction for answering this criterion question. It is derived from decision-making (Beach, 2009; Carver & Scheier, 2012) and emotion research (Lang, 1995), which show that we rely on appraisals of situational cues to decide whether we need to take action or not, and the direction of that action (i.e., approach or avoid). In simplified form, we compare observed events to our expectations for how these events should unfold (see Russell & Friedrich, 2015 for a recent discussion of this in the context of sustainability). If our situation is appraised as consistent with expectations, then we tend to continue in our current thinking and action. If, however, we appraise things as discrepant from expectations, there is a greater likelihood of emotive responding and behavioral change.

The discrepancy test concept has been applied in various guises, including as threat/opportunity framing. It has the advantage of being applicable at the decision, individual, and group levels of analysis (see Ashkanasy & Humphrey, 2014; Jones, 2015), and can be used in practice to categorize situational perceptions of stakeholders at various levels of analysis.

Criterion 2. When do people use thoughtful, informed decision processes? It is not uncommon to hear people asking, "Why don't people stop and think before…," then include a host of bad environmental behaviors. Unfortunately, if Kahneman's Nobel Prize–winning body of work (Kahneman, 2011) is any indication, deliberative thought and decision-making (versus emotive responding, fixed action patterns, heuristic responding) are by far the exception. In terms of science-based practice, however, bringing this question, and several well-founded answers, to the attention of clients may have considerable value for (1) enhancing their own mindful consideration of the problems they are trying to address, (2) understanding which emotions, fixed action patterns, and heuristics are affecting behaviors, and (3) arriving at approaches to these problems that "match" better with the realities of the situation. In fact, it could be argued that the intervention process unfolding here is itself a deliberative process. Discussing this criterion question early in the process probably has considerable value.

Criterion 3. When do people change how they think and act? This is perhaps the most sought-after psychological criterion for sustainability. The good news here is that psychological science and practice provide an incredibly wide and deep body of research, not only about the basic mechanisms of change (i.e., learning, development, and other forms of psychological change), but also about the efficacy of various applied methods for change.

But before considering applied approaches, there is one very important and enduring question underlying any attempts at change: How quickly do various psychological characteristics allow us to attempt to adapt? Aspects of the human system that are more or less changeable can be considered on an *adaptation continuum* (Table 1). On one end, there is generational, genetic change that occurs at the species level in response to environmental change. On the other end, we work as groups to change the world to adapt it to us (artifices to heat and cool, get water, protect from elements, make and gather food, etc.). Between these are adaptations like language that are passed along through social identity (slow changes) and behavioral learning (with concomitant risks of error) that can occur within seconds. Table 1 provides one way of considering the rapidity of adaptation of major psychological characteristics.

Table 1. Adaptive Changeability of Psychological Characteristics (From Slowly to Quickly Changed)

1. Emotive responses (fixed action patterns from the social mammalian brain)

2. Decision biases and heuristics (decision and action shortcuts common across people)

3. Mental abilities (mostly established in early childhood)

4. Social identity and personality (derived through enculturation during young adulthood)

5. Cognitive and moral reasoning (principled responding to unique situations developed through the lifespan)

6. Social learning (developed through the lifespan by copying others' behaviors in unique contexts)

7. Behavioral learning (changes that occur as a result of stimulus-response contingencies)

8. Social systemic innovation (made in the environment by groups to adapt it to themselves)

Methods available for change in applied settings are limited by the ease or rapidity of change. If clients are in a hurry, many of the kinds of change described in Table 1 will not be available as options. To confound the matter further, people have reliable tendencies to see themselves and others as more or less changeable (Burnette, O'Boyle, VanEpps, Pollack, & Finkel, 2013). If clients see humans as unchangeable, then they are less likely to attempt to make change than if they see humans as highly changeable (Burnette et al., 2013).

Given this, it makes some sense that social systemic innovation (item 8 in Table 1) is a very rapid option. It also helps to explain the efficacy of applied areas that take a social-systems approach. Environmental psychologists have demonstrated the value of social-systems approach as a way to influence consumption within specific circumstances (McKenzie-Mohr, 2000), and with the support of key community partners.

Bamberg's (2013) recent work on stages of change also provides a powerful tool for understanding individual sustainable action.

Criterion 4. When do people take action? It should be clear by now that criterion questions 1–3 provide cumulative answers to this criterion question. However, the reasoning derived from psychological answers to question 3 also strongly suggest (again) that it is not individual action but collective action that is desired. So answering this question is actually at the heart of the psychology of sustainability (Bamberg, Rees, & Seebauer, 2015).

Criterion 5. What is likely to "work"? The question of practicality is pervasive in applied psychology. The approach suggested so far is itself practical, if its success in many situations is any indication.

What is not so obvious is that many experienced applied psychologists understand that they are not the ones making the actual decisions here (Jones & Culbertson, 2011). One way to characterize the entire role of scientist-practitioners is as *decision facilitators*. We provide this facilitation through all of the many tools of criterion development, deliberative assessment and feedback, and change inducement. But our role is entirely limited by the choices clients make.

SUGGESTIONS FOR INTERVENTION

However, there are many aspects of intervention integrated with the core steps illustrated by the five criteria.

Table 2 provides a quick description of a few of the kinds of measures available for the assessment and feedback process—steps 2 and 4 in the "common process" of applied psychology described in the section "Fundamental Assumptions." Notice that Table 2 links the individual with broader levels of analysis. For example, a measure of commitment is used as an outcome at the individual level, with the purpose of predicting who will feel the greatest attachment to the organization or community group. Individual scores are then aggregated, and the average and variance of commitment across subgroups can be used as an input for predicting organization-level outcomes. The broader levels of greatest importance in this example are organizational and community levels. It should also be noted that this is neither comprehensive nor a guide for specific situations. Rather, based on an initial criterion discussion, it is an

180 • AN APPLIED APPROACH TO PSYCHOLOGY OF SUSTAINABILITY

Table 2. One Example of a Systems-Oriented Assessment-Feedback Process

	Input measure(s)	Process measure(s)	Outcome measure(s)
Level of analysis			
1. Individual	Mental abilities	Knowledge	Performance ratings
	Big Five personality	Competency	Commitment
	Long-term thinking	Place attachment	Environmental behaviors
2. Group	Mean knowledge	Group work simulation	Team performance
	Variance in knowledge	Group cohesion	
		Recognition of expertise	
3. Organization	Mean commitment	Business unit policies	Triple bottom line
	Top management volunteering	Climate for creativity	
4. Community	Level of education	Income	Parks volunteering
	Income	Problem awareness	Environmental citizenship

example of what may be used to guide practical assessment choices within a specific situation. A deeper discussion of the assessment process is available in Jones (2015).

FEEDBACK PROCESSES AND DECISIONS FOR CHANGE

It should be clear by now that there are no specific prescriptions for change offered here. Rather, applied psychology at best provides an ethically driven *process* for effecting change, rather than any one-size-fits-all "solutions" often seen in practitioner literature.

The exception to this is discussion about feedback, which, when facilitated well, is a powerful source for change (see London, 2015). It is beyond the scope of this article to elaborate on effective feedback discussions. Suffice to say that, when the discovery process described here is accomplished effectively, there is considerable value derived during facilitated feedback discussions. To the extent that all stakeholders' interests have been addressed through criterion definition and choices of assessments, it is likely that feedback will lead to more practical and effective change. Put in more familiar terms, this process is a group process. It not only *involves* many stakeholders; it *relies* on them for adequate criterion definition, assessment, feedback acceptance, and implementation.

CONCLUSION

However recent the science-based practice of human psychology is relative to some of the earth sciences, this article provides both an argument for why we need to use what we know so far, and something about how to do so in applied settings. We do know that there are many forms of mismatch between our early evolutionary environment and the psychological precursors that have led to environments we have created for ourselves through artificial adaptation. We also know that any attempts to manage the problems associated with this mismatch will require a situationally specific process, which engages stakeholders on problems that span across levels of analysis.

This article has provided a four-step approach to accomplishing science-based interventions. Particular attention needs to be paid to stakeholder-change agent relationships and to the ethical conduct of science-based practice, following from common processes in applied psychology. Fortunately, there are substantial research literatures on which to base practices aimed at the five criteria, which are extensively elaborated elsewhere (Jones, 2015; London, 2015).

FURTHER READING

Dilchert, S., & Ones, D. S. (2012). Environmental sustainability in and of organizations. *Industrial and Organizational Psychology: Perspectives on Science and Practice*, 5(4), 503–511.

Gifford, R. (2014). Environmental psychology matters. *Annual Review of Psychology*, 65, 541–579.

Huffman, A. H., & Klein, S. R. (2013). *Green organizations: Driving change with I-O psychology*. New York: Routledge/Taylor & Francis Group.

Jones, R. G. (2015). *Psychology of sustainability: An applied perspective*. New York: Taylor and Francis/Routledge.

Oskamp, S. (2007). Applying psychology to help save the world: Reflections on a career in psychology. *Analyses of Social Issues and Public Policy (ASAP)*, 7(1), 121–136.

Reser, J. P., & Swim, J. K. (2011). Adapting to and coping with the threat and impacts of climate change. *American Psychologist*, 66(4), 277–289.

Robertson, J. L., & Barling, J. (2015). *The psychology of green organizations*. New York: Oxford.

Scott, B. A., Amel, E. L., Koger, S. M., & Manning, C. M. (2016). *Psychology for sustainability* (4th ed.). New York: Routledge.

Stern, P. C. (2011). Contributions of psychology to limiting climate change. *American Psychologist*, 66(4), 303–314.

Swim, J. K., Stern, P. C., Doherty, T. J., et al. (2011). Psychology's contributions to understanding and addressing global climate change. *American Psychologist*, 66(4), 241–250.

Vlek, C., Steg, L., & Hoyle, R. H. (2007). Human behavior and environmental sustainability [Special issue]. *Journal of Social Issues*, 63(1).

REFERENCES

Ashkanasy, N. M., & Humphrey, R. H. (2014). Leadership and emotion: A multilevel perspective. In D. V. Day (Ed.), *The Oxford handbook of leadership and organizations* (pp. 783–804). New York: Oxford University Press.

Austin, J. T., & Villanova, P. (1992). The criterion problem: 1917–1992. *Journal of Applied Psychology*, 77(6), 836–874.

Bamberg, S. (2013). Changing environmentally harmful behaviors: A stage model of self-regulated behavioral change. *Journal of Environmental Psychology*, 34, 151–159.

Bamberg, S., Rees, J., & Seebauer, S. (2015). Collective climate action: Determinants of participation intention in community-based pro-environmental initiatives. *Journal of Environmental Psychology*, 43, 155–165.

Bartram, D. (2005). The great eight competencies: A criterion-centric approach to validation. *Journal of Applied Psychology, 90*(6), 1185–1203.

Beach, L. R. (2009). Decision making: Linking narratives and action. *Narrative Inquiry, 19*(2), 393–414.

Bechtel, R. B. (1996). The paradigm of environmental psychology. *American Psychologist, 51*(11), 1187–1188.

Boiral, O., Paillé, P., & Raineri, N. (2015). The nature of employees' pro-environmental behaviors. In J. L. Robertson & J. Barling (Eds.), *The psychology of green organizations* (pp. 12–32). New York: Oxford University Press.

Burnette, J. L., O'Boyle, E. H., VanEpps, E. M., Pollack, J. M., & Finkel, E. J. (2013). Mind-sets matter: A meta-analytic review of implicit theories and self-regulation. *Psychological Bulletin, 139*(3), 655–701.

Carver, C. S., & Scheier, M. F. (2012). Cybernetic control processes and the self-regulation of behavior. In R. M. Ryan (Ed.), *The Oxford handbook of human motivation* (pp. 28–42). New York: Oxford University Press.

Cialdini, R. (1988). *Influence: Science and practice* (2d ed.). Glenview, IL: Scott, Foresman.

Devine-Wright, P. (2011). Place attachment and public acceptance of renewable energy: A tidal energy case study. *Journal of Environmental Psychology, 31*(4), 336–343.

DuBois, C. L. Z., Astakhova, M. N., & DuBois, D. A. (2013). Motivating behavior change to support organizational environmental sustainability goals. In A. H. Huffman & A. R. Klein (Eds.), *Green organizations* (pp. 186–207). New York: Routledge.

Ermer, E., Cosmides, L., & Tooby, J. (2007). Functional specialization and the adaptationist program. In S. W. Gangestad & J. A. Simpson (Eds.), *The evolution of mind: Fundamental questions and controversies* (pp. 153–160). New York: Guilford Press.

Gattig, A., & Hendrickx, L. (2007). Judgmental discounting and environmental risk perception: Dimensional similarities, domain differences, and implications for sustainability. *Journal of Social Issues, 63*(1), 21–39.

Gifford, R. (2007a). *Environmental psychology: Principles and practice* (4th ed.). Colville, WA: Optimal.

Gifford, R. (2007b). Environmental psychology and sustainable development: Expansion, maturation, and challenges. *Journal of Social Issues, 63*(1), 199–212.

Gifford, R., Scannell, L., Kormos, C., Smolova, L., Biel, A., Boncu, S., Corral, V., Guntherf, H., Hanyu, K., Hine, D., Kaiser, K. G., Korpela, K., Lima, L. M., Mertig, A. G., Mira, R. G., Moser, G., Passafaro, P., Pinheiro, J. Q., Saini, S.,…Uzzell, D. (2009). Temporal pessimism and spatial optimism in environmental assessments: An 18-nation study. *Journal of Environmental Psychology, 29*(1), 1–12.

Giuliani, M. V., & Scopelliti, M. (2009). Empirical research in environmental psychology: Past, present, and future. *Journal of Environmental Psychology, 29*(3), 375–386.

Gottfredson, L. (1997). Mainstream science on intelligence: An editorial with 52 signatories, history and bibliography. *Intelligence, 24*, 13–23.

Hakel, M. D. (2013). Commentary: *Homo economicus*, industrial psychology, and the greater good. In J. Olson-Buchanan, L. K. Bryan, & L. F. Thompson (Eds.), *Using industrial-organizational psychology for the greater good* (pp. 559–566). New York: Routledge.

Hattie, J., Marsh, H. W., Neill, J. T., & Richards, G. E. (1997). Adventure education and outward bound: Out-of-class experiences that make a lasting difference. *Review of Educational Research, 67*(1), 43–87.

Huffman, A. H., & Klein, A. R. (2013). *Green organizations*. New York: Routledge.

Jones, R. G. (2015). *Psychology of sustainability: An applied perspective*. New York: Taylor and Francis/Routledge.

Jones, R. G., & Culbertson, S. S. (2011). Why performance management *will remain* broken: Authoritarian communication. *Industrial and Organizational Psychology, 4*, 179–180.

Kahneman, D. (2011). *Thinking, fast and slow*. New York: Farrar, Straus, and Giroux.

Karlin, B., Davis, N., Sanguinetti, A., Gamble, K., Kirkby, D., & Stokols, D. (2014). Dimensions of conservation: Exploring differences among energy behaviors. *Environment and Behavior, 46*(4), 423–452.

Karlin, B., Zinger, J. F., & Ford, R. (2015). The effects of feedback on energy conservation: A meta-analysis. *Psychological Bulletin, 141*(6), 1205–1227.

Lang, P. J. (1995). The emotion probe: Studies of motivation and attention. *American Psychologist, 50,* 372–285.

Lévy-Leboyer, C. (1976). A review of environmental psychology in the United States. *Revue de Psychologie Appliquée, 26*(4), 609–616.

Lévy-Leboyer, C. (1988). Success and failure in applying psychology. *American Psychologist, 43*(10), 779–785.

Lévy-Leboyer, C. (1993). The chicken and the egg: Which came first? *Applied Psychology: An International Review, 42*(1), 52–54.

Lévy-Leboyer, C., & Duron, Y. (1991). Global change: New challenges for psychology. *International Journal of Psychology, 26*(5), 575–583.

London, M. (2015). *The power of feedback: Giving, seeking, and using feedback for performance improvement.* New York: Routledge/Taylor & Francis Group.

Matthies, E., & Krömker, D. (2000). Participatory planning: A heuristic for adjusting interventions to the context. *Journal of Environmental Psychology, 20*(1), 65–74.

McKenzie-Mohr, D. (2000). Fostering sustainable behavior through community-based social marketing. *American Psychologist, 55*(5), 531–537.

Muchinsky, P. M., & Raines, J. M. (2013). The overgeneralized validity of validity generalization. *Journal of Organizational Behavior, 34*(7), 1057–1060.

Ones, D. S., & Dilchert, S. (2013). Measuring, understanding, and influencing employee green behavior. In A. H. Huffman & S. R. Klein (Eds.), *Green organizations: Driving change with I-O psychology* (pp. 115–148). New York: Routledge.

Osbaldiston, R., & Schott, J. P. (2012). Environmental sustainability and behavioral science: Meta-analysis of proenvironmental behavior experiments. *Environment and Behavior, 44*(2), 257–299.

Price, M. E., & Van Vugt, M. (2015). The service-for-prestige theory of leader-follower relations: A review of the evolutionary psychology and anthropology literatures. In S. M. Colarelli & R. D. Arvey (Eds.), *The biological foundations of organizational behavior* (pp. 169–202). Chicago: University of Chicago Press.

Russell, S., & Friedrich, E. (2015). The relationship between emotions and workplace pro-environmental behaviors. In J. L. Robertson & J. Barling (Eds.), *The psychology of green organizations* (pp. 141–163). New York: Oxford University Press.

Ryan, B., & Wilson, J. R. (2013). Ergonomics in the development and implementation of organisational strategy for sustainability. *Ergonomics, 56*(3), 541–555.

Schultz, P. W. (2014). Strategies for promoting proenvironmental behavior: Lots of tools but few instructions. *European Psychologist, 19*(2), 107–117.

Schwartz, D., Bruine de Bruin, W., Fischhoff, B., & Lave, L. (2015). Advertising energy saving programs: The potential environmental cost of emphasizing monetary savings. *Journal of Experimental Psychology: Applied, 21*(2), 158–166.

Steg, L., & Vlek, C. (2009). Encouraging pro-environmental behaviour: An integrative review and research agenda. *Journal of Environmental Psychology, 29*(3), 309–317.

Swim, J. K., Stern, P. C., Doherty, T. J., et al. (2011). Psychology's contributions to understanding and addressing global climate change. *American Psychologist, 66*(4), 241–250.

Uiterkamp, A. S., & Vlek, C. (2007). Practice and outcomes of multidisciplinary research for environmental sustainability. *Journal of Social Issues, 63*(1), 175–197.

Weber, E. U., & Stern, P. C. (2011). Public understanding of climate change in the United States. *American Psychologist, 66*(4), 315–328.

Whitmarsh, L. (2009). Behavioural responses to climate change: Asymmetry of intentions and impacts. *Journal of Environmental Psychology, 29*(1), 13–23.

Zelezny, L. C. (1999). Educational interventions that improve environmental behaviors: A meta-analysis. *The Journal of Environmental Education, 31*(1), 5–14.

Robert G. Jones

HUMANITARIAN WORK AND ORGANIZATIONAL PSYCHOLOGY

INTRODUCTION

In the psychology of perception, a figure–ground reversal is a dramatic change in how the world is seen. In the blink of an eye, what was before an instant foreground (e.g., the profile of a vase) suddenly becomes a background (e.g., the profile of a soldier). Humanitarian work and organizational psychology is likewise a figure–ground reversal (Carr et al., 2012). It switches emphasis between efficiency and humanity. When efficiency moves back, well-being comes forward. In the process, neither image is completely lost. All that has changed is their relative emphasis. This recognizes that work and organizational psychologists, whatever emphasis they practice, value people and their well-being. It also engages with extant critiques of work psychology: that people, ahead of efficiency, have not always been put first (Baritz, 1960; Brief, 2000; Lefkowitz, 2003, 2017).

Humanitarian work and organizational psychology also reflects a concerted response to humanitarian *deteriorations* in the world of work during the early part of the 21st century. Since the 2007–2008 economic crisis, this world has been witnessing record numbers of people getting into "jobs" (World Bank, 2012). Outside the global workforce of 3.3 billion people in 2019, 172 million were still unemployed, which is for most people a humanitarian and moral scourge. Yet unemployment was at that time also being overshadowed by a storm-cloud statistically 19 times larger (ILO, 2019a). Statistically, the number of people working informally, without formal protections like minimum wages, regular income, or any security from a formal job, was over 2 billion. This meant that a two-thirds majority of the world's 2019 workforce was in vulnerable informal work. Even among the remainder, working in the formal sector, a clear majority (59%) reported "struggling" to make ends meet (ITUC, 2018). Lastly but certainly not least, global wages and income inequality were running "out of control" (Oxfam, 2020).

The unemployed, the informally employed, the precariously employed, the working poor, plus inequalities with the grossly overpaid executive class—these are the groups that work and organizational psychology as a whole has largely underserved and overlooked (Bergman & Jean, 2015; Gloss et al., 2016; ILO, 2013; Reichman, 2014). By the end of 2019, calls for a major reversal of emphasis were clarion. Just before the pandemic started in 2020, the International Labor Organization (ILO) (2019b) identified poor working conditions as the "number one challenge" in the world of work. Meanwhile, the *World Development Report*, which just 7 years earlier had called for "jobs" to save world development (World Bank, 2012), was urging humanity to "Protect *people, not* jobs" (World Bank, 2019, emphasis added).

In a sense, therefore, the COVID-19 pandemic simply underscored preexisting and widespread unsustainability, insecurity, and inequality—including racism and police brutality—across the world of work (OECD, 2020a). It was a megadisruptor to working lives all over the planet. Disruptors make the previously unthinkable thinkable. This included, for example, full-time working from home (for those still employed) as well as public applause for previously undervalued care workers, health workers, bus drivers, and supermarket "trolley gods." Such re-assertions of common humanity are also arguably opportunities for change. So too, unfortunately, are the incoming and returning societal challenges from mass unemployment—forecast at the time to hit women, the young, and ethnic minorities the hardest (OECD, 2020b; UN, 2020). Humanity more than ever needed a plan.

The closest thing humanity already had to such a plan, and a structure that has guided humanitarian work and organizational psychology to date, are the United Nations sustainable development goals (SDGs). Building on their narrower, less work-inclusive predecessors, the millennium development goals(MDGs) (Annan, 2000), the SDGs were initiated in 2016 and are set to run till 2030. They comprise 17 humanitarian development goals, spanning from health and food security to protecting the biosphere for future generations and promoting societal peace over conflict (UN, 2020). In the midst of these 17 goals sits SDG 8, "decent work and economic growth" for all (UN, 2020).

Decent work meets "aspirations all people have for their working lives; for work that is productive, delivers a fair income with security and social protection" (ILO, 2020). In a sense, this wording strives to strike a balance between efficiency (productive, economic growth) and humanity (decent work aspirations, fair income, security, social protection). Since 2020, the COVID-19 pandemic has revealed how difficult striking such balances could be, with lockdowns becoming closedowns for many livelihoods in the name of human life preservation. In this case, putting lives before livelihoods showed how SDG 8 could and did clash with others (e.g., SDG 3—health for all). Humanitarian work and organizational psychology is about striking that wider balance too.

FOUNDATIONS

Using the metaphor of a house, humanitarian work and organizational psychology has articulated a set of foundations for contributing in balanced ways toward the SDGs. Each foundation stone can be viewed as a form of figure–ground reversal, between humanity ("decent work") and efficiency ("economic growth"). Without such checks and balances, efficiency could logically become economic slavery (Cooper, personal correspondence, August 27, 2018).

Ethical.   Putting people *before* jobs, like lives before livelihoods, is first and foremost moral (Lefkowitz, 2003). For middle-class professionals who can afford to work from home, moral implies professional ethics (Lefkowitz, 2017). A recurrent ethical issue that work and organizational psychologists face is a conflict of interest: protecting the interests of employees versus serving the interests of employers (Reichman & Carr, 2020). Codes of ethics tend to foreground the person (General Assembly of the International Union of Psychological Science, 2008); earning a livelihood (including as a work and organizational psychologist) the latter (employers). As a result, it is quite easy for practitioners to become "conditioned" to serving economic power (Lefkowitz, 2017, p. 390).

Take "resilience training" for example. On the surface, this kind of "intervention" has a very humanitarian ethos and motivation. Yet an ever-present risk in such training, insofar as it often concentrates on individual hardiness or grit, is inadvertently allowing unscrupulous employers to increase workloads with impunity. Shining a spotlight on personality takes light away from structures. It can help to avoid the very interventions that would restructure working conditions themselves so that they became more decent and humane (Hodgetts et al., 2020). As a result, according to Hodgetts et al. (2020), resilience training can actually fail, in the longer run, to put people first.

What this example shows is how our own Work and Organizational Psychology systems can inadvertently end up conditioning the service of economic power, such as putting jobs before people (Lefkowitz, 2017). Another example of the same kind of conditioning, less obvious perhaps but more fundamental to the world of working poverty, is job evaluation (Figart, 2000). Through much of the 20th century, some of its advocates wanted to use the idea of objectively valuing a job to help "pay the job not the person," to deliver more "equal pay for equal work," such as equitably across genders (Figart, 2000; SDG 5—gender equality). However, in the early 2020s, SDG 8 still seeks "equal pay for work of equal value" (UN, 2020). Clearly, job evaluation has under-delivered on some of its own core goals.

In retrospect, part of the reason for this under-delivery may be protecting the job more than the person (ILO, 2019b; see also Figart, 2000, for a full historical critique). Job evaluation has continued to rely on preexisting wage markets to set job pay rates. These had become sinkholes, dragging people's wages and well-being ever lower in a "race to the bottom" on wages globally (ILO, 2019a, 2019b). Applauding low-paid frontline workers in the street is an outpouring of appreciation but it may also be a statement about ethics in job evaluation processes and their outcomes. It tells that something was fundamentally wrong with the wider practice of job evaluation. It was serving economic power over works' well-being. Ultimately, job evaluations had put jobs before people, not people before jobs (World Bank, 2019).

Applause makes switching the normative focus thinkable by asking not how cheaply labor can be harnessed by employers, but how valuable it is to human society. Paraphrasing a dictum for job evaluation, pay the person for the job they do (for all). Organizational commitment stops being just about workers serving organizations (*organizational* commitment). It starts being more about organizations serving workers (i.e., organizational *commitment*). Such ethical figure–ground reversals put people first before jobs (Reichman, 2014).

Historical.   Putting people first is a core purpose in humanitarian work. An early example of work psychology in this type of humanitarian sector can be found in the writings of psychologists who consulted to the United States' Peace Corps (Harris, 1973). Called in to help reduce early returns by Peace Corps volunteers from overseas aid assignments, a team of consultant psychologists first tried using a clinical judgment approach to triage applicants, based on their personality traits. This kind of approach failed to stem early returns, and psychology eventually switched to cross-cultural training in the private sector (Carr, 2010; for an exception, see Kealey, 1989). In the meantime, though, a valuable lesson was drawn: reverse the focus from personality alone to its fit with the demands of humanitarian work itself (Harris, 1973).

Putting people first was also a focus in some private sector organizations. An early example in humanitarian work and organizational psychology is the employee assistance program (EAP) (Reichman & Beidel, 1989). Now part of the lexicon of work and organizational psychology, EAPs (sometimes called EASs for employee assistance services) were initially designed in 1971, with the humanitarian goal of providing support services for people with alcohol addiction at work. Thereafter this kind of human service morphed into systems for identifying wider counseling needs across a wider range of humanitarian issues at work, including today's mental health. As such, like resilience training perhaps, EAPs might (sometimes) deflect attention from unethical employers who use EAPs to deflect attention from poor working conditions. Risks notwithstanding, however, EAPs have helped millions of people at work and laid the groundwork for humanitarian work and organizational psychology today.

Between 2000 and 2015, MDGs (SDGs' predecessors) focused on development goals that were aligned with international aid and, to that extent, with humanitarian work (Annan, 2000). During that period, major developments in humanitarian work and organizational psychology included the groundbreaking multi-university, multi-country program: work, organizational and personnel psychology (WOP-P). WOP-P was founded at the University of Valencia, Spain, under the European Union's Erasmus student exchange program. Around that time, too, professional work and organizational associations, including the Society for Industrial and Organizational Psychology (SIOP) and the International Association of Applied Psychology (Division 1—Work & Organizational Psychology), forged links with the United Nations (Saxena, 2018). This was followed by the establishment of the Global Organization for Humanitarian Work Psychology (GoHWP). By the time the MDGs closed, and the SDGs had begun, the ambit had widened to end poverty in all its forms, everywhere (www.un.org). Now, the previous focus on humanitarian work underwent a figure–ground reversal of its own (Carr & MacLachlan, 2014). As well as humanitarian work, attention broadened to include the entire world of work, in all kinds of occupations (Berry et al., 2011).

The term "humanitarian work psychology" captured this dual sidedness nicely.[1] It was a figure–ground reversal between humanitarian work|psychology (the psychology of humanitarian work) and humanitarian|work psychology (the psychology of making work-in-general more humanitarian). Although the title of this article includes "and Organizational" to mark a slight divergence from the more typical label HWP, it makes essentially the same reversal: humanitarian work|and organizational psychology and humanitarian|work and organizational psychology. Yet it also goes slightly further than HWP, namely by reminding the reader to learn from history by keeping an eye on organizational structure.

Conceptual. At first blush, the admonishment "serve people, not jobs" (World Bank, 2019) may seem contrary, even self-contradictory. A centerpiece of work and organizational psychology as most applied psychologists know it is "the job." Yet now it is being questioned. What could possibly go in its place without throwing out the baby (job analysis, description, specification, selection, placement, appraisal, and so on) with the bathwater (most people these days no longer have formal jobs)? In answer, there is a concept, which has taking its origins from outside the discipline and profession, and resonated with the SDGs, that has already been incorporated into humanitarian work and organizational psychology.

The term *sustainable livelihood* grew out of a report on environmental sustainability in economically poor rural communities in the "developing" world (WCED, 1989). Since the 1980s, it has acquired a self-explanatory definition: "a livelihood comprises the capabilities, assets...and activities required for a means of living, a livelihood is sustainable which can cope with and recover from stress and shocks, maintain or enhance its capabilities and assets, and provide sustainable livelihood opportunities for the next generation; and which contributes net benefits to other livelihoods at the local and global levels and in the short and long term" (Chambers & Conway, 1991, p. 6).

This definition cleanly differentiates sustainable livelihood from the more formal and rather individualistic notion of a "job"—economically, socially, and temporally. It also embraces humanitarian work as well as making all working conditions humanitarian. Accordingly, in the 1990s, the concept was extended from rural to urban environments, where most of the world's population now lives (UN, 2014). In the 2000s, it was extended further still, to buffering natural and manmade disasters respectively (Blaikie et al., 2004; Kranz, 2001). It then found its way into the United Nations Rio Conference Declaration, which presaged the SDGs and SDG 8 (Morse & McNamara, 2013).

Sustainable livelihood is a further figure–ground reversal in humanitarian work and organizational psychology. The term reverses a past heavy emphasis on jobs by looking Beyond them, to inquire if people's livelihoods are actually being made, and made sustainably. It puts the social psychology back into work and organizational studies, teaching and services, by stressing that one's livelihood is connected to someone else's livelihood, and vice versa. Such human connections (i.e., shared humanity) are what the applause for often poorly job-evaluated care workers was about.

Political. Reversing the emphasis from "jobs" to sustainable livelihoods is not going to happen without a backlash (Saner & Yiu, 2012, 2014a). There are too many interests vested in the concept of a job (Saner & Yiu, 2014b). Reforms always meet resistance, from those who might be disempowered by the empowerment of others (MacLachlan, 2014). Such political realities imply another reversal. Typically, evidence is assumed to be sufficient in itself to enlighten human decisions about work, and at work, without the need for any active persuasion. What is needed now is a way to *reverse* that emphasis on evidence alone. In other words, what is known and shown by work and organizational research has to be, primarily, persuasive. Logically, in an era of over-rated evidence and fake news, skills of persuasion become even more important to cultivate, arguably, than evidence alone. Those skills have been collectively dubbed as "new diplomacies" (Saner & Yiu, 2012).

These diplomacies are "new" insofar as they include awareness and knowledge of and skills in working with a range of relatively new structures. They already include a range, such as cultivating awareness of the *OECD Guidelines to Multinational Enterprises* (OECD, 2011), acquiring a knowledge of what is actually in these guidelines, and how to effectively use them to advance the *Decent Work Agenda* (ILO, 2020) under the United Nations SDGs (Saner & Yiu, 2014a). They include the SDGs themselves, specifically the skills in monitoring progress on goals, whistle-blowing, safely, when standards are not met, and translating research into policy briefs and other policy-focused forms of communication that are concise, cogent, user friendly, and compelling (Saner & Yiu, 2012, 2014b).

New diplomacies such as these go further than recognized political skills in social astuteness, networking ability, apparent sincerity, and interpersonal influence for example (Ferris et al., 2005). They include knowing how to leverage a range of 21st-century humanitarian structures designed to help promote human rights, across both lives and livelihoods (Reichman & Carr, 2020). An example of such structures being relevant during the COVID-19 pandemic is a call by following the ten human rights-led principles in the "UN Global Compact," a global charter that responsible organizations (from diverse sectors) can sign up to, and commit to, uphold for sustainable livelihoods (Freeman, 2020). Principles and codicils like the Global Compact add to the inherent potential for humanitarian work and organizational psychology, and applied psychologists in general, to contribute toward sustainability (Saner & Yiu, 2014b).

LEVELS

New diplomacies can span individual skills, persuading people in organizations, and influencing them across whole sectors and nations (MacLachlan, 2014). Using the metaphor of a house with different levels, humanitarian work and organizational psychology emphasizes multilevel diplomacy.

Individual.   An example of a relatively individualized perspective into the *humanitarian* space is a study of expatriate aid workers' adaptation and satisfaction in a church charity in sub-Saharan Africa and Southern Asia (Manson & Carr, 2011). As was seen, a person-organization "fit" helps such work. In Manson and Carr (2011), though, there was more than one potential fit, with international headquarters and local community priorities. The authors calibrated these separately and found that individual expatriate workers adapted better when their own values fitted both. In diplomacy terms, the best fitting (happy and efficient) candidate was "aligned" with local values and "harmonized" with organizational ones (Paris Declaration on Aid Effectiveness, 2004). This kind of modification to conventional fit theory, in the humanitarian sphere, can assist in future job selection, placement, and ultimately efficiency (Manson & Carr, 2011).

An example of a relatively individualized perspective in *business* organizations can be found across the banking sector. Around the world, millions of micro-business entrepreneurs may seek to transform their informal own-account business into a formal small-to-medium enterprise (SME), thereby enabling job creation and livelihoods for others. Reputable banks may be seeking to select talented business entrepreneurs for startup and enterprise loans (Klinger et al., 2013). Micro-business entrepreneurs themselves, however, may not have the time nor the education and training to keep detailed records. In the wake of economic recessions, micro-business entrepreneurs may thereby have no chance of convincing nervous banks that they are actually a really good proposition, even though they are.

To help close that gap, Klinger et al. (2013) have reversed the conventional emphasis on job selection, away from selecting "out" of jobs to selecting "in" to service lending provisions; and to a more sustainable livelihood. Klinger et al. have successfully co-designed a battery of culturally competent and safe tests to help banks assess prospective entrepreneurs whose goals are to transition out of informal micro-businesses into more formal SMEs. The goal in

Entrepreneurial Finance Lab is to enable this kind of opportunity without being held back and excluded simply by dint of no access to higher education, or lack of time to keep books. As a result of the EFL approach to selection, SME businesses have grown and thrived, enabling decent job creation and sustainable livelihoods for entrepreneur and employees alike (Klinger et al., 2013).

Organizational. Micro-businesses have been widely developed through self-supporting groups run by women, notably perhaps in micro-credit groups (Yunus, 1999). Self-empowering groups have also been a focus in humanitarian work and organizational psychology (Schein, 2003). Initially focused on motivation "to" find work among single unemployed mothers in the United States, this leading work has been broadened to include the psychological benefits of organized women's groups "at" work, in lower-income economies (Schein, 2011; Schein et al., 2011).

One example is an organization that runs empowerment camps for girls (Berry et al., 2014). The project was co-designed with stakeholders in Lesotho to expand opportunities for girls to have sustainable livelihood choices. They included fostering enterprise development skills that reduce reliance on more precarious forms of occupation such as forced prostitution (Berry et al., 2013). Initial evaluations of the camp's effectiveness in fostering enterprise skills, confidence, and awareness of risks in more radical commerce were reported to be promising (Berry et al., 2013). Similar conclusions were reached with respect to another project focused on women's self-empowerment groups, this time among primary healthcare workers in rural India (for more details, see Meyer et al., 2016).

In the private sector, the training program Student Training for Entrepreneurial Promotion (STEP) has focused on providing courses in enterprise development (Bischoff et al., 2013). Based on action-oriented training, STEP provides young entrepreneurs in lower-income settings with training in conducting a market analysis, developing an operations plan for a business, creating jobs, and learning from business mistakes using feedback principles. Randomized field experiments have indicated that the training program, run with samples of students in Uganda, Kenya, Tanzania, Rwanda, and Liberia, is effective. An evaluation study in Uganda ($n=200$ in each condition, control, and treatment) found that 83% of the STEP trainees after just 36 months had repaid their startup capital (US$100), 78% had made a profit (mean=$50), which was on average 71% higher than businesses in the control. They had also created 47% more new job-based livelihoods than the control (Bischoff et al., 2013).

In their related intervention involving 1,500 entrepreneurs in Togo, West Africa, Campos et al. (2017) compared a no-intervention baseline to personal initiative versus conventional business training to develop a small business. Personal initiative training (again action-oriented) was the most effective, but its effects were also reportedly mediated by a range of additional elements. These included trainable business practices, capital and labor inputs, the diversification of product line, bringing us back to individual entrepreneurs and EFL (Klinger et al., 2013), and access to finance. Such elements jointly mediated the total effect of personal initiative training and its differential effect compared to traditional training (Campos et al., 2017). Thus, both person and situational conditions were crucial for enterprise development.

Societal. At the other end of the individual-level spectrum, humanitarian work and organizational psychology has contributed to policy developments in global health

(MacLachlan, 2014; McAuliffe et al., 2009). In health service "task-shifting," for example, some key healthcare tasks are reallocated from health workers with longer training to health workers with shorter training. The goal is to boost workforce outreach and client inclusion, namely efficiency and humanity (i.e., SDG 3) (Vallieres & McAuliffe, 2016). Thus, a clinical officer who has trained for three years may safely and effectively deliver babies and conduct C-sections without the longer training of medical practitioners qualified in the wider field of obstetrics. This and other forms of task shifting are ultimately about increasing inclusion for otherwise marginalized and underserved client groups in the wider community (Amin et al., 2011). Such cadres are as effective as obstetricians with much longer training and may render healthcare more accessible, cost-effective, and efficient (Buse et al., 2008). Humanitarian work psychology has further supported this change by researching the key challenges faced by mid-level cadres in motivation, career development, support, supervision, and management of resistance from more established medical professions (McAuliffe et al., 2009).

The general goal of making health services more accessible and inclusive has been developed further at a more macro, national level (MacLachlan, 2014; McAuliffe et al., 2009). A leading example is Equiframe, which was designed to check whether any policy in formation actually respects the human rights of vulnerable groups, such as people with disabilities (Amin et al., 2011). Originally developed in consultation with civil society and other groups across a range of countries, Equiframe has already been applied to forming national health policies in countries like Sudan and South Sudan.

Equiframe's protocol includes workforce service questions such as "Does the policy support the capacity-building of health workers and of the system that they work in addressing health needs of vulnerable groups?" (Amin et al., 2011, p. 7). Questions like these form an overall screening protocol for assessing and improving future policies, by pre-proofing them for social protection and inclusion. They are another timely and important reminder that sustainability goals, like SDG 8 (decent work) and SDG 3 (healthy lives and well-being for all), intersect (UN, 2020). More than that, however, they also show how micro-level influences cross over into macro-level policy, and thus become societal (MacLachlan, 2014).

SPACES

Using a metaphor that we have now introduced in multiple sections above, in the same way that one can move between levels of a house crossing levels connotes traversing spaces in-between them. In this metaphor, humanitarian work and organizational psychology foregrounds such spaces ahead of lines. It thereby exposes—and responds to—a range of previously underserved domains.

Wage Intervals. Perhaps the most self-evident of all lines at work, traversing individual, organizational, and societal levels, is wage. The minimum wage (i.e., a legal mandate in the formal sector designed to support subsistence) and/or the living wage (i.e., a voluntary wage that campaigns claim would support a decent quality of life) are familiar terms in public discourse. Unfortunately they have been far less familiar in contemporary applied psychology (Smith, 2015). Invariably "the" minimum and "the" living wage itself are each a specific number, that is, a datum of one. Against that kind of standard setting, a fixed poverty line, are thrown heated arguments about whether it is too high or too low, too generous or too mean, for financial viability or for social inclusion (Carr et al., 2018; Maleka et al., 2018). Yet there are no comparison points. Without such comparison points, there is logically no clear way of resolving whether it could, and maybe should, have been lower or higher.

Logic and psychology 101 would tell us to look for *variation* in wages along a wage *spectrum*. Applied research could then chart and narrate different qualities of work life, and life, as a function of different wage values, along the same wage continuum. These data, quantitative and qualitative combined, might then indicate a wage value at, or range of values within, which quality of life and work life improved or even transformed. Such transformations, if they were found, would signal an escape from working poverty traps (Carr et al., 2016).

Recent research has tested this possibility by exploring narratives of well-being as a function of wage. So far, it has done so quite consistently, for example, across two very different economies, in South Africa (Maleka et al., 2018) and New Zealand (Carr et al., 2018, 2019). These studies detected cusps in quality of work life, first near the legal minimum wage in both countries, when people began to report improvements in quality of work life, and second near each respective living wage, when people clearly began to say quality of work life was no longer poor but good.

Such findings are important because they suggest that reaching and traversing the *space in-between* minimum and living wages could be pivotal in eradicating (working) poverty (Carr et al., 2016). Addressing that possibility systematically is Project Global Living Organizational Wage (Project GLOW, 2020). GLOW has had foundational support (I/O Shaken & Stirred, 2017) from GoHWP and from SIOP. Eventually, GLOW may help to set—and dynamically monitor—the thresholds and qualities of life and work life spaces for minimum and living wage values. In this way, humanitarian work and organizational psychology would serve individual, organizational, and societal goals, especially at times of crisis (McWha-Hermann & Searle, 2020).

What one can see may change once wage is viewed not as a single-datum poverty line but as a continuous variable. From that kind of perspective, it becomes conceivable to locate in context the thresholds that matter for people's everyday living and qualities of life. The same may be true of income inequality, which by definition is fueled by differences in between wages, such as that between factory floor and chief executive officer (CEO) ceiling (ILO, 2013). One way of helping to rein in any runaway income inequality, which before the pandemic inequality indexes were showing was "out of control" (Oxfam, 2020), is by setting thresholds for wage ratios.

According to the ILO (2013), these ratios could be set between minimum and maximum wages, at either organizational or societal levels (Pizzigati, 2018). A CEO who wished to raise their own wage would then also need to raise the wage of the respective shop floor, and thereby the wage of the organization as a whole (ILO, 2013). According to the ILO, this would incentivize greater fairness and, in the process, partly help tackle vertical inequality (i.e., between lower- and higher-paid jobs).

At an institutional level, the very same idea has been advocated to help tackle persistent wage inequalities between expatriate and host counterpart workers, which still occur widely despite their similar qualifications and experience (Marai et al., 2010; McWha-Hermann et al., 2020). Such gaps are a form of horizontal inequality (i.e., between equally skilled and experienced employees). Their "dual salaries" have been found to divide host country from expatriate employees through an insidious process of mutual, "double demotivation" (Carr et al., 2010; MacLachlan et al., 2010). Combating an "economic apartheid" of dual-salary systems (Marai et al., 2010) requires political will and leadership. Policy options for such leadership would include capping expatriate–local salary ratios to thresholds that workers themselves would find fair (Marai et al., 2010; McWha-Herman et al., 2017).

Shades of Formality.   Another line often drawn—and rarely crossed by work psychology services—is between formal and informal work sectors. The exclusion line is shocking given that the informal sector comprises a clear majority of the world's workforce and that the two sectors are often connected by trade along the very same supply chains (ILO, 2019a, 2019b). The global trade in coffee is a familiar and daily example (zapizapu, 2012). The very nature of those production to consumption links is actually that they are inter-organizational. The word *chain* is apt for denoting the conditions that many people in them often work under endure (World Bank, 2019). Notorious exemplars include the exploitation of child miners of cobalt to power smartphones and batteries for e-cars, as well as shoe and other forms of sweatshop in some areas of the garment industry.

Humanitarian work and organizational psychology has started to play a role in counteracting poor working conditions. In rural India, for example, skilled artisans who create exquisite baskets and pottery are under threat locally from the cheaper plastic bag (Saxena et al., 2015). By facilitating supply lines into coffee houses in Chicago, where a fair trade price can be secured for these products, alongside fair traded coffee, differences in quality of life can be made to and by the livelihoods of whole village communities.

At a societal level, humanitarian work psychology can play a further role in promoting social protection for "vulnerable" workers in the informal sector (World Bank, 2019). In Cameroon, for example, an estimated 90% of jobs are informal (Tchagneno et al., 2019). Tchagneno's work is uniquely responsive because it researches how people feel about transitioning to the formal sector, which government policies and training provisions have attempted to do (so far, with little success). Research evidence from Tchagneno et al. (2019) has highlighted motivations that include, for instance, mistrust of government and fear of negative marginal returns from possible taxes and loss of transfers. Knowing such barriers to formalization, and more importantly the opportunities from greater social protection that formality might bring, may aid governments to realign policies and provisions with people's actual perceived priorities and needs, including living wages, sustainable taxes, and transfers.

A similar approach privileging everyday work perspectives from the informal sector has been applied in new work on the psychology of "radical commerce" (Groot & Hodgetts, 2015). Radical commerce includes livelihoods in sectors like the sex industry and other street occupations such as drug dealing, gang-related occupations, and working at traffic intersections in cities (Groot & Hodgetts, 2015). This research recognizes that work skills are required to make any kind of living in a street environment (e.g., making a street intersection your workplace). It pulls no punches because it recognizes that radical commerce may not be sustainable for people's health and well-being in the longer run, while respecting the fact that street life has cultures, artefacts, spaces, and spheres of its own (Groot & Hodgetts, 2015). The research suggests municipal policies that celebrate instead of denigrating or penalizing these spheres, such as providing municipal spaces instead of perpetually moving people on.

Degrees of Employment.   The term "work" psychology implies an exclusion of people who are "not" in work, such as the unemployed. Understandably, with one or two exceptions (e.g., Warr, 1987, and the literature on "downsizing," "rightsizing," and "outplacement," all synonyms for layoffs), unemployment has not traditionally held a very prominent place in most work and organizational psychology textbooks. This is despite its widely evident and documented deleterious effects on people's everyday well-being and psychology (Fryer & Fagan, 2003), and despite repeated economic crises that have caused massive unemployment, particularly among youth (ILO, 2013).

In response to such pandemics of unemployment, humanitarian work and organizational psychologists have reconceptualized the spaces and gradations between youth unemployment and employment (Searle et al., 2014). In their International White Paper on this topic for SIOP, Searle et al. (2014) highlighted a continuum of unemployment, underemployment (in poor-quality jobs that do not respect people's capabilities), and full employment for youth. Highlighting such spaces conceptually is important in both practical and ethical terms. It helps, for instance, in (re)generating options for creating decent work opportunities for youth, from self-entrepreneurship to partnerships between schools and smaller workplaces. The policy recommendations made in Searle et al. (2014) are thus multi-stakeholder, linking job seekers, parent, educators, and employers with policymakers (Carter, 2019).

Policy advocacy has been a core thrust in a related multi-age group approach, from vocational and counselling psychology, namely the psychology of working (Blustein, 2011, 2013). Focused on eradicating poverty for all (SDG 8), the psychology of working approach focuses on people's needs for survival, relational connections, and self-determination, therein intersecting with humanitarian work and organizational psychology (Thompson & Dahling, 2019). An example can be found in access to decent work for immigrants from lower-income countries, many of whom are highly skilled and yet also continue to encounter prolonged periods of unemployment and underemployment in their new home, a widely observed and persistent phenomenon dubbed "brain waste" (Mahroum, 2000).

Such wasted potential is a humanitarian disaster as well as a broken promise to the people who have made the new country their intended home. A crucial part of settling in any new country is finding a sustainable livelihood, one that helps to meet people's everyday needs for sustainable survival, relations, and self-determination across generations (Duffy et al., 2016). Humanitarian work-related research has already engaged with such needs by theorizing the psychological reasons for brain waste (Coates & Carr, 2005; Mace et al., 2005). Discrimination at work is not confined, of course, to new settlers (Marai, 2014; Marai et al., 2010). Ways of redressing them include, for instance, structuring the process to render it more accountable to (and inclusive of) disadvantaged groups (de Kock & Hauptfleisch, 2018; Maynard et al., 2010). Such advances have the potential to resonate and intersect with the Black Lives Matter movement, recently enjoined by the GoHWP. Specifically, GoHWP formed a global task force to help countermand racism in police and policing work.

VISTAS

A vista is a view from elevation, and a house has elevation, which makes it possible to look beyond the horizon. In this case, perhaps, building more inclusive selection could be considered an instantiation of corporate social responsibility (CSR) (Aguinis, 2011). As Rupp and Mallory (2015) showed, CSR has often focused more on the corporate and less on the social forms of responsibility (which means that it intersects with HWP), encouraging public perceptions that it is greenwashing, and more on the cost-benefits (to shareholders) from boosting corporate reputation. Corporations have a major role to play in enabling the SDGs (Foster & Viale, 2020). For example, if CSR begins at home, it could surely require providing decent working conditions for a corporation's own employees and local workforces (Erdogan et al., 2015; Osicki, 2016).

Private sector corporations are not the only form of organizations that can and should work with social responsibility. Civil society and non-government organizations (NGOs), as well as social enterprises and SMEs, may also be both socially and environmentally responsible (Aguinis, 2011). Broadly speaking, such organizational social responsibility would include not-for-profit, non-corporate forms of organization, without ever losing sight of CSR's foundational "triple-bottom line" of people, planet, and profit (Rupp & Mallory, 2015).

People. In the transition from a health crisis to an unemployment crisis, the most vulnerable groups are often youths, migrants, and women (OECD, 2020a, 2020b). According to the OECD (2020a, 2020b), neither standard forms of social protection (such as unemployment benefits) nor less conventional forms (such as job retention and wage subsidy schemes) will in the future suffice to sustain these group's livelihoods. Even before the COVID-19 pandemic started, many of their jobs were at risk from automation, which has early in the 2020s already increased exponentially (Scarpettta, 2020). Such rapid acceleration toward automation raises a new humanitarian challenge for the world of work in the future—addressing livelihood security (UNTF, 2015; World Bank, 2019).

Measuring (in)security of work is an important, foundational step in addressing how insecure people feel at any given time, in any given form of work (Abdul-Nasiru & Gloss, 2014). As time goes on, it will become more important to evaluate if and when it has improved, for example, as a result from implementing a living wage (Seubert & Hopfgartner, 2019). In their research, Seubert and Hopfgartner (2019) have developed a measure of livelihood insecurity at work. This includes multiple dimensions that range from material and institutional forms of felt (in)security to lack of recognition or meaning at work. Such measures could in the future become increasingly important for monitoring and evaluating "what works" to improve livelihood security, as well as decent working conditions, among any at-risk groups and individuals (Di Fabio & Kenny, 2016; Duffy et al., 2020; Pereira et al., 2019; Ribeiro et al., 2016).

Work security for people (the title of this section) is not just an individual-level issue (UNTF, 2015; see also the section "Levels—Individual"). Across 30 nations and 48 states in the United States, Jiang and Probst (2017) found that countries and states with higher income inequality (captured by the Gini coefficient) also showed sharper increases in micro-level burnout from lingering job insecurity at work. As Jiang and Probst (2017) argued, "Psychological demands placed on employees [micro level] as a result of job insecurity [middle level] are compounded when they occur in a context of economic [vertical] inequality [macro level]" (p. 679, brackets added). Studies of horizontal inequality (i.e., equal human capital but discrepant remuneration) found that double demotivation from dual-salary systems was less likely to be moderated by country or by sector than it was by the specific organization in which people were working. This suggested potential intervention points at organizational as well as institutional levels (Carr et al., 2010).

At an institutional level, the COVID-19 pandemic showed how even "unthinkable" interventions (e.g., abolishing dual standards in pay) for many could suddenly materialize. An example is the provision of wage subsidy schemes, as well as job retention programs, by national governments (IMF, 2020). These are not too far from forms of universal basic income (UBI), albeit tied to having a job, and to that extent excluding the unemployed (PSC, 2017). Such differences and others notwithstanding, the idea of a UBI as an alternative form of social protection to, say, minimum wages and state transfers (e.g., unemployment benefits) gained significantly in traction during the COVID-19 pandemic (UN, 2020).

From the perspective of humanitarian work and organizational psychology, such attention created a potential to evaluate how well basic income could help to offset at least some of the livelihood insecurities stemming from increasing automation. Some examples include training people to manage the robots, giving people time to consider decent work options, and motivating employers to pay higher, more competitive wages (Carr et al., 2020). According to the UNDP (2020), a more pressing function that UBI could serve at the time was slowing surges in COVID-19 cases within lower-income, insecure, and informal work settings. This point is consistent with research conducted before the pandemic, showing that state-level social insurance can help to buffer people from the time pressure and financial strain of unemployment and to find higher-quality, more sustainable new livelihoods (Wanberg et al., 2020).

Planet. A third crisis, the most serious, is environmental destruction. This ongoing unfolding disaster may have brought this COVID-19 virus to humanity in the first place, as animal habitats are being increasingly encroached and destroyed (epizootiology). It may also be either exacerbated or tempered by it, for example, by dumped personal protection equipment (PPE) waste versus by people travelling less often to work, depending on what people, humanity, does next. What such examples suggest, though, is that saving the planet may actually be a question not only of organizational and worker behavior, but also (of course!) consumer behavior, such as commuting and habits (SDG 12—sustainable consumption). In that way, the looming vista of biosphere destruction might ultimately become more reversible (SDG 13—climate action).

How can humanitarian work and organizational psychology contribute much more than it has so far toward protecting the Earth's biosphere? Consumer behavior can be affected by fair trade certification, which can then persuade customers to pay more toward a living wage for the primary producer, farm, or factory worker, and possibly enjoy the product or commodity in the process (De Pelsmacker et al., 2005; Lotz et al., 2013). That same line of reasoning may also apply to helping to preserve life in the ocean (SDG 14) and on land (SDG 15), for example, if living wages boosted capacity to manage forests more sustainably and/or helped to conserve marine reserves from exploitative organizations flying under flags of convenience and running slave ships (UN News, 2019). Once again this is a reminder that the SDGs are in fact interconnected, that one livelihood is inseparable from another, that work links to life, and that what ultimately sustains everybody is the respect for the biosphere.

Psychology. Humanitarian work and organizational psychologists, present and future, are not above any other occupation, or apart from the society and environment in which they may live and work. Work psychologists need sustainable livelihoods too. Among the most frequently asked and most pertinent questions at conferences and seminars on humanitarian work and organizational psychology has been "What jobs can I find with this specialism?" In the past, the answer would have been a bit of a fudge—a combination of "research" (not for most), "volunteer work" (not really sustainable for most), and "a balance of commercial consulting and NGO work" (sustainable for some). In the 21st century, perhaps another more widely applicable option has opened: teaching and training students to build their own sustainable livelihoods. This could more overtly include helping others to make theirs. That would mean scaling up from small businesses and social enterprises (Nguyen et al., 2021), adapting them to include, for example, new diplomacies, and practicing humanitarian principles in work and organizational psychology as a responsible employer of other people. The COVID-19 pandemic may have thus become a disruptor that creates new pedagogical and training options toward context-based psychologies of sustainable livelihood.

ACKNOWLEDGMENTS

My thanks go to the expert peer reviewers and editors for their kind, helpful, and constructive feedback on earlier versions of this article. They are greatly appreciated and highly valued.

REFERENCES

Abdul-Nasiru, I., & Gloss, A. (2014). International development and I-O psychology in sub-Saharan Africa: Perspectives from local and expatriate standpoints. In W. Reichman (Ed.), *Industrial and organizational psychology help the vulnerable: Serving the underserved* (pp. 33–49). Palgrave Macmillan.

Aguinis, H. (2011). Organizational responsibility: Doing good and doing well. In S. Zedeck (Ed.), *APA handbook of industrial and organizational psychology, Vol. 3. Maintaining, expanding, and contracting the organization* (pp. 855–879). American Psychological Association.

Amin, M. A., MacLachlan, M., Mannan, H., El Tayeb, S., El Khatim, A., Swartz, L., Munthali, A., Van Rooy, G., McVeigh, J., Eide, A., & Schneider, M. (2011). EquiFrame: A framework for analysis of the inclusion of human rights and vulnerable groups in health policies. *Health and Human Rights, 13*(2), 1–20.

Annan, K. (2000). *We the peoples.* United Nations.

Atkins, S. G., & Foster-Thompson, L. (2012). Online volunteers and Smart-aid. In S. C. Carr, M. MacLachlan, & A. Furnham (Eds.), *Humanitarian work psychology* (pp. 266–292). Palgrave Macmillan.

Baritz, L. (1960). *The servants of power: A history of the use of social science in American industry.* Wesleyan University Press.

Bergman, M. E., & Jean, V. A. (2015). Where have all the workers gone? A critical analysis of the underrepresentativeness of our samples relative to the labor market in the industrial–organizational psychology literature. *Industrial and Organizational Psychology, 9*(1), 84–113. https://doi.org/10.1017/iop.2015.70

Berry, M. O., Kuriansky, J., & Butler, M. (2014). A multidisciplinary approach to solving global problems: The case of psychologists collaborating on a girls' empowerment program in Africa. In W. Reichman (Ed.), *Industrial and organizational psychology help the vulnerable: Serving the underserved* (pp. 73–91). Palgrave Macmillan.

Berry, M. O., Kuriansky, J., Lytle, M. C., Vistman, B., Mosisilli, M. S., Hlothoane, L., & Pebane, J. (2013). Entrepreneurial training for girls' empowerment in Lesotho: A process evaluation of a model programme. *South African Journal of Psychology, 43*(4), 445–458.

Berry, M., Reichman, W., MacLachlan, M., Klobas, J., Hui, H. C., & Carr, S. C. (2011). Humanitarian work psychology: The contributions of organizational psychology to poverty reduction. *Journal of Economic Psychology, 32*(2), 240–247.

Bischoff, K. M., Gielnik, M. M., & Frese, M. (2013). Entrepreneurship training in developing countries. In W. Reichman (Ed.), *Industrial and organizational psychology help the vulnerable: Serving the underserved* (pp. 92–119). Palgrave Macmillan.

Blaikie, P., Cannon, T., Davis, I., & Wisner, B. (2004). *At risk: Natural hazards, people's vulnerability, and disasters.* Routledge.

Blustein, D. L. (2011). A relational theory of working. *Journal of Vocational Behavior, 79*(1), 1–17.

Blustein, D. L. (2013). The psychology of working: A new perspective for a new era. In D. L. Blustein (Ed.), *The Oxford handbook of the psychology of working* (Oxford Handbooks Online). Oxford University Press. https://doi.org/10.1093/oxfordhb/9780199758791.013.0001

Brief, A. P. (2000). Still servants of power. *Journal of Management Inquiry, 9*(4), 342–351.

Buse, K., Ludi, E., & Vigneri, M. (2008). Can project-funded investments in rural development be scaled up? Lessons from the Millennium Villages Project. *Natural Resource Perspectives, 118*(November), 1–6.

Campos, F., Frese, M., Goldstein, M. P., & Iacovone, L. (2017). Training personal initiative beats traditional training in boosting small businesses in West Africa. *Science, 357*(6357), 1287–1290.

Carr, S. C. (Ed.). (2010). *The psychology of global mobility.* Springer.

Carr, S. C. (2020, June 16). *IO words for Covid* [Invited TED-talk]. SIOP Conference, USA.

Carr, S. C., Haar, J., Hodgetts, D., Arrowsmith, J., Parker, J., Young-Hauser, A., Alefaio-Tuglia, S., & Jones, H. (2019). An employee's living wage and their quality of work life: How important household size and income? *Journal of Sustainability Research, 1*(1), 1–19.

Carr, S. C., Hodgetts, D. J., Potgieter, J., & Meyer, I. (2020). Macro-psychology for decent work: Sustainable livelihood. In M. MacLachlan & J. McVeigh (Eds.), *Macro-psychology: A population science for Sustainable Development Goals* (pp. 213–231). Springer.

Carr, S. C., & MacLachlan, M. (2014). Humanitarian work psychology. *The Psychologist, 27*(3), 160–163.

Carr, S. C., MacLachlan, M., & Furnham, A. (2012). *Humanitarian work psychology.* Palgrave Macmillan.

Carr, S. C., Maleka, M., Meyer, I., Barry, M. L., Harr, J., Parker, J., Arrowsmith, J., Yao, C., Hodgetts, D., Jones, H., Young-Hausner, A., Afeaki-Mafile'o, E., Rasmussen, A.-H., Alefaio-Tugia, S., Falealili, B., Mafile'o, K., Pikula, T., Wolfgramm, N., 'Uhila, H.,…, Naithani, A. (2018). How can wages sustain a living? By getting ahead of the curve. *Sustainability Science, 13*(4), 901–917. https://doi.org/10.1007/s11625-018-0560-7

Carr, S. C., McWha, I., MacLachlan, M., & Furnham, A. (Eds.). (2010). Remuneration discrepancies and poverty reduction: Elephant salaries in the international development parlour. *International Journal of Psychology, 45*(5), 321–380.

Carr, S. C., Parker, J., Arrowsmith, J., & Watters, P. A. (2016). The living wage: Theoretical integration and an applied research agenda. *International Labour Review, 155*(1), 1–24.

Carter, A. J. (2019). *Young people, employment, and work: Interventions and solutions.* Routledge.

Chambers, R. C., & Conway, G. R. (1991). *Sustainable rural livelihoods: Practical concepts for the 21st century* [Paper No. 296]. Institute of Development Studies, University of Sussex, Brighton, UK.

Coates, K., & Carr, S. C. (2005). Skilled immigrants and selection bias. *International Journal of Intercultural Relations, 29*(5), 577–599.

de Kock, F. S., & Hauptfleisch, D. B. (2018). Reducing racial similarity bias in interviews by increasing structure: A quasi-experiment using multilevel analysis. *International Perspectives in Psychology: Research, Practice, Consultation, 7*(3), 137–154. https://doi.org/10.1037/ipp0000091

De Pelsmacker, P., Driesen, L., & Rayp, G. (2005). Do consumers care about ethics? Willingness to pay for fair-trade coffee. *The Journal of Consumer Affairs, 39*(2), 363–385.

Di Fabio, A., & Kenny, M. E. (2016). From decent work to decent lives: Positive self and relational management (PS&RM) in the twenty-first century. *Frontiers in Psychology, 7*(March). https://doi.org/10.3389/fpsyg.2016.00361

Duffy, R. D., Blustein, D. L., Allan, B. A., Diemer, M. A., Cinemon, R. E. (2020). Introduction to the special issue: A cross-cultural exploration of decent work. *Journal of Vocational Behavior, 116*(Part A). https://doi.org/10.1016/j.jvb.2019.103351

Duffy, R. D., Blustein, D. L., Diemer, M. A., & Austin, K. L. (2016). The psychology of working theory. *Journal of Counselling Psychology, 63*(2), 127–148.

Erdogan, B., Bauer, T. N., & Taylor, S. (2015). Management commitment to the ecological environment and employees: Implications for employee attitudes and citizenship behaviours. *Human Relations, 68*(11), 1669–1691.

Ferris, G. R., Treadway, D. C., Kolodinsky, R., Hochwarter, W. A., Kacmer, C., & Douglas, C. (2005). Development and validation of the Political Skill Inventory. *Journal of Management, 31*(1), 126–152.

Figart, D. (2000). Equal pay for equal work: The role of job evaluation in an evolving social norm. *Journal of Economic Issues, 34*(1), 1–19.

Foster, L. L., & Viale, T. (2020). The changing nature of work and organizations in sustainable development. In B. J. Hoffman, M. K. Shoss, & L. A. Wegman (Eds.), *The Cambridge handbook of the changing nature of work* (pp. 583–618). Cambridge University Press.

Freeman, D. (2020, June 11). *What does "build back better" really mean? One of the world's top CEOs gives us his take.* UN News. https://news.un.org/en/story/2020/06/1066152

Fryer, D., & Fagan, R. (2003). Poverty and unemployment. In S. C. Carr & T. S. Sloan (Eds.), *Poverty and psychology: From global perspective to local practice* (pp. 87–101). Springer.

General Assembly of the International Union of Psychological Science. (2008, July). *Universal Declaration of Ethical Principles for Psychologists.* International Union of Psychological Science.

Gloss, A., Carr, S. C., Reichman, W., & Abdul-Nasiru, I. (2016). From handmaidens to POSH humanitarians. *Industrial & Organizational Psychology Journal, 10*(3), 1–41.

Gloss, A., McCallum, S., & Foster, L. F. (2016). Putting human capabilities to work: A person-centered approach to international skills development. In I. McWha-Hermann, D. C. Maynard, & M. O'Neill Berry (Eds.), *Humanitarian work psychology and the global development agenda: Cases and interventions* (pp. 85–99). Routledge.

Godbout, J. (2014). Exploring Haiti from an organizational psychology perspective: Lessons learned along the way. In W. Reichman (Ed.), *Industrial and organizational psychology help the vulnerable: Serving the underserved* (pp. 131–141). Palgrave Macmillan.

Groot, S., & Hodgetts, D. (2015). The infamy of begging: A case-based approach to street homelessness and radical commerce. *Qualitative Research in Psychology, 12*(4), 349–366.

Harris, J. J., Jr. (1973). A science of the South Pacific: Analysis of the character of the Peace Corps volunteer. *American Psychologist, 28*(3), 232–247.

Hodgetts, D., Stolte, O., Sonn, C., Drew, N., Nikora, L. W., & Carr, S. C. (2020). *Social psychology and everyday life* (2nd ed.). Macmillan.

I/O Shaken & Stirred. (2017, May 2). *Project GLOW presented by John C. Scott at I/O Shaken & Stirred 2017.* YouTube. https://www.youtube.com/watch?v=zbZafHgqumo

ILO (International Labor Organization). (2013). *World of work report 2013: Repairing the economic and social fabric.* International Labor Organization.

ILO (International Labor Organization). (2019a). *World employment and social outlook: Trends 2019.* International Labor Organization.

ILO (International Labor Organization). (2019b, February 13). *Poor working conditions are main global employment challenge.* https://www.ilo.org/global/about-the-ilo/newsroom/news/WCMS_670171/lang--en/index.htm

ILO (International Labor Organization). (2020). *Decent work agenda.* International Labor Organization.

IMF (International Monetary Fund). (2020). *Policy responses to COVID-19.* International Monetary Fund.

ITUC (International Trade Union Confederation). (2018, December 2). *Global poll: Governments' failure to address low wages and insecure jobs threatens trust in politics and democracy.* https://www.ituc-csi.org/ITUC-Global-Poll-2018

Jiang, L., & Probst, T. M. (2017). The rich get richer and the poor get poorer: Country- and state-level income inequality moderates the job insecurity-burnout relationship. *Journal of Applied Psychology, 102*(4), 672–681.

Kandola, B. (2014). Increasing resilience among people who are homeless. In W. Reichman (Ed.), *Industrial and organizational psychology help the vulnerable: Serving the underserved* (pp. 186–202). Palgrave Macmillan.

Kealey, D. J. (1989). A study of cross-cultural effectiveness: Theoretical issues, practical applications. *International Journal of Intercultural Relations, 13*(3), 387–428.

Klinger, B., Khwaja, A. I., & del Carpio, C. (2013). *Enterprising psychology and poverty reduction.* Springer.

Kranz, L. (2001). *The sustainable livelihood approach to poverty reduction.* Swedish International Development Cooperation Agency.

Lefkowitz, J. (2003). *Ethics and values in industrial–organizational psychology.* Lawrence Erlbaum.

Lefkowitz, J. (2017). *Ethics and values in industrial–organizational psychology* (2nd ed.). Routledge.

Lotz, S., Christandl, F., & Fetchenhauer, D. (2013). What is fair is good: Evidence of consumers' taste for fairness. *Food Quality and Preference, 30*(2), 139–144.

Mace, K. A., Atkins, S. G., Fletcher, R. B., & Carr, S. C. (2005). Immigrant job hunting, labour market experiences, and feelings about occupational life in New Zealand: An exploratory study. *New Zealand Journal of Psychology, 34*(2), 97–109.

MacLachlan, M. (2014). Macropsychology, policy and global health. *American Psychologist, 69*(8), 851–863.

MacLachlan, M., Carr, S. C., & McAuliffe, E. (2010). *The aid triangle: Recognizing the human dynamics of dominance, justice and identity.* Zed Books.

Mahroum, S. (2000). High-skilled globe-trotters: Mapping the international migration of human capital. *R & D Management, 30*(1), 23–32.

Maleka, M., Rugimbana, R., Carr, S. C., Meyer, I., Parker, J., & Barry, M. L. (2018). Reflections on a study conducted in New Zealand and South Africa to ascertain the extent to which living wages are a panacea for quality life for low-income workers. *SAGE Research Methods Cases, Part 2.* https://doi.org/10.4135/9781526449481

Manson, J., & Carr, S. C. (2011). Improving job fit for mission workers by including expatriate and local job exerts in job specification. *Journal of Managerial Psychology, 26*(6), 465–484.

Marai, L. (2014). Dual salary and workers' wellbeing in Papua New Guinea. In W. Reichman (Ed.), *Industrial and organizational psychology help the vulnerable: Serving the underserved* (pp. 120–127). Palgrave Macmillan.

Marai, L., Keibu, V., Kinkin, E., Peniop, P., Salini, C., & Kofana, G. (2010). Remuneration disparities in Oceania: Papua New Guinea and Solomon Islands. *International Journal of Psychology, 45*(5), 350–359.

Maynard, D., Ferdman, B., & Holmes, T. (2010). Mobility and inclusion. In S. C. Carr (Ed.), *The psychology of global mobility* (pp. 211–234). Springer.

McAuliffe, E., Bowie, C., Manafa, O., Maseko, F., MacLachlan, M., Hevey, D., Normand, C., & Chirwa, M. (2009). Measuring and managing the work environment of the mid-level provider. *Human Resource for Health, 7,* 13.

McWha-Hermann, I., Jandric, J., Wakefield, S., Moutou, M., Grund, C., & Carr, S. C. (2017). *Fairness in aid remuneration: Project FAIR*. CHS Alliance. https://www.chsalliance.org/get-support/article/project-fair-webinar-summary-and-follow-up-questions/

McWha-Hermann, I., Maynard, D. C., & O'Neill Berry, M. (Eds.). (2016). *Humanitarian work psychology and the global development agenda: Case studies and interventions*. Routledge.

McWha-Hermann, I., & Searle, R. (2020, May). Living wages are crucial now more than ever. *The Psychologist, 21*. https://www.research.ed.ac.uk/en/publications/living-wages-are-crucial-now-more-than-ever

Meyer, R. D., Kanfer, R., & Burrus, C. (2016). Improving motivation and performance among frontline healthcare workers in rural India: The role of team-based goals and incentives. In I. McWha-Hermann, D. C. Maynard, & M. O. Berry (Eds.), *Humanitarian work psychology and the global development agenda: Case studies and interventions* (pp. 100–112). Routledge.

Morse, S., & McNamara, N. (2013). *Sustainable livelihood approach: A critique of theory and practice*. Springer.

Nguyen, M. H. T., Carr, S. C., Hodgetts, D., & Fauchart, E. (2021, March). Why do some social enterprises flourish in Vietnam? A comparison of human and ecosystem partnerships. *Sustainability, Management and Accounting Policy Journal*. https://www.emerald.com/insight/content/doi/10.1108/SAMPJ-04-2020-0137/full/html

OECD (Organization for Economic Cooperation and Development). (2011). *Guidelines for Multinational Enterprises* (2nd ed.). Organization for Economic Cooperation and Development.

OECD (Organization for Economic Cooperation and Development). (2020a). *One world: Global solidarity for recovery and resilience*. Organization for Economic Cooperation and Development.

OECD (Organization for Economic Cooperation and Development). (2020b). *OECD employment outlook 2020: Worker security and the Covid-19 crisis*. Organization for Economic Cooperation and Development.

Olson-Buchanan, J., Koppes-Bryan, L., & Foster-Thompson, L. (2013). *Using industrial-organizational psychology for the greater good*. Society for Industrial and Organizational Psychology.

Osicki, M. (2016). Leadership development via humanitarian work: IBM's efforts in Nigeria. In I. McWha-Hermann, D. C. Maynard, & M. O'Neill Berry (Eds.), *Humanitarian work psychology and the global development agenda: Cases and interventions* (pp. 56–68). Routledge.

Oxfam. (2020). *Time to care: Unpaid and underpaid care work and the global inequality crisis* [Briefing Paper]. https://indepth.oxfam.org.uk/time-to-care/

Paris Declaration on Aid Effectiveness. (2004). *Paris Declaration on Aid Effectiveness*. United Nations.

Pereira, S., Dos Santos, N., & Pais, L. (2019). Empirical research on decent work: A literature review. *Scandinavian Journal of Work and Organisational Psychology, 4*(1), 4. http://doi.org/10.16993/sjwop.53

Pizzigati, S. (2018). *The case for a maximum wage*. Wiley & Sons.

Project GLOW (Global Living Organisational Wage). (2020). International perspectives on living wages for sustainable livelihoods: Some lessons from Project GLOW. In W. F. Filho, T. (Ed.), *Encyclopaedia of the UN Sustainable Development Goals: Decent work and economic growth* (in press). Oxford University Press.

PSC (Psychologists for Social Change). (2017). *Universal basic income: A psychological impact assessment*. Psychologists for Social Change.

Reichman, W. (Ed.). (2014). *Industrial and organizational psychology help the vulnerable: Serving the underserved*. Palgrave Macmillan.

Reichman, W., & Beidel, B. J. (1989). Implementation of a state police EAP. *Journal of Drug Issues, 19*(July), 369–383.

Reichman, W., & Carr, S. C. (2020). Human rights is the business of business. In N. Rubin (Ed.), *Cambridge handbook of psychology and human rights* (pp. 428–442). Cambridge University Press.

Ribeiro, M. A., Silva, F. L., & Figueiredo, P. M. (2016). Discussing the notion of decent work: Senses of working for a group of Brazilian workers without college education. *Frontiers in Psychology, 7*(February), Article 207. https://www.frontiersin.org/articles/10.3389/fpsyg.2016.00207/full

Rupp, D., & Mallory, D. (2015). Corporate social responsibility: Psychological, person-centric, and progressing. *Annual Review of Organizational Psychology and Organizational Behaviour, 2*, 211–236.

Saner, R., & Yiu, L. (2012). The new diplomacies and humanitarian work psychology. In S. C. Carr, M. MacLachlan, & A. Furnham (Eds.), *Humanitarian work psychology* (pp. 129–165). Palgrave Macmillan.

Saner, R., & Yiu, L. (2014a). Designing learning systems for poverty reduction in least developed countries. In W. Reichman (Ed.), *Industrial and organizational psychology help the vulnerable: Serving the underserved* (pp. 164–182). Palgrave Macmillan.

Saner, R., & Yiu, L. (2014b). Business diplomacy competence: A requirement for implementing the OECD's *Guidelines for Multinational Enterprises. The Hague Journal of Diplomacy, 9*(4), 311–333.

Saxena, M. (2018). *Humanitarian work psychology.* Oxford University Press: Bibliographies.

Saxena, M., Sall, E., Scott, J. C., Rupp, D. E., Saari, L., Thompson, L. F. (2015). News from the SIOP–United Nations team: Exploring work experiences of informal workers and promoting decent work for all. *The Industrial–Organizational Psychologist, 53*(1), 172–175.

Scarpetta, S. (2020). *Future of work: Rebuilding a future that works for all.* International Labor Organization.

Schein, V. E. (2003). The functions of work-related group participation for poor women in developing countries: An exploratory look. *Psychology and Developing Societies, 15*(2), 123–142.

Schein, V. E. (2011). How leaders and companies treat people matters: Voices of women garment assembly workers in Nicaragua. In D. D. Warrick & J. Mueller (Eds.), *Learning from real world cases: Lessons in leadership* (pp. 77–82). Rossi Smith.

Schein, V. E., Marsella, A. J., Wiesenfeld, E., Sanchez, E., Berry, M., & Reichman, W. (2011). Women in self-organized groups at work: Do they promote agency and reduce poverty. *Journal of Managerial Psychology, 26*(6), 508–521.

Searle, R., Erdogan, B., Peiró, J. M., & Kleke, U. K. (2014). *What we know about youth unemployment: Research survey and best practices* [White Papers Series]. Society for Industrial and Organizational Psychology.

Seubert, C., & Hopfgartner, L. (2019). Beyond insecurity: Concept, dimensions and measurement of precarious employment. *Journal of Everyday Activity, 12*(2), 33–45.

Smith, L. (2015). Reforming the minimum wage: Towards a psychological perspective. *American Psychologist, 70*(6), 557–565.

Tchagneno, C., Wassouo, E., Minkoue, P. L., & Doutre, E. (2019). Construction et validation d'une échelle de mesure des représentations sociales du travail informel. *Pratiques Psychologiques, 25*(4), 399–417. https://doi.org/10.1016/j.prps.2018.07.001

Thompson, M. N., & Dahling, J. J. (2019). Employment and poverty: Why work matters in understanding poverty. *American Psychologist, 74*(6), 673–684.

Tumwabaze, C., & MacLachlan, M. (2012). Motivating the teacher workforce in Uganda. In S. C. Carr, M. MacLachlan, & A. Furnham (Eds.), *Humanitarian work psychology* (pp. 166–181). Palgrave Macmillan.

UN (United Nations). (2014). *Revision of world urbanization prospects.* United Nations.

UN (United Nations). (2020). *Shared responsibility, global solidarity: Responding to the socio-economic impacts of Covid-19.* United Nations.

UNDP (United Nations Development Program). (2020). *Temporary basic income to protect the world's poorest people could slow the surge in COVID-19 cases.* United Nations Development Program.

UN News. (2019, November 21). *Deadly life at sea: UN partners spotlight depths of danger in fishing industry.* UN News.

UNTF (United Nations Trust Fund). (2015). *Human security and agenda 2030.* United Nations Trust Fund for Human Security.

Vallieres, F., & McAuliffe, E. (2016). Reaching MDZGs 4 and 5: The application of organizational psychology to maternal and child health programme sustainability in Sierra Leone. In I. McWha-Hermann, D. C. Maynard, & M. O'Neill Berry (Eds.), *Humanitarian work psychology and the global development agenda: Cases and interventions* (pp. 15–27). Routledge.

Wanberg, C. R., van Hooft, E. A. J., Dossinger, K., van Vianen, A. G. M., & Klehe, U. C. (2020). How strong is my safety net? Perceived unemployment insurance, generosity, and implications for job search, mental health and re-employment. *Journal of Applied Psychology, 105*(3), 209–229.

Warr, P. B. (1987). *Work, unemployment and mental health.* Clarendon Press.

WCED (World Commission on Environment and Development). (1989, March). *Our common future.* Brundtland Commission.

World Bank. (2012). *World development report: 2013—Jobs.* World Bank.

World Bank. (2019). *World development report 2018—WDR 2019 presentations.* World Bank. https://pubdocs .worldbank.org/en/808261547222082195/WDR19-English-Presentation.pdf

Yiu, L., & Saner, R. (2016). Humanitarian work psychology: Unique contributions and theoretical development in the context of the global development agenda. In I. McWha-Hermann, D. C. Maynard, & M. O'Neill Berry (Eds.), *Humanitarian work psychology and the global development agenda: Cases and interventions* (pp. 192–199). Routledge.

Yunus, M. (1999). The Grameen Bank. *Scientific American, 281*(5), 114–119.

Zapizapu. (2012, April 5). *Living with coffee (a documentary about fair trade coffee).* YouTube. https://www .youtube.com/watch?v=BwYl69VstPw

NOTE

1. At a meeting held at UCL, London, UK, in 2009, at which the field was suggested by M. MacLachlan and the name by J. Godbout. This meeting also spawned a global task force for humanitarian work psychology (Berry et al., 2011).

Stuart C. Carr

Research Methods

MEDIATOR VARIABLES

OVERVIEW OF CURRENT STATUS

Definition. *Mediator variables* are variables that are intermediate in the causal relation between two other variables. That is, mediator variables (the second variable in the causal chain) transmit changes in the first variable (the cause) to the third variable (the effect). Consider setting three dominoes in a row such that tipping over the first domino causes the second domino to fall, which in turn causes the third domino to fall—a chain reaction. Here the middle domino is an example of a mediator variable because when the first domino falls over, the effect is transmitted to the last domino through the middle domino. If the middle domino (mediator) was removed, then the first domino is prevented from knocking over the third domino. Hence, if mediator variables are not present or are forced to remain unchanged then the first variable, often called the *independent variable, predictor*, or *antecedent*, cannot have its entire effect on the third variable, usually referred to as the *dependent variable, outcome*, or *consequent*. This is why mediator variables are conceptualized as being the intermediate links in a causal chain between two other variables.

Mediator variables are particularly important to psychologists, who are very interested in understanding how or why two variables are related. For example, how does cognitive behavioral therapy (CBT) affect depression? One way CBT has been found to affect depression is by reducing negative thinking (Kaufman, Rohde, Seeley, Clarke, & Stice, 2005). Here negative thinking is the intermediate mediator variable between CBT and depression such that receiving CBT causes a reduction in negative thinking and the reduction in negative thinking reduces depression symptoms. The statistical identification of the mediating mechanisms (e.g., how an intervention works), called *mediation analysis*, may allow for a more targeted treatment or for the addition of components to a treatment to increase its effectiveness. The previous examples are not intended to insinuate that mediation analysis is limited to manipulated causes, however. Observational studies where the antecedent is not directly manipulated by the researcher are candidates for mediation analysis as well.

The two most important words in the definition for mediator variables are *causal* and *intermediate* because these properties are what differentiate mediator variables from other variables that may play a role in the relation between two other variables. For example, a *confounder variable* is a variable that is related to both the independent variable and the outcome, often causally, that explains all or part of the relation between these two variables but is not an intermediate link in a causal chain. A classic example of a confounder variable is the significant positive relation between violent crime and ice cream consumption that can be explained by an increase in temperature during the summer (Le Roy, 2009). Moderating variables are also often confused with mediating variables. A *moderator variable* is a variable that addresses the question of under what circumstances a particular relationship holds between two other variables. That is, the size and direction of the relation between the two other variables depends on the value of the moderator variable, but the moderator does not transmit changes in one variable to the other. For example, if the effect of CBT on depression was stronger for females than males (an effect that has not typically been found; Cuijpers et al., 2014), gender would moderate the effect of the intervention on depression. The distinction between a mediator, a confounder, and a moderator can also be depicted using path model diagrams as in Figure 1.

The Single-Mediator Model. At a minimum, a *mediation model* must include an independent variable, an outcome, and a single mediator variable that transmits all or a portion of the effect that the independent variable has on the outcome, which is called a *single-mediator model*. One of the first mentions of the single-mediator model is the Stimulus Organism Response model where the organism (mediator variable) determines the type of response (outcome) that the stimulus (antecedent) causes (Woodworth, 1926). Early contributions to the single-mediator model were also made by Sewall Wright (1921), who demonstrated that the effect of an antecedent on a consequent through an intermediate variable may be quantified by multiplying the path coefficient between the antecedent and intermediate variable by the path coefficient between the intermediate variable and consequent (i.e., multiplying a and b in Figure 1).

A source of confusion regarding mediator variables is that the moderator/mediator distinction is also often muddled. Though far from being the first or only treatment of mediator variables (e.g., James & Brett, 1984; Judd & Kenny, 1981), the most prominent paper in psychology discussing the single-mediator model and mediator variables in general is the Baron and Kenny (1986) paper in the *Journal of Personality and Social Psychology*, which to-date has

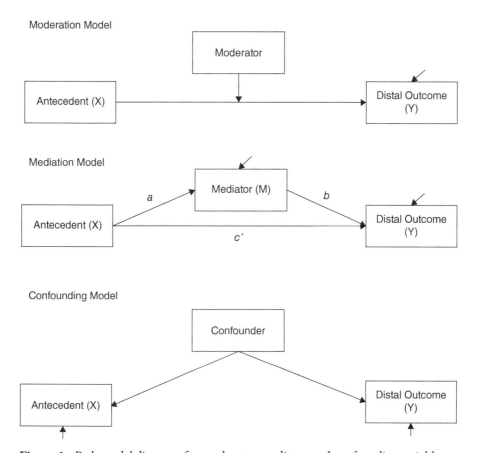

Figure 1. Path model diagrams for moderator, mediator, and confounding variables.

been cited over 40,000 times. There are two main reasons why the Baron and Kenny paper is so highly cited. First, their definition of mediator variables and the distinction between mediator and moderator variables is very clear. Second, they describe a set of four steps that may be used to statistically test for the presence of a mediator variable using a set of three regression equations. These four steps, often referred to as the *Causal Steps Test* of mediation (e.g., MacKinnon, Lockwood, Hoffman, West, & Sheets, 2002), are illustrated in Figure 2.

- Step 1: Test the *overall effect* of the antecedent on the outcome, labeled c, for significance. The reasoning behind this step is that if c is not statistically significant, there is no effect to be mediated.
- Step 2: Assuming c is found to be significant, test the effect of the antecedent on the mediator variable, labeled a, for significance. When the antecedent variable is a directly manipulated variable, such as random assignment to a treatment and control group, the a effect is called the *action theory* (MacKinnon, 2008).
- Step 3: If c and a are significant, test the effect of the mediator on the outcome controlling for the antecedent, b, for significance. As directly manipulating the mediator

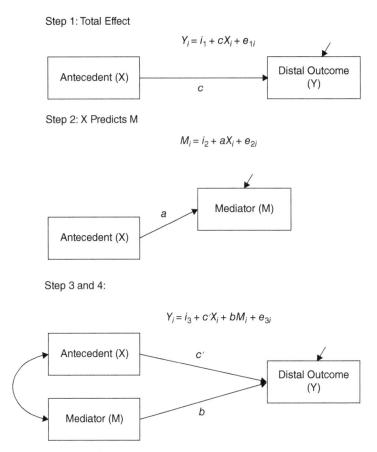

Figure 2. Causal steps.

variable is untenable in most situations, the b effect is called the *conceptual theory* (MacKinnon, 2008).

The testing of Step 4 requires understanding that though a mediator variable transmits the effect of the antecedent to the outcome, it is possible that the mediator variable does not transmit all of the effect. That is, there may still be some effect of the antecedent on the outcome that is not transmitted through the mediator. This potential non-transmitted effect, called the *direct effect* and labeled c', is the effect of the antecedent on the outcome controlling for the mediator. In the event that the entire effect of the antecedent on the outcome passes through the mediator variable, called *complete mediation*, then there should be no direct effect and $c' = 0$. As noted by Baron and Kenny, in psychology rarely is 100% of the variability in a variable explained, so a more likely situation is that part of the effect of the antecedent on the outcome passes through the mediator and part of the effect does not. The case where c' is not exactly zero is called *incomplete mediation*. Because the total effect is just being split into the direct effect and the effect passing through the mediator, if a mediating variable is present then the direct effect should be smaller than the total effect such that:

- Step 4: If c, a, and b are significant, then test the relation $c' < c$. If this step is not passed, then the relationship of the mediator variable to the other two variables is more complex than simple mediation.

If all four steps are passed, then mediation is said to occur. If any of the four steps fail, then mediation does not occur.

Beyond the Causal Steps Test. Though the Causal Steps Test is easy to understand and implement, there are several potential problems with it that have prompted revisions and new statistical tests for mediator variables to be developed. The first issue concerns the testing of the total effect in Step 1. When estimating these effects using multiple regression models where the mediator and outcome are continuous, normally distributed variables, the relation between the effects is $c = (a*b) + c'$ (MacKinnon, Warsi, & Dwyer, 1995). Conceptually this makes sense because the total effect is being split into two pieces: the part of the effect that is being transmitted through the mediator, which is equal to ab and is called the *mediated effect* or *indirect effect* because the antecedent is indirectly affecting the outcome through the mediator, and the part of the effect that is not being transmitted through the mediator, the direct effect. When the mediated effect and direct effect are both in the same direction, called *consistent mediation*, then the total effect will be larger (i.e., farther from zero) than either of the individual effects. But when ab and c' have opposite signs, called *inconsistent mediation*, c will be closer to zero (MacKinnon, Krull, & Lockwood, 2000). If the mediated and direct effects are exactly equal in size, but have different signs, then the direct effect will be equal to zero. Hence, the Causal Steps Test will conclude there is no evidence of mediation because Step 1 will fail, no matter how large the value of the mediated effect. This has led some researchers to recommend dropping Step 1 and Step 4, proceeding only with Steps 2 and 3, which has been called the *Joint Significance Test* (MacKinnon et al., 2002).

The second problem with the Causal Steps Test, inherent to the Joint Significant Test also, is that it does not directly test the mediated effect ab, instead testing a and b separately. Sobel (1982) found a solution by deriving the standard error of the mediated effect. The standard error can then either be divided into the mediated effect and the resulting ratio compared to a normal or t distribution to test for significance, called the *First-Order Standard Error Test* or *Sobel Test*, or used to create a symmetric confidence interval around the mediated effect. While eagerly adopted by psychologists as an alternative to the Causal Steps Test, the First-Order Standard Error Test has a fatal flaw, which is that in most circumstances the mediated effect is not normally distributed—hence the test is usually biased. Tests that do not rely on the mediated effect being normally distributed have been developed to address this issue and are discussed in the "Current Trends in Mediation" section.

A third problem with the Causal Steps Test is that it does not readily translate into more complex models. For example, if the mediator and the outcome variables are not continuous, normally distributed variables, then $c = (a*b) + c'$ may no longer hold, in which case the steps no longer make as much sense. Additionally, what happens when there are multiple mediating variables in the same model? There are several ways in which the relation between multiple mediators in the same model can be conceptualized. Consider the single-mediator model from Figure 1. It is possible that there is another mediator variable that mediates the relation between the first mediator and the outcome, such that the second mediator variable acts as another link in the causal chain between the antecedent and outcome. Returning to the domino example, this would be equivalent to adding a fourth domino between the middle (the first mediator variable) and last dominoes (the outcome); this is known as a *serial* or *sequential mediator model* and is illustrated in Figure 3.

Serial mediator models are common in psychology as illustrated by Tett and Meyer (1993), who hypothesized that organizational commitment (antecedent) has a positive relationship with job satisfaction (mediator #1), which in turn has a negative relationship with intention to quit the job (mediator #2), that ultimately has a positive relationship with actually quitting the job (consequent). This combination of effects would result in organizational commitment having a negative indirect effect on quitting your job through job satisfaction and intentions to quit. Although this model does not hypothesize that organizational commitment has a direct effect on turnover, results from a meta-analysis conducted by Tett and Meyer suggest that there is a negative direct effect. Thus, although this example has a combination of positive and negative hypothesized relationships, it is an example of consistent mediation because the direct and indirect effect are both negative.

Multiple mediator variables can also be added to a model such that the antecedent simultaneously affects both mediator variables, which in turn both affect the outcome, but neither mediator variable transmits the effect of the other. For the domino example this would be equivalent to adding a fourth domino next to the existing middle domino such that the first domino knocks over both the middle dominoes simultaneously, which in turn knock down the last domino, but the middle dominoes do not knock each other over. This configuration, also illustrated in Figure 3, is known as a *parallel* or *stacked mediator model*. An example from health psychology of a parallel mediator model hypothesizes that the effect of a weight-loss intervention for obese men (independent variable) on body weight 6 months later (outcome) was mediated simultaneously by increases in number of steps per day (mediator #1) and decreases in unhealthy meal choices (mediator #2; Young et al., 2015). The mediator variables

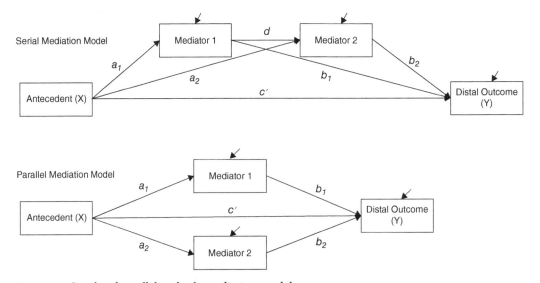

Figure 3. Serial and parallel multiple mediation models.

are parallel because while the two mediator variables may be correlated, increasing steps did not cause a change in meal choices and vice versa.

Multiple mediators increase the complexity of the mediation analysis. An idea that can still be used to cope with this additional complexity, however, is the idea of the total effect of an antecedent on a consequent being equal to the sum of the direct and indirect effects. When there are multiple mediators in a model, there are multiple indirect effects. Each of these indirect effects is unique in that it represents how the effect of the antecedent on the consequent is transmitted through a specific set of mediator variables in a specific order, which is why the effects are called *specific indirect effects* (Bollen, 1987) or *time-specific indirect effects* in autoregressive panel models (Cole & Maxwell, 2003). Using the parallel mediation model in Figure 3, there are two specific indirect effects: a_1b_1 and a_2b_2. The *overall* or *total indirect effect* is equal to the sum of all of the specific indirect effects or $[a_1b_1 + a_2b_2]$. And finally the total effect is then equal to $[a_1b_1 + a_2b_2] + c'$.

Multiple-mediators models can also contain a combination of mediator variables, some serially related, others entered in parallel. For example, Ranby et al. (2009) examined the impact of an intervention designed to decrease unhealthy body behaviors in female student athletes (independent variable) by first causing changes in knowledge, social norms, and mood management (mediators #1–3), which in turn caused changes in outcome expectancies and self-efficacy (mediators #4 and #5), which then changed intentions to use steroids and diet pills (outcome).

Additional Considerations. One of the most important assumptions of the single-mediator model is *temporal precedence*, which states that a cause must precede an effect in time. Thus, to make a strong argument for a variable being a mediator, the measurement of the antecedent, mediator, and consequent must reflect that the antecedent needs time to alter the mediator variable, which in turn needs time to alter the consequent. Therefore, in most cases, longitudinal data measured at a *minimum* of three points in time are needed to adequately assess mediator variables. Due to a variety of factors, including time and resource constraints, however, longitudinal data are used to test for mediation far too rarely. This is particularly problematic because Maxwell and Cole (2007) demonstrated that in most situations, cross-sectional data provide substantially biased estimates of the true longitudinal mediation effects. What this means is that the presence of a statistically significant indirect effect in cross-sectional data *does not* necessarily mean mediation has occurred. That is, not all indirect effects are mediated effects. Another reason for this is that an additional assumption of mediation analysis requires that the causal ordering of the variables is correctly specified and cross-sectional data do not inherently provide any such information regarding the direction of the causal effects. Since effects cannot occur before causes, if the mediator is measured after the antecedent, the mediator cannot cause the antecedent, though it remains the researcher's responsibility to show that the antecedent causes the mediator variable.

Using longitudinal data does not guarantee that all potential timing issues have been correctly addressed, however, because effects do not necessarily remain constant across time. Some effects extinguish, while other effects are delayed. The domino example should make this point readily apparent because if the spacing of the dominoes, or by analogy when the variables in a mediation model are measured, is too wide, then when each domino falls, it cannot knock over the next domino in the chain. Hence, careful consideration needs to be given to the spacing of the measurements of the longitudinal data, which is part of what Collins and Graham (2002) call the *temporal design* of a study, to ensure that each effect is captured at its peak or the mediated effect will be underestimated.

A third assumption of mediation models is that no variables that may explain the relations between the antecedent, mediator, and outcome have been omitted from the model. Omitted variables that have a relationship with the variables in the model may result in biased estimates of the mediated effect, which can lead to incorrect substantive conclusions (e.g., incorrectly concluding that an effect is significant). Note that not controlling for previous levels of the mediator and outcome can also lead to biased estimates (Cole & Maxwell, 2003). The effects of omitted variables on the relation between the antecedent and mediator are minimized with an effective randomization of treatment. Typically, this cannot be done for the mediator, unless individuals are randomized to both the antecedent and mediator variables, which is called *double randomization*. Given the inability to randomly assign the mediator and the knowledge that every model is likely to have some omitted confounder of the mediator-outcome relationship, something must be done to assess the effect that this limitation is having on the parameter estimates. Sensitivity analysis, which is discussed in the "Challenges in Mediation Analysis" section, is a tool that is used to assess the effect that mediator-outcome confounding is having on the estimates.

Even if the assumptions related to longitudinal data, measurement timing, and omitted variables are met, there still may be problems. Yet another assumption of mediation models is that all of the variables are measured without error. In mediation models the effect of violating this assumption is typically that the a and b paths are underestimated, which would make it less likely that the mediated effect is significant (Hoyle & Kenny, 1999). If this was the only possible consequence of measurement error, then measurement error could only force a significant mediated effect to become nonsignificant, but in more complex models the effect of measurement error is not nearly as straightforward. Some paths may be overestimated while others are underestimated (Cole & Preacher, 2014). One way to deal with measurement error is to use latent variable models that correct the estimates of the mediated effect for measurement error.

CURRENT TRENDS IN MEDIATION

Current trends in mediation may be divided into three subsections: (1) computationally intensive approaches that have only been possible with the increase in computational power of personal computers, (2) more complex statistical models that allow for longitudinal data, nesting of data, and categorical variables, and (3) mediation analyses conducted in a causal inference or hypothetical outcomes framework.

Computationally Intensive Approaches. When conducting a mediation analysis, decisions must be made regarding whether the direct and indirect effects are farther from zero than expected by chance, which is typically done using a combination of statistical significance testing (i.e., p-values or confidence intervals) and effect sizes. As discussed previously, neither the Causal Steps Test nor the Joint Significant Test directly tests the mediated effect ab for significance, instead testing the individual effects a and b separately. The First-Order Standard Error (i.e., Sobel) Test does directly test the mediated effect ab, but this test assumes that the sampling distribution of ab is normal, which is typically not the case (MacKinnon et al., 2002). As a result of this shortcoming, computationally intensive approaches that do not rely on normality assumptions have been developed. Many computationally intensive tests of mediation have been developed: three of the most used approaches are described here: the distribution of the product, bootstrapping, and the use of Bayesian methods. In general, any of these three approaches should be used instead of the Causal Steps, Joint Significance, or First-Order Standard Error Tests because they provide more accurate statistical tests and confidence intervals.

Distribution of the Product. The major issue with the First-Order Standard Error Test is that it assumes the mediated effect is normally distributed. Hence, the symmetric confidence intervals created using the first-order standard error are incorrect. But if the actual distribution of the mediated effect was known, it could be used to create correct confidence intervals. The problem is that the distribution of the mediated effect changes shape depending on the values of a, b, and their respective standard errors. MacKinnon and colleagues (MacKinnon, Fritz, Williams, & Lockwood, 2007; MacKinnon, Lockwood, & Williams, 2004; MacKinnon et al., 2002) addressed this issue by creating a program, PRODCLIN, that estimates correct confidence intervals based on the actual distribution of the mediated effect for any values of a and b; this is called the *Distribution of the Product Test*. This work was expanded as a package in the statistical program R by Tofighi and MacKinnon (2011). Due to the distribution of the mediated effect often being skewed, the confidence intervals created by the Distribution of the Product Test are usually asymmetric, meaning that the confidence interval is not centered on the value of ab, but these confidence intervals are interpreted in the same way as symmetric confidence intervals.

Bootstrapping. Another approach to testing the mediated effect that many researchers recommend (e.g., Bollen & Stine, 1990; Lockwood & MacKinnon, 1998; MacKinnon et al., 2004; Preacher & Hayes, 2008; Shrout & Bolger, 2002) that does not rely on the normal distribution is bootstrapping. *Bootstrapping* involves taking repeated samples, called *bootstrap samples*, from the original sample with replacement. For example, consider having a sample of 100 participants from a study—this is the original sample. A bootstrap sample is then created by randomly selecting a sample of 100 cases from this original sample. If the 100 cases in the bootstrap sample were selected without replacing any of the selected cases, the bootstrap sample would be identical to the original sample. If instead each case is replaced after it is selected, then any specific case can be selected multiple times for that bootstrap sample—it is even possible to end up with a bootstrap sample that was made up of all the same case! In general, however, the bootstrap sample will end up with some cases selected from the original sample multiple times and others not selected at all. The mediated effect is then estimated using the data in the bootstrap sample, resulting in a *bootstrap estimate of the mediated effect*.

If a large number of bootstrap samples were taken from the original sample, say 1,000, and then the mediated effect is estimated in each of these bootstrap samples, the result would be 1,000 bootstrap estimates of the mediated effect. If these 1,000 bootstrap estimates of the mediated effect were then sorted from smallest to largest, they would create an *empirical distribution* of the mediated effect (i.e., one based solely on the data) that would closely approximate the actual non-normal distribution of the mediated effect for those specific values of a and b. A 95% confidence interval can then be calculated by finding the bootstrap estimates of the mediated effect that correspond to the 2.5 and 97.5 percentiles of the empirical distribution. The bootstrap confidence interval could then be used to test for statistical significance as with any other confidence interval; this is called the *Percentile Bootstrap Test*. Similar to the Distribution of the Product Test, the Percentile Bootstrap Test will often produce asymmetric confidence intervals. This makes sense, because conceptually these two approaches are doing exactly the same thing. The only difference is that the Distribution of the Product Test is using the actual mathematical distribution to create the confidence intervals, while the Percentile Bootstrap Test is using an empirical distribution based on the data. The Distribution of the Product Test might seem like it is better because it uses the actual distribution, but in more complex mediation models, the computational requirements to find the actual distribution become too difficult to use in practice, while the Percentile Bootstrap Test often works quite well with complex models.

There are several variations on the Percentile Bootstrap Test that are worth mentioning. The *Bias-Corrected Bootstrap Test* includes a correction for potential bias due to skew in the empirical distribution caused by resampling the original data and the *Accelerated Bias-Corrected Bootstrap Test* includes corrections for both skew and kurtosis. In general, both versions of the Bias-Corrected Bootstrap Test perform the same in terms of statistical power and Type I error rate, but recent studies (e.g., Fritz, Taylor, & MacKinnon, 2012) have shown the Bias-Corrected Bootstrap Test has Type I error rates that are too high in many cases, leading researchers to recommend the Percentile Bootstrap Test.

Bayesian. The third computationally intensive approach to mediation analysis discussed here is *Bayesian statistics*. Bayesian approaches to mediation analysis are different from the null hypothesis significance testing most psychologists are trained in, which collectively are known as *frequentist statistics*, because Bayesian statistics do not rely on the idea of sampling error or a p-value. Instead, Bayesian methods for mediation analysis allow the researcher to provide some information about the mediated effect in the population before estimating the effect in the sample using what is known as an *informative prior distribution*. If the research is being conducted in an area where little prior information is available, *uninformative priors* may be used that allow the researcher to maintain the advantages of Bayesian analysis without having to supply an informed prior. While the idea of providing information about the mediated effect before conducting any analyses may seem backwards, Kaplan (2014) notes that the theories and hypotheses that are supposed to be driving the data collection should provide a considerable amount of information about the expected size and direction of the mediated effect. The information provided in the informative prior is then combined with the observed data and new, better estimates of the mediated effect are created in what is known as the *posterior distribution*. Unlike in frequentist statistics, no significance test is performed. Instead, the value of the mediated effect in the posterior distribution must be evaluated based solely on the size of the effect and the variability associated with the effect. It should be noted that methodologists have recommended frequentist statistics for years... (e.g., Wilkinson & APA Task Force on Statistical Inference, 1999), though many psychologists continue to prefer p-values despite the many flaws inherent in them.

Bayesian statistics offer several other advantages for mediation analysis. First, unlike a 95% confidence interval created using frequentist methods, a 95% confidence interval created using Bayesian statistics can actually be interpreted as there being a 95% likelihood that the true value of the mediated effect is within that interval. Second, the more complex the mediation model, the larger the number of parameters that have to be estimated, which usually results in the need for a larger sample size. Bayesian estimation is a tool that may alleviate some of the sample size burden; this is achieved through the incorporation of pre-existing substantive knowledge into the prior distribution as well as the use of exact inference. *Exact inference* simply means that inferences do not rely on large-sample theory, which makes them more ideal for small sample sizes (Yuan & MacKinnon, 2009). Examples from the methodological literature demonstrating the advantages of Bayesian estimation with mediation models are seen in Yuan and MacKinnon for single-level regression as well as multilevel analyses and for multilevel structural equation models (SEM; Hox, van de Schoot, & Matthijsse, 2012).

More Complex Designs

Categorical Mediators and Distal Outcomes. Categorical mediator variables and outcomes expand the typical regression models by introducing data that are not normally distributed. For example, Wyszynski, Bricker, and Comstock (2011) found the effect of a parent's smoking cessation (antecedent) on a child's subsequent smoking behavior as a senior in high school (categorical outcome) was mediated by negative attitudes toward smoking and tobacco refusal self-efficacy (continuous mediator variable). Any combination of continuous/categorical mediator and outcome variables is possible, however—categorical mediator with continuous outcome, continuous mediator with categorical outcome, and both categorical. If viewed through the lens of statistical analysis, the domino example contains a dichotomous mediator as well as a dichotomous outcome because the dominoes may take one of two values (i.e., remain standing or fall over).

The rationale behind analyzing these types of mediating variables is the same as when continuous mediators are being analyzed, but there are some complications. First, a different type of regression must be used when the mediator or the outcome is dichotomous, generally either probit or logistic regression. Second, because the error variances for probit and logistic regression are not estimated, they are fixed, $c - c'$ does not always equal ab because c and c' do not necessarily have the same scale, (MacKinnon & Dwyer, 1993; MacKinnon, Lockwood, Brown, Wang, & Hoffman, 2007). Categorical data in this section are limited to either dichotomous mediators or outcomes. Although not discussed here, count data are another type of data that are often encountered in practice and may be handled in mediation analysis.

Multilevel Mediation. To this point in the discussion, it has been assumed that the data from each participant are independent. Many times in psychology, however, this is not the case, with participants being nested within some structure, such as children nested within classrooms or patients nested within clinics. In these cases, a patient from a given clinic is likely to have more in common with another patient from the same clinic than a patient from a different clinic. Ignoring this non-independence usually results in inflated Type I error rates (Bovaird, 2007), so a different family of models, which go by several names including *multilevel models* and *hierarchical linear models*, is needed to correct for this dependence.

In addition to controlling for clustering, multilevel mediation models allow for some substantively interesting research questions. Specifically, any predictor that is measured for each person (e.g., a treatment administered to a patient) can have an effect that varies depending upon the cluster (e.g., the clinic) in which the treatment was delivered. The term *multilevel* is used because there is variability between individuals (Level 1) and variability between clusters (Level 2) in the same statistical model. Several frameworks exist to study multilevel mediation, but the approach described by Bauer, Preacher, and Gill (2006) is discussed here. In multilevel mediation, the levels of the variables are typically denoted as antecedent level–mediator level–outcome level (Krull & MacKinnon, 2001). Therefore, a 1-1-1 multilevel mediation model would indicate that the antecedent, mediator, and outcome were all person-level variables, not cluster-level variables, while a 2-1-1 multilevel mediation model would mean that the antecedent is measured at the cluster level, which predicts the person-level mediator and outcome. For example, Krull and MacKinnon used a 2-1-1 multilevel mediation model to investigate whether randomly assigning high school football teams to receive an intervention to reduce steroid use or to a control group (cluster-level antecedent) reduced the student's perceived tolerance of steroid use by peers and coaches (person-level mediator), which in turn reduced the student's intentions to use steroids (person-level outcome variable).

Conditional Process Analysis. Although not immediately obvious, in a 2-1-1 multilevel mediation model, both the antecedent and the mediator can have effects that differ between clusters. In the steroid example, it is possible that the effect of perceived tolerance is not the same for all of the football teams (i.e., moderation). Combining mediation and moderation into a single analysis, whether multilevel or single-level, is called a *conditional process model* (Hayes, 2013) where *process* refers to the process of mediation and *conditional* reflects the differential effect of moderation. The term *conditional process model* was coined to replace the often-used terms *moderated mediation* or *mediated moderation* (Muller, Judd, & Yzerbyt, 2005) because of the confusion that surrounds these terms given that researchers have used both terms to describe identical models and both fall within the conditional process model framework. In a conditional process model there is at least one mediator variable and at least one of the paths that make up the mediated effect *ab* is moderated by some fourth variable. Consider the evolution of Fishbein and Ajzen's (1975) Theory of Reasoned Action (TRA) into the Theory of Planned Behavior (TPB; Ajzen, 1991). TRA is a mediation model where the effects of attitudes and subjective norms (both antecedents) on behavior (outcome) are mediated by intentions. Subsequently TRA was expanded to include perceived behavioral control, creating the TPB such that perceived behavioral control is hypothesized to moderate the relationship between intentions and behavior; specifically, intentions are expected to predict behavior better when an individual has higher behavioral control.

Longitudinal Mediation. As described previously, mediation makes an assumption of temporal precedence that requires longitudinal data. When each variable is repeatedly measured across time, an individual's score at the first measurement occasion is likely to be correlated to some degree with his or her score at one or more subsequent measurement occasions, and the non-independence of repeated observations must be accounted for by using statistical models specifically designed for longitudinal data. The first longitudinal model that is discussed is a variation of the regression models that have been discussed previously. If every variable in a single-mediator model is measured at least twice, then the difference between each pair of consecutive scores, called *change scores* or *difference scores*, can be computed. If these change scores are then substituted into the regression equations that are provided in Figure 2, the result is a *change score mediation model*. This model works well for situations where the level of a variable is expected to change between measurements, but this model has several limitations, including the difference score being able to take into account only two repeated-measurements at a time and the fact that the observed difference score is often (Cronbach & Furby, 1970), but not always (MacKinnon, 2008), unreliable.

The second limitation can be addressed through the use of *latent change score models* (LCS; Ferrer & McArdle, 2003), which represent the change between two occasions as a latent variable that is free from measurement error. The mediation version of the LCS, described by MacKinnon (2008), includes a set of LCS models: one for the antecedent, one for the consequent, and one for the mediator. There are several ways in which the mediated effect can be set up with LCS models, including having the observed values of each variable predicting the latent change scores for the subsequent variables in the causal chain, having the latent change scores of each variable predicting the latent change scores for the subsequent variables, or even including a latent variable that measures the change in the latent change scores (i.e., second-order change).

An alternative to change scores are *autoregressive effects*, which occur when a variable's value at one point in time is predicted from one or more previous measurements of the same variable. Though the change score model allows prediction of the change in a variable's value between two successive time points, *autoregressive models* provide for additional flexibility because how many *lags*, that is, the number of previous measurements, to include in the model can be varied. For example, a first-order autoregressive model, AR(1), regresses each measurement on only the previous measurement, while a second-order model, AR(2), regresses each measurement on the previous two measurements (Selig & Preacher, 2009). In the context of mediation, autoregressive models are extremely useful because they can specify not just the autoregressive lags, but also the lags of the mediation effects a, b, and c' (Cole & Maxwell, 2003), allowing for the investigation of many possible time-specific indirect effects. For example, in the autoregressive mediation model in Figure 4 there are five specific indirect effects between the first measurement of the antecedent and the fourth measurement of the outcome. The overall mediated effect of the first measurement of the antecedent on the fourth measurement of the outcome can also be examined.

The change score model examines changes between pairs of successive measurements, while the autoregressive model predicts the value of a variable at one measurement from the same and other variables measured at previous points in time. But what if the goal is to describe the change in the values of a variable across all of the repeated measurements, called a *trajectory*? *Growth curve models* do just that using either a multilevel or a latent variable framework. Growth curve models not only allow the shape of the trajectory to take many forms (e.g., linear, quadratic, exponential decay; Fritz, 2014), but also allow the initial value and rate of growth to vary between individuals. Cheong, Mackinnon, and Khoo (2003) describe a *latent growth curve mediation model* where a dichotomous independent variable changes the trajectory of the mediator across time, which in turn changes the trajectory of the outcome variable.

Because growth curves must be fit independently to each of the continuous variables in the mediation model, the timing of the repeated measurements for each variable must be considered.

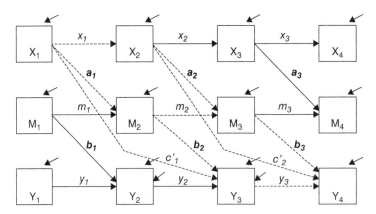

Figure 4. Autoregressive mediation model.

If all variables are measured across the same time span, then the growth processes are occurring simultaneously, resulting in a *parallel process mediation model*. If instead the measurements of the variables are offset to reflect the causal ordering of the variables, then this is known as a *sequential process mediation model*. In parallel process mediation models, it is important to consider that some indirect effects may not be logical. For example, the change in the mediator variable should not be hypothesized to mediate the effect of treatment on the initial status of the consequent. This analysis would be using future data to predict the past when using the change in mediator to predict the starting point of the consequent (Selig & Preacher, 2009).

Causal Mediation. *Causal mediation analysis* is presented in a separate section not because it is new, but because it comes from a seemingly very different perspective from the other models discussed here. Though the discussion of these methods can be complex and intimidating, as with Bayesian methods, the causal methods provide many benefits over traditional methods for mediation analysis (e.g., better estimates of mediated effects, stronger evidence for causality, work better with nonlinear models such as logistic regression), so they warrant a brief overview. Causal mediation analyses come from a *potential outcomes* perspective (Rubin, 1974). The *individual causal effect* of a treatment, which may be thought of as an antecedent with two levels (i.e., $X = 0$ for the control and $X = 1$ for the treatment condition), is defined as the difference in the potential score on an outcome variable Y between what would have happened if participant *i* received the treatment, $Y_i(X_i = 1)$, compared to the potential score on the outcome if participant *i* did not receive the treatment, $Y_i(X_i = 0)$. That is, the individual causal effect of the treatment X for individual *i* is equal to $Y_i(X_i = 1) - Y_i(X_i = 0)$.

The problem with the individual causal effect, however, is that both of these potential outcome scores cannot be observed because participant *i* cannot simultaneously be in the treatment *and* control conditions. Suppose participant *i* was assigned to the treatment condition—then $Y_i(X_i = 1)$ could be observed, which is called the *factual*. Because participant *i* cannot also be assigned to the control, $Y_i(X_i = 0)$ cannot be observed, which is called the *counterfactual* (Splawa-Neyman, 1990). Thus, the individual causal effect can never be directly calculated, which is the *Fundamental Problem of Causal Inference* (Holland, 1986). Instead *average causal effects* are used, which are based on the assumption that randomly assigning participants to the treatment conditions creates equivalent groups of individuals. The average causal effect of the treatment X is the difference in the mean outcome scores for the participants who receive the different treatments (i.e., $E[Y(X=1)] - E[Y(X=0)]$ where E is used to denote the expected population mean) and provides an unbiased estimate of the individual causal effect. While the average causal effect can provide quite a bit of information about the causal relation between the antecedent and the mediator, it does not provide much information about the causal relation between the mediator and the outcome because often it is impossible, either physically or ethically, to randomly assign individuals to levels of the mediator. Causal mediation methods attempt to address this shortcoming of the traditional mediation methods.

Unlike traditional methods, causal mediation analysis has a variety of effects, both direct and indirect (MacKinnon, Valente, & Wurpts, 2015; Muthén & Asparouhov, 2015; Pearl, 2009). The *controlled direct effect* (CDE) is the effect of the treatment on the outcome when the mediator is held constant at some value m and is equivalent to the direct effect c' from traditional mediation analysis when the data are continuous and normally distributed. The CDE is solely a direct effect because the mediator is held constant. There is also the *pure natural direct effect* (PNDE) and *total natural direct effect* (TNDE). The PNDE is the effect the treatment has on the outcome when the mediator is allowed to vary as it would in the control condition. This may be thought of as the effect that the treatment would have if the mediator was maintained at the level it would have taken in the absence of the treatment. The TNDE is the effect of treatment on the outcome when the mediator is allowed to vary as it would in the treatment condition. There are also multiple indirect effects. The *total natural indirect effect* (TNIE) and the *pure natural indirect effect* (PNIE) are similar to the TNDE and PNDE because the TNIE is the indirect effect that the treatment has on the outcome through the mediator when the direct effect is allowed to vary as it would in the treatment condition. The PNIE is conceptually similar except that the treatment effect is allowed to vary as it would in the control condition. The *total effect* may then be computed as the sum of the PNDE and TNIE or the sum of the TNDE and the PNIE.

CHALLENGES IN MEDIATION ANALYSIS

By definition, mediator variables are part of a causal chain. From their undergraduate methods and statistics courses onward, psychologists have learned that *correlation does not equal causation* and *causal effects can only be measured with randomized experiments*. Though the truth of the situation is much more nuanced than these maxims allow, this does present a serious challenge to psychologists who test mediation hypotheses. For example, in a cross-sectional strictly observational study, statistically significant tests of mediation are likely to provide only very weak evidence of mediation occurring. Randomly assigning individuals to levels of the antecedent provides stronger evidence because it should provide a good estimate of the causal effect of the antecedent on the mediator, but unless individuals can also be randomly assigned to levels of the mediator variable, the relation between the mediator and the outcome is still strictly correlations. Using longitudinal data may provide still stronger, but again not conclusive, evidence. Then what can be done? The key to making a strong claim for mediation lies in the testing of the assumptions of the mediation model and creating a preponderance of evidence rather than relying on a single statistical test (MacKinnon, 2008).

Measurement. One of the basic assumptions of all research in psychology is that valid, reliable measures of the variables are being used, but few variables in psychology are completely reliable. Unreliable measures of mediator variables almost always result in biased estimates of the mediated effect in single-mediator models, with the bias in many of these situations resulting in the estimates being too small (Fritz, Kenny, & MacKinnon, 2016). Moving to more complex models with multiple mediator variables results in even more concern about the estimates, not because the bias is necessarily worse, but because the combined effect of unreliability in each of the individual variables in the model on the estimate of the mediated effect is difficult to predict. That is, the estimate of the mediated effect could be too big, too small, opposite in sign, or even unbiased depending on the pattern of relations between variables, the levels of unreliability, and the specific model. Latent variable models can correct for much of the measurement error in mediation models, but a researcher's evidence for mediation may be limited by the reliability of their measures. Hence, psychologists interested in finding evidence for mediation need to stop relying on measures whose reliability is just *good enough*.

Temporal Design. Another unavoidable issue concerns the use of longitudinal data. While cross-sectional data do not meet the assumption of temporal precedence, the use of longitudinal data does not guarantee temporal precedence is met either (Mitchell & Maxwell, 2013). Remember that the timing and spacing of the measurements must be accurate in order to allow the variables to have effects on one another and for those effects to be captured at their peak (Fritz & MacKinnon, 2012). Decisions regarding when and how often to measure the variables in a mediation model must be made largely based on theory. For example, what is the expected pattern of change over time? If the theory includes personality traits that do not change over time or the relation between the antecedent and the mediator is expected to be linear, then many time points may not be necessary. A theory about personality states or nonlinear relationships, such as exponential decay, likely requires many time points spaced in a manner that captures the change over time accurately. Additionally, an incorrect measurement interval or only having a few measurements may lead to incorrect decisions regarding the pattern of change over time or the presence of an effect at all. An optimal temporal design therefore requires researchers to make more specific hypotheses regarding how individual variables change over time before making hypotheses about longitudinal relations between variables, especially ones that involve mediator variables. If a researcher does not have enough information to include the temporal design in the mediation hypothesis, then more work is needed prior to conducting the study.

Sensitivity Analysis. Even if perfectly reliable measures and longitudinal data that are measured at exactly the correct intervals are used, there are still some assumptions of mediation models that are simply not going to be met in a majority of psychology studies. Consider the assumption discussed previously that no variables, such as confounders or additional mediators, are omitted from the model, known as *sequential ignorability*. The omitted variable assumption could be accounted for by simply measuring every variable related to the antecedent, mediator, and outcome variable, and then including them into the model. But it is practically impossible to measure and include every relevant variable, even if they could be identified! This becomes especially true when one considers that the mediation model being tested is almost guaranteed to be just one small piece of a much larger process. Left with no reasonable way to avoid violating this assumption, the effect that violating this assumption has on the mediated effect must be estimated, which is known as *sensitivity analysis* (Cox, Kisbu-Sakarya, Miočević, & MacKinnon, 2014).

While numerous authors have presented methods for conducting a sensitivity analysis (e.g., Imai, Keele, & Tingley, 2010), Liu, Kuramoto, and Stuart (2013) state that all sensitivity analyses come from one of two traditions. Sensitivity analyses that come from a classic statistical tradition attempt to determine how large the effect of an omitted variable is needed for the effect of the mediator variable to be exactly zero, or at least no longer statistically significant. Those that come from the epidemiological tradition, however, attempt to determine how much of the mediated effect can be explained by other related variables. A sensitivity analysis that found only a very weakly related variable would need to be omitted for the effect of the mediator variable to become nonsignificant suggests that the results provide poor evidence for mediation. In contrast, a sensitivity analysis that found the effect of the mediator variable persists unless an improbably or even impossibly important variable is omitted provides strong evidence for mediation. Therefore, a mediation analysis without a sensitivity analysis is incomplete and the reporting of sensitivity analyses along with statistical tests of mediation should be standard in psychology.

Multiple Studies and Multiple Designs.   Finally, just as mediation is a process, establishing that a variable is a mediator is a process. While exactly replicating a mediation study may seem like a waste of time to many busy psychologists, given the recent concerns regarding the nonreplicability of published studies in psychology (e.g., Open Science Collaboration, 2015), exact replications are no sure thing and can provide much needed evidence for a variable being a mediator. Conceptual replications that vary specific contextual factors or measures of variables are likely to provide a wealth of information as well, particularly for conditional process models. But moving beyond replications, multiple studies that examine the different pieces of the mediation model are more likely to provide the necessary strong evidence for a variable being a mediator. Consider a series of studies conducted on the same variables. In the first study, a preliminary cross-sectional observational study is conducted to determine if the proposed antecedent, mediator, and outcome variables are related. In the second study, the author measures these same variables multiple times to determine if there is a longitudinal relation between the variables. In a third study, the researcher manipulates the antecedent variable, randomly assigning individuals to levels of the antecedent to determine if changing the antecedent changes the mediator and outcome. In a fourth study, participants are randomly assigned to levels of the mediator to determine if changing the mediator changes the outcome variable. Taken together, the findings from these four studies provide much stronger evidence of mediation than any of these studies on their own.

CONCLUSIONS

Mediator variables are one of the most frequently hypothesized variable types in psychology because of their scientific value in exploring and explaining relations between variables. Although a plethora of research on mediator variables has been conducted since Baron and Kenny (1986), mediation research is by no means a stagnant field without methodological innovation. Developments in methods to assess mediating variables are developed in many fields (e.g., psychology, epidemiology, statistics, education, and computer science). The challenge for psychologists today is staying abreast of these developments that are published in a wide array of methodological and applied statistical journals, which may be difficult to access for psychologists. Luckily, the Internet has improved access to new developments as well as a host of Web-based tools for conducting and interpreting mediation analyses.

ACKNOWLEDGMENTS

This research was supported in part by a grant from the National Institute on Drug Abuse (DA 009757).

FURTHER READING

This list includes books and articles that will provide a more thorough introduction to past and current trends in assessing mediator variables. Five books are: *Introduction to Mediation, Moderation, and Conditional Process Analysis: A Regression-Based Approach* (Hayes, 2013), *Causal Inference* (Hernán & Robins, 2010), *Causal Inference in Statistics: A Primer* (Pearl, Glymour, & Jewell, 2016), *Introduction to Statistical Mediation Analysis* (MacKinnon, 2008), and *Explanation in Causal Inference: Methods for Mediation and Moderation* (VanderWeele, 2015). Five articles are: James and Brett (1984), Baron and Kenny (1986), MacKinnon, Lockwood, Hoffman, West, and Sheets (2002), Holland (1986), and Muthén and Asparouhov (2015).

REFERENCES

Ajzen, I. (1991). The theory of planned behavior. *Organizational Behavior and Human Decision Processes, 50,* 179–211. http://dx.doi.org/10.1016/0749-5978(91)90020-t

Baron, R. M., & Kenny, D. A. (1986). The moderator-mediator variable distinction in social psychological research: Conceptual, strategic and statistical considerations. *Journal of Personality and Social Psychology, 51,* 1173–1182. http://dx.doi.org/10.1037/0022-3514.51.6.1173

Bauer, D. J., Preacher, K. J., & Gil, K. M. (2006). Conceptualizing and testing random indirect effects and moderated mediation in multilevel models: New procedures and recommendations. *Psychological Methods, 11,* 142–163. http://dx.doi.org/10.1037/1082-989X.11.2.142

Bollen, K. A. (1987). Total, direct, and indirect effects in structural equation models. *Sociological Methodology, 17,* 37–69. http://dx.doi.org/10.2307/271028

Bollen, K. A., & Stine, R. (1990). Direct and indirect effects: Classical and bootstrap estimates of variability. *Sociological Methodology, 20,* 115–140. http://dx.doi.org/10.2307/271084

Bovaird, J. A. (2007). Multilevel structural equation models for contextual factors. In T. D. Little, J. A. Bovaird, & N. A. Wainer (Eds.), *Modeling contextual effects in longitudinal studies* (pp. 151–182). Mahwah, NJ: Lawrence Erlbaum Associates.

Cheong, J., MacKinnon, D. P., & Khoo, S. T. (2003). Investigation of mediational processes using parallel process latent growth curve modeling. *Structural Equation Modeling*, 10, 238–262. http://dx.doi.org/10.1207/s15328007sem1002_5

Cole, D. A., & Maxwell, S. E. (2003). Testing mediational models with longitudinal data: Questions and tips in the use of structural equation modeling. *Journal of Abnormal Psychology*, 112, 558–577. http://dx.doi.org/10.1037/0021-843X.112.4.558

Cole, D. A., & Preacher, K. J. (2014). Manifest variable path analysis: Potentially serious and misleading consequences due to uncorrected measurement error. *Psychological Methods*, 19, 300–315. http://dx.doi.org/10.1037/a0033805

Collins, L. M., & Graham, J. W. (2002). The effect of the timing and spacing of observations in longitudinal studies of tobacco and other drug use: Temporal design considerations. *Drug and Alcohol Dependence*, 68, 85–96. http://dx.doi.org/10.1016/s0376-8716(02)00217-x

Cox, M. G., Kisbu-Sakarya, Y., Miočević, M., & MacKinnon, D. P. (2014). Sensitivity plots for confounder bias in the single mediator model. *Evaluation Review*, 37, 405–431. http://dx.doi.org/10.1177/0193841X14524576

Cronbach, L. J., & Furby, L. (1970). How we should measure "change": Or should we? *Psychological Bulletin*, 74, 68. http://dx.doi.org/10.1037/h0029382

Cuijpers, P., Weitz, E., Twisk, J., Kuehner, C., Cristea, I., David, D., DuRubeis, R. J., Dimidjian, S., Dunlop, B. W., Faramarzi, M., Hegerl, U., Jarrett, R. B., Kennedy, S. H., Kheirkhah, F., Mergl, R., Miranda, J., Mohr, D. C., Segal, Z. V., Siddique, J., Hollon, S. D. (2014). Gender as predictor and moderator of outcome in cognitive behavior therapy and pharmacotherapy for adult depression: An "individual patient data" meta-analysis. *Depression and Anxiety*, 31, 941–951. http://dx.doi.org/10.1002/da.22328

Ferrer, E., & McArdle, J. J. (2003). Alternative structural models for multivariate longitudinal data analysis. *Structural Equation Modeling*, 10, 493–524. http://dx.doi.org/10.1207/s15328007sem1004_1

Fishbein, M., & Ajzen, I. (1975). *Belief, attitude, intention, and behavior: An introduction to theory and research.* Reading, MA: Addison-Wesley.

Fritz, M. S. (2014). An exponential decay model for mediation. *Prevention Science*, 15, 611–622. http://dx.doi.org/10.1007/s11121-013-0390-x

Fritz, M. S., Kenny, D. A., & MacKinnon, D. P. (2016). The combined effects of measurement error and omitting confounders in the single-mediator model. *Multivariate Behavioral Research*, 51, 681–697. http://dx.doi.org/10.1080/00273171.2016.1224154

Fritz, M. S., & MacKinnon, D. P. (2012). Mediation models for developmental data. In B. Laursen, T. Little, & N. Card (Eds.), *Handbook of developmental research methods* (pp. 291–310). New York: Guilford Press.

Fritz, M. S., Taylor, A. B., & MacKinnon, D. P. (2012). Explanation of two anomalous results in statistical mediation analysis. *Multivariate Behavioral Research*, 47, 61–87. http://dx.doi.org/10.1080/00273171.2012.640596

Hayes, A. F. (2013). *Introduction to mediation, moderation, and conditional process analysis: A regression-based approach.* New York: Guilford Press.

Hernán, M. A., & Robins, J. M. (2010). *Causal inference.* Boca Raton, FL: CRC.

Holland, P. W. (1986). Statistics and causal inference. *Journal of the American Statistical Association*, 81, 945–960. http://dx.doi.org/10.1080/01621459.1986.10478354

Hox, J., van de Schoot, R., & Matthijsse, S. (2012). How few countries will do? Comparative survey analysis from a Bayesian perspective. *Survey Research Methods*, 6, 87–93.

Hoyle, R. H., & Kenny, D. A. (1999). Sample size, reliability, and tests of statistical mediation. In R. H. Hoyle (Ed.), *Statistical strategies for small sample research* (pp. 196–222). Thousand Oaks, CA: SAGE.

Imai, K., Keele, L., & Tingley, D. (2010). A general approach to causal mediation analysis. *Psychological Methods*, 15, 309–334. http://dx.doi.org/10.1037/a0020761

James, L. R., & Brett, J. M. (1984). Mediators, moderators and tests for mediation. *Journal of Applied Psychology, 69*, 307–321. http://dx.doi.org/10.1037/0021-9010.69.2.307

Judd, C. M., & Kenny, D. A. (1981). Process analysis: Estimating mediation in treatment evaluations. *Evaluation Review, 5*, 602–619. http://dx.doi.org/10.1177/0193841x8100500502

Kaplan, D. (2014). *Bayesian statistics for the social sciences.* New York: Guilford Press.

Kaufman, N. K., Rohde, P., Seeley, J. R., Clarke, G. N., & Stice, E. (2005). Potential mediators of cognitive-behavioral therapy for adolescents with comorbid major depression and conduct disorder. *Journal of Consulting and Clinical Psychology, 73*, 38–46. http://dx.doi.org/10.1037/0022-006X.73.1.38

Krull, J. L., & MacKinnon, D. P. (2001). Multilevel modeling of individual and group level mediated effects. *Multivariate Behavioral Research, 36*, 249–277. http://dx.doi.org/10.1207/S15327906MBR3602_06

Le Roy, M. (2009). *Research methods in political science: An introduction using MicroCase®* (7th ed.). Boston: Cengage Learning.

Li, Y., Schneider, J. A., & Bennett, D. A. (2007). Estimation of the mediation effect with a binary mediator. *Statistics in Medicine, 26*, 3398–3414. http://dx.doi.org/10.1002/sim.2730

Liu, W., Kuramoto, S. J., & Stuart, E. A. (2013). An introduction to sensitivity analysis for unobserved confounding in non-experimental prevention research. *Prevention Science, 14*, 570–580.

Lockwood, C. M., & MacKinnon, D. P. (1998). Bootstrapping the standard error of the mediated effect. *Proceedings of the Twenty-Third Annual SAS Users Group International Conference* (pp. 997–1002). Cary, NC: SAS Institute.

MacKinnon, D. P. (2008). *Introduction to statistical mediation analysis.* New York: Erlbaum.

MacKinnon, D. P., & Dwyer, J. H. (1993). Estimating mediated effects in prevention studies. *Evaluation Review, 17*, 144–158. http://dx.doi.org/10.1177/0193841x9301700202

MacKinnon, D. P., Fritz, M. S., Williams, J., & Lockwood, C. M. (2007). Distribution of the product confidence limits for the indirect effect: Program PRODCLIN. *Behavior Research Methods, 39*, 384–389. http://dx.doi.org/10.3758/BF03193007

MacKinnon, D. P., Krull, J. L., & Lockwood, C. M. (2000). Equivalence of the mediation, confounding and suppression effect. *Prevention Science, 1*, 173–181. http://dx.doi.org/10.1023/a:1026595011371

MacKinnon, D. P., Lockwood, C. M., Brown, C. H., Wang, W., & Hoffman, J. M. (2007). The intermediate endpoint effect in logistic and probit regression. *Clinical Trials, 4*, 499–513. http://dx.doi.org/10.1177/1740774507083434

MacKinnon, D. P., Lockwood, C. M., Hoffman, J., West, S., & Sheets, V. (2002). A comparison of methods to test mediated and other intervening variable effects. *Psychological Methods, 7*, 83–104. http://dx.doi.org/10.1037/1082-989x.7.1.83

MacKinnon, D. P., Lockwood, C. M., & Williams, J. (2004). Confidence limits for the indirect effect: Distribution of the product and resampling methods. *Multivariate Behavioral Research, 39*, 99–128. http://dx.doi.org/10.1207/s15327906mbr3901_4

MacKinnon, D. P., Valente, M. J., & Wurpts, I. C. (2015, October). *The centrality of the intervention by mediator interaction in causal mediation analysis.* Paper presented at the annual meeting of the Society for Multivariate Experimental Psychology, Redondo Beach, CA.

MacKinnon, D. P., Warsi, G., & Dwyer, J. H. (1995). A simulation study of mediated effect measures. *Multivariate Behavioral Research, 30*, 41–62. http://dx.doi.org/10.1207/s15327906mbr3001_3

Maxwell, S. E., & Cole, D. A. (2007). Bias in cross-sectional analyses of longitudinal mediation. *Psychological Methods, 12*, 23–44. http://dx.doi.org/10.1037/1082-989X.12.1.23

Mitchell, M. A., & Maxwell, S. E. (2013). A comparison of the cross-sectional and sequential designs when assessing longitudinal mediation. *Multivariate Behavioral Research, 48*, 301–339. http://dx.doi.org/10.1080/00273171.2013.784696

Muller, D., Judd, C. M., & Yzerbyt, V. Y. (2005). When moderation is mediated and mediation is moderated. *Journal of Personality and Social Psychology, 89*, 852–863. http://dx.doi.org/10.1037/0022-3514.89.6.852

Muthén, B., & Asparouhov, T. (2015). Causal effects in mediation modeling: An introduction with applications to latent variables. *Structural Equation Modeling*, 22, 12–23. http://dx.doi.org/10.1080/10705511.2014.935843

Open Science Collaboration. (2015). Estimating the reproducibility of psychological science. *Science*, 349 (6251), 943. http://dx.doi.org/10.1126/science.aac4716

Pearl, J. (2009). *Causality* (2d ed.). Cambridge, U.K.: Cambridge University Press.

Pearl, J., Glymour, M., & Jewell, N. P. (2016). *Causal inference in statistics: A primer*. New York: Wiley.

Preacher, K. J., & Hayes, A. F. (2008). Asymptotic and resampling strategies for assessing and comparing indirect effects in multiple mediator models. *Behavior Research Methods*, 40, 879–891. http://dx.doi.org/10.3758/brm.40.3.879

Ranby, K. W., Aiken, L. S., MacKinnon, D. P., Elliot, D. L., Moe, E. L., McGinnis, W., & Goldberg, L. (2009). A mediation analysis of the ATHENA intervention for female athletes: Prevention of athletic-enhancing substance use and unhealthy weight loss behaviors. *Journal of Pediatric Psychology*, 34, 1069–1083. http://dx.doi.org/10.1093/jpepsy/jsp025

Rubin, D. B. (1974). Estimating causal effects of treatments in randomized and nonrandomized studies. *Journal of Educational Psychology*, 66, 688–701. http://dx.doi.org/10.1037/h0037350

Selig, J. P., & Preacher, K. J. (2009). Mediation models for longitudinal data in developmental research. *Research in Human Development*, 6, 144–164. http://dx.doi.org/10.1080/15427600902911247

Shrout, P. E., & Bolger, N. (2002). Mediation in experimental and nonexperimental studies: New procedures and recommendations. *Psychological Methods*, 7, 422–445. http://dx.doi.org/10.1037/1082-989x.7.4.422

Sobel, M. E. (1982). Asymptotic confidence intervals for indirect effects in structural equation models. In S. Leinhardt (Ed.), *Sociological methodology* (pp. 290–312). Washington, DC: American Sociological Association. http://dx.doi.org/10.2307/270723

Splawa-Neyman, J. (1990). On the application of probability theory to agricultural experiments. Essays on Principles. Section 9. *Statistical Science*, 5, 465–472. Originally published in Polish in 1923.

Tett, R. P., & Meyer, J. P. (1993). Job satisfaction, organizational commitment, turnover intention, and turnover: Path analyses based on meta-analytic findings. *Personnel Psychology*, 46, 259–293. http://dx.doi.org/10.1111/j.1744-6570.1993.tb00874.x

Tofighi, D., & MacKinnon D. P. (2011). RMediation: An R package for mediation analysis confidence intervals. *Behavior Research Methods*, 43, 692–700. http://dx.doi.org/10.3758/s13428-011-0076-x

VanderWeele, T. J. (2015). *Explanation in causal inference: Methods for mediation and moderation*. Oxford: Oxford University Press.

Wilkinson, L., & APA Task Force on Statistical Inference. (1999). Statistical methods in psychology journals: Guidelines and explanations. *American Psychologist*, 54, 594–604. http://dx.doi.org/10.1037/0003-066x.54.8.594

Woodworth, R. S. (1926). Dynamic psychology. In C. Murchison (Ed.), *Psychologies of 1925* (pp. 111–126). Worcester, MA: Clark University Press. http://dx.doi.org/10.1037/11020-005

Wright, S. (1921). The theory of path coefficients: A reply to Niles's criticism. *Genetics*, 8, 239–255.

Wyszynski, C. M., Bricker, J. B., & Comstock, B. A. (2011). Parental smoking cessation and child daily smoking: A 9-year longitudinal study of mediation by child cognitions about smoking. *Health Psychology*, 30, 171–176. http://dx.doi.org/10.1037/a0022024

Young, M. D., Lubans, D. R., Collins, C. E., Callister, R., Plotnikoff, R. C., & Morgan, P. J. (2015). Behavioral mediators of weight loss in the SHED-IT community randomized controlled trial for overweight and obese men. *Annals of Behavioral Medicine*, 49, 286–292. http://dx.doi.org/10.1007/s12160-014-9657-0

Yuan, Y., & MacKinnon, D. P. (2009). Bayesian mediation analysis. *Psychological Methods*, 14, 301–322. http://dx.doi.org/10.1037/a0016972

Matthew S. Fritz and Houston F. Lester

MODERATOR VARIABLES

OVERVIEW OF CURRENT STATUS

Definition. When the strength of the association between two variables is conditional on the value of a third variable, this third variable is called a *moderator variable*. That is, the magnitude and even the direction of the relation between one variable, usually referred to as a *predictor* or *independent variable*, and a second variable, often called an *outcome* or *dependent variable*, depend on the value of the moderator variable. Consider baking bread in an oven. In general, the higher the temperature of the oven (independent variable), the faster the bread will finish baking (dependent variable). But consider a baker making two different types of bread dough, one with regular white flour and the other with whole-wheat flour. Keeping the temperature constant, if the bread made with whole-wheat flour took longer to finish baking than the bread made with white flour, then the type of flour would be a moderator variable, because the relation between temperature and cooking time *differs* depending on the type of flour that was used. Note that moderating variables are not necessarily assumed to directly cause the outcome to change, only to be associated with change in the strength and/or the direction of the association between the predictor and the outcome.

Moderator variables are extremely important to psychologists because they provide a more detailed explanation of the specific circumstances under which an observed association between two variables holds and whether this association is the same for different contexts or groups of people. This is one reason why contextual variables and demographic variables, such as age, gender, ethnicity, socioeconomic status, and education, are some of the mostly commonly examined moderator variables in psychology. Moderator variables are particularly useful in experimental psychology to explore whether a specific treatment always has the same effect or if differential effects appear when another condition, context, or type of participant is introduced. That is, moderator variables advance our understanding of the effect. For example, Avolio, Mhatre, Norman, and Lester (2009) conducted a meta-analysis of leadership intervention studies and found that the effect of leadership interventions on a variety of outcome variables differed depending on whether the participants were all- or majority-male compared to when the participants were all- or majority-female.

The most important issue to consider when deciding whether a variable is a moderator of the relation between two other variables is the word *different*, because if the relation between two variables does not differ when the value of the third variable changes, the third variable is not a moderator variable and therefore must be playing some other role, if any. As illustrated in Figure 1, a third variable is a *confounder variable* when it explains all or part of the relation between an independent variable and an outcome, but unlike a moderating variable, the magnitude of the relation between the independent and dependent variable does not change as the value of the confounder variable changes. A classic example of a confounding effect is the significant positive relation between ice cream consumption and violent crime. Ice cream consumption does not cause an increase in violent crime or vice versa; rather, the rise in both can be explained in part by a third variable—warmer temperatures (Le Roy, 2009). Moderator variables are also often confused with *mediator variables*, which are intermediate variables in a causal chain, such that changes in the independent variable (or *antecedent*) cause changes in

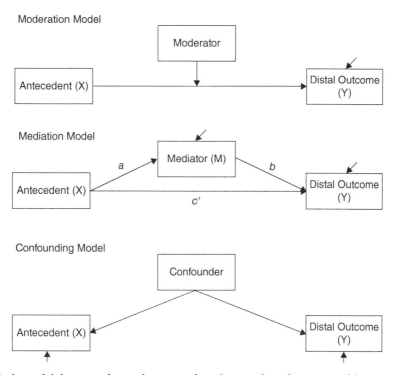

Figure 1. Path model diagrams for mediator, confounding, and moderator variables.

the mediator variable, which then cause changes in the outcome variable (or *consequent*). For example, receiving cognitive-behavioral therapy (CBT; independent variable) has been found to cause reductions in negative thinking (mediating variable), and the reduction in negative thinking in turn reduces depressive symptoms (outcome variable; Kaufman, Rohde, Seeley, Clarke, & Stice, 2005). Moderator variables are not assumed to be part of a causal chain.

Interaction Models. When a moderator variable is present, such that the strength of the relation between an independent and dependent variable differs depending on the value of the moderator variable, the moderator variable is said to *moderate* the relation between the other two variables. The combined effect of the moderator variable with the independent variable is also called an *interaction* to reflect the interplay between the two variables, which differs from the individual effects of the independent and moderator variables on the dependent variable. This means that although the moderator variable changes the relation between the independent variable and outcome, the strength of the relation between the moderator variable and the outcome in turn differs depending on the values of the independent variable. Hence, the independent and moderator variables simultaneously moderate the relation between the other variable and the outcome. When an interaction term is statistically significant, it is not possible to interpret the effect of the independent variable alone because the effect depends on the level of the moderator variable.

Categorical by Categorical (2×2). To illustrate the idea of an interaction, consider the finding by Revelle, Humphreys, Simon, and Gilliland (1980) that the relation between caffeine consumption and performance on a cognitive ability task is moderated by personality type. Specifically, Revelle et al. (1980) used a 2×2 between-subjects analysis of variance (ANOVA) design to examine the impact of consuming caffeine (independent variable; 0 mg or 200 mg) and personality type (moderator variable; introvert vs. extrovert) on cognitive performance (outcome; score on a practice GRE test).[1] Examination of the mean performance for the *main effect* of caffeine, which is the effect of caffeine collapsing across the personality type factor and shown in Figure 2a, demonstrates that the participants who received caffeine performed better than those who did not receive caffeine. Hence, one might categorically conclude that caffeine improves performance for everyone. In turn, the mean performance for the main effect of personality, which is the effect of personality type collapsing across the caffeine factor (Figure 2b), shows that extroverts performed better than introverts. When the means are plotted for the four cross-factor groups in the study (Figure 2c), however, it is apparent that although caffeine increased the performance of the extroverts, it actually decreased the performance of the introverts. Therefore, personality moderates the relation between caffeine and performance. In turn, caffeine moderates the relation between personality and performance because although introverts performed better than the extroverts regardless of caffeine consumption, the difference in performance between introverts and extroverts is larger for those who did not receive caffeine than those who did. Note that the vertical axis only shows a limited range of observed outcome values, so the response scale may have limited the real differences.

Finding a statistically significant interaction term in an ANOVA model tells us that *moderation* is occurring, but provides no further information about the specific form of the interaction (unless one looks at the coefficient for the interaction, which is usually ignored in ANOVA, but will be considered when moderator variables are discussed in the multiple regression context). Full understanding of the relation between the independent and moderator variables requires examination of the interaction in more detail, a process called *probing* (Aiken & West, 1991). Probing an interaction in ANOVA typically involves testing each of the *simple main effects*, which are the effects of the independent variable at each level of the moderator. In the caffeine example, there are two simple main effects of the independent variable at levels of the moderator variable: the simple main effect of caffeine for introverts, represented by the solid line in Figure 2c, and the simple main effect of caffeine for extroverts, represented by the dashed line. The plot makes it clear that caffeine had a larger effect on performance for the extroverts than the introverts (i.e., the ends of the dashed line are farther apart vertically than the ends of the solid line), but the plot alone cannot show whether there is a significant effect of caffeine in either of the personality groups; hence the need for statistical tests.

Another way to conceptualize moderation is to say that moderation occurs when the simple main effects of an independent variable on an outcome are not the same for all levels of the moderator variable. If the effect of caffeine on performance was the same for both introverts and extroverts, the two simple main effects would be the same and the two lines in Figure 2c would be parallel. Instead, the two simple main effect lines are not parallel, indicating different simple main effects (i.e., moderation). Despite the moderating effect of personality on the relation between caffeine and performance illustrated in Figure 2c, the introverts always performed better than the extroverts in this study. As a result, though the lines are not parallel and

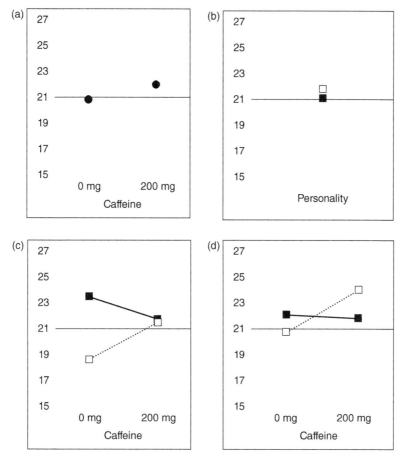

Figure 2. 2×2 Interaction: (a) Main effect of caffeine; (b) Main effect of personality type (black = introvert, white = extrovert); (c) Interaction between caffeine and personality type on Day 1 (black/solid = introvert, white/dotted = extrovert); and (d) Interaction between caffeine and personality on Day 2.
(Redrawn from Revelle et al., 1980)

must cross at some point, the lines do not intersect in the figure. When the simple main effect lines do not intersect within the observed range of values, the interaction is said to be *ordinal* (Lubin, 1961) because the groups maintain their order (e.g., introverts always outperform extroverts). When the simple main effect lines cross within the observed range of values, the interaction is said to be *disordinal* because the groups do not have the same order for all values of the moderator. A disordinal interaction is illustrated in Figure 2d, which again shows the same simple main effects of caffeine on performance for the different personality types, but for individuals who completed the same protocol the following day (Revelle et al., 1980).

What is important to consider when probing an interaction is what effect the moderator has on the relation between the other two variables. For example, the relation between the independent and dependent variables may have the same sign and be statistically significant for all values of the moderator, in which case the moderator only changes the magnitude of the relation. Alternatively, the relation between the independent and dependent variables may not be statistically significant at all values of the moderator, indicating that the relation exists only for specific values of the moderator. A third possibility is that the relation between the independent and dependent variables is statistically significant, but opposite in sign for different values of the moderator. This would indicate that the direction of the relation between the variables depends on the moderator. These are very different interaction effects that the statistical significance of the interaction term alone will not differentiate between, which is why probing interactions is essential to describing the effect of a moderator variable.

There are two additional issues to consider. First, the labeling of one variable as the independent variable and the other variable as the moderator is guided by theory. Because a significant interaction means that caffeine is also moderating the effect of personality on performance, the simple main effects of personality at levels of caffeine may also be considered; in this case, the simple main effect of personality type on performance for the 0 mg caffeine group and the simple main effect of personality type on performance for the 200 mg caffeine group. Since the statistical model is the same regardless of whether personality is the independent variable and caffeine is the moderator or vice versa, the assignment of roles to these variables is left up to the researcher. Second, while the 2×2 ANOVA framework is a simple design that lends itself to probing interactions, splitting a continuous variable at its mean or median in order to force continuous variables to fit into the ANOVA framework is a very bad idea, as it not only results in a loss of information that decreases statistical power, but also increases the likelihood of finding spurious interaction effects (Maxwell & Delaney, 1993).

Categorical by Categorical (3×3). Probing a significant interaction in a 2×2 ANOVA is relatively straightforward because there are only two levels of each factor. When a simple main effect is statistically significant, there is a difference in the average score on the dependent variable between the two levels of the independent variable for that specific value of the moderator. The significant overall interaction then tells us that the difference in the means for the two levels of the independent variable are not the same for both values of the moderator. When there are more than two levels, probing an interaction in ANOVA becomes more complicated. For example, imagine if Revelle et al. (1980) had employed a 3×3 ANOVA design, where participants were randomized to one of three levels of caffeine (e.g., 0, 100, and 200 mg) and personality type was also allowed to have three levels (e.g., introvert, neutral, extrovert). In this case, a significant main effect of caffeine would only tell us that the mean performance in at least one of the caffeine groups was different than the mean performance in the other two groups, collapsing across personality type, but not specifically which caffeine groups differed in mean performance. Determining which groups differed requires a *main effect contrast*, also called a *main comparison*, which specifically compared two or more of the groups. For example, a main effect contrast could be used to examine the mean difference in performance between just the 100 mg and 200 mg groups.

The same issue extends to probing the interaction because a significant interaction in the 3×3 ANOVA case only demonstrates that the simple main effects of caffeine are not the same for all levels personality type (and vice versa), but not specifically how the simple main effects of caffeine are different or for which of the three personality types. One way to probe a 3×3 (or larger) interaction is to first individually test all simple main effects for significance. Then for any simple main effects that are found to be significant (e.g., the effect of caffeine just for introverts), a comparison could be used to test for differences between specific levels of the independent variable for that simple main effect (e.g., 100 mg vs. 200 mg just for introverts), called a *simple effect contrast* or *simple comparison*. Alternatively, instead of starting with simple main effects, a significant interaction effect can be probed by beginning with a main comparison (e.g., 100 mg vs. 200 mg). If the main comparison is significant, then one can test whether the main comparison effect differed as a function of personality type (e.g., does the difference in performance between 100 mg and 200 mg differ between any of the personality types), which is called a *main effect contrast by factor interaction*. If the main effect contrast by factor interaction was significant, the effect can be further examined by testing whether the main effect contrast on the independent variable (e.g., 100 mg vs. 200 mg) differed at specific levels of the moderator (e.g., neutral vs. extrovert). That is, a *contrast by contrast interaction* specifies contrasts on both factors. For example, testing can show whether the difference in mean performance between the 100 mg and 200 mg caffeine groups differed for neutrals compared to extroverts, which essentially goes back to a 2×2 interaction.

Probing interactions in ANOVA when the factors have more than a few levels can lead to a large number of statistical tests. When a large number of these *post hoc tests* are examined, there is a danger that the probability of falsely finding a significant mean difference (i.e., making a Type I error) increases beyond a reasonable level (e.g., 0.05). When that happens, a Type I error correction needs to be applied to bring the probability of falsely finding a significant difference across all of the post hoc tests, called the *experiment wise Type I error rate*, back down to an appropriate level. The most well known of these corrections is the Bonferroni, but Maxwell and Delaney (2004) show that the Bonferroni overcorrects when the number of *post hoc* tests is more than about nine. Alternatives to the Bonferroni include the Dunnett correction for when one reference level is to be compared to each other level of the factor, the Tukey correction for all pairwise comparisons of levels, and the Scheffé correction for all possible *post hoc* tests.

Continuous by Categorical.   Although not discussed in detail here, interactions between categorical variables can also be assessed using multiple regression rather than ANOVA. When one or both of the variables involved in the interaction is continuous, however, multiple regression must be used to test moderation hypotheses (Blalock, 1965; Cohen, 1968). The regression framework permits a moderation hypothesis to be specified with any combination of categorical and continuous variables. Consider the continuous by categorical variable interaction from Sommet, Darnon, and Butera (2015), who examined interpersonal conflict regulation strategies in social situations.[2] When faced with a disagreeing partner, people generally employ either a competitive strategy or conform to their partner's point of view. Specifically, they found that the relation between the number of performance-approach goals (e.g., "did you try to show the partner was wrong"; continuous predictor) and competitive regulation scores (continuous outcome) differs depending on the person's relative academic competence compared to their partner (same, superior, or unspecified; categorical moderator). The significant interaction indicates that performance-approach goals have a higher association with competitive regulation for both superior partners and partners with unspecified competence compared to partners with the same competence (Figure 3).

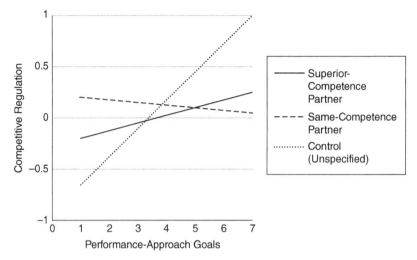

Figure 3. Categorical by continuous variable moderation.
Source: Redrawn from Sommet et al., 2015.

Probing a significant interaction in multiple regression when the predictor is continuous and the moderator variable is categorical differs from probing interactions in ANOVA, but it can be straightforward depending on how the categorical moderator is incorporated into the regression model. There are many methods for representing nominal or ordinal variables in regression equations (e.g., Cohen, Cohen, West, & Aiken, 2003; Pedhauzer, 1997), though this article focuses only on *dummy codes*. Creating dummy codes for a categorical variable with k levels, requires $k - 1$ *dummy variables* $(D_1, D_2, \ldots D_{k-1})$. Using the Sommet et al. (2015) example, where competence has three groups ($k = 3$), two dummy variables are needed: D_1 and D_2. Dummy variables are created by first selecting a *reference group*, which receives a zero on all of the dummy variables. Each of the non-reference groups receives a one for one dummy variable (though not the same dummy variable as any other non-reference group) and a zero for all other dummy variables. If same-competence is selected as the reference group, then one potential set of dummy codes is: D_1 = {same = 0, superior = 1, unspecified = 0} and D_2 = {same = 0, superior = 0, unspecified = 1}. Both dummy variables are then entered into the regression model as predictors. To create the interaction between the predictor and the dummy variables, each of the dummy variables must be multiplied by the continuous predictor and added into the regression model as well. For the interpersonal conflict example, the *overall regression model* for computing predicted competitive regulation scores (^ denotes a predicted score) from the number of performance approach goals, relative academic competency, and the interaction between goals and competency is equal to:

$$\widehat{COMPETE} = b_0 + b_1 GOALS + b_2 D_1 + b_3 D_2 + b_4 GOALS * D_1 + b_5 GOALS * D_2 \quad (1)$$

If regression coefficient b_4, b_5, or both are significant, then there is a significant interaction between goals and competence.

Interpreting and probing the interaction between a continuous predictor and a categorical moderator in regression is much easier when using the overall regression equation. Consider what happens when the values for the competency reference group (i.e., same competence) are substituted into the overall regression model.

$$COM\hat{P}ETE = b_0 + b_1 GOALS + b_2(0) + b_3(0) + b_4 GOALS*(0) + b_5 GOALS*(0)$$
$$= b_0 + b_1 GOALS \quad (2)$$

Since the same-competence group has 0's for D_1 and D_2, the overall regression equation reduces to just include b_0 and b_1. This reduced regression equation represents the relation between performance approach goals and competitive regulation scores for individuals who have the same academic competency as their partners. Equation 2 is called a *simple regression equation* because it is analogous to the simple main effect in ANOVA. The b_1 coefficient, which represents the relation between goals and competitive regulation for individuals with the same competency, is called the *simple slope*. But what do the other coefficients in the overall regression model represent?

If the dummy variable values for the superior-competency group are substituted into the equation and then some terms are rearranged, the result is:

$$COM\hat{P}ETE = b_0 + b_1 GOALS + b_2(1) + b_3(0) + b_4 GOALS*(1) + b_5 GOALS*(0)$$
$$= b_0 + b_1 GOALS + b_2(1) + b_4 GOALS*(1) \quad (3)$$
$$= [b_0 + b_2] + [b_1 + b_4] GOALS$$

Since b_0 and b_1 are the intercept and simple slope for the same competency group, b_2 is the difference in the intercept and b_4 is the difference in simple slope, respectively, between the same- and superior-competency groups. This means that if b_4 is significantly different than zero, the simple slopes for the same- and superior-competency groups are different from one another, and academic competency therefore moderates the relation between goals and competitive regulation. The simple regression equation can also be computed for the unspecified-competency group. These three *simple regression lines* are illustrated in Figure 3 and show that higher performance-approach goal scores are significantly associated with greater competitive regulation behaviors, although it is now known that this effect differs based on the relative level of competence of the partner.

The significance of b_4 and b_5 demonstrates whether or not the relation between the predictor and outcome variable is moderated by the categorical moderator variable, but a significant interaction does not explain whether the relation between the predictor and the outcome is statistically significant in any of the groups. Since b_1 is automatically tested for significance by most statistical software packages, there is no need to worry about testing the simple slope for the reference group. Aiken and West (1991) provide equations for computing the standard errors for testing the other two simple slopes, $[b_1 + b_4]$ and $[b_1 + b_5]$, for significance. Alternatively, the dummy coding could be revised to make another group the reference category (e.g., superior-competence), then the complete model could be re-estimated and the significance of the new b_1 value would test the simple slope for the new reference group.

Another characteristic of the simple regression equations that may be of interest is the *intersection point* of two simple regression lines, which is the value of the predictor variable at which the predicted value of the outcome variable is the same for two different values of the moderator variable. Looking at Figure 3, the superior- and same-competence simple regression lines appear to intersect at around 5 on the performance-approach goals variable. The exact value of the intersection point can be calculated by setting the simple regression equations for these two groups equal to each other and then using algebra to solve for value of goals. While the intersection point is where the predicted scores for two simple regression equations are exactly the same, the points at which the predicted scores for two simple regression lines begin to be statistically different from each other can be computed. Called *regions of significance* (Potthoff, 1964), this is conceptually similar to a confidence interval that is centered-around the intersection point for two simple regression lines. For any value of the predictor closer to the intersection point than the boundaries of the regions of significance, the predicted outcome values for the two simple regression lines are not statistically significantly different from one another. For any value of the predictor farther away from the intersection point than the boundaries of the regions of significance, the predicted outcome values for the two simple regression lines are statistically significantly different from one another.

Continuous by Continuous. Interactions between a continuous predictor and continuous moderator variable can also be examined using the multiple regression framework. An example of a continuous by continuous variable interaction is that although injustice (continuous predictor) has positive relationships with retaliatory responses such as ruminative thoughts and negative emotions (continuous outcomes), mindfulness (continuous moderator) reduces these associations (Long & Christian, 2015). That is, high levels of mindfulness reduce rumination and negative emotions (e.g., anger) by decoupling the self from experiences and disrupting the automaticity of reactive processing. Long and Christian administered measures of mindfulness, perceived unfairness at work, ruminative thoughts, outward-focused anger, and retaliation behavior. They found that lower levels of mindfulness were associated with increased anger, whereas higher mindfulness was associated with lower anger (see Figure 4).

Similar to continuous predictor by categorical moderator interactions in multiple regression, with continuous predictor by continuous moderator interactions each variable is entered into the regression model, then the product of the two variables is entered as a separate predictor variable representing the interaction between these variables. For the anger example, the overall regression model predicting anger from perceived injustice, mindfulness, and the interaction between injustice and mindfulness is equal to:

$$\hat{ANGER} = b_0 + b_1 INJUSTICE + b_2 MINDFUL + b_3 INJUSTICE * MINDFUL \qquad (4)$$

As with a continuous by categorical interaction, interactions between two continuous variables are probed by investigating the simple regression equations of the outcome variable on the predictor for different levels of the moderator. Unlike categorical moderator variables where one can show how the simple slopes differ between the groups, a continuous moderator variable may not necessarily have specific values of interest. If there are specific values of the continuous moderator that are of interest to the researcher, then the simple regression equation can be computed by substituting these values into the overall regression equation.

In the absence of specific values of interest, Aiken and West (1991) recommend examining the mean of the moderator, one standard deviation above the mean, and one standard deviation below the mean. While it may seem that these values are somewhat arbitrary, these three values provide information about what is happening at the average score on the moderator, as well as providing a good range of moderator values without going too far into the tails, where there are likely to be very few observations.

A trick that makes interpreting a continuous by continuous variable interaction easier is to mean center the predictor and moderator variables, but not the outcome variable, prior to creating the interaction term. When injustice and mindfulness are mean centered before they are entered into the complete regression equation and the simple regression equation is calculated for the mean of the moderator, which is zero when the moderator is mean centered, the overall regression model reduces to:

$$\hat{ANGER} = b_0 + b_1 INJUSTICE_C + b_2 MINDFUL_C + b_3 INJUSTICE_C * MINDFUL_C$$
$$= b_0 + b_1 INJUSTICE_C + b_2(0) + b_3 INJUSTICE_C *(0) \qquad (5)$$
$$= b_0 + b_1 INJUSTICE_C$$

Then b_0 and b_1 in the overall regression model are equal to the intercept and simple slope for participants with an average level of mindfulness, rather than for a person with zero mindfulness.

One issue not yet considered is the values of the regression coefficients themselves. There are two possibilities. When the regression coefficients for the predictor and the interaction are opposite in sign, *buffering* or *dampening interactions* occur, which results in larger moderator values decreasing the relationship between the predictor and the outcome. The distinction is based on whether a beneficial phenomenon is being decreased (dampening) or a harmful phenomenon is being decreased (buffering). The mindfulness effect in Figure 4 is a buffering moderator because it further reduces the effect of the independent variable. Alternatively, if the signs of the regression coefficients for the predictor and interaction term are the same, positive or negative, then increasing values of the moderator are related to a larger relationship between the predictor and the outcome variable. This is called a *synergistic* or *exacerbating*

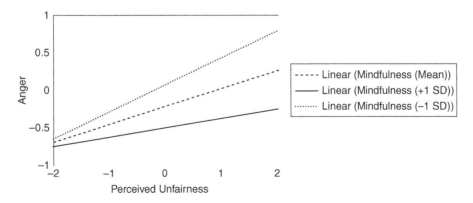

Figure 4. Continuous by continuous interaction.
Source: Adapted from Long & Christian, 2015.

interaction depending on whether the phenomenon being examined is beneficial or harmful to the individual, respectively. Mathematically, buffering and dampening interactions (or synergistic and exacerbating interactions) are identical, so the distinction is based purely on theory.

Standardized Interaction Coefficients. Given many psychologists' preference for reporting standardized regression coefficients, researchers should be aware that when regression models include higher-order terms (e.g., interaction terms or curvilinear terms), the standardized coefficients produced by most statistical software packages are incorrect. Consider the unstandardized regression equation for a dependent variable Y and two predictors X_1 and X_2:

$$\hat{Y} = b_0 + b_1 X_1 + b_2 X_2 \tag{6}$$

The standardized coefficients can be calculated by multiplying each unstandardized coefficient by the standard deviation of the corresponding predictor divided by the standard deviation of Y (Cohen et al., 2003) or equivalently by creating z-scores for Y, X_1, and X_2 (i.e., standardizing the variables by mean centering each variable, then dividing by its standard deviation) and then estimating the model using the standardized variables (Z_Y, Z_{X_1}, and Z_{X_2}) such that:

$$\hat{Z}_Y = b_1^* Z_{X_1} + b_2^* Z_{X_2} \tag{7}$$

where a standardized regression coefficient is denoted with an asterisk.

As previously described, in order to test whether X_2 moderates the relation between Y and X_1, a new variable must be created in the data set that is the product of the two predictors, $X_1 X_2$, and enter it into the regression model as a separate predictor, resulting in the equation:

$$\hat{Y} = b_0 + b_1 X_1 + b_2 X_2 + b_3 X_1 X_2 \tag{8}$$

The software program is unaware that this new predictor $X_1 X_2$ is, in fact, an interaction term and not just another continuous predictor, however. This means that, when the software is calculating the standardized coefficients, it converts all of the variables in the model into z-scores such that the standardized coefficients come from the following regression equation:

$$\hat{Z}_Y = b_1^* Z_{X_1} + b_2^* Z_{X_2} + b_3^* Z_{X_1 X_2} \tag{9}$$

Unfortunately, $Z_{X_1 X_2}$ is not equal to the value of the product term created from standardized variables, $Z_{X_1} Z_{X_2}$. Hence, b_3^* is not the correct estimate of the standardized interaction coefficient. To obtain the correct estimate of the standardized interaction coefficient, a researcher must manually create Z_Y, Z_{X_1}, Z_{X_2}, and $Z_{X_1} Z_{X_2}$, to fit the model:

$$\hat{Z}_Y = b_{1Z} Z_{X_1} + b_{2Z} Z_{X_2} + b_{3Z} Z_{X_1} Z_{X_1} \tag{10}$$

and then use the *unstandardized* value b_{3Z}. While using the unstandardized solutions from a regression of standardized variables to get the correct standardized values of the regression coefficients seems counterintuitive, the discrepancy between the unstandardized coefficient b_{3Z} computed using the standardized variables and the standardized coefficient b_3^* using the unstandardized variables is quite evident in the output. And though the difference in the coefficients may be small, this difference can lead to large differences in inference and interpretation (Aiken & West, 1991; Cohen et al., 2003; Friedrich, 1982).

Curvilinear. Though not always included in discussions of moderator variables, curvilinear change that can be described with a polynomial regression model (i.e., quadratic, cubic, etc.) is a form of moderation, albeit one where a variable moderates itself. Consider the classic finding in psychology that the relation between physiological arousal and task performance is U-shaped (i.e., quadratic; Yerkes & Dodson, 1908), illustrated in Figure 5. If the relation between arousal and performance for very low levels of arousal were described using a straight line, the result would be a regression line with a very steep positive slope. That is, when someone has low arousal, even small increases in arousal can lead to large increases in predicted performance. Describing the same relation for medium levels of arousal would result in a regression line with a very shallow slope, such that a slight increase in arousal would only be met with a slight increase in predicted performance. For very high levels of arousal, the regression line would again have a very steep slope, but now the slope is negative, such that small increases in arousal lead to large decreases in predicted performance. Therefore, the relation between arousal and performance is different depending on the level of arousal, so arousal is both the predictor *and* the moderator variable. This dual role is shown clearly in the regression equation for the quadratic relation between performance and arousal:

$$P\hat{E}RFORM = b_0 + b_1 AROUSAL + b_2 (AROUSAL * AROUSAL) \quad (11)$$

because the squared quadratic term that represents the U-shape is the product of arousal times arousal, the same form as the interaction terms between the predictor and the moderator variable in the two previous examples.

Three-Way Interactions. Up until this point in the discussion of moderators, the focus has been only on the interaction between two variables, an independent variable and a single moderator, which are known as *two-way interactions*. But there is no reason why two or more moderator variables cannot be considered simultaneously. Returning to the Revelle et al.

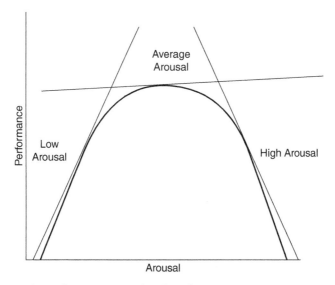

Figure 5. Quadratic relation between arousal and performance.

(1980) example, the researchers believed that time of day also had an impact on the relation between caffeine and performance, so they collected data from participants in the morning on the first day and in the afternoon on the second day. Figures 2c and 2d clearly show that the interaction between caffeine and personality type differs depending on whether the participants completed the study in the morning (Day 1) or in the afternoon (Day 2). That is, personality type moderates the relation between caffeine and performance, but time of day moderates the interaction between personality and caffeine. The moderation of a two-way interaction by another moderator variable is called a *three-way interaction*. As with two-way interactions in ANOVA, a significant three-way interaction is probed by testing a combination of *post hoc* effects including simple main effects, simple comparisons, contrast by factor interactions, and contrast by contrast interactions (Keppel & Wickens, 2004). In regression, probing a significant three-way interaction involves selecting values for both moderator variables and entering these values simultaneously into the overall regression equation to compute the simple regression equations (Aiken & West, 1991). Three-way interactions can also come into play with curvilinear relations. For example, the relation between two variables may be cubic, necessitating a $X3$ term, or the quadratic relation between two variables may vary as a function of a third variable.

There are two very important considerations when examining three-way interactions. First, whenever a higher-order interaction is tested in a model, all lower-order effects must be included in the model. For a three-way interaction, this means that all two-way interactions as well as all main effects must be included in the model (Cohen, 1978). This is more easily illustrated in regression. For example, consider if the two-way interaction between injustice and mindfulness in the Long and Christian (2015) example was found to differ depending on the person's gender.[3] The correct regression equation would be:

$$
\begin{aligned}
A\hat{NGER} = b_0 &+ b_1 INJ + b_2 MIND + b_3 GENDER \\
&+ b_4 INJ * MIND + b_5 INJ * GENDER + b_6 MIND * GENDER \quad (12) \\
&+ b_7 INJ * MIND * GENDER
\end{aligned}
$$

which includes the three-way interaction between injustice, mindfulness, and gender, the three two-way interactions between these variables, as well as the three first-order effects. As described before, when the highest-order term is significant, no lower-order terms should be interpreted without consideration of the levels of the other variables.

CURRENT TRENDS IN MODERATION

After defining moderator variables, providing an overview of the different types of interactions most likely to be encountered by psychologists, and discussing how to probe significant interactions between variables, the next section summarizes current trends in moderation analysis. Recent advances in moderation research have been focused in three areas: (1) moderator variables in the context of clustered data, (2) moderation with latent variables, and (3) models that have both moderator and mediator variables.

Multilevel and Cross-Level Moderation. *Multilevel models* (Raudenbush & Bryk, 2002; Snijders & Bosker, 2012), also called *hierarchical linear models*, *mixed models*, and *random effects models*, are a type of regression model that is used when participants are *nested* or *clustered* within organizational hierarchies, such as patients within hospitals, students within classrooms, or even repeated-measurements within individuals. Nesting is of interest because nested data violates the assumption of independence between participants, which causes the estimates of the standard errors for the regression coefficients to be too small. For example, two children in the same classroom might be expected to be more alike than two children who are in different classrooms. The degree of similarity of participants within a group or cluster is called the *intraclass correlation coefficient*, which is the proportion of the total variance that is shared between groups. Multilevel models work by dividing the total variability in scores on the outcome variable into different levels that reflect the nested structure of the data. Two-level models are most commonly used, although any number of levels are possible, such as students (Level 1) nested within teachers (Level 2) nested within schools (Level 3) nested within school districts (Level 4), and so on. Once the variability in the outcome has been attributed to the different levels of nesting, predictors, moderators, and interactions can then be added to the model to explain the variability at the different levels in the exact same manner as in single-level regression models.

Where multilevel models differ from single-level regression models regarding moderation, however, is that multilevel models can specify how variables occurring at one level influence relationships with variables at another level. Seaton, Marsh, and Craven (2010) use an example of the Big-Fish-Little-Pond effect to illustrate this concept, which states that although individual mathematics ability has a positive relationship with mathematics self-concept, higher school-average ability reduces this association. Here a two-level model is used because the students (Level 1) are nested within schools (Level 2).[4] In a simplified version of their model, Seaton et al. predicted individual mathematics self-concept (outcome variable) from individual mathematics ability (Level 1 predictor):

$$\text{Level 1: } SCONCEPT_{ij} = \beta_{0j} + \beta_{1j}(MATH_{ij} - \overline{MATH_j}) + r_{ij} \tag{13}$$

where i indexes individuals, j indexes schools, r_{ij} is the Level 1 residual, and individual mathematics ability has been centered at the mean for each school.

The Level 1 model is at the student level and predicts self-concept for student i in school j. This model has an intercept (β_{0j}) representing self-concept for mean mathematics ability across all schools and a slope (β_{1j}) representing the effect of mathematics ability on self-concept across all schools. It is possible, however, that the effect of mathematics ability on mathematics self-concept is not the same for all schools. To explain the differences between self-concept and math achievement between students, β_{0j} and β_{1j} are allowed to vary across schools, hence the subscript j and why they are called *random coefficients*. In other words, each school is allowed to have its own intercept and slope. To model the variability in the intercept and slope of the Level 1 model between schools, two Level 2 models are created which are at the school level:

$$\text{Level 2: } \beta_{0j} = \gamma_{00} + u_{0j} \tag{14}$$
$$\beta_{1j} = \gamma_{10} + u_{1i}$$

The Level 1 intercept (β_{0j}) is partitioned into a mean intercept across schools (γ_{00}) and a random effect (u_{0j}), which represents the difference between the mean intercept across schools and the specific intercept for each school. In the same way, the Level 1 slope (β_{1j}) is partitioned into the mean slope across schools (γ_{10}) and a random effect (u_{1j}), which represent the difference in the effect of individual mathematics ability averaged across schools and the effect of individual mathematics ability for a specific school.

Since β_{0j} and β_{1j} are allowed to vary by school, this variability in the random coefficients may be explained by adding school-level predictors to the Level 2 equations. For example, Seaton et al. (2010) added average school mathematics ability, centered at the grand mean, as a Level 2 predictor of both the Level 1 intercept and slope:

$$\begin{aligned} \text{Level1:} \quad & SCONCEPT_{ij} = \beta_{0j} + \beta_{1j}(MATH_{ij} - \overline{MATH_j}) + r_{ij} \\ \text{Level2:} \quad & \beta_{0j} = \gamma_{00} + \gamma_{01}(MATH_j - \overline{MATH}) + u_{0j} \\ & \beta_{1j} = \gamma_{10} + \gamma_{11}(MATH_j - \overline{MATH}) + u_{1j} \end{aligned} \quad (15)$$

While a complete dissection of this model is beyond the scope of the current discussion, when the Level 2 equations are substituted into the Level 1 equation to get:

$$\begin{aligned} SCONCEPT_{ij} = \gamma_{00} \; & + \; \gamma_{01}(MATH_j - \overline{MATH}) + \gamma_{10}(MATH_j - \overline{MATH}) \\ & + \; \gamma_{11}(MATH_{ij} - \overline{MATH_j}) * (MATH_j - \overline{MATH}) \\ & + \; u_{0j} + u_{1j}(MATH_{ij} - \overline{MATH_j}) + r_{ij} \end{aligned} \quad (16)$$

the interaction between student-level mathematics ability and school-level mathematics ability becomes obvious.

When a multilevel model contains a moderating variable from one level and an independent variable from another level, it is called a *cross-level interaction* (Raudenbush & Bryk, 2002). For the current example, students of all abilities had lower mathematics self-concepts if they attended high-ability schools compared to students of similar ability who attended average- or low-ability schools. The decrease in mathematics self-concept was more dramatic for higher-ability students. This phenomenon led Davis (1966) to warn parents against sending their children to "better" schools where the child would be in the bottom of the class. For multilevel models, it is not necessary to create a product term to estimate a cross-level moderation effect. Rather, if a Level 2 variable has a significant effect on the Level 1 slope, the moderation hypothesis is supported. Interactions between variables at the same level (e.g., a Level 1 predictor and Level 1 moderator) must still be entered manually.

Moderator variables in multilevel models share many of the challenges of moderators in single-level regression. For example, centering is recommended in multilevel models to facilitate interpretation, unless the predictors have a meaningful zero point. When adding Level 1 explanatory variables, centering becomes especially important. There are two ways to center Level 1 variables: grand mean centering (individuals centered around the overall mean) and group mean centering (individuals centered around group means). To avoid confusing a within-group relationship with a between-group relationship, it is recommended to group mean center Level 1 predictors, while grand mean centering Level 2 predictors. For more about centering in multilevel applications, see Enders and Tofighi (2007).

Moderation in Structural Equation Models. *Structural equation modeling* (SEM) is a collection of techniques that can be used to examine the relations between combinations of observed variables (*manifest*; e.g., height) and unobservable construct variables (*latent*; e.g., depression). As such, SEM can be used for examining many research questions, including: theory testing, prediction, estimating effect sizes, mediation, group differences, and longitudinal differences (Kline, 2011). SEMs can include both a *measurement model*, which describes the relation between each latent construct and the observed items used to measure individuals' scores on that latent construct, and a *structural model*, which specifies the relations between latent constructs, as well as manifest variables.

Multiple-Group Analysis.   Testing for moderation in SEM can be conducted in multiple ways. If both the predictor and the moderator are manifest variables, then an interaction term can be computed by taking the product of the predictor and moderator, which is then added to the SEM as a new variable, just as in multiple regression. Provided the moderator is an observed categorical variable, moderation can also be tested in SEM using a multiple-group analysis. In a *multiple-group analysis*, the SEM model is fit with the path between the predictor and the outcome variable constrained to be the same in all moderator groups, and then a second time with the path unconstrained, such that the effect is allowed to be different for each group. The overall fit of the two models (i.e., constrained vs. unconstrained) is then compared. If the unconstrained model does not fit significantly better than the constrained model, then the effect is the same for all of the groups and moderation is not present. If the unconstrained model fits significantly better than the constrained model, however, it is concluded that the effect is different for at least one of the groups and moderation is present.

When variables are not perfectly reliable, as routinely occurs in psychology, it is often preferable to create latent variables to provide a mechanism for explicitly modeling measurement error. Latent moderator approaches are divided into *partially latent variable* approaches, where at least one variable is latent and at least one variable is observed, and *fully latent variable* approaches, where all variables are latent (Little, Bovaird, & Widaman, 2006; Marsh, Wen, & Hau, 2006). A multiple-group analysis with a latent predictor variable is a partially latent variable approach since the moderator must be observed. Two other historical partially latent approaches include using factor scores in regression and a two-stage least-squares method (Bollen, 1995), although these methods are generally inferior to SEM approaches and therefore are not recommended. Fully latent approaches can also implemented within the context of an SEM (e.g., creating a third latent variable to represent the interaction of the two other latent variables), but some issues exist concerning the practicality and interpretation of a latent construct that represents the interaction between two other latent constructs. Several approaches have been proposed for modeling fully latent interactions (see Marsh et al., 2007, for a review), but most approaches are based on the Kenny and Judd (1984) product indicator model.

Invariance.   One of the most common reasons for testing for moderation with latent variables in SEM is invariance testing (Mellenbergh, 1989; Meredith, 1993). *Invariance testing* is used to determine the degree to which a specific model fits the same in different groups or across time. Invariance is tested by imposing progressively stricter constraints across the groups and then comparing the model fit of the constrained model to a model with fewer constraints. Two types of invariance are discussed: factorial invariance and structural invariance.

Factorial invariance tests the factor structure or the measurement model across groups or time. Five levels of factorial invariance are commonly tested. The first level, *dimensional invariance,* is used to test whether the number of latent factors is the same across groups—this level of invariance is more commonly assumed than tested. The next level, *configural invariance,* tests whether the general pattern of item loadings on the latent constructs is the same across groups. If the factor loadings are found not just to have the same general pattern but to be exactly equal across groups, the model has *loading* or *weak invariance* across groups, which is the third level of factorial invariance. Loading invariance is the minimal level of invariance needed as evidence that a construct has the same interpretation across groups or time. The next level is *intercept* or *strong invariance,* which occurs when, in addition to the observed item loadings, the item intercepts are also equal across groups. The final level of factorial invariance is *strict* or *error invariance,* in which the observed item loadings, intercepts, and relations between the residual error terms are equal across groups. With strict factorial invariance, we have evidence that the measurement portion of the model is exactly the same across groups. In other words, this states that any group differences in scores are not due to how the constructs were measured, but rather are due to differences in mean ability levels or differences in the relationships between variables (Angoff, 1993; Millsap, 2011). We can also test for differences between groups in their average level and variability on a latent construct. *Factor (co)variance invariance* constrains the factor variances and covariances to be equal across groups, and if this is met, then the variance across groups is homogeneous. The highest level of factorial invariance is *latent mean invariance,* in which the latent means are constrained to be equal across groups. This is equivalent to a latent *t*-test or ANOVA, for which homogeneity of variance is an assumption.

To test for group differences that are due to differences in the relations between variables, *structural invariance* is used, which assumes full factorial invariance and imposes additional constraints on the regression coefficients in the structural model across groups. This is what is generally tested within the multiple-group SEM analysis described previously, which tests whether the path coefficients are the same across observed groups. It is not necessary for group membership to be observed, however. When subgroups are hypothesized, *latent class analysis* (McCutcheon, 1987) is a method used to identify individuals' memberships in latent groups (i.e., classes), based on responses to a set of observed categorical variables. The latent group membership can be extracted and included in SEMs as a latent moderating variable. Additionally, changes in class membership over time can be examined using *latent transition analysis* (Collins & Lanza, 2010).

A different context in which latent variable models are useful is for modeling measurement error when the moderator variables or the corresponding independent variable have missing data. Enders, Baraldi, and Cham (2014) showed that re-specifying manifest independent and moderator variables as latent variables with one indicator each, factor loadings of one, and residual errors of zero preserves the intended interpretations but deals with the missing data using the multivariate normality assumptions in maximum likelihood estimation. Latent variables can easily be centered by constraining the latent means to zero, which provides meaningful and interpretable results without the need for transformations. Alternatively, multiple imputation has been shown to produce similar results as maximum likelihood, so the methods are interchangeable for this purpose.

Conditional Process Models. Given that the structural model is often used to reflect causal relations between variables, another topic that can be discussed in the context of SEM is moderation of mediated effects. *Conditional process models* combine moderator and mediator variables in the same model (Hayes, 2013) with *process* standing for the causal process that is mediation and *conditional* representing the differential effects of moderation. Consider the Theory of Planned Behavior (TPB; Ajzen, 1991), which is an example of a conditional process model. In the TPB, changes in attitudes and subjective norms (antecedent variables) change intentions (mediator variable), which in turn change observed behaviors (outcome variable), but the relation between intention and behavior differs depending on the level of an individual's perceived behavioral control (moderator variable). The minimum requirements for a conditional process model are a single mediator variable and a single moderator variable, but conditional process models can be much more complex with multiple mediator and moderator variables operating simultaneously. This is the main reason the general term *conditional process model* has begun to replace the rather confusing historical terms *moderated mediation* (e.g., Little, Card, Bovaird, Preacher, & Crandall, 2007) and *mediated moderation* (Baron & Kenny, 1986). Though these terms were meant to indicate whether the researcher was examining possible moderation of a significant mediated effect (i.e., moderated mediation) or investigating whether a variable mediated a significant moderation effect (i.e., mediated moderation), in practice these terms have been used interchangeably because they can be used to describe identical statistical models. Since both are just special cases of conditional process models, we suggest that psychologists are better off referring to all models that contain both moderators and mediators as conditional process models because this requires that the researcher explain in detail the specific model being estimated, which is clearer all around.

Numerous authors have described how to test conditional process model hypotheses using the multiple regression framework (e.g., Hayes, 2013). These methods work quite well and significant interactions can be probed in much the same way as previously described for traditional regression models. When conditional process models become complex and at least one of the moderator variables is categorical, however, a better way to test for moderation is to use a multiple-group structural equation model. In the conditional process model case, a multiple-group SEM can be used to simultaneously test the mediation model across groups and directly test for differences in the mediation process between groups. For example, in Mplus (Muthén & Muthén, 2015), it is possible to formally test the difference between the mediated effects when the moderator variable is dichotomous. This direct testing of group differences makes this method superior to methods that conduct the same analysis separately for each group (e.g., for males and then for females) and indirectly compare the results for differences.

CURRENT CHALLENGES

By definition, moderator variables illustrate the extent to which relations between variables are dependent on other factors including characteristics related to personality, environment, and context. Identifying moderation effects is particularly important for psychologists not only to better understand how mental processes are related to behaviors, but also to ensure that, in the effort to help, harm is not accidentally caused to specific groups of individuals. Therefore, a comprehensive plan to examine all potential moderator variables should be an integral piece of any research study in psychology. Determining if a variable moderates the relation between two other variables poses several challenges to researchers, however, including the need to identify when a treatment causes harm to specific individuals, ensuring adequate statistical power to detect a moderation effect, and the difficulty in probing and interpreting complex moderation effects correctly. In this section, these issues are discussed, along with potential strategies for limiting their impact.

Treatment Interactions.   As discussed previously, one of the key reasons psychologists should be interested in moderating variables is that they provide information on how the effect of a treatment, such as a CBT or behavioral prevention intervention, may function differently for groups of individuals. The effect of a treatment can vary depending on a number of different moderator variables, including demographic variables such as gender or ethnicity (Judd, McClelland, & Smith, 1996), a participant's aptitude, called an *aptitude by treatment interaction* (Cronbach & Snow, 1977), or a participant's pre-treatment level of an outcome or mediator variable, called a *baseline by treatment interaction* (Fritz et al., 2005). When present, these effects provide information that may then be used to tailor a treatment to be more effective for specific at-risk individuals. More important than improving the effectiveness of a treatment, however, is making sure there are no iatrogenic effects of the treatment. An *iatrogenic effect* occurs when a treatment causes an unplanned, harmful effect. For example, consider an intervention designed to prevent teenagers from using marijuana that actually increases marijuana use for some individuals. Iatrogenic effects are easily missed when they occur in only a small percentage of a sample, but ethically these effects need to be identified. Therefore, it is crucial that all theoretically relevant variables that may moderate the effect of a treatment be measured and tested.

Statistical Power.   Theoretical moderating variables are not always supported by empirical research, however (e.g., Zedeck, 1971). When we fail to reject a null hypothesis of no moderating effect, there are two potential reasons why: either the null hypothesis is true and the variable truly does not moderate the effect, or the null hypothesis is false but it was not detected by the statistical test conducted (i.e., a Type II error occurred). To prevent incorrect conclusions about moderation effects, the probability of detecting a true effect, or *statistical power*, must be high. The single biggest issue with detecting moderation, other than ensuring that potential moderator variables are measured and tested in the first place, is that interaction effects tend to explain much less variance than main effects (McClelland & Judd, 1993). Hence, even studies that are adequately powered to find main effects are likely to be woefully unpowered when it comes to detecting moderator variables. Some of the factors that result in the under-powering of studies in psychology are beyond control—when studying a rare disorder, it may be impossible to adequately power a study simply by increasing the sample size. But there are other ways to increase statistical power for detecting moderation effects. For example, McClelland (2000) discusses several methods for increasing the statistical power of a study without increasing the sample size, such as using more reliable measures. And McClelland and Judd (1993) show that oversampling extreme cases can increase the statistical power for tests of moderation.

Part of the cause of these underpowered studies, however, is that psychological theories are rarely specific enough to include hypotheses about effect sizes for main effects, let alone interactions. A larger concern is the conflation of the size of an effect with the theoretical importance of an effect. Too many psychologists interpret Cohen's (1988) small, medium, and large designations of effect sizes as being a measure of an effect's theoretical importance. Cohen did not intend for large to mean important and small to mean unimportant. Instead, these categories were presented as examples of effect sizes found in a very specific area (abnormal social psychology) that needed to be recalibrated for each area of psychology and set of variables. Therefore, an effect that explains 9% of the variance in a variable (a medium effect using Cohen's designations) may explain so little variance as to be completely disregarded by one area of psychology, yet so large as to be unobtainable in another area. Regardless of the cause, the consequences of under-powering studies to find moderation are the same: an inability to provide context for effects, resulting in a poorer understanding of the world.

Multicollinearity. Another issue that must be considered when testing interactions is multicollinearity between the variables and the interaction terms. *Multicollinearity* occurs when predictors in a multiple regression are highly correlated with one another and can cause excessively large standard errors, reducing the statistical power to detect an interaction even further. Since the interaction terms are just the product of the predictors, it is not surprising that the individual predictors and the interaction terms can be highly correlated. Aiken and West (1991) show that centering the predictors prior to creating an interaction term can decrease the correlation between the predictors and the interaction term by removing the *nonessential multicollinearity*, which is an artificial relation caused by the scaling of the predictors, while leaving the real relation, called *essential multicollinearity*. Others (e.g., Hayes, 2013) have questioned whether multicollinearity is an issue with interactions and whether centering actually addresses multicollinearity because the highest-order term, in this case the interaction term, is unaffected by centering of the lower-order terms.

Too Many Variables. When all theoretically hypothesized moderators are measured and we have adequate power to test the effect of each moderator, we run into a new problem: too many variables. It is easy to see how nearly every variable in a regression model could be moderated by every other variable in the model. But including too many interaction terms can result in an increased risk of making a Type I error, along with extremely large standard errors and potential computational difficulties. In addition, moderating relationships can be difficult to disentangle from multicollinearity and curvilinear relationships between other variables (Ganzach, 1997). Multicollinearity between independent variables can lead to a significant interaction term when the true interaction is not significant (Busemeyer & Jones, 1983; Lubinski & Humphreys, 1990) or may cause the interaction term to have a curvilinear appearance although the true interaction is not curvilinear. A moderating effect may also be erroneously found when there is a curvilinear relationship between the dependent and independent variables, but the model is mis-specified by excluding curvilinear terms. Lubinski and Humphreys (1990) illustrate the difficulty of distinguishing between an interaction model and a model with a curvilinear effect in which two variables are highly correlated.

The problem of too many variables is compounded when we consider that the effect of a moderator variable on the relation between an independent and dependent variable may not just differ depending on values of a second moderator variable (i.e., a three-way interaction), but also on a fourth or fifth moderator variable. Returning to the Revelle et al. (1980) example, suppose that the moderation effect of time of day on the two-way interaction between caffeine and personality type was itself different for gender (a four-way interaction). And suppose the four-way interaction between caffeine, personality type, time of day, and gender was moderated by whether the participant routinely drank highly caffeinated beverages such as coffee and soda (a five-way interaction). While four-way and higher interactions may be of interest to a researcher, an added complexity inherent to higher-order interactions is that, as described before, to properly specify a model with higher-order interactions, all lower-order interaction terms must be included in the model (Cohen, 1978; Cohen et al., 2003). For example, in an ANOVA with five factors, to correctly estimate the five-way interaction between all five factors, all possible four-way (five with five factors), three-way (nine with five factors), and two-way interactions (ten with five factors), as well as the main effects of the five factors must be included, for a total of 30 effects!

A final concern is that interactions that involve more than three variables can become very difficult to interpret in any meaningful way. This is particularly problematic in ANOVA models with large numbers of factors since many software programs automatically include all possible interactions between the factors. While failing to include an interaction term in a model is equivalent to explicitly saying the interaction effect is exactly zero, taking a kitchen-sink approach and testing all possible interactions is generally a poor strategy. Instead, researchers should test all moderation effects hypothesized by the underlying theory being studied and use diagnostic tools such as plots of residuals to determine if specific unhypothesized interactions may exist in the data, making sure to note that these additional analyses are exploratory.

CONCLUSIONS

Moderation and moderator variables are one of the most common analyses in the psychological, social, and behavioral sciences. Regardless of the phenomenon being studied, it is helpful to more fully understand for whom and in what context an effect occurs. Moderation variables help researchers test hypotheses about how the strength and/or direction of the relation between two variables may differ between individuals. Though the basic methods for analyzing moderation effects have not changed dramatically in the past 25 years, new tools have been developed to aid researchers in probing and interpreting significant interactions. The challenge for psychologists today is to include moderator variables in their theories, then plan studies that not only measure these potential moderator variables, but also are adequately powered to find moderation effects.

SOFTWARE

A majority of the interaction models and probing of significant interaction terms described here can be conducted using any general statistical software package. For psychology, popular general statistical software packages to examine moderation include:

SPSS (https://www.ibm.com/spss), SAS (http://www.sas.com/en_us/software/analytics/stat.html), Stata (http://www.stata.com/products/), and R (https://www.r-project.org/).

While many of these more general statistical programs can also be used to test for moderation in multilevel and SEM models, specialized software may be preferred. For multilevel models, HLM is often used. For SEM models, especially those that include latent variables, Mplus, LISREL, Amos, EQS, or R may be preferred. For power analyses, two excellent programs are G-Power and Optimal Design.

ACKNOWLEDGMENTS

This research was supported in part by a grant from the National Institute on Drug Abuse (DA 009757).

SOFTWARE RESOURCES

Arbuckle, J. L. (2014). Amos (Version 23.0) [computer software]. Chicago: IBM SPSS. http://ibm-spss-amos.software.informer.com/23.0/

Bentler, P. M. (2014). EQS (Version 6.2) [computer software]. Los Angeles, CA: MVSoft, Inc. http://www.mvsoft.com/eqs60.htm

Faul, F., Erdfelder, E., Buchner, A., & Lang, A.-G. (2014). G-Power (version 3.1.9.2) [computer software]. http://www.gpower.hhu.de/en.html

IBM. (2016). SPSS Statistics. (Version 23.0) [computer software]. Armonk, NY: IBM Corp. http://www-03.ibm.com/software/products/en/spss-statistics

Joreskog, K. G., & Sorbom, D. (2016). LISREL (Version 8.8) [computer software]. Skokie, IL: Scientific Software International, Inc. http://www.ssicentral.com/lisrel/new.html

Muthén, L. K., & Muthén, B. O. (2016). Mplus (Version 7.4) [computer software]. Los Angeles: Muthén & Muthén. https://www.statmodel.com/orderonline/categories.php?category=Mplus-Software

R Core Development Team. (2016). R (Version 3.3) [computer software]. Vienna, Austria: R Foundation for Statistical Computing. https://www.r-project.org/

Raudenbush, S. W., Bryk, A. S., & Congdon, R. (2016). HLM (Version 7) [computer software]. Skokie, IL: Scientific Software International, Inc. http://www.ssicentral.com/hlm/

SAS Institute. (2016). SAS (Version 9.4) [computer software]. Cary, NC: SAS Institute Inc. http://www.sas.com/en_us/software/analytics/stat.html

Spybrook, J., Bloom, H., Congdon, R., Hill, C., Martinez, A., & Raudenbush, S. (2011). Optimal Design [computer software]. https://sites.google.com/site/optimaldesignsoftware/home

StataCorp. (2015). Stata Statistical Software (Version 14) [computer software]. College Station, TX: StataCorp LP. http://www.stata.com/products/

FURTHER READING

Aiken, L. S., & West, S. G. (1991). *Multiple regression: Testing and interpreting interactions.* Newbury Park, NJ: SAGE.

Baron, R. M., & Kenny, D. A. (1986). The moderator–mediator variable distinction in social psychological research: Conceptual, strategic, and statistical considerations. *Journal of Personality and Social Psychology, 51,* 1173–1182.

Cohen, J., Cohen, P., West, S. G., & Aiken, L. S. (2003). *Applied multiple regression/correlation analysis for the behavioral sciences* (3d ed.). Mahwah, NJ: Lawrence Erlbaum.

Dawson, J. F., & Richter, A. W. (2006). Probing three-way interactions in moderated multiple regression: Development and application of a slope difference test. *Journal of Applied Psychology, 91*(4), 917–926.

Hayes, A. F. (2013). *Introduction to mediation, moderation, and conditional process analysis: A regression-based approach*. New York: Guilford Press.

Hoffman, L. (2015). Between-person analysis and interpretation of interactions. In L. Hoffman (Ed.), *Longitudinal analysis: Modeling within-person fluctuation and change* (pp. 29–78). New York: Routledge.

Jaccard, J. (1997). *Interaction effects in factorial analysis of variance*. Thousand Oaks, CA: SAGE.

Jaccard, J., & Turrisi, R. (2003). *Interaction effects in multiple regression* (2d ed.). Thousand Oaks, CA: SAGE.

Keppel, G., & Wickens, T. D. (2004). *Design and analysis* (4th ed.). Upper Saddle River, NJ: Pearson.

Preacher, K. J., Curran, P. J., & Bauer, D. J. (2006). Computational tools for probing interactions in multiple linear regression, multilevel modeling, and latent curve analysis. *Journal of Educational and Behavioral Statistics, 31*(4), 437–448.

REFERENCES

Aiken, L. S., & West, S. G. (1991). *Multiple regression: Testing and interpreting interactions*. Newbury Park, NJ: SAGE.

Ajzen, I. (1991). The theory of planned behavior. *Organizational behavior and human decision processes, 50*, 179–211.

Angoff, W. H. (1993). Perspectives on differential item functioning methodology. In P. W. Holland & H. Wainer (Eds.), *Differential item functioning* (pp. 3–23). Hillsdale, NJ: Erlbaum.

Avolio, B. J., Mhatre, K., Norman, S. M., & Lester, P. (2009). The moderating effect of gender on leadership intervention impact. *Journal of Leadership & Organizational Studies, 15*, 325–341.

Baron, R. M., & Kenny, D. A. (1986). The moderator–mediator variable distinction in social psychological research: Conceptual, strategic, and statistical considerations. *Journal of Personality and Social Psychology, 51*, 1173–1182.

Blalock, H. M. (1965). Theory building and the statistical concept of interaction. *American Sociological Review, 30*(3), 374–380.

Bollen, K. A. (1995). Structural equation models that are nonlinear in latent variables: A least-squares estimator. *Sociological Methodology, 25*, 223–252.

Busemeyer, J. R., & Jones, L. E. (1983). Analysis of multiplicative combination rules when the causal variables are measured with error. *Psychological Bulletin, 93*, 549–562.

Cohen, J. (1968). Multiple regression as a general data-analytic system. *Psychological Bulletin, 70*, 426–443.

Cohen, J. (1978). Partialed products are interactions; Partialed powers are curve components. *Psychological Bulletin, 85*, 858–866.

Cohen, J. (1988). *Statistical power analyses for the behavioral sciences* (2d ed.). Mahwah, NJ: Lawrence Erlbaum.

Cohen, J., Cohen, P., West, S. G., & Aiken, L. S. (2003). *Applied multiple regression/correlation analysis for the behavioral sciences* (3d ed.). Mahwah, NJ: Lawrence Erlbaum.

Collins, L. M., & Lanza, S. T. (2010). *Latent class and latent transition analysis: With applications in the social, behavioral, and health sciences*. Hoboken, NJ: Wiley.

Cronbach, L., & Snow, R. (1977). *Aptitudes and instructional methods: A handbook for research on interactions*. New York: Irvington.

Davis, J. (1966). The campus as a frog pond: An application of the theory of relative deprivation to career decisions for college men. *American Journal of Sociology, 72*, 17–31.

Dawson, J. F., & Richter, A. W. (2006) Probing three-way interactions in moderated multiple regression: Development and application of a slope difference test. *Journal of Applied Psychology, 91*(4), 917–926.

Enders, C. K., Baraldi, A. N., & Cham, H. (2014). Estimating interaction effects with incomplete predictor variables. *Psychological Methods, 19*, 39–55.

Enders, C. K., & Tofighi, D. (2007). Centering predictor variables in cross-sectional multilevel models: A new look at an old issue. *Psychological Methods, 12*(2), 121–138.

Faul, F., Erdfelder, E., Buchner, A., & Lang, A.-G. (2009). Statistical power analyses using G*Power 3.1: Tests for correlation and regression analyses. *Behavior Research Methods, 41*, 1149–1160.

Friedrich, R. J. (1982). In defense of multiplicative terms in multiple regression equations. *American Journal of Political Science, 26*, 797–833.

Fritz, M. S., MacKinnon, D. P., Williams, J., Goldberg, L., Moe, E. L., & Elliot, D. (2005). Analysis of baseline by treatment interactions in a drug prevention and health promotion program for high school male athletes. *Addictive Behaviors, 30*, 1001–1005.

Ganzach, Y. (1997) Misleading interaction and curvilinear terms. *Psychological Methods, 2*, 235–247.

Hayes, A. F. (2013). *Introduction to mediation, moderation, and conditional process analysis: A regression-based approach*. New York: Guilford Press.

Judd, C. M., McClelland, G. H., & Smith, E. R. (1996). Testing treatment by covariate interactions when treatment varies within subjects. *Psychological Methods, 1*, 366–378.

Kaufman, N. K., Rohde, P., Seeley, J. R., Clarke, G. N., & Stice, E. (2005). Potential mediators of cognitive-behavioral therapy for adolescents with comorbid major depression and conduct disorder. *Journal of Consulting and Clinical Psychology, 73*, 38–46.

Kenny, D. A., & Judd, C. M. (1984). Estimating the nonlinear and interactive effects of latent variables. *Psychological Bulletin, 96*, 201–210.

Keppel, G., & Wickens, T. D. (2004). *Design and analysis* (4th ed.). Upper Saddle River, NJ: Pearson.

Kline, R. (2011) *Principles and practice of structural equation modeling* (3d ed.). New York: Guilford Press.

Le Roy, M. (2009). *Research methods in political science: An introduction using MicroCase*®. (7th ed.). Boston: Cengage Learning.

Little, T. D., Bovaird, J. A., & Widaman, K. F. (2006). Powered and product terms: Implications for modeling interactions among latent variables. *Structural Equation Modeling, 13*, 497–519.

Little, T. D., Card, N. A., Bovaird, J. A., Preacher, K. J., & Crandall, C. S. (2007). Structural equation modeling of mediation and moderation with contextual factors. In T. D. Little, J. A. Bovaird, & N. A. Card (Eds.), *Modeling contextual effects in longitudinal studies* (pp. 207–230). New York: Psychology Press.

Long, E., & Christian, M. (2015). Mindfulness buffers retaliatory responses to injustice: A regulatory approach. *Journal of Applied Psychology, 100*(5), 1409–1422.

Lubin, A. (1961). The interpretation of significant interaction. *Educational and Psychological Measurement, 21*, 807–817.

Lubinski, D., & Humphreys, L. G. (1990). Assessing spurious "moderator effects": Illustrated substantively with the hypothesized ("synergistic") relation between spatial and mathematical ability. *Psychological Bulletin, 107*, 385–393.

Marsh, H. W., & Parker, J. W. (1984). Determinants of student self-concept: Is it better to be a relatively large fish in a small pond even if you don't learn to swim as well? *Journal of Personality and Social Psychology, 47*, 213–231.

Marsh, H. W., Wen, Z., & Hau, K. T. (2006). Structural equation models of latent interaction and quadratic effects. In G. R. Hancock & R. O. Mueller (Eds.), *Structural equation modeling: A second course* (pp. 225–265). Charlotte, NC: Information Age.

Marsh, H. W., Wen, Z., Hau, K. T., Little, T. D., Bovaird, J. A., & Widaman, K. F. (2007). Unconstrained structural equation models of latent interactions: Contrasting residual-and mean-centered approaches. *Structural Equation Modeling, 14*, 570–580.

Maxwell, S. E., & Delaney, H. D. (1993). Bivariate median splits and spurious statistical significance. *Psychological Bulletin, 113*, 181–190.

Maxwell, S. E., & Delaney, H. D. (2004). *Designing experiments and analyzing data* (2d ed.). New York: Psychology Press.

McClelland, G. H. (2000). Increasing statistical power without increasing sample size. *American Psychologist, 55*, 963–964.

McClelland, G. H., & Judd, C. M. (1993). Statistical difficulties of detecting interactions and moderator effects. *Psychological Bulletin, 114*, 376–390.

McCutcheon, A. L. (1987). *Latent class analysis*. Newbury Park, CA: SAGE.

Mellenbergh, G. J. (1989). Item bias and item response theory. *International Journal of Educational Research, 13*, 127–143.

Meredith, W. (1993). Measurement invariance, factor analysis and factorial invariance. *Psychometrika, 58*, 525–543.

Millsap, R. E. (2011) *Statistical approaches to measurement invariance*. New York: Routledge.

Muthén, L. K., & Muthén, B. O. (2015). *Mplus User's Guide* (7th ed.). Los Angeles: Muthén & Muthén.

Pedhauzer, E. J. (1997). *Multiple regression analysis in behavioral research: Explanation and prediction* (3d ed.). Fort Worth, TX: Wadsworth Publishing.

Potthoff, R. F. (1964). On the Johnson-Neyman technique and some extensions thereof. *Psychometrika, 29*, 241–256.

Preacher, K. J., Curran, P. J., & Bauer, D. J. (2006). Computational tools for probing interactions in multiple linear regression, multilevel modeling, and latent curve analysis. *Journal of Educational and Behavioral Statistics, 31*(4), 437–448.

Raudenbush, S. W., & Bryk, A. S. (2002). *Hierarchical linear models: Applications and data analysis methods* (2d ed.). London: SAGE.

Revelle, W., Humphreys, M. S., Simon, L., & Gilliland, K. (1980). The interactive effect of personality, time of day, and caffeine: A test of the arousal model. *Journal of Experimental Psychology: General, 109*, 1–31.

Seaton, M., Marsh, H. W., & Craven, R. (2010). Big-fish-little-pond effect: Generalizability and moderation: Two sides of the same coin. *American Educational Research Journal, 47*, 390–433.

Snijders, T., & Bosker, R. (2012). *Multilevel analysis: An introduction to basic and advanced multilevel modeling* (2d ed.). London: SAGE.

Sommet, N., Darnon, C., & Butera, F. (2015). To confirm or to conform? Performance goals as a regulator of conflict with more-competent others. *Journal of Educational Psychology, 107*, 580–598.

Yerkes, R. M., & Dodson, J. D. (1908). The relation of strength of stimulus to rapidity of habit formation. *Journal of Comparative Neurology of Psychology, 18*, 459–482.

Zedeck, S. (1971). Problems with the use of "moderator" variables. *Psychological Bulletin, 76*, 295–310.

NOTES

1. For illustrative purposes, we are drawing the details for the example from Figure 3 of Revelle et al. (1980), which combines results across multiple studies. Though the results presented here approximate those of Revelle et al., they are not based on the actual data, so the reader is encouraged to read Revelle et al.'s thoughtful and much more thorough discussion of the actual results.

2. As with the Revelle et al. (1980) example, only part of the overall Sommet et al. (2015) study is used for illustration, and the reader is encouraged to read the original paper for a complete discussion of the results.

3. Gender was not found to be a significant moderator in Long and Christian (2015), it is being used here only for illustrative purposes.

4. In the original Seaton et al. (2010) paper, a third level (country) was included in the model but has been removed here for simplicity.

Matthew S. Fritz and Ann M. Arthur

MULTILEVEL MODELING METHODS

INTRODUCTION

Human behavior develops in many different contexts. For instance, employees perform jobs in organizations, primary school students learn in schools, children grow up in families, and athletes (e.g., basketball players) play on sports teams. Some properties of these contexts (e.g., organizations, schools, families, and teams) influence human behavior (Lewin, 1936). For instance, an organization's climate influences employee engagement and performance (Spell, Eby, & Vandenberg, 2014). To estimate and understand these relationships, researchers need appropriate methods that take into account that the involved variables reside at different levels[1] (e.g., the organization and the employee) and that the data to be analyzed present a nested structure (e.g., employees are nested in organizations).

Disregarding the nested structure of data and performing the statistical analysis at the lower level (e.g., employees) by means of ordinary least squares (OLS) regression can have important undesirable consequences (González-Romá & Hernández, 2017). OLS regression assumes that observations are independent, and this assumption is violated in the case of nested data (Preacher, Zhang, & Zyphur, 2011). Individuals who are members of the same collective (e.g., work unit, school class, family, sports team) tend to have similar perceptions, affective experiences, attitudes, and behaviors (Barsade & Knight, 2015). Different processes (e.g., social interaction, emotional contagion, vicarious learning) can explain this similarity, which means that, in nested data, individual observations are generally non-independent. Bliese and Hanges (2004) showed that using OLS regression at the lower level to analyze nested data can lead to Type I and Type II errors. Specifically, this practice can lead to an increase in Type I error (i.e., the probability of rejecting the null hypothesis when it is true) when a researcher is interested in estimating the relationship between a higher-level variable (e.g., organizational climate) and a lower-level one (e.g., employee performance). It can lead to an increase in Type II error and loss of statistical power (i.e., the inability to reject the null hypothesis when it is false) when the interest is in estimating the relationship between two lower-level variables (e.g., employee job satisfaction and performance) in a sample providing nested data (e.g., employees nested in teams).

In order to avoid these problems, multilevel modeling is one of the techniques that can be used. The goals of this article are to provide an introduction to conventional multilevel modeling[2] methods that have evolved from multiple regression and offer updated guidelines for applying these methods, based on recent methodological research. The rest of this article is structured as follows. First, an introduction to the logic underlying multilevel modeling methods is offered. Second, the article shows how a number of basic multilevel models are built and discusses the meaning of their parameters. This is done by providing examples with real data and SPSS syntax that readers can use to practice on their own. Third, the article shows how more complex models, including mediation and moderation, are built and estimated. Fourth, some recommendations about sample sizes for testing multilevel effects are presented. Finally, some limitations are discussed, and some of the research opportunities offered by these methods are highlighted.

The focus of this article is two-level models in which individuals are nested within units (e.g., groups, teams, organizations). However, this approach can be extended to three-level designs (e.g., individuals nested within teams, which are nested within organizations) and longitudinal designs in which data collected at different occasions are nested within individuals (see Heck, Thomas, & Tabata, 2013).

THE LOGIC UNDERLYING MULTILEVEL MODELING METHODS

To show the logic underlying multilevel modeling methods, a hypothetical example will be used. Imagine that an organizational psychologist working in a large organization thinks that: (1) employee job satisfaction varies across the organization's work units; (2) employee satisfaction is positively influenced by the climate of organizational support in the work units to which employees belong (i.e., shared perceptions about the extent to which unit members believe the unit is supported by the organization and their managers; henceforth, unit climate); and (3) the negative relationship between employee job stress and job satisfaction (an individual-level relationship) varies across units, and this variation depends on units' climate, so that when the latter variable is high, the job stress–job satisfaction relationship is weakened. Each of these expected relationships involves variables that reside at different levels. These relationships are typically represented as shown in Figure 1.

Imagine that to ascertain whether her ideas are supported by empirical evidence, the organizational psychologist estimates the job stress–job satisfaction individual-level relationship in each unit of her organization. To do so, she estimates the following simple regression model: $Y = a + b\,X + e$, where Y is the outcome variable (job satisfaction), X is the predictor variable (job stress), a is the regression intercept, b is the regression coefficient or slope, and e is the residual term. This simple regression equation can be rewritten using a multilevel notation and considering the nested structure of the data as follows:

$$Y_{ij} = \beta_{0j} + \beta_{1j} X_{ij} + r_{ij} \qquad (1)$$

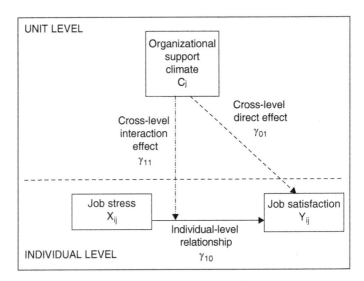

Figure 1. Typical representation of cross-level direct and interaction effects.

where Y_{ij} is the score on the outcome variable (job satisfaction) of subject i from unit j, X_{ij} is the score on the predictor variable (job stress) of subject i from unit j, β_{0j} is the regression intercept estimated in each unit (j), β_{1j} is the regression coefficient (slope) estimated in each unit (j), and r_{ij} is the residual term of the regression equation in each unit (j). Because in this equation the outcome and the predictor are individual-level variables, equation 1 is an individual-level equation (or Level-1 equation).

Suppose that our organizational psychologist represents the regression lines obtained for each unit and obtains a graph similar to the one displayed in Figure 2 (for clarity, only the regression lines for 10 units are displayed).

Figure 2 shows that the relationship between job stress and job satisfaction varies across units (as our organizational psychologist suspected). Different units have different regression lines. Actually, there are differences across units in the regression intercept (β_{0j}, the point at which the regression lines cross the Y-axis) and the regression slope (β_{1j}). In these 10 units, the value of the intercept varies between 5.24 and 2.12, and the value of the (unstandardized) slope varies between .08 and –.75. Our organizational psychologist is interested in ascertaining whether unit climate can explain part of this variability in intercepts and slopes across units. Therefore, she writes the following simple regression equations with the $Y = a + bX + e$ form:

$$\beta_{0j} = \gamma_{00} + \gamma_{01} C_j + U_{0j} \qquad (2)$$

$$\beta_{1j} = \gamma_{10} + \gamma_{11} C_j + U_{1j} \qquad (3)$$

where C_j represents the score on the predictor (unit climate) of unit j, γ_{00} and γ_{10} are two regression intercepts, γ_{01} and γ_{11} are two regression coefficients (slopes) that estimate the relationship between C_j, on the one hand, and β_{0j} and β_{1j}, on the other, and U_{0j} and U_{1j} are the corresponding residual terms. It is important to highlight two important characteristics of these two equations: (1) the outcome variables (β_{0j} and β_{1j}) are not typical substantive variables (as job satisfaction is, in equation 1), they are the regression intercepts and

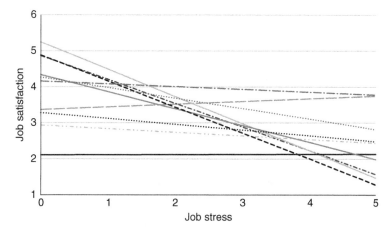

Figure 2. Regression lines obtained after regressing job satisfaction on job stress in 10 work units.

slopes, which vary across units; (2) the outcome and predictor variables are unit-level variables. Thus, equations 2 and 3 are unit-level equations (or Level-2 equations).

The set composed of equations 1, 2, and 3 represents a multilevel model in which different relationships are specified at different levels of analysis (the individual level, equation 1, and the unit level, equations 2 and 3). Multilevel modeling methods allow researchers to estimate the parameters involved in Level-1 and Level-2 equations. These parameters and other components of multilevel models are denoted by using a specific terminology. *Random coefficients* are parameter estimates that are allowed to vary across Level-2 units (e. g., work units). In our example, β_{0j} and β_{1j} are random coefficients. Note that the j subscript indicates that they can vary across work units. *Fixed effects* are parameter estimates that do not vary across Level-2 units. In our example, γ_{00}, γ_{01}, γ_{10}, and γ_{11} are fixed effects (note that they do not have a j subscript). *Random effects* represent the variation in random coefficients across Level-2 units. They are denoted by the Level-2 residual terms U_{0j} and U_{1j}. It is assumed that these residuals follow a normal distribution, with a zero mean and variances $\sigma^2_{\tau_{00}}$ and $\sigma^2_{\tau_{11}}$, respectively. The *variance-covariance components* of the multilevel model are these variances in the Level-2 residuals ($\sigma^2_{\tau_{00}}$ and $\sigma^2_{\tau_{11}}$), the covariance of the Level-2 residuals ($\sigma_{\tau_{10}}$), and the variance in the Level-1 residual r_{ij}[3], which is denoted by σ^2.

BASIC MULTILEVEL MODELS

In this section, a series of basic multilevel models is presented with the goal of showing how multilevel models can be built. In real research practice, the precise form of each multilevel model will depend on the researcher's hypotheses. However, this series offers sufficient initial understanding about the usefulness and flexibility of multilevel modeling techniques.

The Baseline Model with Random Intercepts.

This model (a.k.a. the null model, the unconditional model, or the one-way Analysis of Variance (ANOVA) model) allows researchers to decompose the variance in the outcome variable into two components: a within-unit component and a between-unit component. Note that, in multilevel studies, researchers expect the outcome variable to vary across the study units. In our example, the organizational psychologist thinks job satisfaction varies across the organization's units. The baseline model with random intercepts is generally the first multilevel model to estimate because it shows whether the aforementioned expectation is supported by the data.

The Level-1 equation for this model is:

$$Y_{ij} = \beta_{0j} + r_{ij} \tag{4}$$

As mentioned above, Y_{ij} is the score on the outcome variable (job satisfaction) of subject i from unit j, β_{0j} is the regression intercept of each unit (j), and r_{ij} is the residual term. In this model, β_{0j} represents the mean of each unit on the outcome variable. Remember that in a simple regression model like $Y = a + bX + e$, the value for the intercept (a) is given by $a = \overline{Y} - b\overline{X}$. If there is no predictor, then the intercept equals the average on the outcome variable ($\overline{Y}$).

The number of Level-2 equations equals the number of random coefficients in the corresponding Level-1 equation. In the baseline model, there is only one random coefficient in equation 4—β_{0j}; thus, only one Level-2 equation is needed, in which β_{0j} is the criterion variable:

$$\beta_{0j} = \gamma_{00} + U_{0j} \qquad (5)$$

where γ_{00} represents the grand-mean of the outcome variable in the population, and U_{0j} is a random effect that represents the variability in β_{0j} around γ_{00} across units. Note that there is no predictor in equations 4 and 5.

Equation 4 can be rewritten by replacing β_{0j} with the right-hand term from equation 5, which yields the so-called combined model:

$$Y_{ij} = \gamma_{00} + U_{0j} + r_{ij} \qquad (6)$$

This model shows that the variance in the outcome variable has two components: the variance in $U_{0j} (\sigma^2_{\tau 00})$, and the variance in $r_{ij} (\sigma^2)$. More formally, we can write the following:

$$\mathrm{Var}\left(Y_{ij}\right) = \mathrm{Var}\left(U_{0j} + r_{ij}\right) = \sigma^2_{\tau_{00}} + \sigma^2 \qquad (7)$$

where $\sigma^2_{\tau_{00}}$ estimates the variance in the intercept (β_{0j}) across units (the between component), and σ^2 represents the within-unit variance in the outcome variable (the within component). Once the two variance components are estimated, one can compute the proportion of variance in the outcome variable that resides between units by means of the intraclass correlation coefficient (ICC):

$$ICC = \frac{\sigma^2_{\tau_{00}}}{\sigma^2_{\tau_{00}} + \sigma^2}$$

This ratio yields the proportion of the total variance in the outcome variable $(\mathrm{Var}(Y_{ij}) = \sigma^2_{\tau_{00}} + \sigma^2)$ that corresponds to variance between units $(\sigma^2_{\tau_{00}})$. In our example, the ICC would help the organizational psychologist to ascertain whether employee job satisfaction varies across the organization's units, as she expects. Simulation studies suggest that when ICC > .05, nested data should be analyzed with multilevel method techniques. However, when ICC $\leq$ 0.05, the consequences of ignoring the nested structure of the data and analyzing the data by means of OLS regression are negligible (Finch & French, 2011).

Using the data and the syntax offered in the supplemental material, the baseline model was tested. The data came from a sample of 641 employees who were members of 197 units of a large organization. The baseline model was tested with the Mixed Models module of IBM SPSS software (version 24).[4] Because the number of Level-2 units is large, maximum likelihood estimation methods were used.

According to equation 6, the baseline model provides an estimation for three parameters: a fixed parameter γ_{00}, and the variances in U_{0j} and r_{ij}, $\sigma^2_{\tau_{00}}$ and σ^2, respectively. The results showed that the values obtained for these parameters are 3.16, .28, and .09, respectively. The value obtained for γ_{00} means that the grand mean for job satisfaction in the study sample equals 3.16 (on a scale from "1. Very unsatisfied" to "5. Very satisfied"). With the valued obtained for $\sigma^2_{\tau_{00}}$ and σ^2, the corresponding ICC can be computed:

258 • MULTILEVEL MODELING METHODS

$$ICC = \frac{\sigma_{\tau_{00}}^2}{\sigma_{\tau_{00}}^2 + \sigma^2} = \frac{.09}{.09 + .28} = .24$$

This result means that 24% of the variance in job satisfaction corresponds to differences between units. It provides empirical support for our organizational psychologist's expectation that employee job satisfaction varies across the organization's units. Because the outcome variable varies substantially within and between units, a multilevel analytical approach is justified.

SPSS also offers several criteria for the model fit. One of them is: -2 log likelihood function, which under maximum likelihood estimation methods can be used to compare the fit of two nested models. In our example, the value obtained for the baseline model is 1147.51.

The One Way Analysis of Covariance (ANCOVA) Model with Random Effects. With this model, researchers can ascertain whether a given individual-level predictor significantly explains the within-unit variance in the outcome variable. Coming back to our example, the next step would be to include job stress as an individual-level predictor of job satisfaction in the multilevel model (see Figure 1).

Before moving ahead, a few lines should be devoted to the issue of predictor centering. In psychology, researchers are frequently interested in constructs that are measured with arbitrary scales that do not have a meaningful zero point. One way to handle this problem is by centering the model predictors (Enders & Tofighi, 2007). In multilevel research, Level-1 predictors can be centered by using two different approaches. When centering at the grand mean (CGM), the grand mean of the predictor $(\overline{X}_T)$ is subtracted from each individual score (X_{ij}), so that the centered predictor equals $x_{ij} = X_{ij} - \overline{X}_T$. With the centering within cluster method (CWC, also called group-mean centering), the mean of the cluster or unit to which a given subject belongs $(\overline{X}_j)$ is subtracted from the respective individual scores, so that the centered predictor equals $x_{ij} = X_{ij} - \overline{X}_j$. In both cases, a value of zero means that the value of the predictor for a given subject equals the corresponding mean. Choosing the right option in multilevel research is quite important because the meaning of multilevel parameters can change depending on the centering option used. More importantly, as Enders and Tofighi (2007) highlight, "the decision to use CGM or CWC . . . depends heavily on one's substantive research questions" (pp. 134–135). We strongly recommend reading Enders and Tofighi's (2007) article to understand the implications of the centering issue. Because a cross-level interaction effect is of substantive interest in our example, we decided to center our Level-1 predictor (job stress) within cluster.

As to Level-2 predictors (e.g., unit climate), CGM is the only centering option available. Here, an alternative is to use the predictor in its raw metric. Because CGM is the recommended approach for a larger number of situations (see Enders & Tofighi, 2007, p. 135), and it gives meaning to a zero value, we decided to center our Level-2 predictor at the grand mean. The Level-1 equation for this model is the following:

$$Y_{ij} = \beta_{0j} + \beta_{1j} x_{ij} + r_{ij} \tag{8}$$

where x_{ij} is the CWC Level-1 predictor (job stress).

There are two random coefficients in equation 8: β_{0j} and β_{1j}. Therefore, this model has two Level-2 equations, one for β_{0j} and the other for β_{1j}. These equations are the following:

$$\beta_{0j} = \gamma_{00} + U_{0j} \qquad (5)$$

$$\beta_{1j} = \gamma_{10} \qquad (9)$$

The Level-2 equation for β_{0j} is the same as the one we had for the baseline model because we did not enter any Level-2 predictors into the model. An important point to highlight is that equation 9 establishes that the regression coefficient or slope estimating the individual-level relationship between x_{ij} (job stress) and Y_{ij} (job satisfaction) is constant (and equal to γ_{10}) across all the work units. The fixed parameter γ_{10} represents the pooled individual-level relationship between the predictor and the outcome variables. Note that because it is assumed that β_{1j} has a constant value across units, there is no random effect (U_{1j}) in equation 9; this model only assumes random effects for the intercept (U_{0j}). These are specific characteristics of this model that will be relaxed later.

As mentioned above, the meaning of multilevel parameters can change depending on the centering option used (Enders & Tofighi, 2007; Raundenbush & Bryk, 2002). To illustrate this, next we show the different meaning of β_{0j} using CGM or CWC in this model. Remember that, in a simple regression, the value for the intercept (a) is given by $a = \overline{Y} - b\overline{X}$. In CGM, the values for X_{ij} are transformed into the following deviation scores: $X_{ij} - \overline{X}_T$. Then, the intercept for each j unit can be obtained as follows:

$$\beta_{0j} = \overline{Y}_j - \beta_{1j}(\overline{X}_j - \overline{X}_T) \qquad (10)$$

Equation 10 shows that under CGM, β_{0j} represents the mean of each unit on the outcome variable ($\overline{Y}_j$), adjusted for differences among units in the predictor ($\overline{X}_j - \overline{X}_T$), and taking the regression slope into account (β_{1j}).

In CWC, the values for X_{ij} are transformed into the following deviation scores: $x_{ij} = X_{ij} - \overline{X}_j$. For each unit, the average of x_{ij} equals zero. Then, the intercept for each j unit is:

$$\beta_{0j} = \overline{Y}_j \qquad (11)$$

Equation 11 shows that under CWC, β_{0j} represents the unadjusted mean of each unit on the outcome variable.

Equation 8 can be rewritten by replacing β_{0j} and β_{1j} with the right-hand terms from equations 5 and 9, yielding the following combined model:

$$Y_{ij} = \gamma_{00} + \gamma_{10}x_{ij} + U_{0j} + r_{ij} \qquad (12)$$

Comparing the combined models for the baseline model and the one-way ANCOVA model (equations 6 and 12, respectively), it can be seen that the difference lies in the new fixed parameter (γ_{10}) estimating the relationship between the predictor (job stress) and the outcome variable (job satisfaction). Equation 12 provides an estimation of four parameters: two fixed parameters, γ_{00} and γ_{10}, and the variances in U_{0j} and r_{ij}, $\sigma^2_{\tau_{00}}$, and σ^2, respectively. Using the data and the corresponding SPSS syntax offered in the supplemental material, the one-way ANCOVA model was tested.

The results obtained show that model fit was improved. The fit for the baseline model was 1147.51, whereas this measure equals 1097.4 for the one-way ANCOVA model. The reduction in fit suggests that the fit of the last model is better than the fit of the former one. The difference in fit between two nested[5] models can be statistically tested because it follows a chi-square distribution with degrees of freedom equal to the difference in the number of parameters estimated in each model. The difference in the fit measure is 1147.51 – 1097.4 = 50.11. The difference in the number of parameters estimated under the two models is 1. A chi-square value of 50.11 with 1 degree of freedom is statistically significant ($\chi^2 = 50.11, df = 1, p < .01$). Therefore, it can be concluded that the fit of the one-way ANCOVA model is significantly better than the fit of the baseline model.

The results obtained for the fixed parameters were $\gamma_{00} = 3.16$ and $\gamma_{10} = -.23 \left(p < .01 \right)$. This last result means that, as expected, there is a statistically significant individual-level relationship between job stress and job satisfaction. The results obtained for the variance components were $\sigma^2_{\tau_{00}} = .10$ and $\sigma^2 = .25$. The inclusion of a Level-1 predictor in the model produced a decrease in the within-unit variance (σ^2) from .28 in the baseline model to .25 in the present one. We can estimate the proportion of within-unit variance explained by the Level-1 predictor (job stress) by computing the following pseudo-R^2 coefficient:

$$pseudoR^2 = \frac{\sigma^2_{M1} - \sigma^2_{M2}}{\sigma^2_{M1}} = \frac{.28 - .25}{.28} = .11$$

where M1 and M2 refer to the baseline and one-way ANCOVA models, respectively. The result obtained shows that job stress explains 11% of the with-unit variance in job satisfaction.

The Random-Coefficients Regression Model.   In the previous models, only the intercept β_{0j} was a random coefficient that was allowed to vary across units. The last model also included β_{1j} in the Level-1 equation, but it was constrained to assume a constant value across units ($\beta_{1j} = \gamma_{10}$). In the random-coefficients regression model, this last restriction is relaxed, and the two Level-1 regression coefficients (β_{0j} and β_{1j}) are allowed to vary across units. Note that in some situations (as in our example), the analyst thinks the examined individual-level relationship (e.g., job stress → job satisfaction) varies across units, and this variation depends on a Level-2 property (e.g., unit climate). To obtain empirical evidence about the existing variation in slopes across units, the random-coefficients regression model can be compared to the one-way ANCOVA model because the latter assumes that this variation is null.

The Level-1 equation for this model is the same as in the previous case because no new Level-1 predictor has been added:

$$Y_{ij} = \beta_{0j} + \beta_{1j} x_{ij} + r_{ij} \tag{8}$$

The two Level-2 equations, one for β_{0j} and the other for β_{1j}, are:

$$\beta_{0j} = \gamma_{00} + U_{0j} \tag{5}$$

$$\beta_{1j} = \gamma_{10} + U_{1j} \tag{13}$$

Note that equation 13 includes a random effect for the slope (β_{1j}), meaning that the slope estimating the relationship between job stress and job satisfaction in each unit can vary across units.

By replacing β_{0j} and β_{1j} in equation 8 with the right-hand terms from equations 5 and 13, the following combined model is obtained:

$$Y_{ij} = \gamma_{00} + U_{0j} + \left(\gamma_{10+}U_{1j}\right)x_{ij} + r_{ij} = \gamma_{00} + U_{0j} + \gamma_{10}x_{ij} + U_{1j}x_{ij} + r_{ij} \qquad (14)$$

$$Y_{ij} = \gamma_{00} + \gamma_{10}x_{ij+}U_{0j} + U_{1j}x_{ij} + r_{ij}$$

The difference between this combined model and the previous one (equation 12) lies in the inclusion of the random effects for the slope (U_{1j}).

According to equation 14, the random-coefficients regression model provides an estimation for two fixed parameters: γ_{00} and γ_{10}. Moreover, it provides estimations for the variances in U_{0j}, U_{1j}, and r_{ij}: $\sigma^2_{\tau_{00}}$, $\sigma^2_{\tau_{11}}$, and σ^2, respectively.[6] Thus, the total number of parameters to estimate is five. Using the data and the corresponding SPSS syntax offered in the supplemental material, the random-coefficients regression model was tested. The values obtained for the parameters also included in the previous model (γ_{00}, γ_{10}, $\sigma^2_{\tau_{00}}$, and σ^2) were similar to the values shown before. The value for the new parameter ($\sigma^2_{\tau_{11}}$) was .021.

The fit measure for this model was smaller than the one obtained for the previous model (1095.71 vs. 1097.40). However, the difference in fit between the two models was not statistically significant ($\chi^2 = 1.69, df = 1, p > .05$). This result would suggest that β_{1j} does not vary across units (contrary to what our organizational psychologist expected). However, a simulation study conducted by LaHuis and Ferguson (2009) found that this method has low statistical power when there are significant cross-level interactions. They recommended "against using significant slope variance as a prerequisite for testing hypothesized cross-level interactions and suggest[ed] that they should be tested regardless of the significance of slope variance" (pp. 432–433). Similarly, based on the idea that the tests of the statistical significance of the slope variance may be underpowered, the recommendation made by Aguinis, Gottfredson, and Culpepper (2013, p. 1502) was "to proceed with the cross-level interaction test even when the null hypothesis of no slope variance is retained when there is a strong theory-based rationale for a particular hypothesis." Therefore, assuming that there were theoretical reasons to expect that unit climate buffers the individual-level, negative relationship between job stress and job satisfaction, our organizational psychologist decided to proceed with the testing of the expected cross-level interaction effect.

The Intercepts-as-Outcomes Model. In this model, researchers model the variability in the Level-1 intercept (β_{0j}) across units by including Level-2 predictors (e.g., unit climate) in the corresponding Level-2 equation. The Level-1 equation is the same as in the two previous models:

$$Y_{ij} = \beta_{0j} + \beta_{1j}x_{ij} + r_{ij} \qquad (8)$$

Because our organizational psychologist expects job satisfaction (the outcome variable) to be positively influenced by work units' organizational support climate (C_j), this variable is included as a Level-2 predictor in the Level-2 equation for β_{0j}:

$$\beta_{0j} = \gamma_{00} + \gamma_{01}C_j + U_{0j} \qquad (15)$$

$$\beta_{1j} = \gamma_{10} + U_{1j} \qquad (13)$$

The Level-2 equation for β_{1j} is the same as in the previous model. However, depending on the research hypotheses, β_{1j} can be assumed to be constant across units (as in the one-way

ANCOVA model). This is the case when researchers are not interested in cross-level interactions (for an example, see Naumann & Bennett, 2000).

As equation 2 shows, the new fixed parameter γ_{01} estimates the relationship between two work unit variables: unit climate (C_j) and units' intercept (β_{0j}). It is important to highlight this because γ_{01} has frequently been incorrectly interpreted as estimating the relationship between a higher-level predictor (such as C_j) and the involved individual-level variable (Y_{ij}) (see LoPilato and Vandenberg, 2015, and González-Romá, 2019, for examples and a detailed explanation of this issue). The meaning of β_{0j} depends on the specific multilevel model tested and the approach used to center the Level-1 predictor (as shown above). When the key research question focuses on estimating the influence of a Level-2 predictor on the outcome variable, the recommended centering approach is CGM (Enders & Tofighi, 2007). As we saw above, under CGM, β_{0j} is an adjusted unit mean in the outcome variable. Therefore, in this case, γ_{01} would estimate the relationship between a unit variable and units adjusted mean on the outcome.

By replacing β_{0j} and β_{1j} in equation 8 with the right-hand terms from equations 15 and 13, the following combined model is obtained:

$$Y_{ij} = \gamma_{00} + \gamma_{01}C_j + U_{0j} + (\gamma_{10+}U_{1j})x_{ij} + r_{ij} = \gamma_{00} + \gamma_{01}C_j + U_{0j} + \gamma_{10}x_{ij+}U_{1j}x_{ij} + r_{ij}$$
$$Y_{ij} = \gamma_{00} + \gamma_{01}C_j + \gamma_{10}x_{ij+}U_{0j} + U_{1j}x_{ij} + r_{ij} \tag{16}$$

The difference between this combined model and the previous one (equation 14) lies in the new fixed effect γ_{01} associated with C_j. This parameter is said to estimate a "cross-level direct effect" (see Figure 1).

According to equation 16, the intercepts-as-outcomes model provides an estimation for three fixed parameters: γ_{00}, γ_{01}, and γ_{10}. Moreover, it also provides estimations for the variances in U_{0j}, U_{1j}, and r_{ij}: $\sigma^2_{\tau_{00}}$, $\sigma^2_{\tau_{11}}$, and σ^2, respectively. Thus, the total number of parameters to estimate is six. The fit measure for this model was smaller than the one obtained for the previous model (1071.32 vs. 1095.71). The difference in fit between the two models was statistically significant ($\chi^2 = 24.39, \mathrm{df} = 1, p < .05$).

The estimated value for the new fixed parameter (γ_{01}) was .21 ($p < .01$). Because we centered the Level-1 predictor within cluster, and in this situation, β_{0j} equals units' mean on the outcome variable, this result means that there is a significant positive relationship between units' climate and units' average score on job satisfaction (see equation 15). This result provides empirical evidence supporting our organizational psychologist's expectation that unit climate is related to job satisfaction.

The inclusion of a significant predictor (C_j) reduced the variance in the intercept (β_{0j}) across units ($\sigma^2_{\tau_{00}}$), from .10 in the previous model to .08 in the present one. The proportion of between-unit variance in the intercept explained by the Level-2 predictor (unit climate) can be estimated by computing the following pseudo-R^2 coefficient:

$$pseudo\ R^2 = \frac{\sigma^2_{\tau_{00}M3} - \sigma^2_{\tau_{00}M4}}{\sigma^2_{\tau_{00}M3}} = \frac{.10 - .08}{.10} = .20$$

where M3 and M4 refer to the random-coefficients regression and intercepts-as-outcomes models, respectively. The result obtained shows that unit climate (C_j) explains 20% of the between-unit variance in the Level-1 intercept across units. The values obtained for the other four parameters (γ_{00}, γ_{10}, $\sigma^2_{\tau_{11}}$, and σ^2) were the same as in the previous model.

The Intercepts-and-Slopes-as-Outcomes Model.

Remember that the organizational psychologist in our example thinks that *units'* climate has a buffering effect on the negative, individual-level relationship between job stress and job satisfaction. This effect represents an interaction because the strength of the relationship depends on a third variable. Moreover, it is called a "cross-level interaction" because the moderator (unit climate, C_j) is a unit-level variable, whereas the relationship involved is an individual-level one. In the intercepts-and-slopes-as-outcomes model, researchers model the variability in the Level-1 slope (β_{1j}) across units by including Level-2 predictors in the corresponding Level-2 equation. The Level-1 equation is the same as in the three previous models because no additional Level-1 predictor has been added:

$$Y_{ij} = \beta_{0j} + \beta_{1j} x_{ij} + r_{ij} \tag{8}$$

Because units' climate (C_j) is expected to impact on the slope estimating the individual-level job stress–job satisfaction relationship (β_{1j}), C_j is included as a Level-2 predictor in the Level-2 equation for β_{1j}:

$$\beta_{0j} = \gamma_{00} + \gamma_{01} C_j + U_{0j} \tag{15}$$

$$\beta_{1j} = \gamma_{10} + \gamma_{11} C_j + U_{1j} \tag{17}$$

By replacing β_{0j} and β_{1j} in equation 8 with the right-hand terms from equations 15 and 17, we obtain the following combined model:

$$\begin{aligned} Y_{ij} &= \gamma_{00} + \gamma_{01}C_j + U_{0j} + (\gamma_{10} + \gamma_{11} C_j + U_{1j})x_{ij} + r_{ij} \\ &= \gamma_{00} + \gamma_{01}C_j + U_{0j} + \gamma_{10}x_{ij+} \gamma_{11}C_j x_{ij+} U_{1j}x_{ij} + r_{ij} \\ &= \gamma_{00} + \gamma_{01}C_j + \gamma_{10}x_{ij+}\gamma_{11}C_j x_{ij+} U_{0j} + U_{1j}x_{ij} + r_{ij} \end{aligned} \tag{18}$$

The difference between this combined model and the previous one (equation 16) is the new fixed effect γ_{11} associated with the product term $C_j x_{ij}$. This parameter is said to estimate a "cross-level interaction" (see Figure 1).

According to equation 18, the intercepts-as-outcomes model provides an estimation for four fixed parameters: γ_{00}, γ_{01}, γ_{10}, and γ_{11}. Moreover, it also offers estimations for the variances in U_{0j}, U_{1j}, and r_{ij}: $\sigma^2_{\tau_{00}}$, $\sigma^2_{\tau_{11}}$, and σ^2, respectively. Thus, the total number of parameters to estimate is six. The fit measure for this model was smaller than the one obtained for the previous model (1067.36 vs. 1071.32). Moreover, the difference in fit between the two models was statistically significant ($\chi^2 = 3.96, df = 1, p < .05$). The value obtained for the new fixed parameter (γ_{11}) was $-.10$ ($p < .05$). Thus, there is a significant cross-level interaction effect through which unit climate has an influence on the Level-1 slope (β_{1j}) estimating the individual-level relationship between job stress and job satisfaction (see equation 17). To interpret the direction of the cross-level interaction effect, researchers can use Preacher, Curran, and Bauer's (2006) tools (http://www.quantpsy.org/interact/index.htm), which provide estimates and graphical representations of simple slopes.

The inclusion of a relevant predictor (C_j) reduced the variance in the slope (β_{1j}) across units ($\sigma^2_{\tau_{11}}$) from .021 in the previous model to .019 in the present one. The proportion of between-unit variance in the slope explained by the Level-2 predictor (unit climate) can be estimated by computing the following pseudo-R^2 coefficient:

$$pseudo\ R^2 = \frac{\sigma^2_{\tau_{11}M4} - \sigma^2_{\tau_{11}M5}}{\sigma^2_{\tau_{11}M4}} = \frac{.021 - .019}{.021} = .10$$

where M4 and M5 refer to the intercepts-as-outcomes and the intercepts-and-slopes-as-outcomes models, respectively. The result obtained shows that unit climate (C_j) explains 10% of the between-unit variance in the Level-1 slope across units. The values obtained for the other five parameters (γ_{00}, γ_{01}, γ_{10}, $\sigma^2_{\tau_{00}}$, and σ^2) were the same as in the previous model.

SAMPLE SIZE RECOMMENDATIONS FOR ESTIMATING BASIC MULTILEVEL MODELS

To ensure that the results and conclusions obtained when testing cross-level direct and interaction effects are appropriate, it is important to consider what combinations of sample sizes at both levels prevent bias and type I errors and foster the precision and statistical power of the estimates. According to the studies reviewed by González-Romá and Hernández (2017), although parameter estimates are typically unbiased with a small number of relatively small groups (e.g., 20 groups of 10 or even 10 groups of 5), researchers should try to sample a larger number of groups (approximately 30) in order to obtain adequate standard errors (SEs) to test for the significance of cross-level effects and build the corresponding confidence intervals.

Regarding power, González-Romá and Hernández (2017) concluded that the number of units seems to be more important than the number of individuals per unit, especially for cross-level direct effects. Again, 30 groups of approximately 20 to 40 individuals each seem to be enough to reach a power of 0.80 (Bell, Morgan, Schoeneberger, Kromrey, & Ferron, 2014). Regarding cross-level interactions, Mathieu, Aguinis, Culpepper, and Chen (2012) found that power was larger than 0.80 with 40 groups of 18. With small groups (3–7 individuals), even more than 100 groups did not reach enough power according to conventional standards.

MORE COMPLEX MULTILEVEL MODELS AND EFFECTS

Multilevel researchers are not only interested in cross-level direct and interaction effects. To understand the mechanisms underlying the (causal) relationship of interest, they often propose and test for mediators (e.g., Donati, Zappala, & González-Romá, 2016). If the strength and even the direction of these indirect influences are expected to depend on third variables that act as moderators, conditional mediation models (i.e., moderated mediation and mediated moderation) come into play (e.g., Pan, Sun, & Chow, 2012).

With conventional multilevel methods, different types of multilevel mediation models are possible. For the simplest case of a single mediator, there are three possible models: 1-1-1, 2-1-1, and 2-2-1, where the numbers indicate the level of the predictor X, the mediator M, and the outcome Y, respectively[7] (Krull & MacKinnon, 2001). Examples of each of these models are depicted in Figure 3. In all three cases, similarly to when OLS methods are applied, two regression coefficients need to be estimated and tested (see Fritz & Lester, 2016): *a*, which is obtained by regressing M on X, and *b*, which is obtained by regressing Y on M, controlling for the effect of X (*c*). Then, the indirect effect of X on Y via M can be obtained by means of the product *ab*. The statistical significance of this indirect "effect" must be tested using appropriate methods for non-normal distributions, such as Monte Carlo confidence intervals or the product of coefficients method (see MacKinnon, Lockwood, & Williams, 2004; Preacher & Selig, 2012). However, considering the possible different levels of the variables involved in the mediation chain and the two sources of variance involved in nested data (between- and

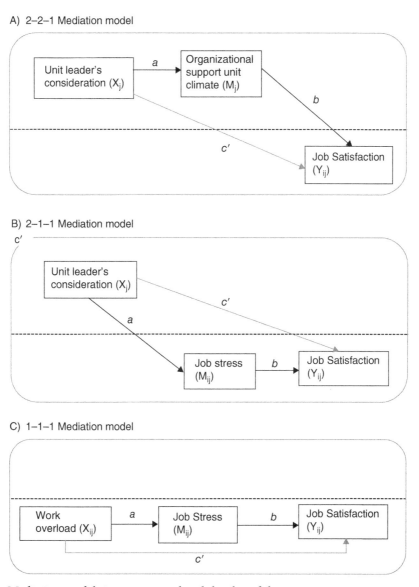

Figure 3. Mediation models in conventional multilevel modeling.

within-group variance), we need to take some considerations into account when testing and interpreting indirect effects.

On the one hand, when either X or both X and M are Level-2 variables (as in 2-1-1 and 2-2-1 models, respectively), only between-group indirect effects can be estimated (see Zhang, Ziphur, & Preacher, 2009) because Level-2 variables remain constant within groups and, thus, cannot explain within-group variance. On the other hand, when conducting multilevel analysis by using raw or CGM Level-1 scores (in models 2-1-1 and 1-1-1), the indirect effect conflates between-group and within-group variance, leading to incorrect conclusions about mediation (Zhang et al., 2009). In order to unconflate these variances, the CWC(M) centering option has been recommended (e.g., Enders & Tofighi, 2007; Zhang et al., 2009). In CWC(M), the Level-1 variables X and M are centered within cluster (CWC), and their group means ($\overline{X}_j$ and $\overline{M}_j$) are reintroduced in the model as Level-2 predictors of random intercepts. These Level-2 additional variables, $\overline{X}_j$ and $\overline{M}_j$, can be centered at the grand mean to make the interpretation of the intercept more meaningful. Next, closer attention is paid to the three types of mediation models mentioned.

The 2-2-1 Multilevel Mediation Model. In a 2-2-1 mediation model (Figure 3, Panel A), both X_j (unit leader's consideration) and M_j (organizational support unit climate) are Level-2 variables. Therefore, both a and b, as well as the indirect effect ab, are fixed coefficients that can only reflect between-unit variance across Level-2 units. In this case, conflated variance is not a concern because all the relationships in the model reflect between-unit effects.

To estimate a, M_j is regressed on X_j (a Level-2 regression):

$$\text{Level-2}: M_j = \gamma_{00}^a + \gamma_{01}^a \ X_j + U_{0j}^a \tag{21}$$

The value for $a(X_j \rightarrow M_j)$ is given by γ_{01}^a.
The multilevel regression equations involved in the estimation of b are:

$$\text{Level-1}: Y_{ij} = \beta_{0j}^b + r_{ij}^b \tag{22}$$

(see in Figure 3A that there is no Level-1 predictor)

$$\text{Level-2}: \beta_{0j}^b = \gamma_{00}^b + \gamma_{01}^b \ X_j + \gamma_{02}^b \ M_j + U_{0j}^b \tag{23}$$

The value for $b[M_j \rightarrow \beta_{0j}^b$ (unit intercept in the outcome variable), controlling for $X_j]$ is given by γ_{02}^b.

Thus, the indirect effect ab is given by $\gamma_{01}^a \cdot \gamma_{02}^b$. This is a between-unit indirect effect. In the example data, it equals .034 (.26 × .13) (see detailed results in Table 1). Because bootstrap can be problematic and computationally complex in multilevel contexts (McNeish, 2017), we used the product of coefficients method $\left(P = ZaZb, \text{where } Za = a / SE_a, \text{and } Zb = b / SE_b\right)$ (MacKinnon, Lockwood, Hoffman, West, & Sheets, 2002) and the Monte Carlo-based confidence interval method [for the latter, see Rockwood and Hayes's (2017) macro for SPSS (MLmed) and Tofighi and MacKinnon (2011) for R program (Rmediation)]. As Table 1 shows, the indirect effect was statistically significant with both approaches.

The 2-1-1 Multilevel Mediation Model. The second example in Figure 3 (panel B) depicts a 2-1-1 model (unit leader's consideration → job stress → job satisfaction). As mentioned

Table 1. Indirect Effects in Mediation Models

Model Tested	a	SEa	Za	b	SEb	Zb	P	Indirect Effect ab	SE ab	95% Monte Carlo CI
Model 2-2-1:										
Between-group effects	.26**	.03	8.67	.13**	.04	3.25	28.18	.03	.01	$[.01; .06]$
Model 2-1-1:										
Between-group effects	−.17**	.05	−3.4	−.31**	.04	−7.75	26.35**	.05	.02	$[.02; .09]$
Within-group effects	—	—	—	−.23**	.03	−7.67	—	—	—	—
Model 1-1-1:										
Within-group effects	.19**	.04	4.75	−.21**	.03	−7.00	−33.25**	−.04	.01	$[−.06; −.02]$
Between-group effects	.26**	.05	5.20	−.35**	.05	−7.00	−36.40**	−.09	.02	$[−.14; −.05]$

Notes: ** $p < .01$; SE: standard error; $Z_a = a/SE_a$. $Z_b = b/SE_b$. $P = Z_a Z_b$; CI: confidence interval.

earlier, a Level-2 predictor can only show indirect effects at the between-unit level because it is constant within units, regardless of the level at which the mediator is located. When using the CWC(M) centering option, the indirect between-unit effect of X on Y through M is estimated unequivocally. Although the within-unit effect of m_{ij} ($m_{ij} = M_{ij} - \overline{M}_j$) is also estimated, it is irrelevant for obtaining the indirect between effect.

If the CWC(M) centering recommendations are followed, the 2-1-1 multilevel regression equations required to estimate a are:

$$\text{Level-1}: M_{ij} = \beta_{0j}^a + r_{ij}^a \tag{24}$$

$$\text{Level-2}: \beta_{0j}^a = \gamma_{00}^a + \gamma_{01}^a X_j + U_{0j}^a \tag{25}$$

The value for $a[X_j \rightarrow \beta_{0j}^a$ (unit intercept in the mediator)] is given by γ_{01}^a. The multilevel regression equations for b are:

$$\text{Level-1}: Y_{ij} = \beta_{0j}^b + \beta_{1j}^b m_{ij} + r_{ij}^b \tag{26}$$

$$\text{Level-2}: \beta_{0j}^b = \gamma_{00}^b + \gamma_{01}^b X_j + \gamma_{02}^b \overline{M}_j + U_{0j}^b \tag{27}$$

$$\beta_{1j}^b = \gamma_{10}^b \tag{28}$$

The value for $b[\overline{M}_j \rightarrow \beta_{0j}^b$ (unit intercept in the outcome variable), controlling for X_j] is given by γ_{02}^b.

Therefore, the between-unit indirect effect ab is given by: $\gamma_{01}^a \cdot \gamma_{02}^b$. In our example, $\gamma_{01}^a \cdot \gamma_{02}^b = -.17 \times -.31 = .053$, which is statistically significant ($p < .05$) according to both the product of coefficients method and the Monte Carlo confidence interval (see Table 1).

The 1-1-1 Multilevel Mediation Model. The final example in Figure 3 (Panel C) depicts a 1-1-1 mediation model (work overload → job stress → job satisfaction), with all the effects considered at the individual level (but in a nested data sample). Therefore, the indirect effect of interest is a within-unit effect. If the CWC(M) approach is followed, the 1-1-1 multilevel regression equations required to estimate a are:

$$\text{Level-1}: M_{ij} = \beta_{0j}^a + \beta_{1j}^a x_{ij} + r_{ij}^a \tag{29}$$

where $x_{ij} = X_{ij} - \bar{X}_j$

$$\text{Level-2}: \beta_{0j}^a = \gamma_{00}^a + \gamma_{01}^a \bar{X}_j + U_{0j}^a \tag{30}$$

$$\beta_{1j}^a = \gamma_{10}^a \tag{31}$$

The value for $a(x_{ij} \to M_{ij})$ is given by γ_{10}^a.
The multilevel regression equations to estimate b are:

$$\text{Level-1}: Y_{ij} = \beta_{0j}^b + \beta_{1j}^b x_{ij} + \beta_{2j}^b m_{ij} + r_{ij}^b \tag{32}$$

$$\text{Level-2}: \beta_{0j}^b = \gamma_{00}^b + \gamma_{01}^b \bar{X}_j + \gamma_{02}^b \bar{M}_j + U_{0j}^b \tag{33}$$

$$\beta_{1j}^b = \gamma_{10}^b \tag{34}$$

$$\beta_{2j}^b = \gamma_{20}^b \tag{35}$$

The value for $b(m_{ij} \to Y_{ij})$, controlling form x_{ij}) is given by γ_{20}^b.

Therefore, the within-unit indirect effect ab is given by: $\gamma_{10}^a \cdot \gamma_{20}^b$. In our example, $\gamma_{10}^a \cdot \gamma_{20}^b = -.19 \times -.21 = -.04$, which was statistically significant (see Table 1). Note that for the sake of parsimony, we assumed that the Level-1 regression coefficients are fixed parameters that do not vary across units (see equations 31 and 35). If these coefficients varied across units, then the covariance between the random components (if any) would have to be incorporated when computing the within-unit indirect effect $[(\gamma_{10}^a + U_{1j}^a)(\gamma_{20}^b + U_{2j}^b)]$. In this case, MLmed could be used to test for the indirect effect that incorporates the covariance between the random variables, following Bauer, Preacher, and Gil's (2006) approach.

Although the indirect effect of interest is the within-unit effect shown above, this model also allows researchers to estimate the corresponding between-unit indirect effect, given by $\gamma_{01}^a \cdot \gamma_{02}^b$. In the example, $\gamma_{01}^a \cdot \gamma_{02}^b = .26 \times -.35 = -.09$. Once the two indirect effects are estimated, researchers can test for their difference and ascertain whether a contextual effect exists (Enders & Tofighi 2007). With our results: contextual indirect effect $= ab_{between} - ab_{within} = -.091 - (-.038) = -.053$, Monte Carlo 95% confidence interval: $-.10$; $-.01$. Thus, the two indirect effects are statistically different. These results show that modeling between-unit effects provides additional explanatory power, supporting the need to consider the effects of work overload at both levels.

Cross-Level Moderation in 1-1-1 Mediation Models. Although moderators may play a role at different levels and in different types of mediation models, the final model considered focuses on a cross-level interaction in a 1-1-1 model (see Figure 4). Here, the second mediation path (job stress→ job satisfaction) is moderated by a Level-2 variable: organizational support unit climate (C_j). For simplicity, it is assumed that only path b varies across units. As in the previous model, the interest is in the within-unit indirect effect that varies according to C_j.

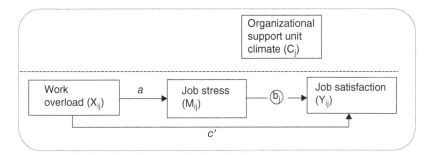

Figure 4. Conditional multilevel mediation model.

The multilevel equations to estimate coefficient a are:

$$\text{Level-1}: M_{ij} = \beta_{0j}^{a} + \beta_{1j}^{a} x_{ij} + r_{ij}^{a} \tag{36}$$

$$\text{Level-2}: \beta_{0j}^{a} = \gamma_{00}^{a} + \gamma_{01}^{a} \overline{X}_{j} + U_{0j}^{a} \tag{37}$$

$$\beta_{1j}^{a} = \gamma_{10}^{a} \tag{38}$$

The value for a is given by γ_{10}^{a}.

The multilevel regression equations to estimate the b coefficients are:

$$\text{Level-1}: Y_{ij} = \beta_{0j}^{b} + \beta_{1j}^{b} x_{ij} + \beta_{2j}^{b} m_{ij} + r_{ij}^{b} \tag{39}$$

$$\text{Level-2}: \beta_{0j}^{b} = \gamma_{00}^{b} + \gamma_{01}^{b} \overline{X}_{j} + \gamma_{02}^{b} \overline{M}_{j} + \gamma_{03}^{b} C_{j} + \gamma_{04}^{b} \overline{M}_{j} C_{j} + U_{0j}^{b} \tag{40}$$

$$\beta_{1j}^{b} = \gamma_{10}^{b} \tag{41}$$

$$\beta_{2j}^{b} = \gamma_{20}^{b} + \gamma_{21}^{b} C_{j} + U_{2j}^{b} \tag{42}$$

The value for b is given by $\gamma_{20}^{b} + \gamma_{21}^{b} C_{j}$. The coefficient testing for the cross-level interaction is γ_{21}^{b}. The within-unit indirect effect conditional to specific values of the moderator C_{j} is $\gamma_{10}^{a}(\gamma_{20}^{b} + \gamma_{21}^{b} C_{j}) = \gamma_{10}^{a}\gamma_{20}^{b} + \gamma_{10}^{a}\gamma_{21}^{b} C_{j}$. In our example, the cross-level interaction ($\gamma_{21}^{b} = -.11$) is statistically significant ($p < .05$). MLmed can be used to obtain the within index of moderated mediation and the size and significance of indirect effects across different values of the moderator. In our example, the within index of moderated mediation is statistically significant: 95% Monte Carlo confidence interval: −.04; −.003.

Finally, only some extensions of the basic multilevel models have been considered, due to space limitations. However, the logic underlying model construction can be easily generalized to more complex models with several sequential or parallel mediators and/or multiple moderators at different levels.

SAMPLE SIZE RECOMMENDATIONS FOR ESTIMATING MORE COMPLEX MODELS

According to the simulation studies reviewed by González-Romá and Hernández (2017), the estimates of the indirect effects are generally accurate, even with small samples, for all types of models (for example, in the 2-1-1 model only 10 groups of 5–10 individuals; Krull & MacKinnon, 1999). In addition, Zhang et al. (2009) showed that when the between and within variance components are differentiated in a 2-1-1 model, the CWC(M) approach shows good control of the Type I error rates for the different sample size combinations assessed by the authors: from 20 groups of 30 individuals to 120 groups of 5. A more recent study focusing on 2-1-1 models (McNeish, 2017) shows that Type I error rates are acceptable across different numbers of groups (10 to 100) and observations (7–14 to 80–160 per group). For 1-1-1 models with random coefficients, Bauer et al. (2006) showed that Monte Carlo–based confidence intervals led to false-positive rates below the nominal level when the number of groups was 25 and there were only 4 individuals per group. With more groups and/or individuals per group, the Type I error rates were adequately controlled for.

Regarding power, Zhang et al. (2009) showed that in 2-1-1 mediation models, there was more power when including more groups with fewer observations per group than the other way around. Specifically, using the Sobel (1982) test to assess whether the indirect effect was significant, they concluded that a minimum of 75 groups of 8 was necessary to reach acceptable power. However, more recently, McNeish (2017) showed that, in 2-1-1 models, Monte Carlo confidence intervals reach power levels larger than .80 with only 25 groups of 7–14 individuals. Monte Carlo confidence intervals, compared to other methods, have also shown the highest power levels in simulated 1-1-1 models (Bauer et al., 2006) and in 2-2-1 (Kelcey, Dong, Spybrook, & Cox, Shen, 2017a) and 2-1-1 group-randomized simulation studies (Kelcey, Dong, Spybrook, & Cox, 2017b). For example, Kelcey et al. (2017a) showed that, for a medium-size indirect effect, acceptable power (.80) was reached with 30 Level-2 units of 20 individuals if the model included covariates. The required Level-2 sample was twice as large when the model did not include covariates. For the 2-1-1 model, Kelcey et al. (2017b) showed that, for a medium-size indirect effect, the Monte Carlo interval test reached acceptable power with approximately 36 groups of 20 individuals when covariates explained about 75% of the variance of the outcome. When the percentage of variance was 25%, the number of Level-2 units increased to 64. In the latter two studies, results from the simulated samples were similar to the results obtained with the formulas proposed by the authors (see the PowerUp Mediator software). For multilevel conditional mediation, more research is needed.

LIMITATIONS

The conventional multilevel approach presented here is flexible enough to accommodate different research questions and models. However, it has a number of limitations that must be considered. Some of them are related to general regression-based models, and others are specific to the conventional multilevel approach.

First, when applying conventional multilevel methods, the outcome variable in the model has to be a Level-1 outcome. Thus, cross-level effects are constrained to top-down effects. This fact has barred research on bottom-up effects in psychology (e.g., Neal & Griffin, 2006). MSEM opens up the possibility of testing bottom-up effects, or a combination of bottom-up and top-down effects, because both can be modeled by means of MSEM (see Preacher, Zyphur, & Zang, 2010).

Second, in multilevel research, there are two possible sources of error or unreliability: one due to measurement error and one due to sampling error. However, under conventional multilevel modeling, variables are assumed to be error-free. MSEM, however, allows researchers to consider both types of errors. Measurement error is controlled for by modeling the constructs of interest as latent variables with multiple indicators. Sampling error is an issue when Level-1 variables are aggregated at the unit level to represent Level-2 variables (e.g., the case of unit climate, which is obtained from unit members' individual responses aggregated at the unit level). The problem is that often only a small sample of subjects from each unit is used to compute unit means. MSEM allows researchers to control for sampling error by considering the unit mean as a latent variable measured with a certain amount of precision by the observed unit mean (Marsh et al., 2009).

Third, the assessment of model fit with conventional multilevel methods is problematic because there are no clear comparison models or easily interpretable fit indices (Curran, 2003). However, fit indices used in the SEM literature can be employed to assess MSEM models. In this case, indices that provide specific fit information for each level of analysis are especially useful (Ryu & West, 2009).

Finally, for the sake of simplicity, the models presented in this article involve continuous variables. When the outcome variables are categorical and count variables, they can be analyzed by means of conventional multilevel methods (for example in SPSS, by using the generalized linear mixed model; see Heck, Thomas, & Tabata, 2012). However, as the models become more complex (e.g., including categorical mediators), MSEM becomes a more flexible approach. In this regard, research is needed to ascertain how well multilevel modeling works when models include categorical variables.

Despite the benefits of the MSEM approach, there is an important drawback that can impede its use: sample size requirements. González-Romá and Hernández (2017) concluded that, when using MSEM with multiple indicators, at least 100 work units of 15 individuals should be sampled. Focusing on mediation, McNeish (2017) reported that most MSEM studies (89%) did not reach the minimum number of 100 Level-2 units, and that most models in the MSEM studies reviewed (75%) could have been tested by conventional multilevel modeling. Using simulated data, he showed that conventional multilevel modeling performs better with small samples and can be trustworthy even with 10 Level-2 units. Another possibility is to use Bayesian estimation methods, which in MSEM have been shown to be a reasonable option when the number of Level-2 units is small (e.g., 25) (Hox, Moerbeek, Kluytmans, & van de Schoot, 2014). In this regard, McNeish (2017) points out that using the diffuse default prior distributions of popular software can result in poor estimates because the additional information that is added through the priors can detract from the information obtained from the small amount of data available.

RESEARCH OPPORTUNITIES

Multilevel modeling offers new research opportunities to extend knowledge about phenomena of interest. By partitioning the variance of lower-level variables into their within and between components (for example, by means of CWC(M)), it is possible to investigate effects that may operate at different levels. This includes indirect effects that develop at both within- and between-unit levels and interactions that involve only between components and/or within and between components (see Preacher et al., 2010). The awareness of these opportunities will contribute to the formulation of more concrete and richer hypotheses (González-Romá & Hernández, 2017). In addition, this variance partition will allow researchers to test for contextual effects and determine whether relationships observed at a specific level (e.g., within units) can be generalized to another level (e.g., across units). Moreover, when longitudinal data are available, variance partition will help researchers to determine whether the time needed for a process to develop at the individual level is similar to the time frame needed for the same process to develop at the unit level.

CONCLUSION

Human behavior takes place in many different contexts that can influence individuals' behavior. To investigate this influence, researchers need methods that consider that the variables involved reside at different levels and the specific characteristic of nested data. The multilevel modeling methods presented here respond to these demands. With this article, we hope to help interested researchers understand the logic underlying these methods, build multilevel models, and test them. By doing so, researchers will contribute to extending knowledge about psychological phenomena from a more comprehensive and integral perspective.

REFERENCES

Aguinis, H., Gottfredson, R. K., & Culpepper, S. A. (2013). Best-practice recommendations for estimating cross-level interaction effects using multilevel modeling. *Journal of Management, 39,* 1490–1528.

Barsade, S. C., & Knight, A. P. (2015). Group affect. *Annual Review of Organizational Psychology and Organizational Behavior, 2,* 21–46.

Bauer, D. J., Preacher, K. J., & Gil, K. M. (2006). Conceptualizing and testing random indirect effects and moderated mediation in multilevel models: New procedures and recommendations. *Psychological Methods, 11,* 142–163.

Bell, B. A., Morgan, G. B., Schoeneberger, J. A., Kromrey, J. D., & Ferron, J. M. (2014). How low can you go? An investigation of the influence of sample size and model complexity on point and interval estimates in two-level linear models. *Methodology, 10,* 86–92.

Bliese, P. D., & Hanges, P. J. (2004). Being both too liberal and too conservative: The perils of treating grouped data as though they were independent. *Organizational Research Methods, 7,* 400–417.

Curran, P. J. (2003). Have multilevel models been structural equation models all along? *Multivariate Behavioral Research, 38,* 529–569.

Donati, S., Zappalà, S., & González-Romá, V. (2016). The influence of friendship and communication network density on individual innovative behaviours: A multilevel study. *European Journal of Work and Organizational Psychology, 25,* 583–596.

Enders, C. K., & Tofighi, D. (2007). Centering predictor variables in cross-sectional multilevel models: A new look at an old issue. *Psychological Methods, 12,* 121–138.

Finch, W. H., & French, B. F. (2011). Estimation of MIMIC model parameters with multilevel data. *Structural Equation Modeling, 18,* 229–252.

Fritz, M. S., & Lester, H. F. (2016). Mediator variables. *Oxford Research Encyclopedia of Psychology.* http://dx.doi.org/10.1093/acrefore/9780190236557.013.19

González-Romá, V. (2019). Three issues in multilevel research. *The Spanish Journal of Psychology, 22*(e4), 1–7.

González-Romá, V., & Hernández, A. (2017). Multilevel modeling: Research-based lessons for substantive researchers. *Annual Review of Organizational Psychology and Organizational Behavior, 4,* 183–210.

Heck, R. H., & Thomas, S. L. (2015). *An introduction to multilevel modeling techniques: MLM and SEM approaches using Mplus.* New York: Routledge.

Heck, R. H., Thomas, S., & Tabata, L. (2012). *Multilevel modeling of categorical outcomes using IBM SPSS.* New York: Routledge Academic.

Heck, R., Thomas, S., & Tabata, L. (2013). *Multilevel and longitudinal modeling with IBM SPSS.* New York: Routledge.

Hox, J., Moerbeek, M., Kluytmans, A., & Van De Schoot, R. (2014). Analyzing indirect effects in cluster randomized trials. The effect of estimation method, number of groups and group sizes on accuracy and power. *Frontiers in Psychology, 5,* 78.

Hui, C. H., Chiu, W. C., Yu, P. L., Cheng, K., & Tse, H. H. (2007). The effects of service climate and the effective leadership behaviour of supervisors on frontline employee service quality: A multi-level analysis. *Journal of Occupational and Organizational Psychology, 80,* 151–172.

Kelcey, B., Dong, N., Spybrook, J., & Cox, K. (2017). Statistical power for causally defined indirect effects in group-randomized trials with individual-level mediators. *Journal of Educational and Behavioral Statistics, 42,* 499–530.

Kelcey, B., Dong, N., Spybrook, J., & Shen, Z. (2017). Experimental power for indirect effects in group-randomized studies with group-level mediators. *Multivariate Behavioral Research, 52,* 699–719.

Krull, J. L., & MacKinnon, D. P. (1999). Multilevel mediation modeling in group-based intervention studies. *Evaluation Review, 23,* 418–444.

Krull, J. L., & MacKinnon, D. P. (2001). Multilevel modeling of individual and group level mediated effects. *Multivariate Behavioral Research, 36,* 249–277.

LaHuis, D. M., & Ferguson, M. W. (2009). The accuracy of significance tests for slope variance components in multilevel random coefficient models. *Organizational Research Methods, 12,* 418–435.

LaHuis, D. M., Hartman, M. J., Hakoyama, S., & Clark, P. C. (2014). Explained variance measures for multilevel models. *Organizational Research Methods, 17,* 433–451.

Lewin, K. (1936). *Principles of topological psychology.* New York: McGraw-Hill.

LoPilato, A. C., & Vandenberg, R. J. (2015). The not-so-direct cross-level direct effect. In C. E. Lance & R. J. Vandenberg (Eds.), *More statistical and methodological myths and urban legends* (pp. 292–310). New York: Routledge.

MacKinnon, D. P., Lockwood, C. M., & Williams, J. (2004) Confidence limits for the indirect effect: Distribution of the product and resampling methods. *Multivariate Behavioral Research, 39,* 99–128.

MacKinnon, D. P., Lockwood, C. M., Hoffman, J. M., West, S. G., & Sheets, V. (2002). A comparison of methods to test mediation and other intervening variable effects. *Psychological Methods, 7,* 83–104.

Marsh, H. W., Lüdtke, O., Robitzsch, A., Trautwein, U., Asparouhov, T., Muthén, B., & Nagengast, B. (2009). Doubly-latent models of school contextual effects: Integrating multilevel and structural equation approaches to control measurement and sampling error. *Multivariate Behavioral Research, 44,* 764–802.

Mathieu, J. E., Aguinis, H., Culpepper, S. A., & Chen, G. (2012). Understanding and estimating the power to detect cross-level interaction effects in multilevel modeling. *Journal of Applied Psychology, 97,* 951–966.

McNeish, D. (2017). Multilevel mediation with small samples: A cautionary note on the multilevel structural equation modeling framework. *Structural Equation Modeling: A Multidisciplinary Journal, 24,* 609–625.

Naumann, S. E., & Bennett, N. (2000). A case for procedural justice climate: Development and test of a multilevel model. *Academy of Management Journal, 43,* 881–889.

Neal, A., & Griffin, M. A. (2006). A study of the lagged relationships among safety climate, safety motivation, safety behavior, and accidents at the individual and group levels. *Journal of Applied Psychology, 91,* 946–953.

Pan, W., Sun, L. Y., & Chow, I. H. S. (2012). Leader-member exchange and employee creativity: Test of a multilevel moderated mediation model. *Human Performance, 25,* 432–451.

Preacher, K. J., Zyphur, M. J., & Zhang, Z. (2010). A general multilevel SEM framework for assessing multilevel mediation. *Psychological Methods, 15,* 209–233.

Preacher, K. J., Zhang, Z., & Zyphur, M. J. (2011). Alternative methods for assessing mediation in multilevel data: The advantages of multilevel SEM. *Structural Equation Modeling, 18,* 161–182.

Preacher, K. J., & Selig, J. P. (2012). Advantages of Monte Carlo confidence intervals for indirect effects. *Communication Methods and Measures, 6*, 77–98.

Preacher, K. J., Curran, P. J., & Bauer, D. J. (2006). Computational tools for probing interactions in multiple linear regression, multilevel modeling, and latent curve analysis. *Journal of Educational and Behavioral Statistics, 31*, 437–448.

Raudenbush, S. W., & Bryk, A. S. (2002). *Hierarchical linear models: Applications and data analysis methods.* Thousand Oaks, CA: SAGE.

Rockwood, N. J., & Hayes, A. F. (2017, May). *MLmed: An SPSS macro for multilevel mediation and conditional process analysis.* Poster presented at the annual meeting of the Association of Psychological Science (APS), Boston.

Ryu, E., & West, S. G. (2009). Level-specific evaluation of model fit in multilevel structural equation modeling. *Structural Equation Modeling, 16*, 583–601.

Sobel, M. E. (1982). Asymptotic confidence intervals for indirect effects in structural equation models. *Sociological Methodology, 13*, 290–312.

Spell, H. B., Eby, L. T., & Vandenberg, R. J. (2014). Developmental climate: A cross-level analysis of voluntary turnover and job performance. *Journal of Vocational Behavior, 84*, 283–292.

Tofighi, D., & MacKinnon, D. P. (2011). RMediation: An R package for mediation analysis confidence intervals. *Behavior Research Methods, 43*, 692–700.

Zhang, Z., Zyphur, M. J., & Preacher, K. J. (2009). Testing multilevel mediation using hierarchical linear models problems and solutions. *Organizational Research Methods, 12*, 695–719.

APPENDIX

Annotated SPSS syntax to estimate the basic multilevel models presented in the article

Only key and new elements are mentioned for each model. These elements are highlighted in bold type. See Heck et al.'s (2013) book to learn how to run these models by using the SPSS graphical user interface (GUI).

MODEL 1. The baseline model with random intercepts

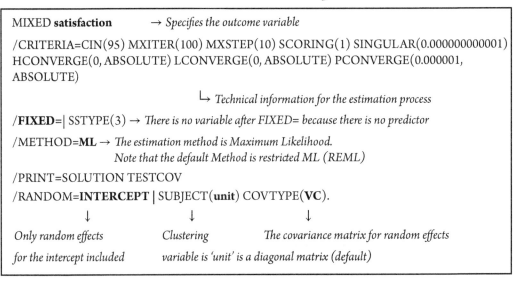

MULTILEVEL MODELING METHODS • 275

MODEL 2. The one-way ANCOVA model with random effects

MIXED satisfaction **WITH stressCWC** → *Specifies the new predictor in the model*

 /CRITERIA=CIN(95) MXITER(100) MXSTEP(10) SCORING(1) SINGULAR (0.000000000001) HCONVERGE(0,

   ABSOLUTE) LCONVERGE(0, ABSOLUTE) PCONVERGE(0.000001, ABSOLUTE)

 /FIXED=**stressCWC** | SSTYPE(3) → *Estimates the fixed effect γ_{10} associated with the stress-satisfaction relationship*

 /METHOD=ML

 /PRINT=SOLUTION TESTCOV

 /RANDOM=INTERCEPT | SUBJECT(unit) COVTYPE(VC).

MODEL 3. The random-coefficients regression model

MIXED satisfaction WITH stressCWC

 /CRITERIA=CIN(95) MXITER(100) MXSTEP(10) SCORING(1) SINGULAR(0.000000000001) HCONVERGE(0,

   ABSOLUTE) LCONVERGE(0, ABSOLUTE) PCONVERGE(0.000001, ABSOLUTE)

 /FIXED=stressCWC | SSTYPE(3)

 /METHOD=ML

 /PRINT=SOLUTION TESTCOV

 /RANDOM=INTERCEPT **stressCWC** | SUBJECT(unit) COVTYPE(VC).

                    ↓

The random effects for the slope associated
with job stress (β_{1j}) are included in the model

MODEL 4. The intercepts-as-outcomes model

MIXED satisfaction WITH **supportTEAMGMC** stressCWC → *The Level 2 variable (C_j) is included in the model*

 /CRITERIA=CIN(95) MXITER(100) MXSTEP(10) SCORING(1) SINGULAR(0.000000000001) HCONVERGE(0,

   ABSOLUTE) LCONVERGE(0, ABSOLUTE) PCONVERGE(0.000001, ABSOLUTE)

 /FIXED=**supportTEAMGMC** stressCWC | SSTYPE(3) → *Estimates the fixed effect γ_{01}, the cross-level direct effect*

 /METHOD=ML

 /PRINT=SOLUTION TESTCOV

 /RANDOM=INTERCEPT stressCWC | SUBJECT(unit) COVTYPE(VC).

MODEL 5. *The intercepts-and-slopes-as-outcomes model*

MIXED satisfaction WITH supportTEAMGMC stressCWC

 /CRITERIA=CIN(95) MXITER(100) MXSTEP(10) SCORING(1) SINGULAR(0.000000000001) HCONVERGE(0,

ABSOLUTE) LCONVERGE(0, ABSOLUTE) PCONVERGE(0.000001, ABSOLUTE)

/FIXED=supportTEAMGMC stressCWC **supportTEAMGMC*stressCWC** | SSTYPE(3)

$$\downarrow$$

Estimates the fixed effect γ_{11} associated with the interaction term $(C_j\, x_{ij})$, the cross-level interaction

/METHOD=ML

/PRINT=SOLUTION TESTCOV

/RANDOM=INTERCEPT stressCWC | SUBJECT(unit) COVTYPE(VC).

MODEL 2–1–1
(unit leader's consideration → job stress → job satisfaction

Coefficient *a* (unit leader's consideration → job stress)

 MIXED stress WITH ConsiderationTEAMGMC

  /CRITERIA=CIN(95) MXITER(100) MXSTEP(10) SCORING(1) SINGULAR(0.000000000001) HCONVERGE(0,

   ABSOLUTE) LCONVERGE(0, ABSOLUTE) PCONVERGE(0.000001, ABSOLUTE)

  /FIXED=**ConsiderationTEAMGMC** | SSTYPE(3) → *Estimates the fixed effect γ_{01}^{a} (the cross-level direct effect) (between)*

 /METHOD=ML

 /PRINT=SOLUTION TESTCOV

 /RANDOM=INTERCEPT | SUBJECT(unit) COVTYPE(VC).

Coefficient *b* (job stress → job satisfaction, controlling for unit leader's consideration)

MIXED satisfaction WITH ConsiderationTEAMGMC stressTEAMGMC stressCWC

 /CRITERIA=CIN(95) MXITER(100) MXSTEP(10) SCORING(1) SINGULAR(0.000000000001) HCONVERGE(0,

  ABSOLUTE) LCONVERGE(0, ABSOLUTE) PCONVERGE(0.000001, ABSOLUTE)

 /FIXED=ConsiderationTEAMGMC **stressTEAMGMC stressCWC** | SSTYPE(3)

$$\downarrow \qquad\qquad \downarrow$$

Estimates the fixed effect γ_{02}^{a} (the cross-level direct effect) (between)   *Estimates the fixed effect γ_{10}^{b} (the relationship between the level-1 variables) (within)*

/METHOD=ML

/PRINT=SOLUTION TESTCOV

/RANDOM=INTERCEPT | SUBJECT(unit) COVTYPE(VC).

MULTILEVEL MODELING METHODS · 277

Annotated SPSS syntax to estimate the mediation model presented in the article (see Figure 3)

MODEL 2–2–1

(unit leader's consideration → unit climate for support → job satisfaction

---

Coefficient *a* (unit leader's consideration → uunit climate for support)

REGRESSION → *No variable is considered at the individual level, OLS regression is run*

 /MISSING LISTWISE
 /STATISTICS COEFF OUTS R ANOVA
 /CRITERIA=PIN(.05) POUT(.10)
 /NOORIGIN
 /DEPENDENT supportTEAMGMC
 /METHOD=ENTER **ConsiderationTEAMGMC.** → *Estimates the fixed effect* γ_{01}^{a}
 (between)

Coefficient *b* (unit climate for support → job satisfaction, controlling for unit leader's consideration)

MIXED satisfaction WITH ConsiderationTEAMGMC supportTEAMGMCt
 /CRITERIA=CIN(95) MXITER(100) MXSTEP(10) SCORING(1)
SINGULAR(0.000000000001) HCONVERGE(0,
 ABSOLUTE) LCONVERGE(0, ABSOLUTE) PCONVERGE(0.000001, ABSOLUTE)
 /FIXED=ConsiderationTEAMGMC **supportTEAMGMC** | SSTYPE(3) → *Estimates the*
 fixed effect γ_{02}^{b} *(the cross-level direct effect) (between)*

 /METHOD=ML
 /PRINT=SOLUTION TESTCOV
 /RANDOM=INTERCEPT | SUBJECT(unit) COVTYPE(VC).

MODEL 1–1–1

(work overload → job stress → job satisfaction)

Coefficient *a* (work overload → job stress)
 MIXED stress WITH overloadTEAMGMC overloadCWC
 /CRITERIA=CIN(95) MXITER(100) MXSTEP(10) SCORING(1)
SINGULAR(0.000000000001) HCONVERGE(0,
 ABSOLUTE) LCONVERGE(0, ABSOLUTE) PCONVERGE(0.000001, ABSOLUTE)

 /FIXED=**overloadTEAMGMC**   **overloadCWC** | SSTYPE(3)
              ↓   ↓
 Estimates the fixed effect γ_{01}^{a} *Estimates the fixed effect* γ_{10}^{a}
 (the cross-level direct effect)   *(the relationship between the level-1*
 (between)   *variables) (within)*

/METHOD=ML

/PRINT=SOLUTION TESTCOV

/RANDOM=INTERCEPT | SUBJECT(unit) COVTYPE(VC).

Coefficient *b* (job stress → job satisfaction, controlling for work overload)

MIXED satisfaction WITH overloadTEAMGMC stressTEAMGMC overloadCWC stressCWC

/CRITERIA=CIN(95) MXITER(100) MXSTEP(10) SCORING(1) SINGULAR(0.000000000001) HCONVERGE(0,

ABSOLUTE) LCONVERGE(0, ABSOLUTE) PCONVERGE(0.000001, ABSOLUTE)

/FIXED=overloadTEAMGMC **stressTEAMGMC** overloadCWC **stressCWC** | SSTYPE(3)

↓ ↓

Estimates the fixed effect γ_{02}^{b} (the cross-level direct effect) (between)

Estimates the fixed effect γ_{20}^{b} (the relationship between the level-1 variables) (within)

/METHOD=ML

/PRINT=SOLUTION TESTCOV

/RANDOM=INTERCEPT | SUBJECT(unit) COVTYPE(VC).

Annotated SPSS syntax to estimate the conditional mediation model presented in the article (see Figure 4)

Conditional mediation: 1-1-1 mediation with a Level-2 moderator in the second path

(work overload → (job stress → job satisfaction)*unit climate for support)

Coefficient *a* (work overload → job stress) –same model as 1-1-1 mediation

MIXED stress WITH overloadTEAMGMC overloadCWC

/CRITERIA=CIN(95) MXITER(100) MXSTEP(10) SCORING(1) SINGULAR(0.000000000001) HCONVERGE(0,

ABSOLUTE) LCONVERGE(0, ABSOLUTE) PCONVERGE(0.000001, ABSOLUTE)

/FIXED=**overloadTEAMGMC** **overloadCWC** | SSTYPE(3)

↓ ↓

Estimates the fixed effect γ_{01}^{a} (the cross-level direct effect) (between)

Estimates the fixed effect γ_{10}^{a} (the relationship between the level-1 variables) (within)

/METHOD=ML

/PRINT=SOLUTION TESTCOV

/RANDOM=INTERCEPT | SUBJECT(unit) COVTYPE(VC).

Coefficient *b* (job stress → job satisfaction, controlling for work overload), conditional to the Level-2 moderator: unit climate for support

MIXED satisfaction WITH overloadTEAMGMC stressTEAMGMC overloadCWC stressCWC supportTEAMGMC

/CRITERIA=CIN(95) MXITER(100) MXSTEP(10) SCORING(1) SINGULAR(0.000000000001) HCONVERGE(0, ABSOLUTE) LCONVERGE(0, ABSOLUTE) PCONVERGE(0.000001, ABSOLUTE)

/FIXED= overloadTEAMGMC **stressTEAMGMC** supportTEAMGMC overloadCWC
stressCWC
supportTEAMGMC*stressTEAMGMC

supportTEAMGMC*stressCWC | SSTYPE(3)   ↓   ↓

                                                                    ↓

                                        Estimates the fixed effect γ_{02}^{b} *Estimates the fixed*

                                    ↓   *(between)*

effect γ_{20}^{b} *Estimates the between*

                                                (within)   *interaction*

Estimates the within interaction

                effect $\gamma_{04}^{b}\left(\overline{M}_j \, C_j\right)$

    effect $\gamma_{21}^{b}\left(x_{ij} \, C_j\right)$

/METHOD=ML

/PRINT=SOLUTION TESTCOV

/RANDOM=INTERCEPT **stressCWC** | SUBJECT (unit) COVTYPE(VC).

                        ↓

        The slope associated with job stress
        is allowed to vary at random

NOTES

1. A level refers to a specific position in a series of nested arrangements; for instance, employees are nested in organizations.
2. Because of space limitations, multilevel structural equation modeling (MSEM) methods are out of the scope of this article. Interested readers may consult Heck and Thomas (2015).
3. It is also assumed that r_{ij} follows a normal distribution with a zero mean.
4. Readers interested in learning how to test multilevel models using SPSS can read Heck, Thomas, and Tabata (2013).
5. Two models are nested when the difference between them lies in a given set of parameters. In the present case, the baseline model is nested within the one-way ANCOVA model because the latter includes an additional parameter (γ_{10}) not included in the former model.
6. Note that in this model the covariance between U_{0j} and $U_{1j}\left(\sigma_{\tau_{10}}\right)$ can also be estimated. This covariance provides an estimation of the relationship between the Level-1 intercept and slope. To keep the focus on $\sigma_{\tau_{11}}^{2}$, we did not estimate $\sigma_{\tau_{10}}$.
7. Conventional multilevel methods assume that outcome variables reside at lower levels of analysis and do not influence higher-level variables. MSEM does not adopt this assumption (Preacher et al., 2010).

Vicente González-Romá and Ana Hernández

TEMPORAL DYNAMICS IN ORGANIZATIONAL PSYCHOLOGY

INTRODUCTION

Time plays an important role in organizational life because it surrounds us in everything we do. For example, employers and employees use time as a metric to determine whether events happen on time, ahead of time, or behind schedule (Blount & Janicik, 2001). Furthermore, time provides employees with the means to understand current work experiences given that present experiences are inherently connected to past experiences and anticipation of the future (Shipp & Jansen, 2011). The passage of time is moreover used to discern whether, when, and why a phenomenon has evolved or changed over time (Roe, 2008). Time is also directly included in numerous constructs studied in the field of Organizational Psychology such as time pressure, deadlines, and time schedules (Sonnentag, 2012). As a result, scholars have increasingly paid attention to the role of time in the fields of Organizational Behavior (see Bluedorn, 2002; George & Jones, 2000; Griep & Hansen, 2020), Behavioral and Social Sciences (see Levine, 2003; McGrath & Tschan, 2004), and Organizational Psychology (see Albert, 2013; Ancona, Goodman, Lawrence, & Tushman, 2001; Mitchell & James, 2001; Roe, 2008). These scholars, among others, have argued that the inclusion of time and temporal dynamics is essential to better explain "when" a phenomenon occurs, "what" aspects of the phenomenon are being influenced, "how" these aspects are being influenced, and "why" this influence occurs (see also Griep & Hansen, 2020). The role of time is of the utmost importance for the field of Organizational Psychology because "the substance of organizational behavior—its constructs—exist in and through time" (George & Jones, 2000, p. 666). Moreover, Roe (2014a, 2014b) has coined the term *temporal footprint of work* to refer to the idea that neither the behavior of employees nor the activities of organizations can be defined without reference to time. Hence, it should come as no surprise that the field of Organizational Psychology is guided by the principles of time and temporal dynamics.

Despite the crucial role of time and temporal dynamics, it receives little acknowledgment in the Organizational Psychology literature. In fact, in most published articles, the methodologies (approximately only 4% rely on a time-sensitive method; Roe, 2014a, 2014b), the findings, and their conclusions make no reference to time (for a critical review, see Roe, 2008). The Organizational Psychology literature and theories are rather ambiguous in their use of the word *time* and *temporal dynamics*. Although several so-called process theories—such as Valence-Expectancy Theory (Vroom, 1964), Goal-Setting Theory (Locke & Latham, 1990), and Self-Regulation Theory (Bandura, 1991)—claim to describe unfolding processes over time, they are actually rather static and atemporal descriptions of human behavior, triggering a series of "snapshot-like" empirical studies. The idea that Organizational Psychology is devoted to the study of processes and guided by the principles of time and temporal dynamics is a utopia at best. This stands in stark contrast with the numerous worries expressed by scholars about this inconsistency in the literature and its detrimental consequences for the validity and accuracy of the field's accumulated knowledge (see Ancona et al., 2001; George & Jones, 2000; Mitchell & James, 2001; Roe, 2008; Roe, Gockel, & Meyer, 2012). According to these researchers, the field of Organizational Psychology should incorporate the role of time and temporal dynamics to fully understand the processes underlying the development and impact of emotions, attitudes, and behaviors in the workplace. The authors of this article agree with the statement that "advancing theories that address the dynamics of how important phenomena emerge, evolve, and change over time is the next frontier" (Kozlowski, 2009, p. 3) and that that frontier is now upon us.

The objective of this article is to help scholars begin to address the temporal shortcomings in the extant Organizational Psychology literature. First, the article highlights what is meant by time and temporal dynamics in Organizational Psychology. Second, it offers a review of how time has been considered in the Organizational Psychology literature since the turn of the century. Third, it suggests possible future trends for the inclusion of time and temporal dynamics in theory building and empirical research in the field of Organizational Psychology. In doing so, the article hopes to both inspire and help direct future research in Organizational Psychology to acknowledge and incorporate the important role of time and temporal dynamics.

WHAT DO WE MEAN BY TIME AND TEMPORAL DYNAMICS IN ORGANIZATIONAL PSYCHOLOGY?

Objective and Subjective Time.   Broadly speaking, time can be subdivided into "objective clock time" and "subjective time experiences" (Ancona et al., 2001; Bluedorn & Denhardt, 1988; Fried & Slowik, 2004). Shipp and Fried (2014a, 2014b) explicate the differences between objective and subjective time. They define *objective clock time* as a view of time that is (a) unidirectional (time progresses from past to present to future in a linear way), (b) homogeneous (each unit of time is similar to the next unit of time; each second is identical to the next second), and (c) absolute (time is identical across individuals and contexts). In other words, time is what a clock shows. In classical, non-relativistic physics it is a scalar quantity and, like length, mass, and charge, is usually described as a fundamental quantity. In contrast, Shipp and Fried (2014a, 2014b) define *subjective time* as a view of time that is (a) cognitively cyclical (one may switch back and forth between a focus on the past, present, and future and may do so in any direction), (b) heterogeneous (some moments pass more quickly than others; time flies when you are having fun versus time seems to slow down when you are bored), and (c) interpretative (experiences of time differ between individuals and contexts can only be understood with reference to an individual's experience and in context). In other words, time refers to one's subjective experience, or sense, of time, which is measured by one's personal perception of the duration of the indefinite and unfolding of events within a specific context.

Time Issues and Temporal Dynamics.   Research on temporal dynamics examines how certain phenomena emerge (i.e., onset), evolve or fluctuate, and/or dissolve (i.e., offset) over time (McCormick, Reeves, Downes, Li, & Ilies, 2020; Vantilborgh, Hofmans, & Judge, 2018). Key considerations in this regard concern *the unit that is assumed to change over time* (e.g., individuals, work characteristics, teams, organizations), *the total length or duration of the time span that is of interest* (e.g., 1 week, 6 months, 3 decades), *the regularity or irregularity of time intervals* *at which measurements are collected* (e.g., minutes, months, years), *the assumed patterns of change* (e.g., linear, nonlinear), and *the relevant starting and end points of the investigation* (e.g., Monday through Friday, early to late adulthood; see also Zacher & Rudolph, 2020). In addition to the direction of changes with time (e.g., increases, maintenance, or decreases in a construct), researchers can also focus on the rate or speed of change over time (i.e., velocity; Johnson & Howe, 2013). For example, research has shown that changes in the rate of goal progress (i.e., disturbances, interruptions) are more frustrating than changes to the amount of progress made (Beck, Scholer, & Hughes, 2017).

The extent of temporal change indicates whether a construct is more dynamic or stable. For example, psychologists have traditionally assumed that people's personality is "set like plaster" after the age of 30 years (Costa & McCrae, 1994). In contrast, 21st-century scholars agree that personality characteristics can change during adulthood and up until old age due to changes in social roles and the environment, including the work context (Woods, Wille, Wu, Lievens, & De Fruyt, 2019). Relatedly, organizational scholars have examined individuals' "affect spin"—the trait variability of dynamic affective states—as a buffer of emotion regulation demands on well-being outcomes (Beal, Trougakos, Weiss, & Dalal, 2013). Moreover, the broader context of temporal dynamics is important. Researchers may, for example, be interested in changes across historical time (e.g., a comparison of working conditions across decades; see Wegman, Hoffman, Carter, Twenge, & Guenole, 2018), changes across the human life span independent of historical time (e.g., a comparison of younger and older workers' cognitive abilities or observation of changes in cognitive abilities as workers get older), or the influence of period effects (e.g., wars, natural catastrophes, pandemics). Regarding the latter, researchers may examine how the COVID-19 pandemic has influenced changes in workers' attitudes toward telework or perceived organizational support.

Scholars can further focus on the underlying mechanisms and boundary conditions of changes in phenomena over time. For example, research suggests that people's social and emotional priorities change with age; the factor assumed to cause these changes is not time itself but a decrease in future time perspective as people get older, triggering an increased focus on the present moment (Carstensen, 2006). Furthermore, dynamic research is concerned not only with within-unit changes or stability in a construct, but also with between-unit differences in within-unit development, as well as antecedents and consequences of its development (Nesselroade, 1991; Wang et al., 2017). For example, depending on individual differences (e.g., personality) or contextual characteristics (e.g., organizational support), organizational newcomers may use different socialization tactics that, in turn, influence their personal adjustment to work over time (Song, Liu, Shi, & Wang, 2017).

HOW HAS TIME BEEN CONSIDERED IN ORGANIZATIONAL PSYCHOLOGY RESEARCH?

To better understand how organizational psychologists have approached the concept of time in their research, the authors of this article conducted a search for the word "time" within the Industrial and Organizational Psychology field (code 3600) on the PsycInfo database for the period 2000–2020. This search revealed 268 entries (journal articles, books, book chapters, and publicly available dissertations in English). Figure 1 summarizes two trends that can be

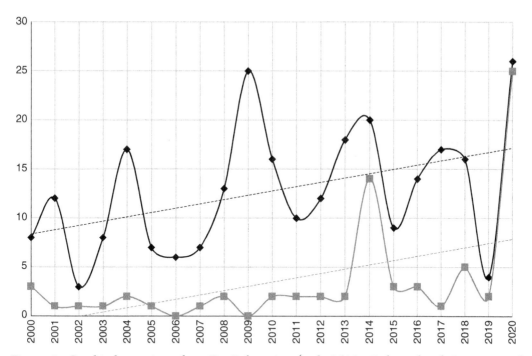

Figure 1. Graphical overview of our PsycInfo review (code 3600—Industrial and Organizational Psychology) for the keyword "time." Note: The black solid line with diamonds refers to the number of publications referencing the word "time"; the black dashed line refers to the linear trend in the number of publications referencing the word "time"; the gray line with squares refers to the number of publications referencing the word "time" in relation to methodology, subjective time perceptions, or time in theory development; and the gray dashed line refers to the linear trend in the number of publications referencing the word "time" in relation to methodology, subjective time perceptions, or time in theory development.

seen when screening these 268 entries in light of time and temporal dynamics. First, there appears to be an overall increasing trend (see black dotted line for the linear trend) in the number of entries that refer to time and temporal dynamics in the Organizational Psychology literature. However, a closer inspection of each of these 268 entries indicates that only 73 entries referred to time or temporal dynamics in relation to how the literature defines time (see "Objective and Subjective Time" and "Time Issues and Temporal Dynamics"). This implies that 72.76% of all entries did not refer to objective or subjective time, and/or did not include time as the focal construct in their manuscript, and/or did not focus on crucial time issues or temporal dynamics, and/or did not focus on the role of time in theory development. Nonetheless, inspection of Figure 1 (see gray dotted line for the linear trend) still reveals an increasing trend in the Organizational Psychology literature with respect to the number of entries that refer to time in relation to methodology, subjective time perceptions, or time in theory development.

An important note to make is that Figure 1 reveals two peaks (2014 and 2020) in the number of publications that reference time in methodology or subjective time. These peaks conjoin with the publication of Shipp and Fried's (2014a, 2014b) book series on "how time impacts individuals" and "how time impacts groups, organizations and methodological choice" and the publication of Griep and Hansen's (2020) *Handbook on the Temporal Dynamics of Organizational Behavior*. A more in-depth review of all 268 titles and abstracts revealed that the most popular approach in the Organizational Psychology literature has been that of "time as a construct or variable" (43.28%), followed by "time as future prediction" (29.48%), "time in theory development or improvement" (18.28%), and "time in methodology" (8.96%).

The following sections present more detail on each of these different approaches to the concept of time in the Organizational Psychology literature. Readers should note that although this article provides an overview of the different sections ranging from most common to least common use of the concept of time, it will devote most of its time (pun intended) to the two least common usages of the concept of time and time dynamics in the Organizational Psychology literature. That is, the article will place most attention on "time in theory development or improvement" (18.28%) and "time in methodology" (8.96%) because, as will become clear when reading the remainder of the article, these approaches to time and temporal dynamics are the most closely related to how the literature defines time (see "Objective and Subjective Time" and "Time Issues and Temporal Dynamics"). Moreover, better insights into these two approaches results in the development of essential elements that "good" time-sensitive theory and research should adhere to, akin to proposing some possible future trends for the inclusion of time and temporal dynamics in theory building and empirical research.

Time as a Construct or Variable.   The most popular approach (43.28% of all entries) to time and temporal dynamics in the Organizational Psychology literature has been that of time as a defining element of a construct or variable of interest. Within this approach to time and temporal dynamics there appear to be three distinct approaches to time and time dynamics: (a) subjective aspects of time (i.e., psychological constructs related to the concept of time that can be affected by individual differences), (b) objective aspects of time (i.e., aspects of time that are inherent to the definition of a psychological construct and are not, or are to a far lesser extent, influenced by individual differences), and (c) elapsed time (i.e., time that has passed between moment X and moment Y). The majority of work has been done on subjective and objective aspects of time, while far less is known about elapsed time.

Overview of Literature on Subjective Aspects of Time.   Scholars have investigated, for instance, constructs related to time that can be classified as subjective time such as future time perspective and orientations, time pressure, time constraints, time orientation, time demands, and individual time perceptions. For example, Baltes, Wynne, Sirabian, Krenn, and De Lange (2014) found that higher *future time perspective* positively influenced regulatory focus, which in turn influenced the use of selection, optimization, and compensation behaviors (i.e., a series of coping strategies) among older workers. In their meta-analyses, Rudolph, Kooij, Rauvola, and Zacher (2018) and Kooij, Kanfer, Betts, and Rudolph (2018) found that occupational future time perspective and future time perspective were positively related to job satisfaction, organizational commitment, work engagement, work continuance intentions, well-being and health, and task and contextual performance, and negatively related to retirement intentions and risk-taking behaviors. As a final example, Yeung, Fung, and Chan (2020) found that individuals who perceived an open-ended future time perspective reported more positive emotions and used more passive and constructive strategies than did those with a limited future time perspective. Other scholars studied the influence of *negative time aspects* (i.e., time constraints, time demands, and time pressure). For example, Chu and Spires (2001) found that the experience of time constraint makes employees more prone to process information faster, process less information, and use less rigorous decision strategies, which ultimately reduces performance and increases error rates. In contrast, the opposite results were found for the experience of time control. Collinson and Collinson (2004) found that leaders may intensify work (i.e., more work needs to be done in less time) and erode how employees can utilize their free time as a way to exercise power, control, and discipline, whereas Syrek, Apostel, and Antoni (2013) found that transformational leadership mitigates the positive relationship of time pressure to work–life balance and exhaustion. Finally, some scholars have focused on *individual perceptions of time* (see Levasseur, Shipp, Fried, Rousseau, & Zimbardo, 2020) For example, Rhee (2007) found that the effects of position-related networks (measured by network size and density) on promotion are affected by the temporal distribution of ties (measured by whether a tie was formed before or after an employee's positional change), while the effects of person-related networks are insensitive to temporal effects. Lee and Park (2012) examined how temporal distance to career entry influences the perceived importance of self-efficacy and outcome expectations concerning a career pursuit and found that time in interaction with other contextual variables (i.e., perceived support and barriers, as well as country) predicts the perceived importance of career-related self-efficacy and outcome expectations.

Overview of Literature on Objective Aspects of Time. Other studies have focused on constructs related to time that can be classified as objective time such as time management, work and leisure time and their trade-off, work-time arrangements or restrictions, timing, and time delay. For example, Danko (2011) studied *time management techniques* of executive and middle manager professionals; participants in this study believed that (a) productivity, (b) deadlines, calendars, priorities, and organization, and (c) management were responsible for effective time management. Furthermore, several scholars have studied whether *time spent in paid labor is voluntary or constrained by demands of the employer*. Their general conclusion is that many employees are overworked by their employers (Clarkberg & Moen, 2001), and employees are often bound to an incessant time clock, forcing a good proportion to work overtime and experience loss in leisure time (Adler & Adler, 2001; Cornelius & Skinner, 2008; Grotto, 2015; Klumb & Perrez, 2004), akin to feeling a need to have as many "billable" hours as possible (Devoe, 2008; Epstein & Kalleberg, 2004; Yakura, 2001), which in turn increases family stress and conflict (Blair-Loy, 2004; Dugan, Matthews, & Barnes-Farrell, 2012; Epstein & Kalleberg, 2004; Schneider & Waite, 2005), reduces mental health (Kleiner, Schunck, & Schömann, 2015), and increases negative affective states (Sonnentag, Reinecke, Mata, & Vorderer, 2018). In contrast, other scholars (e.g., Farnworth & Fossey, 2003) found that employees have a relatively equal distribution of work, recreation, and rest, and that the average person's actual use of time has changed little in the last 40 years. This implies that our tempo—pace of life or time pressure—did not change but our temporality—the temporal character of occupation that is imbued with meaning in relation to one's sense of past, present, and future—did change negatively. Next, some work has been done on *working-time arrangements and restrictions* (often in relation to dual-earner couples). These scholars often distinguish between different temporal dimensions of employment relationships (e.g., working-time schedules, work-time intensity, time–money exchange) when arguing that these temporal reorganizations of employment and their outcomes may differ between genders, age groups, cultures, and countries due to societal, regulatory, or political differences (Cornelius & Skinner, 2008; Epstein, 2004; Fagan, 2001; Grotto, 2015; Kalleberg & Epstein, 2001; Levin, 2004). Finally, some scholars have focused on *time and time delay*. For example, Santos, Passos, Uitdewilligen, and Nübold (2016) studied the role of temporal leadership behaviors in coordinating team members' efforts, avoiding time-related conflicts, and ensuring that teams perform well. They found that conflict mediates the relationship between leadership behaviors and team performance as well as between shared temporal cognitions and team performance. Nakashima, Daniels, and Laurin (2017) studied the interactive effect of timing in announcing restrictive organizational policies on employee support and found that leaders should consider announcing restrictive policies well in advance to secure the support of their followers.

Overview of Literature on Elapsed Time. A final approach to time and temporal dynamics is that of time as an instrumental construct or elapsed time; the clock time that has passed between separate moments in time and how the passing of time is related to outcomes under study. In these types of studies, time tends to serve as a factor in, for example, a before–after (quasi-) experimental design or a (quasi-) longitudinal design in which the interest is not in the evolution of a variable over time but rather lies in predicting an increase/decrease in variable Y based on variable X. Some scholars have studied the effect of one variable on another variable by using a *time lag of a few days, weeks, months, or years*. For example, Gevers, van Eerde, and Rutte (2001) studied the effect of group self-regulatory actions that may impede or foster the timeliness of group projects by measuring perceived time pressure, group potency, planning, and reflexivity, as well as the project's progress at the start of the project and after the project deadline (13 weeks later). Morris (2005) found that the negative effect of time pressure on visual discrimination (as an operationalization of task performance) was sustained over a period of 30 minutes of interrupted task performance time. Using different time frames across five different studies, Converse (2006) found that individuals adjust their behavior in accordance with the demands of a given situation, which supports an adaptive view of self-regulatory behavior over time.

Time as a Construct or Variable: Concluding Remarks. This overview clearly demonstrates that organizational psychologists are aware of the importance and relevance of time and time-related constructs for understanding employee behavior, organizational functioning, and their interaction. Although the use of time as a defining element of a construct or variable of interest was the most popular approach to time and temporal dynamics in the Organizational Psychology literature in the period 2000–2020, Figure 2 (see medium gray line with triangles) demonstrates a slight decreasing trend in its general popularity and a steep decreasing trend in its popularity since 2017.

Time as Future Prediction.
The second most popular way (29.48% of all entries) in which organizational psychologists have used the concepts of time is to refer to predictions about the future of Organizational Psychology rather than time as dynamic aspects. The reference to time in these entries is not only not in line with how the literature defines time (see

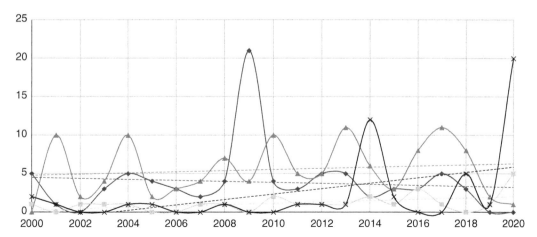

Figure 2. Graphical overview of our in-depth review of all 268 titles and abstracts. Note: The medium gray line with triangles refers to "time as a construct or variable" (43.28%), the medium gray dashed line refers to the linear trend in the number of publications using "time as a construct or variable"; the dark gray line with diamonds refers to "time as future prediction" (29.48%); the dark gray dashed line refers to the linear trend in the number of publications using "time as future prediction"; the black line with crosses refers to "time in theory development or improvement" (18.28%); the black dashed line refers to the linear trend in the number of publications using "time in theory development or improvement"; the light gray line with squares refers to "time in methodology" (8.96%); and the light gray dashed line refers to the linear trend in the number of publications using "time in methodology."

"Objective and Subjective Time" and "Time Issues and Temporal Dynamics"), but the concept of time is not even part of the construct and/or psychological phenomena under investigation. Because "time" is merely used to talk about future directions of a field of research, the overview of the literature will not be as detailed as in the other sections.

Overview of Literature on Time as Future Prediction. When reviewing the literature, it becomes evident that most entries reference time to express personal opinions about the field's future, evaluate the current state of the field, and/or set an agenda for the future. For example, Smith and colleagues (2000) present their opinions on the demands of literacy in the workplace in the next millennium and highlight various topics, including problem solving, technology, multiple literacies, the use of information, and employers' belief about workers' abilities. Aycan (2000) and Aycan and Gelfand (2012) critically evaluate the past, present, and future of cross-cultural industrial and organizational theory and research. Denisi (2010) discusses opportunities for growth and evolution for the Academy of Management for the next decade. Kozlowski (2017) reflects on his experiences as editor of the *Journal of Applied Psychology* and suggests desirable directions for future evolutions of the journal, including focusing on multi-level system dynamics as core capabilities. A plethora of manuscripts deal with *attempts to predict the future of work and where, how, when, and why work is conducted* (e.g., Bergman & Karlsson, 2011; Cooper, 2005; Das, 2004; Fisscher, 2005; Fossland, 2013; Furnham, 2000; Griep et al., 2019; Hesselbein & Goldsmith, 2009; Khanna & New, 2008; Kuhn, 2006; Mayrhofer & Schneidhofer, 2009; Nickel, 2015; Sanchez & Levine, 2012; Ulrich & Smallwood, 2009; Weick, 2005; Winsborough & Chamorro-Premuzic, 2013; Ybema, 2004).

In doing so, they discuss topics such as flexible work arrangements; remote, virtual, and telework; distributed or virtual teams; the advent and use of offsite communal share- or cowork spaces; the uptake of "gig" working; and the rapidly changing economy. Finally, several scholars talk about *what leaders can expect in tomorrow's world and how they should adapt their leadership accordingly* (Cockerell, 2009; Goldsmith, 2006; Guttman, 2009; Hill, 2009; Kennedy, 2009; Kouzes & Posner, 2009; Martin, Epitropaki, Thomas, & Topakas, 2010; Moe, 2018; Ulrich & Smallwood, 2009).

Time as Future Prediction: Concluding Remarks. This brief overview showcases the misuse of the term "time" to merely refer to future directions of a field of research. Although the use of time to talk about future predictions was the second most popular approach to time and temporal dynamics in the Organizational Psychology literature in the period 2000–2020, Figure 2 (see dark gray line with diamonds) demonstrates a relatively stable trend (with the exception of a large spike in 2009) in the number of publications referencing time as a future prediction.

Time in Theory. The third most popular—despite a low number of entries—approach (18.28% of all entries) to time and temporal dynamics in the Organizational Psychology literature has been that of time as an element in theory development and/or improvement. This approach to time and time dynamics is of crucial importance to the future success of the field because the literature's current consensus is one in which scholars have neglected the role of time and temporal dynamics in theory building, measurement, data analyses, interpretation and discussion of results, and proposition of theoretical and practical relevance (e.g., Albert, 2013; Ancona et al., 2001; George & Jones, 2000; Griep & Hansen, 2020; Mitchell & James, 2001). When reading the arguments made by these authors, there appear to be two main reasons as to why time has not received the attention it deserves in the development and improvement of theory.

First, theory in Organizational Psychology—and related domains such as Organizational Behavior—deny the role of time either explicitly (i.e., reject the role of time or embrace the notion of stability) or implicitly (i.e., ignore the possible effect of time or prefer to develop a "one size fits all" theory). Some theories (for a few of many examples, see Vroom's valence-expectancy theory of motivation, Locke and Latham's goal-setting theory, and Ajzen's theory of planned behavior) in Organizational Psychology have *explicitly rejected the importance of time* despite the fact that they position themselves as process theories. Although all these theories propose that one's actions in the future are directly linked to past and current experiences, they do not reference time and explicitly reference the "ahistorical" nature of their propositions (see Vroom, 1964, p. 17). When reading this, it is good to keep in mind that these so-called process theories have significantly influenced later theory developments in the field of Organizational Psychology and related domains such as Organizational Behavior. Less explicit, but still denying the role of time and temporal dynamics, are *theories that assume stability of constructs over time.* This generally applies to theories focusing on abilities, personality traits, personnel selection, self-regulation, motivation, goal orientations, work–family experiences, work design, and leadership (e.g., Bandura, 1991; Bass & Avolio, 1993; Deci & Ryan, 2012; Greenhaus & Powell, 2006; Locke & Latham, 1990; Oakes, Ferris, Martocchio, Buckley, & Broach, 2001; Oldham & Hackman, 2010; Tsaousis & Nikolaou, 2001). Although, theoretically, time could play an important role here—and several scholars have criticized the dominant focus on stability—the original assumption is that time has no effect or that its effect is simply random noise or error variance (Molenaar, 2004). In making this assumption, these theories—and their derived empirical studies—assume that behavior is stable. As a corollary they fail to provide information on when it happens, how long it lasts, how it changes, why it changes, and so forth.

Second, at a methodological level, organizational psychologists tend to select measurement instruments, research designs, analytical techniques, and "quick and dirty" cross-sectional or semilongitudinal approaches to research questions out of habit or due to a lack of knowledge and/or interest in how to handle temporal data. In doing so, they ignore the fact that their approach most likely does not fit the process nature of their hypotheses. That is, most studies still use cross-sectional or semilongitudinal methods to analyze associations between variables, while their hypotheses and research questions point toward an unfolding or developmental process, temporal effect, or causal effect, demonstrating a misfit between the theoretical propositions and the methods used to test these temporal phenomena (Ployhart & Vandenberg, 2010; Roe, 2008; Sonnentag, 2012). Several explanations have been offered as to why Organizational Psychology researchers continue to embrace this theory–method misfit: (a) *there is no theoretical or empirical guidance about how to conduct a more time-sensitive study* (fake news: see "Overview of Literature on Time in Theory" and "Time in Theory: Concluding Remarks and Ways Forward"); (b) *there are no guidelines in place that allow researchers to find and convince organizations and respondents to take part in more time-sensitive study* (fake news; for excellent overviews, see Beal, 2015; Bolger, Davis, & Rafaeli, 2003; Fisher & To, 2012; Ohly, Sonnentag, Niessen, & Zapf, 2010); (c) *there are insufficient methodological and analytical tools and resources available to conduct time-sensitive data analyses* (fake news; although the field of Organizational Psychology is slow in picking up new methods, there are plenty of resources available on dynamic research methods such as time series analyses, survival analyses, growth and discontinuous growth analyses, computational modeling, multilevel analyses, and mixture modeling; for excellent examples, see Bliese & Lang, 2016; Bliese & Ployhart, 2002; Bliese, Adler, & Flynn, 2017; Bollen & Brand, 2010; Morin & Marsh, 2015; Morin, Meyer, Creusier, & Biétry, 2016; Morin & Wang, 2016; Morin et al., 2017; Muthén, 2002; Vancouver & Scherbaum, 2008; Vancouver, Wang, & Li, 2020; Wang, Zhou, & Zhang, 2016; Zyphur et al., 2019); and (d) *there is too much pressure to conduct research and publish in short periods of time* (partially true; the idea of "publish or perish" indeed favors short-term experiments and cross-sectional studies. When universities and granting agencies do not implement the idea of "slow science" as part of their merit and tenure systems and provide researchers with the necessary time to conduct proper time-sensitive research, well-intended initiatives by individual researchers such as the "Future of Work and Organizational Psychology" remain nothing more than armchair philosophy with no systematic impact).

Overview of Literature on Time in Theory. Fried and Slowik (2004, p. 405) describe advances in conceptualizing the role of time within Organizational Psychology and related fields as "esoteric and far from becoming common knowledge." Despite this rather gloomy and pessimistic view (partially supported by the fact that very few publications deal with this topic; see Figure 2, black line with crosses), there appears to be an increasing trend (with two large spikes in 2014 and 2020) in the number of publications referencing the importance of time and temporal dynamics in improving theory and research (see Figure 2, black line with crosses). Organizational psychologists have indeed become increasingly aware of the fact that time should receive more attention in building better theory and research. At a conceptual level, George and Jones (2000) describe six important time dimensions that are especially relevant to theory building and the proposition of time-related questions that can serve as a guide or template for improving theory building through the incorporation of temporality into the what, how, and why of theories: (a) the past, future, and present and the subjective experience of time; (b) time aggregations; (c) duration of steady states and rates of change; (d) incremental versus discontinuous change; (e) frequency, rhythms, and cycles; and (f) spirals and intensity. Applying some of the principles, Shipp and Jansen (2011) and Jansen and Shipp (2013) expand the person–organization fit literature by focusing on fit narratives—composed of retrospective, current, and anticipated fit and woven together by a theme—as a tool that helps individuals make sense of their fit experiences through temporal influence and temporal comparison processes. Relatedly, Hernandez and Guarana (2018) developed and tested the temporal intricacies of job engagement. Specifically, they examine the interplay of employees' temporally relevant perspectives of fit (i.e., retrospect, current, and anticipated) within their ongoing membership to the organization and refined both person–organization fit and job engagement theories by including employees' temporally constructed psychological experiences. In another example, Mohammed and Nadkarni (2014) integrate the concept of shared temporal cognition, temporal transactive memory systems, and polychronicity diversity in theory on team performance. Leroy, Shipp, Blount, and Licht (2015) introduce the construct of synchrony preference—one's willingness to adapt one's pace and rhythm within social interactions for the purpose of creating synchrony with others—into the theory and research on adaptability. In doing so, they demonstrate that synchrony preference predicts flexible pacing behaviors, interpersonal facilitation, contribution to team synchrony, contribution to team performance, and job dedication. Griep, Vantilborgh, Hansen, and Conway (2018) edited a special issue on the role of time in psychological contract processes, and Rousseau, Hansen, and Tomprou (2018) update psychological contract theory to recognize the dynamic nature of the psychological contract as a "dynamic phase model." In a related field of study, Outlaw, Colquitt, Baer, and Sessions (2019) integrate the concept of timeliness—defined as the degree to which procedures are started and completed within an acceptable time frame—within traditional justice literature to build time-sensitive predictions with regard to "how long" it took for procedures to be perceived as fair rather than just focusing on "how fair" procedures were perceived to be. Tang, Richter, and Nadkarni (2020) recognized that the extant Organizational Psychology literature is fragmented due to a lack of conceptual clarification and integration of temporal constructs. To address this fragmentation, they synthesize temporal research from different disciplines (i.e., Strategy, Entrepreneurship, Organizational Theory, Organizational Behavior) and introduce a framework that allocates temporal constructs according to their basic conceptual nature (trait–state) and level of analysis (individual–collective). Their framework categorizes four generic types of subjective time—individual temporal disposition, individual temporal state, collective temporal state, and collective temporal disposition—which form the foundations for a future research agenda. Finally, two edited books (Griep & Hansen, 2020; Shipp & Fried, 2014a, 2014b) on temporal dynamics and the concept of time have largely contributed to a more dynamic, process-oriented, and person-centered approach to Organizational Psychology theory and empirical studies.

Time in Theory: Concluding Remarks and Ways Forward. This overview demonstrates that organizational psychologists are increasingly becoming aware of incorporating time and temporal dynamics in theory development and/or improvement; Figure 2 (see black line with crosses) indeed demonstrates a sharp increasing trend since 2004. Despite this increased interest in, and recognition of, time and time dynamics in theory, the Organizational Psychology literature continues to struggle with defining the necessary aspects and characteristics of time-sensitive theory. In order to advance the field of Organizational Psychology, *we recognize that theory should contain the following essential elements for it to be considered time-sensitive*: (a) constructs and psychological phenomena should be clearly defined with reference to the time window within which the construct or psychological phenomenon is expected to fluctuate and/or change; (b) relationships between constructs should be defined in relation to time and/or the unfolding nature of a construct or psychological phenomena should be specified; (c) temporal features—such as when phenomena occur, how long they are expected to last, how fast they are expected to change, which developmental form they are expected to take, which form of change they are expected to follow (linear versus nonlinear), which type of change they are expected to follow (incremental versus discontinuous or stabilization versus destabilization), whether constructs of phenomena are expected to follow phases, rhythms, cycles, spirals, or other more complex forms of change—should be defined and describes in detail; and (d) temporal metrics should be defined with reference to the specific timescales, time frames, and time lags that should to be used to measure the construct or psychological phenomenon.

Time in Methodology.

The final approach to time and temporal dynamics in the Organizational Psychology literature (8.96% of entries) pertains to the role of time in methodology. This approach to time and time dynamics is of crucial importance as well (see "Time in Theory") because to generate more valid knowledge, organizational psychologists do not only need time-sensitive theories, they also need a better understanding of the appropriate methodological and analytical tools that are needed to answer their time-sensitive research questions.

Overview of Literature on Time in Methodology. The introduction of techniques to gather sequential data by means of experience sampling techniques, diary methods, ecological momentary assessment, and intensive longitudinal techniques is arguably the most important driver of the increased use of time and temporal dynamics in research methods and analyses (e.g., Beal, 2015; Bolger et al., 2003; Ohly et al., 2010). Specifically, the field of Organizational Psychology has increasingly relied on repeated observations from the same participants or groups of participants to study temporal order in psychological processes—such as learning, adaptation, psychological contracts, personality, emotions, organizational change, in-role and extra-role performance, work design, work values, organizational justice, decision-making, motivation, teams, job attitudes, leadership, workplace safety, work–family conflict and enrichment, and employee well-being (for an overview, see Griep & Hansen, 2020)—by means of a wide range of time-sensitive analytical techniques such as multilevel analyses (e.g., Bolger

& Laurenceau, 2013; Griep & Vantilborgh, 2018a; Hülsheger, 2016; Judge, Simon, Hurst, & Kelley, 2014; Kozlowski, Chao, Grand, Braun, & Kuljanin, 2016; Vantilborgh et al., 2018), growth and discontinuous growth analyses (e.g., Bliese & Lang, 2016; Bliese & Ployhart, 2002; Bliese et al., 2017; Griep & Vantilborgh, 2018b; Grimm, Ram, & Estabrook, 2016), latent change score models (e.g., Voelkle & Oud, 2015), longitudinal analyses (Schonfeld & Rindskopf, 2007; Singer, Willett, & Willett, 2003), time series analyses (Molenaar, 1985), and mixture modeling (Morin & Marsh, 2015; Morin & Wang, 2016; Morin et al., 2016, 2017; Muthén, 2002).

Time in Methodology: Concluding Remarks and Ways Forward.   Despite the increased use of methodologies and techniques in which time and time dynamics are explicitly included (see Figure 2, light gray line with squares to represent the number of publications referencing time in methodology), there is still a fundamental limitation to consider with respect to how time is dealt with conceptually and analytically in these methods. That is, while these methods account for the fact that time affects what happens *within* respondents (or a group of respondents) over time, it generally does not account for what happens *to* these respondents over time. For example, people may change roles within a team, department, or organization; teams may change in composition; individual, team, or organizational goals and objectives may change; and the economic and political landscape may change. These macro-, meso-, and microlevel changes indicate that employees and their organizations *exist and behave in time* and that *time affects how they exist and behave*. While these novel methodologies account for the former, they often fail to account for the latter. As a consequence, they introduce an important contextual limitation, namely that findings are only valid for the specific episode during which the observations were made. This implies that replications may give different results (i.e., different magnitude and possible direction of effects) depending on the time period (e.g., early or late; less or more varied moments; short or long follow-up) in which the study took place.

POSSIBLE TRENDS FOR THE FUTURE OF TIME AND TEMPORAL DYNAMICS IN ORGANIZATIONAL PSYCHOLOGY

There are several promising directions for future research in Organizational Psychology that more strongly incorporates the role of time and temporal dynamics. In this section, we briefly cover these directions in the hope that they will help to advance the literature and contribute to meaningful practical applications. First, we deem it important that organizational psychologists adopt a dynamic and temporal perspective when thinking about research topics and associated methodologies (see also "Overview of Literature on Time in Methodology"). In particular, research designs should fit the dynamics inherent in theoretical models (i.e., a synergy of theory, method, and application). For instance, when testing a "process theory," cross-sectional and/or between-person designs should be avoided. Similarly, researchers should only test mediation models when their study design involves collecting data on all constructs at three (or ideally more) separate time points from the same individuals. Advanced research designs and analytical strategies, such as latent growth curve modeling, latent change score modeling, and random intercept cross-lagged panel models, allow for the investigation of level–level, level–change, and change–change relationships among constructs (e.g., Zacher,

Schmitt, Jimmieson, & Rudolph, 2019). At the same time, it is important to use reliable and valid (multi-item) measures in longitudinal research that are "time-invariant," meaning that, for instance, the indicator loadings of latent variables do not differ significantly across measurement occasions (see also "Time in Methodology: Concluding Remarks and Ways Forward").

Second, when researchers develop a new theory, or refine an existing theory, it is imperative that they explicitly address and incorporate temporal dynamics—including changes in key constructs over time as well as the mechanisms and boundary conditions of proposed changes—into theory (see also "Time in Theory: Concluding Remarks and Ways Forward"). This involves, for instance, thinking about why, when, and for how long certain changes in key constructs occur. As human experiences and behaviors are inherently dynamic, nearly all theories in Organizational Psychology should have a temporal dimension. For example, in a theory article on "achieving work–family balance," Hirschi, Shockley, and Zacher (2019) outline how "time to deadline" moderates the influences of work and family demands, resources, and barriers on the selection of relevant action regulation strategies. In addition, these researchers suggest that the selection of these regulation strategies follows a temporal process during which individuals consider the availability, malleability, and time-bounded nature of their work and family goals.

Third, there are a number of important topics in the field of Organizational Psychology that should increasingly be studied from a dynamic and temporal perspective. For instance, Zacher and Rudolph (2020) demonstrate a lack of theorizing and research on temporal changes in job design, leadership, teams and diversity, and human resource management, leaving the corpus of knowledge on these topics to remain underdeveloped. Studying changing individuals who work in dynamic contexts requires dynamic approaches to person–environment fit (see Jansen & Shipp, 2019; Shipp & Jansen, 2011). For instance, researchers have argued that, to better understand the relationship between age and occupational well-being, empirical work has to take into account age-related changes of individuals as well as temporal changes in the work environment, including the job, team, and organization (Zacher, Feldman, & Schulz, 2014).

Fourth, scholars should consider indicators of both subjective and objective time together in their studies (e.g., chronological versus subjective age, time left until retirement versus occupational future time perspective, actual time available versus perceived time pressure) in order to offer a full perspective on time (see also Jansen & Shipp, 2019). For example, it may be interesting to examine effects of the fit or misfit between the objective and subjective time indicators on outcomes using polynomial regression analysis with response surface plots. It could be the case that individuals whose objective and subjective time are congruent are more successful than those who experience incongruity. In addition, both theory and research should consider timing issues (i.e., when things happen), cycles and rhythms, as well as discontinuities more often, rather than just focusing on average developmental patterns in psychological constructs.

Finally, the discussion sections of many (cross-sectional or experimental) articles state something along the lines of, "future research should conduct longitudinal studies to better disentangle the direction of effects." However, at the same time, there are expectations to produce ever more papers within increasingly shorter time intervals in universities and research communities. Thus, we recommend that researchers, university administrators, grant funding agencies, and policymakers recognize that high-quality temporal research is not only time- but also resource-consuming. At the same time, such research contributes greatly toward our understanding of temporal processes and mechanisms and, thus, greatly benefits the development of more effective interventions and other practical applications.

CONCLUSION

The goal of this article is to help scholars address the temporal shortcomings in the Organizational Psychology literature and to propose future trends for the inclusion of time and temporal dynamics in theory building and empirical research. The article has presented a review (PsycInfo database 2000–2020) of the Industrial and Organizational Psychology literature. This review reveals that the most popular approach to the concept of time has been that of "time as a construct or variable" (43.28%), followed by "time as future prediction" (29.48%), "time in theory development or improvement" (18.28%), and "time in methodology" (8.96%). Based on this overview and discussion of the literature, the article has presented four essential aspects and characteristics that "good" time-sensitive theory and research should adhere to. Finally, the article has created awareness of possible future trends for the inclusion of time and temporal dynamics in theory building and empirical research. In doing so, it is the authors' hope to inspire future theorists and scholars to adopt a more dynamic way of thinking and studying the complexities of human emotions, attitudes, and behavior.

REFERENCES

Adler, P. A., & Adler, P. (2001). Off-time labor in resorts: The social construction of commercial time. *American Behavioral Scientist, 44*(7), 1096–1114. http://doi.org/10.1177/00027640121956674

Albert, S. (2013). *When: The art of perfect timing.* San Francisco, CA: Jossey-Bass.

Ancona, D. G., Goodman, P. S., Lawrence, B. S., & Tushman, M. L. (2001). Time: A new research lens. *Academy of Management Review, 26*(4), 645–663. http://doi.org/10.5465/amr.2001.5393903

Aycan, Z. (2000). Cross-cultural industrial and organizational psychology: Contributions, past developments, and future directions. *Journal of Cross-Cultural Psychology, 31*(1), 110–128. http://doi.org/10.1177/0022022100031001009

Aycan, Z., & Gelfand, M. J. (2012). Cross-cultural organizational psychology. In S. W. Kozlowski (Ed.), *The Oxford handbook of organizational psychology* (pp. 1103–1160). New York: Oxford University Press.

Baltes, B. B., Wynne, K., Sirabian, M., Krenn, D., & De Lange, A. (2014). Future time perspective, regulatory focus, and selection, optimization, and compensation: Testing a longitudinal model. *Journal of Organizational Behavior, 35*(8), 1120–1133. http://doi.org/10.1002/job.1970

Bandura, A. (1991). Social cognitive theory of self-regulation. *Organizational Behavior and Human Decision Processes, 50*(2), 248–287.

Bass, B. M., & Avolio, B. J. (1993). Transformational leadership and organizational culture. *Public Administration Quarterly, 17*(1), 112–121.

Beal, D. J. (2015). ESM 2.0: State of the art and future potential of experience sampling methods in organizational research. *Annual Review of Organizational Psychology and Organizational Behavior, 2,* 383–407. http://doi.org/10.1146/annurev-orgpsych-032414-111335

Beal, D. J., Trougakos, J. P., Weiss, H. M., & Dalal, R. S. (2013). Affect spin and the emotion regulation process at work. *Journal of Applied Psychology, 98*(4), 593–605. http://doi.org/10.1037/a0032559

Beck, J. W., Scholer, A. A., & Hughes, J. (2017). Divergent effects of distance versus velocity disturbances on emotional experiences during goal pursuit. *Journal of Applied Psychology*, *102*(7), 1109–1123. http://doi.org/10.1037/apl0000210

Bergman, A., & Karlsson, J. C. (2011). Three observations on work in the future. *Work, Employment and Society*, *25*(3), 561–568.

Blair-Loy, M. (2004). Work devotion and work time. In C. F. Epstein & A. L. Kalleberg (Eds.), *Fighting for time: Shifting boundaries of work and social life* (pp. 282–316). New York, NY: Russell Sage Foundation.

Bliese, P. D., Adler, A. B., & Flynn, P. J. (2017). Transition processes: A review and synthesis integrating methods and theory. *Annual Review of Organizational Psychology and Organizational Behavior*, *4*, 263–286. http://doi.org/10.1146/annurev-orgpsych-032516-113213

Bliese, P. D., Edwards, J. R., & Sonnentag, S. (2017). Stress and well-being at work: A century of empirical trends reflecting theoretical and societal influences. *Journal of Applied Psychology*, *102*(3), 389–402. http://doi.org/10.1037/apl0000109

Bliese, P. D., & Lang, J. W. (2016). Understanding relative and absolute change in discontinuous growth models: Coding alternatives and implications for hypothesis testing. *Organizational Research Methods*, *19*(4), 562–592. http://doi.org/10.1177/1094428116633502

Bliese, P. D., & Ployhart, R. E. (2002). Growth modeling using random coefficient models: Model building, testing, and illustrations. *Organizational Research Methods*, *5*(4), 362–387. http://doi.org/10.1177/109442802237116

Blount, S., & Janicik, G. A. (2001). When plans change: Examining how people evaluate timing changes in work organizations. *Academy of Management Review*, *26*(4), 566–585. http://doi.org/10.5465/amr.2001.5393892

Bluedorn, A. C. (2002). *The human organization of time: Temporal realities and experience*. Stanford, CA: Stanford University Press.

Bluedorn, A. C., & Denhardt, R. B. (1988). Time and organizations. *Journal of Management*, *14*(2), 299–320. http://doi.org/10.1177/014920638801400209

Bolger, N., Davis, A., & Rafaeli, E. (2003). Diary methods: Capturing life as it is lived. *Annual Review of Psychology*, *54*, 579–616. http://doi.org/10.1146/annurev.psych.54.101601.145030

Bolger, N., & Laurenceau, J. P. (2013). *Intensive longitudinal methods: An introduction to diary and experience sampling research*. New York, NY: Guilford Press.

Bollen, K. A., & Brand, J. E. (2010). A general panel model with random and fixed effects: A structural equations approach. *Social Forces*, *89*(1), 1–34. http://doi.org/10.1353/sof.2010.0072

Carstensen, L. L. (2006). The influence of a sense of time on human development. *Science*, *312*(5782), 1913–1915. http://doi.org/10.1126/science.1127488

Chu, P. C., & Spires, E. E. (2001). Does time constraint on users negate the efficacy of decision support systems? *Organizational Behavior and Human Decision Processes*, *85*(2), 226–249. http://doi.org/10.1006/obhd.2000.2940

Clarkberg, M., & Moen, P. (2001). Understanding the time-squeeze: Married couples' preferred and actual work-hour strategies. *American Behavioral Scientist*, *44*(7), 1115–1136. http://doi.org/10.1177/0002764201044007005

Cockerell, L. (2009). The organization of the future will foster an inclusive environment. In F. Hesselbein & M. Goldsmith (Eds.), *The organization of the future: Vol. 2. Visions, strategies, and insights on managing in a new era* (pp. 245–257). San Francisco, CA: Jossey-Bass.

Collinson, D. L., & Collinson, M. (2004). The power of time: Leadership, management, and gender. In C. F. Epstein & A. L. Kalleberg (Eds.), *Fighting for time: Shifting boundaries of work and social life* (pp. 219–246). New York, NY: Russell Sage Foundation.

Converse, P. D. (2006). *Self-regulation over time: Resource depletion and learned industriousness*. Unpublished dissertation, Michigan State University, East Lansing, MI.

Cooper, C. L. (2005). The future of work: Careers, stress and well-being. *Career Development International, 10*(5), 369–399. http://doi.org/10.1108/13620430510615319

Cornelius, N., & Skinner, D. (2008). The careers of senior men and women: A capabilities theory perspective. *British Journal of Management, 19*(1), 141–149. http://doi.org/10.1111/j.1467%968551.2008.00579.x

Costa, P. T., Jr., & McCrae, R. R. (1994). Set like plaster? Evidence for the stability of adult personality. In T. F. Heatherton & J. L. Weinberger (Eds.), *Can personality change?* (pp. 21–40). Washington, DC: American Psychological Association.

Danko, M. P. (2011). *A phenomenological study of time management.* Unpublished dissertation, University of Phoenix, Phoenix, AZ.

Das, T. K. (2004). Time-span and risk of partner opportunism in strategic alliances. *Journal of Managerial Psychology, 19*(8), 744–759. http://doi.org/10.1108/02683940410568239

Deci, E. L., & Ryan, R. M. (2012). Self-determination theory. In P. A. M. Van Lange, A. W. Kruglanski, & E. T. Higgins (Eds.), *Handbook of theories of social psychology* (pp. 416–436). New York, NY: Russell Sage Foundation.

Denisi, A. S. (2010). Challenges and opportunities for the academy in the next decade: 2009 Presidential address. *Academy of Management Review, 35*(2), 190–201. http://doi.org/10.5465/amr.35.2.zok190

Devoe, S. E. (2008). *When time is money: The effect of organizational practices on the evaluation and use of time.* Unpublished dissertation, Stanford University, Stanford, CA.

Dugan, A. G., Matthews, R. A., & Barnes-Farrell, J. L. (2012). Understanding the roles of subjective and objective aspects of time in the work–family interface. *Community, Work & Family, 15*(2), 149–172. http://doi.org/10.1080/13668803.2011.609656

Epstein, C. F. (2004). Border crossings: The constraints of time norms in transgressions of gender and professional roles. In C. F. Epstein & A. L. Kalleberg (Eds.), *Fighting for time: Shifting boundaries of work and social life* (pp. 317–340). New York, NY: Russell Sage Foundation.

Epstein, C. F., & Kalleberg, A. L. (2004). *Fighting for time: Shifting boundaries of work and social life.* New York, NY: Russell Sage Foundation.

Fagan, C. (2001). The temporal reorganization of employment and the household rhythm of work schedules: The implications for gender and class relations. *American Behavioral Scientist, 44*(7), 1199–1212. http://doi.org/10.1177/00027640121956728

Farnworth, L. J., & Fossey, E. (2003). Occupational terminology interactive dialogue: Explaining the concepts of time use, tempo and temporality. *Journal of Occupational Science, 10*(3), 150–153.

Fisher, C. D., & To, M. L. (2012). Using experience sampling methodology in organizational behavior. *Journal of Organizational Behavior, 33*(7), 865–877. http://doi.org/10.1002/job.1803

Fisscher, O. (2005). The necessary nature of future firms: Attributes of survivors in a changing world. *Creativity and Innovation Management, 14*(4), 438–440.

Fossland, T. (2013). Negotiating future careers: A relational perspective on skilled migrants' labour market participation. *Journal of Management Development, 32*(2), 193–203. http://doi.org/10.1108/0262171 1311305692

Fried, Y., & Slowik, L. H. (2004). Enriching goal-setting theory with time: An integrated approach. *Academy of Management Review, 29*(3), 404–422. http://doi.org/10.5465/amr.2004.13670973

Furnham, A. (2000). Work in 2020: Prognostications about the world of work 20 years into the millennium. *Journal of Managerial Psychology, 15*(3), 242–254. http://doi.org/10.1108/EUM000000 0005321

George, J. M., & Jones, G. R. (2000). The role of time in theory and theory building. *Journal of Management, 26*(4), 657–684. http://doi.org/10.1177/014920630002600404

Gevers, J. M., van Eerde, W., & Rutte, C. G. (2001). Time pressure, potency, and progress in project groups. *European Journal of Work and Organizational Psychology, 10*(2), 205–221. http://doi.org/10.1080 /13594320143000636

Goldsmith, M. (2006). E-coaching: Using the new technology to develop tomorrow's leaders. In M. Goldsmith & L. Lyons (Eds.), *Coaching for leadership: The practice of leadership coaching from the world's greatest coaches* (pp. 213–220). San Diego, CA: Pfeiffer.

Greenhaus, J. H., & Powell, G. N. (2006). When work and family are allies: A theory of work–family enrichment. *Academy of Management Review, 31*(1), 72–92. http://doi.org/10.5465/amr.2006.19379625

Griep, Y., Cooper, C., Robinson, S., Rousseau, D. M., Hansen, S. D., Tomprou, M.,…Linde, B. J. (2019). Psychological contracts: Back to the future. In Y. Griep & C. Cooper (Eds.), *Handbook of research on the psychological contract at work*. Cheltenham, UK: Edward Elgar.

Griep, Y., & Hansen, S. D. (Eds.). (2020). *Handbook on the temporal dynamics of organizational behavior*. Cheltenham, UK: Edward Elgar.

Griep, Y., & Vantilborgh, T. (2018a). Let's get cynical about this! Recursive relationships between psychological contract breach and counterproductive work behaviour. *Journal of Occupational and Organizational Psychology, 91*(2), 421–429. http://doi.org/10.1111/joop.12201

Griep, Y., & Vantilborgh, T. (2018b). Reciprocal effects of psychological contract breach on counterproductive and organizational citizenship behaviors: The role of time. *Journal of Vocational Behavior, 104,* 141–153. http://doi.org10.1016/j.jvb.2017.10.013

Griep, Y., Vantilborgh, T., Hansen, S. D., & Conway, N. (2018). Unravelling the role of time in psychological contract processes. *Frontiers in Psychology, 9,* 813. http://doi.org/10.3389/fpsyg.2018.00813

Grimm, K. J., Ram, N., & Estabrook, R. (2016). *Growth modeling: Structural equation and multilevel modeling approaches*. New York, NY: Guilford Press.

Grotto, A. R. (2015). On-demand: When work intrudes upon employees' personal time: Does gender matter. In M. J. Mills (Ed.), *Gender and the work–family experience: An intersection of two domains* (pp. 201–223). Cham, Switzerland: Springer International.

Guttman, H. M. (2009). The new high-performance, horizontal organization. In F. Hesselbein & M. Goldsmith (Eds.), *The organization of the future: Vol. 2. Visions, strategies, and insights on managing in a new era* (pp. 268–281). San Francisco, CA: Jossey-Bass.

Hernandez, M., & Guarana, C. L. (2018). An examination of the temporal intricacies of job engagement. *Journal of Management, 44*(5), 1711–1735. http://doi.org/10.1177/0149206315622573

Hesselbein, F., & Goldsmith, M. (Eds.). (2009). *The organization of the future 2: visions, strategies, and insights on managing in a new era*. Hoboken, NJ: John Wiley & Sons.

Hill, M. L. (2009). Closing commentary: The future of intercultural competence in an era of globalization. In M. A. Moodian (Ed.), *Contemporary leadership and intercultural competence: Exploring the cross-cultural dynamics within organizations* (pp. 281–282). Thousand Oaks, CA: SAGE.

Hirschi, A., Shockley, K. M., & Zacher, H. (2019). Achieving work–family balance: An action regulation model. *Academy of Management Review, 44*(1), 150–171. http://doi.org/10.5465/amr.2016.0409

Hülsheger, U. R. (2016). From dawn till dusk: Shedding light on the recovery process by investigating daily change patterns in fatigue. *Journal of Applied Psychology, 101*(6), 905–914. http://doi.org/10.1037/apl0000104

Jansen, K. J., & Shipp, A. J. (2013). A review and agenda for incorporating time in fit research. In J. Billsberry & A. Kristof-Brown (Eds.), *Organizational fit: Key issues and new directions* (pp. 195–221). New York, NY: Wiley.

Jansen, K. J., & Shipp, A. J. (2019). Fitting as a temporal sensemaking process: Shifting trajectories and stable themes. *Human Relations, 72*(7), 1154–1186.

Johnson, R. E., & Howe, M. (2013). The importance of velocity, or why speed may matter more than distance. *Organizational Psychology Review, 3*(1), 62–85. http://doi.org/10.1177/2041386612463836

Judge, T. A., Simon, L. S., Hurst, C., & Kelley, K. (2014). What I experienced yesterday is who I am today: Relationship of work motivations and behaviors to within-individual variation in the five-factor model of personality. *Journal of Applied Psychology, 99*(2), 199–221. http://doi.org/10.1037/a0034485

Kalleberg, A. L., & Epstein, C. F. (2001). Introduction: Temporal dimensions of employment relations. *American Behavioral Scientist, 44*(7), 1064–1075. http://doi.org/10.1177/00027640121956656

Kennedy, D. (2009). Leadership by perpetual practice. In F. Hesselbein & M. Goldsmith (Eds.), *The organization of the future: Vol. 2. Visions, strategies, and insights on managing in a new era* (pp. 321–335). San Francisco, CA: Jossey-Bass.

Khanna, S., & New, J. R. (2008). Revolutionizing the workplace: A case study of the future of work program at Capital One. *Human Resource Management, 47*(4), 795–808. http://doi.org/10.1002/hrm.20245

Kleiner, S., Schunck, R., & Schömann, K. (2015). Different contexts, different effects? Work time and mental health in the United States and Germany. *Journal of Health and Social Behavior, 56*(1), 98–113. http://doi.org/10.1177/0022146514568348

Klumb, P. L., & Perrez, M. (2004). Why time-sampling studies can enrich work: Leisure research. *Social Indicators Research, 67*(1/2), 1–10. http://doi.org/10.1023/B:SOCI.0000007332.92810.21

Kooij, D. T. A. M., Kanfer, R., Betts, M., & Rudolph, C. W. (2018). Future time perspective: A systematic review and meta-analysis. *Journal of Applied Psychology, 103*(8), 867–893. http://doi.org/10.1037/apl0000306

Kouzes, J. M., & Posner, B. Z. (2009). To lead, create a shared vision. *Harvard Business Review, 87*(1), 20–21.

Kozlowski, S. W. J. (2009). Editorial. *Journal of Applied Psychology, 94*(1), 1–4.

Kozlowski, S. W. J. (2017). Reflections on the *Journal of Applied Psychology* for 2009 to 2014: Infrastructure, operations, innovations, impact, evolution, and desirable directions. *Journal of Applied Psychology, 102*(3), 580–588.

Kozlowski, S. W., Chao, G. T., Grand, J. A., Braun, M. T., & Kuljanin, G. (2016). Capturing the multilevel dynamics of emergence: Computational modeling, simulation, and virtual experimentation. *Organizational Psychology Review, 6*(1), 3–33. http://doi.org/10.1177/2041386614547955

Kuhn, T. (2006). A "demented work ethic" and a "lifestyle firm": Discourse, identity, and workplace time commitments. *Organization Studies, 27*(9), 1339–1358. http://doi.org/10.1177/0170840606067249

Lee, S. A., & Park, H. S. (2012). Influence of temporal distance on the perceived importance of career-related self-efficacy and outcome expectations. *Career Development Quarterly, 60*(3), 194–206. http://doi.org/10.1002/j.2161%960045.2012.00016.x

Leroy, S., Shipp, A. J., Blount, S., & Licht, J. G. (2015). Synchrony preference: Why some people go with the flow and some don't. *Personnel Psychology, 68*(4), 759–809. http://doi.org/10.1111/peps.12093

Levasseur, L., Shipp, A. J., Fried, Y., Rousseau, D. M., & Zimbardo, P. G. (2020). New perspectives on time perspective and temporal focus. *Journal of Organizational Behavior, 41*(3), 235–243. http://doi.org/10.1002/job.2435

Levin, P. (2004). Gender, work, and time: Gender at work and at play in futures trading. In C. F. Epstein & A. L. Kalleberg (Eds.), *Fighting for time: Shifting boundaries of work and social life* (pp. 249–281). New York, NY: Russell Sage Foundation.

Levine, M. (2003). Times, theories and practices in social psychology. *Theory & Psychology, 13*(1), 53–72. http://doi.org/10.1177/0959354303013001762

Locke, E. A., & Latham, G. P. (1990). *A theory of goal setting & task performance.* Englewood Cliffs, NJ: Prentice Hall.

Martin, R., Epitropaki, O., Thomas, G., & Topakas, A. (2010). A review of leader-member exchange research: Future prospects and directions. In G. P. Hodgkinson & J. K. Ford (Eds.), *International review of industrial and organizational psychology* (Vol. 25, pp. 35–88). New York, NY: Wiley.

Mayrhofer, W., & Schneidhofer, T. M. (2009). The lay of the land: European career research and its future. *Journal of Occupational and Organizational Psychology, 82*(4), 721–737. http://doi.org/10.1348/096317909X471347

McCormick, B. W., Reeves, C. J., Downes, P. E., Li, N., & Ilies, R. (2020). Scientific contributions of within-person research in management: Making the juice worth the squeeze. *Journal of Management, 46*(2), 321–350. http://doi.org/10.1177/0149206318788435

McGrath, J. E., & Tschan, F. (2004). *Temporal matters in social psychology: Examining the role of time in the lives of groups and individuals.* Washington, DC: American Psychological Association.

Mitchell, T. R., & James, L. R. (2001). Building better theory: Time and the specification of when things happen. *Academy of Management Review, 26*(4), 530–547. http://doi.org/10.5465/amr.2001.5393889

Moe, T. R. (2018). *Exploring the leadership skills needed by frontline expatriate leaders to lead the global international workforce of the future.* Unpublished dissertation, Colorado Technical University, Colorado Springs, CO.

Mohammed, S., & Nadkarni, S. (2014). Are we all on the same temporal page? The moderating effects of temporal team cognition on the polychronicity diversity–team performance relationship. *Journal of Applied Psychology, 99*(3), 404–422. http://doi.org/10.1037/a0035640

Molenaar, P. C. (1985). A dynamic factor model for the analysis of multivariate time series. *Psychometrika, 50*(2), 181–202. http://doi.org/10.1007/BF02294246

Molenaar, P. C. (2004). A manifesto on psychology as idiographic science: Bringing the person back into scientific psychology, this time forever. *Measurement, 2*(4), 201–218. http://doi.org/10.1207/s15366359mea0204_1

Morin, A. J. S., Boudrias, J.-S., Marsh, H. W., McInerney, D. M., Dagenais-Desmarais, V., Madore, I., & Litalien, D. (2017). Complementary variable- and person-centered approaches to the dimensionality of psychometric constructs: Application to psychological wellbeing at work. *Journal of Business and Psychology, 32*(4), 395–419. http://doi.org/10.1007/s10869-016-9448-7

Morin, A. J., & Marsh, H. W. (2015). Disentangling shape from level effects in person-centered analyses: An illustration based on university teachers' multidimensional profiles of effectiveness. *Structural Equation Modeling: A Multidisciplinary Journal, 22*(1), 39–59. http://doi.org/10.1080/10705511.2014.919825

Morin, A. J. S., Meyer, J. P., Creusier, J., & Biétry, F. (2016). Multiple-group analysis of similarity in latent profile solutions. *Organizational Research Methods, 19*(2), 231–254. http://doi.org/10.1177/1094428115621148

Morin, A. J. S., & Wang, J. C. K. (2016). A gentle introduction to mixture modeling using physical fitness data. In N. Ntoumanis & N. Myers (Eds.), *An introduction to intermediate and advanced statistical analyses for sport and exercise scientists* (pp. 183–210). London, UK: Wiley.

Morris, C. S. (2005). *Effects of voluntary control on performance response under stress.* Unpublished dissertation, University of Central Florida, Orlando, Florida.

Muthén, B. O. (2002). Beyond SEM: General latent variable modeling. *Behaviormetrika, 29*(1), 81–117. http://doi.org/10.2333/bhmk.29.81

Nakashima, N. A., Daniels, D. P., & Laurin, K. (2017). It's about time: Divergent evaluations of restrictive policies in the near and distant future. *Organizational Behavior and Human Decision Processes, 142*, 12–27. http://doi.org/10.1016/j.obhdp.2017.07.005

Nesselroade, J. R. (1991). Interindividual differences in intraindividual change. In L. M. Collins & J. L. Horn (Eds.), *Best methods for the analysis of change: Recent advances, unanswered questions, future directions* (pp. 92–105). Washington, DC: American Psychological Association.

Nickel, J. W. (2015). Ethical protections for future persons: Is their present non-existence a serious problem? *Journal of Business Ethics, 127*(4), 717–722. http://doi.org/10.1007/s10551-014-2181-0

Oakes, D. W., Ferris, G. R., Martocchio, J. J., Buckley, M. R., & Broach, D. (2001). Cognitive ability and personality predictors of training program skill acquisition and job performance. *Journal of Business and Psychology, 15*(4), 523–548. http://doi.org/10.1023/A:1007805132107

Ohly, S., Sonnentag, S., Niessen, C., & Zapf, D. (2010). Diary studies in organizational research. *Journal of Personnel Psychology, 9*, 79–93. http://doi.org/10.1027/1866-5888/a000009

Oldham, G. R., & Hackman, J. R. (2010). Not what it was and not what it will be: The future of job design research. *Journal of Organizational Behavior, 31*(2–3), 463–479. http://doi.org/10.1002/job.678

Outlaw, R., Colquitt, J. A., Baer, M. D., & Sessions, H. (2019). How fair versus how long: An integrative theory-based examination of procedural justice and procedural timeliness. *Personnel Psychology, 72*(3), 361–391. http://doi.org/10.1111/peps.12309

Ployhart, R. E., & Vandenberg, R. J. (2010). Longitudinal research: The theory, design, and analysis of change. *Journal of Management, 36*(1), 94–120. http://doi.org/10.1177/0149206309352110

Rhee, M. (2007). The time relevance of social capital. *Rationality and Society, 19*(3), 367–389. http://doi.org/10.1177/1043463107080451

Roe, R. A. (2008). Time in applied psychology: The study of "what happens" rather than "what is". *European Psychologist, 13*(1), 37–52. http://doi.org/10.1027/1016-9040.13.1.37

Roe, R. A. (2014a). Test validity from a temporal perspective: Incorporating time in validation research. *European Journal of Work and Organizational Psychology, 23*(5), 754–768. http://doi.org/10.1080/1359432X.2013.804177

Roe, R. A. (2014b). Performance, motivation and time. In A. J. Shipp & Y. Fried (Eds.), *Time and work: Vol. 1. How time impacts individuals* (pp. 63–110). London, UK: Routledge.

Roe, R. A., Gockel, C., & Meyer, B. (2012). Time and change in teams: Where we are and where we are moving. *European Journal of Work and Organizational Psychology, 21*(5), 629–656. http://doi.org/10.1080/1359432X.2012.729821

Rousseau, D. M., Hansen, S. D., & Tomprou, M. (2018). A dynamic phase model of psychological contract processes. *Journal of Organizational Behavior, 39*(9), 1081–1098. http://doi.org/10.1002/job.2284

Rudolph, C. W., Kooij, D. T., Rauvola, R. S., & Zacher, H. (2018). Occupational future time perspective: A meta-analysis of antecedents and outcomes. *Journal of Organizational Behavior, 39*(2), 229–248. http://doi.org/10.1002/job.2264

Sanchez, J. I., & Levine, E. L. (2012). The rise and fall of job analysis and the future of work analysis. *Annual Review of Psychology, 63*, 397–425. http://doi.org/10.1146/annurev-psych-120710-100401

Santos, C. M., Passos, A. M., Uitdewilligen, S., & Nübold, A. (2016). Shared temporal cognitions as substitute for temporal leadership: An analysis of their effects on temporal conflict and team performance. *Leadership Quarterly, 27*(4), 574–587. http://doi.org/10.1016/j.leaqua.2015.12.002

Schneider, B., & Waite, L. (2005). Timely and timeless: Working parents and their children. In S. M. Bianchi, L. M. Casper, & B. R. King (Eds.), *Work, family, health, and well-being* (pp. 67–79). Mahwah, NJ: Lawrence Erlbaum.

Schonfeld, I. S., & Rindskopf, D. (2007). Hierarchical linear modeling in organizational research: Longitudinal data outside the context of growth modeling. *Organizational Research Methods, 10*(3), 417–429. http://doi.org/10.1177/1094428107300229

Shipp, A. J., & Fried, Y. E. (Eds.). (2014a). *Time and work: Vol. 1. How time impacts individuals.* London, UK: Routledge.

Shipp, A. J., & Fried, Y. E. (Eds.). (2014b). *Time and work, Vol. 2: How time impacts groups, organizations and methodological choices.* London, UK: Routledge.

Shipp, A. J., & Jansen, K. J. (2011). Reinterpreting time in fit theory: Crafting and recrafting narratives of fit in medias res. *Academy of Management Review, 36*(1), 76–101. http://doi.org/10.5465/amr.2009.0077

Singer, J. D., Willett, J. B., & Willett, J. B. (2003). *Applied longitudinal data analysis: Modeling change and event occurrence.* New York, NY: Oxford University Press.

Smith, M. C., Mikulecky, L., Kibby, M. W., Dreher, M. J., & Dole, J. A. (2000). RRQ snippet: What will be the demands of literacy in the workplace in the next millennium? *Reading Research Quarterly, 35*(3), 378–383.

Song, Y., Liu, Y., Shi, J., & Wang, M. (2017). Use of proactive socialization tactics and socialization outcomes: A latent growth modeling approach to understanding newcomer socialization process. *Academy of Management Discoveries, 3*(1), 42–63. http://doi.org/10.5465/amd.2014.0142

Sonnentag, S. (2012). Psychological detachment from work during leisure time: The benefits of mentally disengaging from work. *Current Directions in Psychological Science, 21*(2), 114–118. http://doi.org/10.1177/0963721411434979

Sonnentag, S., Reinecke, L., Mata, J., & Vorderer, P. (2018). Feeling interrupted—being responsive: How online messages relate to affect at work. *Journal of Organizational Behavior, 39*(3), 369–383. http://doi.org/10.1002/job.2239

Syrek, C. J., Apostel, E., & Antoni, C. H. (2013). Stress in highly demanding IT jobs: Transformational leadership moderates the impact of time pressure on exhaustion and work–life balance. *Journal of Occupational Health Psychology, 18*(3), 252–261. http://doi.org/10.1037/a0033085

Tang, S., Richter, A. W., & Nadkarni, S. (2020). Subjective time in organizations: Conceptual clarification, integration, and implications for future research. *Journal of Organizational Behavior, 41*(2), 210–234. http://doi.org/10.1002/job.2421

Tsaousis, I., & Nikolaou, I. E. (2001). The stability of the five-factor model of personality in personnel selection and assessment in Greece. *International Journal of Selection and Assessment, 9*(4), 290–301. http://doi.org/10.1111/1468-2389.00181

Ulrich, D., & Smallwood, N. (2009). Organization is not structure but capability. In F. Hesselbein & M. Goldsmith (Eds.), *The organization of the future: Vol. 2. Visions, strategies, and insights on managing in a new era* (pp. 13–26). San Francisco, CA: Jossey-Bass.

Vancouver, J. B., & Scherbaum, C. A. (2008). Do we self-regulate actions or perceptions? A test of two computational models. *Computational and Mathematical Organization Theory, 14*(1), 1–22. http://doi.org/10.1007/s10588-008-9021-7

Vancouver, J. B., Wang, M., & Li, X. (2020). Translating informal theories into formal theories: The case of the dynamic computational model of the integrated model of work motivation. *Organizational Research Methods, 23*(2), 238–274. http://doi.org/10.1177/1094428118780308

Vantilborgh, T., Hofmans, J., & Judge, T. A. (2018). The time has come to study dynamics at work. *Journal of Organizational Behavior, 39*(9), 1045–1049. http://doi.org/10.1002/job.2327

Voelkle, M. C., & Oud, J. H. (2015). Relating latent change score and continuous time models. *Structural Equation Modeling: A Multidisciplinary Journal, 22*(3), 366–381.

Vroom, V. H. (1964). *Work and motivation.* New York, NY: Wiley.

Wang, M., Beal, D. J., Chan, D., Newman, D. A., Vancouver, J. B., & Vandenberg, R. J. (2017). Longitudinal research: A panel discussion on conceptual issues, research design, and statistical techniques. *Work, Aging and Retirement, 3*(1), 1–24. http://doi.org/10.1093/workar/waw033

Wang, M., Zhou, L., & Zhang, Z. (2016). Dynamic modeling. *Annual Review of Organizational Psychology and Organizational Behavior, 3*, 241–266. http://doi.org/10.1146/annurev-orgpsych-041015-062553

Wegman, L. A., Hoffman, B. J., Carter, N. T., Twenge, J. M., & Guenole, N. (2018). Placing job characteristics in context: Cross-temporal meta-analysis of changes in job characteristics since 1975. *Journal of Management, 44*(1), 352–386. http://doi.org/10.1177/0149206316654545

Weick, K. E. (2005). Managing the future: Foresight in the knowledge economy. *Academy of Management Review, 30*(4), 871–873. http://doi.org/10.5465/amr.2005.18378884

Winsborough, D., & Chamorro-Premuzic, T. (2013). Consulting psychology in the digital era: Current trends and future directions. *Consulting Psychology Journal: Practice and Research, 65*(4), 319–324. http://doi.org/10.1037/a0035698

Woods, S. A., Wille, B., Wu, C. H., Lievens, F., & De Fruyt, F. (2019). The influence of work on personality trait development: The demands–affordances Transactional (DATA) model, an integrative review, and research agenda. *Journal of Vocational Behavior, 110*, 258–271. http://doi.org/10.1016/j.jvb.2018.11.010

Yakura, E. K. (2001). Billables: The valorization of time in consulting. *American Behavioral Scientist, 44*(7), 1076–1095. http://doi.org/10.1177/0002764201044007003

Ybema, S. (2004). Managerial postalgia: Projecting a golden future. *Journal of Managerial Psychology, 19*(8), 825–841. http://doi.org/10.1108/02683940410568284

Yeung, D. Y., Fung, H. H., & Chan, D. K. S. (2020). Roles of age and future time perspective of the work relationship in conflict management: A daily diary study. *International Journal of Stress Management.* Advance online publication. http://doi.org/10.1037/str0000155

Zacher, H., Feldman, D. C., & Schulz, H. (2014). Age, occupational strain, and well-being: A person–environment fit perspective. In P. L. Perrewé, C. C. Rosen, & J. R. B. Halbesleben (Eds.), *Research in occupational stress and well-being* (pp. 83–111). Bingley, UK: Emerald Group.

Zacher, H., & Rudolph, C. W. (2020). How a dynamic way of thinking can challenge existing knowledge in organizational behavior. In Y. Griep & S. D. Hansen (Eds.), *Handbook on the temporal dynamics of organizational behavior* (pp. 8–25). Cheltenham, UK: Edward Elgar.

Zacher, H., Schmitt, A., Jimmieson, N. L., & Rudolph, C. W. (2019). Dynamic effects of personal initiative on engagement and exhaustion: The role of mood, autonomy, and support. *Journal of Organizational Behavior, 40*(1), 38–58. http://doi.org/10.1002/job.2277

Zyphur, M. J., Allison, P. D., Tay, L., Voelkle, M. C., Preacher, K. J., Zhang, Z., . . . Diener, E. (2019). From data to causes I: Building a general cross-lagged panel model (GCLM). *Organizational Research Methods, 23*(4), 651–687. http://doi.org/10.1177/1094428119847278

Yannick Griep and Hannes Zacher

GENERAL CODING AND ANALYSIS IN QUALITATIVE RESEARCH

INTRODUCTION

Coding and analysis are at the heart of qualitative projects. Indeed, they connect study design and data gathering to the final form the project takes, be it a report, chapter, article, book, or other way of "writing up" your findings. For qualitative research, the metaphor proposed for coding and analysis is that of translating.[1] Just as someone might translate a story from English to French, qualitative researchers take data from "informants" in the field and attempt to translate insights from their worldview to an academic audience. As with translating, it involves both technique (how to do it) and a mindset (how to think about). As with all translations, there will be slippage in the process; however, coding and analysis can be done well or poorly, with the latter resulting in undue "violence to experience" (Pratt, 2008). Both necessitate knowing two cultures (and languages) well—the informants' as well as that of academics—and being able to move back and forth from one to the other. Such movement, however, is not simply a technical replacement of one word for another, but involves active judgment to preserve meanings. Where the metaphor breaks down, perhaps, is that coding and analysis should not result in "theoretical description": simply being able to restate what your informants know using extant academic concepts. Rather, the aim is to build or elaborate new theory, leveraging insights from your informants to improve and extend academic understanding.

KNOWING THE LANGUAGE

Saldaña (2021, p. 5) provides an often-cited explanation of a code as "a word or short phrase that symbolically assigns a summative, salient, essence-capturing, and/or evocative attribute for a portion of language-based or visual data." Codes can be either emergent or a priori, meaning that they either arise from the data or they are predetermined based on extant theorizing (Blair, 2015). Emergent codes are often associated with inductive research and a priori codes with deductive research. However, as many qualitative scholars will note, both kinds of coding can be used even in research that is largely inductive. For example, the use of sensitizing concepts (Bowen, 2006) and the like, especially in grounded theory, suggest that both inductive and deductive coding may occur in a given qualitative analysis. Others note that grounded theory is essentially an abductive process (Timmermans & Tavory, 2012) which is different than both deduction and induction (Locke et al., 2008).[2]

Taking the general meaning of analysis as a systematic way of approaching data for the purpose of better understanding it, coding can be viewed as one type of or one part of analysis. The stance taken here is that coding data is part of a broader analytical effort. Outside of coding, researchers may record impressions of their time in the field in analytic memos (Locke, 2001; Strauss & Corbin, 1998), in narratives or chronologies (Langley, 1999), in semiotic clusters (Feldman, 1995), or in field notes (Spradley, 1979). Analysis draws on these practices to facilitate intuitive leaps, flashes of insight, and moments of doubt and discovery (Locke et al., 2008) that may be evoked—at least in part—by coding, but may also draw upon impressions from extant research, or one's own unique experiences in the field, or from other areas of one's life (Locke, 2001).

Coding and analysis, in turn, are part of a larger qualitative analysis cycle comprised of research design, data gathering, and writing up one's findings in some form, such as for publication. This process is depicted in Figure 1. Study design involves several things including crafting a research question, determining your context and your sampling strategy, deciding what types of data you will gather, and how you will implement the study (see Alvesson & Sandberg, 2013; Creswell & Creswell, 2018; Marshall & Rossman, 1999; Pratt, 2016). Study design influences coding and analysis. At a most basic level, research questions and study design (e.g., sampling) will delimit the data one collects and therefore what one analyzes. To illustrate, the author's work on Amway distributors began with interviewing active and former distributors and he contrasted these groups in his later analysis (Pratt, 2000a, 2000b).[3]

Data gathering, as the name implies, involves getting the archival, interview, observation, video, or other data you will need that will serve as the raw materials for your analysis. In qualitative research, data gathering and data analysis occur together in an iterative fashion as noted by the double arrows in Figure 1 (see "constant comparative method" in "'How to' Knowledge About Analysis: Grounded Theory"). Indeed, one common mistake among those new to qualitative research is waiting until the end of one's data collection to begin any analysis of one's data.[4] Because qualitative research tends to start broadly and then home in on certain elements in one's context (see "Levels of Knowing: Analysis"), waiting to analyze data until the end of a study likely means that all of the data collection has been very general,

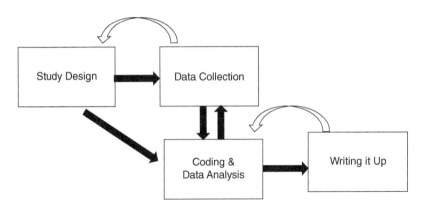

Figure 1. Qualitative research process.

resulting in a large amount of very superficial data (see also "Levels of Knowing: Coding"). Coding and analysis often result in writing up one's findings in some form (e.g., report, chapter, journal, or book). As anyone who has written a journal article can attest, through the review process one might realize that additional coding and analysis is required to better understand one's data, which may result in further data collection or even a redesign of the original study (see curved arrows in Figure 1).

Not fully featured in Figure 1, but true of coding and analysis, is their dynamic nature (see also "live" coding in Locke et al., 2015). Researchers not only move back and forth among data collection, coding, and analysis, but they will also iterate among old codes and new ones, as well as among emerging and extant theory. Coding itself often occurs in "rounds" whereby the data is coded, and then later recoded multiple times as the analytic process progresses. Thus, even when qualitative analyses are written up as being more-or-less linear, the process of coding and analysis is decidedly nonlinear.

LEVELS OF KNOWING: CODING

Since the close of the 20th century, there have been an increasing number of sources for researchers to draw upon that focus specifically on the mechanics of the coding process itself. Such sources are replete with examples of texts and what codes were given for them and why. Perhaps the most comprehensive source is Saldaña's (2021) *The Coding Manual for Qualitative Researchers*, which boasts 43 different approaches to coding. Resources about coding can be divided into one of two different types: those that focus specifically on the mechanics of coding and those that guide the reader on how to think about coding.

"How to" Knowledge of Coding. Central to "how to" treatments of coding are responding to basic questions that a novice researcher may ask when initially approaching their data. These questions include but are not limited to when to code one's data, how much data one should code, how granular should one's coding be (e.g., word-by-word, incident-by-incident, etc.), how many codes should be produced, how codes should be named, and relatedly, what types of codes should be employed.[5] In general, the answers to these questions will depend on one's research question as well as the specific methodological approach one is taking.

With regard to when to begin coding, there are a number of factors to consider. For example, broad research questions may require some interactions at the field site to get a better idea of whether and how one's research question may be answered in this context. Similarly, engagement in coding depends on your methodological approach. Some, like ethnography, require a certain amount of cultural expertise before certain types of coding can be employed (see "'How to' Knowledge About Analysis: Ethnography"). For analytic approaches such as grounded theory, data is coded while data collection is still ongoing. Of course, it is important to distinguish between analysis and coding when determining engaging with one's data. Engaging with one's data early on via memos, field notes, impressions, and the like are important as one considers whether and how one's data corresponds with one's research question.[6] Formal coding, however, may only occur after one has had enough time in the field to begin to contextualize one's understanding of one's data.

Coding may also be constrained by one's data collection schedule. To illustrate, if an organization provides access once a month for a week to collect data, one may decide to wait for the "off" weeks to engage in coding. Researchers may also design into their data collection periods of time when they will exit the field and code data. Some researchers will collect 10 or so interviews, code them, and then collect a dozen more, code again, and the cycle repeats. Planning for breaks in data collection in order to engage with one's data allows the researcher an opportunity to refine their data collection, which will, in turn, influence subsequent coding and analysis.

Regarding how much of one's data you code also depends on several factors. For example, if one's research question was about how different employees used the term *authentic* one would likely first identify this word-in-use or "in vivo" and then code around its use for its meaning. However, if one was interested in inducing a theory about how organizational practices either inhibit or promote expressions of authenticity, then one would code more broadly around practices and individual perceptions. As a general rule, the broader and more inductive one is when doing one's coding, the more data one will code.

Concerning the level of granularity, coders can make predetermined choices to focus on individual words, go line-by-line, or code for larger chunks such as incidents (Charmaz, 2014) or broad life stories (Atkinson, 1998). To illustrate choices about granularity, Table 1 provides a coded excerpt of an interview with an Amway distributor. Amway is a direct-selling organization where distributors (a.k.a. Independent Business Owners) buy and sell products via the Amway Corporation. In this interview, a distributor was being asked about something the interviewer had heard: that Amway was about more than money.

The initial coding in the first paragraph demonstrates line-by-line coding, which grounded theorists refer to as a "microanalysis" (Strauss & Corbin, 1998). These codes show how Amway distributors develop people and in doing so, develop friendships in the process, which the interviewee sees as different from those outside of Amway. In particular, she notes that although Amway distributors did not treat her differently once her husband died, those outside of Amway, especially married couples, did so (e.g., she was a threat to marriages). The advantage of line-by-line coding is that you can pick up on a lot of themes that may be missed if you coded this as a larger block of data. For example, you could miss her traditional upbringing

306 • GENERAL CODING AND ANALYSIS IN QUALITATIVE RESEARCH

Table 1. An Illustration of Different Granularity of Coding of an Interview Excerpt

Interviewer: I heard on a tape by an Amway Emerald about how Amway is about more than making money. I hear that at all the seminars too. If you could just expand on that a little bit? You were just talking about ministering to people.

Informant: I probably just said it all right there, that it does go beyond. You're seeing people develop [**developing people**], what I was talking about earlier. The friendships that you develop [**making friendships**]. Again, I can make a comparison because of the death of my husband and people always talk about what do widows [**death of husband**] and/or widowers, but I can't speak to widowers, men remarry fairly rapidly after the death of a spouse [**can't hang out with widowers after the death of her husband**] statistically, I read a little bit about it, but you always, we've always heard these things about [**rumors about how people treat widows**] well suddenly you're on the outside, you have couples that are friends and now you're the threat [**post-husband's-death seen as threat to married couples**] because you're the single woman. I'm going oh for corn sake, am I a threat? That depends on [**but is she a threat to other's marriages as a widow?**] the faithfulness of couples I guess and that's changed a lot but I was brought up, I guess, pretty [**her marriage threat level depends on the faithfulness of other couples**] traditionally, very traditionally, you know my husband was my husband and that was it [**raised traditionally**] and I hope, I believe that was the same for him, for me, that we were faithful to one another in all ways [**was faithful to husband and vice versa**]. So, I didn't go looking around saying, boy there's a really neat looking guy particularly [**didn't notice other guys when married**], I had one and I was happy so you hear all this stuff about couples and threatening [**more on how widows are threats to other married couples**] and you're not invited out anymore and all that and I thought, nah, no problem you know I'm friendly and all this and it happened [**didn't think it would happen to her but did**].

Although we had been cut off from couples that sort of interchange of dinner out and having my husband's office, you know the people that work in his office, over for dinner and that sort of thing, we had drifted away from that because we got so involved in the Amway business and those people went other places [**drifted from husband's office friends while in Amway**]. But I found it even with people I considered friends at church and they feel awkward, it's just that people don't know what to do with you I concluded and in Amway that doesn't happen. You're still friends, you still work together and it doesn't matter [**awkward with church members but not with Amway friends**] if you as I jokingly say, you're a couple, a single, or a half a couple [**couple, single, or "half a couple"**], meaning one works the business, the other does not and if we have a potluck supper, we don't say now we have to have all these couples and seat them. We might have 15 women and 5 men or 12 men and 7 women or whatever. We never give it a second thought to socially, I guess is what I'm talking about, seeing that when people say friendships develop in the business, what I'm giving you is a little comparison of what happens when somebody is widowed and is not involved in the Amway business. I found out, by golly, what they said is true is really true [**Amway friends don't care about gender or marital status**]. You start, I said I don't want to hang around with a bunch of 60-year-old ladies. Don't sound like fun to me and that's what widowed people end up doing and if, come to singles group to church and so forth because they don't have that camaraderie anymore and in Amway, I found nothing changed [**After husband died, Amway relationships didn't change**]. As a matter of fact, I'm sponsoring more young couples. I was concerned that might be a problem when I present the business and I'm sponsoring more young couples than I, we did earlier. We used to jokingly call it "Sigfried and his harem" so that was an affirmation we shouldn't have, early days you sponsored a lot of housewives who wanted to earn a little extra money so we had Sigfried and his harem and now I have almost, I'm thinking going to things, couple in their 30s, even 20s and that's delightful. Some of them call me Mom, I'm grandma Smith to one of the kids [**Grandma Smith to some in downline**]. That's great, in more of a counselor capacity, maybe than a good buddy,

Table 1. Continued

that's really neat to have cross culturally, cross age, friendships, one of my closest friends in my business is an 83 year old person and we don't see eye to eye on half of the things in life but we're good friends, that's the beauty of it so that's what Amway is, more than, because we are freer for some reason because, I've thought of it because you're involved with people's finances in a sense and their interest in making more money for some reason, so you're already beyond the hello, how are you, what do you like to eat for dinner? You're a little more deeply into how that person ticks so you end up talking about religion, politics which are no-nos in social situations [**being in business opens doors to asking deeper questions**]. I'm going, that's what's interesting, come on. But we talk more about philosophies, what do you want out of life, and I don't think we ever talked about those things with our social friends.

Note: Coding is provided in brackets.

or her faithfulness to her marriage. Although they might not seem important on a first pass, it could be helpful to know how Amway distributors think about marriage in relation to other parts of the business (Pratt, 2000b). However, some find this level of granularity overwhelming as one can end up with many, many codes.

Rather that sticking to a specific level of granularity a priori, a researcher may also decide to code for "meaningful chunks" of data. Of course, what is a meaningful chunk of data is in the eye of the beholder. In the second paragraph of this excerpt, the data is coded using broader swaths of data to home in on some similar themes raised in the more granular coding: that after the loss of her husband, non-Amway relationships changed, but Amway relationships did not. "Meaningful chunks" can be paragraphs, several lines, or even a word or two. "Grandma Smith," for example, was coded as it indicated a familial relationship. This code also reinforces the point that once you know about someone's finances by being in business with them, you have moved beyond superficialities and can ask deeper questions of one another.

It is important to note that changes in granularity may occur as researchers become more familiar with their data and are in later stages of coding. For example, the broader chunks around what non-Amway people do and what Amway people do may be possible because of the more fine-grained analysis done in the first paragraph. Put another way, when considering granularity, one might consider whether one is trying to figure out what is going on in an interview, that is what is meaningful, or whether one has some idea of what is meaningful and is looking for how that meaningfulness appears in the data. One's progress in a research project may also influence what is coded or recoded. For example, one may wish to "go deeper" into some parts of one's data, thus these data will likely be recoded whereas other data may not.

Although there are not hard and fast rules with regard to how granular to code data, there are some best practices. For example, it is often best when initially coding to code everything even if it does not, on the surface, seem that important. It may be that something seemingly irrelevant comes to take on greater importance as coding proceeds. If you code everything, however, you may wish to be less granular on areas that—in your initial read—do not seem critical. For example, another coder with another research question could have simply coded the first paragraph as "Amway and non-Amway relationships" as an initial placeholder, and if relationships became more important later in the analysis, the coder could go back to these broadly coded areas and recode. One exception to the "code everything" prescription, however, are data that are clearly outside of your research question. For example, one may choose to not code the small talk that often begins an interview.

Of course, decisions about what you will code and at what level of granularity you will code will directly impact the number of codes one produces. As Elliott (2018, p. 2852) notes:

> Friese (2014) warns that the number of codes should not swell into the thousands . . . Other figures gathered by Saldaña (2016) range between 50–300 codes (Friese, 2014); 80–100 codes divided into 15–20 categories, eventually grouped into 5–7 major concepts (Litchtman, 2013); or 30–40 codes. (MacQueen et al., 2009)

Rather than attempting to achieve a "magic number," it is better to understand a basic tension in coding. You need enough codes to provide a foundation for your analysis, but not so many that the researcher is overwhelmed.[7] How a researcher resolves this tension will depend on a variety of factors, including one's analytical approach, one's research question, and even one's personal preferences. As will be discussed, the number of codes will also vary depending on where in the analytical process one is.

Another "how to" question involves what codes should look like. Although suggestions range, the reader should consider Abraham Lincoln's response to a question about how long a man's legs should be. He is quoted as saying, "long enough to reach the ground." Similarly, codes should be long enough that the coder remembers what they were trying to capture with the code: no longer or no shorter. Alternatively, one may facilitate recollection by recording what codes mean in a coding log. Some codes, especially in early rounds of coding may be *in vivo* codes. In the Table 1 excerpt, "half a couple" is an in vivo code that refers to how informants refer to married couples where only one member is active in building an Amway business. Other codes are not from the informants and are longer to represent certain ideas in the data such as "Post-husband's-death seen as threat to married couples."

As discussed in "Levels of Knowing: Analysis," codes may also look different as one's coding progresses. This difference is captured in the distinction between "first cycle" or initial codes and "second cycle," which involves finding patterns among codes later in one's analysis (Miles et al., 2020; Saldaña, 2021). The codes in Table 1 are "first cycle." However, later rounds of coding may involve codes that are abstractions of these earlier codes. That is, later codes may be more theoretical, abstract, and etic, while initial codes (e.g., "half a couple") may be more emic. There are several types of codes common to earlier and later stages of analysis that can be utilized. Miles et al. (2020), for example, identify descriptive, process, emotion, values, and general pattern codes, to name just a few. As with all decisions about coding, the types of codes employed should be guided by a researcher's general analytic approach (e.g., axial codes in grounded theory) as well as one's research question (e.g., using process codes if you have a process-oriented research question) and progress in the research project.

In sum, "how to" knowledge of coding involves the mechanics of sitting down with a set of data and knowing what to code and how to code it. Central issues here are when and how much of the data to code, the granularity of codes, and what the codes themselves look like. This knowledge also involves knowing how codes might change (e.g., become more abstract) through different rounds of coding. The latter insight begins to move the discussion away from the mechanics of coding toward how to think about coding more generally.

How to Think About Coding. Taking a step back from the various "how to" questions about coding are broader considerations such as why one codes and how to think about the coding process itself. The issue of how to think about noncoding ways of interacting with one's data, as well as analysis more broadly, will be covered in "'How to' Knowledge: Moving From Understanding Informants' Worldviews to Constructing Theory" as well as "How to Think About Analysis" (see also "Knowing the Language"). With regard to why someone should engage in coding, Linnenberg and Korsgaard (2019, pp. 261–262) suggest several benefits of coding such as: facilitating deep engagement with one's data; making key data easier to retrieve throughout the coding process; reducing and organizing the amount of data you need to consider; strengthening the linkages between research questions and findings by creating a "chain of evidence"; and when done well, reflecting the worldview and voice of one's informants. Locke et al. (2015) also note that coding can either shut down or open up new possibilities. They contrast "static" coding with "live" coding to get at another important reason to code one's data: to facilitate discovery.

Thinking reflexively about *why* one is coding opens the door for understanding *how* researchers might think about the coding processes in pursuit of these aims. To illustrate, Grodal et al. (2021) note that since coding involves identifying categories, scholars should draw upon insights from research on categorization to inform how they code their data. They break down coding data into a variety of "moves" that represent different ways of approaching the coding process. For example, one can code by "focusing on puzzles" whereby the coder focuses "on the part of the data that is most surprising or salient to the researchers" (Grodal et al., 2021, p. 593). What differentiates these treatments of coding from the "how to" is that this level of knowledge focuses on how to use codes (e.g., to get at puzzles) to achieve certain ends (e.g., understanding an informant's worldview).[8]

In a similar vein, scholars have also explored how to think about coding as a series of "actions in movements" including "making codes," "organizing to code," and "putting patterns together" (Locke et al., 2022, pp. 272–273). These various moves do not indicate stages or phases that a coder undergoes in a linear fashion; rather, they delineate the various functions that coding entails. For example, making codes involves the crafting of the coding label itself and Locke et al. (2022) offer some ways in which researchers can go about fulfilling this function (e.g., drawing on data or literature, looking at and refining prior codes). Organizing to code involves preparing for a coding activity such as using the literature to narrow the focus of the research project. Finally, putting patterns together involves making connections within data, across data and the literature, or even across literatures (Locke et al., 2022, p. 273). Researchers enact these moves organically as they engage in data and extant literature; in this way, coding is never a mechanistic process whereby the same moves, moments, or coding activities are enacted in the same way across different projects. Rather, coding moves, moments, and activities are all customized to a specific research project.

As researchers move from basics about "how to code" such as code length and granularity to "how to think about coding," the boundaries between coding and analysis become blurrier. Indeed, the latter moves beyond the application of labels or categories to data. Although coding is only a part of analysis, this level of knowledge about coding reminds us that the two are inexorably intertwined and the distinctions are not clean and neat. However, analysis involves reflexive activities that transcend the coding process. If qualitative research is a translation process, coding is about understanding what has been said by looking at the words and phrases of the speaker. Analysis, however, involves the art of knowing the nuance and subtlety of the meanings behind the words.

LEVELS OF KNOWING: ANALYSIS

There are a wide variety of ways to analyze qualitative data (Pratt et al., 2022), including semiotics, phenology, narrative analysis, discourse analysis, case studies, grounded theory, and ethnography, to name a few. Analytic approaches differ by discipline, ontology, epistemology, as well as the extent to which they also include information on study design. To introduce both how qualitative analysis can be done and to provide a comparison for inducing some general principles of qualitative analysis, two prominent methods were chosen to review: (a) Spradley's (1979) ethnographic method and (b) grounded theory, largely from the perspective of Strauss and Corbin (1998).[9]

"How to" Knowledge About Analysis: Ethnography. Spradley's (1979) ethnographic approach involves grounding one's analysis in the distinctive language of one's informants. His approach involves three distinct types of analyses: domain, taxonomic, and componential. These analyses must be done in this order as later analyses build on the previous ones. In this way, ethnographic analysis is perhaps more structured than grounded theory (see "'How to' Knowledge About Analysis: Grounded Theory"). However, both follow a similar logic of abstracting up from codes that begin very close to the data.

The domain analysis compares different names or labels that informants use in terms of their semantic relationships. Semantic relationships might involve inclusion, function, cause–effect, or more (see Spradley, 1979, p. 11). An illustration of a domain analysis can be found in Figure 2. The semantic relationship illustrated in this figure is inclusion ("is a type of"). The point of this analysis was to identify all of the Amway terms (i.e., the "included terms") that referred distributors, which is the overarching "cover term." As Figure 2 illustrates, there are many terms in Amway that could be included as a type of distributor, including someone who

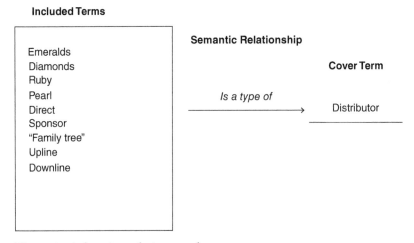

Figure 2. A domain analysis example.

is a sponsor, who is an "emerald," and who is part of one's "downline." The goal of a domain analysis is to get a broad understanding of the "cultural scene" and to begin to understand the categories one's informants use in describing this scene. As the analysis continues, one begins to fill out these categories.

The next step of analysis (which follows from asking informants to expand on what one has learned via "structural" questions) digs deeper into a category to better specify how various parts of a category relate to the whole. For example, returning to the cover term of "distributors," one could explore how different types of distributors relate to each other. From a taxonomic standpoint, distributors can be sorted as active, inactive (not currently building their Amway business), or former (also referred to as "losers"). An example of a taxonomic analysis can be found in Figure 3. As indicated, in comparing Figures 2 and 3, as one changes the focus of one's analysis, some terms may drop out and some may be added.

By sorting terms into "buckets," a taxonomic analysis shows that even among the domain of distributors, there are many different types. But this analysis does not comprehensively explore these differences, which is the purpose of a third type of analysis: componential. To conduct a componential analysis of distributors, one would start by more deeply linking different distributors to one's larger group of codes, such as activities. For example, active distributors listen to Amway books and tapes and listen to their upline sponsors (more senior distributors). An illustration of this step of the analysis can be found in Figure 4.

For a complete componential analysis, however, one would need to do a similar analysis of both former and inactive distributors and then compare all three. Table 2 shows what a more complete componential analysis might look like. Contrast is indicated by bold versus regular font. This pattern of results highlights where key differences are among the distributor types.[10] For example, former distributors differed from active and inactive distributors in that the latter listened to Amway books and tapes, listened to their upline, and did not engage in "stinkin' thinkin'" (harbor negative thoughts). Taken together, it suggests that former distributors did

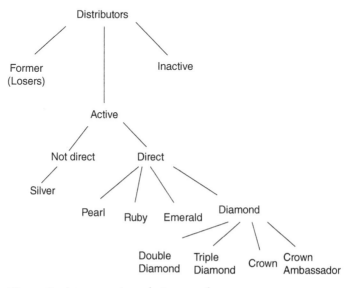

Figure 3. A taxonomic analysis example.

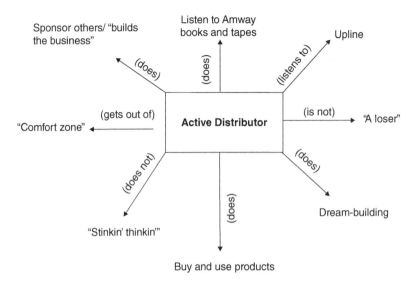

Figure 4. A partial componential analysis example.

not engage in many of the activities related to "positive programming" whereas other distributors did. By contrast, inactive distributors differed from both active and former distributors in that the latter engaged in dream-building activities. Dream-building involves goal-setting whereby distributors personalize large goals (e.g., buy a certain type of car) to motivate them to build their Amway business. Dream-building results in individuals not feeling good about who they are now, which came to be understood as a type of sensebreaking (Pratt, 2000a). Finally, active distributors differ from both former and inactive distributors in that they were able to get out of their comfort zone and engaged in both dream-building and positive programming.

From this analysis, it is not a huge leap to arrive at the figure that was published in Pratt (2000a). The original model is represented in Figure 5. Looking straight across, active members were involved in dream-building (sensebreaking) and positive programming (sensegiving) and thus bought into Amway's worldview in its entirety and positively identified with Amway (i.e., saw Amway as a large part of how they defined themselves). By not engaging in dream-building, inactive distributors never felt they needed to improve or change so didn't build their businesses, but liked the people in Amway and listened to Amway's messaging (i.e., positive programming). Because of the strong messages from their Amway upline about building their business, inactive distributors often felt some guilt in not being "better distributors" and thus came to a push-pull attachment to Amway referred to as ambivalent identification. Finally, those who quit Amway believed that they could be better than they were (due to successful sensebreaking) but did not trust Amway distributors or Amway-related sources to help them out. As a result, they came to hate Amway (i.e., disidentified). A fuller discussion of moving from coding and analysis in this model can be found in "'How to' Knowledge: Moving From Understanding Informants' Worldviews to Constructing Theory."

"How to" Knowledge About Analysis: Grounded Theory. There are many published explanations of how to do grounded theory, so this section will be brief (see Charmaz, 2014;

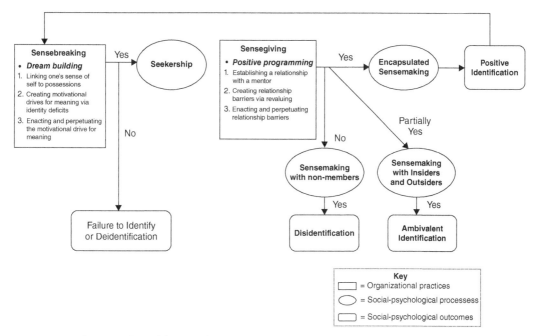

Figure 5. A theoretical model example.
Source: Pratt (2000a).

Glaser, 1992; Glaser & Strauss, 1967; Locke, 2001; Strauss & Corbin, 1998). Although there are different varieties of grounded theory, the approach tends to involve three overlapping and iterative phases that revolve around three different types of coding: open, axial or focused, and selective. Open coding helps the researcher get an initial sense of their informants' worldview and is done "close to the data": it should not reflect researchers' expectations or use abstract theoretical terms. To help minimize their preconceptions, researchers should engage in bracketing, whereby they "work to surface and examine our biases and pre-existing theoretical commitments specifically so that they can be 'bracketed' out" (Locke, 2001, p. 46).

The examples in Table 1 illustrate open coding. Open codes may be in-vivo codes such as "half a couple" or can utilize language in the common vernacular. For example, one can code "Amway friends" and "non-Amway friends" without referring to broader theoretical constructs like "relational ties." Open coding is complemented by the noncoding technique of "memoing" whereby the researcher writes notes reflecting on the codes and how they might relate to each other (e.g., are they in the same category with certain properties or do they vary along certain dimensions?).[11] This comparison of codes to previous ones and mapping out their relationships, known as the constant comparative method, occurs throughout each phase of grounded theory (Glaser & Strauss, 1967). As open coding continues, the researcher will begin to identify not only categories from their data, but also subcategories.

The second part of grounded theorizing involves abstracting up from data fragments to create broader concepts. As Locke (2001) notes, there is a shift here from comparing fragments of data to each other toward comparing fragments of data to concepts. Strauss and Corbin (1998) refer to this part of the analysis as axial coding. In axial coding, one compares

Table 2. A Complete Componential Analysis

Contrast set	Dimensions of contrast							
	Sponsors others/"builds the business"	Listens to Amway books and tapes	Upline	"A loser"	Engages in team-building	Buys and uses products	Engages in stinkin' thinkin'	**Get out of "comfort zone"**
Active	**Does**	**Does**	**Listens to**	**Is not**	**Does**	Does	**Does not**	Does
Inactive	Does not	**Does occasionally**	**Listens to**	**Is not**	Does not	Does	**Does not**	**Does not**
Former	Some did, some did not	Did not	Distrusts	Is	**Did**	Did	Did	**Did not**

the properties and dimensions of concepts that were beginning to be articulated during open coding. Such comparisons may involve "questioning" one's data—by asking "why or how come, where, when, how, and with what results"—to better understand how concepts relate to each other in terms of structure and process (Strauss & Corbin, 1998, p. 127). Charmaz (2014) offers an alternative to this more structured approach in the second part of grounded theorizing which she refers to as focused coding. She sees using focused coding as a flexible means to "synthesize, analyze, and conceptualize larger segments of data" (Charmaz, 2014, p. 138). However, common to both approaches are abstracting from one's initial codes to create more abstract conceptualizations that reflect the voice of one's informants. Moreover, as with open coding, both axial and focused coding are done concurrently with memoing.

A third part of a grounded theory analysis is "selective coding" which is "the process of integrating and refining the theory" (Strauss & Corbin, 1998, p. 143). Although referred to as "coding," this part is more analytical than the previous two. For Strauss and Corbin (1998), one begins by identifying the central or core category which represents the main story or theme one wants to develop from the data. Returning to the Amway example, the central category here would be "types of identification." This central category organizes the rest of the data to explain why some people love, hate, are ambivalent, or never identify with being an Amway distributor. Not surprisingly, pinpointing a central category is difficult and may involve "trying on" a few of them to see which will work. Strauss and Corbin (1998) suggest different types of memoing (e.g., writing a storyline that represents one's data) are central to identifying the central category and eventually developing a theory. They also suggest reviewing old memos and reflecting on them throughout this process.

Once a general theory is sketched out, one needs to refine one's model. This involves, among other things, removing some categories and building up others. With regard to the former, landing on one's emerging theory will necessitate not using some of the categories or subcategories of codes that one has developed. To illustrate, focusing on identification in Figure 5 meant largely dropping codes around "prospecting" or recruiting new distributors. With regard to the latter, a researcher needs to "validate" their theory by ensuring that it reflects the raw data they have collected. In this process, a researcher may also find some categories and concepts are underdeveloped: that is, are not well-supported or validated by one's data. In this case, more data may need to be gathered or more analysis may need to be done to arrive at "theoretical saturation," which is "the point at which gathering more data about a theoretical category reveals no new properties nor yields any further theoretical insights about the emerging grounded theory" (Charmaz, 2014, p. 345).

When building new theory, Strauss and Corbin (1998) emphasize the importance of creating one's own concepts. They strongly advise against using extant literature to identify what is core to one's data as existing constructs are likely to be a poor fit with one's data. The analogy here is looking for a custom fit for a suit by picking one off a rack. However, to extend the analogy, the literature can help one decide the type of suit one wants to buy, even if one is not choosing something directly off the rack. Indeed, as long as one does not simply affix existing theory to one's data, existing literature can be helpful in figuring out how to position one's work to an academic audience. Although not discussing grounded theory, per se, Locke et al. (2022, p. 269) suggest three broad uses of theory when engaging in the analysis of data:

(a) the literature as a direct source of codes independent of engaging with the data, (b) the literature as a source of definitions and concepts that help delimit the field of/sensitize researchers to possibilities in their data, and (c) the literature as a source of ideas that researchers use to help make sense of and theorize about the categorization schemes in the project.

To wrap up this part of analysis, researchers may also check with one or more members of the community they studied to see if they find the theory recognizable. This process is also referred to as a type of "member check."[12] "Recognizable" is key in that one's theory may not reflect informants' own particular circumstances, and they may disagree with a researcher's interpretation of the data. Such disagreements may lead to fruitful conversations about what the researcher may have missed. Overall, informants should be able to see how the researcher might have come to the conclusions they have. One member of Amway noted when viewing an earlier version of Figure 5 that "I don't find it altogether flattering but I agree with it."

Although Strauss and Corbin (1998) do not offer many visuals to represent their various phases of analysis (cf., Corbin & Strauss, 2008), likely due to the relatively unstructured and iterative nature of grounded theory, Gioia et al. (2012) recommend that those engaging in grounded theory create a data structure. To provide a parallel to the various examples of ethnographic analyses in Figures 2–4 and Table 2, an example of a partial grounded theory data structure is illustrated in Figure 6.

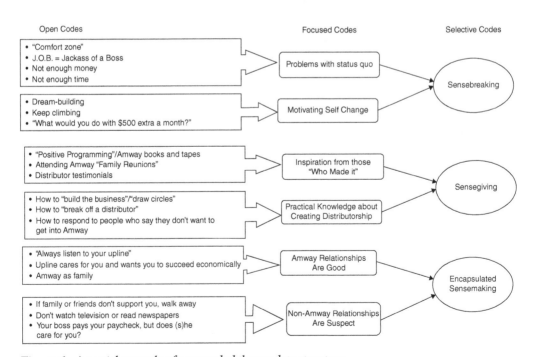

Figure 6. A partial example of a grounded theory data structure.

"How to" Knowledge: Moving From Understanding Informants' Worldviews to Constructing Theory. Both ethnography and grounded theory involve a movement from analysis to building theory. One could, for example, see similarities among the componential analysis of Table 2, the data structure of Figure 6, and the theoretical model of Figure 5. Yet the coding diagrams and structures are not the model. Indeed, there are a variety of judgments that go into how to order, link, and most broadly weave together a set of findings (parts) into a more comprehensive whole. There are a variety of analytical tools that can facilitate this transition. Although some of these tools are discussed in treatments of coding, this article separates them out here in the discussion of analysis as they extend beyond assigning a descriptive label to a piece of data.

Data reduction techniques are one such tool. Contact summary forms, for example (Miles et al., 2020), provide the researcher an opportunity to summarize in a page what they believe is most critical to a particular interview.[13] Unlike coding, especially initial coding, which breaks down meanings into very small chunks, contact summary forms allow the researcher to get at a more holistic view of a given interview, observation set, video segment, or the like. The term *summary* does not mean that one simply reduces what was said into a small number of words; rather, it is the place for a researcher to record themes that arose and identify what was interesting. Personally, the author often reviews his completed contact summary forms for a set of interviews (e.g., 10 or so) to have a broader sense of the data before breaking data down in initial coding. Alternatively, one may "try on" different theoretical lenses to see what new insights they evoke. Feldman (1995), for example, discusses the use of deconstruction, dramaturgy, ethnomethodology, and semiotics to structure analyses in such a way as to help guide interpretations of and facilitate discovery within her data (see also "metatheoretical analysis").

Another critical set of analytical tools are documents where one records ideas, hunches, and anything that comes to mind during coding and analysis—and even during data collection. In grounded theory this is known as memoing (Strauss & Corbin, 1998) but there is a similar practice in ethnography that involves taking field notes or keeping a field journal (see Emerson et al., 2011; Pratt & Sala, 2021; Spradley, 1979). Reflexive documents allow one to come into conversation with one's data in a more unstructured way and it may bring together not only data, but personal experiences, insights from conversations with others, ideas from existing literature, and more. To illustrate, creating a storyline memo about identification among distributors, which involves writing a long abstract of the central findings of one's data (Strauss & Corbin, 1998), was critical for understanding the process of identification management among distributors. The memo included the organization's attempts to engage in sensebreaking (invalidating one's identity) and sensegiving (providing needed information for making sense) and ultimately how distributors responded to these attempts via various forms of identification. Writing as a story where the organization acted and distributors reacted provided coherence among the various codes that had been created and served as the scaffolding for Figure 5.

Building on these sources, one should never forget the role of the researcher and the physical feelings that are elicited in their own bodies as one moves from coding structures to broader theorizing. Locke et al. (2008) suggest paying attention and even cultivating doubt to open a researcher up to new perspectives in their data. Such doubt may stem from possibly entering the field with preconceived notions that are not met or simply when one's own experiences seem at odds with that of one's informants. In addition to cultivating doubt, others discuss being open to "surprise" (Pratt, 2000a) or "discovery" (Locke et al., 2015) that may come from being perplexed by what one's data mean. Such doubt may also be facilitated by having a strong knowledge of existing research. This is not using the literature to explain one's data, but rather to question it. For example, with regard to the Amway example used throughout, one surprising finding early in the analysis process was that distributors used to make salient work–family conflicts. Indeed, they would remind distributors who were attending events that they left their children behind at home. This seemed counterintuitive with regard to existing research theorizing that organizations minimize such conflicts! However, this insight was important for better understanding the motivation for Amway distributors and led to an entirely different study of network marketing organizations (Pratt & Rosa, 2003).

Another tool for moving from coding to theorizing is the creation of artifacts such as figures or diagrams (Locke et al., 2022). To illustrate, as major concepts and categories are formed, a researcher might decide to write them each on a whiteboard and then play around with how they might relate to each other (e.g., Sala & Pratt, in press). In Figure 5, the storyline was how individuals reacted via different types of identification to different organizational practices. This action–reaction frame ordered the concepts in a specific way. However, if the author was interested in cocreation of identity, he might have instead paired certain individual and organizational concepts together (e.g., individual's life circumstances connected with organizational sense-breaking practices) before further ordering them. What is important here is to be clear what perceptually is figure and what is ground in your theorizing. In the Amway example, there are contributions to both identification and sensemaking. However, the author chose to view sensemaking in service of identification, thereby making identification figure and sensemaking ground. It would be a very different paper, and would be framed for a very different academic audience, if it was about how Amway influences sensemaking (sensemaking as figure), and one outcome happened to be identification (identification as ground).

How to Think About Analysis.   Looking at analyses from both ethnography and grounded theory suggests both a general logic as well as general practices regarding how to think about qualitative analyses. With regard to the former, inductive qualitative analyses involve understanding your informants' worldview and translating that understanding to build and improve academic theories. Understanding the worldview of your informants occurs in two steps. First, both domain analyses (ethnography) and open coding (grounded theory) involve in vivo coding and other ways of staying close to one's data. In this way, the researcher starts by understanding various "pieces" of the informant's worldview, similar to understanding the vocabulary of a language (see Figures 2 and 6). This phase of coding is critical as it provides the foundation for what follows.

Second, the researcher must understand how the pieces fit together. What are the "verbs" (processes and practices)? Who or what are the "subjects" of these verbs (e.g., a leader, a crisis) and what are the "objects" that are associated with them (e.g., outcomes)? This is largely the focus of a taxonomic analysis (ethnography), and begins in open coding and continues in axial or focused coding (grounded theory). But just as a string of sentences would not make a good translation, these understandings must cohere into a more holistic understanding of an informant's worldview. The sentence must become a story. More specifically, the researcher creates a "theory" that is about the context where the researcher gathered data (cf., "substantive theories"—Glaser & Strauss, 1967).

Once the worldview of the informant is well understood, the next step is to more fully engage with extant academic theory to begin translating your informant's worldview into new academic theory. To make this translation, however, means that the researcher must also be "fluent" in the theoretical area in which they would like to contribute. Continuing the Amway example, the author had to know about the different types of identification (Dukerich et al., 1998) and that no one had examined what organizational practices might be related to these different types. However, fluency will often need to extend beyond a specific theoretical area. To illustrate, understanding the relationship among the practices and different identification types meant delving into several other areas of research, including theories of goal-setting, extended self, identity-transforming organizations, social identity, conversion, sensemaking, socialization, as well as various types of "attachment" such as commitment and person–organization fit (Pratt, 2000a). Thus, although one "translates" into a general area of research, because of the "off the rack" nature of extant theorizing, customizing one's findings to craft new theory may involve understanding and borrowing from a much larger set of theories.

Another way to think about analysis is in terms of general practices. Central to inductive research is the interplay between concrete and abstract as well as parts and wholes. A cursory glance at both grounded theory and ethnography could lead one to the impression that there is a linear movement from concrete (e.g., in vivo codes) to the abstract (a theoretical model). However, viewing analysis in this way misses a fundamental part of it: the iterating among the concrete and the abstract (Locke et al., 2022). As one builds categories and taxonomies, for example, it is essential to go back to the data to see if these abstractions actually fit the data. Thus, there is a constant interweaving of concrete and abstract throughout the process.

Relatedly, another way to think about qualitative analysis is the movement between parts and wholes. Analysis involves trying to understand different fragments of informants' experiences and putting them together into a narrative or otherwise holistic understanding of their worldview. But again, this process is not linear. Getting a holistic understanding of data by data reduction, for example, may be followed with a very detailed understanding of data "parts" via the use of codes which are eventually compiled into a new whole, which is validated (or not) by going back to the parts, which can lead to a new sense of the whole, and so on. This process is dynamic, and neither parts nor wholes are fixed. Similarly, as one translates into academic language, there is a need to both connect with specific theories, but also create a new theoretical whole that resonates with one's data and both connects to but is different from the component theories.

When viewed in light of this common logic and these practices, some common pitfalls for analysis become apparent. First, sometimes inductive researchers get criticized for simply "finding what they are looking for" and not really being inductive (Pratt & Bonaccio, 2016). This problem would result if researchers spent too little time understanding their informants' worldview and moved too quickly to extant research. A similar problem is engaging in theoretical description. Here, the issue is less that the researcher had a preconceived notion of what they would find, but rather they end up strongly favoring extant theorizing to explain what they found and drowning out informants' voices. Theoretical description can also occur when an analysis has not moved enough from parts to wholes. Indeed, noting how multiple findings might be predicted by several extant theories would be missing the whole. To illustrate the difference between theoretical description and building theory, one could look at

Figure 5. If the author stopped by equating dream-building with certain theories like the extended self and goal-setting theory in steps 1–3, that would be theoretical description. However, seeing how the various theoretical insights work together to create "sensebreaking" or a fundamental challenging of who one is (Pratt, 2000a, p. 464) was critical for building new theory.

Another analytical problem is "reinventing the wheel." Here, extant theory is given too little weight, and as a result, data are used to create a theory that essentially already exists. To illustrate, a former student of mine was going through his data and proudly announced that he had a huge insight. It was a study of rural doctors, some of whom had joined larger managed care organizations and others who decided to remain independent. There was a lot of anger among those who did not "sell out" (in their words) to the larger managed care organization toward those physicians who did. My student said that based on the data, those physicians who decided to stay independent came to view themselves as a group or community and they lumped all of those doctors who did not together as enemies. What he said was true to the data, but unfortunately, he had just rediscovered ingroup–outgroup bias! Readers (such as reviewers) will likely pick up on this pitfall and ask how the findings from the study are different from what is already known. Of course, these pitfalls are posed in relatively extreme terms and the balance between honoring the wisdom of one's informants and the wisdom of the extant theory is difficult in practice. What is critical is that the researcher does not see this as an "either/or" problem but honors both.

LOST IN TRANSLATION? HOW DO RESEARCHERS KNOW WHEN THEY'VE DONE IT RIGHT?

The "Introduction" began by viewing coding and analysis as a translation process. To close, the notion of what a "good" translation is will be briefly addressed. It is only briefly addressed as treatments of what a good qualitative analysis is could be (and have been) the topic of entire papers and at least parts of books. What makes for a good translation is currently contested in the field, as is how to refer to good qualitative research (e.g., rigorous, trustworthy, convincing). That said, scholars appear to range along a continuum of appropriate standards for assessing good qualitative research: at one end is "similar to quantitative, positive research" and at the other is "unique to qualitative research."

Some believe that a good qualitative analysis should echo the same criteria used by quantitative researchers. For example, Yin (2003) uses analogs to construct validity, internal validity, external validity, and reliability when discussing how to assess the "goodness" of a qualitative analysis. Lincoln and Guba (1985) take a more interpretivist stance but echo these criteria by eliciting standards of credibility, transferability, dependability, and confirmability. Each of these criteria are summarized, defined, and illustrated in Table 3 (see also Pratt et al., 2020).

At the other end of the continuum is the belief that qualitative research is different enough from quantitative research that it should be held to a different set of standards. However, there is yet to be consensus on just what those standards should be. As noted in Table 3, some scholars suggest criteria that are unique to specific types of qualitative research, such as ethnography or process-oriented research (Gehman et al., 2018; Langley, 1999; Locke & Golden-Biddle, 1997). Most recently, Grodal et al. (2021) suggest that qualitative research can be made more

Table 3. Different Criteria for Establishing Trustworthiness in Qualitative Research

Position and key source	Characteristic	Defining questions	Illustrative practices
Naturalistic inquiry (Lincoln & Guba, 1985)	Credibility	To what degree has the investigator given voice to the different constructions of reality found in one's data? Credibility is assessed by those one has studied.	"Prolonged engagement" (p. 301); "persistent observation" (p. 304); triangulation (e.g., different data sources, methods, investigators, etc.); "peer debriefing" (p. 308); "negative case analysis" (p. 309); "referential adequacy" (p. 313); "member checks" (p. 314)
	Transferability	Is there contextual similarity between the context one is studying and other contexts? The burden of proof regarding such a comparison lies with those who want to compare findings to other contexts more than it is with the original investigator.	Providing a lot of details (e.g., thick description) to "show," not "tell," the reader the findings
	Dependability	Has the investigator taken into account "both factors of instability and factors of phenomenal or design induced change"? (p. 299)	All the practices of credibility plus "stepwise replication" within the dataset (p. 317) and "inquiry audit" (p. 317)
	Confirmability	Was there a process for verifying the data? Confirmability is a characteristic of the data, not the investigator.	Inquiry audit; triangulation; "reflexive journal"; "audit trail" (p. 319); "audit process" (p. 320)
Case studies/ positivism (Yin, 2003)	Construct validity	Can the data be verified? This is a quality of the data, not the investigator.	"Use multiple sources of evidence; establish a chain of evidence; have key informants review draft" (p. 34)
	Internal validity	Is there a causal relationship between variables or constructs?	"Do pattern-matching; do explanation-building; address rival explanations; use logic models" (p. 34)
	External validity	Can findings be generalized and to what domain?	"Use theory in single-case studies; use replication logic in multiple case studies" (p. 34)
	Reliability	Can it be replicated across cases in the study?	"Use case study protocol; develop case study database" (p. 34)

(Continued)

322 • GENERAL CODING AND ANALYSIS IN QUALITATIVE RESEARCH

Table 3. Continued

Position and key source	Characteristic	Defining questions	Illustrative practices
Ethnographic[a] (Locke & Golden-Biddle, 1997)	Authenticity	Communicating that the author was in the field and did not do violence to the experience of the informants	"Particularizing everyday life" (p. 601); "delineating the relationship in the field" (p. 603); "depicting the disciplined pursuit and analysis of data" (p. 604); "qualifying personal biases" (p. 605)
	Plausibility	Does the academic audience "buy" it in that it (a) makes sense and (b) makes a contribution? (p. 600)	"Normalizing unorthodox methodologies" (p. 605); "drafting the reader" (p. 606); "legitimizing the atypical" (p. 606); "smoothing the contestable" (p. 608); "differentiating findings—a singular contribution" (p. 609); "building dramatic anticipation" (p. 610)
	Criticality	Does the study make the author rethink their assumptions about the field or their own work?	"Carving out room to reflect" (p. 610); "provoking the recognition and examination of differences" (p. 610); "imagining new possibilities" (p. 611)
Process research[b] (Gehman et al., 2018; Langley, 1999)	Longitudinal data	Have you studied things over time?	Showing that your data fit with the timespan of the examined process; interviewing people about factual events if being retrospective or in real time if trying to understand how individuals' interpretation of events evolve; using one or a combination of different analytical strategies: narrative, quantification; attend to risk of retrospective reconstruction
Pratt et al. (2022)	Competence	Has the researcher demonstrated knowledge of various analytic moves and has used them well?	Appropriate citing of methodological sources; detailed description of data sources and why they were gathered; provide rationale for analytic choices

Table 3. Continued

Position and key source	Characteristic	Defining questions	Illustrative practices
	Integrity	Do the various analytical moves fit together?	Coherence between research question and design such as using a longitudinal design and/or timeline for process theorizing; coherence between research question and sampling, such as sampling for different attachment types when exploring identification
	Benevolence	Has the researcher maintained fidelity to their data? Has the researcher done "violence to experience"?	Long time in the field; using raw data rather than just explanations of the data; gathered data from different groups in order to get multiple perspectives; noting surprises that arise in analysis

Note: [a] It is important to note that Locke and Golden-Biddle (1997) are arguing why ethnographic work is convincing, not trustworthy. Their arguments are included here in this table as they are about what makes for good qualitative research.

[b] Langley does not use the term *trustworthiness* in her descriptions but does lay out the fundamentals of process research.

Source: Adapted and expanded from Pratt et al. (2020).

rigorous by better incorporating insights from categorization research and provide several categorization moves. Pratt et al. (2022) also take a general approach to qualitative methods and offer analytical moves that communicate to readers a sense of trustworthiness by demonstrating competence, integrity, and benevolence (see Table 3). Building on qualitative papers published in top journals, they provide several examples of how different moves can be used to show each. They are clear to point out, however, that the specific moves that are to be used to show trustworthiness—and the degree to which one relies most heavily on competence, benevolence, or integrity moves—will depend on the scholar's research question.

One should not take a lack of consensus on standards for good qualitative research as meaning "anything goes." Rather it is incumbent on the researcher to argue which standards they have applied and why they have done so. One's standards will depend on one's analytical approach (and one's ontological stance on that approach) and the specifics of the scholar's research project. Moreover, as with a good translation, good qualitative research will respect the voices of one's informants and be generous when contributing to extant research.

ACKNOWLEDGMENTS

I would like to thank Martha Feldman, Karen Locke, Kevin Rockmann, and an anonymous reviewer for their comments on an earlier draft of this article.

REFERENCES

Alvesson, M., & Sandberg, J. (2013). *Constructing research questions: Doing interesting research*. SAGE.

Atkinson, R. (1998). *The life story interview*. SAGE.

Basit, T. (2003). Manual or electronic? The role of coding in qualitative data analysis. *Educational Research*, 45(2), 143–154. https://doi.org/10.1080/0013188032000133548

Behfar, K., & Okhuysen, G. A. (2018). Perspective—Discovery within validation logic: Deliberately surfacing, complementing, and substituting abductive reasoning in hypothetico-deductive inquiry. *Organization Science*, 29(2), 323–340.

Blair, E. (2015). A reflexive exploration of two qualitative data coding techniques. *Journal of Methods and Measurement in the Social Sciences*, 6(1), 14–29. https://doi.org/10.2458/v6i1.18772

Bowen, G. A. (2006). Grounded theory and sensitizing concepts. *International Journal of Qualitative Methods*, 5(3), 12–23.

Charmaz, K. (2014). *Constructing grounded theory* (2nd ed.). SAGE.

Corbin, J., & Strauss, A. (2008). *Basics of qualitative research* (3rd ed.). SAGE.

Creswell, J. W., & Creswell, J. D. (2018). *Research design qualitative: Quantitative and mixed methods approaches* (5th ed.). SAGE.

Dukerich, J., Kramer, R. M., & Parks, J. M. (1998). The dark side of identification. In D. Whetten & P. Godrey (Eds.), *Identity in organizations: Developing theory through conversations* (pp. 245–256). SAGE.

Eisenhardt, K. (2020). What is the Eisenhardt method, really? *Strategic Organization*, 19(1), 147–160. https://journals.sagepub.com/doi/10.1177/1476127020982866

Elliott, V. (2018). Thinking about the coding process in qualitative data analysis. *The Qualitative Report*, 23(11), 2850–2861. https://www.proquest.com/docview/2155621346?pq-origsite=gscholar&fromopenview=true

Emerson, R. M., Fretz, R. I., & Shaw, L. L. (2011). *Writing ethnographic fieldnotes* (2nd ed.). University of Chicago Press.

Feldman, M. (1995). *Strategies for interpreting qualitative data*. SAGE.

Gehman, J., Glaser, V. L., Eisenhardt, K. M., Gioia, D., Langley, A., & Corley, K. G. (2018). Finding theory–method fit: A comparison of three qualitative approaches to theory building. *Journal of Management Inquiry*, 27(3), 284–300.

Gioia, D. A., Corley, K. G., & Hamilton, A. L. (2012). Organizational research. *Organizational Research Methods*, 16(1), 15–31.

Glaser, B. G. (1992). *Basics of grounded theory analysis*. Sociology Press.

Glaser, B. G., & Strauss, A. L. (1967). *The discovery of grounded theory: Strategies for qualitative research*. Aldine De Gruyter.

Grodal, S., Anteby, M., & Holm A. (2021). Achieving rigor in qualitative analysis: The role of active categorization in theory building. *Academy of Management Review*, 46(3), 591–612. https://doi.org/10.5465/amr.2018.0482

Langley, A. (1999). Strategies for theorizing from process data. *Academy of Management Review*, 24(4), 691–710.

Lincoln, Y. S., & Guba, E. G. (1985). *Naturalistic inquiry*. SAGE.

Linnenberg, M. S., & Korsgaard, S. (2019). Coding qualitative data: A synthesis guiding the novice. *Qualitative Research Journal*, 19(3), 259–270. https://doi.org/10.1108/QRJ-12-2018-0012

Locke, K. (2001). *Grounded theory in management research*. SAGE.

Locke, K., Feldman, M., & Golden-Biddle, K. (2015). Discovery, validation, and live coding. In K. Elsbach & R. Kramer (Eds.), *Handbook of qualitative organizational research* (pp. 371–380). Routledge.

Locke, K., Feldman, M., & Golden-Biddle, K. (2022). Coding practices and iterativity: Beyond templates for analyzing qualitative data. *Organizational Research Methods*, 25(2), 262–284. https://doi.org/10.1177/1094428120948600

Locke, K., & Golden-Biddle, K. (1997). Constructing opportunities for contribution: Structuring intertextual coherence and "problematizing" in organizational studies. *Academy of Management Journal, 40*(5), 1023–1062.

Locke, K., Golden-Biddle, K., & Feldman, M. S. (2008). Perspective—Making doubt generative: Rethinking the role of doubt in the research process. *Organization Science, 19*(6), 907–918.

Marshall, C., & Rossman, G. (1999). *Designing qualitative research* (3rd ed.). SAGE.

Miles, M. B., Huberman, A. M., & Saldaña, J. (2020). *Qualitative data analysis: A methods sourcebook* (4th ed.). SAGE.

Pratt, M. G. (2000a). The good, the bad, and the ambivalent: Managing identification among Amway distributors. *Administrative Science Quarterly, 45*(3), 456–493.

Pratt, M. G. (2000b). Building an ideological fortress: The role of spirituality, encapsulation, and sensemaking. *Studies in Cultures, Organizations and Societies, 6*(1), 35–69.

Pratt, M. G. (2008). Fitting oval pegs into round holes: Tensions in evaluating and publishing qualitative research in top-tier North American journals. *Organizational Research Methods, 11*(3), 481–509.

Pratt, M. G. (2016). Crafting and selecting research questions and contexts in qualitative research. In K. Elsbach & R. Kramer (Eds.), *The handbook of qualitative organizational research* (pp. 177–185). Taylor & Francis.

Pratt, M. G., & Bonaccio, S. (2016). Qualitative research in I/O psychology: Myths, maps and moving forward. *Industrial and Organizational Psychology: Perspectives on Science and Practice, 94*(4), 693–715.

Pratt, M. G., Kaplan, S., & Whittington, R. (2020). Editorial essay: The tumult over transparency: Decoupling transparency from replication in establishing trustworthy qualitative research. *Administrative Science Quarterly, 65*(1), 1–19.

Pratt, M. G., & Rosa, J. A. (2003). Transforming work-family conflict into commitment in network marketing organizations. *Academy of Management Journal, 46*(4), 395–418.

Pratt, M. G., & Sala, G. R. (2021). A researcher's toolkit for observational methods. *Oxford Research Encyclopedia of Business and Management.* https://doi.org/10.1093/acrefore/9780190224851.013.283

Pratt, M. G., Sonenshein, S., & Feldman, M. S. (2022). Moving beyond templates: A bricolage approach to conducting trustworthy qualitative research. *Organizational Research Methods, 25*(2), 211–238.

Sala, G. R., & Pratt, M. G. (In-press). How organizations influence interpersonal trust repair: The case of a French antiterrorist unit. *Academy of Management Journal.* https://doi.org/10.5465/amj.2020.1093

Saldaña, J. (2021). *The coding manual for qualitative researchers* (4th ed.). SAGE.

Spradley, J. P. (1979). *The ethnographic interview.* Holt, Rinehart and Winston.

Strauss, A., & Corbin, J. (1998). *Basics of qualitative research: Techniques and procedures for developing grounded theory* (2nd ed.). SAGE.

Timmermans, S., & Tavory, I. (2012). Theory construction in qualitative research: From grounded theory to abductive analysis. *Sociological Theory, 30*(3), 167–186.

Yin, R. (2003). *Case study research: Design and methods* (3rd ed.). SAGE.

NOTES

1. Unless otherwise specified, the discussion of coding and analysis will pertain to inductive or at least abductive qualitative research rather than deductive qualitative research.
2. For a thoughtful discussion of abduction and its broader role in research, see Behfar and Okhuysen (2018).
3. Sampling using contrasts is similar to analytical moves in the Eisenhardt method (Eisenhardt, 2020).
4. Most qualitative approaches suggest early engagement with the data in some form (e.g., taking field notes), although one must always take care to not narrow your interpretations too early in the data collection process.

5. Coders may struggle with the decision about whether to code their data manually or use a Computer Aided Qualitative Data Analysis Software (CAQDAS). This decision may be influenced by many factors, including the amount of data one has as well as one's experience and comfort with either practice. A researcher may also use a mixed approach such as starting coding by hand and moving to CAQDAS to help store and recall codes. A thoughtful discussion of this decision can be found in Saldaña (2021). It is important to note that, at least for now (and perhaps barring new advances in artificial intelligence), coding always involves judgments of the researcher.

6. Most qualitative approaches suggest early engagement with the data in some form (e.g., taking field notes), although one must always take care to not narrow your interpretations too early in the data collection process.

7. This tension may be more central to some forms of coding than others. For example, complaints about being overloaded with codes are common when using grounded theory.

8. It is important to note that some treatments of coding do blend both types of knowledge. Saldaña (2021), for example, does not just stick to mechanics, but also discusses "how to think about" coding knowledge. For example, he distinguishes between "lumping" and "splitting," whereby coding can also be used to capture the holistic essence of a relatively large segment or to break down and analyze smaller segments of data (see Table 1 for examples).

9. Anselm Strauss and Juliet Corbin have several editions of the same book beyond this one. This particular edition, however, focused more squarely on coding and analytic procedures than some later editions (e.g., Corbin & Strauss, 2008).

10. It is important to start by what did not distinguish among the distributors, which was buying and using products. This was not surprising because in order to be a distributor at any point, one needed to at least buy Amway products.

11. In exploring how codes relate to each other, researchers will explore both similarities and differences. Thus, grounded theory is different from Spradley's (1979) ethnographic analysis where differences are only systematically explored later in the analysis (via a componential analysis).

12. In addition to sharing theory (or theoretical models) with members, member checks may also involve sharing the transcript of an interview—or sharing quotes or excerpts of data that will be used in a publication—with the interviewee. However, the purpose of these is to check on the accuracy of the quotes or transcript, not to check the interpretation of these data.

13. Contact summary forms are not traditionally part of either grounded theory or ethnography.

Michael G. Pratt

The Environment
of Organizations

INDUSTRIAL AND ORGANIZATIONAL PSYCHOLOGY FROM A GLOBAL PERSPECTIVE

INTRODUCTION

In the first two decades of the 21st century, industrial-organizational psychology has become a field of global science. As globalization accelerates, worldwide enterprises, labor, and business are increasingly connected, and scientific knowledge of management and workplace psychology is also boosted for the globalizing business. As pointed out by Ones et al. (2015, p. xxv), "IWO (industrial, work, and organizational) research is not solely conducted and published by those in North America and Europe. Knowledge is generated, replicated, and disseminated worldwide." Indeed, the globalization trend in both the business world and the research community has witnessed the generation of new scientific knowledge in industrial-organizational psychology.

While globalization, as a complex process, has been defined in different ways across disciplines, the commonality is that globalization refers to the processes through which different parts of the world connect in various dimensions, including economy, politics, communication, physical environment, and culture (Beck, 2018; Tomlinson, 1999). The globalizing scientific research in the field of industrial-organizational psychology, as a microcosm of globalization, is rooted in the globalization of business, labor, and researchers.

First, economics and business activities are becoming more global. In the second decade of the 21st century, more than 82,000 MNEs (multinational enterprises) manage at least 810,000 subsidiaries overseas, and the 500 largest MNEs have an annual sale of about one-third of the global output (Peng, 2016). In particular, the past 20 years have seen dramatic growth in emerging markets (or developing countries), such as Brazil, Russia, India, China, and South Africa (BRICS), where many business opportunities are attracting investors worldwide. Undoubtedly, international business has become an important part of the global economy.

Second, the labor force supply is increasingly global. For example, expatriates and expatriate managers are no longer rare occupations (Takeuchi et al., 2005, 2009, 2019; van der Laken et al., 2019; Wang & Takeuchi, 2007). International assignment of employees has become an increasingly used human resource management (HRM) practice for multinational organizations to enhance organizational effectiveness. In addition, the increasing usage of information technology has enabled global information sharing for worldwide workers. In 2021, the number of Internet users reached more than 5 billion, which represented more than 65% of the global population (Internet World Stats, 2022). The widespread digital technology united global workers and created new ways of international communication and cooperation (Colbert et al., 2016).

Third, although the overrepresentation of Western and industrialized countries persists, industrial-organizational psychology is also experiencing a globalization trend. In the 21st century, researchers from many areas and regions of the world conduct research in the field of industrial-organizational psychology. It is fair to say that the current industrial-organizational psychology research community is becoming increasingly international, and the knowledge creation process involves an interplay between the global research community and global organizations. Insights from the international academic community, especially under-representative countries and regions, are important to reverse the POSH bias (i.e., "Professionals who hold Official jobs in a formal economy and who enjoy relative Safety from discrimination while also living in High-income countries"; Gloss et al., 2017, p. 329) in I-O psychology. Therefore, to embark on unbiased, humanistic, and practically important findings under the context of globalization, the current trend for I-O psychology to become more globalized and unbiased should be further encouraged.

With the globalization background, several streams of research in industrial-organizational psychology are worth noting. First, an emerging body of studies is focused on the usage of new technology and the development of new economic forms that are changing the global workforce. It is time for both researchers and practitioners to refresh their understanding of employees in the workplace. Second, the knowledge about HRM practices is being updated for globalizing business. For the success of global organizations, it is crucial to have effective HRM through recruitment, selection, training, and performance management. Third, in a globalized and cross-cultural setting, diversity-related challenges and solutions have drawn much attention. To make the workplace inclusive for employees from all over the world, it is important to understand the cross-cultural differences and diversity of their backgrounds as well as to initiate workplace inclusion practices (Li, Kleshinski, et al., 2021).

CHANGING GLOBAL WORKFORCE: DIGITAL WORKERS, NEW ECONOMY, AND GLOBAL UNCERTAINTY

Rapid globalization is witnessing several dramatic changes that are happening to the global workforce and their managers: (a) the development of digital technology and the changing nature of work in global organizations; (b) new economic forms (e.g., platform economy, gig economy, and knowledge economy); and (c) the threats and opportunities to workers and managers in a world with increasing global uncertainty.

Digital Workforce. Digital technology has become more accessible to the global population in the past 20 years. From 2000 to 2021, the number of Internet users has grown by more than 13 times, reaching more than 5 billion users, covering more than 65% of the global population (Internet World Stats, 2022). It is worth noting that though Western developed countries have a higher penetration rate of Internet usage (e.g., 94% for North America and 88% for Europe in 2021), other non-Western countries grow faster in their Internet coverage. From 2000 to 2021, the number of Internet users grew by more than 23 times in Asia, more than 26 times in Latin America, and more than 59 times in the Middle East (Internet World Stats, 2022). With the popularization of the Internet, the usage of emails, smartphones, and social media has changed people's lives and work globally (Colbert et al., 2016).

Further, the tremendous development of artificial intelligence (AI) has made it possible to apply many AI-based technology or tools in global organizations, such as autonomous vehicles, smart robotics, and virtual agents (McKinsey Global Institute, 2017). These applications have become visible in various industries such as high tech/telecom, automotive/assembly, financial services, retail, media/entertainment, education, health care, and tourism, especially in North America, Asia, and Europe (McKinsey Global Institute, 2017; Popkova & Parakhina, 2018; Soni et al., 2020).

It is not difficult to realize that the popularity of digital technology and the increasing usage of AI are changing the global workforce into a "digital workforce" (Colbert et al., 2016). The increasing usage of information technology is changing the nature of work and the methods of completing work tasks considerably. Briggs and Makice (2012) proposed the concept of "digital fluency" to describe workers' proficiency and comfort in achieving desired outcomes using technology. Digital equipment (e.g., computers/laptops, smartphones) and digital applications (e.g., virtual meetings, emails, and social media) have become so prevalent that they are frequently used in employees' daily working routines (Colbert et al., 2016). In addition, AI-based tools are increasingly utilized in the workplace to facilitate human work (Tang et al., 2021). For instance, AI-based tools and big data have been used for human resources management (HRM) such as personnel selection and performance evaluations (Oswald et al., 2020). AI has also been considered promising for organizational decision-making and problem-solving (Von Krogh, 2018).

The availability of digital technology also deepened the process of globalization by promoting the global divisions of labor and global business cooperation. For example, outsourcing a business function or an organizational fragmentation to the workers in another country (i.e., hiring call center representatives from another country with lower human cost) becomes easier with information and communication technology (ICT), which provides a different possible approach for multinational enterprises' (MNE) economic activities (Buckley &

Strange, 2015). Indeed, it is quite convenient for members of global virtual teams across different time zones to collaborate by using information technologies such as videoconferencing, email, decision support software, and shareware (Maynard et al., 2012).

There is no doubt that the development of digital technology has increased workers' productivity all over the world. However, the dramatic global change in digital technologies also brings some challenges to workers, managers, and policymakers. For example, the speed of global technological development varies, which may lead to inequality in the global distribution of income (Buckley & Strange, 2015). Further, the digital job requirement also puts the "digital natives" (i.e., a generation of young people born in the digital age) at an advantage over the "digital immigrants" (i.e., an older generation who learned to use computers in adult life; Prensky, 2001; Wang et al., 2013), which may lead to age discrimination toward the older workers in the workplace. Further, the recent development of AI has raised the debate of whether human jobs will be completely replaced by AI ("automation," as compared to "augmentation," which means humans collaborate closely with machines to perform a task; Raisch & Krakowski, 2021). Though there are occupational and industrial differences (Felten et al., 2021), employees' fear that their jobs could be replaced by AI has been found to increase their depression and cynicism, especially for older workers (Brougham & Haar, 2018). Moreover, the increasing use of the Internet and mobile technologies blurs the work–life boundary, which can be harmful to employees' well-being (Nam, 2014).

New Forms of Economy. Coupled with the increasing usage of digital technologies, another significant change for the global workforce is the various new forms of economy. Related to the development of technology, knowledge workers who "think for a living" are recognized as critical for organizational productivity (Davenport, 2005; Dekas et al., 2013). As the society transforms into post-industrial states where industrial production and business activities shift from manual to non-manual, knowledge work characterized by the processing of non-routine problems and creative thinking has received great attention from both managers and researchers (Reinhardt et al., 2011).

In addition to the broader trend of the development of knowledge economy and knowledge workers, other new forms of economy are also emerging in the global market. For example, the "gig economy" has emerged as a modern employment practice. The "gig economy" is defined as "people using apps to sell their labor" (Taylor et al., 2017, p. 25). Although the absolute number of workers in the gig economy remains small (e.g., 4.4% of adults in Great Britain in 2017; Lepanjuuri et al., 2018), this new form of economy has implications for the future form of work for humans, characterized with fragmented work and increasing casualization (Wood et al., 2019). Related to but different from the "gig economy," the digital platform-based economy is also emerging and covers an increasing share of economic and societal activities. Digital platforms, such as Amazon, Facebook, Google, Instagram, and YouTube, make it easier to build a business and earn income (Cutolo & Kenney, 2020). At the same time, it is also changing the ways in which workers are connected with the organization and external customers (Cutolo & Kenney, 2020; Tschang, 2021). Further, the "sharing economy," such as Airbnb, Uber, and TaskRabbit, also is developing rapidly (Gerwe & Silva, 2020), changing the traditional understanding of the nature of work.

Workers and Managers Under Global Uncertainty. Despite the development of information technology and the emerging new forms of economy, the global workforce is also under a dark cloud of increasing global uncertainty. The once-in-a-century pandemic has caused a widespread economic, societal, and political mess for global production and global cooperation (Phan, 2021). For example, COVID-19-related events have been found to increase employees' perceived job insecurity (i.e., employees' subjective perceptions of threats to the continuity and stability of their current employment) and lead to employees' emotional exhaustion and organizational deviance (Lin et al., 2021). Similarly, consuming news information has been found to induce a feeling of uncertainty that will further harm employees' daily goal progress and creativity (Yoon et al., 2021). In addition to the threats of COVID-19 itself to employees, a series of societal and economic impacts are also transmitted to the global workforce. Restricted travel, mobility regulations, and lockdowns of economy have a devastating impact on the global economy and the globalization process (Shrestha et al., 2020). The COVID-19 pandemic and relevant reactions of individuals and organizations might have long-lasting influences on globalization. On the one hand, communication technologies spawned in the pandemic can benefit post-COVID globalization. For example, adjustments for remote work (e.g., virtual meetings and flexible worktime) may remain as organizational routines and facilitate collaboration across the globe. On the other hand, organizations may refrain from collaborating with global suppliers/manufacturers as the pandemic exposes the vulnerability of the global supply chain, slowing down globalization progress.

In an era of VUCA (i.e., volatility, uncertainty, complexity, and ambiguity; Bennett & Lemoine, 2014), organizational managers are required to show greater resilience to ensure organizational effectiveness and keep employees' high organizational commitment when life-threatening events happen to the organizations. Resilience represents "the multiple ways in which humans, organizations, and other systems respond to destabilizing disturbances to adapt to the challenges imposed by their environments" (Mithani, 2020, p. 513). For managers and employees in an era of uncertainty, it is important to have the capacity to overcome unprecedented changes in the external environment and adapt to the changes (Mithani, 2020). For organizational leaders, using appropriate leadership behaviors will reduce the uncertainty of organizational members, whereas some other behaviors may be even more detrimental for organizations under global uncertainty. For example, Kim et al. (2021) found that CEOs' narcissism will increase middle managers' perceived uncertainty and thus make them more likely to show laissez-faire leadership (i.e., middle managers' withdrawal from leadership). Kim et al. also found that this effect was stronger when the business experienced threats due to COVID-19. In addition, it has been suggested that leaders can support employees' mental health during crisis through means such as demonstrating supportive listening and communicating available resources (Smith, 2020).

HUMAN RESOURCE MANAGEMENT IN A GLOBALIZED CONTEXT

Human resource management (HRM) has always been a key element in leveraging human capital and translating it into competitive advantages (Li et al., 2018, 2022; Li, Gong, et al., 2021). Under the globalization context, human capital and the human resource (HR) practices used to manage and exploit human capital become increasingly important (Collings et al., 2019; Crook et al., 2011). During this process, the fundamental issue is how to align HRM with the changing nature of human capital and the competitive environment, wherein a critical question is whether companies of different origins and their HR practices are converging or diverging (Al Ariss & Sidani, 2016; Bader et al., 2021; Peiró, 2014). The convergence perspective argues that universal HR systems will emerge due to gradually homogenous economic systems caused by the continuous progress of industrialization and technology. In contrast, the divergence view holds that distinct HR systems will continue to exist due to insurmountable barriers of institutional contexts. Integrating these two views, the contingent perspective argues that certain practices are converging while others are diverging and focus our effort on elaborating the contingency. Supporting such a perspective, the literature shows both convergence and divergence are underway for multiple domains in HR, including recruitment, selection, training, and performance management. In addition, some novel HR practices have emerged as the products of globalization.

Recruitment.   Recruitment, or the process through which companies reveal information (i.e., signals) about themselves to attract prospective talent, is of greater importance in the context of globalization (Rynes et al., 1991; Uggerslev et al., 2012). The combination of convergence and divergence is manifested in the evolution of recruitment practices globally (Huo et al., 2002). This combination can be easily observed in multinational companies, which have to strike a balance between standardization and localization. For example, after analyzing recruiting messages on company websites of Fortune 1000 firms, Banks et al. (2019) found that companies tended to standardize recruiting signals in multiple subsidiaries. However, some localized signals have also been identified, such as emphasis on team-based culture and inclusiveness toward veterans in the context of the United States. Meanwhile, the strength of signals varied in different subsidiaries. Similarly, it has been shown that discriminatory information in job advertisements of multinational companies is a function of the regulations of both the home countries (standardization) and the host countries (i.e., localization). Interestingly, Siegel et al. (2019) suggested that multinational companies might conduct recruitment in a way deliberately departing from local norms or institutions. Specifically, they found that multinational companies in South Korea tried to attract and hire female employees (an excluded group in the local market) via female-friendly HR practices as an effort to exploit well-qualified human capital overlooked by local companies. Research attention has also been paid to how to craft recruiting signals to attract applicants qualified for specific job requirements. For example, communicating global travel requirements in job advertisements can attract applicants with a global mindset by increasing their perceived job fit (Phillips et al., 2014).

Selection and Training.   In contrast to other HR practices, selection and training practices mainly exhibit a convergent trend in the context of globalization. That is, companies need to select and train employees with cross-cultural competence. Cross-cultural competence captures whether an individual can work with people from different cultural backgrounds successfully by employing a set of relevant knowledge, skills, and personal attributes (Johnson et al., 2006). Cross-cultural competence has been associated with various psychological, behavioral, and performance outcomes at the individual level and the team level (Leung et al., 2014).

Since cross-cultural competence cannot be observed or measured directly, personnel selection usually uses international experience as a proxy (Caligiuri et al., 2009). The reasons are twofold. First, international experience provides cultural knowledge, which is an important component of cross-cultural competence (Johnson et al., 2006). Second, international experience per se has been associated with various outcomes, such as global leadership effectiveness (Caligiuri & Tarique, 2012), CEO compensation (Carpenter et al., 2001), expatriate adjustment (Takeuchi et al., 2019), and job promotion (Zhu et al., 2016).

Empirical evidence has supported the view that international experience should be taken into account in personnel selection. For example, Rickley (2019) has found a positive association between subsidiary executives' international experience and the institutional distance between home countries and host countries, suggesting that managers with rich international experience are appointed to positions with high cross-cultural requirements. International experience also contributes to one's ascendance to CEO positions, especially in highly international companies (Magnusson & Boggs, 2006). Further, international experience-based personnel selection is not confined to the selection of top managers and expatriates. Valued by an increasing number of companies, international experience has become a powerful signal of capacity for employees of various occupational groups (Andresen et al., 2021). Moreover, employees with rich international experience typically have higher external employability, which increases their bargaining power with regard to compensation and promotion (Andresen et al., 2021). The selection based on international experience is so prevalent that some scholars even caution against discrimination on the basis of international experience, especially in cases where international experience is not necessarily a genuine requirement (Bano & Nadeem, 2018).

In addition to selecting human capital with cross-cultural competence, companies are developing training systems to help build it internally as well. For example, catalyzed by the globalization of the economy, multinational companies use cross-cultural training and development activities to improve these competencies of international assignees (Caligiuri & Tarique, 2012). Cross-cultural training can effectively improve trainees' adjustment and performance in international assignments by equipping them with high confidence in cross-cultural interactions, sophisticated relational skills, and multiple cognitive perspectives (Black & Mendenhall, 1990; Morris & Robie, 2001). Through multiple techniques including developing attribution skills, imparting cross-cultural knowledge, cultivating host-culture appropriate behaviors, honing language skills, promoting successful adjustment, and practicing potential situations, cross-cultural training produces competent employees in the global business arena (Littrell & Salas, 2005).

Performance Management. Performance management practices exhibit a combination of convergence and divergence as well. On the one hand, advanced and sophisticated performance management systems have been transferred from the West to the world, especially by multinational companies. For instance, an analysis of foreign multinational companies in the United Kingdom showed that U.S. multinational companies had more sophisticated pay and performance management practices than other firms (Ferner & Almond, 2013). In addition, individualized pay-for-performance originating in the United States has been adopted in other countries around the world. The extent of adoption is determined by cultural and institutional factors such as labor regulation and the degree of masculinity (Gooderham et al., 2018). Some promising findings have justified the introduction of Western performance management systems. For example, Korean firms introducing profit sharing, an incentive system emphasizing employee participation and cooperation, have enhanced employee attitudes compared with those solely governed by traditional seniority-based pay. The beneficial effect was mediated through improved distributive and interactional justice (Kwon et al., 2008).

On the other hand, divergence in performance management systems still exists due to institutional differences. For example, Cooke and Huang (2011) investigated the performance management systems of Chinese IT firms acquired by U.S. multinational companies. They found that though the acquirers tried to align HR practices with their strategies by adopting sophisticated performance management techniques, they encountered resistance from Chinese managers due to cultural and institutional factors. Similarly, Yahiaoui et al. (2021) investigated the performance appraisal systems of the subsidiaries of French multinational companies in the Middle East and North Africa region. Their results suggest that performance appraisal in these areas is highly dependent on sociocultural values, such as emotional bonds between managers and subordinates, fear of losing face, paternalism, and confrontation avoidance, which lead to managers' preference for providing subjective appraisal and reluctance to give negative feedback.

Some evidence also indicates the coexistence of convergence and divergence in performance management. For example, data from 472 multinational companies across 22 countries showed that distal contexts (cultural, legal, and economic contexts) of both the home countries and the host countries were associated with performance appraisal systems, resulting in hybridized systems (Morley et al., 2021). Taken together, it seems that the evolution of performance management practices will continue to balance both the convergent and divergent aspects to achieve success in a globalized business environment.

In addition to the general trend of performance management systems in the context of globalization, attention has also been paid to two specific topics: managerial compensation management and performance management systems for expatriates. First, managerial compensation has important implications for the interactional actions of a company (especially a multinational company), wherein risk plays a major role. For example, since international diversification involves higher risks arising from diverse competitors, customers, cultures, and institutions, managers with higher levels of stock ownership are more likely to turn to business diversification from international diversification to lower their risk-bearing (Alessandri & Seth, 2014). Similarly, though risky long-term investments such as international acquisitions are critical to shareholders' benefits, CEOs near retirement, especially those with higher value of in-the-money option holdings and equity holdings, are more likely to adopt a short-term view and are reluctant to engage in international acquisitions as an effort to minimize the risk and conserve their legacies (Matta & Beamish, 2008). In contrast, top managers whose compensation portfolios are largely based on long-term performance (e.g., restricted stock options, long-term management incentive plans) are more inclined to make international acquisitions (Datta et al., 2009). Managerial compensation also influences coordination between subsidiaries within a company. For example, managerial incentive pay based on company-wide performance (in contrast to mere subsidiary performance) can facilitate knowledge sharing among subsidiaries (Fey & Furu, 2008). This evidence suggests that managerial compensation should be reconsidered in a globalized context to better serve the interests of both internal and external shareholders. Second, the growing number of expatriates also directs scholars' attention to performance management systems for expatriates. Studies have investigated the critical elements of performance management systems for expatriates, and it has been found that fairness, clear performance expectations, and the incorporation of career development are perceived as important predictors of performance appraisal system success, whereas the evaluation frequency and the consideration of local environment are not (Martin & Bartol, 2003).

DIVERSITY-RELATED CHALLENGES IN GLOBALIZATION

With the acceleration of globalization, the business world is becoming unprecedently diverse, connected, and flexible as a result of the increasing number of cross-cultural and intercultural business activities. Culture, defined by Hofstede (1993) as "the collective programming of the mind that distinguishes one group or category of people from another," is playing a critical role in globalization. Culture and globalization have been enhancing each other mutually in history. During the first half of the 20th century, when large numbers of migrants fluxed into the United States, the dominant view of cultural studies stressed the cultural transformation of alien workers and was "culture blind" to the diversity and inclusion issues (Gelfand et al., 2017). Since the late 20th century, milestones in globalization (e.g., the invention of the Internet, the universal use of personal computers) have brought culture to the spotlight and led to a wider perspective of culture at the workplace (Gelfand et al., 2017).

Today, individuals and organizations are both experiencing drastic changes at different levels to adapt to a more culturally diverse work environment and more culturally demanding tasks. For example, individuals often have to collaborate with coworkers from culturally different social groups or work in a foreign country as expatriate workers for a short or long time period. To perform effectively in these situations, they need to learn specific skills and knowledge to solve culture-related conflicts, manage identity threats (Ramarajan & Reid, 2020), and adjust to social norms related to culture. As for organizations, expanding business to other parts of the world requires knowledge on collaborating with local partners, norms and habits of local customers, and laws and regulations of local governments. A more diverse workforce also poses challenges to human resource management within the firm (Atwater et al., 2009). The fruitful findings accumulated in culture studies provide implications for organizations and individuals to address the challenges and embrace the gains of a more culturally diverse working environment.

As such, literature has expanded on several related topics, including how cultural diversity impacts the generalizability of management practices across different countries and regions, what challenges firms tend to encounter when establishing relationships with local firms, how routine jobs have been changed by cultural diversity, and racial discrimination and bias in the workplace. Previous studies differentiated between cross-cultural research, which focuses on the comparison of different or similar phenomena under different cultural environments, and intercultural research, which provides a different perspective on how individuals and organizations cope with settings where different cultures coexist.

Generalizability of Management Practices in Cross-Cultural Settings.   Whether management practices and management research findings can be generalized across countries or cultures is a great concern for managers of multinational organizations. In cross-cultural studies, culture mainly plays two roles in theories: as the antecedent of workplace outcomes, or as the boundary condition of studied relationships (Tsui et al., 2007).

Culture has direct effects on organizational processes and outcomes at both the micro and macro levels (Daniels & Greguras, 2014) through region-level cultures and individual-level perceived cultures. Early management studies relate cultures directly to countries, which constrained examination of more detailed mechanisms through which cultures impact outcomes at the workplace. More recent studies elaborated culture into more concrete dimensions and tested how different dimensions of culture influence individuals' behaviors and attitudes. As Tsui et al. (2007) summarized in a literature review covering over 20 management journals, the most studied culture-value dimension is the continuum of individualism/collectivism, followed by power distance and its variants. Culture-value dimension from Global Leadership and Organizational Behavior Effectiveness (GLOBE; i.e., performance orientation, assertiveness, future orientation, humane orientation, institutional collectivism, in-group collectivism, gender egalitarianism, power distance, and uncertainty avoidance) also received great attention from management scholars (Tsui et al., 2007).

At the individual level, individuals' perceptions of cultural dimensions may impact an individual's attitudes and behavior. For example, perceived power distance impacts individuals' use of feedback channels (Hwang & Francesco, 2010; Sully de Luque & Sommer, 2000), voice behavior (Botero & Van Dyne, 2009), and job attitudes (Bochner & Hesketh, 1994). At the organization level, business conditions, including the expense of starting a business and construction permits, employment conditions, and investor regulations, differ drastically across different countries (Nicholls-Nixon et al., 2011). Further, local culture, laws, and politics fundamentally impact organizational decision-making and strategies. In particular, individualism and collectivism play important roles in firm behavior. For instance, Martin et al. (2007) found that country-level in-group collectivism and welfare socialism significantly decreased the bribery activity of a firm. Li and Haleblian (2022) also found that culture dimensions, including collectivism and uncertainty avoidance, along with the country's regulatory pressures impact a firm's bid premium in acquisition. Li and Liang (2015) proposed a Confucian social model to explain why private-firm chief executive officers sought political appointments and how it benefited their business success under this special cultural setting.

Culture is also an important boundary condition for relationships between antecedents and workplace outcomes. For example, individualism/collectivism influences how job embeddedness predicts employees' turnover intention (Ramesh & Gelfand, 2010). While collectivists usually enjoy more intimate and long-term relationships with coworkers and denser networks at work, people under individualistic cultures may prefer individual autonomy and independence. Therefore, the negative relationship between job embeddedness and employee turnover was stronger in collectivist cultures than in individualistic cultures (Ramesh & Gelfand, 2010). Further, because work is considered as contributing to the family instead of competing with it, the negative relationship between work–family conflict and satisfaction is weaker in collectivistic cultures (Allen et al., 2020). Several cultural dimensions from the GLOBE study also moderate the relationships between company corporate social responsibility and employees' affective organizational commitment. Specifically, human orientation and institutional collectivism strengthen this positive relationship, while power distance weakens it (Mueller et al., 2012).

Although these studies emphasize the differences across cultures and the same practice has varied effects under different cultural settings, other studies suggest that some findings remain the same when tested in other countries. For example, Fisher (2014) found that the negative effect of role overload on organizational commitment did not vary as a function of culture in a study examining 6,264 employees working across 18 countries. Other studies suggest that individual culture orientation and region-level culture do not always serve as boundary conditions in the workplace. For instance, Kirkman et al. (2009) found that the employees' power distance orientation weakened the relationship between transformational leadership and perceived procedural justice because employees with a higher power distance orientation expect leaders not to envision but to give direct orders to them. However, they found the moderating effect does not hold for country-level power distance.

Interfirm Relationships in Intercultural Settings. In the era of globalization, firms need to have transactions and interactions with firms from other cultural backgrounds. Interfirm relationships have been changed by increased levels of environmental uncertainty (i.e., "instability and unpredictability of the external environment"; Abdi & Aulakh, 2017) and behavioral uncertainty (i.e., lack of "common grounds and shared frameworks among collaborating firms"; Abdi & Aulakh, 2017) in intercultural settings. To cope with the uncertainty of operating in a foreign country, partnering with a local firm is a common strategy taken by many firms. However, as Liu and Maula (2016) pointed out, venture-level uncertainty and country-level uncertainty had different impacts on the decision to partner with a local firm. Venture-level certainty requires investment firms to have local network information and venture-specific knowledge, to which only local partners have access, and thus venture-level certainty increases the likelihood of partnering. To the opposite, country-level uncertainty resulting from weak legal enforcement makes it more critical for firms to have major ownership and makes it riskier for firms to collaborate with local firms.

Acquisition is another form of relationship between home firms and local firms in different cultural contexts. Zhu et al. (2019) found that culture dimensions that were related to informal institution building (i.e., collectivism and humane orientation) enhanced the post-acquisition integration and firm performance because acquired foreign targets were more likely to be viewed as an interdependent part by acquirers and to have received support from acquirers in collectivistic and humane cultures. On the other hand, culture dimensions that were related to formal institutions regulating firm behavior (i.e., shareholder orientation and property rights protection) decreased integration and firm performance because they prioritized the interests of the acquirer.

Work in Intercultural Settings. A more diverse workforce poses challenges to employees to work with culturally diverse individuals. The increasing frequency of business activities across borders also requires employees to adapt to a different cultural setting while managing their own cultural identity. Extant studies have shown that the impact of working in intercultural settings on performance is dependent on boundary conditions including individual differences and organizational contexts. Managers can modify recruitment and selection practices to maintain a "culturally intelligent" workforce, develop a culturally friendly working environment, and take reasonable strategies to tackle intercultural conflicts.

Intercultural communication has been attached much importance in globalization because many business activities feature dense communication needs (e.g., negotiation, collaboration, coordination). Liu et al. (2010) proposed that the quality of communication in intracultural and intercultural settings is composed of three dimensions—clarity, responsiveness, and comfort—which are critical for negotiation outcomes. They also found that all three communication qualities had lower scores in intercultural settings than in intracultural settings. Conflict can inhibit high-quality communication. Intercultural task conflict is often the task conflict arising from cultural diversity among collaborators. Chua and Jin (2020) found that intercultural task conflict had a positive impact on reaping the rewards of cultural diversity conditioned on the gender of conflict dyads (i.e., beneficial for women), while intercultural relationship conflict generally hurt creative collaboration. Intercultural communication is often mediated by communication technology and embedded in virtual team settings. Technical language violations and etiquette violations may induce negative perceptions about the communicator (Vignovic & Thompson, 2010).

Expatriate employees are becoming an important part of the workforce. Employees may voluntarily move to a new country and become expatriate workers or may be selected by organizations to work in a foreign branch. Research shows that foreign workers have a higher turnover rate and lower psychological well-being compared with local workers (Ang et al., 2007). Thus, it is critical for organizations to dispatch employees who are fit to work in a foreign country. Volpone et al. (2018) found that a minority status in the home country helps individuals to acculturate to a new country because they have experiences working with dissimilar others. Work design for expatriate workers also impacts their socialization and return intentions. Firth et al. (2014) found that expatriates with high challenge stressors maintained a high level of work adjustment over the course of socialization, while the level of work adjustment of employees with low challenge stressors dropped quickly after the first month. In addition to job demands, studies also investigated how resources impact expatriates' retention. Ren et al. (2014) differentiated the reactive demand-based and proactive resource-based mechanisms underlying expatriates' adjustment and retention. They found that positive framing significantly enhanced expatriates' adjustment and relationship building indirectly benefited their retention through improving their job embeddedness. These studies provide practical implications for managing expatriates in a foreign country.

Biases and Discrimination Related to Diversity.   While a diverse workforce has been unprecedentedly prevalent, biases and discrimination related to diversity remain in the workplace and persistently hamper the performance and well-being of employees and hinder organizations' success (Li, Koopmann, et al., 2021). Discrimination against minorities often includes intersectional invisibility at the workplace (Smith et al., 2019), unfair payment and rewards (Hernandez et al., 2019), and gender and ethnic harassment (Raver & Nishii, 2010). These discrimination behaviors are exacerbated when racial minority identity is combined with other kinds of minority identities (e.g., gender and sexuality; Smith et al., 2019). Racial discrimination at the workplace exists in a vast variety of industries, ranging from competitive sports (Nardinelli & Simon, 1990; Price & Wolfers, 2010) to the emerging shared economy (Edelman et al., 2017).

Research suggests that the reasons behind discrimination are diverse and complex. Evaluation biases are closely tied to stereotypes, and people might experience stereotype threat if they engage in behaviors against the stereotypes related to their social groups (Lee et al., 2015). On the other hand, Sy et al. (2010) found that when an individual's race matches that person's stereotype (e.g., an Asian engineer), the perceptions of leadership offered by the person would be higher. In salary negotiations, employers expect black job seekers to negotiate less and punish them by lowering the starting point salary when they violate such stereotypes (Hernandez et al., 2019). Besides stereotypes, Hekman et al. (2017) found that women and minorities were discouraged from engaging in "diversity-valuing behaviors." Women and minorities received lower performance ratings when they engaged in diversity-valuing behaviors, while white male leaders were rewarded when they engaged in such behaviors. Discrimination related to diversity at the workplace not only puts racial minorities at an economic disadvantage but also severely impacts their psychological well-being (Ong et al., 2009).

As Small and Pager (2020) pointed out, discrimination is not always intentional but can be unconscious and automatic. A potential race-neutral practice can still have discriminant consequences because the preexisting context of the organization is discriminant. For example, referral-based hiring procedures can result in recruiting new employees of a similar racial composition to the current workforce in the organization. Small and Pager's (2020) observation implies the importance of developing and maintaining a diverse and inclusive workforce. Equally important is to cultivate an inclusive climate in organizations that values the unique value and contribution of diverse employees and enhances their belongingness to the organization. Shore et al. (2011) proposed a 2×2 theoretical framework of inclusion based on employees' perceived belongingness and value of their uniqueness. On the one end of the spectrum, the high-belongingness/high-value-in-uniqueness combination leads to the most positive experiences related to inclusion. Employees of different social groups feel they are insiders of their workgroup, and their uniqueness is greatly valued. On the other end of the spectrum, the combination of low belongingness and low value in uniqueness results in feelings of exclusion, namely the perceptions that employees are not treated as insiders and their unique values in the workgroup are not respected, either. Between these two ends, high belongingness and low value in uniqueness (i.e., assimilation) might jointly lead to employees' conformity, and low belongingness and high value in uniqueness (i.e., differentiation) might lead minority employees to feel excluded. Taken together, simultaneously treating employees from diverse social groups as organizational insiders and valuing their unique characteristics can promote an inclusive climate. To achieve this, organizations can adopt a number of diversity-specific practices. For example, Wang and Fang (2020) recommended that five types of management practices could be used in combination to foster inclusion of age-diverse employees, including age-inclusive management, peer mentoring between employees of different age groups, participative decision-making, ensuring job security, and providing training to counter age-related stereotypes. Combinations of different practices are more effective than single practices in cultivating inclusive cultures.

FUTURE DIRECTIONS

Though industrial-organizational psychology research has been conducted in the global context for years, there are still many opportunities to bring novel insights to both the theory and practice under the background of globalization. This section mentions some ongoing and new areas for future study of global organizations.

Emerging Global Phenomena and Building New Theories. The past two decades have witnessed many new industrial-organizational psychology phenomena in global organizations, such as the prevalence of the Internet and smartphones, the development of AI, and the emergence of new employment relationships (e.g., the gig economy). These new phenomena bring many opportunities for theory building and a better understanding of organizations in the globalized society (Eisenhardt & Graebner, 2007). For example, AI has been increasingly used by global firms in recent years, but research on AI's impacts on employee productivity and well-being is still rare; more research is needed to understand how organizations can best leverage AI in the workplace (Raisch & Krakowski, 2021). Regarding methodology, qualitative studies and/or case studies, together with multi-method studies, may be extremely helpful in understanding these new phenomena worldwide. Future research may thus examine these emerging phenomena with multi-methods in global organizations for theory building.

Measuring and Analyzing Cultural Differences. Though the research on cross-cultural differences is fruitful, measurement and analyses of culture "has been and still is a problem" (Aycan & Gelfand, 2012, p. 1142). As a response to this problem in cross-cultural research, scholars have suggested using additional innovative methodologies to measure cultures, such as descriptive norm measures (i.e., what others do in the cultural context), implicit measures, and qualitative measures of culture (Aycan & Gelfand, 2012). In addition to different measurement instruments, researchers may also consider new analytical procedures to study cross-cultural differences. A state-of-the-art methodological technique—latent profile analysis (LPA)—may be used as an additional tool for this purpose. To date, theory and empirical evidence about culture have been mainly restricted to a paradigm of dimension division (e.g., Hofstede, 2011). Though dimensionalizing cultures is an effective approach to understanding cultural differences, this paradigm is prone to many theoretical and methodological criticisms, such as how many dimensions are appropriate, the assumption of homogeneity within countries (Shaiq et al., 2011), and whether these dimensions are distinguishable from each other (Minkov & Kaasa, 2021).

As a complement to this approach, latent profile analysis (or latent class procedures) may be considered as an equally valid approach for examining cultural differences. While the dimensional approach focuses on "capturing the interrelatedness (often in the form of covariance or latent factor) among different variables and using this interrelatedness to infer the underlying processes or causes" (Wang & Hanges, 2011, p. 24), the latent profile analysis considers "the interrelatedness between or among different variables as a function of the unobserved heterogeneity of the population" (p. 24). The latent profile analysis is especially appropriate when the research objective is to identify and understand the unobserved subpopulation where cultural differences may exist. This is because, with the latent profile analysis, researchers can specify the unobserved heterogeneity in their data, which may reflect the cultural differences in unobserved subgroups (Wang & Hanges, 2011; Zhang et al., 2022). Therefore, future research may consider using latent profile analysis and other new methodology for better measurement and analyses of cultural differences.

Moving from Highlighting Differences to Better Global Cooperation. While many valuable research efforts have been focused on cultural differences for organizations in globalization contexts, future research may also pay more attention to how to enhance global organizations' interorganizational cooperation and intraorganizational inclusion. While it is always important to first understand the global diversity of culture, the general goal of industrial-organizational psychology research is not only to document the differences but also to promote cooperation when recognizing the uniqueness of each culture. To this end, future research may examine what challenges organizations may face in global cooperation and how global organizations can effectively enhance their cooperation when interacting with a different culture. Further, at the intraorganizational level, future research may investigate how organizations can make the workplace more inclusive to employees with diverse cultural backgrounds through effective human resource management. To date, the research on workplace diversity and inclusion has a focus on race and ethnicity, especially in the United States, for many historical reasons. Whereas this line of research is undoubtedly important, in a globalization background, research on workplace inclusion should also consider a variety of other characteristics, such as national origin, language, disability, age, gender, religion, sexual orientation, political views, and socioeconomic status (Burmeister et al., 2020; Klein & Wang, 2010; Li, Gong, et al., 2021; Wang et al., 2015). Therefore, future research may investigate how organizations can endorse inclusion practices more effectively in a variety of domains.

CONCLUSION

The world is becoming more connected than it ever was. Globalization improves economic efficiency by enhancing global labor division and cooperation, but also brings challenges to organizations and managers. In the first two decades of the 21st century, the interplay between the global workforce and industrial-organizational psychologists has enriched our understanding of the workplace in the globalization process. However, there is still much room for theory building, especially given the fast-growing usage of information technology and artificial intelligence, new forms of economy, and increasing global uncertainty. It is crucial for global organizations to use human resource management tools appropriately for employees from all over the world, understand the cross-cultural differences in both their international cooperation and internal corporate management, and be inclusive of employees with diverse backgrounds. We hope that the accumulation of industrial-organizational psychology knowledge eventually contributes to a better workplace in the global village.

FURTHER READING

Abdi, M., & Aulakh, P. S. (2017). Locus of uncertainty and the relationship between contractual and relational governance in cross-border interfirm relationships. *Journal of Management*, 43(3), 771–803. https://doi.org/10.1177/0149206314541152

Al Ariss, A., & Sidani, Y. (2016). Comparative international human resource management: Future research directions. *Human Resource Management Review, 26*(4), 352–358. https://doi.org/10.1016/j.hrmr.2016.04.007

Aycan, Z., & Gelfand, M. J. (2012). Cross-cultural organizational psychology. In S. W. J. Kozlowski (Ed.), *The Oxford handbook of organizational psychology* (pp. 1103–1160). Oxford University Press.

Bader, A. K., Bader, B., Froese, F. J., & Sekiguchi, T. (2021). One way or another? An international comparison of expatriate performance management in multinational companies. *Human Resource Management, 60*(5), 1–16. https://doi.org/10.1002/hrm.22065

Colbert, A., Yee, N., & George, G. (2016). The digital workforce and the workplace of the future. *Academy of Management Journal, 59*(3), 731–739. https://doi.org/10.5465/amj.2016.4003

Gelfand, M. J., Aycan, Z., Erez, M., & Leung, K. (2017). Cross-cultural industrial organizational psychology and organizational behavior: A hundred-year journey. *Journal of Applied Psychology, 102*(3), 514–529. https://psycnet.apa.org/doi/10.1037/apl0000186

Peiró, J. M. (2014). Roles and responsibilities of international psychology organizations in improving psychology education and training. In R. K. Silbereisen, P. L. J. Ritichie, & J. Pandey (Eds.), *Psychology education and training: A global perspective* (pp. 231–241). Psychology Press.

Raisch, S., & Krakowski, S. (2021). Artificial intelligence and management: The automation–augmentation paradox. *Academy of Management Review, 46*(1), 192–210. https://doi.org/10.5465/amr.2018.0072

Small, M. L., & Pager, D. (2020). Sociological perspectives on racial discrimination. *Journal of Economic Perspectives, 34*(2), 49–67. https://doi.org/10.1257/jep.34.2.49

Tsui, A. S., Nifadkar, S. S., & Ou, A. Y. (2007). Cross-national, cross-cultural organizational behavior research: Advances, gaps, and recommendations. *Journal of Management, 33*(3), 426–478. https://doi.org/10.1177/0149206307300818

REFERENCES

Abdi, M., & Aulakh, P. S. (2017). Locus of uncertainty and the relationship between contractual and relational governance in cross-border interfirm relationships. *Journal of Management, 43*(3), 771–803. https://doi.org/10.1177/0149206314541152

Al Ariss, A., & Sidani, Y. (2016). Comparative international human resource management: Future research directions. *Human Resource Management Review, 26*(4), 352–358. https://doi.org/10.1016/j.hrmr.2016.04.007

Alessandri, T. M., & Seth, A. (2014). The effects of managerial ownership on international and business diversification: Balancing incentives and risks. *Strategic Management Journal, 35*(13), 2064–2075. https://doi.org/10.1002/smj.2222

Allen, T. D., French, K. A., Dumani, S., & Shockley, K. M. (2020). A cross-national meta-analytic examination of predictors and outcomes associated with work–family conflict. *Journal of Applied Psychology, 105*(6), 539–576. https://psycnet.apa.org/doi/10.1037/apl0000442

Andresen, M., Lazarova, M., Apospori, E., Cotton, R., Bosak, J., Dickmann, M., Kase, R., & Smale, A. (2021). Does international work experience pay off? The relationship between international work experience, employability and career success: A 30-country, multi-industry study. *Human Resource Management Journal, 32*(3), 1–24. https://doi.org/10.1111/1748-8583.12423

Ang, S., Van Dyne, L., Koh, C., Ng, K. Y., Templer, K. J., Tay, C., & Chandrasekar, N. A. (2007). Cultural intelligence: Its measurement and effects on cultural judgment and decision making, cultural adaptation and task performance. *Management and Organization Review, 3*(3), 335–371. https://doi.org/10.1111/j.1740-8784.2007.00082.x

Atwater, L., Wang, M., Smither, J. W., & Fleenor, J. W. (2009). Are cultural characteristics associated with the relationship between self and others' ratings of leadership? *Journal of Applied Psychology, 94*(4), 876–886. https://doi.org/10.1037/a0014561

Aycan, Z., & Gelfand, M. J. (2012). Cross-cultural organizational psychology. In S. W. J. Kozlowski (Ed.), *The Oxford handbook of organizational psychology* (pp. 1103–1160). Oxford University Press.

Bader, A. K., Bader, B., Froese, F. J., & Sekiguchi, T. (2021). One way or another? An international comparison of expatriate performance management in multinational companies. *Human Resource Management, 60*(5), 1–16. https://doi.org/10.1002/hrm.22065

Banks, G. C., Woznyj, H. M., Wesslen, R. S., Frear, K. A., Berka, G., Heggestad, E. D., & Gordon, H. L. (2019). Strategic recruitment across borders: An investigation of multinational enterprises. *Journal of Management, 45*(2), 476–509. https://doi.org/10.1177/0149206318764295

Bano, A., & Nadeem, S. (2018). Exploring discrimination on the basis of international experience: The colonial mindset bias in the context of Pakistan. *Human Resource Management, 57*(1), 211–233. https://doi.org/10.1002/hrm.21824

Beck, U. (2018). *What is globalization?* John Wiley & Sons.

Bennett, N., & Lemoine, J. (2014). What VUCA really means for you. *Harvard Business Review, 92.*

Black, J. S., & Mendenhall, M. (1990). Cross-cultural training effectiveness: A review and a theoretical framework for future research. *Academy of Management Review, 15*(1), 113–136. https://doi.org/10.5465/amr.1990.11591834

Bochner, S., & Hesketh, B. (1994). Power distance, individualism/collectivism, and job-related attitudes in a culturally diverse work group. *Journal of Cross-Cultural Psychology, 25*(2), 233–257. https://doi.org/10.1177/0022022194252005

Botero, I. C., & Van Dyne, L. (2009). Employee voice behavior: Interactive effects of LMX and power distance in the United States and Colombia. *Management Communication Quarterly, 23*(1), 84–104. https://doi.org/10.1177/0893318909335415

Briggs, C., & Makice, K. (2012). *Digital fluency: Building success in the digital age.* SociaLens.

Brougham, D., & Haar, J. (2018). Smart technology, artificial intelligence, robotics, and algorithms (STARA): Employees' perceptions of our future workplace. *Journal of Management & Organization, 24*(2), 239–257. https://doi.org/10.1017/jmo.2016.55

Buckley, P. J., & Strange, R. (2015). The governance of the global factory: Location and control of world economic activity. *Academy of Management Perspectives, 29*(2), 237–249. https://doi.org/10.5465/amp.2013.0113

Burmeister, A., Wang, M., & Hirschi, A. (2020). Understanding the motivational benefits of knowledge transfer for older and younger workers in age-diverse coworker dyads: An actor–partner interdependence model. *Journal of Applied Psychology, 105*(7), 748–759. https://doi.org/10.1037/apl0000466

Caligiuri, P., & Tarique, I. (2012). Dynamic cross-cultural competencies and global leadership effectiveness. *Journal of World Business, 47*(4), 612–622. https://doi.org/10.1016/j.jwb.2012.01.014

Caligiuri, P., Tarique, I., & Jacobs, R. (2009). Selection for international assignments. *Human Resource Management Review, 19* (3), 251–262. https://doi.org/10.1016/j.hrmr.2009.02.001

Carpenter, M. A., Sanders, W. G., & Gregersen, H. B. (2001). Bundling human capital with organizational context: The impact of international assignment experience on multinational firm performance and CEO pay. *Academy of Management Journal, 44*(3), 493–511. https://doi.org/10.5465/3069366

Chua, R., & Jin, M. (2020). Across the great divides: Gender dynamics influence how intercultural conflict helps or hurts creative collaboration. *Academy of Management Journal, 63*(3), 903–934. https://doi.org/10.5465/amj.2016.1319

Colbert, A., Yee, N., & George, G. (2016). The digital workforce and the workplace of the future. *Academy of Management Journal, 59*(3), 731–739. https://doi.org/10.5465/amj.2016.4003

Collings, D. G., Mellahi, K., & Cascio, W. F. (2019). Global talent management and performance in multinational enterprises: A multilevel perspective. *Journal of Management, 45*(2), 540–566. https://doi.org/10.1177/0149206318757018

Cooke, F. L., & Huang, K. (2011). Postacquisition evolution of the appraisal and reward systems: A study of Chinese IT firms acquired by US firms. *Human Resource Management, 50*(6), 839–858. https://doi.org/10.1002/hrm.20457

Crook, T. R., Todd, S. Y., Combs, J. G., Woehr, D. J., & Ketchen, D. J., Jr. (2011). Does human capital matter? A meta-analysis of the relationship between human capital and firm performance. *Journal of Applied Psychology, 96*(3), 443–456. https://doi.org/10.1037/a0022147

Cutolo, D., & Kenney, M. (2020). Platform-dependent entrepreneurs: Power asymmetries, risks, and strategies in the platform economy. *Academy of Management Perspectives, 35*(4). https://doi.org/10.5465/amp.2019.0103

Daniels, M. A., & Greguras, G. J. (2014). Exploring the nature of power distance: Implications for micro- and macro-level theories, processes, and outcomes. *Journal of Management, 40*(5), 1202–1229. https://doi.org/10.1177/0149206314527131

Datta, D. K., Musteen, M., & Herrmann, P. (2009). Board characteristics, managerial incentives, and the choice between foreign acquisitions and international joint ventures. *Journal of Management, 35*(4), 928–953. https://doi.org/10.1177/0149206308329967

Davenport, T. H. (2005). *Thinking for a living: How to get better performances and results from knowledge workers*. Harvard Business Press.

Dekas, K. H., Bauer, T. N., Welle, B., Kurkoski, J., & Sullivan, S. (2013). Organizational citizenship behavior, version 2.0: A review and qualitative investigation of OCBs for knowledge workers at Google and beyond. *Academy of Management Perspectives, 27*(3), 219–237. https://doi.org/10.5465/amp.2011.0097

Edelman, B., Luca, M., & Svirsky, D. (2017). Racial discrimination in the sharing economy: Evidence from a field experiment. *American Economic Journal: Applied Economics, 9*(2), 1–22. https://doi.org/10.1257/app.20160213

Eisenhardt, K. M., & Graebner, M. E. (2007). Theory building from cases: Opportunities and challenges. *Academy of Management Journal, 50*(1), 25–32. https://doi.org/10.5465/amj.2007.24160888

Felten, E., Raj, M., & Seamans, R. (2021). Occupational, industry, and geographic exposure to artificial intelligence: A novel dataset and its potential uses. *Strategic Management Journal, 42*(12), 2195–2217. https://doi.org/10.1002/smj.3286

Ferner, A., & Almond, P. (2013). Performance and reward practices in foreign multinationals in the UK. *Human Resource Management Journal, 23*(3), 241–261. https://doi.org/10.1111/1748-8583.12001

Fey, C. F., & Furu, P. (2008). Top management incentive compensation and knowledge sharing in multinational corporations. *Strategic Management Journal, 29*(12), 1301–1323. https://doi.org/10.1002/smj.712

Firth, B. M., Chen, G., Kirkman, B. L., & Kim, K. (2014). Newcomers abroad: Expatriate adaptation during early phases of international assignments. *Academy of Management Journal, 57*(1), 280–300. https://doi.org/10.5465/amj.2011.0574

Fisher, D. M. (2014). A multilevel cross-cultural examination of role overload and organizational commitment: Investigating the interactive effects of context. *Journal of Applied Psychology, 99*(4), 723–736. https://psycnet.apa.org/doi/10.1037/a0035861

Gelfand, M. J., Aycan, Z., Erez, M., & Leung, K. (2017). Cross-cultural industrial organizational psychology and organizational behavior: A hundred-year journey. *Journal of Applied Psychology, 102*(3), 514–529. https://psycnet.apa.org/doi/10.1037/apl0000186

Gerwe, O., & Silva, R. (2020). Clarifying the sharing economy: Conceptualization, typology, antecedents, and effects. *Academy of Management Perspectives, 34*(1), 65–96. https://doi.org/10.5465/amp.2017.0010

Gloss, A., Carr, S., Reichman, W., Abdul-Nasiru, I., & Oestereich, W. (2017). From handmaidens to POSH humanitarians: The case for making human capabilities the business of I-O psychology. *Industrial and Organizational Psychology, 10*(3), 329–369. https://doi.org/10.1017/iop.2017.27

Gooderham, P., Fenton-O'Creevy, M., Croucher, R., & Brookes, M. (2018). A multilevel analysis of the use of individual pay-for-performance systems. *Journal of Management, 44*(4), 1479–1504. https://doi.org/10.1177/0149206315610634

Hekman, D. R., Johnson, S. K., Foo, M. D., & Yang, W. (2017). Does diversity-valuing behavior result in diminished performance ratings for non-white and female leaders? *Academy of Management Journal, 60*(2), 771–797. https://doi.org/10.5465/amj.2014.0538

Hernandez, M., Avery, D. R., Volpone, S. D., & Kaiser, C. R. (2019). Bargaining while Black: The role of race in salary negotiations. *Journal of Applied Psychology, 104*(4), 581–592. https://psycnet.apa.org/doi/10.1037/apl0000363

Hofstede, G. (1993). Cultural constraints in management theories. *Academy of Management Perspectives, 7*(1), 81–94. https://doi.org/10.5465/ame.1993.9409142061

Hofstede, G. (2011). Dimensionalizing cultures: The Hofstede model in context. *Online Readings in Psychology and Culture, 2*(1). https://doi.org/10.9707/2307-0919.1014

Huo, Y. P., Huang, H. J., & Napier, N. K. (2002). Divergence or convergence: A cross-national comparison of personnel selection practices. *Human Resource Management, 41*(1), 31–44. https://doi.org/10.1002/hrm.10018

Hwang, A., & Francesco, A. M. (2010). The influence of individualism–collectivism and power distance on use of feedback channels and consequences for learning. *Academy of Management Learning & Education, 9*(2), 243–257. https://doi.org/10.5465/amle.9.2.zqr243

Internet World Stats. (2022). *World internet users—Statistics.* http://www.internetworldstats.com/stats.htm

Johnson, J. P., Lenartowicz, T., & Apud, S. (2006). Cross-cultural competence in international business: Toward a definition and a model. *Journal of International Business Studies, 37*(4), 525–543. https://doi.org/10.1057/palgrave.jibs.8400205

Kim, J., Lee, H. W., Gao, H., & Johnson, R. E. (2021). When CEOs are all about themselves: Perceived CEO narcissism and middle managers' workplace behaviors amid the COVID-19 pandemic. *Journal of Applied Psychology, 106*(9), 1283–1298. https://psycnet.apa.org/doi/10.1037/apl0000965

Kirkman, B. L., Chen, G., Farh, J. L., Chen, Z. X., & Lowe, K. B. (2009). Individual power distance orientation and follower reactions to transformational leaders: A cross-level, cross-cultural examination. *Academy of Management Journal, 52*(4), 744–764. https://doi.org/10.5465/amj.2009.43669971

Klein, K. M., & Wang, M. (2010). Deep-level diversity and leadership. *American Psychologist, 65*(9), 932–934. https://doi.org/10.1037/a0021355

Kwon, S., Kim, M. S., Kang, S. C., & Kim, M. U. (2008). Employee reactions to gainsharing under seniority pay systems: The mediating effect of distributive, procedural, and interactional justice. *Human Resource Management, 47*(4), 757–775. https://doi.org/10.1002/hrm.20243

Lee, S. Y., Pitesa, M., Thau, S., & Pillutla, M. M. (2015). Discrimination in selection decisions: Integrating stereotype fit and interdependence theories. *Academy of Management Journal, 58*(3), 789–812. https://doi.org/10.5465/amj.2013.0571

Lepanjuuri, K., Wishart, R., & Cornick, P. (2018). *The characteristics of those in the gig economy.* UK Department for Business, Energy and Industrial Strategy.

Leung, K., Ang, S., & Tan, M. L. (2014). Intercultural competence. *Annual Review of Organizational Psychology and Organizational Behavior, 1*(1), 489–519. https://doi.org/10.1146/annurev-orgpsych-031413-091229

Li, C., & Haleblian, J. (2022). The influence of nation-level institutions on acquisition premiums: A cross-country comparative study. *Journal of Management, 48*(4), 878–904. https://doi.org/10.1177/01492063211010219

Li, X. H., & Liang, X. (2015). A Confucian social model of political appointments among Chinese private-firm entrepreneurs. *Academy of Management Journal, 58*(2), 592–617. https://doi.org/10.5465/amj.2012.1067

Li, Y., Gong, Y., Burmeister, A., Wang, M., Alterman, V., Alonso, A., & Robinson, S. (2021). Leveraging age diversity for organizational performance: An intellectual capital perspective. *Journal of Applied Psychology, 106*(1), 71–91. https://doi.org/10.1037/apl0000497

Li, Y., Kleshinski, C. E., Wilson, K. S., & Zhang, K. (2021). Age differences in affective responses to inclusion experience: A daily diary study. *Personnel Psychology*, 1–28. https://doi.org/10.1111/peps.12484

Li, Y., Koopmann, J., Lanaj, K., & Hollenbeck, J. R. (2021). An integration-and-learning perspective on gender diversity in self-managing teams: The roles of learning goal orientation and shared leadership. *Journal of Applied Psychology*. Advance online publication. https://doi.org/10.1037/apl0000942

Li, Y., Shao, Y., Wang, M., Fang, Y., Gong, Y., & Li, C. (2022). From inclusive climate to organizational innovation: Examining internal and external enablers for knowledge management capacity. *Journal of Applied Psychology*. Advance online publication. https://doi.org/10.1037/apl0001014

Li, Y., Wang, M., van Jaarsveld, D. D., Lee, G. K., & Ma, D. G. (2018). From employee-experienced high-involvement work system to innovation: An emergence-based human resource management framework. *Academy of Management Journal, 61*(5), 2000–2019. https://doi.org/10.5465/amj.2015.1101

Lin, W., Shao, Y., Li, G., Guo, Y., & Zhan, X. (2021). The psychological implications of COVID-19 on employee job insecurity and its consequences: The mitigating role of organization adaptive practices. *Journal of Applied Psychology, 106*(3), 317–329. https://psycnet.apa.org/doi/10.1037/apl0000896

Littrell, L. N., & Salas, E. (2005). A review of cross-cultural training: Best practices, guidelines, and research needs. *Human Resource Development Review, 4*(3), 305–334. https://doi.org/10.1177/1534484305278348

Liu, L. A., Chua, C. H., & Stahl, G. K. (2010). Quality of communication experience: Definition, measurement, and implications for intercultural negotiations. *Journal of Applied Psychology, 95*(3), 469–487. https://psycnet.apa.org/doi/10.1037/a0019094

Liu, Y., & Maula, M. (2016). Local partnering in foreign ventures: Uncertainty, experiential learning, and syndication in cross-border venture capital investments. *Academy of Management Journal, 59*(4), 1407–1429. https://doi.org/10.5465/amj.2013.0835

Magnusson, P., & Boggs, D. J. (2006). International experience and CEO selection: An empirical study. *Journal of International Management, 12*(1), 107–125. https://doi.org/10.1016/j.intman.2006.01.002

Martin, D. C., & Bartol, K. M. (2003). Factors influencing expatriate performance appraisal system success: An organizational perspective. *Journal of International Management, 9*(2), 115–132. https://doi.org/10.1016/S1075-4253(03)00030-9

Martin, K. D., Cullen, J. B., Johnson, J. L., & Parboteeah, K. P. (2007). Deciding to bribe: A cross-level analysis of firm and home country influences on bribery activity. *Academy of Management Journal, 50*(6), 1401–1422. https://doi.org/10.5465/amj.2007.28179462

Matta, E., & Beamish, P. W. (2008). The accentuated CEO career horizon problem: Evidence from international acquisitions. *Strategic Management Journal, 29*(7), 683–700. https://doi.org/10.1002/smj.680

Maynard, M. T., Mathieu, J. E., Rapp, T. L., & Gilson, L. L. (2012). Something(s) old and something(s) new: Modeling drivers of global virtual team effectiveness. *Journal of Organizational Behavior, 33*(3), 342–365. https://doi.org/10.1002/job.1772

McKinsey Global Institute. (2017). *Artificial intelligence: The next digital frontier?*. https://www.calpers.ca.gov/docs/board-agendas/201801/full/day1/06-technology-background.pdf

Minkov, M., & Kaasa, A. (2021). A test of the revised Minkov–Hofstede model of culture: Mirror images of subjective and objective culture across nations and the 50 US states. *Cross-Cultural Research, 55*(2–3), 230–281. https://doi.org/10.1177/10693971211014468

Mithani, M. A. (2020). Adaptation in the face of the new normal. *Academy of Management Perspectives, 34*(4), 508–530. https://doi.org/10.5465/amp.2019.0054

Morley, M. J., Murphy, K. R., Cleveland, J. N., Heraty, N., & McCarthy, J. (2021). Home and host distal context and performance appraisal in multinational enterprises: A 22 country study. *Human Resource Management, 60*(5), 715–736. https://doi.org/10.1002/hrm.22056

Morris, M. A., & Robie, C. (2001). A meta-analysis of the effects of cross-cultural training on expatriate performance and adjustment. *International Journal of Training and Development, 5*(2), 112–125. https://doi.org/10.1111/1468-2419.00126

Mueller, K., Hattrup, K., Spiess, S. O., & Lin-Hi, N. (2012). The effects of corporate social responsibility on employees' affective commitment: A cross-cultural investigation. *Journal of Applied Psychology, 97*(6), 1186–1200. https://psycnet.apa.org/doi/10.1037/a0030204

Nam, T. (2014). Technology use and work-life balance. *Applied Research in Quality of Life, 9*(4), 1017–1040.

Nardinelli, C., & Simon, C. (1990). Customer racial discrimination in the market for memorabilia: The case of baseball. *The Quarterly Journal of Economics, 105*(3), 575–595. https://doi.org/10.2307/2937891

Nicholls-Nixon, C. L., Davila Castilla, J. A., Sanchez Garcia, J., & Rivera Pesquera, M. (2011). Latin America management research: Review, synthesis, and extension. *Journal of Management, 37*(4), 1178–1227. https://doi.org/10.1177/0149206311403151

Ones, D. S., Sinangil, H. K., Viswesvaran, C., & Anderson, N. (2015). *The SAGE handbook of industrial, work & organizational psychology: Managerial psychology and organizational approaches.* SAGE.

Ong, A. D., Fuller-Rowell, T., & Burrow, A. L. (2009). Racial discrimination and the stress process. *Journal of Personality and Social Psychology, 96*(6), 1259–1271. https://psycnet.apa.org/doi/10.1037/a0015335

Oswald, F. L., Behrend, T. S., Putka, D. J., & Sinar, E. (2020). Big data in industrial-organizational psychology and human resource management: Forward progress for organizational research and practice. *Annual Review of Organizational Psychology and Organizational Behavior, 7,* 505–533. https://doi.org/10.1146/annurev-orgpsych-032117-104553

Peiró, J. M. (2014). Roles and responsibilities of international psychology organizations in improving psychology education and training. In R. K. Silbereisen, P. L. J. Ritichie, & J. Pandey (Eds.), *Psychology education and training: A global perspective* (pp. 231–241). Psychology Press.

Peng, M. W. (2016). *Global business.* Cengage Learning.

Phan, P. H. (2021). Where is management theory in an age of crises? *Academy of Management Perspectives, 35*(3), 331–333. https://doi.org/10.5465/amp.2021.0128

Phillips, J. M., Gully, S. M., McCarthy, J. E., Castellano, W. G., & Kim, M. S. (2014). Recruiting global travelers: The role of global travel recruitment messages and individual differences in perceived fit, attraction, and job pursuit intentions. *Personnel Psychology, 67*(1), 153–201. https://doi.org/10.1111/peps.12043

Popkova, E. G., & Parakhina, V. N. (2018). Managing the global financial system on the basis of artificial intelligence: Possibilities and limitations. In E. Popkova (Eds.), *International Conference Project, "The future of the Global Financial System: Downfall or harmony"* (pp. 939–946). Springer. https://doi.org/10.1007/978-3-030-00102-5_100

Prensky, M. (2001). Digital natives, digital immigrants. *On the Horizon, 9*(5), 1–6. https://doi.org/10.1108/10748120110424843

Price, J., & Wolfers, J. (2010). Racial discrimination among NBA referees. *The Quarterly Journal of Economics, 125*(4), 1859–1887. https://doi.org/10.1162/qjec.2010.125.4.1859

Raisch, S., & Krakowski, S. (2021). Artificial intelligence and management: The automation–augmentation paradox. *Academy of Management Review, 46*(1), 192–210. https://doi.org/10.5465/amr.2018.0072

Ramarajan, L., & Reid, E. (2020). Relational reconciliation: Socializing others across demographic differences. *Academy of Management Journal, 63*(2), 356–385. https://doi.org/10.5465/amj.2017.0506

Ramesh, A., & Gelfand, M. J. (2010). Will they stay or will they go? The role of job embeddedness in predicting turnover in individualistic and collectivistic cultures. *Journal of Applied Psychology, 95*(5), 807–823. https://psycnet.apa.org/doi/10.1037/a0019464

Raver, J. L., & Nishii, L. H. (2010). Once, twice, or three times as harmful? Ethnic harassment, gender harassment, and generalized workplace harassment. *Journal of Applied Psychology, 95*(2), 236–254. https://doi.org/10.1037/a0018377

Reinhardt, W., Schmidt, B., Sloep, P., & Drachsler, H. (2011). Knowledge worker roles and actions—Results of two empirical studies. *Knowledge and Process Management, 18*(3), 150–174. https://doi.org/10.1002/kpm.378

Ren, H., Shaffer, M. A., Harrison, D. A., Fu, C., & Fodchuk, K. M. (2014). Reactive adjustment or proactive embedding? Multistudy, multiwave evidence for dual pathways to expatriate retention. *Personnel Psychology, 67*(1), 203–239. https://doi.org/10.1111/peps.12034

Rickley, M. (2019). Cultural generalists and cultural specialists: Examining international experience portfolios of subsidiary executives in multinational firms. *Journal of Management, 45*(2), 384–416. https://doi.org/10.1177/0149206317748745

Rynes, S. L., Bretz, R. D., Jr., & Gerhart, B. (1991). The importance of recruitment in job choice: A different way of looking. *Personnel Psychology, 44* (3), 487–521. https://doi.org/10.1111/j.1744-6570.1991.tb02402.x

Shaiq, H. M. A., Khalid, H. M. S., Akram, A., & Ali, B. (2011). Why not everybody loves Hofstede? What are the alternative approaches to study of culture? *European Journal of Business and Management, 3*(6), 101–111.

Shore, L. M., Randel, A. E., Chung, B. G., Dean, M. A., Holcombe Ehrhart, K., & Singh, G. (2011). Inclusion and diversity in work groups: A review and model for future research. *Journal of Management, 37*(4), 1262–1289. https://doi.org/10.1177%2F0149206310385943

Shrestha, N., Shad, M. Y., Ulvi, O., Khan, M. H., Karamehic-Muratovic, A., Nguyen, U. S. D., Baghbanzadeh, M., Wardrup, R., Aghamohammadi, N., Cervantes, D., Nahiduzzaman, K. M., Zaki, R. A., & Haque, U. (2020). The impact of COVID-19 on globalization. *One Health, 11*, 100180. https://doi.org/10.1016/j.onehlt.2020.100180

Siegel, J., Pyun, L., & Cheon, B. Y. (2019). Multinational firms, labor market discrimination, and the capture of outsider's advantage by exploiting the social divide. *Administrative Science Quarterly, 64*(2), 370–397. https://doi.org/10.1177/0001839218769634

Small, M. L., & Pager, D. (2020). Sociological perspectives on racial discrimination. *Journal of Economic Perspectives, 34*(2), 49–67. https://doi.org/10.1257/jep.34.2.49

Smith, A. N., Watkins, M. B., Ladge, J. J., & Carlton, P. (2019). Making the invisible visible: Paradoxical effects of intersectional invisibility on the career experiences of executive Black women. *Academy of Management Journal, 62*(6), 1705–1734. https://doi.org/10.5465/amj.2017.1513

Smith, R. (2020, May 1). How CEOs can support employee mental health in a crisis. *Harvard Business Review*.

Soni, N., Sharma, E. K., Singh, N., & Kapoor, A. (2020). Artificial intelligence in business: From research and innovation to market deployment. *Procedia Computer Science, 167*, 2200–2210. https://doi.org/10.1016/j.procs.2020.03.272

Sully de Luque, M. F., & Sommer, S. M. (2000). The impact of culture on feedback-seeking behavior: An integrated model and propositions. *Academy of Management Review, 25*(4), 829–849. https://doi.org/10.5465/amr.2000.3707736

Sy, T., Shore, L. M., Strauss, J., Shore, T. H., Tram, S., Whiteley, P., & Ikeda-Muromachi, K. (2010). Leadership perceptions as a function of race–occupation fit: The case of Asian Americans. *Journal of Applied Psychology, 95*(5), 902–919. https://doi.org/10.1037/a0019501

Takeuchi, R., Li, Y., & Wang, M. (2019). Expatriates' performance profiles: Examining the effects of work experiences on the longitudinal change patterns. *Journal of Management, 45*(2), 451–475. https://doi.org/10.1177/0149206317741195

Takeuchi, R., Wang, M., Marinova, S. V., Yao, X. (2009). Role of domain-specific facets of perceived organizational support during expatriation and implications for performance. *Organization Science, 20*(3), 621–634. https://doi.org/10.1287/orsc.1080.0403

Takeuchi, R., Wang, M., & Marinova, S. V. (2005). Antecedents and consequences of psychological workplace strain during expatriation: A cross-sectional and longitudinal investigation. *Personnel Psychology*, 58(4), 925–948. https://doi.org/10.1111/j.1744-6570.2005.00809.x

Tang, P. M., Koopman, J., McClean, S. T., Zhang, J. H., Li, C. H., De Cremer, D., Lu, Y., & Ng, C. T. S. (2021). When conscientious employees meet intelligent machines: An integrative approach inspired by complementarity theory and role theory. *Academy of Management Journal*, 65(3), 1019–1054. https://doi.org/10.1111/j.1744-6570.2005.00809.x

Taylor, M., Marsh, G., Nicol, D., & Broadbent, P. (2017). *Good work: The Taylor review of modern working practices*. Department for Business, Energy & Industrial Strategy.

Tomlinson, J. (1999). *Globalization and culture*. University of Chicago Press.

Tschang, F. T. (2021). Platform-dependent entrepreneurs: Participants in an expanding universe of platforms? *Academy of Management Perspectives*, 35(4), 696–701. https://doi.org/10.5465/amp.2020.0140

Tsui, A. S., Nifadkar, S. S., & Ou, A. Y. (2007). Cross-national, cross-cultural organizational behavior research: Advances, gaps, and recommendations. *Journal of Management*, 33(3), 426–478. https://doi.org/10.1177/0149206307300818

Uggerslev, K. L., Fassina, N. E., & Kraichy, D. (2012). Recruiting through the stages: A meta-analytic test of predictors of applicant attraction at different stages of the recruiting process. *Personnel Psychology*, 65(3), 597–660. https://doi.org/10.1111/j.1744-6570.2012.01254.x

Van der Laken, P. A., Van Engen, M. L., Van Veldhoven, M. J. P. M., & Paauwe, J. (2019). Fostering expatriate success: A meta-analysis of the differential benefits of social support. *Human Resource Management Review*, 29(4), 100679. https://doi.org/10.1016/j.hrmr.2018.12.003

Vignovic, J. A., & Thompson, L. F. (2010). Computer-mediated cross-cultural collaboration: Attributing communication errors to the person versus the situation. *Journal of Applied Psychology*, 95(2), 265–276. https://doi.org/10.1037/a0018628

Volpone, S. D., Marquardt, D. J., Casper, W. J., & Avery, D. R. (2018). Minimizing cross-cultural maladaptation: How minority status facilitates change in international acculturation. *Journal of Applied Psychology*, 103(3), 249–269. https://doi.org/10.1037/apl0000273

Von Krogh, G. (2018). Artificial intelligence in organizations: New opportunities for phenomenon-based theorizing. *Academy of Management Discoveries*, 4(4), 404–409. https://doi.org/10.5465/amd.2018.0084

Wang, M., Burlacu, G., Truxillo, D., James, K., & Yao, X. (2015). Age differences in feedback reactions: The roles of employee feedback orientation on social awareness and utility. *Journal of Applied Psychology*, 100(4), 1296–1308. https://doi.org/10.1037/a0038334

Wang, M., & Fang, Y. (2020). Age diversity in the workplace: Facilitating opportunities with organizational practices. *Public Policy & Aging Report*, 30(3), 119–123. https://doi.org/10.1093/ppar/praa015

Wang, M., & Hanges, P. J. (2011). Latent class procedures: Applications to organizational research. *Organizational Research Methods*, 14(1), 24–31. https://doi.org/10.1177/1094428110383988

Wang, Q. E., Myers, M. D., & Sundaram, D. (2013). Digital natives and digital immigrants: Towards a model of digital fluency. *Business & Information Systems Engineering*, 5(6), 409–419. https://doi.org/10.1007/s12599-013-0296-y

Wang, M., & Takeuchi, R. (2007). The role of goal orientation during expatriation: A cross-sectional and longitudinal investigation. *Journal of Applied Psychology*, 92(5), 1437–1445. https://doi.org/10.1037/0021-9010.92.5.1437

Wood, A. J., Graham, M., Lehdonvirta, V., & Hjorth, I. (2019). Good gig, bad gig: Autonomy and algorithmic control in the global gig economy. *Work, Employment and Society*, 33(1), 56–75. https://doi.org/10.1177/0950017018785616

Yahiaoui, D., Nakhle, S. F., & Farndale, E. (2021). Culture and performance appraisal in multinational enterprises: Implementing French headquarters' practices in Middle East and North Africa subsidiaries. *Human Resource Management, 60*(5), 771–785. https://doi.org/10.1002/hrm.22063

Yoon, S., McClean, S. T., Chawla, N., Kim, J. K., Koopman, J., Rosen, C. C., Trougakos, J. P., & McCarthy, J. M. (2021). Working through an "infodemic": The impact of COVID-19 news consumption on employee uncertainty and work behaviors. *Journal of Applied Psychology, 106*(4), 501–517. https://doi.org/10.1037/apl0000913

Zhang, N., Wang, M., & Xu, H. (2022). Disentangling effect size heterogeneity in meta-analysis: A latent mixture approach. *Psychological Methods, 27*(3), 373–399. https://doi.org/10.1037/met0000368

Zhu, H., Ma, X., Sauerwald, S., & Peng, M. W. (2019). Home country institutions behind cross-border acquisition performance. *Journal of Management, 45*(4), 1315–1342. https://doi.org/10.1177/0149206317699520

Zhu, J., Wanberg, C. R., Harrison, D. A., & Diehn, E. W. (2016). Ups and downs of the expatriate experience? Understanding work adjustment trajectories and career outcomes. *Journal of Applied Psychology, 101*(4), 549–568. https://doi.org/10.1037/apl0000073

Mo Wang, Chengquan Huang, Junhui Yang, and Zhefan Huang

CROSS-CULTURAL ISSUES IN INDUSTRIAL, WORK, AND ORGANIZATIONAL PSYCHOLOGY

INTRODUCTION

Since 2010, there has been a proliferation of cross-cultural research and practice in industrial, work, and organizational psychology (IWOP). Although previously looked upon as a niche domain, cross-cultural IWOP has become increasingly prominent. Its importance is further evidenced in a recent collaboration among industrial, work, and organizational psychologists who presented a Declaration of Identity that was endorsed by scholars worldwide. Included in the declaration is the recognition of IWOP as an international profession in its own right, with ethical responsibilities to societies at large (Kożusznik & Glazer, 2021).

Including cross-cultural perspectives in the field of IWOP contributes to a deeper understanding of people's experiences and behaviors associated with work and organizations. These contributions are all the more apparent when scholars and practitioners find themselves at a loss for explaining why a theory did not hold up or why an intervention did not work in new contexts. Indeed, "best practices" are not always portable to different countries. In a comprehensive review of cross-cultural industrial and organizational psychology, Glazer (2002) pointed out that, up to that point in time, any semblance of cross-cultural IWOP research had been more about the portability of IWOP theories to different countries rather than methodologically rigorous cross-cultural comparisons. Similarly, in searching through more than 2,000 articles published in 13 English-language applied and organizational psychology journals from between 1980 and 1989, Erez (1994) found that only 21 were true cross-cultural studies. As Gelfand et al. (2017) noted, most scholarship in IWOP did not consider culture until well into the 2000s, with a burgeoning of scholarship around the 2010s, as the notion of cross-cultural competence gained popularity.

Much of the cross-cultural IWOP focus has been on the "O" topics rather than the "I" topics. In the domain of industrial psychology, concepts related to selection and placement, training and development, and performance management are studied. The focus of industrial psychology is on how to select the best employees through various methods of assessments, to develop employees' skills to contribute to the workforce, and to appraise employee performance. Cross-cultural research in these domains is limited, although there is increasing awareness of the need to test the efficacy of selection, including personality assessments across cultures (e.g., Ion et al., 2016, 2017; van de Vijver & Poortinga, 1997). Certainly, these topic areas are linked to many of the "O" topics that are covered in this entry and are deserving of more attention.

This contribution provides a snapshot of the history of cross-cultural IWOP research, the role of cultural values and cultural context in IWOP, and multiculturalization of businesses around the globe. It then delves into several cross-cultural IWOP topics that have received increased attention in the last decade. In particular, this article focuses on a few salient topics that have fueled insights and debates in IWOP literature to date, including organizational culture; leadership; occupational safety, stress, and health; precarious and decent work; trust; and workplace diversity and inclusion. This contribution concludes with some thoughts on the future of cross-cultural IWOP research and practice.

INDUSTRIAL, WORK, AND ORGANIZATIONAL PSYCHOLOGY'S INITIAL INCLUSION OF CULTURE

Notable early researchers in the field, such as Walter Dill Scott, considered a father of industrial psychology, along with Hugo Münsterberg, were both trained in Leipzig, Germany, under Wilhelm Wundt. However, whereas Münsterberg was from Prussia, Scott was from the United States, and both launched branches of applied psychology scholarship that are recognized as part of IWOP. Despite studying under Wundt, who is known for having a perspective that societal culture explains some of the psychological processes that influence outcomes, neither Münsterberg nor Scott considered culture a major contributor to people's affects, behaviors, or cognitions. Still, several of their contributions were also not devoid of contextual influences. For example, Robert Yerkes, a member of Scott's research group of psychologists that created the U.S. Army Alpha test, identified a test-design problem as the selection test failed on account of test takers' illiteracy, in part due to them being immigrants to the United States.

Founded in Europe in 1920, the International Association for Applied Psychology (IAAP) developed out of a necessity to take psychological principles into applied settings. Within the United States, Division 14 of the American Psychological Association (APA), currently known as the Society for Industrial and Organizational Psychology, was founded in 1945 (Bryan & Pickren, 2021). The Canadian Society for Industrial/Organizational Psychology (C-SIOP) was established in 1975, and in 1981, in response to a seemingly culture-bound APA Division 14, the European Network of Organizational Psychologists was constituted to address matters in Europe. A decade later, in 1991, the European Association for Work and Organizational Psychology (EAWOP) was established and open to people from around the globe. Over a decade after that (in 2005), the Society for IO Psychology South Africa took form. In 2009, the Alliance for Organizational Psychology (a.k.a. the Alliance) grew out of a desire to formally connect SIOP, EAWOP, IAAP, and, later, C-SIOP. By 2021, the Alliance connected associations and societies focused on IWOP from every inhabited continent (more than 20 countries). Still, even in 2021, in an edited book on the history of industrial and organizational (IO) psychology, there is a chapter that addresses IWOP around the world but not one that addresses cross-cultural findings (Bryan, 2021). From a historical perspective, the field of IWOP is still in its adolescence, and the role of culture within IWOP is truly in its infancy.

Notable examples of when culture began to be recognized as an important consideration in IWOP include literary debates on psychological theories, such as goal-setting theory in the 1980s (Erez, 2018; Latham et al., 1988), when occasionally authors recognized that a possible reason for their inconsistent findings was cultural differences. Specifically, Miriam Erez, Chris Earley, Ed Locke, and Gary Latham put the work of goal setting on an international stage (Erez, 2018; Erez & Earley, 1987; Latham et al., 1988). Around that same time, Earley (1989, 1993) identified cultural differences in group and team behaviors, comparing employees in the United States and China.

Erez's (2018) article describes various ways that culture influences workplace motivation and satisfaction. Goal-setting theory appears to be the most portable motivational theory across cultures. Not only was it validated in East Asia as well as in Western settings (Matsui et al., 1987, as cited in Erez, 2018, p. 3), but the theory can also be applied in different ways to suit the culture for which it is intended. For example, in a country such as Israel, where power distance is low, it is particularly important to have employees participate in setting their goals because they tend to respond negatively to having goals assigned to them but perform very well when they were able to provide input in setting their goals (Erez, 2018).

INDUSTRIAL, WORK, AND ORGANIZATIONAL PSYCHOLOGY AS A CULTURALLY IMPACTED DISCIPLINE

In a review of published articles, Erez (2018) found only 14 papers on cross-cultural IWOP research between 1960 and 1989 despite the fact that there were whispers of the importance of a cultural focus in IWOP even before 1960. For example, in 1951, W. Edwards Deming presented a novel philosophy outlining 14 principles to ensure total quality in managing projects and people in his *Quality Control Handbook*. His ideas were shaped by statistical and mathematical models for rectifying quality issues in manufacturing at the Western Electric Company's Hawthorn plant in the mid-1920s. However, they were not embraced by American industry. Instead, throughout the 1950s, Deming presented his principles to Japanese companies that were striving to make an economic return after the devastation of World War II. The results of Japanese companies' adoption of Total Quality Management (TQM) were so astounding that in the 1970s, many U.S. companies decided to adopt it too. By the mid-1980s, it became evident that TQM was not going to yield the same stellar results in the United States as in Japan. Consequently, researchers began to test cultural implications on the efficacy of TQM (e.g., Sousa-Poza et al., 2001). Attempting to explain the success or failure of TQM, scholars took to another groundbreaking theory of cultural values that was being developed in the 1970s—Hofstede's (1976, 1980) cultural values. These cultural values would come to be used as notable explanations for variations in the efficacy of TQM in different countries.

Hofstede's (1980, 2001) research incorporated a more quantitative approach to understanding and comparing cultures than had been used in earlier years by influential anthropologists (Munroe & Munroe, 1997). As a social psychologist working with IBM in the 1960s and 1970s, he developed and analyzed employee survey data related to experiences and values in the work setting. In his analyses, he noticed that employees within global regions often had similarities in their responses. Using the items in the internal organizational survey, Hofstede (1980) developed four dimensions that could be used to describe—and compare—various societal cultures. These dimensions include collectivism versus individualism, masculinity versus femininity, uncertainty avoidance, and power distance. Shortly after Hofstede's work was published, the Chinese Culture Connection (1987) identified Confucian work dynamism, which Hofstede (2001) adapted as short-term versus long-term orientation; more recently Minkov and Hofstede (2011) introduced indulgence versus restraint. However, the first four cultural values dimensions continue to dominate most cross-cultural IWOP research that compares societal cultures. Perhaps because of its origins, rooted in organizations and organizational research, Hofstede's cultural values became and maintained a dominant role in cross-cultural IWOP since the 1970s.

Criticism regarding Hofstede's (1980) methodology resulted in the development of a more rigorous approach to discovering both cultural and individual values (Schwartz, 1992; Schwartz & Sagiv, 1995). Cultural values have been conjectured to directly affect work centrality, norms about working, and work values (Schwartz, 1999) and found to relate to reward allocation (Fischer et al., 2007). Individual values were found to relate to perceptions of justice (Fischer & Smith, 2006), organizational citizenship behavior (Cohen & Liu, 2011), and organizational commitment (Glazer et al., 2004; Wasti, 2003), to name a few.

A more recent approach to measuring societal cultural values and their relationship with various organizational behaviors comes from the Global Leadership and Organizational Behavior Effectiveness (GLOBE) project (House et al., 2004). The GLOBE (https:// globeproject.com/) project reflects a collaborative effort with nearly 500 researchers in 150 countries. The project sought to include both etic (cultural-universals) and emic (cultural-specific) perspectives on organizational behaviors across the globe. Similar to Hofstede's (1980) research, GLOBE also focuses on geopolitical boundaries as the basis for cultural units; however, GLOBE also focused on specific subgroups, such as both Anglophone and Francophone samples in Canada. The GLOBE project expands the cultural values lens to nine dimensions: uncertainty avoidance, assertiveness, gender differentiation/egalitarianism, performance orientation, humane orientation, in-group collectivism, institutional collectivism, power distance, and future orientation. Critically, the GLOBE studies also distinguish between societal values as aspirational or that which is desired (i.e., what *should be* in a society) versus enacted or that which is practiced (i.e., what societal practices *actually are*). Together these cultural values have been shown to relate to different leadership styles around the world (Dorfman et al., 2012).

At the same time as the GLOBE cultural values and leadership styles were coming to light, Leung et al. (2002) were testing a new cultural characteristic, social axioms, or generalized beliefs that might help in understanding cross-cultural behavior, for example, workplace cynicism (e.g., Kwantes & Bond, 2019). More recently, Gelfand et al. (2011) presented the notion of cultural tightness versus looseness, reflecting the extent to which people are expected to follow societal norms and the degree to which there are strong sanctions toward those who do not follow the status quo. Cultural tightness and looseness have been linked to a number of organizational behaviors, including effective leadership (e.g., Aktas et al., 2016).

The preponderance of studies incorporating culture into IWOP research clearly shows the importance of understanding societal culture's impact on organizations, institutions, work, and workers. Context matters, and it matters deeply. Merely transferring existing theories and practices of IWOP to new contexts without a clear understanding of whether those theories and practices make sense across cultures is unlikely to be successful. Rather, careful cross-cultural research in IWOP is required. Currently, most large organizations are global to some extent (Erez & Shokef, 2008), and global supply chains are critical for most companies (Meyer et al., 2020). Failure to implement a cross-cultural focus results in a myopic, localized view of organizational and employee experiences. Thus, current work in cross-cultural IWOP strives to understand culture's impact on organizations, workers, and their work environments.

INDUSTRIAL, WORK, AND ORGANIZATIONAL PSYCHOLOGY AND THE GLOBALIZATION OF WORK AND ORGANIZATIONS

Globalization is a process wherein changes in technology, geographic dispersion, and cultural diversification have intensified the reach of work beyond the confines of an organization's immediate boundaries (Erez, 2018). Through globalization and the multiculturalization of workforces both internationally and domestically, many employees are interacting with people from other cultures on a far more regular basis than in the past (Gelfand et al., 2017). Globalization has thus resulted in a broadening, rather than a narrowing, of the range of IWOP topics and has spurred attention to how culture has impacted understanding in some key IWOP theoretical domains.

Organizational Culture.　Different societal contexts have different expectations, norms, and challenges (Matsumoto, 2007). Societal cultures often play a large role in how employees ascribe meanings in organizations, including their organizational culture. Organizational culture, as nested within societal culture, has had a strong appeal to both IWOP theorists and practitioners (Erez & Gati, 2004). Organizational culture has often been measured in the same way as societal culture—with a focus on either values or behavioral norms. Early quantitative work examining organizational culture was values-focused. Hofstede and colleagues (1990) explored ways to use value dimensions to describe organizational culture. Based on interviews of carefully selected employees, they determined that three values, security, authority, and work centrality, were key to understanding all organizational cultures. Using values to understand organizational culture as a parallel to using values to understand societal culture may have some utility (Glazer, 2021) yet it does not always replicate well (Bond, 1997). Despite the obvious potential links between organizational and societal cultures, the constructs at the two levels are not necessarily isomorphic (Hofstede, 2001; Kwantes & Dickson, 2011).

This recognition has spurred other ways to understand organizational culture—notably that of defining organizational culture as behavioral norms and expectations. Cooke and Szumal (1993), for example, operationalize organizational culture as resulting from the assumptions, beliefs, and behavioral expectations that are shared by employees of an organization.

Organizational culture conceptualized in this way can be an effective means to compare organizational behaviors across societies, as evident in research linking it to perceptions of leadership and personal effectiveness in multiple societal contexts (Kwantes & Boglarsky, 2007), as well as in specific contexts, such as Crete (Rovithis et al., 2017), France (Minvielle et al., 2008), China (Head, 2002), and even Antarctica (Sarris & Kirby, 2007). Behavioral norms and expectations in organizations are somewhat reflective of the norms and expectations of the society within which the organization exists, and there is some indication that alignment between cultural expectations at the societal and organizational levels can increase satisfaction and motivation (Kwantes & Boglarsky, 2003, 2006).

Although values and behavioral norms are discrete constructs (Fischer et al., 2009), they are not unrelated (Kwantes & Dickson, 2011). The values in an organization and society tend to guide the norms and expectations; however, the specific nature of this relationship is still unclear. For example, the GLOBE studies (House et al., 2004) found that practices and values did not always align in their data, and in fact, the correlations between them were often negative at the country level (Brodbeck et al., 2008). These disparate findings constitute an area of ongoing focus for cross-cultural IWOP.

Societal culture has an impact on organizational culture and vice versa (Dickson et al., 2014; Erez & Gati, 2004). Key to understanding the bidirectional influences of organizational and societal cultures is how individuals in societies develop and share values, attitudes, and norms of behaviors (Kwantes & Dickson, 2011). Thus, culture may be seen as a form of sensemaking (Harris, 1994) whereby individuals draw on available and salient information to understand what values are operating in a context and what ensuing behaviors are expected.

Leadership.   Leadership is one of the most common themes of IWOP and one of the first IWOP areas to be impacted by increased interest in cross-cultural research. In 1979, Bass et al. came to the conclusion that managers in different parts of the world often differ with respect to values and practices in the workplace. The GLOBE project (House et al., 2004) explicitly focused on both etic (universally accepted) and emic (culturally specific) leadership practices (Chhokar et al., 2008) noting that organizational leadership around the world has the same goal of influencing, motivating, and coordinating employee efforts, yet the way these goals are enacted can vary greatly from culture to culture and society to society. Aktas et al. (2016) examined the relationship between cultural tightness–looseness in relation to leadership styles (autocratic, charismatic, self-protective, autonomous, team, and humane-oriented leadership), finding that autonomous leadership (i.e., leaders who rely on their own abilities rather than seek feedback and collaboration from others) was perceived to be more effective by individuals in tight cultures. Furthermore, individuals' perceived effectiveness of team-oriented leadership and charismatic leadership was negatively associated with tightness. Watts et al. (2020) explored the relationship between transformational leadership and innovation as moderated by uncertainty avoidance. They noted that Latin American, Latin European, and East European countries tended to score high on uncertainty avoidance, and therefore, to stimulate employee innovations, organizations operating in those regions may benefit from investing in supervisor transformational leadership development. They also conjectured that transformational leaders are particularly effective in high uncertainty avoidant cultures because they are able to "project a positive image of the future that provides their employees with direction and meaning, which in turn reduces anxiety and uncertainty" (Watts et al., 2020, p. 2).

Beyond culture-specific leadership effectiveness, globalization has increased interest in global, or pancultural, leadership effectiveness. Caligiuri and Tarique (2012) found that to be an effective global leader, one must demonstrate high levels of cultural flexibility and tolerance of ambiguity, as well as low levels of ethnocentrism. Furthermore, "non-work cross-cultural experiences are related to dynamic cross-cultural competencies" and "high contact organization-initiated cross-cultural experiences are positively related to cultural flexibility and tolerance of ambiguity" (Caligiuri & Tarique, 2012, p. 619). Altogether, these findings suggest that it is beneficial for individuals, especially global leaders, to have experiences interacting with people from other cultures.

As organizations are becoming increasingly interdependent around the globe, the ability to understand cross-cultural differences is an increasingly important component of organizational success (Gupta & Govindarajan, 2002). A key to this understanding is a global mindset, or "the cognitive ability that helps individuals figure out how to best understand and influence individuals, groups, and organizations from diverse social/cultural systems" (Clapp-Smith et al., 2007, p. 106). Global mindsets for leaders are often considered an important competitive advantage and one that is too often ignored at an organization's "peril" (Beechler & Baltzley, 2008, p. 40).

Relatedly, cultural competence and cultural intelligence are receiving increasing attention in the field of IWOP (Kwantes & Glazer, 2017; Liao & Thomas, 2020). Broadly, cross-cultural competence reflects the ability to deal well with individuals from different societal cultural backgrounds (Li, 2020). Cultural intelligence goes beyond this to focus on intercultural effectiveness as resulting from an interacting system of knowledge and skills that an individual consciously draws on in a selective manner to suit a particular situation (Liao & Thomas, 2020). These two approaches to examining leadership effectiveness across cultures provide a lens for understanding how culture and leadership can interact to result in effective leadership.

A more recent interest in IWOP leadership studies has been in the area of ethical leadership. Although the preponderance of research into ethical leadership has shown multiple benefits for the organization and subordinates, the definition of ethical leadership that is most commonly accepted hinges on "normatively accepted conduct" (Brown et al., 2005, p. 120). Norms and normatively accepted behaviors vary greatly across societies, so it is no surprise that what constitutes "ethical leadership" behaviors can also vary widely from context to context. Resick and colleagues (2011) explicitly examined the relationship between societal culture and descriptions of both ethical and unethical leadership. They found that the more similar societal cultures were, the more similar descriptions of ethical leadership were. This finding highlights the importance of understanding similarities and differences in leadership expectations in both multinational organizations and organizations that work across societal culture divides. Clear connections between societal values and expectations and the way those impact perceptions—and even definitions—of ethical leadership have been found (Kimura & Nishikawa, 2018).

Occupational Safety, Stress, and Health. The domain of occupational safety, stress, and health has received an abundance of attention yet while studies have often been conducted within countries, until the early 2000s, few had been conducted cross-culturally (Glazer, 2002). Cultural and contextual norms appear to play an important role in the experience of stressors, coping abilities, and reported strains (Glazer, 2008). For example, the experience of employee burnout can vary greatly between countries (Pines, 2004; Schaufeli & Janczur, 1994) and furthermore, the implications of stressors on strains were found to vary in a four-country cross-cultural study of nurses (Glazer & Beehr, 2005). In a larger cross-cultural study with more than 6,000 managers from 24 countries, the perception of workload was greater in individualistic countries than in collectivistic countries even when the actual work hours were the same (Yang et al., 2012).

Organizations in individualistic countries, as compared to those in collectivistic countries are also more likely to have a transactional employee–organization relationship (Fitzsimmons & Stamper, 2014). In individualistic countries, employees are presented with opportunities for economic gain in exchange for work performance contributions. They typically prefer being given autonomy in deciding how to get their work done more than people in collectivistic countries. Both managers and employees understand this type of relationship to be quid pro quo, and there is much less psychological attachment as compared with organizations in collectivistic countries, which place a greater value on employee–organizational relationships. Considering that strain or friction occurs when there is a misalignment in expectations, employees in individualistic countries might seek to balance their investments and returns and, therefore, may view work stressors, such as long hours, as too heavy an investment in the organization. A perceived higher workload may be because they feel that their investment is not being matched and that work is getting in the way of other priorities. This conjecture also tracks with the findings from Masuda and colleagues (2012), which revealed a preference among people in individualistic countries for flexible work arrangements, such as flextime, part-time work, a compressed workweek, and telecommuting, that give employees some control of their time. Flexible work arrangements are a research domain that gained traction in the early 2000s. *Flexible work arrangement* refers to an employee's autonomy in deciding when, where, and how an individual works, and it can be both formally codified or informally agreed on. Research has also shown that managers in individualistic countries that offered flextime were more satisfied with their job, less likely to report turnover intentions, and less likely to report experiencing time-based and strain-based work–family conflict (Masuda et al., 2012).

Research on flexible work arrangements is part of a larger domain of research, specifically that of work–family or work–nonwork conflict. Work–nonwork conflict focuses on stressors a person might experience due to competing expectations between work and nonwork (e.g., family) roles. With a proliferation of research in work–nonwork conflict, it has come to be recognized that cultural context is an important factor influencing whether people experience work–nonwork expectations as a source of strain or not (Allen et al., 2020; Shockley et al., 2018). Allen and colleagues' (2020) meta-analysis shows a weaker relationship between work–nonwork conflict and satisfaction among workers in collectivistic countries than in individualistic countries, suggesting that where the roles are interdependent, there is less attitudinal strain. Such findings have important implications for the management of work–nonwork conflict among workers working across geographic borders. This domain garnered even more attention when the SARS-CoV-2 global pandemic work-from-home orders were issued (CultureAmp, 2020; Rudolph et al., 2021).

IWOP scholars have also been joining business and social psychology scholars in focusing on ways to help international assignees adjust to work and nonwork life in a foreign country. Given the high costs associated with failed international assignments and early returns home (Morris & Robie, 2001), researchers have been examining topics such as blogging as a coping resource (e.g., Nardon et al., 2015), family adjustment as a factor affecting expatriate assignment fulfillment (Ali et al., 2003), and even repatriation of those completing their assignments (e.g., Froese et al., 2021; Kraimer et al., 2012). One of the greatest financial losses for organizations sending workers abroad has been losing international assignees' institutional knowledge upon their return home, as repatriates often leave their employers within 1 to 2 years of their return because their role identities have changed (Kraimer et al., 2012). A better understanding of the cross-cultural competencies required to successfully navigate both foreign assignments and the demands of a return home would benefit from closer IWOP attention.

Precarious and Decent Work. Humanitarian work psychologists have begun to address topics that affect well over 60% of work-eligible adults, including conditions for precarious workers and decent work. Precarious workers tend to be poorly compensated in work, scheduled to work during unspecified or inconsistent work hours, work in poor and unsafe environmental conditions, have ill-defined reporting structures, sometimes work in social isolation, and have limited work protections through defined and upheld standards. The precarious nature of their work renders their jobs insecure, lacking in benefits, and with uncertain pay (Milczarek et al., 2008). Despite the increasingly unstable labor market and heightened vulnerability, these jobs are essential, but the value of the work and the workers who perform them are often overlooked in societies. To begin addressing these issues, researchers have begun focusing on decent work (Pereira et al., 2019).

The ILO first defined the concept of decent work in 1999 as an institutional effort to ensure security, gender equality, freedom, and human dignity by enabling all people to achieve fair wages, voice their opinions freely, enjoy work–nonwork balance, and personally develop. With increasing global economic dependencies, social inequalities have become more visible. Social scientists have been observing a preponderance of organizations taking advantage of social and economic inequalities in order to keep production costs and consumer prices down while maximizing profits. Unfortunately, where there are economic disparities, there are typically poor working conditions (Pereira et al., 2019). An international group of IWOP professionals formed the Global Organization for Humanitarian Work Psychology (GOHWP) in the early 2010s, with a specific focus on how IWOP can address the humanitarian aspects of work (Carr, 2021). However, there remains a dearth of IWOP research on decent work and a particular need to study this topic in the Global South, which is especially adversely impacted by social and economic disparities.

Trust and Trustworthiness. Trust is critical to good working relationships and to successful organizational functioning. The interdependent nature of work in organizations and the fact that business and organizational environments are constantly evolving make it impossible to agree ahead of time on all aspects of work and how to handle contingencies that may arise. This uncertainty necessitates trust, which is inherently a dynamic social construction

(Costa et al., 2018; Wright & Ehnert, 2010), The societal context is therefore critical for understanding the development of trust and the role trust plays in organizational settings.

Although personalities can impact the extent to which an individual has the propensity to trust others (Alarcon et al., 2018), trust and perceptions of trustworthiness are essentially always context-bound (Bachmann, 2010). Trust is fundamentally based on risk and reflects a "leap of faith" (Moellering, 2006) with a willingness to be vulnerable to the actions of another. As such, trust and perceptions of the trustworthiness of the "other" are inextricably linked (Mayer et al., 1995). Certain behaviors and exchanges are expected from individuals in specific organizational roles in order for individuals to be considered trustworthy; these expectations are rooted in societal expectations and vary according to societal culture (Kwantes & Kartolo, 2021). For example, managers in different cultural contexts place different emphases on attributes of employees in determining whether they are trustworthy (Brett & Mitchell, 2020) and use different cultural cues and actions for determining trustworthiness (Bürger et al., 2006).

Societal culture also affects how organizational functioning promotes or inhibits trust in the workplace. "Organizations and their employees are increasingly enmeshed in complex interdependencies across national, organization and professional borders, meaning that people from different 'cultures' are being asked to manage unfamiliar relationships with unfamiliar parties. Such contexts demand trust" (Dietz et al., 2010, p. 4). Societal-level collectivism impacts individual propensity to trust (Westjohn et al., 2022); however, organizations can intervene in this relationship to increase trust propensity.

Individuals' attitudes toward organizations tend to be personal (Malone & Fiske, 2013) and can extend to considering if organizations themselves are trustworthy. Perceived trust in organizations is based, in part, on predictability, perceptions of organizational justice, and organizational support (Vanhala et al., 2011). Furthermore, people in different cultures place different emphases on these factors. For example, an organization's compliance with legal mandates may be less important for determining the trustworthiness of organizations for East Asians than for North Americans (Caldwell & Clapham, 2003).

Assessments of whether another individual may be trusted are inextricably linked with cultural norms (Lau et al., 2008). In the absence of other information, the most fundamental heuristic used to determine trustworthiness is how much the other is "like me" (Farmer et al., 2014). Within multicultural workplaces, this comparison has created challenges for developing trust among coworkers, leading IWOP scholars to pay particular attention to trust in work teams (Costa et al., 2018).

Societal culture plays a large role in determining what expectations are for specific role behaviors in organizations, including leadership and followership roles (Blair & Bligh, 2018). Moreover, expected attributes of trustworthy leadership differ by cultural context (Kwantes & Kartolo, 2021), and different influence tactics are accepted as legitimate in different societies (Kennedy et al., 2003). Power distance, or the value for hierarchy, for example, has been found to be of particular importance to trust in supervisors, with evidence that supervisor–subordinate congruence in expectations related to supervisor power-enhanced trust (Guzman & Fu, 2022).

Trust in teams includes interpersonal trust and trust that reflects an assessment of the trustworthiness of the team as a whole (Costa et al., 2018). Multinational teams inherently have varied cultural perspectives that can impact trust in team members, as well as organizational effectiveness. Such teams may be long-standing in nature, or temporary, or even ad hoc. In this latter situation, in which the typical time and interaction for the development of trust may not be possible, "swift trust" (Meyerson et al., 1996) may play an intermediary role to facilitate team interaction across cultures. Rather than having a history of interactions and behaviors to determine the trustworthiness of another team member, employees draw on characteristics and stereotypes to make quick judgments about the trustworthiness of another. Swift trust is, however, vulnerable to interpretations of how team members behave and is therefore extremely fragile when team members come from different cultures. Some evidence suggests that positive and effective cross-cultural communication is able to sustain the swift trust until team members have a longer history of interactions to draw on for determining trustworthiness (Jarvenpaa & Leidner, 1999).

Diversity, Equity, and Inclusion in the Workplace.   The workforce of organizations inside geopolitical borders has undergone increasing multiculturalization and is receiving increasing attention in IWOP around the world. In many industrialized countries, immigration has been increasing (Turner, 2019), and the resulting impetus to be more inclusive of those with varying cultural traditions, values, and beliefs has become stronger. Indeed, cultural differences within the same workplace can have impactful consequences. For example, depending on cultural beliefs, the same organizational behaviors may be perceived as in-role or as extra-role (Kwantes et al., 2008), and levels of commitment to the organization may also differ (Glazer & De La Rosa, 2008). These variations could have real implications for both behaviors and performance evaluations.

Organizations are increasingly challenged to provide greater equity and inclusion to all employees, regardless of cultural background, yet there are some significant steps that could still be taken. For example, CultureAmp (2022) found that while 71% of organizations in their global survey indicated a focus on diversity, equity, and inclusion efforts, only 34% of organizations provide appropriate resources to support these efforts, and only 27% know how to assess whether these efforts were successful. Nonetheless, there are some notable efforts at organizational and societal levels to address these challenges. For example, Germany's Seat, SA, is focused on increasing inclusivity across generations, genders, LGBTQ community, and nationalities (B. R. Heller, personal communication, January 19, 2022). Also, some countries, such as Canada and Australia, are increasingly paying attention to organizational and labor issues related to Indigenous peoples—issues that were formerly totally ignored. New Zealand exemplifies a country where research that explicitly includes both Indigenous (Maori) and later settler viewpoints has flourished (see Haar & Brougham, 2016). Yet, IWOP has not begun to explore immigrant or Indigenous cultural issues in the workplace in a substantive manner.

ROLE OF CULTURE IN INDUSTRIAL, WORK, AND ORGANIZATIONAL PSYCHOLOGY IN THE FUTURE

In today's research, theory, and practice of IWOP, cultural context is still struggling to find its place. IWOP professionals still fail to consider that phenomena in one cultural context might not generalize to another cultural context. The role of culture in IWOP continues to be an add-on consideration. Even though there is greater international connectedness amongst scholars, as well as IWOP-related associations, through the Alliance for Organizational Psychology, culturally infused IWOP is still budding. In fact, most IWOP-related graduate programs do not have any courses or training in cross-cultural IWOP, although professors might pay homage to culture by assigning a cross-cultural reading here and there (Glazer et al., 2014, 2021).

The need to focus more on cross-cultural aspects of IWOP remains only partially addressed despite its urgency. Globalization is increasing at a pace that is faster than the scholarly activity that can describe, explain, and predict employee behavior in cross-cultural environments. International collaborative work arrangements have changed course; the manner and place in which office workers around the globe are working continue to shift. Companies around the world have been revisioning where and how business takes place. In fact, of 349 companies around the world that had little remote work prior to March 2020, roughly 33% plan to keep more than half their employees working remotely, about 40% will have less than half of their employees work remotely, and less than 20% will return to mostly in-person work (CultureAmp, 2020). The anticipation of global virtual teams proliferating (Glazer et al., 2012) is no longer a prediction. Global virtual teams are now a normal work context for office workers in multinational enterprises. IWOP scholars have not had sufficient exploration of the cyber environment as a replacement for the physical environment. Small two-dimensional boxes and avatars are now replacing human connection. This limited human connection is a cause for concern and an area that IWOP scholars must dive into; the implications of minimal to no human contact are concerns that will require more attention in the coming years.

During a nearly 2-year period (starting March 2020) of restricted international travel, there was an increased domestic focus on how equitable access to education and employment opportunities for people of underserved backgrounds could be improved. Organizations are increasingly expected to be agents of social change through employment equity and affirmative action legislation. Not only are governments, such as those in Canada and the United States, passing nondiscriminatory and equity employment legislation, but calls for these changes are reaching the ears of accounting auditors who are striving to capture the intangible costs and benefits of increasing workplace diversity. This movement to focus on intangibles in organizational change efforts is being captured through audits of organizations' environmental, social, and governance practices (Knachel & Porter, 2021). Now, more than ever, the calls for IWOP to be involved in diversity, equity, and inclusion in the workplace are getting louder (Brief, 2018).

A focus on inclusion requires expanding lenses beyond office and company workers to workers at the fringe who are often willing to work in the service sectors and in unskilled labor jobs, such as migrant workers. These workers disproportionately face health threats in their work (Hargreaves et al., 2019), often placing them in one of the most vulnerable employment sectors (Moyce & Schenkar, 2018). A related international development in IWOP is a greater focus on humanitarian work psychology that centers on decent work in which little to none exists for precarious, informal, and impoverished workers (Saxena, 2017). This global focus on decent work is another demonstration of IWOP's contributions to improving work lives, but the scholarship, again, is not cross-cultural.

Looking toward the future of IWOP research, attention must be given to health-promoting leadership and activities for workers of every kind in environments of every kind. In 2015, the

ILO's conception of decent work was integrated into the 2030 United Nations Sustainable Development Goals, as Goal 8:

> We envisage a world of universal respect for human rights and human dignity, the rule of law, justice, equality and non-discrimination; of respect for race, ethnicity and cultural diversity; and of equal opportunity permitting the full realization of human potential and contributing to shared prosperity. A world which invests in its children and in which every child grows up free from violence and exploitation. A world in which every woman and girl enjoys full gender equality and all legal, social and economic barriers to their empowerment have been removed. A just, equitable, tolerant, open and socially inclusive world in which the needs of the most vulnerable are met.
> (United Nations, 2015)

Indeed, there is much to anticipate looking forward as the future of IWOP unfolds to embrace culture as a core valued human dimension that can enrich a more connected world with respect and decency.

REFERENCES

Aktas, M., Gelfand, M. J., & Hanges, P. J. (2016). Cultural tightness-looseness and perceptions of effective leadership. *Journal of Cross-Cultural Psychology, 47,* 294–309.

Alarcon, G. M., Lyones, J. B., Christensen, J. C., Bowers, M. A., Klosterman, S. L., & Capiola, A. (2018). The role of propensity to trust and the five factor model across the trust process. *Journal of Research in Personality, 75,* 69–82.

Ali, A., van der Zee, K., & Sanders, G. (2003). Determinants of intercultural adjustment among expatriate spouses. *International Journal of Intercultural Relations, 27,* 563–580.

Allen, T. D., French, K. A., Dumani, S., & Shockley, K. M. (2020). A cross-national meta-analytic examination of predictors and outcomes associated with work–family conflict. *Journal of Applied Psychology, 105*(6), 539–576. https://doi.org/10.1037/apl0000442

Bachmann, R. (2010). Towards a context-sensitive approach to researching trust in inter-organizational relationships. In M. K. Saunders, S. Skinner, G. Dietz, N. Gillespie, & R. J. Lewicki (Eds.), *Organizational trust: A cultural perspective* (pp. 87–106). Cambridge University Press.

Bass, B. M., Burger, P. C., Doktor, R., & Barrett, G. V. (1979). *Assessment of managers: An international comparison.* Free Press.

Beechler, S., & Baltzley, D. (2008). Creating a global mindset. *Chief Learning Officer, 7*(6), 40–45.

Blair, B. A., & Bligh, M. C. (2018). Looking for leadership in all the wrong places: The impact of culture on proactive followership and follower dissent. *Journal of Social Issues, 74*(1), 129–143.

Bond, M. H. (1997). Adding value to the cross-cultural study of organizational behavior: Reculer pour mieux sauter. In P. C. Earley & M. Erez (Eds.), *New perspectives on international industrial/organizational psychology* (Ch. 10, pp. 256–275). New Lexington Press.

Brett, J. M., & Mitchell, T. (2020). Research: How to build trust with business partners from other cultures. *Harvard Business Review Digital Articles,* 2–8. https://hbr.org/2020/01/research-how-to-build-trust-with-business-partners-from-other-cultures

Brief, A. P. (2018). How much has America changed in 50 years? An organizational psychologist's take on social justice progress since the Civil Rights Act of 1964. In A. J. Colella & E. B. King (Eds.), *The Oxford handbook of workplace discrimination* (pp. 411–418). Oxford University Press.

Brodbeck, F. C., Chhokar, J. S., & House, R. J. (2008). Culture, leadership in 25 societies: Integration, conclusions, and future directions. In J. S. Chhokar, F. C. Brodbeck, & R. J. House (Eds.), *Culture and leadership across the world: The GLOBE book of in-depth studies of 25 societies* (pp. 1023–1084). Erlbaum.

Brown, M. E., Trevino, L. K., & Harrison, D. A. (2005). Ethical leadership: A social learning perspective for construct development and testing. *Organizational Behavior and Human Decision Processes, 97*(2), 117–134.

Bryan, L. K. (Ed.). (2021). *Historical perspectives in industrial and organizational psychology* (2nd ed.). Routledge.

Bryan, L. K., & Pickren, W. (2021). Industrial and organizational psychology: An evolving science and practice. In L. K. Bryan (Ed.), *Historical perspectives in industrial and organizational psychology* (2nd ed., pp. 1–20). Routledge.

Bürger, J., Luke, M., & Indeláová, H. (2006). Interpersonal trust in German–Czech work relations: Mutual expectations and suggestions for improvement. *Journal of Organisational Transformation & Social Change, 3*(2), 173–199.

Caldwell, C., & Clapham, S. E. (2003). Organizational trustworthiness: An international perspective. *Journal of Business Ethics, 46,* 349–364.

Caligiuri, P., & Tarique, I. (2012). Dynamic cross-cultural competencies and global leadership effectiveness. *Journal of World Business, 47,* 612–622.

Carr, S. C. (2021). Humanitarian work and organizational psychology. In J. M. Peiró (Ed.), *Oxford research encyclopedia of psychology.* Oxford University Press. https://doi.org/10.1093/acrefore/9780190236557.013.828

Chhokar, J. S., Brodbeck, F. C., & House, R. J. (Eds.). (2008). *Culture and leadership across the world: The GLOBE book of in-depth studies of 25 societies.* Erlbaum.

Chinese Culture Connection. (1987). Chinese values and the search for culture-free dimensions of culture. *Journal of Cross- Cultural Psychology, 18,* 143–164.

Clapp-Smith, R., Luthans, F., & Avolio, B. (2007). The role of psychological capital in global mindset development. In M. Javidan, R. M. Steers, & M. A. Hitt (Eds.), *The global mindset, advances in international management, Vol 19* (pp. 105–130). Emerald.

Cohen, A., & Liu, Y. (2011). Relationships between in-role performance and individual values, commitment, and organizational citizenship behavior among Israeli teachers. *International Journal of Psychology, 46*(4), 271–287. https://doi.org/10.1080/00207594.2010.539613

Cooke, R. A., & Szumal, J. L. (1993). Measuring normative beliefs and shared behavioral expectations in organizations: The reliability and validity of the Organizational Culture Inventory. *Psychological Reports, 72,* 1299–1330. https://doi.org/10.2466/pr0.1993.72.3c.1299

Costa, A. C., Fulmer, C. A., & Anderson, N. R. (2018). Trust in work teams: An integrative review, multilevel model, and future directions. *Journal of Organizational Behavior, 39*(2), 169–184.

CultureAmp. (2020). *How companies are embracing a new future: Organizational responses to people issues raised by COVID-19.* https://www.cultureamp.com/resources/all-ebooks/how-companies-are-embracing-a-new-future

CultureAmp. (2022). *Workplace diversity, equity, & inclusion report: Understanding the DEI landscape.* https://www.cultureamp.com/workplace-dei-report-2022#top

Dickson, M., Kwantes, C. T., & Magomaeva, A. B. (2014). Societal and organizational culture: Connections and a future agenda. In B. Schneider & K. Barbera (Eds.), *The Oxford handbook of organizational climate and culture* (pp. 276–296). Oxford University Press.

Dietz, G., Gillespie, N., & Chao, G. T. (2010). Unravelling the complexities of trust and culture. In M. K. Saunders, S. Skinner, G. Dietz, N. Gillespie, & R. J. Lewicki (Eds.), *Organizational trust: A cultural perspective* (pp. 3–41). Cambridge University Press.

Dorfman, P., Javidan, M., Hanges, P., Dastmalchian, A., & House, R. (2012). GLOBE: A twenty-year journey into the intriguing world of culture and leadership. *Journal of World Business, 47*(4), 504–518.

Earley, P. C. (1989). Social loafing and collectivism: A comparison of the United States and the People's Republic of China. *Administrative Science Quarterly, 34,* 565–581.

Earley, P. C. (1993). East meets West meets Mideast: Further explorations of collectivistic and individualistic work groups. *Academy of Management Journal, 36*(2), 319–348.

Erez, M. (1994). Toward a model of cross-cultural industrial and organizational psychology. In H. C. Triandis, M. D. Dunnette, & L. M. Hough (Eds.), *Handbook of industrial and organizational psychology: Vol. 4* (2nd ed., pp. 559–608). Consulting Psychologists Press.

Erez, M. (2018). From local to cross-cultural to global work motivation and innovation. In M. Gelfand, C.-y. Chiu, & Y-y. Hong (Eds.), *Handbook of advances & culture and psychology* (Vol. 7., pp. 217–260). Oxford University Press. https://doi.org/10.1093/oso/9780190879228.003.0005

Erez, M., & Earley, P. C. (1987). Comparative analysis of goal-setting strategies across cultures. *Journal of Applied Psychology, 72,* 658–665.

Erez, M., & Gati, E. (2004). A dynamic, multi-level model of culture: From the micro level of the individual to the macro level of a global culture. *Applied Psychology: An International Review, 53,* 583–598.

Erez, M., & Shokef, E. (2008). The culture of global organizations. In P. B. Smith, M. F. Peterson, & D. C. Thomas (Eds.), *The handbook of cross-cultural management* (pp. 285–300). SAGE.

Farmer, H., McKay, R., & Tsakiris, M. (2014). Trust in me: Trustworthy others are seen as more physically similar to the self. *Psychological Science, 25*(1), 290–292.

Fischer, R., Ferreira, M.C., Assmar, E., Redford, P., Harb, C., Glazer, S., Cheng, B. S., Jian, D.Y., Wong, C., Kumar, N., Kaertner, J., Hofer, J. & Achoui, M. (2009). Individualism-collectivism as descriptive norms: Development of a subjective norm approach to culture measurement. *Journal of Cross-Cultural Psychology, 40*(3), 187–213.

Fischer, R., & Smith, P. B. (2006). Who cares about justice? The moderating effect of values on the link between organisational justice and work behaviour. *Applied Psychology: An International Review, 55,* 541–562.

Fischer, R., Smith, P. B., Richey, B. Ferreira, M. C., Assmar, E., Maes, J., & Stumpf, S. (2007). How do organizations allocate rewards? The predictive validity of national values, economic and organizational factors across six nations. *Journal of Cross-Cultural Psychology, 38,* 3–18.

Fitzsimmons, S. R., & Stamper, C. L. (2014). How societal culture influences friction in the employee-organization relationship. *Human Resource Management Review, 24,* 80–94.

Froese, F. J., Stoermer, S., Reiche, B. S., & Klar, S. (2021). Best of both worlds: How embeddedness fit in the host unit and the headquarters improve repatriate knowledge transfer. *Journal of International Business Studies, 52,* 1331–1349. https://doi.org/10.1057/s41267-020-00356-4

Gelfand, M. J., Aycan, Z., Erez, M., & Leung, K. (2017). Cross-cultural industrial organizational psychology and organizational behavior: A hundred-year journey. *Journal of Applied Psychology, 102,* 514–529.

Gelfand, M. J., Raver, J. L., Nishii L., Leslie, L. M., Lun, I., Lim, B. C., Duan, L., Almaliach, A., Ang, S., Arnadottir, J., Aycan, Z., Boehnke, K., Boski, P., Cabecinhas, R., Chan, D., Chhokar, J. D'Amato, A., Ferrer, M., Fischlmayr, I. C., . . . Yamaguchi, S. (2011). Differences between tight and loose cultures: A 33-nation study. *Science, 332,* 1100–1104.

Glazer, S. (2002). Past, present, and future of cross-cultural studies in industrial and organizational psychology. In C. Cooper & I. T. Robertson (Eds.), *International review of industrial and organizational psychology* (Vol. 17, pp. 145–185). Wiley. https://doi.org/10.1002/9780470696392

Glazer, S. (2008). Cross-cultural issues in stress and burnout. In J. R. B. Halbesleben (Ed.), *Handbook of stress and burnout in health care* (pp. 79–93). Nova Science.

Glazer, S. (2021). Organizational role ambiguity as a proxy for uncertainty avoidance. *International Journal of Intercultural Relations, 85,* 1–12. https://doi.org/10.1016/j.ijintrel.2021.08.011

Glazer, S., & Beehr, T. A. (2005). Consistency of the implications of three role stressors across four countries. *Journal of Organizational Behavior, 26,* 467–487. https://doi.org/10.1002/job.326

Glazer, S., Daniel, S. C., & Short, K. M. (2004). A study of the relationship between organizational commitment and human values in four countries. *Human Relations, 57*, 323–345. https://doi.org/10.1177/1470595807088319

Glazer, S., & De La Rosa, G. M. (2008). Immigrant status as a potential correlate of organizational commitment. *International Journal of Cross-Cultural Management, 8*(1), 5–22.

Glazer, S., Kozusznik, M. W., & Shargo, I. A. (2012). Global Virtual Teams: A cure for – or a cause of – stress. In P. L. Perrewé, J. Halbesleben, & C. Rosen (Eds.), *Research in occupational stress and well being, volume 10: The role of the economic context on occupational stress and well being* (pp. 213–266). Emerald. https://doi.org/10.1108/S1479-3555(2012)0000010010

Glazer, S., Moliner, C., & Carmona, C. (2014). Differences in educational training models and implications from international collaborations. In R. L. Griffith, L. F. Thompson, & B. K. Armon (Eds.), *Internationalizing the curriculum in organizational psychology* (pp. 79–104). Springer. https://doi.org/10.1007/978-1-4614-9402-7

Glazer, S., Moon, S., Ayman, R., & Berger, R. (2021). Preparing for a career: Essential KSAs and experiences. In E. L. Shoenfelt (Ed.), *Mastering the job market: Career issues for master's level industrial-organizational psychologists* (pp. 37–59). Oxford University Press. https://doi.org/10.1093/oso/9780190071172.001.0001

Gupta, A. K., & Govindarajan, V. (2002). Cultivating a global mindset. *Academy of Management Executive, 16*(1), 116–126.

Guzman, F. A., & Fu, X. (2022). Leader–subordinate congruence in power distance values and voice behaviour: A person–supervisor fit approach. *Applied Psychology: An International Review, 71*(1), 271–295.

Haar, J. M., & Brougham, D. (2016). Organisational-based self-esteem: A within country comparison of outcomes between Maori and New Zealand Europeans. *Journal of Management & Organization, 22*(5), 720–735.

Hargreaves, S., Rustage, K., Nellums, L. B., McAlpine, A., Pocock, N., Devakumar, D., Aldridge, R. W., Abubakar, I., Kristensen, K. L., Himmels, J. W., Friedland, J. S., & Zimmerman, C. (2019). Occupational health outcomes among international migrant workers: A systematic review and meta-analysis. *Lancet Global Health, 7*, e872–e882.

Harris, S. G. (1994). Organizational culture and individual sensemaking: A schema-based perspective. *Organization Science, 5*, 309–321.

Head, T. C. (2002). Organization development and the People's Republic of China: An interesting partnership. *OD Practitioner, 1*, 38–42.

Heller, B. R. (2022, January 19). Diversity & inclusion: A business case [at SA-SEAT]. Invited presentation at a joint session hosted by University of Barcelona and The University of Baltimore [virtual].

Hofstede, G. (1980). *Culture's consequences: International differences in work-related values*. SAGE.

Hofstede, G. (2001). *Culture's consequences: Comparing values, behaviors, institutions, and organizations across nations* (2nd ed.). SAGE.

Hofstede, G. (1976). Nationality and espoused values of managers. *Journal of Applied Psychology, 61*(2), 148–155.

Hofstede, G., Neuijen, B., & Ohavy, D. D. (1990). Measuring organizational cultures: A qualitative and quantitative study across twenty cases. *Administrative Science Quarterly, 35*, 286–316.

House, R. J., Hanges, P. J., Javidan, M., Dorfman, P. W., & Gupta, V. (Eds.). (2004). *Culture, leadership, and organizations: The GLOBE study of 62 societies*. SAGE.

Ion, A., Iliescu, D., Aldhafri, S., Rana, N., Ratanadilok, K., Widyanti, A., & Nedelcea, C. (2017). A cross-cultural analysis of personality structure through the lens of the HEXACO model. *Journal of Personality Assessment, 99*, 25–34. https://doi.org/10.1080/00223891.2016.1187155

Ion, A., Iliescu, D., & Illie, A., & Ispas, D. (2016). The emic-etic approach to personality measurement in personnel selection. *Personality and Individual Differences, 97*, 55–60.

Jarvenpaa, S. L., & Leidner, D. E. (1999). Communication and trust in global virtual teams. *Organization Science, 10*(6), 791–815.

Kennedy, J. C., Fu, P. P., & Yukl, G. (2003). Influence tactics across twelve cultures. *Advances in Global Leadership, 3*, 127–147. https://doi.org/10.1016/S1535-1203(02)03007-1

Kimura, T., & Nishikawa, M. (2018). Ethical leadership and its cultural and institutional context: An empirical study in Japan. *Journal of Business Ethics, 151*(3), 707–724.

Knachel, E., & Porter, B. (2021). Do ESG matters affect accounting and financial reporting today? *Heads Up, 28*(6), 1–4. https://dart.deloitte.com/USDART/home/publications/deloitte/heads-up/2021/esg-affect -financial-reporting

Kożusznik, B., & Glazer, S. (2021). Hearing the international voices of professionals in industrial, work, and organizational psychology: A declaration of identity. *The Industrial-Organizational Psychologist, 58*(4). https://www.siop.org/Research-Publications/Items-of-Interest/ArticleID/5049/ArtMID/19366 /preview/true

Kraimer, M. L., Shaffer, M. A., Harrison, D. A., & Ren, H. (2012). No place like home? An identity strain perspective on repatriate turnover. *Academy of Management Journal, 55*, 399–420.

Kwantes, C. T., & Boglarsky, C. A. (2003). *Individual level outcomes of the relationship between social and organizational cultures* [Poster presentation]. International Association for Cross-Cultural Psychology, Sixth European Regional Congress, Budapest, Hungary. https://www.humansynergistics.com/Files /ResearchAndPublications/Individual%20Level%20Outcomes.pdf

Kwantes, C. T., & Boglarsky, C. A. (2006). Organizational cultures across national boundaries: Results of a cluster analysis. *Applied Multivariate Research, 12*(2), 107–124.

Kwantes, C. T., & Boglarsky, C. A. (2007). Perceptions of organizational culture, leadership effectiveness and personal effectiveness across six countries. *Journal of International Management, 13*(2), 204–230.

Kwantes, C. T., & Bond, M. H. (2019). Social cynicism and organizational justice in relation to organizational cynicism. *Personality and Individual Differences, 151*, Article 109391. https://doi.org/10.1016 /j.paid.2019.04.046

Kwantes, C. T., & Dickson, M. W. (2011). Organizational culture in a societal context: Lessons from GLOBE and beyond. In N. N. Ashkanasy, C. Wilderom, & M. F. Peterson (Eds.), *The handbook of organizational culture and climate* (2nd ed., pp. 494–514). SAGE.

Kwantes, C. T., & Glazer, S. (2017). Culture, organizations, and work: Clarifying concepts. In S. Glazer & C. T. Kwantes (Series Eds.), SpringerBriefs in *Culture, organizations, & work*. Springer.

Kwantes, C. T., Karam, C. M., Kuo, B. C. H., & Towson, S. (2008). Organizational citizenship behaviours: The influence of culture. *International Journal of Intercultural Relations, 32*, 229–243.

Kwantes, C. T., & Kartolo, A. B. (2021). A 10 nation exploration of trustworthiness in the workplace. *Interpersona: An International Journal on Personal Relationships, 15*(2), 146–166.

Latham, G. R., Erez, M., & Locke, E. (1988). Resolving scientific disputes by the antagonists: Application of the Erez-Latham dispute regarding participation. *Journal of Applied Psychology, 73*, 753–772.

Lau, D. C., Lam, L. W., & Salamon, S. D. (2008). The impact of relational demographics on perceived managerial trustworthiness: Similarity or norms? *Journal of Social Psychology, 148*(2), 187–209.

Leung, K., Bond, M. H., de Carrasquel, S. R., Muñoz, C., Hernández, M., Murakami, F., Yamaguchi, S., Bierbrauer, G., & Singelis, T. M. (2002). Social axioms: The search for universal dimensions of general beliefs about how the world functions. *Journal of Cross-Cultural Psychology, 33*, 286–302.

Li, M. (2020). An examination of two major constructs of cross-cultural competence: Cultural intelligence and intercultural competence. *Personality & Individual Differences, 164*, Article 110105. https://doi.org /10.1016/j.paid.2020.110105

Liao, Y., & Thomas, D. C. (2020). Cultural intelligence in the world of work: Past, present, future. In S. Glazer & C. T. Kwantes (Series Eds.), Springer Series in *Emerging cultural perspectives in work, organizational, and personnel studies*. Springer.

Malone, C., & Fiske, S. T. (2013). *The human brand: How we relate to people, products, and companies.* Jossey-Bass.

Masuda, A. D., Poelmans, S. A., Allen, T. D., Spector, P. E., Lapierre, L. M., Cooper, C. L., Abarca, N., Brough, P., Ferreiro, P., Fraile, G., Lu, L., Lu, C., Siu, O. L., O'Driscoll, M. P., Simoni, A. S., Shima, S., & Moreno-Velazquez, I. (2012). Flexible work arrangements availability and their relationship with work-to-family conflict, job satisfaction, and turnover intentions: A comparison of three country clusters. *Applied Psychology: An International Review, 61,* 1–29.

Matsumoto, D. (2007). Culture, context, and behavior. *Journal of Personality, 75*(6), 1287–1320.

Mayer R. C., Davis, J. H., & Schoorman, F. D. (1995). An integrative model of organizational trust. *The Academy of Management Review, 20*(3), 709–734.

Meyer, K. E., Li, C., & Schotter, A. P. J. (2020). Managing the MNE subsidiary: Advancing a multi-level and dynamic research agenda. *Journal of International Business Studies, 51,* 538–576. https://doi.org/10.1057/s41267-020-00318-w

Meyerson, D., Weick, K. E., & Kramer, R. M. (1996). Swift trust and temporary groups. In R. M. Kramer & T. R. Tyler (Eds.), *Trust in organizations: Frontiers of theory and research* (pp. 166–195). SAGE.

Milczarek, M., Brun, E., & González, E. R. (2008, April 8–9). Emerging psychosocial risks related to occupational safety and health—An expert forecast. *EU-OSHA Seminar on Emerging Psychosocial Risks Related to OSH.* https://osha.europa.eu/en/tools-and-resources/seminars/emerging-psychosocial-risks-related-osh

Minkov, M., & Hofstede, G. (2011). The evolution of Hofstede's doctrine. *Cross Cultural Management, 18*(1), 10–20.

Minvielle, E., Aegerter, P., Dervaux, B., Boumendil, A., Retbif, A., Jars-Guincestre, M., & Guidet, B. (2008). Assessing organizational performance in intensive care units: A French experience. *Journal of Critical Care, 23,* 236–244.

Moellering, G. (2006). *Trust: Reason, routine, reflexivity.* Elsevier.

Morris, M. A., & Robie, C. (2001). A meta-analysis of the effects of cross-cultural training on expatriate performance and adjustment. *International Journal of Training and Development, 5,* 112–125.

Moyce, S. C., & Schenkar, M. (2018). Migrant workers and their occupational health and safety. *Annual Review of Public Health, 39,* 351–365.

Munroe, R. L., & Munroe, R. M. (1997). A comparative anthropological perspective. In J. W. Berry, Y. H. Poortinga, & J. Pandey (Eds.), *Handbook of cross-cultural psychology, Vol. I, Theory and method* (pp. 171–213). Allyn & Bacon.

Nardon, L., Aten, K., & Gulanowski, D. (2015). Expatriate adjustment in the digital age: The co-creation of online social support resources through blogging. *International Journal of Intercultural Relations, 47,* 41–55.

Pereira, S., Dos Santos, N., & Pais, L. (2019). Empirical research on decent work: A literature review. *Scandinavian Journal of Work and Organizational Psychology, 4*(1), 1–15. https://doi.org/10.16993/sjwop.53

Pines, A. M. (2004). Why are Israelis less burned out? *European Psychologist, 9,* 69–77.

Resick, C. J., Martin, G. S., Keating, M. A., Dickson, M. W., Kwan, H. K., & Peng, C. (2011). What ethical leadership means to me: Asian, American, and European perspectives. *Journal of Business Ethics, 101*(3), 435–457.

Rovithis, M., Linardakis, M., Merkouris, A., Patiraki, E., Vassilaki, M., & Philalithis, A. (2017). Organizational culture among levels of health care services in Crete (Greece). *Applied Nursing Research, 36,* 9–18.

Rudolph, C. W., Allan, B., Clark, M., Hertel, G., Hirschi, A., Kunze, F., Shockley, K., Shoss, M., Sonnentag, S., & Zacher, H. (2021). Pandemics: Implications for research and practice in industrial and organizational psychology. *Industrial and Organizational Psychology, 14*(1–2), 1–35.

Sarris, A., & Kirby, N. (2007). Behavioral norms and expectations on Antarctic stations. *Environment and Behavior, 39*(5), 706–723.

Saxena, M. (2017). Workers in poverty: An insight into informal workers around the world. *Industrial and Organizational Psychology: Perspectives on Science and Practice, 10*(3), 376–379. https://doi.org/10.1017/iop.2017.29

Schaufeli, W. B., & Janczur, B. (1994). Burnout among nurses. A Polish-Dutch comparison. *Journal of Cross-Cultural Psychology, 25*, 95–113.

Schwartz, S. H. (1992). Universals in the content and structure of values: Theoretical advances and empirical tests in 20 countries. *Advances in Experimental Social Psychology, 25*, 1–65. https://doi.org/10.1016/S0065-2601(08)60281-6

Schwartz, S. H. (1999). Some theoretical and practical implications. *Applied Psychology: An International Review, 48*(1), 23–47. https://doi.org/10.1017/cbo9780511620799.007

Schwartz, S. H., & Sagiv, L. (1995). Identifying culture-specifics in the content and structure of values. *Journal of Cross-Cultural Psychology, 26*, 92–116.

Shockley, K. M., French, K. A., & Yu, P. P. (2018). A comprehensive review and synthesis of the cross-cultural work-family literature. In K. M. Shockley, W. Shen, & R. C. Johnson (Eds.), *The Cambridge handbook of the global work-family interface* (pp. 9–68). Cambridge University Press.

Sousa-Poza, A., Nystrom, H., & Wiebe, H. (2001). A cross-cultural study of the differing effects of corporate culture on TQM in three countries. *International Journal of Quality & Reliability Management, 18*, 744–761.

Turner, R., on behalf of the *PLoS Medicine* editors. (2019). Migrants and refugees: Improving health and well-being in a world on the move. *PLoS Medicine, 16*(7), e1002876.

United Nations. (2015). *Transforming our world: The 2030 Agenda for Sustainable Development.* https://sdgs.un.org/sites/default/files/publications/21252030%20Agenda%20for%20Sustainable%20Development%20web.pdf

van de Vijver, F. J. R., & Poortinga, Y. H. (1997). Towards an integrated analysis of bias in cross-cultural assessment. *European Journal of Psychological Assessment, 13*, 29–37. https://doi.org/10.1027/1015-5759.13.1.29

Vanhala, M., Puumalainen, K., & Blomquist, K. (2011). Impersonal trust: The development of the construct and the scale. *Personnel Review, 40*(4), 485–513.

Wasti, S. A. (2003). The influence of cultural values on antecedents of organizational commitment: An individual-level analysis. *Applied Psychology: An International Review, 52*, 533–554.

Watts, L. L., Steele, L. M., & Den Hartog, D. N. (2020). Uncertainty avoidance moderates the relationship between transformational leadership and innovation: A meta-analysis. *Journal of International Business Studies, 51*, 138–145. https://doi.org/10.1057/s41267-019-00242-8

Westjohn, S. A., Magnusson, P., Franke, G. R., & Peng, Y. (2022). Trust propensity across cultures: The role of collectivism. *Journal of International Marketing, 30*, 1–17. https://doi.org/10.1177/1069031X211036688

Wright, A., & Ehnert. I. (2010). Making sense of trust across cultural contexts. In M. K. Saunders, S. Skinner, G. Dietz, N. Gillespie, & R. J. Lewicki (Eds.), *Organizational trust: A cultural perspective* (pp. 107–126). Cambridge University Press.

Yang, L., Spector, P. E., Sanchez, J. I., Allen, T. D., Poelmans, S., Cooper, C. L., Lapierre, L. M., O'Driscoll, M. P., Abarca, N., Alexandrova, M., Anoniou, A-S., Beham, B., Brough, P., Çarikçi, I., Ferreiro, P., Fraile, G., Geurts, S., Kinnunen, U., Lu, C, ...Woo, J-M. (2012). Individualism-collectivism as moderator of the work demands-strains relationship: A cross-level and cross-national examination. *Journal of International Business Studies, 43*, 424–443.

Sharon Glazer and Catherine Kwantes

THE GROUP DYNAMICS OF INTERORGANIZATIONAL COLLABORATION

INTRODUCTION

The aims of this article are: (a) to draw attention to a type of group that has largely been neglected by social psychologists doing group research, namely, groups consisting of individuals representing different organizations; (b) to discuss the relational dynamics of these groups as understood from a systems-psychodynamic perspective; and (c) to share some insights on how to help group members gain an understanding of these dynamics. The neglect of the multiparty group is to be regretted as the effectiveness of interorganizational collaboration is crucial in dealing with societal and organizational challenges. This article presents a systems-psychodynamic perspective that focuses on the deeper emotional dynamics of working across organizational boundaries. It is not a standard empirical article, although it will provide illustrations of action research projects, where through engaging in a "helping" relationship (Schein, 2011) the researcher gained understanding from within.

I will start with pointing at the relevance of such multiparty groups and sketching the complexity of its dynamics. Subsequently, I will briefly address how existing notions in social psychology deal with aspects of these groups yet do not capture the dynamics in their entirety. I will then describe the lens that I use to understand these groups better, namely, systems-psychodynamics. Thereafter, I will focus on two action research projects to illustrate what a systems-psychodynamic perspective adds to our understanding of multiparty group dynamics. The article ends with some reflections on the use of this perspective in the context of understanding and developing interorganizational collaborative relations.

THE MULTIORGANIZATIONAL GROUP

Large-scale collaboration between different organizations is a feature of today's society—which has been dubbed a network society (Castells, 2009). For example, the delivery of health and social care relies on the collaboration and coordination of multiple organizations, the same applies to how education is organized, how safety in society is managed, and so on. The private sector is characterized by many joint ventures and strategic alliances, while the public and private worlds come together in public–private partnerships. Interorganizational collaboration refers to a process involving two or more legally independent organizations that come together to address a concern or an opportunity; they develop a joint goal while also serving the interests of the individual organizations (Gray, 1989; Schruijer & Vansina, 2008). The process is emergent and starts from being underorganized as there are no shared goals from the start, there is no legitimate authority, and trust is likely to be absent. While dealing with and capitalizing on the differences (in interests, sectors, perspectives, identities) and their interdependencies, they come to a shared problem definition, formulate a joint goal, and develop trust. Parties organize and govern themselves as they work together while keeping their legal autonomy intact (Gray, 1989; Gray & Purdy, 2018; Huxham & Vangen, 2005; Trist, 1983).

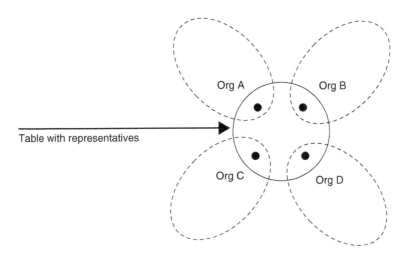

Figure 1. A multiparty group consisting of individuals representing four different organizations.

Collaboration is based on human activity. It is individuals who convene to start a process to decide which challenge needs addressing and which parties are to be involved. It is individuals who develop a common goal toward which different parties contribute. And it is individuals who monitor the realization of these goals and play a decisive role in the governance of collaborative processes. When I say individuals, I mean people who represent their organizations, while of course they are also individuals with their unique makeup. Besides the organizational level and the individual level there is a third level, as these individuals representing organizations come together to develop and realize collaboration—they form a (temporary) group (cf. referent organization, Trist, 1983). And of course there is the wider societal context.

Such a multiparty group may (or may not) meet regularly around a metaphoric or real table in order to organize themselves (see Figure 1).

A table is the setting where protagonists come together to create and sustain collaborative relationships between their respective organizations. The convening of stakeholders is not a given though, as the idea of bringing all stakeholders together may instill a fear of chaos. Indeed, the situation is a complex one considering the three systems levels mentioned: individuals and their interpersonal relationships, organizations as represented by individuals and interorganizational relationships enacted by these representatives, and a group made up of these individuals/representatives dealing with here-and-now group dynamics. The larger societal context, a fourth system level, also affects what is happening around the table. The setting is complex, with these different system levels operating simultaneously and influencing one another (Curşeu & Schruijer, 2018; Schilke & Cook, 2013); with the diversity of interests, perspectives, identities, and power positions present (Schruijer & Vansina, 2008); with the ambiguities that are inherent to wicked problems with which multiparty systems often deal (Weber & Khademian, 2008); and with the likely underorganization, at least at the start (Gray, 1989).

In collaboration, and its development, the task is to come to a shared problem definition that makes clear what the protagonists want to work on and what not, exploring their interdependencies and arriving at a shared goal that will realize something individual parties cannot do on their own—a shared goal that also serves the interests of the participating organizations (Gray, 1989; Schruijer & Vansina, 2008). Working with the diversity around the table (in interests, perspectives, identities) is a crucial element of collaboration. Diversity, however, often gives rise to stereotyping and win–lose behavior. The protagonists around the table have to engage in the difficult job of building trustworthy relationships with the other representatives (e.g., Vangen & Huxham, 2003), while also working toward the interests of their constituent organizations, facing a so-called dual conflict (Adams, 1976). (Becoming too close to the other representatives may upset the constituents [who may feel that the interests are not well served or that their representative is siding with the other parties], while firmly sticking to a [possibly restrictive] mandate will impede developing relationships around the table [see also Stephenson, 1981].) Those engaged in developing collaborative relationships also need to be able to deal with the complexities and ambiguities involved: there is no leader, at least no one with formal positional authority, no shared goal is present from the start, it is not always clear what the different interests entail, membership may change, trust has not been developed yet, and neither is there a common identity.

A SOCIAL PSYCHOLOGICAL PERSPECTIVE ON MULTIORGANIZATIONAL GROUP DYNAMICS

Understanding group dynamics has a long tradition in social psychology (Cartwright & Zander, 1968; Forsyth, 2018; Shaw, 1981). Many insights have been obtained that are relevant for comprehending the dynamics around a multiparty table, for example, regarding social influence processes. As it appears, groups and individuals tend to reduce or avoid differences. Groups homogenize over time (Schneider, 1987), majorities can pressure minorities into conforming (e.g., Asch, 1953; Cialdini & Goldstein, 2004), people prefer similarity rather than difference when it comes to friendships, partner choice, and selection processes (e.g., Berscheid & Reis, 1998; Goldberg, 2005), groups tend to avoid conflict (e.g., Janis, 1972), yet do engage in (destructive) relational conflict while much less so in (constructive) task conflict (Jehn, 1995). Also, the literature shows that besides homogenizing processes, individuals can resist majority pressures (Asch, 1953); minorities can, under certain conditions, also have an impact on majorities and thus create change (Jetten & Hornsey, 2013; Moscovici, 1980).

Such insights are of great importance in studying the dynamics around the table among protagonists representing various organizations. Yet a key difference between small groups and a multiorganizational group is exactly this multiorganizational dimension with all the complexities and ambiguities involved. Most social psychological research into diverse or heterogeneous groups (e.g., Horwitz & Horwitz, 2007) only looks at demographic or cognitive differences. The fact that these individuals may represent different organizations with diverse interests, identities, or perspectives, is largely ignored.

Two research streams may inform the understanding of groups consisting of different organizations: the first on intergroup relations and the other on the concept of multiteams. The social psychological literature on the determinants and processes of intergroup relations provides a host of relevant insights for understanding the dynamics of interorganizational relationships (Schruijer, 2008). It explains why members of groups or organizations engage in stereotyping, self-serving attributions, and relational conflict, either because they compete for scarce resources (Sherif, 1966) or because they want to distinguish themselves positively vis-à-vis relevant outgroups, so as to arrive at a positive social identity provided by one's own in-group (Tajfel & Turner, 1979). Power differences influence such dynamics as do the permeability of group or organization boundaries, among other variables. Mechanisms for resolving conflict have also been identified, such as creating a superordinate goal, creating a superordinate identity, or ensuring that all parties involved can derive a positive social identity compared to a relevant outgroup through using different comparison dimensions (Brown & Gaertner, 2003). The identified mechanisms are highly relevant yet do not provide sufficient insight into: (a) how to arrive at a desired and internalized common goal or identity; and (b) how one can do so while simultaneously maintaining a clear focus on one's own interests and cultivating a sufficiently strong positive in-group identity. Further, the insights are mostly generated in an experimental situation involving two groups only, whereas real-life collaborative processes among multiple organizations are much more complex.

The literature on multiteams taps into the functioning and success of multiteam systems where multiple special teams, crossing boundaries within and between organizations, collaborate in healthcare, new product development, disaster response, and disease prevention, often dealing with wicked problems (Shuffler & Carter, 2018; Shuffler, Jiménez-Rodríguez, & Kramer, 2015). Boundary spanning, mutual adjustment, and coordination and control mechanisms are pointed to as important for the success of these systems. However, this literature does not seem to address in depth the functioning of what they call the leader team, that is, the team with the leaders of the different component teams as member. Such composite team I call the multiparty group (which, by the way, not necessarily consists of [only] leaders of their constituent parties). As so often in science, the multiteam literature has been developed separately from the group dynamics literature and from the multiparty collaboration literature.

Finally, the original interest in understanding the deeper, often unconscious, emotional life of groups has waned (Schruijer & Curşeu, 2014). The phenomenon of groupthink (Janis, 1972) is an example showing the fruitful influence of psychodynamic thinking on studying the dynamics of groups. It describes an emotional climate of concurrence seeking in groups under duress and shows how such groups fail to use the diversity in ideas, perspectives, and opinions within the group so as to jointly ward off anxieties. Although much research in (largely nomothetic) social psychology demonstrates the difficulties of working with difference constructively, getting a grasp of the deeper emotional reality of groups as a whole in context seems absent from today's academic literature (while Janis [1972] is criticized, as research testing elements of the groupthink proposition [Fuller & Aldag, 1998; Turner & Pratkanis, 1998] provides for only partial support).

Overall then, social psychological research has highlighted many relevant aspects of intragroup and intergroup interactions, yet does not fully capture the complex dynamics of multiorganizational groups. The emphasis of social psychologists on the experiment as the method par excellence has prevented researchers studying the dynamics of real groups as they unfold over time (Schruijer, 2012). It is not surprising then that group dynamics (in the sense of understanding the deeper emotional climate of groups as a whole in context) has declined and the study of group processes became disconnected from psychodynamics (Schruijer & Curşeu, 2014). The multiteam literature is promising yet does not address the dynamics of delegates around the table. And although literature exists on multiorganizational relationships and its social aspects, for example regarding the need to involve and empower the various stakeholders (Gray, 1989), how the presence or absence of trust affects the outcomes of collaboration (Laan, Noorderhaven, Voordijk, & DeWulf, 2011), how trust can be built (Vangen & Huxham, 2003), and what leadership means in the context of interorganizational collaboration (Huxham & Vangen, 2000), this literature barely looks closely at the actual emotional dynamics around the table (e.g., Merkus et al., 2017).

A SYSTEMS-PSYCHODYNAMIC PERSPECTIVE ON MULTIORGANIZATIONAL GROUP DYNAMICS

A systems-psychodynamic perspective aims to provide insights into the (conscious and unconscious) dynamic processes in groups and organizations, in their context, and how to work with these dynamics in ways that benefit the social system. Its body of knowledge derives from psychoanalysis and systems theory. The focus, though, is not on individuals and their private lives and not on pathological dynamics—it does address work systems, the present and relevant history of these systems, and their "normal" (but possibly dysfunctional) dynamics. It is through individual behavior that system dynamics are played out. The relevant notion here is "person-in-role": the intersection of the person and the system s/he belongs to (e.g., Newton, Long, & Sievers, 2018). It is individuals who have emotions, yet rather than originating from their private worlds, it is postulated that many tensions are triggered by the organization and its tasks. As individuals tend to avoid anxieties as well as threats to self-esteem, socially defensive processes may result. The operation of defensive processes occurs largely at an unconscious level. The unconscious consists, from a systems-psychodynamic perspective, not only of unacceptable infantile desires—this perspective understands "unconscious" as containing socially repressed elements as well as inner representations and experiences of the social system too (Long & Harney, 2018; Vansina & Vansina-Cobbaert, 2008).

Psychoanalytic thinking offers inspiration for understanding emotional dynamics and unconscious processes (through notions such as inner conflict and ambivalence, defense against anxiety, transference and countertransference, projection and projective identification), and by focusing on the importance of certain conditions for engaging in fruitful professional work (such as providing space for reflection, containing, and holding, and by emphasizing the importance of the relationship between the professional [therapist, consultant, action researcher] on the one hand and client on the other). Systems theory brings in organizational context by understanding organizational functioning in terms of its primary task, the organizational structure and design, its formal hierarchy, the division of labor, and so on.

Key notions within a systems-psychodynamic perspective are, for example, "basic assumptions," referring to Bion's (1961) work on unconscious and ineffective modes of group functioning that are a consequence of task-related tensions (French & Simpson, 2010); "social defenses" (Jaques, 1953; Menzies-Lyth, 1960), pertaining to how warded-off anxieties, stirred up by the task, can be expressed by dysfunctional organizational routines, structures, and cultures (often undermining professed values and beliefs [e.g., Long, 2008; Stein, 2007, 2019]); "organization-in-the-mind" (Armstrong, 2005), a concept that refers to how the organization, its goals, tasks, and activities, are represented internally by those working in it, based on their experiences and their concomitant feelings; and "transitional change" (Amado & Ambrose, 2001; Amado & Vansina, 2005), regarding notions of how to create conditions for aligning the organization members' inner worlds with a changing outer (organizational) world and working through the tensions that go along with change.

In-depth understanding calls for an idiographic methodology. It is about *Verstehen* rather than *Erklären*. The purpose is not to generalize or to unearth causal relationships between variables, but to arrive at a rich description of a particular group or organization as it wrestles with its tasks. On the one hand, it resembles those ethnographical approaches that are self-reflexive (taking a subjective position and working with one's inner experiences and emotions [Zilber & Zanoni, 2020]), while on the other it is different as a systems-psychodynamic researcher will share his or her subjective sense-making with the social system so as to arrive at a joint understanding, thus actively intervening (unless one observes from a distance without having the intention of helping achieve change or when emotional dynamics of social systems are inferred from published texts or archives).

Although systems-psychodynamic researchers indeed may use archival data, or alternatively, base their conclusions on interviews, working with observations seems most appropriate when it concerns the in-depth emotional dynamics of small groups. Questionnaires tap into conscious behavior, while experiments reduce the complexity of reality too much—they may generate valuable insights concerning the causal relationship between variables, yet their internal validity is obtained through compromising external validity. In-depth interviews may provide deeper insight into individual inner worlds or those of groups. However, interviews are often about an issue or about emotions rather than catching these dynamics in the here-and-now as they are experienced.

In observing, one tries to be receptive to the various ways the system's (recent) past is expressed in language, actions and interactions, images, symbols, and artifacts. One is attentive to what is being said or done between the lines, and one tries to listen to the music behind the words and actions. Since one does not know what will enfold, a fixed observation scheme is inadequate. To be open to all possible dynamics, a stance of not knowing is desirable, very much like Keats' concept of "negative capability": "when a man is capable of being in uncertainties, mysteries, doubts, without any irritable reaching after fact and reason" (Keats, 1899, p. 277). It embodies a stance of wonder and being able to stay with the complexity without reducing it too quickly by invoking known concepts (cf. Bion, 1970).

Observing is a subjective activity—different observers may notice different elements of the total puzzle. It is a subjectivity that is deliberately chosen as it can be very helpful in trying to understand what is happening in the observed group. The thoughts and emotions that are stirred up in oneself may relate to what the group is struggling with through processes of projective identification. Thus, a systems-psychodynamic observer has a dual focus: s/he observes what is going on out there, while also being attentive to what is going on in one's inner world. Obviously, one is not a member of the group (having a different role), neither does one become emotionally immersed: one is close enough to sense the dynamics yet removed enough to keep one's autonomy.

The position taken is also an active one: rather than staying with one's own sense-making, it is shared with the group involved, and group members are invited to also share their (individual and partial) experiences and so arrive at a joint and more complete understanding of what is or has been going on (cf. Krantz, 2018; Vansina & Vansina-Cobbaert, 2008). Such sharing is preferably done with a sense of wonder, from a stance of not knowing yet with a willingness to find out, and without judgment, so as to encourage group members to share their experiences and to signal that the observer is not superior or knows better and that his or her observations are tentative. It is a process of "sharing, comparing and finding out" (Bridger, 1990), a joint inquiry through the creation of and working with reflective space (Krantz, 2018; Vansina, 2005). Such spaces can be taken during meetings (as in process consultation), can be organized in special review sessions, or can be part of the design of working conferences.

For more detailed discussions of a systems-psychodynamic perspective on groups and organizations, I refer to Fotaki, Long, and Schwartz (2012), Hirschhorn (1990), and Vansina and Vansina-Cobbaert (2008).

MULTIPARTY GROUP DYNAMICS IN PRACTICE

A systems-psychodynamic perspective on interorganizational relationships can enrich our understanding of its group dynamics (e.g., Gould, Ebers, & Clinchy, 1999; Prins, 2010; Schruijer & Vansina, 2008). Unfortunately, academic literature that presents systems-psychodynamic action-oriented research is scarce. I will now turn to how such a perspective can be worked with in practice and the kind of insights it offers, based on my own work. First, I will briefly describe the group dynamics in an infrastructural project I was involved in where stakeholders came together in a novel way so as to more successfully collaborate. Then I will describe a simulation that I have been playing for many years in which participants, divided over seven groups, work with their interdependencies in facing social, economic, and ecological challenges. I will present its main dynamics, while also sharing how the simulation can be worked with as a learning tool.

Highway. One example pertains to an infrastructural project involving the reconstruction of a major highway. The megaproject lasted for years—my involvement for approximately half a year. In this period I observed and worked with a group that consisted of representatives of various parties, among which was a governmental organization that was the principal agent, various contractors (some being competitors), and employers' associations (Schruijer, 2020). This unprecedented informal group, with no formal status, came together regularly to discuss the progress of the project. The idea was to identify the problems, mobilize the constituencies, and solve the issues, so as to prevent them escalating to a formal contract table where a win–lose atmosphere traditionally prevails, as tendering is based on the lowest price, more work normally needs doing, the question then becomes who is going to pay for it, and finally parties end up in court. I interviewed the members individually (inviting them to reflect on the project and its context as well as their own role in it), while also being present at various meetings.

The protagonists felt they had built trust over organizational boundaries, which was a wholly new experience for them. The atmosphere around the table seemed one of harmony and unity and initially the members seemed quite satisfied with the project's progress. However, during the individual interviews, various frustrations were expressed. One pertained to the effectiveness of the informal table, which they doubted. They were concerned about meeting the deadline, a deadline that was sacred to them (failing was not an option) and felt very committed to (in actual fact, they had very ambitiously expedited the deadline by various years). Parties were especially frustrated with one contractor who was to build a tunnel. All contractors were on schedule yet this one was causing a delay, they felt. However, the concerns remained time and time again undiscussed at their informal table, acting in contradiction to the table's raison d'être. Instead, they were active in finding days which could be saved in the planning and engaged in scapegoating. There were other signals that the apparent harmony concealed tensions—despite their busy schedules, the protagonists were always on time but started late and seemed hesitant to leave after the meeting was over. And there was humor, which helped release the unvoiced tensions. Also members from the constituents and from a governing body found it hard to express their concerns and to discuss these with project team.

The denial of problems at the table, the failure to confront one another, and engaging in scapegoating seemed to serve as a defense against possible failure. This defensive avoidance helped the protagonists to continue to believe they could meet the deadline. They, by the way, were convinced that being one day too late would be a disaster, despite the fact that they had accelerated the project by years. Constructive confrontation of the diversity of interests, opinions, and ideas did not take place. Interestingly, I became aware of my own hesitation to intervene, triggered by an unclarity in my contracted mandate—was I to intervene during meetings or only in specially dedicated reflective spaces?

At some point I was actively invited to intervene—I shared my observations on how they seemed to avoid delicate issues. During the discussion that followed, they became acutely aware that the tunnel builder was not present at the informal meetings. They also came to realize that the tunnel problems had arisen due to a new safety law that was introduced after it was contracted, which required a wholly new design. Through joint exploration, both in the meetings and in a larger working conference, we came to understand the scapegoating and the defensive avoidance as a consequence of, among other factors, a fear of destroying the burgeoning collaborative climate around the table (Harvey, 1999; Janis, 1972). Constructive action was taken and the project could move forward.

Their collusion and defensive avoidance occurred in the context of: (a) the ambitions the protagonists had themselves to show the world collaboration was possible (despite the traditional win–lose climate); (b) the negative press of megaprojects as always being delayed and underbudgeted; (c) pressures to succeed, put on the project leader by his constituent organization; (d) the constituents of both the principal agent and the contractors who doubted whether the protagonists could really change the existing distrustful interorganizational relationships; and (e) a nationwide fraud scandal involving contractors and government officials that came to light some 20 years ago.

What a systems-psychodynamic perspective in particular adds to action research, to mainstream research on group processes, or to an organizational development practice, is its sensitivity to the deeper and often unconscious emotional life of the group as a whole that arises as a consequence of task-related tensions, in a social, political, economic, cultural, historical context. It looks inward by unearthing unconscious dynamic processes while it simultaneously looks outward by understanding these dynamics as arising from tensions around the task and the group's context. Such a perspective also aims to help the client system become aware of the dynamics, owning up to them, and thus to create space for action. In the highway case it involved understanding the defensive avoidance that had been going on, which had escaped the awareness of the protagonists. It could be jointly explored and treated as a phenomenon that was not to be blamed on individual actions or those of individual parties but was a relational and systemic phenomenon (that all contributed toward and thus all could do something about it).

The Simulation: The Yacht Club. The simulation "The Yacht Club" aims to give participants an experience of the group dynamics that emerge when working across organizational boundaries (Vansina, Taillieu, & Schruijer, 1998). It helps them learn from experience about interorganizational dynamics, what leadership entails when there is no formal hierarchy, and how one deals with the ambiguity, complexity, and diversity present. The simulation is based on real events as they emerged in the St. Petersburg area during the early 1990s. It has been used multiple times, in open programs and in-company workshops (Schruijer & Vansina, 2008; Vansina & Taillieu, 1997).

The events depicted evolved around the major social and economic changes as a consequence of the dismantling of the Soviet Union. A major shipyard, situated on the island of Kotlin just outside of St. Petersburg, faced serious problems as it built marine ships yet no orders were coming through anymore. The shipyard was exploring new markets yet it needed to reorganize, for which investments were needed. Being the largest employer on the island, unemployment would have serious consequences. The local authority was concerned about the developments and made its town hall available for interested parties to address these. The breakdown of the Soviet Union also offered possibilities. There was a yacht club on the island that wanted to expand its activities. The same applied to a yacht club near St. Petersburg. Both yacht clubs hoped to attract rich Russians as well as foreign tourists. A Finnish yacht club had indeed expressed interest to link up with these yacht clubs. There was a bank that had capital and was interested in lending it out. Finally, there was a group of rich Russian entrepreneurs who had money to invest and wanted to make more money; they had an emotional tie to the island.

The total number of participants per simulation varies between 18 and 30. They are asked not to role-play (e.g., to play "a Russian"), but to identify as much as possible with the interests of their party. No assignment is given—it is up to the participants how to spend their time. They can build relationships or stay in their own room, as they please. Before individuals are assigned to their parties (based on their preferences), a timetable is shared which specifies how they can interact: during so-called visiting times they can visit or receive (members of) other parties yet not more than three parties are allowed to be present in the same room. Visiting is alternated with so-called town hall meetings. Each party can send a delegate to the town hall table (again, this is not required), and the constituents can, if they want, take a seat behind their representatives and send notes to him or her during the meeting (only the representatives are allowed to speak during such meetings). Another ground rule pertains to playing as realistically as possible, with the data provided and the parties present: one may intend to talk to the central government in Moscow, for example, but cannot actually do so as Moscow is not a party in the simulation. Further, one may think ahead but one must work with the data available and check assumptions on their reality basis. Finally, the simulation is played real time—a minute is a minute. The simulation lasts for just over a full day.

Two or three facilitators observe the between-party and within-party interactions—they do not intervene. Extensive notes are taken and during the simulation observations are briefly exchanged among one another. After the simulation is ended, much of the second day is spent reviewing, during which facilitators and participants try to jointly make sense of the dynamics in the simulation, while also attending to the here-and-now group dynamics as they unfold during reviewing. Also, the results of questionnaires that were distributed at various moments are fed back and discussed. Often a follow-up session is organized to explore how the context (the organization when it concerns an in-company program; the educational program when it concerns a business school) affected the dynamics in the simulation.

Each simulation results in different group dynamics—early events have an impact on later events, the participants bring in their life experiences and work histories, their present organizational or educational memberships have an impact, and so on. Still there are commonalities as generic difficulties need to be to addressed, such as arriving at a joint problem definition, building trust, facing diversity, formulating a common goal, representing one's organization while simultaneously building relationships with the other representatives. Some frequently occurring dynamics (see also Schruijer & Vansina, 2008; Vansina et al., 1998) include:

- Intergroup stereotyping: the young entrepreneurs are often stereotyped as the mafia, the shipyard as powerless, the yacht clubs are quickly dismissed as too small to be able to contribute, the bank is seen as too reactive, and the public authority is seen as bureaucratic and lethargic. Such stereotypes easily become self-fulfilling prophecies.
- The double conflict of representatives is visible in the town hall. Representatives feel dependent on the support from their constituencies and strengthened by the notes they receive. Yet these notes also pressurize them to say something, thus increasing the stress experienced by the delegate as s/he tries to make a connection with the other delegates.
- Instead of open power play (which also occurs), the dynamics can be collusive. Parties go through the motions of meeting, without conflict. At the end of the simulation they feel satisfied, thinking they have collaborated well. Yet they avoided all tensions, which became a goal in itself, and did not engage in the necessary task conflict.
- The purpose of the town hall table often remains undefined. The table erodes into a place where the tensions in the multiparty system are acted out through positional bargaining, scapegoating, stereotyping, and power play. The allotted time for town hall discussion is mostly not fully used. The more competitive the dynamic, the less time is spent in the town hall.
- What is often omitted is to define a joint problem. Parties come to the table with their own problem perceptions but fail to come to a joint problem definition and decide what to work on together. Instead of taking the time to explore interdependencies so as to formulate a joint goal, a vague goal emerges and becomes a kind of veil behind which parties can work to achieve their own interests.
- Group pressures normally arise at the end of the simulation, when participants have to strike a deal because of a self-imposed deadline. The final town hall meeting often ends in a discussion where anyone doubting the deal that is about to be accepted is shut up.

THE GROUP DYNAMICS OF INTERORGANIZATIONAL COLLABORATION · 381

Sometimes the party with a critical voice can stay firm and prevent a fake deal being agreed upon. It faces disbelief, despair, irritation, or anger.

- A mixture exists of wanting to stay independent but not wanting to be excluded either. Sometimes parties are excluded from the town hall meetings or their contributions are ridiculed. A common type of exclusion is defining the problem as an island problem and demanding that all parties contribute. The non-island parties often do not address such a comment openly—although resistance is visible.
- The dynamic between the local authority and the other parties is almost always complex. The public authority takes the chair, often stating that it is neutral and wants to facilitate the meetings. No agreement is explicitly asked for, while no one questions it. Still, the public authority has an interest and serves it by invoking its power, for example through granting permissions. Facilitating while also having an interest is quite impossible. Over time frustration with the public authority mounts.
- A co-occurring dynamic is that the public authority is put in the chairing position by the other parties, either passively by not questioning its role or actively, by asking for guidelines. Moreover, the public authority also puts itself into that role, based on what it (consciously or unconsciously) assumes local authorities do, scripted on their real-life experiences.
- Groups get stuck in their dynamics, which seem to get more extreme over time. When the dynamic changes it is often because one or more members have the capacity to make impactful process remarks at the town hall table and invite the group to question what is going on. Unfortunately, process remarks are hardly made.
- Organizational or educational contexts become expressed in the simulation dynamics. In one run the participants were always striking deals, any deal would do. During reviewing the participants became aware of how dominant deal-making was in their organization. In a simulation for a business school (Schruijer, 2015), there were expressions of grandiosity and omnipotence, with aggressive and instrumental intergroup interactions, lack of empathy, denials of interdependence and of difference, and splitting. Some individuals were rather narcissistically inclined, but actually almost all interactions could be characterized as such. Individuals' propensity (or in Bion's words "valency" [Bion, 1961]) for narcissism exposed group narcissism and had to be understood in an educational context where there was strong pressure to succeed, both as a business school (accreditation was in the air) and as a student (an anxiety to fail was instilled at the start of the simulation as someone mentioned that half of the students had failed an earlier exam).

It is through the joint reviewing, having stepped out of "the heat," that the participants become aware of the dynamics in the simulation. Reflective space is needed in order to understand what was happening and to gauge the relational and systemic dimensions of the dynamics. On the whole participants can sense the distrust and "we–they" thinking while playing (although it is generally felt that the others are doing the distrusting and the stereotyping...), yet the dynamics of defensive avoidance are mostly missed and are only uncovered while reviewing. The same applies to the seductive dynamics between the public authority and the other parties, as depicted. At the end of the workshop, participants have gained an experience in working across organizational boundaries and learned through joint sense-making about multiparty dynamics. It means they also had a learning experience in how to organize and enter a reflective space constructively.

The simulation can be an unique element in a larger action research process. Via the simulation, when discussing how one's own organization or educational institute has impacted the dynamics in the simulation, participants can learn about their own real-life organization. Through the experiences gained in the simulation, they have a way to address the dynamics in their own organization more directly. The simulation thus may be a welcome bypass to get in touch with difficult dynamics in the real world. The simulation and the way we work with it is, in systems-psychodynamic terms, intended as a step in a transitional change process that helps participants understand the need for change, envisage new ways forward, and work through the tensions that are inherent to change (Amado & Ambrose, 2001; Amado & Vansina, 2005).

Simultaneously, the simulation is a research tool. It helps the action researcher learn about multiparty group dynamics that are, on the one hand, never the same, yet, on the other, present recurring patterns. The joint reviewing also opens up talking about the back home organization and thus brings in these experiences as well. Following an inductive logic, as well as an abductive logic (where one tries to make sense of surprising facts and allows for inference and intuition [Long & Harney, 2018]), one can develop hypotheses that are relevant for understanding the here-and-now dynamics, yet also help in generating insights that are relevant across simulations. For example, using both quantitative (questionnaires) and qualitative data (observations), a field experiment was constructed retrospectively, comparing a simulation that excluded parties at the town hall table versus one that did not, thus studying the impact of exclusion on systemic goal achievement and systemic dynamics (Curseu & Schruijer, 2020).

FINAL REFLECTIONS

In this article I have pointed to the importance of understanding the group dynamics of multiparty groups. I have briefly described the systems-psychodynamic perspective on such groups and how I work with it. I would describe the added value of a systems-psychodynamic perspective on multiparty group dynamics, gained through an action research approach, as follows. First, the perspective generates a holistic, rich, and embedded insight into persons-in-role who interact as a group within a particular context. It helps to see the systemic and relational dimensions of the dynamics, rather than thinking in terms of individual qualities.

Second, a systems-psychodynamic perspective draws attention to the fact that, even when one does attend to the here-and-now dynamics, the emotional dynamics may not be directly available. Not for those observed and not for those doing the observing; jointly sharing and reviewing the experiences by both insiders and relative outsiders is often needed to arrive at a deeper understanding of what actually is going on (Vansina, 2005). A clear example pertains to the collusive dynamics where group members avoid all possible disagreement and think they have collaborated well (Gray & Schruijer, 2010; Schruijer, 2018). It makes for deep learning among the participants, who during reviewing come in touch with their pussyfooting behavior and its underlying fears. After initial embarrassment they can feel quite relieved, realizing it is a common and human phenomenon.

Third, joint sense-making through sharing and comparing experiences during a reviewing phase provides participants in systems-psychodynamically oriented action research with a deep insight into their own here-and-now group dynamics and the context thereof. Through that understanding, alternative behaviors and conditions, which are needed for that, can be explored. Actionable knowledge can thus be generated (Argyris, 4). A researcher taking up a helping position, characteristic of action research, may get access to multiparty tables, that is, tables where the action really is—an access that is not evident when staying within positivistic academic role boundaries. One might argue that lack of rigor may be an issue; however, in my view the advantage of more relevance tips the scale convincingly in the direction of the approach advocated in this article.

It is important to realize that one needs special skills to be able to observe the deeper emotional dynamics of the group as a whole and to use oneself as an instrument. Such skills are not taught at universities, as psychodynamic thinking as well as group dynamics have largely disappeared from the psychology curriculum (Redmond & Shulman, 2008; Schruijer, 2013; Schruijer & Curşeu, 2014). Such skills need to be developed through engaging with practice, experiential learning, and professional guidance. Various institutions exist that may organize relevant training, of which the Tavistock Institute of Human Relations is probably the best known.

Despite academic conditions that are not optimal for doing the research I have been advocating, there has been a marked increased interest in systems-psychodynamics among organization scholars, as expressed by high-profile journal publications (including Arnaud, 2012; Fotaki et al., 2012; French & Simpson, 2010; Stein, 2007, 2019) and books that have been written for a wide audience (Long, 2008; Vansina & Vansina-Cobbaert, 2008). Accessible classics are still for sale (such as DeBoard, 1978; Hirschhorn, 1990). Further, although action research is not very popular in university settings (Levin & Greenwood, 2007), highly interesting action research projects are being conducted, including ones that concern interorganizational relations (e.g., Coghlan & Coughlan, 2015; Huzzard, Ahlberg, & Ekman, 2000; Yström, Ollila, Agogué, & Coghlan, 2019), and sometimes even within the realm of multiparty psychodynamics (Prins, 2010).

REFERENCES

Adams, J. S. (1976). The structure and dynamics of behavior in organizational boundary roles. In M. D. Dunnette (Ed.), *Handbook of industrial and organizational psychology* (pp. 1175–1199). Chicago, IL: Rand McNally.

Amado, G., & Ambrose, T. (Eds.). (2001). *The transitional approach to change*. London, UK: Karnac.

Amado, G., & Vansina, L. (Eds.). (2005). *The transitional approach in action*. London, UK: Karnac.

Argyris, C. (2004). Actionable knowledge. In C. Knudsen & H. Tsoukas (Eds.), *The Oxford handbook of organization theory* (pp. 423–452). Oxford, UK: Oxford University Press.

Armstrong, D. (2005). *Organization in the mind*. London, UK: Karnac.

Arnaud, G. (2012). The contribution of psychoanalysis to organization studies and management: An overview. *Organization Studies, 33*, 1105–1120.

Asch, S. (1953). *Social psychology*. New York, NY: Prentice Hall.

Berscheid, E., & Reis, H. T. (1998). Interpersonal attraction and close relationships. In S. Fiske, D. Gilbert, G. Lindzey, & E. Aronson (Eds.), *Handbook of social psychology* (Vol. 2, pp. 193–281). New York, NY: Random House.

Bion, W. R. (1961). *Experiences in groups and other papers*. London, UK: Tavistock Publications.

Bion, W. R. (1970). *Attention and interpretation*. London, UK: Tavistock Publications.

Bridger, H. (1990). Courses and working conferences as transitional learning institutions. In E. Trist & H. Murray (Eds.), *The social engagement of social science*. London, UK: Free Association Books.

Brown, R., & Gaertner, S. (Eds.). (2003). *Intergroup processes*. Oxford, UK: Blackwell.

Cartwright, D., & Zander, A. (1968). *Group dynamics: Research and theory*. New York, NY: Harper & Row.

Castells, M. (2009). *The rise of the network society*. London, UK: Wiley-Blackwell.

Cialdini, R., & Goldstein, N. (2004). Social influence: Compliance and conformity. *Annual Review of Psychology, 55*, 591–621.

Coghlan, D., & Coughlan, P. (2015). Effecting change and learning in networks through network action learning. *Journal of Applied Behavioral Science, 51*, 375–400.

Curşeu, P., & Schruijer, S. (2018). Cross-level dynamics of collaboration and conflict in multi-party systems: An empirical investigation using a behavioural simulation. *Administrative Sciences, 8*, 1–14.

Curşeu, P., & Schruijer, S. (2020). Participation and goal achievement of multiparty collaborative systems dealing with complex problems: A natural experiment. *Sustainability, 12*, 987. http://doi.org/10.3390/su12030987

DeBoard, R. (1978). *The psychoanalysis of organizations: A psychoanalytic approach to behaviour in groups and organizations*. London, UK: Routledge.

Forsyth, D. (2018). *Group dynamics*. Boston, MA: Cengage Learning.

Fotaki, M., Long, S., & Schwartz, H. (2012). Psychoanalytic perspectives on organizations: What can psychoanalysis offer organization studies today? *Organization Studies, 33*, 1105–1255.

French, R. B., & Simpson, P. (2010). The "work group": Redressing the balance in Bion's "Experiences in Groups." *Human Relations, 63*, 1859–1878.

Fuller, S., & Aldag, R. (1998). Organizational tonypandy: Lessons from a quarter century of the groupthink phenomenon. *Organizational Behavior and Human Decision Processes, 73*, 163–184.

Goldberg, C. (2005). Relational demography and similarity-attraction in interview assessments and subsequent offer decisions. *Group & Organization Management, 30*, 597–624.

Gould, L., Ebers, R., & Clinchy, R. (1999). The systems psychodynamics of a joint venture: Anxiety, social defenses and the management of mutual dependence. *Human Relations, 52*, 697–722.

Gray, B. (1989). *Collaborating: Finding common ground for multiparty problems*. San Francisco, CA: Jossey-Bass.

Gray, B., & Purdy, J. (2018). *Collaborating for our future: Multistakeholder partnerships for solving complex problems*. Oxford, UK: Oxford University Press.

Gray, B., & Schruijer, S. (2010). Integrating multiple voices: Working with collusion. In C. Steyaert & B. van Looy (Eds.), *Relational practices, participative organizing* (pp. 121–135). Bingley, UK: Emerald.

Harvey, J. (1999). *How come everytime I get stabbed in the back my fingerprints are on the knife?* San Francisco, CA: Jossey-Bass.

Hirschhorn, L. (1990). *The workplace within: Psychodynamics of organizational life*. Cambridge, MA: MIT Press.

Horwitz, S., & Horwitz, I. (2007). The effects of team diversity on team outcomes: A meta-analytic review of team demography. *Journal of Management, 33*, 987–1015.

Huxham, C., & Vangen, S. (2000). Leadership in the shaping and implementation of collaboration agendas: How things happen in a (not quite) joined-up world. *Academy of Management Journal, 43,* 1159–1175.

Huxham, C., & Vangen, S. (2005). *Managing to collaborate: The theory and practice of collaborative advantage.* Abingdon, UK: Routledge.

Huzzard, T., Ahlberg, B., & Ekman, M. (2000). Constructing interorganizational collaboration: The action researcher as boundary subject. *Action Research,* 1–21.

Janis, I. (1972). *Victims of groupthink.* Boston, MA: Houghton Mifflin.

Jaques, E. (1953). On the dynamics of social structure: A contribution to the psychoanalytical study of social phenomena deriving from the views of Melanie Klein. *Human Relations, 6,* 3–24.

Jehn, K. (1995). A multimethod examination of the benefits and detriments of intragroup conflict. *Administrative Science Quarterly, 40,* 256–282.

Jetten, J., & Hornsey, M. (2013). Deviance and dissent in groups. *Annual Review of Psychology, 65,* 461–485.

Keats, J. (1899). *The complete poetical works and letters of John Keats, Cambridge edition.* Boston, MA: Houghton Mifflin.

Krantz, J. (2018). Work culture analysis and reflective space. In S. Long (Ed.), *Socioanalytic methods.* Abingdon, UK: Routledge.

Laan, A., Noorderhaven, N., Voordijk, H., & DeWulf, G. (2011). Building trust in construction partnering projects: An exploratory case-study. *Journal of Purchasing & Supply Management, 17,* 98–108.

Levin, M., & Greenwood, D. (2007). The future of universities: Action research and the transformation of higher education. In P. Reason & H. Bradbury (Eds.), *The SAGE handbook of action research.* London, UK: SAGE.

Long, S. (2008). *The perverse organization and its deadly sins.* London, UK: Karnac.

Long, S., & Harney, M. (2018). The associative unconscious. In S. Long (Ed.), *Socioanalytic methods.* Abingdon, UK: Routledge.

Menzies-Lyth, I. (1960). Social systems as a defense against anxiety. *Human Relations, 13,* 95–121.

Merkus, S., Willems, T., Schipper, D., van Marrewijk, A., Koppenjan, J, Veenswijk, M., & Bakker, H. (2017). A storm is coming? Collective sensemaking and ambiguity in an inter-organizational team managing railway system disruptions. *Journal of Change Management, 17,* 228–248.

Moscovici, S. (1980). Towards a theory of conversion behavior. In L. Berkowitz (Ed.), *Advances in experimental social psychology* (Vol. 13, pp. 209–239). New York, NY: Academic Press.

Newton, J., Long, S., & Sievers, B. (2018). *Coaching in depth: The organizational role analysis approach.* London, UK: Routledge.

Prins, S. (2010). From competition to collaboration: Critical challenges and dynamics in multiparty collaboration. *Journal of Applied Behavioral Science, 46,* 281–312.

Redmond, J., & Shulman, M. (2008). Access to psychoanalytic ideas in American undergraduate institutions. *Journal of the American Psychoanalytic Association, 56,* 391–408.

Schein, E. (2011). *Helping: How to offer, give and receive help.* Oakland, CA: Berrett-Koehler.

Schilke, O., & Cook, K. (2013). A cross-level process theory of trust development in interorganizational relationships. *Strategic Organization, 11,* 281–303.

Schneider, B. (1987). The people make the place. *Personnel Psychology, 40,* 437–453.

Schruijer, S. (2008). The psychology of interorganizational relations. In S. Cropper, M. Ebers, C. Huxham, & P. Smith Ring (Eds.), *The Oxford handbook of interorganizational relations* (pp. 417–440). New York, NY: Oxford University Press.

Schruijer, S. (2012). Whatever happened to the term 'European' in European social psychology? A study of the ambitions in founding the European Association of Experimental Social Psychology. *History of Human Sciences, 25,* 88–107.

Schruijer, S. (2013). Are we losing the group in the study of group dynamics? Three illustrations. In L. Vansina (Ed.), *Humanness in organizations: A psychodynamic contribution* (pp. 71–89). London, UK: Karnac.

Schruijer, S. (2015). The narcissistic group dynamics of multiparty systems. *Team Performance Management, 21*, 310–319.

Schruijer, S. (2018). The role of collusive dynamics in the occurrence of organizational crime: A psychoanalytically informed social psychological perspective. *Administrative Sciences, 8*, 24. http://doi.org/10.3390/admsci8030024

Schruijer, S. (2020). Developing collaborative interorganizational relationships: An action research approach. *Team Performance Management, 26*, 17–28.

Schruijer, S., & Curşeu, P. (2014). Looking at the gap between the social psychological and psychodynamic perspectives on group dynamics historically. *Journal of Organizational Change Management, 27*, 232–245.

Schruijer, S., & Vansina, L. (2008). Working across organizational boundaries: Understanding and working with the psychological dynamics. In L. Vansina & M.-J. Vansina-Cobbaert (Eds.), *Psychodynamics for consultants and managers: From understanding to leading meaningful change* (pp. 390–410). London, UK: Wiley.

Shaw, M. (1981). *Group dynamics: The psychology of small group behavior.* New York, NY: McGraw-Hill.

Sherif, M. (1966). *In common predicament: Social psychology of intergroup conflict and cooperation.* Boston, MA: Houghton Mifflin.

Shuffler, M. L., & Carter, D. M. (2018). Teamwork situated in multiteam systems: Key lessons learned and future opportunities. *American Psychologist, 73*, 390–406.

Shuffler, M. L., Jiménez-Rodríguez, M., & Kramer, W. S. (2015). The science of multiteam systems: A review and future research agenda. *Small Group Research, 46*, 659–699.

Stein, M. (2007). Oedipus Rex at Enron: Leadership, Oedipal struggle, and organizational collapse. *Human Relations, 60*, 1387–1410.

Stein, M. (2019, November 16). The lost good self: Why the whistleblower is hated and stigmatized. *Organization Studies.* https://doi.org/10.1177/0170840619880565

Stephenson, G. (1981). Intergroup bargaining and negotiation. In J. C. Turner & H. Giles (Eds.), *Intergroup behaviour.* Oxford, UK: Basil Blackwell.

Tajfel, H., & Turner, J. (1979). An integrative theory of intergroup conflict. In W. Austin & S. Worchel (Eds.), *The social psychology of intergroup relations* (pp. 7–24). Monterey, CA: Brooks/Cole.

Trist, E. (1983). Referent organizations and the development of inter-organizational domains. *Human Relations, 36*, 269–284.

Turner, M., & Pratkanis, A. (1998). Twenty-five years of groupthink theory and research: Lessons from the evaluation of a theory. *Organizational Behavior and Human Decision Processes, 73*, 105–115.

Vangen, S., & Huxham, C. (2003). Nurturing collaborative relations: Building trust in interorganizational collaboration. *Journal of Applied Behavioral Science, 39*, 5–31.

Vansina, L. (2005). The art of reviewing. In G. Amado & L. Vansina (Eds.), *The transitional approach in action* (pp. 227–254). London, UK: Karnac.

Vansina, L., & Taillieu, T. (1997). Diversity in collaborative task-systems. *European Journal of Work and Organizational Psychology, 6*, 129–255.

Vansina, L., Taillieu, T., & Schruijer, S. (1998). "Managing" multiparty issues: Learning from experience. In W. Pasmore & R. Woodman (Eds.), *Research in organizational change and development* (Vol. 11, pp. 159–183). Greenwich, CT: JAI Press.

Vansina, L., & Vansina-Cobbaert, M.-J. (2008). *Psychodynamics for consultants and managers: From understanding to leading meaningful change.* London, UK: Wiley.

Weber, E. P., & Khademian, A. M. (2008). Wicked problems, knowledge challenges, and collaborative capacity builders in network settings. *Public Administration Review, 68*, 334–349.

Yström, A., Ollila, S., Agogué, M., & Coghlan, D. (2019). The role of a learning approach in building an interorganizational network aiming for collaborative innovation. *Journal of Applied Behavioral Science, 55*, 27–49.

Zilber, T., & Zanoni, P. (2020, August 12). Templates of ethnographic writing in organization studies: Beyond the hegemony of the detective story. *Organizational Research Methods.* http://doi.org/10.1177/1094428120944468

Sandra Schruijer

Individuals in Organizations

JUDGMENT AND DECISION-MAKING PROCESSES

INTRODUCTION

Work life is filled with many consequential decisions. Which project should be funded? Which market should be expanded into? Who should be hired? Who made a good impression during an interview? Which employee performed best last month? Most decisions share a number of important features, such as uncertainty about what will happen in the future and multiple dimensions along which options differ and must be evaluated. The field of judgment and decision-making (JDM) has explored the basic processes by which people assess uncertainties and evaluate options. This article describes the emergence of behavioral approaches to decision-making (in contrast to mathematically derived rational models), reviews a number of central ideas from the field of JDM, and illustrates their relevance to important organizational questions.

RATIONAL MODELS, VIOLATIONS, AND THE BEHAVIORAL APPROACH

Rational models of decision-making are the underlying principles for many aspects of business education and research, including areas such as finance and strategy. These models are based on fundamental mathematical analyses underlying economics and statistics (Bernoulli,

1954; Savage, 1954; von Neumann & Morgenstern, 1944). At the heart of these models is a set of assumptions that yield a single optimal answer. These assumptions include actors who have consistent preferences and who integrate information using basic rules of math. By assuming consistent preferences, these rational models imply that an individual will be unaffected by incidental features of how information is presented.

Starting with Herbert Simon in the 1950s, research on organizations has long recognized that actors are boundedly rational—they are inconsistent and they use simplifying strategies to make decisions (Cyert & March, 1963; Simon, 1955). This behavioral approach to decision-making has been extremely generative. Many social scientists, most prominently Daniel Kahneman and Amos Tversky, have proposed systematic ways in which people deviate from rational models—and, as importantly, have tried to account for these deviations by describing a set of basic, robust psychological processes.

Thus, the field of JDM was born with a dual focus: the identification of violations of rationality that represent dangers that people need to avoid and the identification of psychological processes that provide explanatory and predictive insights about how people make decisions. To illustrate this dual contribution, consider early work by Kahneman and Tversky (1973) on what they called cognitive heuristics. In one study, they gave participants brief professional profiles that were described as being drawn at random from an overall set composed of either 70 engineers and 30 lawyers (for one group of subjects), or the reverse distribution (30 engineers and 70 lawyers). The profiles varied in detail, sometimes sounding more typical of one profession versus the other (e.g., "he likes mathematical puzzles" is more typical of engineers). After reading the profile, subjects were asked the probability that the target person was an engineer or lawyer. People depended almost exclusively on whether the description sounded like an engineer or lawyer and very little on the composition of the pool. This was perhaps most strikingly illustrated with a deliberately uninformative profile: "Dick is a 30-year-old man. He is married with no children. A man of high ability and high motivation, he promises to be quite successful in his field. He is well liked by his colleagues." People reported that Dick has a 50–50 chance of being a lawyer or engineer—thereby ignoring the base rate represented in the original distribution that was skewed either 70–30 or 30–70.

Kahneman and Tversky (1973) argued that people neglect a statistical principle—attending to base rates—and instead rely on a cognitive shortcut, or heuristic, which they called "representativeness." They argued that people quickly and automatically assess the similarity of an individual description and professional category and, in this case, neglect relevant distributional data that is also important to judging probabilities. This kind of bias can be significant in a number of practical areas, such as diagnosing the causes of a problem. In medicine, doctors have a saying, "when you hear hoofbeats, think horses, not zebras," to keep themselves focused on likely conditions and not overreact to data that are suggestive of very rare diseases. Kahneman and Tversky (1973) argued that representativeness leads to a number of other statistical violations, such as failing to regress to the mean in prediction and overreacting to streaks in random data. For example, subjects who were asked to predict a student's grade point average (GPA) using a reliable indicator (the student's GPA percentile) and an unreliable indicator (the student's percentile score on a test of concentration) predicted with equal confidence and extremity. One of the main insights that has come out of the analytical revolution in sports at the start of the 21st century, in American baseball among other sports, is that a season's worth of data is not as reliable an indicator of underlying ability as a career's worth of data; prior to the analytical revolution, teams hired players based on small samples of recent high performance, only to be sorely disappointed (see Thaler and Sunstein's [2003] review of Michael Lewis's [2004] book *Moneyball*). When observing high performance in a small sample, one's best estimate of the true quality of an individual (or firm) should be regressive to account for the unreliability of the sample.

This early work of Kahneman and Tversky (1973) illustrates the dual goals of JDM research. First, how would a rational person judge a probability or make a prediction? The answer is to rely on base rates and to regress forecasts when predictive cues are imperfect. Second, how do people actually judge a probability or make a prediction? The answer is to rely on judgments of similarity: Does this person sound like an engineer? Did this person perform well on a previous test? Initially, JDM had a large impact on a variety of fields because it called into question assumptions of rationality. And, practically, it affected business training because it seemed important to help future managers avoid biases and rely on economic and statistical principles (such as using base rates and regressing predictions appropriately). But the focus on violations eventually transitioned to a focus on understanding the psychology of judgment and choice.

PSYCHOLOGICAL PROCESSES IN DECISION-MAKING

Research has argued that several general categories of psychological processes underlie decision-making (Arkes, 1991). These processes are general and basic, meaning that they arise across many domains of life and work—they influence personal decisions about health and finance, and they influence professional decisions among doctors, lawyers, and managers (Fischhoff & Broomell, 2020). One feature that these basic processes have in common is that they tend to be intuitive processes, which means that they are rapid, automatic, and require little effort (Kahneman, 2011). In fact, they often occur with very little awareness. To the extent they can yield poor decisions, the lack of awareness becomes an important obstacle in trying to correct them—an issue discussed in the section "Improving Decisions." Rather than attempting to provide an exhaustive list of all of the documented biases that these processes produce, this section describes the general psychological processes that guide decision-making. Focusing on a select number of well-known biases that arise from these processes facilitates illustrating their consequences. Many resources go more deeply into the extensive list of heuristics and biases in decision-making, such as Bazerman and Moore (2012), Gigerenzer and Gaissmaier (2011), Kahneman (2011), and Shah and Oppenheimer (2008).

Associative-Memory Processes. Are there more or fewer than 300 countries in the United Nations? Most people will answer fewer. And if they were originally asked to make a comparison with the number 50, they would answer more. How do these starting points affect a final judgment? Many decades of research show that these arbitrary anchors leak into final judgments: Higher numbers yield higher answers. One of the main explanations for this anchoring effect is that, by initially considering the original answer, people automatically bring to mind evidence consistent with it—in psychological terms, evidence is recruited through associative-memory processes. (In addition, as people try to adjust their initial guess, it is an effortful process, and they tend to stop when they reach a plausible number [Epley, 2004].) This effect is most prominent when people have not first thought independently for themselves. It has consequences for many business activities, such as how to run a team meeting or how to prepare for a negotiation: A party that speaks first may anchor the ensuing discussion on their opening point.

One crucial idea coming out of the behavioral revolution in decision-making research is the idea of search—how people gather and evaluate information to choose between alternatives (Cyert & March, 1963). Because rational models are often based either on the assumption of perfect information or of rational agents paying an effort cost to search for fungible information, they neglect the importance of how people recruit evidence. Research in associative processes yields essential insights regarding this process of search. For example, Tversky and Kahneman (1973) describe the availability heuristic in which people overweight the most readily available information in their cognitive search for evidence. The ease of recall of information is heavily influenced by what was seen recently or what is highly salient (such as the vividness of a plane crash). Reliance on memory can lead to flaws in reasoning such as inattention to base rates, as less vivid statistical information may be less readily available in one's mind (plane deaths per mile of travel are much lower than automobile deaths per mile of travel). Another associative process with profound consequences for decision-making is confirmation bias. People tend to test a belief by first searching in favor of their existing assumption over other possible views and by giving more weight to information that is consistent with that belief (Koriat et al., 1980; Nickerson, 1998). Confirmation bias leads people to hold on to potentially false beliefs because it creates a self-fulfilling prophecy of how information is sought and weighed—a problem that is worsened by social media bubbles and biased Internet searches.

Psychophysical Processes. Imagine facing the following decision (Bazerman & Moore, 2012): You are the chief executive officer of a company faced with a difficult choice. Because of worsening economic conditions, 6,000 people will have to be fired to reduce payroll costs and avoid serious financial problems. Two alternative programs to combat the firings have been proposed to you. The estimates of the consequences of the programs are as follows:

If Program A is adopted, 2,000 jobs will be saved.

If Program B is adopted, there is a one-third probability that 6,000 jobs will be saved, and a two-thirds probability that no jobs will be saved.

Which of the programs would you select? Most people are risk averse—they prefer to save the certain 2,000 jobs rather than gambling on an unlikely chance of saving all jobs and a more likely chance of saving none. Risk aversion is a common assumption in rational models of economics and is intuitive to many laypeople. (Economists assume that there are diminishing marginal returns to money because the first dollar or euro meets more important needs than the thousandth unit, leading people to prefer sure, smaller amounts to gambles.) Now imagine the same situation, but facing different alternative plans:

If Program C is adopted, 4,000 people will be fired.

If Program D is adopted, there is a one-third probability that nobody will be fired, and a two-thirds probability that 6,000 will be fired.

Which of the programs would you select? Facing these program options, most people are risk seeking. It is unappealing to accept a certain loss of 4,000 jobs. Instead, gambling on Program D gives one a fighting chance of avoiding any job losses; and if one loses the gamble, 6,000 job losses does not seem that much worse than 4,000.

The astute reader will have already seen that these two scenarios in fact describe the same final outcomes given that 6,000 are slated to lose their jobs: To save 2,000 jobs (Program A) is to allow 4,000 to be fired (Program C). To save 6,000 jobs is to avoid any job loss (the first stem in Programs B and D); to save no jobs is to see 6,000 fired (the second clause in Programs B and D).

This famous example of gain-loss framing (adapted from Tversky & Kahneman, 1981) was once again influential because it contributed to the dual goals of JDM research. First, this inconsistency of preference for identical outcomes violates basic assumptions in theories of rational choice, such as expected utility theory. Second, the fact that people make different decisions for gains and losses starts to reveal some important, fundamental aspects of the psychology of evaluation. Although the idea of diminishing marginal utility had been a cornerstone of economics for more than a century (Menger, 1871), Kahneman and Tversky (1979) recognized that the principle was both broader and more psychological: People exhibit diminishing sensitivity to large magnitudes and become numb to changes when values are high. This is a general psychophysical phenomenon that holds when people judge the loudness of sounds or the weight of objects. It is this insensitivity to changes in large numbers that in part leads us to prefer the safe Program A when deciding among gains, but to gamble on Program D when deciding among losses—because both 4,000 and 6,000 lost jobs sound large and about equally tragic.

Kahneman and Tversky (1979) included this psychological principle in a theory of choice called prospect theory, which proposed that assessments of value are guided by a function like that shown in Figure 1. The *x*-axis represents outcomes and the *y*-axis represents the psychological feelings associated with those outcomes. The function reflects three key insights: First, judgments are made relative to a reference point that divides the world into feelings of gains and losses. The reference point itself is malleable and can shift depending on what information one attends to—for example, one could compare a salary offer to one's current salary, a colleague's salary, or an industry norm, each of which could make the offer seem like a loss or a

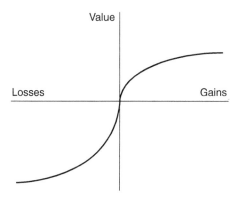

Figure 1. The shape of the value function proposed by Kahneman and Tversky (1979) in prospect theory. Graphic is original to this article.

gain. Second, people are sensitive to changes in gains and losses but show diminishing sensitivity as magnitudes grow larger in either a positive or negative direction. This is reflected in Figure 1 by the fact that both curves become flatter as values deviate more from the reference point. It is this psychophysical property that leads people to be risk averse when deciding among gains but to gamble when deciding among losses. Third, the value function shows greater steepness in the domain of losses than the domain of gains, reflecting the fact that people find it very aversive to lose $1,000 and will work harder to avoid the loss than they would to achieve a comparable $1,000 gain. For example, most people would be reluctant to play a 50–50 gamble in which they could win $1,000 and lose only $500. Psychologically, losses loom larger than gains and result in loss aversion. Loss aversion—which is more properly thought of as an emotional process than a psychophysical one—has been used to explain a number of phenomena relevant to organizations, including a status quo bias that makes us resistant to change efforts (Samuelson & Zeckhauser, 1988). People feel the pain of losing rights and resources they currently possess (e.g., sole decision authority over hiring) more greatly than they value hypothetical gains on other dimensions (e.g., more resources for hiring) that might in fact have greater objective value.

A number of other judgment processes have also been explained by psychophysical processes. For example, diminishing sensitivity suggests that once one has made a $20,000 investment in a new project that is not turning out well, people may escalate their commitment because spending $2,000 more does not seem like much (Kelly & Milkman, 2013). Likewise, diminishing sensitivity explains why consumers are more likely to choose to reduce a stereo speaker's noise output from 0.01% to 0.003% than to choose to increase a stereo speaker's signal output from 99.990% to 99.997% (Wong & Kwong, 2005). Other aspects of judgment and choice are also influenced by psychophysics. Identical information can be scaled such that the difference between alternatives appears small or large by using a different base (Pandelaere et al., 2011). For example, people find a more expensive but higher quality cell plan more attractive than an alternative when the more expensive plan is described as costing $5 more per month rather than $60 per year (Burson et al., 2009). The per-month frame makes the magnitude of difference seem small and negligible, whereas the per-year frame makes it seem more significant, despite the fact that the information is identical.

Emotional and Motivational Processes.   Research in JDM from 1970 to 1990 largely focused on cognitive processes, including ones that are associative and psychophysical. These initial steps away from rational reasoning started by considering the actual architecture of reasoning. But starting in the 1980s, there was a realization that information processing was only part of the picture—a missing piece was the feelings and emotions that accompany decisions (Finucane et al., 2000; Lerner et al., 2015; Loewenstein et al., 2001). For example, research on risky decision-making proposed that people anticipate regretting their decisions (Bell, 1982; Loomes & Sugden, 1982). One reason people choose a sure $10 over a coin flip for $20 is diminishing sensitivity (as described earlier); but another is an asymmetry in the opportunity to feel bad. If one chooses the gamble, there's a 50% chance of ending up with nothing and knowing one could have had $10. (There's also a 50% chance of coming out ahead, but, because of loss aversion, coming out behind is more painful than coming out ahead is enjoyable.) Choosing the sure $10 not only guarantees winning, it also leaves ambiguous the outcome of the road not taken—which can be useful if it allows a decision maker to use the ambiguity to conclude "I probably wouldn't have won." Interestingly, one can eliminate the emotional safety of the sure thing if the coin is flipped regardless of the choice, and one has a 50% chance of seeing that one could have won $20 because of a successful coin flip. In a world with full feedback there is no place to hide, and choosing the sure thing loses some of its appeal. Consequently, in the presence of full feedback, people become less risk averse (Larrick & Boles, 1995). For additional research on regret and disappointment, see Mellers (2000), Reb and Connolly (2010), and Zeelenberg (1999).

The emotions of regret and disappointment arise from the decision process itself—patterns of outcomes make one feel good or bad about one's decision. But emotions can also influence decisions incidentally. Imagine an employee angered at work by the denial of promotion—the feeling of anger can linger and easily spill over into aggressive, risky driving on the way home. Laboratory research has shown just such spillovers (Lerner & Keltner, 2000). Emotions differ not only in valence (positive or negative) but also in other characteristics, such as whether they create a feeling of certainty or uncertainty and whether or not one feels in control. For example, anger is marked by feelings of certainty and control; fear is marked by uncertainty and lack of control. Thus, momentary anger, regardless of the source, can create a mindset in which people are more likely to take on risks because they feel both certainty and control.

A number of other decision processes reflect the operation of needs and desires. There is a large body of research showing that people favor small outcomes in the present over larger future outcomes. The degree of preference for present outcomes is highly myopic. It implies a discount rate that is overly shortsighted compared to rates typically assumed in economic models (Urminsky & Zauberman, 2015). An influential interpretation of this pattern is that immediate gains and losses are psychologically vivid and salient, leading to a present bias, and anything in the future is diminished in comparison (Laibson, 1997). There is also a large body of work showing that our reasoning is often not dispassionate, but motivated: If someone has a desired conclusion, such as picking a specific job candidate to hire or project to fund, they unconsciously give more attention and credence to favorable information and underweight unfavorable information (Ditto et al., 1998; Kunda, 1990). Political polarization is a major source of everyday motivated reasoning as each side gives more weight to their evidence and arguments and dismisses the merits of opposing views.

Rule-Based Processes.   Many decisions are guided by simple rules, norms, and habits that are either learned from experience or from others directly (including parents, teachers, and colleagues) or indirectly (books, media, etc.). Many adults were told as kids "waste not, want not" as an explanation for why they had to clean their plate. This rule of thumb is one reason why people may be more inclined to stick with a project that is not turning out well if it was preceded by a large investment.

This final category is not strictly parallel to the first three (associative, psychophysical, and emotional processes). The first three describe very basic psychological processes that influence a wide range of decision contexts. They are domain general. Rules, norms, and habits tend to be tied to specific situations, and they are learned either from experience or from others. In addition, bad rules can also be replaced by good rules ("waste not, want not" can be replaced by "don't cry over spilt milk" or "you have to know when to hold 'em and know when

DUAL SYSTEM THEORIES OF DECISION-MAKING

to fold 'em"). Nisbett and colleagues conducted a number of studies looking at how education shapes people's knowledge of basic economic and statistical principles (summarized in Nisbett, 1993). The acquisition and possession of effective rules is an important concept underlying the frameworks discussed in "Dual System Theories of Decision-Making" and "Learning Environments and Expertise."

DUAL SYSTEM THEORIES OF DECISION-MAKING

Since the start of the 21st century, JDM research has adopted a dual systems framework for describing decision-making (Kahneman, 2011; Sloman, 1996; Stanovich & West, 1998). The first system consists of processes that are rapid and automatic. These include the categories of associationistic, psychophysical, and emotional processes. A key feature of these automatic processes is that they produce an intuitive response very quickly and without effort. The second system consists of processes that are slower and more deliberate—they are generally conscious and serial, and depend on access to specific kinds of strategies and knowledge (Evans & Stanovich, 2013). Adding the numbers 734 and 217 requires a slow and serial process—one typically facilitates this calculation by using a strategy of putting one number on top of another on a page and then adding one column of digits at a time. Kahneman captured these two systems in the title of his bestselling 2011 book, *Thinking, Fast and Slow*.

JDM researchers have gathered extensive evidence on the potential pitfalls of system 1 fast thinking—cognitive shortcuts that are generally adaptive produce consistent errors when overapplied to inappropriate situations. System 2 slow thinking is proposed to play two roles: (a) to monitor the outputs of system 1 processes for errors and to correct them; and (b) to engage in deliberative processing that uses rules and knowledge. The main evidence for the benefit of slow thinking comes from research that uses an individual difference measure known as the Cognitive Reflection Task (CRT, Frederick, 2005). The test consists of a mere three items, one of which asks the question: "A bat and a ball cost $1.10. The bat costs one dollar more than the ball. How much does the ball cost?" The immediate, intuitive answer is the ball must cost 10 cents. However, reflection shows that if the bat also cost one dollar more than the ball, it would cost $1.10, and the two objects together would cost $1.20. The correct answer is that the ball costs five cents and the bat costs $1.05. The CRT measures the tendency to reflect on answers and double-check the accuracy of one's intuition.

The CRT has been used to predict many instances of better decision performance. People who score higher on the CRT are more patient when waiting for future outcomes, more likely to maximize the expected value of gambles, more likely to rely on base rates and the law of large numbers when forming estimates, and less likely to commit the conjunction fallacy that derives from probabilistic reasoning by representativeness and to commit other errors in statistical reasoning (Cokely & Kelley, 2009; Frederick, 2005; Koehler & James, 2010; Obrecht et al., 2009; Oeschssler et al., 2009). See Toplak et al. (2011) for a review of the CRT's relationship with performance in heuristics and biases tasks.

The dual system argument, however, has been criticized on several grounds. First, the terminology suggests distinct cognitive systems in which the parts within a system are inherently related—perhaps even physically and biologically. Instead, the systems are better understood as a framework for organizing processes by their properties—are they rapid and automatic, or are they slow and controlled? Beyond that, however, the processes grouped within a "system" are not inherently linked. Second, the main evidence for dual systems has come from reliance on an individual difference measure, the CRT, which means the association is open to a variety of third-variable interpretations. For example, some specific cognitive abilities (e.g., problem-solving skills) could jointly explain both CRT scores and performance in bias tasks. The CRT does require some mathematical skill, and it is related to measures of intelligence as well as mathematical ability. And research that has tried to improve decision-making by instructing subjects to make a slow, reflective decision finds that they are no better at solving traditional JDM items testing statistical biases than is the control group (Lawson et al., 2020). Thus, the CRT appears to measure more than simple reflection—it measures both a reflective thinking style and a set of abilities necessary to do math well.

When Sloman (1996) originally proposed that some processes are intuitive, rapid, and automatic (system 1) and others are slower and deliberate (system 2), he called the second system the "rule-based" system because he proposed it also depends on specific knowledge. Consider another classic problem posed by Tversky and Kahneman (1983): Linda is 31 years old, single, outspoken, and very bright. She majored in philosophy. As a student, she was deeply concerned with issues of discrimination and social justice, and also participated in antinuclear demonstrations.

Rank these from most (= 1) to least (= 3) probable.

1. Linda is a bank teller.
2. Linda is active in the feminist movement.
3. Linda is a bank teller and is active in the feminist movement.

Because the description of Linda is more consistent with her being a feminist than a bank teller, many people rank option 3 as more likely than option 1. But a conjunction of events can never be more likely than a constituent event (a violation of a basic rule of statistics and logic). Because of the representativeness heuristic, however, people rely on similarity when answering this question intuitively, rather than the formal rule of logic known as the "conjunction rule". But to answer this question correctly, one not only has to resist the intuitive appeal of using similarity when answering, but one also has to know and understand how conjunctions are related to their constituent events. Lawson et al. (2020) assessed knowledge of the basic rule by asking a conjunction question that had no misleading or tempting answer: Imagine Sally owns a car. Rank the following from most likely (= 1) to least likely (= 3):

1. The car has Bluetooth speakers.
2. The car is painted green.
3. The car has Bluetooth speakers and is painted green.

This simple question directly tests whether people understand that any construction with the word "and" has to be less likely than either element included in the statement. If people do not understand this rule, it seems unlikely that they can solve the Linda problem correctly. Possession of the basic rule or strategy is necessary but not sufficient for answering harder questions accurately. And, in fact, Kahneman originally proposed that optimal decision-making is dependent both on reflection and possession of relevant knowledge:

A task will be too difficult if (1) System 1 favors an incorrect answer, and (2) System 2 is incapable of applying the correct rule, either because the rule is unknown or because the cues that would evoke it are absent.
(Kahneman, 2000, p. 682)

Lawson et al. (2020) discovered, in fact, that CRT score interacted with possession of rules (such as a basic understanding of the conjunction rule) to predict subjects' success at answering problems such as the Linda question. This line of argument suggests that thinking style alone is not sufficient to improve decision-making—it also matters what knowledge one can bring to bear. The section "Learning Environments and Expertise" considers how people acquire relevant knowledge to make effective decisions within specific task domains.

LEARNING ENVIRONMENTS AND EXPERTISE

The classic problems studied in JDM are like those presented here—a word problem in what may be an unfamiliar context and that is designed to tap the use of a very general statistical or economic principle, such as using base rates or applying the conjunction rule. An alternative view of understanding decision-making is to think in terms of important problems and domains, such as professional areas like finance or medicine, and identifying the key knowledge that one needs to possess in these areas. In this domain-specific view, the fundamental problem of decision-making is learning specific relationships in the relevant domains so that accurate knowledge can guide everyday decisions.

For example, the principle of compounding is an important one in making financial decisions. If one carries a credit card balance, paying too little each month leads to a debt spiral. On the flip side, if a young employee starts saving for retirement early, compounding will greatly grow retirement savings. People's (incorrect) intuitions are that retirement savings grow in a linear way (McKenzie & Liersch, 2011). In contrast, financial service professionals are trained in compounding, use it regularly, receive feedback on it, and consequently develop intuitions around it. This is the heart of developing expertise—the chance to practice different actions and receive feedback on their consequences.

In many domains, the chance to gain and use knowledge is rare, and feedback may be nonexistent. Most people will take out mortgages only a few times in their life, years apart. Robin Hogarth (2001) has described environments with small samples and delayed or ambiguous feedback as "wicked"—they are either unhelpful or occasionally systematically misleading. Other environments, however, are "kind"—they provide timely, accurate feedback and allow the decision maker to acquire a large sample. For example, even before the advent of complex computer simulations, and despite the stereotype, meteorologists were actually quite accurate forecasters (Murphy & Winkler, 1977). When they say there is a 70% chance of rain, rain in fact happens about 70% of the time on average. The reason meteorologists develop strong forecasting skills are that there are available cues (e.g., barometric pressure); past data to learn from; and, after making the prediction, immediate and clear feedback (i.e., whether it rained or not). This "kind" environment is the ideal environment in which to hone professional decision-making skills.

A second major component in developing expertise is the existence of a canon of valid knowledge (Larrick & Feiler, 2016). The description of knowledge as "valid" presupposes that understandable relationships exist in a domain. This criterion distinguishes, for example, medicine from astrology. Medicine is a helpful example to consider how expertise is developed. In the case of medicine, prior research has created a canon of scientifically supported relationships. This knowledge is incomplete, and certainly some current knowledge is even inaccurate. But it represents a sea change from medicine at the start of the 20th century (not to mention bloodletting and leeches from even earlier times). This knowledge is transmitted through book learning but also, importantly, through "kind" learning environments in which doctors in training practice diagnosing and treating patients with rapid, accurate feedback in the form of attending doctors and other interns and residents.

IMPROVING DECISIONS

JDM research has focused considerably more attention on identifying decision biases than on developing techniques to reduce them. In recent years this has changed with the rise of behavioral economics. The key argument from behavioral economics is that we can merge the psychological insights of JDM and rational standards from economics to help people make better decisions for themselves and others.

Techniques for improving decisions can be organized around two main approaches. One approach assumes that the best way to help people are techniques "external" to the decision maker. The key argument is to provide a tool or to change a situation so that decision makers are not dependent on their own flawed intuitions, but are "nudged" in a helpful direction. The other approach explores the possibility of improving decision-making through techniques that are "internal" to the decision maker—providing individuals with strategies and processes that give them a new way of thinking that they can retain and apply to new situations.

External Interventions.   One technique for helping people make better decisions is to change the environment in which they make their decision. Consider the decision to be an organ donor. Classic economic theory assumes that people have well-defined preferences for helping others—they precisely know the utility they gain from being altruistic to others. It turns out, however, that the decision to be an organ donor is fundamentally shaped by a subtle feature of the situation: Do you opt into being a donor or opt out (Johnson & Goldstein, 2003)? Across European countries that are often very similar in culture and socioeconomic status (such as Denmark and Sweden), those countries that set the default option as donating end up with 90% or more people electing to donate; those countries that set the default option as not donating end up with less than 20% electing to donate. Default options exert inordinate influence. These effects have been explained in part by the status quo bias as well as several other psychological processes (Smith et al., 2013).

Thaler and Sunstein (2009) proposed that armed with the knowledge of such behavioral insights, those responsible for designing decisions—for example, policymakers and human resources (HR) representatives—can "nudge" people to make better decisions for both themselves and society. By changing how a choice is presented, policymakers can affect the behavior of the people making that choice. The powerful organ donation example illustrates a tool that can be applied to achieve other societal benefits. The effect of defaults can also be used to increase retirement savings (discussed in "Applications of JDM to Workplace Issues"). This increase benefits both employees and society. Thaler and Sunstein (2009) argue that there are many places where those who design systems can intervene as "choice architects" to help simplify decisions (as in the case of overly complicated healthcare plans) and to make it easy to pick the more beneficial decision (as in the case of savings for retirement). There is a growing body of work on the effectiveness of many kinds of nudges that go beyond defaults (Johnson et al., 2012). For example, interventions that keep information salient, such as text reminders to enroll in financial support at community college, help people complete important tasks (Castleman & Page, 2016). Likewise, helping people evaluate their outcomes as good or bad motivates them to improve. When energy bills convey not just energy use and cost, but a comparison to the energy use of nearby neighbors, people are motivated to reduce their energy use (Allcott & Rogers, 2014). These descriptive norms serve as reference points that create clear regions of gains and losses: They turn an otherwise ambiguous kilowatt number into a point of comparison that indicates whether one is in fact succeeding or failing.

Other forms of external interventions involve enhancing individual decisions with additional support such as quantitative tools. JDM research has often argued that, on average, models are more accurate than human judges because they attend to a set of relevant predictor variables and use them consistently (and fairly) across cases (Dawes, 1979). Scott Highhouse (2008) has argued for the effectiveness of using quantitative models in hiring and evaluation, and lamented the enduring psychological attraction of relying on intuition instead. With the explosion of big data, a number of fields have become interested in exploring the contrast between the benefits of algorithms for prediction and evaluation with the human aversion to ceding important decisions to a formula (Dietvorst et al., 2015).

A second big data technique similar to algorithms is relying on the wisdom of crowds (Surowiecki, 2005). When making a quantitative estimate under uncertainty, it is possible to reduce error by averaging together the judgments of different forecasters or evaluators. Interestingly, there are diminishing returns to crowd size, and 5 to 10 people's judgments approach the benefits gained from much larger samples (Mannes et al., 2014). In fact, the largest reduction in error is realized by the second judgment—leading to the simple prescription of going outside one's own head to ask someone else for his or her advice. Benefits of aggregation are greatest when people have thought independently and draw on separate experiences or training. Importantly, many kinds of judgments benefit from aggregation, including "soft" dimensions such as collegiality, and there are many methods available besides averaging, such as voting or pooling options. Bond et al. (2008) asked a group of MBA students to name the goals they would most like to achieve in their summer internship. They then showed the students a longer list generated by pooling the goals of other MBA students. The majority of students rated some goals from the pool to be as or more important than the goals they generated for themselves.

Internal Interventions. An alternative approach to improving decision-making is to help people reason in a better way. As discussed in "Dual System Theories of Decision-Making," some research has implied that slowing down a decision process should lead to greater accuracy. However, it appears that people also need the right strategies and rules to gain accurate insights for many decisions. To offer an extreme example: People often deviate from Bayes' theorem when combining base rates with new information (Kahneman, 2011). Simply slowing down is unlikely to produce the right insights without additional knowledge about the appropriate strategy.

In the 1980s, Richard Nisbett and his colleagues looked at the potential to train people on simple statistical and economic rules such as appreciating larger samples and ignoring sunk costs (summarized in Nisbett, 1993). More recently Carey Morewedge and colleagues (2015) have examined whether an immersive video game–like experience can help train people to identify and avoid basic decision biases, such as anchoring and confirmation bias. Both of these programs have found positive results. There is always a question in training, however, about whether the knowledge persists over time and whether people have the ability to recognize when to apply a rule or strategy "in the wild" after training.

Research on "naturalistic decision making" (Zsambok & Klein, 2014) focuses on the development of expertise through individual and collective experience. Gary Klein and his collaborators have studied how specific professions and job roles, such as firefighters, develop shared expertise that is transmitted to new members of their community. This view of decision-making focuses less on rational standards derived from statistic and economics and more on learning and using domain-specific relationships that allow one to assess a situation and the best response: How quickly will a fire of this size, burning these materials, and under this weather condition spread? For many professions, the right way to think about effective decision-making is to draw on the principles laid out in "Learning Environments and Expertise." Is there a canon of valid insights developed through scientific experimentation or through experience that can help one navigate this domain (e.g., medicine, finance)? Can individuals acquire this knowledge not just through book learning, but through a "kind" environment in which they receive clear, fast feedback on their decisions?

A positive answer to these questions lies in constructing a friendly process. For decades, airplane pilots have spent considerable time in flight simulators in order to help them learn about unusual circumstances (such as a bird strike) and turn abstract book knowledge into automatic associations and responses. With the ready availability of technology, it is worth considering whether simulator training could become a common practice in organizations, to help employees navigate both common and uncommon situations they might encounter (customer service, ethical decisions with suppliers, etc.). Combining consciously learning principles from books with a gamelike simulator that provides repeated experiences with feedback helps turn abstract knowledge into automatic responses. In sum, domain-specific training aims to convert system 2 processes (conscious reflection) into system 1 processes (intuitive responses) through a "kind" learning environment.

Consider a final, more speculative approach to improving decision-making that stands in direct contrast to the notion of domain-specific expertise: Can people learn general decision-making skills that can be applied across situations? Historically, rational decision-making has been defined in terms of economic and statistical models that prescribe reaching a specific, optimal conclusion. An alternative view of effective decision-making is to consider using reliably better processes (i.e., even if they do not guarantee optimal outcomes every time, they lead to better outcomes on average). This suggestion is in the spirit of "thinking slowly" associated with the dual-system framework, but it prescribes more fully the most useful steps in thinking slowly (Larrick, 2009). In proposing an idea he called "value-focused thinking," Ralph Keeney (1996) argued that one of the hardest parts of making decisions is thinking broadly enough to identify the right decision. Interestingly, Keeney spent the 1970s developing and analyzing very sophisticated math to measure utility functions to optimize decisions. By the mid-1990s, he came to argue that the real challenge in decision-making is setting up the right decision by asking questions such as (a) What are the things I care about (recall the MBAs pursuing their internships in Bond et al., 2008)? (b) Can I find or create choice options that will help me achieve those goals? And (c) What are the range of outcomes and circumstances that could arise that will affect the outcomes I experience? In this view, slow decision-making is really a process of building up a broad and complete representation of a problem (Heath & Heath, 2013; Johnson, 2018; Soll et al., 2016). An open and speculative question is whether training in these methods would be beneficial.

APPLICATIONS OF JDM TO WORKPLACE ISSUES

There are many ways in which a JDM perspective can shed light on basic questions in industrial-organizational (IO) psychology, and Scott Highhouse and colleagues have written at length about these connections (Highhouse et al., 2013; Zhang & Highhouse, 2018). Three core topics in IO psychology include how managers help improve employee well-being, how managers evaluate and select employees, and how managers motivate employees. Specific applications include employee retirement savings, evaluation of job candidates, and goal setting.

Retirement Savings. One notable example of applying principles from JDM to work behavior is how to improve employee involvement in retirement savings plans. In the United States, these plans are voluntary. They also offer an extremely attractive return. Contributions are deducted from pre-tax income, which means that there is an immediate gain from not having to pay income tax. Further, any money that employees do contribute to retirement savings plans grows tax free, meaning that compounding is not reduced by annual taxes of any kind. Finally, these individual retirement contributions are often matched in some form by employers. When an employer matches dollar for dollar, this represents an immediate 100% rate of return with no taxes. Rational models of employee behavior assume that they optimally sequence savings and expenditures over a lifetime (Modigliani, 1986). Optimality assumes reasonable intertemporal trade-offs (not impatience), in which people would wisely invest for the future, starting at a young age. Put simply, retirement programs in the United States offer such an attractive return that any rational model would predict full participation.

However, research shows that U.S. employees have invested in these voluntary programs at a low rate. Given the huge financial implications of these decisions, it is surprising that retirement savings, like organ donations, are heavily influenced by initial defaults. Traditionally, these voluntary programs were "opt-in" programs. By default, new employees were not enrolled in the program—to enroll, they had to complete the right paperwork and make decisions about allocations. This creates many small barriers—keeping track of the paperwork, finding the time to complete it, and making investment decisions that can be a bit intimidating to people unfamiliar with mutual funds, stocks, and bonds. In contrast, if employees are automatically enrolled in a company's retirement plan at the beginning of employment—but are free to "opt out"—they stay enrolled and significantly improve their savings (Beshears et al., 2009; Madrian & Shea, 2001). Additional interventions have involved using automatic increases in contributions and have configured the contributions as a portion of a new pay raise—this framing means the contribution is experienced as a diminished gain and not a loss (Thaler & Benartzi, 2004). Importantly, automatic enrollments and increases do not come at the cost of other savings. Research by Raj Chetty and colleagues (Chetty et al., 2014) in Denmark showed that, for 85% of individuals who are passive investors, automatic enrollment and automatic increases in retirement contributions in fact increase an investor's overall savings. By making enrollment the default, the status quo bias (partly determined by loss aversion) helps employees become better savers.

Evaluation of Job Candidates.   One of the insights that motivated Daniel Kahneman to study the flaws of intuitive reasoning was witnessing the use of interviews while serving in the Israeli Army in the 1950s. He quickly recognized that, statistically, this is a noisy sample prone to bias. Researchers using a JDM lens have critiqued interviews on a number of grounds (Highhouse, 2008). First, interviews are a small sample of information and therefore inherently noisy, but they feel informative. Second, the questions that are usually asked provide answers that correlate poorly with success on future tasks (except, perhaps, rapport with strangers). For example, talking about programming skills is not as valuable as directly drawing on a large sample of programming output, either directly through tests or indirectly through grade point average (GPA) in relevant classes. In a series of empirical studies, Dana et al. (2013) found that interviewers become more confident in their assessment of a person's ability even when presented with random responses, and it leads interviewers to rely less on valid predictors of future performance (such as GPA) and more on the confident impressions they have formed during the interview. Finally, it is common in interviews for interviewers to form rapid judgments and then gather evidence supporting their initial impressions through confirmation bias and motivated reasoning. In a qualitative study of law firms, Lauren Rivera (2012) found that it was common for partners conducting the interview to find similarities in colleges, hobbies, and sports relatively early in an interview and then—if found—continue discussing those topics in the rest of the interview.

IO psychology has long recognized weaknesses in unstructured interviews and has spent decades arguing for the merits of structured and semi-structured interviews to prevent some of the preceding problems (Levashina et al., 2014). Structured interviews do a better job of making sure a complete sample of information is gathered (across a range of attributes) and ensures that the samples are more comparable because they have not "drifted" into finding similarities and hobbies, which is a major obstacle to creating a diverse workforce. The shortcomings of using intuition at all, however, suggests that even further steps would be beneficial. First, forecasting models could be used much more extensively than they currently are (Highhouse, 2008). By their nature, models can combine more quantitative measures, such as GPA, with more subjective measures, such as a wisdom-of-crowd assessment of an applicant's collegiality. The key outcome a model can accomplish is attending to a complete set of attributes and applying consistent weights. A complete and consistent process increases accuracy and is a hallmark of procedural fairness. Second, interviews can be augmented or replaced by "work sample tests" that directly test the required skills needed for the job—this yields a more predictive sample than talking about those skills (Knight, 2017).

Finally, another issue that arises in hiring is reliance on similarity judgments in assessing likely future success. These predictions by representativeness can ignore crucial information about candidates (such as other, reliable metrics that could help to form accurate base rates in performance predictions) and often focus on superficial qualities (Kahneman & Tversky, 1973). To borrow another example from sports, after Stephen Curry's success in the NBA, shorter, mixed-race guards were more likely to be drafted, purely because of their physical resemblance to Curry (Lewis, 2016). These judgments are particularly problematic because the formation of exemplars is backward looking—if an industry or role has been male dominated, the exemplar to which new candidates are compared (and judged by their similarity) will likely be male, thus precluding women and minorities from access into these roles. One method to reduce bias is to remove demographic variables at key points of evaluation (but not at all points in time, as knowledge of race and gender is critical to creating a diverse workforce). In a famous study of auditions for major U.S. orchestras, Goldin and Rouse (2000) provide evidence that having applicants perform behind a screen helped contribute to more women being hired between 1970 and 2000. Appropriate use of blinding prevents the operation of the automatic, associative effects that arise from similarity and stereotyped judgments. A survey reported in Fath et al. (in press) shows that, among 900 members of the Society for Human Resource Management (SHRM), a majority of HR professionals have heard of blinding, but only a minority have ever used it or worked at a firm that uses it. This seems like a promising area to use the insights of JDM to improve hiring and evaluation processes.

Goal Setting. Another core area of JDM research—the psychological principles captured in the value function of prospect theory (Kahneman & Tversky, 1979) shown in Figure 1—provides insights about how goals motivate (Locke & Latham, 2013) and how they can also lead to predictable problems (Ordóñez et al., 2009; Ordóñez & Wu, 2014). Locke and Latham (2013) have systematically developed a compelling body of experimental work showing that specific, challenging goals lead people to perform better on tasks compared to other work motivations, such as being told to "do one's best" or being given either vague or modest goals. Moreover, goals motivate even in the absence of financial incentives. Thus, goal setting has become a basic tool in management practice for motivating others.

Heath et al. (1999) proposed that prospect theory's value function can explain many goal setting effects and predict some new ones. The key insight is that goals serve as reference points, creating a region of gains (exceeding a goal) and losses (falling short of a goal); as a result, evaluation of outcomes is subject to both loss aversion and diminishing sensitivity. Suppose one has set a goal of reviewing and archiving 30 files by the end of the day Friday. As one starts pursuing the goal, one is working one's way out of the domain of losses, where the marginal value of making a unit of progress is twice as satisfying as that experienced if accomplishing a unit after meeting the goal. With a goal of 30, it is more satisfying to move from file 26 to 27 than to move from 33 to 34. In addition, satisfaction with progress is also influenced by the psychophysics of diminishing sensitivity. In gains this is intuitive—once one has reached the goal of 30, one feels less marginal satisfaction reaching 31, 32, and so on. But diminishing sensitivity also makes progress unsatisfying when one is far from the goal on the loss side of the function—this can be thought of as "the starting problem" (and is directly related to the "goal gradient" hypothesis [Kivetz et al., 2006]). If one frames work in terms of the final goal (archiving 30 files), the first step from 0 to 1 seems like a drop in the bucket, and other activities (like cleaning one's desk) are relatively more attractive.

The idea that goals serve as reference points has been used to explain and predict a number of phenomena (Ordóñez & Wu, 2014). For example, an early puzzle in the goal-setting literature was why people who pursued challenging goals felt less satisfied with their final performance than people who had no goal at all (Garland, 1984). The resolution depends on what serves as the reference point. People who have no specific goal use their starting point as a reference point and experience each unit of accomplishment as a larger (but diminishing) gain; but people with a specific goal experience each unit of accomplishment as a shrinking loss and finally feel a sense of gain only when reaching the goal—if they even manage to (Wallace & Etkin, 2018). The reference point perspective has been used to explain the benefits of using sub-goals to increase motivation (Amir & Ariely, 2008); why goals induce risky, unethical behavior (Schweitzer et al., 2004); and why the lowest point of motivation might be in the middle of task, when one is far from marking progress relative to either the starting or ending point (Bonezzi et al., 2011).

CONCLUSION

This article has provided a brief history of JDM research and concluded with example applications to workplace decisions. The history highlights three main contributions of JDM. At its founding, JDM asked two basic questions: To what extent do people deviate from rational models? What is the psychology of how people make decisions? Since the start of the 20th century, a third question has been added to the field: How can insights about behavior help people make better decisions for themselves and society? This question has led to vibrant streams of research in field settings. There will be growing opportunities to bring JDM insights into the workplace.

REFERENCES

Allcott, H., & Rogers, T. (2014). The short-run and long-run effects of behavioral interventions: Experimental evidence from energy conservation. *American Economic Review, 104*(10), 3003–3037.

Amir, O., & Ariely, D. (2008). Resting on laurels: The effects of discrete progress markers as subgoals on task performance and preferences. *Journal of Experimental Psychology: Learning, Memory, and Cognition, 34*(5), 1158–1171.

Arkes, H. (1991). Costs and benefits of judgment errors: Implications for debiasing. *Psychological Bulletin, 110*(3), 486–498. https://doi.org/10.1037/0033-2909.110.3.486

Bateson, J., Wirtz, J., Burke, E., & Vaughan, C. (2013). When hiring, first test, and then interview. *Harvard Business Review, 92*(1), 4.

Bazerman, M. H., & Moore, D. A. (2012). *Judgment in managerial decision making.* John Wiley & Sons.

Bell, D. E. (1982). Regret in decision making under uncertainty. *Operations Research, 30*(5), 961–981. https://doi.org/10.1287/opre.30.5.961

Bernoulli, D. (1954). Exposition of a new theory on the measurement of risk [translation by L. Sommer of D. Bernoulli, 1738, Specimen theoriae novae de mensura sortis. *Papers of the Imperial Academy of Science of Saint Peterburg, 5, 175–192*]. *Econometrica, 22*(1), 23–36.

Beshears, J., Choi, J. J., Laibson, D., & Madrian, B. C. (2009). The importance of default options for retirement saving outcomes: Evidence from the United States. In J. R. Brown, J. B. Liebman, & D. A. Wise (Eds.), *Social security policy in a changing environment* (pp. 167–195). University of Chicago Press.

Bond, S. D., Carlson, K. A., & Keeney, R. L. (2008). Generating objectives: Can decision makers articulate what they want? *Management Science, 54*(1), 56–70.

Bonezzi, A., Brendl, C. M., & De Angelis, M. (2011). Stuck in the middle: The psychophysics of goal pursuit. *Psychological Science, 22*(5), 607–612.

Burson, K. A., Larrick, R. P., & Lynch, J. G., Jr. (2009). Six of one, half dozen of the other: Expanding and contracting numerical dimensions produces preference reversals. *Psychological Science, 20*(9), 1074–1078.

Castleman, B. L., & Page, L. C. (2016). Freshman year financial aid nudges: An experiment to increase FAFSA renewal and college persistence. *Journal of Human Resources, 51*(2), 389–415.

Chetty, R., Friedman, J. N., Leth-Petersen, S., Nielsen, T. H., & Olsen, T. (2014). Active vs. passive decisions and crowd-out in retirement savings accounts: Evidence from Denmark. *Quarterly Journal of Economics, 129*(3), 1141–1219.

Cokely, E. T., & Kelley, C. M. (2009). Cognitive abilities and superior decision making under risk: A protocol analysis and process model evaluation. *Judgment and Decision Making, 4*(1), 14.

Cyert, R. M., & March, J. G. (1963). *A behavioral theory of the firm.* Prentice-Hall.

Dana, J., Dawes, R., & Peterson, N. (2013). Belief in the unstructured interview: The persistence of an illusion. *Judgment and Decision Making, 8*(5), 512–520.

Dawes, R. M. (1979). The robust beauty of improper linear models in decision making. *American Psychologist, 34*(7), 571–582.

Dietvorst, B. J., Simmons, J. P., & Massey, C. (2015). Algorithm aversion: People erroneously avoid algorithms after seeing them err. *Journal of Experimental Psychology: General, 144*(1), 114–126.

Ditto, P. H., Scepansky, J. A., Munro, G. D., Apanovitch, A. M., & Lockhart, L. K. (1998). Motivated sensitivity to preference-inconsistent information. *Journal of Personality and Social Psychology, 75*(1), 53–69.

Enke, B., Gneezy, U., Hall, B., & Martin, D. (2020). *Cognitive biases: Mistakes or missing stakes?* [CESifo Working Paper, No. 8168]. Center for Economic Studies and Ifo Institute (CESifo).

Epley, N. (2004). A tale of tuned decks? Anchoring as accessibility and anchoring as adjustment. In D. J. Koehler & N. Harvey (Eds.), *Blackwell handbook of judgment and decision making* (pp. 240–257). John Wiley & Sons.

Evans, J. St. B. T., & Stanovich, K. E. (2013). Dual-process theories of higher cognition: Advancing the debate. *Perspectives on Psychological Science, 8*(3), 223–241. https://doi.org/10.1177/1745691612460685

Fath, S., Larrick, R. P., Soll, J. B., & Zhu, S. (in press). Putting on blinders to size people up. *Sloan Management Review.*

Finucane, M. L., Alhakami, A., Slovic, P., & Johnson, S. M. (2000). The affect heuristic in judgments of risks and benefits. *Journal of Behavioral Decision Making, 13*(1), 1–17.

Fischhoff, B., & Broomell, S. B. (2020). Judgment and decision making. *Annual Review of Psychology, 71,* 331–355.

Frederick, S. (2005). Cognitive reflection and decision making. *Journal of Economic Perspectives, 19*(4), 25–42.

Garland, H. (1984). Relation of effort–performance expectancy to performance in goal-setting experiments. *Journal of Applied Psychology, 69,* 79–84.

Gigerenzer, G., & Gaissmaier, W. (2011). Heuristic decision making. *Annual Review of Psychology, 62*(1), 451–482.

Goldin, C., & Rouse, C. (2000). Orchestrating impartiality: The impact of "blind" auditions on female musicians. *American Economic Review, 90*(4), 715–741.

Heath, C., & Heath, D. (2013). *Decisive: How to make better choices in life and work.* Random House.

Heath, C., Larrick, R. P., & Wu, G. (1999). Goals as reference points. *Cognitive Psychology, 38,* 79–109.

Highhouse, S. (2008). Stubborn reliance on intuition and subjectivity in employee selection. *Industrial and Organizational Psychology*, *1*(3), 333–342.

Highhouse, S., Dalal, R. S., & Salas, E. (Eds.). (2013). *Judgment and decision making at work*. Routledge.

Hogarth, R. M. (2001). *Educating intuition*. University of Chicago Press.

Johnson, E. J., & Goldstein, D. (2003). Do defaults save lives? *Science*, *302*(5649), 1338–1339.

Johnson, E. J., Shu, S. B., Dellaert, B. G. C., Fox, C. R., Goldstein, D. G., Haubl, G., Larrick, R. P., Payne, J. W., Peters, E., Schkade, D., Wansink, B., & Weber, E. U. (2012). Beyond nudges: Tools of a choice architecture. *Marketing Letters*, *23*(2), 487–504.

Johnson, S. (2018). *Farsighted: How we make the decisions that matter the most*. Penguin.

Kahneman, D. (2000). A psychological point of view: Violations of rational rules as a diagnostic of mental processes. *Behavioral and Brain Sciences*, *23*(5), 681–683.

Kahneman, D. (2011). *Thinking fast and slow*. Farrar, Straus and Giroux.

Kahneman, D., & Tversky, A. (1973). On the psychology of prediction. *Psychological Review*, *15*, 237–251.

Kahneman, D., & Tversky, A. (1979). Prospect theory: An analysis of decisions under risk. *Econometrica*, *47*(2), 262–291.

Keeney, R. L. (1996). *Value-focused thinking*. Harvard University Press.

Kelly, T. F., & Milkman, K. L. (2013). Escalation of commitment. In E. H. Kessler (Ed.), *Encyclopedia of management theory* (pp. 256–259). SAGE.

Kivetz, R., Urminsky, O., & Zheng, Y. (2006). The goal-gradient hypothesis resurrected: Purchase acceleration, illusionary goal progress, and customer retention. *Journal of Marketing Research*, *43*(1), 39–58.

Knight, R. (2017, June 12). 7 practical ways to reduce bias in your hiring practice. *Harvard Business Review*. https://hbr.org/2017/06/7-practical-ways-to-reduce-bias-in-your-hiring-process

Koehler, D., & James, G. (2010). Probability matching and strategy availability. *Memory & Cognition*, *38*(6), 667–676.

Koriat, A., Lichtenstein, S., & Fischhoff, B. (1980). Reasons for confidence. *Journal of Experimental Psychology: Human Learning and Memory*, *6*(2), 107–118.

Kunda, Z. (1990). The case for motivated reasoning. *Psychological Bulletin*, *108*(3), 480–498.

Laibson, D. (1997). Golden eggs and hyperbolic discounting. *Quarterly Journal of Economics*, *112*(2), 443–478.

Larrick, R. P. (2009). Broaden the decision frame to make effective decisions. In E. Locke (Ed.), *Handbook of principles of organizational behavior* (pp. 461–480). Wiley.

Larrick, R. P., & Boles, T. L. (1995). Avoiding regret in decisions with feedback: A negotiation example. *Organizational Behavior and Human Decision Processes*, *63*(1), 87–97.

Larrick, R. P., & Feiler, D. C. (2016). Expertise in decision making. In G. Wu & G. Keren (Eds.), *The Wiley Blackwell handbook of judgment and decision making* (pp. 696–721). Wiley.

Lawson, M. A., Larrick, R. P., & Soll, J. B. (2020). Comparing fast thinking and slow thinking: The relative benefits of interventions, individual differences, and inferential rules. *Judgment and Decision Making*, *15*(5), 660–684.

Lerner, J. S., & Keltner, D. (2000). Beyond valence: Toward a model of emotion-specific influences on judgement and choice. *Cognition & Emotion*, *14*(4), 473–493.

Lerner, J. S., Li, Y., Valdesolo, P., & Kassam, K. S. (2015). Emotion and decision making. *Annual Review of Psychology*, *66*(1), 799–823.

Levashina, J., Hartwell, C. J., Morgeson, F. P., & Campion, M. A. (2014). The structured employment interview: Narrative and quantitative review of the research literature. *Personnel Psychology*, *67*(1), 241–293.

Lewis, M. (2004). *Moneyball: The art of winning an unfair game*. Norton.

Lewis, M. (2016). *The undoing project: A friendship that changed the world*. Penguin UK.

Locke, E. A., & Latham, G. P. (Eds.). (2013). *New developments in goal setting and task performance*. Routledge.

Loewenstein, G. F., Weber, E. U., Hsee, C. K., & Welch, N. (2001). Risk as feelings. *Psychological Bulletin, 127*(2), 267–286.

Loomes, G., & Sugden, R. (1982). Regret theory: An alternative theory of rational choice under uncertainty. *Economic Journal, 92*(368), 805–824.

Madrian, B. C., & Shea, D. F. (2001). The power of suggestion: Inertia in 401(k) participation and savings behavior. *Quarterly Journal of Economics, 116*(4), 1149–1187.

Mannes, A. E., Soll, J. B., & Larrick, R. P. (2014). The wisdom of select crowds. *Journal of Personality and Social Psychology, 107*(2), 276–299.

Mckenzie, C. R. M., & Liersch, M. J. (2011). Misunderstanding savings growth: Implications for retirement savings behavior. *Journal of Marketing Research, 48*(SPL), S1–S13.

Mellers, B. (2000). Choice and the relative pleasure of consequences. *Psychological Bulletin, 126,* 910–924.

Menger, K. (1871). *Principles of economics* (J. Dingwall & B. F. Hoselitz, Trans.). Institute for Humane Studies.

Modigliani, F. (1986). Life cycle, individual thrift, and the wealth of nations. *Science, 234*(4777), 704–712.

Morewedge, C. K., Yoon, H., Scopelliti, I., Symborski, C. W., Korris, J. H., & Kassam, K. S. (2015). Debiasing decisions: Improved decision making with a single training intervention. *Policy Insights from the Behavioral and Brain Sciences, 2*(1), 129–140.

Murphy, A. H., & Winkler, R. L. (1977). Reliability of subjective probability forecasts of precipitation and temperature. *Journal of the Royal Statistical Society: Series C (Applied Statistics), 26*(1), 41–47.

Nickerson, R. S. (1998). Confirmation bias: A ubiquitous phenomenon in many guises. *Review of General Psychology, 2*(2), 175–220.

Nisbett, R. E. (1993). *Rules for reasoning.* Lawrence Erlbaum.

Obrecht, N. A., Chapman, G. B., & Gelman, R. (2009). An encounter frequency account of how experience affects likelihood estimation. *Memory & Cognition, 37*(5), 632–643.

Oeschssler, J., Roider, A., & Schmitz, P. W. (2009). Cognitive abilities and behavioral biases. *Journal of Economic Behavior & Organization, 72*(1), 147–152.

Ordóñez, L. D., Schweitzer, M. E., Galinsky, A. D., & Bazerman, M. H. (2009). Goals gone wild: The systematic side effects of overprescribing goal setting. *Academy of Management Perspectives, 23*(1), 6–16.

Ordonez, L. D., & Wu, G. (2014). Goals and decision making. In S. Highhouse, R. S. Dalal, & E. Salas (Eds.), *Judgment and decision making at work* (pp. 123–139). Routledge.

Pandelaere, M., Briers, B., & Lembregts, C. (2011). How to make a 29% increase look bigger: The unit effect in option comparisons. *Journal of Consumer Research, 38*(2), 308–322.

Reb, J., & Connolly, T. (2010). The effects of action, normality, and decision carefulness on anticipated regret: Evidence for a broad mediating role of decision justifiability. *Cognition and Emotion, 24*(8), 1405–1420.

Rivera, L. A. (2012). Hiring as cultural matching: The case of elite professional service firms. *American Sociological Review, 77*(6), 999–1022.

Samuelson, W., & Zeckhauser, R. (1988). Status quo bias in decision making. *Journal of Risk and Uncertainty, 1*(1), 7–59.

Savage, L. J. (1954). *The foundations of statistics.* John Wiley.

Schweitzer, M. E., Ordóñez, L., & Douma, B. (2004). Goal setting as a motivator of unethical behavior. *Academy of Management Journal, 47*(3), 422–432.

Shah, A. J., & Oppenheimer, D. M. (2008). Heuristics made easy: An effort reduction framework. *Psychological Bulletin, 134*(2), 207–222.

Simon, H. A. (1955). A behavioral model of rational choice. *Quarterly Journal of Economics, 69*(1), 99–118.

Sloman, S. A. (1996). The empirical case for two systems of reasoning. *Psychological Bulletin, 119*(1), 3–22.

Smith, N. C., Goldstein, D. G., & Johnson, E. J. (2013). Choice without awareness: Ethical and policy implications of defaults. *Journal of Public Policy & Marketing, 32*(2), 159–172. https://doi.org/10.1509/jppm.10.114

Soll, J. B., Milkman, K. L., & Payne, J. W. (2016). A user's guide to debiasing. In G. Wu & G. Keren (Eds.), *The Wiley Blackwell handbook of judgment and decision making* (pp. 924–951). Wiley.

Stanovich, K. E., & West, R. F. (1998). Individual differences in rational thought. *Journal of Experimental Psychology: General, 127*(2), 161–188.

Surowiecki, J. (2005). *The wisdom of crowds.* Anchor.

Thaler, R. H., & Benartzi, S. (2004). Save More Tomorrow™: Using behavioral economics to increase employee saving. *Journal of Political Economy, 112*(S1), S164–S187.

Thaler, R. H., & Sunstein, C. R. (2003). Market efficiency and rationality: The peculiar case of baseball. *Michigan Law Review, 102*, 1390–1403.

Thaler, R. H., & Sunstein, C. R. (2009). *Nudge: Improving decisions about health, wealth, and happiness.* Penguin.

Toplak, M. E., West, R. F., & Stanovich, K. E. (2011). The Cognitive Reflection Test as a predictor of performance on heuristics-and-biases tasks. *Memory & Cognition, 39*(7), 1275–1289.

Tversky, A., & Kahneman, D. (1973). Availability: A heuristic for judging frequency and probability. *Cognitive Psychology, 5*(2), 207–232.

Tversky, A., & Kahneman, D. (1981). The framing of decisions and the psychology of choice. *Science, 211*(4481), 453–458.

Tversky, A., & Kahneman, D. (1983). Extensional versus intuitive reasoning: The conjunction fallacy in probability judgement. *Psychological Review, 90*(4), 293–315.

Urminsky, O., & Zauberman, G. (2015). The psychology of intertemporal preferences. *The Wiley Blackwell handbook of judgment and decision making* (pp. 141–181). Wiley Blackwell.

von Neumann, J., & Morgenstern, O. (1944). *The theory of games and economic behavior.* Princeton.

Wallace, S. G., & Etkin, J. (2018). How goal specificity shapes motivation: A reference points perspective. *Journal of Consumer Research, 44*(5), 1033–1051.

Wong, K. F. E., & Kwong, J. Y. Y. (2005). Comparing two tiny giants or two huge dwarfs? Preference reversals owing to number size framing. *Organizational Behavior and Human Decision Processes, 98*(1), 54–65.

Zeelenberg, M. (1999). Anticipated regret, expected feedback and behavioral decision making. *Journal of Behavioral Decision Making, 12*(2), 93–106.

Zhang, D. C., & Highhouse, S. (2018). Judgment and decision making in the workplace. In D. S. Ones, N. Anderson, C. Viswesvaran, & H. K. Sinangil (Eds.), *The SAGE handbook of industrial, work & organizational psychology: Personnel psychology and employee performance* (pp. 611–633). SAGE.

Zsambok, C. E., & Klein, G. (Eds.). (2014). *Naturalistic decision making.* Psychology Press.

Richard P. Larrick and M. Asher Lawson

WORK MOTIVATION

DEFINING WORK MOTIVATION

Motivation is one of the most researched topics in the field of industrial/organizational psychology for a variety of reasons, including (a) the prevalent belief that all behavior is at least partially influenced by motivation (Baumeister, 2016; Pinder, 2008); (b) empirical findings demonstrating that motivation relates to a wide array of individual effectiveness, attitudinal, and well-being outcomes (Gagné & Deci, 2005; Gagné et al., 2010); and (c) the potential for organizations to increase the motivation of their employees through the design of work, incentives, features of the work environment, and changes to organizational policies and practices (Humphrey et al., 2007; Kanfer et al., 2017). In short, motivation touches nearly every facet of work life and every topic of research in the organizational sciences (Gagné & Deci, 2005). Given the centrality of work in modern life, it may even be argued that work motivation is at the center of the human condition and the health and functioning of society (Kanfer et al., 2017).

Motivation can be defined as an unobservable force that directs, energizes, and sustains behavior over time and across circumstances (Diefendorff & Chandler, 2011). In the context of work, motivation directs attention toward work-related goals, energizes the expenditure of effort toward those goals, and leads to persistence in the pursuit of goals over time. Because motivation is an abstract, internal construct that must be inferred from behavior, it has been operationalized in research in a variety of ways, including goal level, cognitive effort, attentional focus, time on task, resource allocation, and physiological arousal, to name a few (Diefendorff & Chandler, 2011).

This article provides an overview of the core, fundamental concepts in the scientific literature on work motivation. Given the substantial research on this topic, this article is not intended to be a comprehensive review. Rather, it focuses on select variables and processes relevant to motivation, as well as interventions to improve work motivation. First, the article argues for the importance of goals as a central organizing concept in research on motivation, followed by a discussion of the fundamental role of discrepancies within self-regulatory processes and motivated behavior. This is followed by a discussion on motivated activity in terms of approach or avoid tendencies and as emanating from the self or from the environment. Finally, the article concludes with a discussion of practical implications and interventions that organizations can use to improve employee motivation.

THE GOAL CONCEPT AS A CENTRAL ORGANIZING STRUCTURE

Goals can be defined as internal representations of desired end states (Austin & Vancouver, 1996) that direct attention, energize action, and increase persistence (Locke & Latham, 2002). Goals exist in a hierarchy, with more short-term, concrete goals lower in the hierarchy, and more long-term, abstract goals higher in the hierarchy. Lower level goals represent the means by which higher level goals are attained; often several lower level goals must be achieved in order for a higher level goal to be met (Diefendorff & Lord, 2008; Lord & Levy 1994). Within the work domain, longer term career goals may be at or near the top of the hierarchy, and more proximal performance goals (e.g., annual goals), project goals, and daily task goals may be at the lower end of the hierarchy, representing the means by which the long-term career goals may be accomplished. For example, in order to achieve a high-level goal of being a branch manager, an employee might need to meet annual performance targets. This involves successfully completing various shorter term project goals, which requires attainment of even more narrow goals spanning weeks, days, hours, and even minutes.

Goals can vary along a number of features or qualities (Austin & Vancouver, 1996). For instance, goals can be process-oriented and focused on maintaining some standard (e.g., always be courteous to customers) or outcome-oriented and focused on accomplishing some performance objective (e.g., sell 10 cars this week). Similarly, goals can be set for learning a task (e.g., mastery goals) or for demonstrating competence to others (e.g., performance goals; Klein et al., 2008). A key finding from research on goal setting theory (Locke & Latham, 1990, 2002) is that difficult, specific goals that are accepted by the individual result in better performance than goals that are easy and general (e.g., "do your best") or that do not garner commitment from the individual.

Multiple Goals. Individuals may set and/or pursue multiple goals at the same time. In everyday life, juggling multiple goals is likely the normal state of affairs. When multiple goals exist, they may be conflicting (e.g., competing for the same resources and actions), complementary (e.g., requiring different resources or actions at different times), or compatible (e.g., requiring the same resources and actions to simultaneously attain multiple goals) (Klein et al., 2008). When multiple goals are in conflict, prioritization is needed. When deciding how to spread limited resources across goals, dual goal expectancy may be useful to consider (Schmidt & Dolis, 2009). Dual goal expectancy (expectancy for accomplishing two goals) moderates the relationship between relative goal progress (goal proximity) and subsequent resource allocation. When dual expectancy is high (i.e., there is a high expectancy of accomplishing both goals), individuals will allocate resources based on need (i.e., invest more resources in the more deficient goal). When dual expectancy is low (i.e., low expectancy of accomplishing both goals), individuals will allocate effort to maximize the possibility of reaching at least one goal, investing more time in the task that is relatively closer to completion (Schmidt & Dolis, 2009).

Emotions have also been found to influence effort allocation in the pursuit of multiple goals. Emotions interact with goal proximity to shape expectancy judgments, which then influence effort allocation to the focal/nonfocal goal (Louro et al., 2007). When a goal is far from being attained, the experience of positive emotions can lead to more effort allocation to the goal than the experience of negative emotions. That is, individuals tend to pursue goals associated with positive affect. However, when the goal is near attainment, these positive emotions can lead to less effort to the focal goal compared to the experience of negative emotions (i.e., negative affect signals a larger discrepancy and recruits more effort). A variety of other factors can influence how multiple goals are pursued, and investigating these factors is an important area for future research.

Phases of the Motivation Process. Lewin and colleagues (1944) noted that goal-based processes can be broken down into two main phases: the goal setting phase and the goal striving phase. The goal setting phase involves selecting a goal by considering the feasibility (i.e., expectancy) and desirability (i.e., valence) of different potential goals. This phase involves a deliberative mindset whereby individuals consider the advantages and disadvantages of different goals and select the goal with the highest motivational force. Once a goal is selected, individuals have "crossed the Rubicon" (i.e., passed a point of no return; Heckhausen, 1986) and move into the goal striving phase, which is accompanied by an implemental mindset. Here, individuals may engage in planning (i.e., if a plan is not in place or the path forward is otherwise unclear) and goal pursuit (i.e., expending effort and persisting toward the goal over time). The implemental mindset is focused on what is needed to accomplish the goal rather than the potential advantages and disadvantages of a goal. Once goal striving is complete, an individual will evaluate the outcome and return to cognitions about the feasibility and desirability of the goal, which can be considered when selecting the next goal.

Goal Setting/Goal Choice. The most prominent model of goal choice is expectancy theory (Vroom, 1964). Expectancy theory consists of three components: valence (i.e., desirability) of outcomes associated with goal accomplishment, expectancy (i.e., feasibility), or the probability that one's effort will result in successful goal pursuit (e.g., "I can accomplish this goal if I put forth the effort"), and instrumentality, or the belief that accomplishing the goal will lead to desired outcomes (e.g., "If I accomplish this goal, I will obtain the outcomes I desire"). Expectancy typically decreases as goal difficulty increases, but valence often increases with goal difficulty as more challenging activities are often accompanied by more valuable outcomes, such as satisfying psychological needs, receiving more praise or financial rewards, or enhanced self-esteem. Perceptions of goal expectancy are influenced by a variety of factors, including the individual's knowledge, skills, and abilities (Kozlowski & Bell, 2006), prior experience (i.e., success or failure; Campion & Lord, 1982), attributions (i.e., the causal attributions made for past experiences; Donovan & Williams, 2003), and perceived barriers or enablers (e.g., environmental conditions that impede goal progress; Mathieu et al., 1992). Perceptions of valence are also shaped by a variety of factors, including the needs or values of the individual (Klein et al., 2008) and the rewards associated with goal attainment (Ek et al., 2016). In the work context, rewards typically focus on monetary incentives for performance. Empirical research has also found that personality (e.g., Barrick et al., 2002), goal orientation (e.g., mastery, performance-prove, or performance-avoid orientation; Klein & Lee, 2006), national culture (e.g., Sue-Chan & Ong, 2002), and affect (e.g., Klinger & Cox, 2004) can influence expectancy and valence judgments of goals. Instrumentality is also important, to the extent that there is not a guarantee that goal accomplishment will result in receipt of the valued outcome (e.g., receiving praise from one's boss for a job well done may or may not happen). Theoretically, expectancy, valence, and instrumentality combine to form the overall motivational force for a goal. When comparing two or more goals, individuals are predicted to choose the goal with the highest motivational force.

In many organizational settings, goals may be assigned rather than freely chosen by individuals. In the case of assigned goals, goal commitment, or the degree to which a person has internalized a goal and made it their own, is a necessary condition for the goal to impact behavior. Hollenbeck et al. (1989) developed a model in which expectancy and valence judgments are the primary determinants of goal commitment. One factor that helps build commitment to assigned goals is involving individuals in the goal establishment process—referred to as participative goal setting (Sue-Chan & Ong, 2002). Research has found that participative goal setting builds a sense of choice and ownership over the goal, which enhances the likelihood that individuals will be able to satisfy their psychological needs for autonomy, competence, and relatedness in the pursuit of the goal.

Goal Striving (Effort and Persistence). Goal striving refers to one's efforts to attain a goal and involves flexibly allocating resources to goal pursuit over time and across changing circumstances (Richard & Diefendorff, 2011). Resources are often operationalized as effort exertion or the amount of time dedicated to a task. Key determinants of resource allocation are the person's perceived goal progress (i.e., how far they are from completing the activity) and self-efficacy for the activity (i.e., how confident they are in performing the activity, which is conceptually similar to expectancy) (Bandura, 2000).

With regard to estimating goal progress, affect can influence whether people believe they are on track for goal attainment or not and, as a result, how much more effort is needed. Positive affect signals a smaller discrepancy and can lead to less effort ("coasting"), whereas negative affect signals a larger discrepancy and can lead to high effort (Carver & Scheier, 1998). For self-efficacy, the effects are more complex. Ample evidence suggests that at the between-person level, higher self-efficacy is associated with better performance than lower self-efficacy. However, at the within-person level, moments when self-efficacy is high can result in lower resource allocation and worse performance compared to moments when self-efficacy is low (Vancouver et al., 2001). With low self-efficacy, the person does not feel confident and, as a result, allocates more resources to the task to ensure success. Vancouver et al. (2008) demonstrated that at the within-person level of analysis, self-efficacy can have a positive relationship with the decision to pursue an activity (i.e., to agree to do a task or not), but after the point of agreeing to the task, further increases in self-efficacy are associated with a reduction in resource allocation (i.e., less effort). In other words, moments when one is very confident can result in the allocation of fewer resources to an accepted or chosen task compared to moments when one is not very confident.

In addition to concerns with momentary affect and self-efficacy levels, research has also examined a variety of problems that can derail successful goal striving, including (a) procrastination or missing opportunities to initiate action, (b) being preoccupied with other goals (e.g., not fully disengaging from a prior goal) or negative thoughts and emotions (e.g., worry, anxiety, fear of failure), and (c) prematurely withdrawing effort from goal pursuit (e.g., because of the consummatory force and waning motivation, the emergence of an attractive alternative, or resource depletion).

Difficulties initiating action can contribute to problems in goal striving. Many theories of motivation implicitly assume that action is initiated immediately after a motivational tendency arises. However, the initial motivational tendency and the start of goal pursuit can occur at separate points in time, which can lead to the possibility of procrastination (Heckhausen, 1991). Implementation intentions (Gollwitzer, 1999), or the strategic automatization of goal initiation, may be an effective way to address the issue of starting action in a timely manner. With an implementation intention, the individual forms an "if–then" contingency that passes behavioral control of action initiation to an environmental event (i.e., if a certain time, place, or person is encountered, then goal pursuit can occur). This implies (a) the selection of a critical future situation in which action will be initiated and (b) the selection of an effective goal-directed behavior, which is then linked mentally to the chosen critical situation. Because a situation has been mentally linked to a certain goal-directed behavior, once the situation is encountered, the intended behavior is initiated immediately, efficiently, and without conscious intent or deliberation. This decreases the probability of procrastination and missing an opportunity to start goal pursuit.

Individuals can also have difficulties with goal striving because they are preoccupied with other thoughts, goals, or emotions. In essence, competing thoughts and emotions are consuming attentional and regulatory resources needed for successful goal pursuit. This situation calls for goal shielding, which can involve both cognitive (e.g., clearing one's mind and being fully present or downregulating negative emotions) and environmental efforts (e.g., removing distractions) to keep mental resources focused on goal pursuit and away from other goals or internal states (e.g., negative affect and ruminative thoughts).

Goal striving can also fail because motivation for the task wanes and the availability of regulatory resources needed to persist are diminished. There is evidence that working on a task for a long period of time can instigate a consummatory force that makes continuing to work on the task increasingly less appealing (even for highly valued tasks; Heckhausen, 1991). A similar finding has emerged in the resource depletion literature (Baumeister et al., 1996), although the findings from this work suggest that acts of self-control consume resources and that performance on a subsequent task that requires self-control will suffer as a result of the reduced resources. Inzlicht and Schmeichel (2012) argued that this resource depletion effect corresponds to a reduced desire to persist with the task, which is similar to the notion of the consummatory force producing waning motivation. For either explanation, incentives can help individuals persist longer. Furthermore, breaks can replenish resources, restore task motivation, and help ensure successful persistence during goal striving.

DISCREPANCIES STIMULATE MOTIVATION

Hull's (1943) drive theory argues that discrepancies from a desired state (e.g., food deprivation and sleep deprivation) are the primary source of motivation for pursuing activities. This notion has since been incorporated into a wide variety of motivational theories and is a central aspect of what may be the most elaborated model of dynamic motivational processes: control theory (Carver & Scheier, 1998; Powers, 1973). The central organizing structure in control theory is the negative feedback loop, which acts to compare the current state (i.e., performance) to the desired state (i.e., goal). Negative discrepancies (i.e., performance is less than the goal) result in an increase in effort/resources, whereas positive discrepancies (i.e., performance is higher than the goal) result in a decrease in effort/resources and perhaps an allocation of resources to some other activity.

Critics of control theory suggest it (a) is too mechanistic and treats individuals as passive, machine-like entities that merely react to discrepancies and (b) does not account for the agentic nature of humans who are actively constructing their environments by setting new goals that effectively create discrepancies (e.g., Locke & Latham, 2002). However, the establishment of new goals in control theory can be explained by the goal hierarchy concept whereby higher order goals that reflect longer term, growth-based objectives such as living according to one's values or striving to reach an ideal future self are the source of lower level goals. These higher order goals may never be fully achieved and, as a result, provide a renewable and ongoing source of new goals. The emergence of these new subgoals creates discrepancies that then need to be reduced.

ALL BEHAVIOR INVOLVES APPROACH OR AVOIDANCE MOTIVATION

The distinction between approach and avoidance motivation is fundamental to understanding the goals individuals choose and the way in which they regulate their behavior during goal pursuit. Approach motivation suggests that behaviors are directed toward seeking out or pursuing pleasurable or rewarding stimuli, whereas avoidance motivation suggests that behaviors are aimed at moving away from or preventing contact with unpleasant or punishing stimuli (Elliot, 1999; Higgins, 1997). Approach motivation often involves attempting to eliminate the discrepancy between the current state and desirable outcome, whereas avoidance motivation often involves attempting to maximize the discrepancy between the current state and an undesirable outcome.

A particular theory emphasizing the distinction between approaching success and avoiding failure is regulatory focus theory (Higgins, 1997). According to this theory, promotion focus reflects approach-oriented striving and involves the pursuit of ideals and attainment of gains, whereas prevention focus reflects an avoidance orientation and striving to prevent losses. Promotion focus is activated when the desired end-states are aspirations and accomplishments, with goal striving being characterized by a sense of eagerness and excitement. Prevention focus is activated when the desired end-states are safety and security, with goal striving being characterized by a sense of vigilance and threat detection. The framing of goals and performance feedback (e.g., focusing on gains versus losses) can activate a promotion or prevention mindset, which impacts their accompanying goal striving efforts (Crowe & Higgins, 1997; Roney et al., 1995). Furthermore, promotion focus and prevention focus lead to different types of positive and negative emotions. Success in achieving a promotion-focused activity leads to happiness and excitement, whereas failure in achieving a promotion-focused activity leads to sadness and dejection. In contrast, success in achieving a prevention-focused activity (i.e., in preventing an undesirable outcome) leads to calmness, whereas failure around a prevention-focused activity leads to anxiety and agitation (Higgins et al., 1997).

In addition to outlining how approach and avoidance mindsets might be represented in specific goals and everyday activities, these motivational concepts have been found to exist at the trait level, suggesting personality and even biological underpinnings. Perhaps the best example of this approach is Gray's (1987) behavioral inhibition system (BIS) and behavioral activation system (BAS), which were initially developed based on animal models of brain-based processes and then extended to humans. The main proposition is that these two systems lead individuals to react differently to rewards and punishments. BIS sensitivity is the emotional responsiveness to negative stimuli or punishment and the tendency to avoid or escape such stimuli. Due to their tendency to react strongly to negative events, individuals with high BIS sensitivity often experience more negative affect on average (Gable et al., 2000). Consequently, high BIS sensitivity is often associated with negatively valenced emotions such as anxiety and distress (Kimbrel et al., 2012; Meyer et al., 2005). Because the activation of BIS leads individuals to avoid undesirable events and to inhibit their behaviors, it is also linked to low levels of overall engagement with the environment and stronger negative reactions when unpleasant events occur.

On the other hand, BAS sensitivity represents reactivity to positive stimuli or rewards and the tendency to move toward arousal-enhancing events. In contrast to BIS sensitivity, high BAS sensitivity leads to more positive affect by the selection of positive situations or daily events (Gable et al., 2000). The activation of BAS has been associated with discrete emotions such as happiness and elation (Carver & Scheier, 1998; Carver & White, 1994). Individuals with high BAS sensitivity are motivated to seek stimulating events and to desire goal achievement. The absence of positive stimuli can strongly affect people with high BAS due to their sensitivity toward such stimuli. For example, when high BAS individuals are ostracized (i.e., experiencing a lack of positive social interaction), they exhibit stronger negative reactions than low BAS individuals (Ferris et al., 2019). Moreover, the sensation-seeking tendency of high BAS was found to positively relate to workplace deviance (Diefendorff & Mehta, 2007), whereas more achievement-based approach tendencies were found to negatively relate to deviance.

At an even broader dispositional level, Elliot and Thrash (2002) demonstrated that there are approach and avoidance temperaments represented in motivational, affective, and personality trait structures. In particular, a latent approach motivation tendency is represented by BAS, trait positive affectivity, and extraversion, whereas a latent avoidance motivation tendency is represented by BIS, trait negative affectivity, and neuroticism. These broad tendencies were found to relate to performance and mastery goals such that people with higher approach temperament tend to focus more on goals concerning competence and task mastery, whereas people with higher avoidance temperament focus more on goals concerning avoiding incompetence.

Approach and Avoidance Motivation Can Occur at the Same Time.   Approach and avoidance motivation are often discussed as two separate processes. However, there are situations in which both approach and avoidance motivation can be simultaneously activated. Approach–avoidance conflicts occur when individuals are motivated to avoid negative consequences and approach positive outcomes at the same time (Robinson et al., 2016). Drawing a connection to expectancy theory (Vroom, 1964), some expected outcomes may be positive (i.e., acclaim for a great performance), whereas others may be negative (i.e., ridicule for a poor performance). When the outcomes are negatively valenced, they may be simultaneously associated with moving closer to avoidance goals and further from approach goals. Conversely, positively valenced outcomes may be associated with moving closer to approach goals and further from avoidance goals. In the presence of these motivational conflicts, uncertainty and anxiety can emerge and distract individuals from the goal striving process. Another situation in which both motivations can be activated is when avoidance motivation (i.e., desire to avoid a threat) and the associated anxiety produces high levels of approach motivation as a way to escape the threat, what McGregor et al. (2010) labeled reactive approach motivation. Specifically, they argued that anxiety may be alleviated not just by avoiding the negative stimuli but also by redirecting efforts to simultaneously approach a desirable stimulus. In other words, approach goals can be a strategy to ameliorate the negative impact of avoidance goals.

ALL MOTIVATION EMANATES FROM THE SELF OR THE ENVIRONMENT

All motivation emanates from the self, the environment, or some combination of the two. In essence, goals can emerge from one's self-structure (i.e., personal goal hierarchy), or they can be imposed by situational factors, such as strong incentives or punishment and the demands or expectations of others. Goals quite often reflect a mixture of these two motivational origins, such as when individuals pursue internal desires (e.g., to explore, grow, or be challenged) that also reflect the preferences of others and connect to tangible incentives.

In its purest form, the distinction between pursuing activities for internal reasons and pursuing them for external reasons aligns with the difference between intrinsic motivation (i.e., doing things because they are fun or interesting) and extrinsic motivation (i.e., doing things to receive a reward or avoid receiving a punishment). In short, intrinsic motivation comes entirely from within the self and is driven by inherent interest in and enjoyment of activities (Gagné & Deci, 2005). Extrinsic motivation, on the other hand, is outcome focused and involves engaging in tasks or activities that are instrumental for attaining external rewards or avoiding external punishment (Deci et al., 2017). In summary, intrinsic motivation comes from the self, whereas extrinsic motivation is driven at least in part by one's environment. Typically, intrinsic motivation leads individuals to perform well and is associated with desirable well-being outcomes, whereas external motivation, over time, has been shown to lead to worse outcomes (Deci et al., 2017). The distinction of intrinsic versus extrinsic motivation is central to cognitive evaluation theory (Deci, 1975; Deci & Ryan, 1985b), which also provided early evidence that external inducements for a behavior can reduce (or crowd out) existing intrinsic motivation for that behavior.

Later work on self-determination theory (Deci & Ryan, 1985a) expanded on these ideas by elaborating on different types of extrinsic motivation, with some being experienced as highly controlling (as in the original formulation) but others being experienced as more autonomous. The subsections on "Different Types of Extrinsic Motivation" and "The Role of Basic Psychological Need Satisfaction" detail (a) the different forms of external motivation and how motivation may become more integrated with the self and experienced as autonomous and (b) the role of psychological needs in contributing to more autonomous forms of motivation.

Different Types of Extrinsic Motivation.   In differentiating the types of extrinsic motivation, self-determination theory (Ryan & Deci, 2000) argued that not all extrinsic motivation is experienced as equally controlling and that some forms of extrinsic motivation might be experienced as autonomous (i.e., emanating from the self). Autonomous motivation occurs when one takes part in an activity in which there is a sense of choice about doing so and there is the feeling that the activity is aligned with internal values. In contrast, controlled motivation is done for the attainment of rewards or the avoidance of negative consequences (Deci et al., 2017). Intrinsic motivation is clearly autonomous, but some forms of extrinsic motivation can also be experienced as autonomous. Here, the activity may not be inherently fun or interesting (i.e., not intrinsically motivating), but it strongly aligns with one's personal values or goals and is subjectively experienced as volitional. This motivation is termed "integrated regulation" and is the most autonomous form of extrinsic motivation (Gagné & Deci, 2005). A somewhat less autonomous form of motivation is "identified regulation," in which the person understands and accepts the importance of legitimacy of the action, but the reasons for performing the action are not fully aligned with the self. Nonetheless, pursuit of the activity feels autonomous because the reasons are understood and valued.

Shifting to the controlled forms of extrinsic motivation, "introjected regulation" occurs when actions or behaviors are driven by guilt avoidance. In essence, the person has come to self-administer psychological rewards or punishments for the activity, but there is not a personal endorsement of the action. In comparison, "external regulation" is the most controlled form of extrinsic motivation and is driven solely for the purpose of avoiding negative consequences or obtaining rewards (Gagné & Deci, 2005). With this form of motivation, there is no integration with one's sense of self, values, or beliefs.

Importantly, individuals can simultaneously experience high levels of two or more of these motivations, as demonstrated in various studies using cluster or profile analysis (e.g., Moran et al., 2012). That is, multiple internal and external motivators may be present for different people in different situations. Furthermore, motivations for pursuing activities can change over time, with factors that were once external (controlling) becoming internal (autonomous) through the process of internalization.

The Role of Basic Psychological Need Satisfaction. According to self-determination theory, a key determinant of whether individuals are motivated for autonomous reasons is whether their basic psychological needs are being satisfied by the environment (Ryan & Deci, 2017). These three needs are the need for autonomy, need for competence, and need for relatedness. Autonomy needs can be met by acting in a way that entails a sense of choice and volition, competence needs can be met by having the opportunity to demonstrate one's capabilities and succeed at tasks, and relatedness needs can be met by having the opportunity to connect with and feel accepted by others (Deci et al., 2017). Thus, if one feels autonomous, competent, and connected to others when pursing an activity, it is likely the activity will feel more aligned with one's self-structure and be more autonomously motivating. High motivation without satisfaction of these needs would almost certainly correspond to high controlled motivation. Satisfying one or two needs might be enough to momentarily experience autonomous motivation, but all three needs must be satisfied for longer term autonomous motivation (and well-being) to be achieved.

ALIGNMENT OF WORK ENVIRONMENT FEATURES WITH INTERNAL MOTIVATION

The fact that people typically hold jobs in which they are paid to perform work for others (i.e., managers and company owners) naturally produces a context in which controlled forms of motivation are high in organizations. However, features of the work environment and the job itself can help satisfy individuals' psychological needs and make work more personally meaningful and more autonomously motivating.

Job Characteristics. Hackman and Oldham (1975) developed the job characteristics model, which states that there are five key job characteristics along which all jobs vary, and higher levels of these characteristics produce higher levels of job satisfaction and motivation and better performance outcomes. These characteristics include autonomy (i.e., having discretion of over how work is performed), task significance (i.e., performing work that positively impacts others), task identity (i.e., producing a complete piece of work or product as opposed to pieces or work), feedback from the job (i.e., getting knowledge of results), and skill variety (i.e., being able to use different skills). High levels of these job characteristics are thought to enrich jobs and lead individuals to feel more engaged in performing their work and, as a result, more competent. Humphrey et al. (2007) updated this model by expanding the number of job characteristics and linking these variables to a variety of outcomes and mediating mechanisms, including experienced meaningfulness. Their findings support the self-determination theory idea that alignment of activities with one's self-structure is experienced as more autonomous and produces better well-being and effectiveness outcomes.

Social Factors.   Humphrey et al. (2007) proposed that the job characteristics model can include social characteristics of the job and work environment, including the degree of social support, interdependence, feedback from others, and interactions from outside of the organization. These social factors clearly relate to the need for relatedness because they provide opportunities for high-quality social contact with others (Greguras & Diefendorff, 2009). These factors may also help people feel more competent (e.g., when they receive feedback from others who appreciate their efforts) and more autonomous (e.g., people want to do things for valued others). Interactions from outside of the organization (e.g., serving customers) may also serve as a means to meet relatedness needs, as these can be met not only by feeling cared for but also by caring for and demonstrating kindness to others (Weinstein & Ryan, 2010). Beyond this social focus, simply working in teams might contribute to satisfaction of all three psychological needs, particularly when there are shared intrinsic work values at the team level (Schreurs et al., 2014).

PRACTICAL IMPLICATIONS

Organizations can influence employee motivation through various factors, such as the design of work, provision of incentives, and the design of the work environment (Humphrey et al., 2007). Building on points discussed broadly throughout the motivation literature, there are several specific practices that organizations can follow to increase or maintain the motivation of their employees. Although these recommendations are not comprehensive, they can provide a starting point for organizational interventions. Furthermore, these recommendations may not be suitable in every situation, and motivational intervention should be tailored to the particular organization under consideration. Practitioners should always consult the most up-to-date research evidence so that evidence-based interventions are used.

Setting Appropriate Goals.   One established finding in the goal setting literature is that specific, difficult goals lead to a high level of effort and performance (Locke & Latham, 2002). Thus, organizations may seek to encourage the setting of difficult goals to increase employee motivation. However, organizations should be aware of the nature of employees' work (e.g., deadlines and workload) and consider possible unintended consequences of applying the principles of goal setting theory. For instance, goals that are too difficult may lead to exhaustion and resource depletion (Welsh & Ordonez, 2014), increase the potential for individuals to cut corners and sacrifice quality (Ordóñez et al., 2009), or even engage in unethical actions to attain the goals (Schweitzer et al., 2004; Welsh & Ordóñez, 2014). This may lead to increased risk-taking and other unethical behavior (e.g., cheating and being dishonest), both of which can have real-life negative consequences for the organization, the employee, and customers. The harmful effect of difficult goals is likely to be amplified when difficult goals are set consecutively. If left unchecked, the organization may even cultivate a culture wherein unethical behaviors are indirectly supported through the relentless use of overly difficult goals. Another aspect to consider is whether goals are overly specific and become the singular focus.

These goals may lead to lack of attention to other critical features of the work environment and neglect of aspects of employees' performance not directly tied to the goal (Ordóñez et al., 2009). Therefore, organizations should (a) consider providing or participatively setting (with employees) goals with an appropriate level of difficulty, (b) avoid setting too many consecutive high-difficulty goals, and (c) be sure to consider a broad set of outcomes so that unintended harm does not occur.

Balancing Intrinsic and Extrinsic Motivation.   Previous research has often associated intrinsic motivation with desirable outcomes and extrinsic motivation with undesirable outcomes (Deci et al., 2017). However, this view has shifted as research in the early 21st century reveals that extrinsic motivation and intrinsic motivation can both be beneficial in different circumstances, sometimes even interacting to influence performance (Gagne & Deci, 2005). Cerasoli et al. (2014) found that whereas intrinsic motivation predicted the quality of performance, extrinsic motivation (i.e., incentives) was a strong predictor of the quantity of performance. Thus, organizations should consider how the performance standard is defined before introducing external incentives. Easy, repetitive tasks that concern quantity (and are not internally motivated) may benefit from external rewards. Complex or creative tasks that depend more on quality may benefit more from internal sources of motivation. For complex, quality-focused tasks, organizations should avoid making extrinsic factors salient because it may interfere with the effects of intrinsic motivation (Cerasoli et al., 2014).

Because motivation is a dynamic construct, time is also an important factor when organizations seek to maximize employees' motivation. Benedetti et al. (2015) found that although intrinsic and extrinsic factors exerted positive effects on psychological vitality and satisfaction early in the day, extrinsic factors negatively impacted these outcomes by the end of the day. This change may be due to the gradual decline of employee cognitive resources throughout the day. As such, there may be some benefit to completing extrinsically motivated tasks earlier in the day rather than saving them until the end of the day.

Increasing Self-Efficacy.   As previously noted, self-efficacy can have a complex relationship with resource allocation and performance. Individuals with higher self-efficacy have greater goal commitment and better performance compared to individuals with lower self-efficacy (Locke & Latham, 2002; Sue-Chan & Ong, 2002). Furthermore, within persons, self-efficacy can positively influence employees' goal choice and task persistence in unambiguous situations (Sun et al., 2014; Vancouver & Purl, 2017). However, within persons, an overconfidence effect can occur where individuals feel highly efficacious and do not exert as much effort. As such, any attempt to increase self-efficacy should take efforts to inform individuals of the perils of overconfidence and strive to have employees be appropriately confident.

Research has proposed various methods that organizations can use to increase self-efficacy, which complement Bandura's (2000) strategies of enactive mastery (experiencing success), vicarious learning (watching others successfully perform the task), verbal persuasion (having someone express confidence in a person), and enhancing psychological states (putting someone at ease as a way to make them feel comfortable with pursuing the goal). First, organizations may want to involve employees in the process of goal setting (participative goal setting) instead of merely assigning goals (Sue-Chan & Ong, 2002). Asking for employees' input may make goals more personally meaningful and assist employees in understanding the level of performance that is expected. Second, implementation intentions have been found to successfully increase employees' self-efficacy (Legrand et al., 2017). Implementation intentions can act as mental "scripts" guiding employees' behavior when the scripts are cued in specific situations. Legrand and colleagues (2017) found that having implementation intentions can help employees to be both more persistent in the goal striving process and flexible in goal choice when disengagement from goals is beneficial or desirable. Finally, organizations may consider providing employees with opportunities for self-management training. Self-management training involves helping employees assess their work, monitor their work environment, and set appropriate goals (Frayne & Geringer, 2000). By teaching multiple strategies for managing oneself and the environment, self-management can increase employees' self-efficacy and goal attainment. As previously mentioned, organizations should be cautious when employees' self-efficacy is too high because it can reduce employees' resource allocation and performance (Beck & Schmidt, 2012; Vancouver et al., 2001).

Creating Opportunities for Resource Replenishment. Goal striving can be a resource-consuming activity, especially when employees have to attain consecutive high goals or strive for goals that are not internally motivating (Moller et al., 2006; Welsh & Ordóñez, 2014). Research has found that when individuals experience depletion, their performance decreases (Shoss et al., 2013). Thus, a recovery period may be needed to avoid the harmful effect of self-regulatory resources depletion. Research suggests that on a daily basis, having breaks with relaxing activities, entertaining cognitive activities, and socialization can enhance employees' performance through increased positive affect (Kim et al., 2018; Trougakos et al., 2008). Vacations have also been shown to decrease employees' exhaustion and help employees avoid further depletion (Fritz & Sonnentag, 2006).

CONCLUSION

Employee motivation can be influenced by various factors, some of which can be controlled by the organizations. Tasks and goals are key aspects in determining employees' motivation and performance. Unobtainable goals or goals that are beyond employees' capacity can reduce their effort and performance or even encourage destructive behaviors. Moreover, organizations should match the type of rewards (intrinsic and external) with the needed performance standards (e.g., external for simple, repetitive tasks focused on quantity; intrinsic for complex, novel tasks focused on quality). Although extrinsic sources of motivation can be beneficial, organizations should be careful to avoid external rewards that have been found to negatively impact intrinsic motivation (e.g., engagement and completion contingent rewards; Deci et al., 1999). Organizations may instead choose to focus on external rewards that have been found to be beneficial for intrinsic motivation, such as positive verbal feedback (Deci et al., 1999). Self-efficacy is an important factor that organizations might want to enhance for increasing motivation, with the understanding that high levels of self-efficacy can be detrimental to performance in some cases and low self-efficacy may lead to insufficient effort in other cases. Calibrating self-efficacy to be an accurate and realistic picture of one's competence may be useful, and opportunities for resource replenishment may be desirable for increasing and maintaining desired levels of employee motivation.

424 • WORK MOTIVATION

A final consideration is the influence of culture on employee motivation. Cultural norms and values can affect goal choice, goal expectancy, goal pursuit, and self-efficacy (Oettingen et al., 2008). For example, Niles (1998) found that although both Sri Lankans and Australians preferred individual achievement as a means of strengthening work ethic, the Sri Lankan sample's achievement orientation was directed toward collectivistic goals (emphasis on the group), whereas the Australian sample's achievement orientation was directed toward individualistic goals (emphasis on the individual). Further elaborating on the cultural difference of individualism versus collectivism, Triandis and Bhawuk (1997) proposed differences between horizontal (reflecting an emphasis on equality) and vertical (reflecting an emphasis on hierarchy and inequality) individualism and collectivism. Specifically, they suggested that horizontal individualists will expect each group member to have unique goals, whereas vertical individualists will expect some group members to select goals that place others at a disadvantage; and horizonal collectivists will expect all group members to share goals, whereas vertical collectivists will expect group members to accept differences in goals within the group. Another commonly discussed cultural difference is the dimension of power distance or the degree of inequality among people that the population of a country considers as normal and acceptable (Hofstede, 1983). Research has found that whereas participation in the goal setting process is beneficial in terms of self-efficacy, goal commitment, and performance for low-power distance individuals, it does not yield the same benefits for high-power distance individuals (Sue-Chan & Ong, 2002). Understanding cultural differences and how they influence employees' values and behavior will help organizations identify appropriate interventions for increasing motivation at work.

FURTHER READING

Carver, C. S., & Scheier, M. F. (1998). *On the self-regulation of behavior.* Cambridge University Press.

Carver, C. S., & White, T. L. (1994). Behavioral inhibition, behavioral activation, and affective responses to impending reward and punishment: The BIS/BAS scales. *Journal of Personality and Social Psychology, 67*(2), 319–333.

Deci, E. L., & Ryan, R. M. (2000). The "what" and "why" of goal pursuits: Human needs and the self-determination of behavior. *Psychological Inquiry, 11*(4), 227–268.

Elliot, A. J. (2006). The hierarchical model of approach–avoidance motivation. *Motivation and Emotion, 30*(2), 111–116.

Erez, M., & Earley, P. C. (1987). Comparative analysis of goal-setting strategies across cultures. *Journal of Applied Psychology, 72*(4), 658.

Kanfer, R. (1990). Motivation theory and industrial and organizational psychology. In M. D. Dunnette & L. M. Hough (Eds.), *Handbook of industrial and organizational psychology* (2nd ed., Vol. 1, pp. 75–170). Consulting Psychologist Press.

Kanfer, R., Chen, G., & Pritchard, R. D. (2008). *Work motivation: Past, present, and future.* Taylor & Francis.

Karoly, P. (1993). Mechanisms of self-regulation: A systems view. *Annual Review of Psychology, 44*, 23–52.

Latham, G. (2007). *Work motivation: History, theory, research, and practice.* SAGE.

Mitchell, T. R. (1997). Matching motivational strategies with organizational contexts. *Research in Organizational Behavior, 19*, 57–149.

Mitchell, T. R., & Daniels, D. (2002). Motivation. In W. Borman, D. Ilgen, & R. Klimoski (Eds.), *Handbook of psychology, Vol. 12: Industrial/organizational psychology* (pp. 225–254). Wiley.

Powers, W. T. (1973). *Behavior: The control of perception.* Aldine.

Pritchard, R. D., & Ashwood, E. L. (2008). *Managing motivation: A manager's guide to diagnosing and improving motivation.* Routledge.

Steers, R. M., Mowday, R. T., & Shapiro, D. L. (2004). The future of work motivation theory. *Academy of Management Review, 29*(3), 379–387. https://doi.org/10.5465/amr.2004.13670978

REFERENCES

Austin, J. T., & Vancouver, J. B. (1996). Goal constructs in psychology: Structure, process, and content. *Psychological Bulletin, 120*(3), 338–375. https://doi.org/10.1037/0033-2909.120.3.338

Bandura, A. (2000). Self-efficacy: The foundation of agency. In W. Perrig & A. Grob (Eds.), *Control of human behavior, mental processes, and consciousness: Essays in honor of the 60th birthday of August Flammer* (pp. 17–34). Erlbaum.

Barrick, M. R., Stewart, G. L., & Piotrowski, M. (2002). Personality and job performance: Test of the mediating effects of motivation among sales representatives. *Journal of Applied Psychology, 87*(1), 43–51. https://doi.org/10.1037/0021-9010.87.1.43

Baumeister, R. F. (2016). Toward a general theory of motivation: Problems, challenges, opportunities, and the big picture. *Motivation and Emotion, 40*(1), 1–10. https://doi.org/10.1007/s11031-015-9521-y

Baumeister, R. F., Smart, L., & Boden, J. M. (1996). Relation of threatened egotism to violence and aggression: The dark side of high self-esteem. *Psychological Review, 103*(1), 5–33. https://doi.org/10.1037/0033-295X.103.1.5

Beck, J. W., & Schmidt, A. M. (2012). Taken out of context? Cross-level effects of between-person self-efficacy and difficulty on the within-person relationship of self-efficacy with resource allocation and performance. *Organizational Behavior and Human Decision Processes, 119*(2), 195–208. https://doi.org/10.1016/j.obhdp.2012.06.009

Benedetti, A. A., Diefendorff, J. M., Gabriel, A. S., & Chandler, M. M. (2015). The effects of intrinsic and extrinsic sources of motivation on well-being depend on time of day: The moderating effects of workday accumulation. *Journal of Vocational Behavior, 88*, 38–46. https://doi.org/10.1016/j.jvb.2015.02.009

Campion, M. A., & Lord, R. G. (1982). A control systems conceptualization of the goal-setting and changing process. *Organizational Behavior & Human Performance, 30*(2), 265–287. https://doi.org/10.1016/0030-5073(82)90221-5

Carver, C. S., & Scheier, M. F. (1998). *On the self-regulation of behavior.* Cambridge University Press. https://doi.org/10.1017/CBO9781139174794

Carver, C. S., & White, T. L. (1994). Behavioral inhibition, behavioral activation, and affective responses to impending reward and punishment: The BIS/BAS scales. *Journal of Personality and Social Psychology, 67*(2), 319–333. https://doi.org/10.1037/0022-3514.67.2.319

Cerasoli, C. P., Nicklin, J. M., & Ford, M. T. (2014). Intrinsic motivation and extrinsic incentives jointly predict performance: A 40-year meta-analysis. *Psychological Bulletin, 140*(4), 980–1008. https://doi.org/10.1037/a0035661

Crowe, E., & Higgins, E. T. (1997). Regulatory focus and strategic inclinations: Promotion and prevention in decision-making. *Organizational Behavior and Human Decision Processes, 69*(2), 117–132. https://doi.org/10.1006/obhd.1996.2675

Deci, E. L. (1975). The intrinsic motivation of behavior. In *Intrinsic motivation* (pp. 93–125). Plenum. https://doi.org/10.1007/978-1-4613-4446-9_4

Deci, E. L., Koestner, R., & Ryan, R. M. (1999). A meta-analytic review of experiments examining the effects of extrinsic rewards on intrinsic motivation. *Psychological Bulletin, 125*(6), 627. https://doi.org/10.1037/0033-2909.125.6.627

Deci, E. L., Olafsen, A. H., & Ryan, R. M. (2017). Self-determination theory in work organizations: The state of a science. *Annual Review of Organizational Psychology and Organizational Behavior, 4*, 19–43. https://doi.org/10.1146/annurev-orgpsych-032516-113108

Deci, E. L., & Ryan, R. M. (1985a). *Intrinsic motivation and self-determination in human behavior*. Plenum. https://doi.org/10.1007/978-1-4899-2271-7

Deci, E. L., & Ryan, R. M. (1985b). Cognitive evaluation theory. In E. Deci & R. Ryan (Eds.), *Intrinsic motivation and self-determination in human behavior* (pp. 43–85). Springer. https://doi.org/10.1007/978-1-4899-2271-7_3

Diefendorff, J. M., & Chandler, M. M. (2011). Motivating employees. In S. Zedeck (Ed.), *APA handbook of industrial and organizational psychology, Vol. 3. Maintaining, expanding, and contracting the organization* (pp. 65–135). American Psychological Association. https://doi.org/10.1037/12171-003

Diefendorff, J. M., & Lord, R. G. (2008). Goal-striving and self-regulation processes. In R. Kanfer, G. Chen, & R. D. Pritchard (Eds.), *Work motivation: Past, present, and future* (pp. 151–196). Routledge.

Diefendorff, J. M., & Mehta, K. (2007). The relations of motivational traits with workplace deviance. *Journal of Applied Psychology, 92*(4), 967–977. https://doi.org/10.1037/0021-9010.92.4.967

Donovan, J. J., & Williams, K. J. (2003). Missing the mark: Effects of time and causal attributions on goal revision in response to goal-performance discrepancies. *Journal of Applied Psychology, 88*(3), 379–390. https://doi.org/10.1037/0021-9010.88.3.379

Ek, K. E., Miltenberger, R. G., & Valbuena, D. (2016). Promoting physical activity among school-age children using feedback, goal setting, and rewards. *Behavior Analysis, 16*(1), 41–46. http://dx.doi.org/10.1037/bar0000029

Elliot, A. J. (1999). Approach and avoidance motivation and achievement goals. *Educational Psychologist, 34*(3), 169–189. https://doi.org/10.1207/s15326985ep3403_3

Elliot, A. J., & Thrash, T. M. (2002). Approach–avoidance motivation in personality: Approach and avoidance temperaments and goals. *Journal of Personality and Social Psychology, 82*(5), 804–818. https://doi.org/10.1037/0022-3514.82.5.804

Ferris, D. L., Fatimah, S., Yan, M., Liang, L. H., Lian, H., & Brown, D. J. (2019). Being sensitive to positives has its negatives: An approach/avoidance perspective on reactivity to ostracism. *Organizational Behavior and Human Decision Processes, 152*, 138–149. https://doi.org/10.1016/j.obhdp.2019.05.001

Frayne, C. A., & Geringer, J. M. (2000). Self-management training for improving job performance: A field experiment involving salespeople. *Journal of Applied Psychology, 85*(3), 361–372. https://doi.org/10.1037/0021-9010.85.3.361

Fritz, C., & Sonnentag, S. (2006). Recovery, well-being, and performance-related outcomes: The role of workload and vacation experiences. *Journal of Applied Psychology, 91*(4), 936–945. https://doi.org/10.1037/0021-9010.91.4.936

Gable, S. L., Reis, H. T., & Elliot, A. J. (2000). Behavioral activation and inhibition in everyday life. *Journal of Personality and Social Psychology, 78*(6), 1135–1149. https://doi.org/10.1037/0022-3514.78.6.1135

Gagné, M., & Deci, E. L. (2005). Self-determination theory and work motivation. *Journal of Organizational Behavior, 26*(4), 331–362. https://doi.org/10.1002/job.322

Gagné, M., Forest, J., Gilbert, M. H., Aubé, C., Morin, E., & Malorni, A. (2010). The Motivation at Work Scale: Validation evidence in two languages. *Educational and Psychological Measurement, 70*(4), 628–646. https://doi.org/10.1177/0013164409355698

Gollwitzer, P. M. (1999). Implementation intentions: Strong effects of simple plans. *American Psychologist, 54*(7), 493–503. https://doi.org/10.1037/0003-066X.54.7.493

Gray, J. A. (1987). Perspectives on anxiety and impulsivity: A commentary. *Journal of Research in Personality, 21*(4), 493–509. https://doi.org/10.1016/0092-6566(87)90036-5

Greguras, G. J., & Diefendorff, J. M. (2009). Different fits satisfy different needs: Linking person–environment fit to employee commitment and performance using self-determination theory. *Journal of Applied Psychology, 94*(2), 465–477. https://doi.org/10.1037/a0014068

Hackman, J. R., & Oldham, G. R. (1975). Development of the Job Diagnostic Survey. *Journal of Applied Psychology, 60*(2), 159–170. https://doi.org/10.1037/H0076546

Heckhausen, H. (1986). Why some time out might benefit achievement motivation research. In J. H. L. van den Bercken, E. E. J. De Bruyn, & Th. C. M. Bergen (Eds.), *Achievement and task motivation* (pp. 7–39). Swets & Zeitlinger.

Heckhausen, H. (1991). *Motivation and action* (P. K. Leppmann, Trans.). Springer-Verlag. https://doi.org/10.1007/978-3-642-75961-1

Higgins, E. T. (1997). Beyond pleasure and pain. *American Psychologist, 52*(12), 1280–1300. https://doi.org/10.1037/0003-066X.52.12.1280

Higgins, E. T., Shah, J., & Friedman, R. (1997). Emotional responses to goal attainment: Strength of regulatory focus as moderator. *Journal of Personality and Social Psychology, 72*(3), 515–525. https://doi.org/10.1037/0022-3514.72.3.515

Hofstede, G. (1983). The cultural relativity of organizational practices and theories. *Journal of International Business Studies, 14*(2), 75–89.

Hollenbeck, J. R., Williams, C. R., & Klein, H. J. (1989). An empirical examination of the antecedents of commitment to difficult goals. *Journal of Applied Psychology, 74*(1), 18–23. https://doi.org/10.1037/0021-9010.74.1.18

Hull, C. A. (1943). *Behaviour system and principles of behaviour.* Appleton-Century-Crofts.

Humphrey, S. E., Nahrgang, J. D., & Morgeson, F. P. (2007). Integrating motivational, social, and contextual work design features: A meta-analytic summary and theoretical extension of the work design literature. *Journal of Applied Psychology, 92*(5), 1332–1356. https://doi.org/10.1037/0021-9010.92.5.1332

Inzlicht, M., & Schmeichel, B. J. (2012). What is ego depletion? Toward a mechanistic revision of the resource model of self-control. *Perspectives on Psychological Science, 7*(5), 450–463.

Kanfer, R., Frese, M., & Johnson, R. E. (2017). Motivation related to work: A century of progress. *Journal of Applied Psychology, 102*(3), 338–355. https://doi.org/10.1037/apl0000133

Kim, S., Park, Y., & Headrick, L. (2018). Daily micro-breaks and job performance: General work engagement as a cross-level moderator. *Journal of Applied Psychology, 103*(7), 772–786. https://doi.org/10.1037/apl0000308

Kimbrel, N. A., Nelson-Gray, R. O., & Mitchell, J. T. (2012). BIS, BAS, and bias: The role of personality and cognitive bias in social anxiety. *Personality and Individual Differences, 52*(3), 395–400. https://doi.org/10.1016/j.paid.2011.10.041

Klein, H. J., Austin, J. T., & Cooper, J. T. (2008). Goal choice and decision processes. In R. Kanfer, G. Chen, & R. D. Pritchard (Eds.), *Work motivation: Past, present, and future* (pp. 101–150). Routledge.

Klein, H. J., & Lee, S. (2006). The effects of personality on learning: The mediating role of goal setting. *Human Performance, 19*(1), 43–66. https://doi.org/10.1207/s15327043hup1901_3

Klinger, E., & Cox, W. M. (2004). Motivation and the theory of current concerns. In W. M. Cox & E. Klinger (Eds.), *Handbook of motivational counseling: Concepts, approaches, and assessment* (pp. 3–27). Wiley.

Kozlowski, S. W. J., & Bell, B. S. (2006). Disentangling achievement orientation and goal setting: Effects on self-regulatory processes. *Journal of Applied Psychology, 91*(4), 900–916. https://doi.org/10.1037/0021-9010.91.4.900

Legrand, E., Bieleke, M., Gollwitzer, P. M., & Mignon, A. (2017). Nothing will stop me? Flexibly tenacious goal striving with implementation intentions. *Motivation Science, 3*(2), 101–118. https://doi.org/10.1037/mot0000050

Lewin, K., Dembo, T., Festinger, L., & Sears, P. S. (1944). Level of aspiration. In J. M. Hunt (Ed.), *Personality and the behavior disorders* (pp. 333–378). Ronald Press.

Locke, E. A., & Latham, G. P. (1990). *A theory of goal setting & task performance.* Prentice-Hall.

Locke, E. A., & Latham, G. P. (2002). Building a practically useful theory of goal setting and task motivation: A 35-year odyssey. *American Psychologist, 57*(9), 705–717. https://doi.org/10.1037/0003-066X.57.9.705

Lord, R. G., & Levy, P. E. (1994). Moving from cognition to action: A control theory perspective. *Applied Psychology, 43*(3), 335–367. https://doi.org/10.1111/j.1464-0597.1994.tb00828.x

Louro, M. J., Pieters, R., & Zeelenberg, M. (2007). Dynamics of multiple-goal pursuit. *Journal of Personality and Social Psychology, 93*(2), 174–193. https://doi.org/10.1037/0022-3514.93.2.174

Mathieu, J. E., Tannenbaum, S. I., & Salas, E. (1992). Influences of individual and situational characteristics on measures of training effectiveness. *Academy of Management Journal, 35*(4), 828–847. https://doi.org/10.2307/256317

McGregor, I., Nash, K., Mann, N., & Phills, C. E. (2010). Anxious uncertainty and reactive approach motivation (RAM). *Journal of Personality and Social Psychology, 99*(1), 133–147. https://doi.org/10.1037/a0019701

Meyer, B., Olivier, L., & Roth, D. A. (2005). Please don't leave me! BIS/BAS, attachment styles, and responses to a relationship threat. *Personality and Individual Differences, 38*(1), 151–162. https://doi.org/10.1016/j.paid.2004.03.016

Moller, A. C., Deci, E. L., & Ryan, R. M. (2006). Choice and ego-depletion: The moderating role of autonomy. *Personality and Social Psychology Bulletin, 32*(8), 1024–1036. https://doi.org/10.1177/0146167206288008

Moran, C. M., Diefendorff, J. M., Kim, T. Y., & Liu, Z. Q. (2012). A profile approach to self-determination theory motivations at work. *Journal of Vocational Behavior, 81*(3), 354–363. https://doi.org/10.1016/j.jvb.2012.09.002

Niles, F. S. (1998). Individualism–collectivism revisited. *Cross-Cultural Research, 32*(4), 315–341.

Oettingen, G., Sevincer, A. T., & Gollwitzer, P. M. (2008). Goal pursuit in the context of culture. In R. M. Sorrentino & S. Yamaguchi (Eds.), *Handbook of motivation and cognition across cultures* (pp. 191–211). Elsevier. https://doi.org/10.1016/B978-0-12-373694-9.00009-X

Ordóñez, L., Schweitzer, M. E., Galinsky, A. D., & Bazerman, M. H. (2009). Goals gone wild: How goals systematically harm individuals and organizations. *Academy of Management Perspectives, 23*(1), 6–16. https://doi.org/10.5465/amp.2009.37007999

Pinder, C. C. (2008). *Work motivation in organizational behavior.* Psychology Press.

Powers, W. T. (1973). Feedback: Beyond behaviorism: Stimulus–response laws are wholly predictable within a control-system model of behavioral organization. *Science, 179*(4071), 351–356. https://doi.org/10.1126/science.179.4071.351

Richard, E. M., & Diefendorff, J. M. (2011). Self-regulation during a single performance episode: Mood-as-information in the absence of formal feedback. *Organizational Behavior and Human Decision Processes, 115*(1), 99–110. https://doi.org/10.1016/j.obhdp.2010.11.008

Robinson, M. D., Boyd, R. L., & Persich, M. R. (2016). Dispositional anger and the resolution of the approach–avoidance conflict. *Emotion, 16*(6), 838–849. https://doi.org/10.1037/emo0000189

Roney, C. J., Higgins, E. T., & Shah, J. (1995). Goals and framing: How outcome focus influences motivation and emotion. *Personality and Social Psychology Bulletin, 21*(11), 1151–1160. https://doi.org/10.1177/01461672952111003

Ryan, R. M., & Deci, E. L. (2000). Intrinsic and extrinsic motivations: Classic definitions and new directions. *Contemporary Educational Psychology, 25*(1), 54–67. https://doi.org/10.1006/ceps.1999.1020

Ryan, R. M., & Deci, E. L. (2017). *Self-determination theory: Basic psychological needs in motivation, development, and wellness.* Guilford. https://doi.org/10.1521/978.14625/28806

Schmidt, A. M., & Dolis, C. M. (2009). Something's got to give: The effects of dual-goal difficulty, goal progress, and expectancies on resource allocation. *Journal of Applied Psychology, 94*(3), 678–691. https://doi.org/10.1037/a0014945

Schreurs, B., van Emmerik, I. H., Van den Broeck, A., & Guenter, H. (2014). Work values and work engagement within teams: The mediating role of need satisfaction. *Group Dynamics, 18*(4), 267–281.

Schweitzer, M. E., Ordóñez, L., & Douma, B. (2004). Goal setting as a motivator of unethical behavior. *Academy of Management Journal, 47*(3), 422–432. https://doi.org/10.5465/20159591

Shoss, M. K., Eisenberger, R., Restubog, S. L. D., & Zagenczyk, T. J. (2013). Blaming the organization for abusive supervision: The roles of perceived organizational support and supervisor's organizational embodiment. *Journal of Applied Psychology, 98*(1), 158–168. https://doi.org/10.1037/a0030687

Sue-Chan, C., & Ong, M. (2002). Goal assignment and performance: Assessing the mediating roles of goal commitment and self-efficacy and the moderating role of power distances. *Organizational Behavior and Human Decision Processes, 89*(2), 1140–1161. https://doi.org/10.1016/S0749-5978(02)00017-1

Sun, S., Vancouver, J. B., & Weinhardt, J. M. (2014). Goal choices and planning: Distinct expectancy and value effects in two goal processes. *Organizational Behavior and Human Decision Processes, 125*(2), 220–233. https://doi.org/10.1016/j.obhdp.2014.09.002

Triandis, H. C., & Bhawuk, D. P. S. (1997). Culture theory and the meaning of relatedness. In P. C. Earley & M. Erez (Eds.), *New perspectives on international industrial/organizational psychology* (pp. 13–52). New Lexington Press.

Trougakos, J. P., Beal, D. J., Green, S. G., & Weiss, H. M. (2008). Making the break count: An episodic examination of recovery activities, emotional experiences, and positive affective displays. *Academy of Management Journal, 51*(1), 131–146. https://doi.org/10.5465/amj.2008.30764063

Vancouver, J. B., More, K. M., & Yoder, R. J. (2008). Self-efficacy and resource allocation: Support for a nonmonotonic, discontinuous model. *Journal of Applied Psychology, 93*(1), 35–47. https://doi.org/10.1037/0021-9010.93.1.35

Vancouver, J. B., & Purl, J. D. (2017). A computational model of self-efficacy's various effects on performance: Moving the debate forward. *Journal of Applied Psychology, 102*(4), 599–616. https://doi.org/10.1037/apl0000177

Vancouver, J. B., Thompson, C. M., & Williams, A. A. (2001). The changing signs in the relationships among self-efficacy, personal goals, and performance. *Journal of Applied Psychology, 86*(4), 605–620. https://doi.org/10.1037/0021-9010.86.4.605

Vroom, V. H. (1964). *Work and motivation*. Wiley.

Weinstein, N., & Ryan, R. M. (2010). When helping helps: Autonomous motivation for prosocial behavior and its influence on well-being for the helper and recipient. *Journal of Personality and Social Psychology, 98*(2), 222–244. https://doi.org/10.1037/a0016984

Welsh, D. T., & Ordóñez, L. D. (2014). The dark side of consecutive high performance goals: Linking goal setting, depletion, and unethical behavior. *Organizational Behavior and Human Decision Processes, 123*(2), 79–89. https://doi.org/10.1016/j.obhdp.2013.07.006

James M. Diefendorff, Megan E. Kenworthy, Faith C. Lee, and Linh K. Nguyen

EMPLOYEE WORK EXPERIENCES, FEELINGS, AND MORALITY

INTRODUCTION

How does work influence employees' feelings, and what are the downstream consequences of these feelings for moral behavior? Although the term *feelings* has been defined in a variety of different ways, from physical perception (e.g., touch) to the conscious experience of emotion, within the field of organizational psychology it is most widely used interchangeably with affect. Feelings comprise both feeling states (what one feels at the moment) and feeling tendencies—what one tends to feel in general, across time and situations. In affect terminology this distinction is identical to that between affective states and affective traits that reflect dispositional affectivity (Barsade & Gibson, 2007; Watson, 2000). Feeling states concern both emotions and moods, which fluctuate over time, from one day (or week) to another, or from one moment to another. Whereas emotions are intense, short-lived experiences that include a subjective feeling, a physiological, expressive, and behavioral-tendency component, moods are more diffused and last longer, and do not always have a clear referent or cause (Elfenbein, 2007).

Most relevant to this article is that feeling states may explain why and how events and experiences at work, and their intervening psychological mechanisms, affect employees. After Watson and Tellegen's (1985) seminal article proposing a structural model of mood, and the impactful opening sentence of that article, "Psychology has rediscovered affect" (p. 219), organizational psychology followed suit, with Barsade et al. (2003) proclaiming that an "[a]ffective revolution" had been taking place in organizational behavior and psychology. Many others have discussed this affective revolution and delineated the areas of organizational psychology theory and research where affect and affective processes have been considered (e.g., Ashkanasy & Dorris, 2017; Mitchell, 2018), with Barsade and Gibson (2007) simply explaining that "affect permeates organizations" (p. 36) and then continuing by detailing the many contributions that the study of affect has made in organizational behavior and psychology.

The large body of extant work on affect and feelings in organizations has given scholars a broad understanding of the role of feelings and feeling processes in explaining how and why work influences employee behavior (for an overview of the contributions of this literature, see Ashkanasy & Dorris, 2017). More specific to moral behaviors, however, are how discrete moral feelings (emotions) trigger moral processes and cognitions that influence ethical behavior. A model is proposed that links work experiences and features to ethical behavior through employees' moral emotions and cognitive processes (e.g., moral disengagement). This focus on the linkages between moral feelings and behaviors is timely and important in the context of a burgeoning interest in behavioral ethics (De Cremer & Moore, 2020) and also a renewed interest in unethical behaviors that occur in organizations (e.g., incivility, Schilpzand et al., 2016; unethical pro-organizational behavior, Umphress & Bingham, 2011).

At a general level, perhaps the most influential organizational theory linking work events to behavior through affective states is Affective Events Theory (AET; Weiss & Cropanzano, 1996). In short, AET proposes that events that employees experience at work have immediate affective consequences (they are "affective events") by changing employees' affective states or generating specific emotional reactions. In turn, these affective consequences (i.e., state affect) influence proximal behaviors such as organizational citizenship behavior (OCB) and also contribute to the formation of stable work attitudes. Indeed, following Weiss and Cropanzano, and starting with the study by Weiss, Nicholas, and Daus (1999) where the authors measured affect at work four times daily over 16 days and showed (and studied) the within-individual variability in affective state scores, there has been a flourishing stream of research examining within-individual effects of state affect on various behaviors (e.g., OCB; Ilies et al., 2006).

Among its many contributions, by focusing on immediate affective reactions and on the effects of changes in affective states on behavior, AET "draws much needed attention to the streams of events that can unfold in workplaces" (Brief & Weiss, 2002, p. 284), and it has laid the ground for studying psychological processes through which events that are experienced by employees during their workday influence affective state and the further (mediated) consequences on behaviors and other outcomes. Notably, although AET in its original formulation considers job satisfaction a stable attitude, starting with the study of Ilies and Judge (2002), work attitudes too have been studied as fluctuating states (see also Ilies & Judge, 2004). Although much of the early research testing AET-inspired effects of affective states has conceptualized affect broadly, by examining either pleasantness (e.g., Weiss, Nicholas, & Daus, 1999) or positive and negative affect (e.g., Ilies & Judge, 2002), research that focused on discrete emotions (e.g., guilt, shame) or on narrow "affects" (i.e., subdimensions of broad affect that correspond to discrete emotions; see Watson & Clark, 1994) has quickly ensued (see, e.g., Judge et al., 2006, for a study of discrete experiences of guilt and hostility at work), and this article takes that approach.

In short, the experience of discrete emotional/feeling states (or affects) and not of broad affective states (e.g., positive and negative affect) is proposed to be at the core of the relationships detailed in this article. More specifically, this article focuses on moral emotions: guilt, shame, empathy (compassion), and gratitude. The focus on moral emotions is due to a desire to understand how work experiences and events shape employees' ethical (moral) behavior; this is in line with the idea of considering thematically related (vs. topographically similar) constructs when developing theoretical explanations for organizational phenomena by proposing and testing models that include relationship among such constructs (e.g., Ilies et al., 2007; Organ, 1994). The section "The Moral Emotions" details each of the moral emotions that employees may experience, as well as some of the workplace-specific affective events that could trigger the experience of these moral emotions. Following this, the section "Behavioral Outcomes of Moral Emotions" details the association between the moral emotions and moral behaviors.

THE MORAL EMOTIONS

Moral emotions refer to a constellation of emotions that are deemed to be essential toward our understanding of when and why people are motivated to "do the right thing" (Haidt, 2003; Tangney et al., 2007). Moral emotions are facilitated when individuals encounter moral situations, such as when the welfare of others is under threat (Haidt, 2003). These moral emotions serve as a signal as to whether we have fallen short of (or met) personal or societal standards of moral behavior, and therefore influence our subsequent moral behaviors. The section "The Moral Emotions: Guilt and Shame" first defines and discusses the self-conscious, intrapersonal emotions of shame and guilt. The sections "The Moral Emotions: Compassion and Empathy" and "The Moral Emotions: Gratitude" focus on the self-transcendent, interpersonal emotions of compassion (and by association empathic processes) and gratitude, and their associations with work events and behaviors.

Guilt and Shame. Guilt and shame are negative feelings that are elicited when individuals perceive that they themselves or their behaviors have fallen short of certain moral standards, or when they feel that others are passing negative judgments on them, and are therefore collectively known as self-condemning moral emotions (Greenbaum et al., 2019; Leary, 2002). Shame involves negative feelings about our evaluations of the failings of our moral *character* or internal attributes that are personally uncontrollable (Harvey et al., 2017; Tangney, 1999), while guilt focuses on the moral violations of our more mutable behaviors, as opposed to our internal moral character (Morris & Keltner, 2000). Individuals may feel guilty not only because of their own behaviors but also in response to, or when they witness, others' moral violations (Barclay et al., 2005; Rothschild et al., 2012). As examples of situational affective events that elicit guilt in the workplace, survivors of layoffs often report feeling guilty, particularly when they judged the process as procedurally or interactionally unjust for those who were let go (Brockner et al., 1990). Similarly, employees who appraised that their positive outcomes were a result of biased procedures reported feeling higher levels of guilt (Weiss, Suckow, & Cropanzano, 1999).

Notably, while some theorists consider shame and guilt to be separate emotions with distinct antecedents and behavioral correlates—for example, the experience of guilt purportedly motivates repentance and a desire to make amends or perform corrective actions (e.g., Ilies et al., 2013), while shame is associated with withdrawal or denial of one's faults (Greenbaum et al., 2019)—empirically, these emotions are highly correlated with each other and are related to similar consequences and behaviors (Barclay et al., 2005; Bonner et al., 2017). Research in organizational behavior has found that employees are likely to feel both shame and guilt when they perform unethical behaviors or have harmed another, such as lying, counterproductive work behaviors, or pro-organizational unethical behavior (e.g., Ilies et al., 2013; Tang et al., 2020; Umphress & Bingham, 2011), and that both guilt and shame can (in some circumstances) motivate reparative behavior or behavior that restores their positive self-evaluations (e.g., Bonner et al., 2017; Grant & Wrzesniewski, 2010; Ilies et al., 2013), although, theoretically, guilt should have more pronounced effects in motivating reparative actions.

Because feelings of guilt and shame can be felt in anticipation—i.e., *before* individuals commit unethical behaviors (Lickel et al., 2005; Tangney & Dearing, 2002)—these emotions have anticipatory effects in that they can prevent individuals' engagement in unethical behaviors. Furthermore, individuals with a higher dispositional tendency to experience guilt or shame—i.e., shame- or guilt-proneness—are more attuned to potential moral transgressions and their negative repercussions, which would serve as a deterrent against committing transgressive behaviors. In some sense, shame- and guilt-proneness can therefore have inherent reparatory proprieties because of the higher sensitivity to moral transgressions associated with these dispositional tendencies. Indeed, one study has documented that employees' guilt-proneness strengthens the indirect relationship between engagement in unethical pro-organizational behaviors, guilt, and subsequent organizational citizenship behaviors (Tang et al., 2020).

Compassion and Empathy.   Aside from guilt and shame, which are primarily focused on the self, other moral emotions include self-transcendent emotions, that is, emotions that shift the focus from the individual's personal needs and goals to focus on others, such as compassion and gratitude (Haidt & Morris, 2009). By shifting interest from the self toward other-interest, these self-transcendent emotions are positively associated with engagement in ethical behaviors and practices (e.g., corporate social responsibility, Kollen, 2016; prosocial behavior,

Grant & Gino, 2010), and reduced unethical behaviors (e.g., Ford et al., 2018). This section first defines compassion and its related construct of empathy, as well as their relation to morality, followed by gratitude in the section "The Moral Emotions: Gratitude."

Compassion refers to feeling concern for and being emotionally moved by others' suffering coupled with a desire to help (Goetz et al., 2010). As such, compassion has been thought to be a key emotional response in explaining moral behavior (e.g., Haidt, 2003). Consistent with this positive view, research has found that compassion is positively associated with other-oriented, prosocial behaviors (e.g., Batson & Shaw, 1991). More recent research, however, has examined the boundary conditions of the compassion–prosocial behavior link, noting that this relationship is weakened when the perceiver is unable to cope with the costs associated with helping, or if they perceive that the sufferer deserves the negative outcome (Cameron & Payne, 2012; Goetz et al., 2010). Indeed, individuals often do not behave in moral or prosocial ways when they encounter someone who is suffering, and instead engage in cognitive reappraisals or moral flexibility in order to regulate their feelings of compassion (Cameron & Payne, 2012; Scheffer et al., 2021).

Here, it should be noted that compassion is distinct from empathy, which is a term that is often used interchangeably with compassion. While compassion is a complementary, other-oriented emotion elicited in response to another's suffering, empathy has both cognitive and affective components and refers to the ability or process by which individuals take another's perspective and become emotionally moved by their situation (Aw et al., 2020). As such, compassion is one specific emotional response that *results* from empathic processes, and we may empathize with others in both positive and negative situations, giving rise to other shared emotional states including empathic joy, empathic anger, and compassion (Goetz et al., 2010; Morelli et al., 2015). Nevertheless, as a precursor of compassion and related other-oriented emotions and behaviors, empathy has often been heralded as a moral virtue (Batson et al., 1995; Eisenberg & Miller, 1987). Empathy and its related processes allow individuals to take a proverbial walk in another's shoes, moving attention away from a self-centric perspective toward feeling care and concern for others' well-being (Aw et al., 2020; Eisenberg & Miller, 1987), and the relationship between dispositional empathy and compassion is akin to that between guilt-proneness and guilt.

While empathy, compassion, and their family of related emotions (e.g., sympathy) have not been extensively examined in the organizational setting, preliminary evidence suggests that these emotions and processes have been linked to prosocial behaviors and positive employee attitudes and outcomes (e.g., Aw et al., 2020; Dutton et al., 2014; Kamdar et al., 2006). Perceiving a coworker who is suffering and in need of help would, in the vein of Affective Events Theory, trigger empathic processes and affective reactions such as compassion and sympathy, which in turn lead to helping behaviors (Dutton et al., 2014).

The relationship between empathy, compassion, and (un)ethical behaviors is somewhat more complex, however, with some research showing that individuals may be willing to help others (a prosocial, ethical behavior) even at the expense of violating other moral rules. For instance, in a series of experiments, Batson et al. (1995) found that manipulations of empathy led to participants allocating resources in ways that demonstrated prosociality but violated justice principles. As this article will explain in relation to moral disengagement, such feelings of compassion may enable individuals to engage in moral justifications, such that they are committing unethical acts "for the greater good."

Gratitude. As mentioned in the brief introduction on moral emotions, gratitude too is a positive self-transcendent emotion that is relevant in the discussion of moral and prosocial behavior. Gratitude refers to feelings of appreciation that one feels in response to the beneficial actions of another (Fehr et al., 2017). In other words, individuals experience gratitude when others' actions have positive implications for the self, and gratitude can also inspire feelings of indebtedness. In addition to being an interpersonal emotion that can strengthen social bonds between individuals (Algoe, 2012), gratitude has been theorized to be a "moral reinforcer" that is elicited in response to others' moral, prosocial behaviors to the self (McCullough et al., 2001), as it encourages recipients of good deeds to reciprocate prosocial behaviors, that is, to "pay it forward." Such reciprocation can in its own right be viewed as a moral principle, where we "treat others how we would like to be treated," and addresses notions of equity and obligations to another whose actions have benefited us (Gouldner, 1960). Indeed, the lack of gratitude is seen as a moral failing (McCullough et al., 2001), which suggests that feelings of (in)gratitude play a crucial role in informing and motivating individuals to behave (im)morally.

Within the organizational context, experiencing gratitude is not only associated with organizational citizenship behaviors (Ford et al., 2018), strengthened bonds with coworkers (e.g., Ma et al., 2017), and increased attention to corporate social responsibility (Andersson et al., 2007), but *receiving* others' gratitude also has benefits for the self, by energizing employees and motivating subsequent positive interpersonal interactions and behaviors (Lee et al., 2019; Tang et al., 2022). As such, expressing (and receiving) gratitude can inspire further prosocial and moral behaviors (McCullough et al., 2001), increases cooperation even at the expense of the self (DeSteno et al., 2010), and is also associated with reduced aggression and hostility (DeWall et al., 2012).

Similar to empathy and compassion, however, the relationship between gratitude and unethicality may not be that straightforward. Although gratitude has typically been examined in a positive light—i.e., in relation to helping behaviors and strengthening interpersonal bonds—some preliminary research has explored the "dark side" of gratitude. For example, the social-alignment hypothesis (Ng et al., 2017) proposes that feeling grateful to another may result in the individual being more sensitive to their benefactor's needs, beliefs, and behaviors, and therefore may increase the willingness of the individual to adopt their benefactor's behaviors and values, or even the group's norms. This could have potential negative implications for unethical behaviors in the workplace, in that feeling grateful to one's coworker or supervisor could lead to employees conforming to unethical behavioral norms or making decisions that would benefit their benefactors (or their groups) despite possible moral violations. Similarly, one study found that when leaders expressed gratitude to employees who performed unethical pro-organizational behaviors, this gratitude reinforced employees' unethical behavior and increased their engagement in subsequent unethical behavior (Liu et al., 2022). These studies thus highlight the potentially complex relationships that such positive, purportedly moral emotions may have for moral behaviors at work.

BEHAVIORAL OUTCOMES OF MORAL EMOTIONS

As noted, the goal of this article is to examine relationships between moral emotions and (un) ethical behaviors in the workplace. This includes, but is not limited to, traditional counterproductive work behaviors (CWBs; or deviance), incivility, unethical pro-organizational behaviors (UPBs), as well as prosocial, organizational citizenship behaviors (OCBs). The section "Behavioral Outcomes of Moral Emotions: Counterproductive Work Behaviors" first defines these (classes of) behaviors and briefly reviews some research findings, and subsequently explains how showing moral emotions both influence and are influenced by these behaviors.

Counterproductive Work Behaviors. CWBs are behaviors that violate organizational norms or threaten the well-being of the organization or its members (Aquino et al., 1999; Robinson & Bennett, 1995). These behaviors may be interpersonally or organizationally directed and can include gossiping, theft, drug and alcohol abuse at work, sexual harassment, discrimination, tardiness, and dishonesty. Given the high cost of CWBs for organizations, researchers have been interested in unpacking the antecedents of CWBs, with particular attention being paid to the individual difference factors that predict CWB engagement, including trait anger and anxiety, the Big Five personality traits, as well as the Dark Triad (e.g., Ellen et al., 2021). Beyond personality, however, some research on the within-individual level has also examined the influence of negative affective events on CWBs, with studies demonstrating how negative events during the workday (e.g., being bullied) were linked to negative emotions and greater engagement in CWBs (Weiss & Beal, 2005). On the flip side, employees who *perform* deviant behaviors may too experience negative emotions, such that employees who engage in CWBs are more likely to feel guilt and shame for their actions, and to attempt corrective actions that can assuage their guilt (e.g., Ilies et al., 2013).

Incivility. A more specific form of interpersonally targeted counterproductive workplace behavior involves incivility. Incivility refers to treating others in a rude, discourteous, or demeaning manner and signals a lack of respect for others (Schilpzand et al., 2016). Incivility has been described as a low-intensity behavior with ambiguous intent (Andersson & Pearson, 1999) and therefore may appear to be somewhat milder as an unethical behavior compared to others, such as with aggression, abusive supervision, theft, and substance abuse. Incivility is nevertheless costly for organizations due to its ubiquity in the workplace (Taylor & Locklear, 2022), with an estimated cost of US$14,000 per employee annually (Pearson & Porath, 2005).

Experiencing incivility can have negative implications for employees' job satisfaction, commitment, turnover, performance, and physical and emotional well-being, with supervisor-perpetrated incivility having stronger negative effects compared to coworker or outsider incivility (Giumetti et al., 2013; Hershcovis & Barling, 2010; Lim & Cortina, 2005; Porath & Erez, 2007). From an emotional standpoint, research has found that although experiencing incivility often triggers anger, victims often also report feeling guilt, sadness, and fear, depending on their appraisals of the uncivil event (Bunk & Magley, 2013). Both experiencing and witnessing incivility can have implications for employees' (un)ethical behaviors, such that exposure to incivility predicted subsequent engagement in CWB (and reduced OCBs), particularly for those who had higher negative affectivity or belonged to groups that had high levels of incivility (Mao et al., 2019; Penney & Spector, 2005; Welbourne & Sariol, 2016). Indeed, experiencing incivility incites retaliatory behaviors in a bid to "get even" with the perpetrator. In one study, perception of customer incivility and mistreatment was associated with greater retaliation, that is, customer sabotage, in order to redress this perceived interpersonal injustice (Skarlicki et al., 2008). Beyond perpetrator–victim incivility, experiencing incivility may also lead to "trickle-down" or ripple effects, such that employees who experience incivility from one source (e.g., managers), would be more likely to instigate incivility toward coworkers or subordinates (e.g., Mawritz et al., 2012; Wayne et al., 2008).

Unethical Pro-Organizational Behaviors. Since 2010, there has been increasing interest in unethical behaviors that are not driven by self-interest but rather are for the apparent good of the organization (Umphress & Bingham, 2011), otherwise known as UPBs. These involve behaviors that violate moral principles or laws but are nevertheless intended to benefit the organization, such as promoting an ineffective product to a customer to increase sales or lying to protect the organization's reputation. UPBs are of particular interest as an unethical behavior due to its documented antecedents—namely, that positive social exchange relationships and organizational identification increase the likelihood of employee UPB, as well as its relation to neutralization, a form of moral disengagement that "eliminates social controls that inhibit unethical or deviant acts and frees an individual to perform unethical acts" (Bandura, 1999; Umphress & Bingham, 2011, p. 626).

Within the framework of social exchange theory, receiving resources or benefits from one party triggers the norm of reciprocity (Blau, 1964). Positive social exchange relationships with one's leader, team members, or organization, particularly when employees also identify with the organization, would therefore instigate behaviors that serve to benefit the other, because they are *obliged* or indebted to return the favor even at the expense of moral violations (Umphress & Bingham, 2011). Specific to UPBs and neutralization, the norm of reciprocity invokes an equity principle that can justify engagement in UPBs (Umphress & Bingham, 2011), such that *not* reciprocating could also be seen as ingratitude and is therefore unethical. In these instances, the moral obligation to repay interpersonal debts could take precedence over societal or individual ethical principles. More relevant to emotions in the workplace is that feelings of gratitude could serve as an indicator of positive social exchange relationships and could foster indebtedness associated with others' positive actions for the self, thus facilitating subsequent engagement in UPB.

Organizational Citizenship Behaviors. Finally, it is also important to discuss OCBs as an example of a positive, moral behavior in the workplace. Moral emotions are relevant in influencing employee engagement not only in unethical behaviors, but also in proactive, *ethical* behaviors. OCBs are extra-role behaviors that are outside of employees' job duties but nevertheless are important for the effective functioning of the organization. Similar to CWBs, OCBs may be examined as both interpersonally and organizationally directed. Interpersonal OCBs (OCB-I) are also known as prosocial or helping behaviors, as they are voluntary behaviors intended to benefit others in the workplace (Organ, 2018), while organizationally directed OCBs refers to more general conscientious behaviors that serve the organization's purpose. OCB-Is, or prosocial behaviors, are particularly relevant to this discussion, as these behaviors often involve a willingness to help others even at a cost to oneself or one's scarce resources, because it is the right thing to do, that is, an ethical behavior.

Emotion–Behavior Links. Most organizational research linking emotions to behavior has been looking either at linking negative emotions to unethical behavior (e.g., anger to incivility; Meier & Semmer, 2013) or at the links between positive emotions and "good behavior" (e.g., positive affect to OCBs; Ilies et al., 2006). However, a more nuanced approach, focusing on the motivational properties of moral emotions, is required. For example, guilt (elicited, for example, by making employees aware of the negative consequences of their counterproductive behaviors; Ilies et al., 2013) can motivate employees to engage in behaviors that are beneficial for organizations (e.g., OCBs). Conversely, positive affect, which has been traditionally linked to increased OCBs, can lead to negative behaviors, such as incivility, in certain circumstances (e.g., when employees are low on perspective taking and unable to consider the consequences of their [unethical] actions on others; Ilies et al., 2020). More specifically, positive affect has been theorized to stimulate cognitive flexibility and creativity, characteristics that facilitate moral disengagement (Ilies et al., 2020). Importantly, emotions and affect at work are often elicited by experiences and events (Weiss & Cropanzano, 1996), such as with the survivors' reactions described earlier in "The Moral Emotions: Guilt and Shame" (Brockner et al., 1990), or, of course, when employees are being treated unjustly themselves. Furthermore, employees' own behaviors (e.g., CWBs) can generate moral feelings, especially when employees are being made aware of the negative implications of their behaviors (Ilies et al., 2013; Tang et al., 2020).

MECHANISMS: MORAL DISENGAGEMENT AND LICENSING

It is proposed that psychological mechanisms, specifically moral disengagement and moral licensing, can explain how affective reactions to work experiences or events, that is, moral emotions, lead to employees' engagement in the (im)moral behaviors described in the "Behavioral Outcomes of Moral Emotions" section (De Cremer & Moore, 2020), including unethical pro-organizational behaviors (UPBs) and counterproductive work behaviors, but also prosocial behaviors.

In particular, research in behavioral ethics has relied on moral disengagement theory as a framework to explain why ordinarily good employees may do bad things (Bandura, 1999; Ogunfowora et al., 2022). According to Bandura (1999), moral behavior is governed by a self-regulatory system that monitors the individual's moral behavior in light of internal moral standards or principles. Behaving in ways that violate these standards (even the mere anticipation of such behaviors) would typically lead to negative internal reactions, such as guilt or self-condemnation, which can deter individuals from behaving unethically or motivate them to make reparations after unethical behaviors. However, individuals often (consciously or unconsciously) apply cognitive tactics—known as moral disengagement strategies—to sidestep these moral self-regulatory systems, such as by suppressing or disrupting our negative emotional responses, thus freeing them to engage in unethical behaviors or make questionable decisions.

According to moral disengagement theory (Bandura, 1999), moral disengagement strategies include moral justification, diffusion or displacement of responsibility, and dehumanization, among others. For example, employees who believe that they have been treated unfairly at work may be more willing to justify their retaliation against the organization, such as through theft of organizational property, by reasoning to themselves (moral justification) that they are simply righting a wrong or restoring inequity. Through such justification, they will be less likely experience guilt from their actions, as they believe they deserve or have earned the right to take organizational property, or to treat others with disrespect because they deserve it (blaming the victim). Notably, while Bandura (1999) suggests that moral disengagement strategies are invoked prior to individuals conducting unethical acts, others have theorized that moral disengagement can be applied retrospectively to justify one's unethical behavior (e.g., Detert et al., 2008; Shu et al., 2011).

The moral emotions are typically argued to deactivate or weaken moral disengagement— foreseeing the harm that one's actions may have on others through empathic processes, feeling compassion for and identification with others, and the anticipatory guilt and shame associated with unethical behaviors would make it more difficult for individuals to justify or distort the impact of their actions on others (De Cremer & Moore, 2020; Ogunfowora et al., 2022). While gratitude has not been studied in the context of moral disengagement, it is likely that the role of gratitude in interpersonal bonding, relational identification, and motivating reciprocal, "pay-it-forward" prosocial behaviors may also reduce individuals' likelihood of employing moral disengagement tactics, as being treated fairly prevents individuals from using these tactics (Moore & Gino, 2013).

That said, positive moral emotions such as compassion and gratitude may also trigger moral disengagement under certain circumstances. Behaving altruistically and morally may sometimes conflict (Batson et al., 1995), such that empathy-induced compassion can lead to immoral behavior (e.g., violating equity principles) for the sake of improving others' welfare, or illegally helping others who are victims of inequity even at great cost to themselves, also known as the "Robin Hood Effect" (Gino & Pierce, 2009), as individuals are able to justify that their unethical actions are in actual fact the "right thing to do." Supporting this idea, a study in the organizational context found that identification with and compassion for similar others increases the likelihood of employees helping customers through illegal helping behaviors (Gino & Pierce, 2010). Feeling gratitude to the group or leader may also encourage moral justification in the vein of committing unethical acts for the greater good of the group, such as with UPBs (Liu et al., 2022), or by strengthening ingroup/outgroup distinctions and therefore encouraging dehumanization of others, freeing individuals to perform immoral behavior.

In addition to facilitating engagement in unethical behaviors, moral disengagement tactics may also *reduce* engagement in prosocial or moral behaviors. For instance, while empathy and compassion are often positively associated with prosociality and helping, scholars in these areas have long documented instances where empathy fails to lead to prosocial helping, also known as compassion collapse (Cameron, 2017; Cameron & Payne, 2012). Indeed, caring for others, as with empathy and compassion, can be costly for helpers, leading to burnout or compassion fatigue (e.g., Figley, 1995). Individuals may therefore be motivated to *avoid* compassion to conserve their resources by distancing themselves from perceived victims (Scheffer et al., 2022), by engaging in strategies that resemble moral disengagement—for instance, in derogating outgroups, distancing themselves from the victim, or blaming the victims (Cameron et al., 2016; Zaki, 2014). In these ways, employees may adopt moral disengagement strategies to avoid engaging in ethical, prosocial behaviors.

While moral disengagement can be examined as a state, in relation to our momentary affective reactions, as just described, there are also individual differences in individuals' *propensity* to disengage morally (Detert et al., 2008; Moore et al., 2012; Ogunfowora et al., 2022). A meta-analysis by Ogunfowora et al. (2022), for example, has found that moral identity, honesty–humility, conscientiousness, and trait empathy influenced employees' tendency to disengage from moral standards. Particularly relevant to the discussion on emotions, moral disengagement, and moral behavior is trait empathy—an individual difference factor that determines the degree to which individuals are able to take another's perspective and feel concern for or be emotionally moved by their situation (Eisenberg & Miller, 1987). Empathic processes play an important role in facilitating prosocial and moral behaviors. Because individuals who are higher in dispositional empathy are more likely to relationally identify with others and to be attuned to their psychological needs and emotional states (Aw et al., 2020; Bandura, 1986), these individuals would therefore be less likely to utilize moral disengagement strategies, such as distorting potential harm to victims, or to dehumanize others (Detert et al., 2008), as they are better able to envision and feel how their (un)ethical actions may help or hurt others.

Similarly, guilt- and shame-proneness have been found to be negatively related to moral disengagement and, by extension, to employees' engagement in organizational misconduct (Detert et al., 2008; Ogunfowora et al., 2022). Theorists have reasoned that these individuals would be less able to "switch off" or disrupt anticipatory negative affective reactions, that is, guilt and shame, that result from misbehaving, and therefore are less able to justify their unethical behavior or push responsibility and blame toward others (Moore et al., 2012; Ogunfowora et al., 2022).

In addition to moral disengagement, moral licensing is another psychological process that disinhibits and frees employees to engage in unethical behaviors (Klotz & Bolino, 2013; Miller & Effron, 2010). Moral licensing theory proposes that engaging in ethical behaviors boosts employees' moral self-image and grants them a moral license, or idiosyncratic credits, that frees them to conduct deviant behaviors without compromising their overall moral image. Supporting moral licensing theory, some research has found that employees who behave altruistically and performed higher levels of organizational citizenship behaviors (OCBs) were more psychologically entitled and subsequently engaged in higher levels of interpersonal and organizational counterproductive work behaviors (Yam et al., 2017), and that ethical leader behaviors on one day were positively associated with next-day abusive supervision, an effect that was mediated by moral licensing (Lin et al., 2016).

While the moral emotions have yet to be examined in relation with moral licensing, theorists have suggested that the experience of self-transcendent emotions (e.g., elevation) prevents moral licensing as these emotions affirm the individual's innate willingness and intrinsic motivation to behave prosocially without an increase in psychological entitlement (e.g., Thomson & Siegel, 2017). Similarly then, citizenship and ethical behaviors inspired by the positive moral emotions of gratitude and compassion, or conversely as a result of self-condemnation in the form of guilt and shame, could reduce moral licensing and immoral behaviors, as employees perceive their behaviors to be voluntary and expected of them, instead of being morally praiseworthy or to be rewarded.

Further, there may be individual differences in one's propensity to grant moral licenses to their OCB engagement—specifically, Klotz and Bolino (2013) theorize that the more central one's moral character is to their self-concept—i.e., the stronger one's moral identity— behaving consistently with this identity would not elevate their moral self-regard, as "such behavior merely reflects how they define themselves and what they value" (p. 298). Following this argument, it is proposed that individuals higher in dispositional empathy, compassion, and gratitude would similarly attribute their moral prosocial behaviors to their internal motivations and what is expected of them, and be less likely to grant themselves a moral license after performing OCBs.

CONCLUSION AND FUTURE RESEARCH DIRECTIONS

Drawing on Affective Events Theory (AET) and the behavioral ethics literature, this article demonstrates how AET is a useful framework linking affective events and moral emotions to moral behaviors in the workplace. Further, integrating this large body of research evidence outlines a model delineating how the various moral emotions of guilt, shame, compassion, and gratitude can influence employee engagement in (un)ethical behaviors, through moral licensing and moral disengagement. Figure 1 shows a model where various workplace events can elicit different moral emotions, and the ways in which these moral emotions may differentially increase (or decrease) moral disengagement or moral licensing, engagement in (un)ethical behaviors, and the individual antecedents that could serve as boundary conditions for these proposed relationships.

Nevertheless, there remain important avenues for future research. First, there is a lack of studies linking the discrete moral emotions to moral licensing and moral disengagement—particularly with regard to the positive moral emotions of gratitude and compassion. Relatedly, much of past research is focused on the four moral emotions of guilt, shame, compassion, and gratitude; yet other discrete emotions have also been associated with unethical behavior in organizations, even if they are not considered classically moral emotions. For example, past research has linked envy, fear, pride, and anger to moral behaviors (Gino & Pierce, 2009; Kouchaki & Desai, 2015; O'Reilly et al., 2016; Tang et al., 2020). A more thorough examination of how the individual discrete emotions may facilitate or hinder moral disengagement and might lead to downstream effects on ethical behavior would therefore be valuable in contributing to the behavioral ethics literature.

Further, while affective and moral individual differences discussed in this article (e.g., dispositional empathy, moral identity, guilt- and shame-proneness) are important potential moderators and predictors of the relationships between the moral emotions, moral disengagement, and moral licensing, also relevant are contextual characteristics in shaping employees'

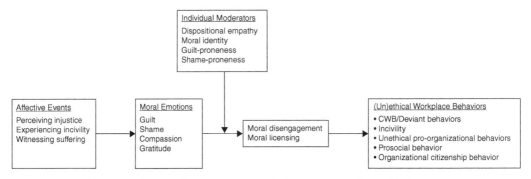

Figure 1. Model linking the moral emotions to workplace events and moral behaviors.

behaviors (e.g., job autonomy and organizational culture), as well as other individual differences (e.g., emotion regulation tendencies), that go beyond the scope of this article. Future research could therefore have a more comprehensive investigation of both individual differences and situational boundary conditions of these effects.

In sum, the hope is that the review and integration in this article effectively summarizes the research on moral emotions and moral behaviors into an overall framework, and provides several avenues for future research that could serve as a springboard for future work in this field.

FURTHER READING

Ashkanasy, N. M., & Dorris, A. D. (2017). Emotions in the workplace. *Annual Review of Organizational Psychology and Organizational Behavior, 4,* 67–90.

Bandura, A. (1999). Moral disengagement in the perpetration of inhumanities. *Personality and Social Psychology Review, 3,* 193–209.

De Cremer, D., & Moore, C. (2020). Toward a better understanding of behavioural ethics in the workplace. *Annual Review of Organizational Psychology and Organizational Behaviour, 7,* 369–393.

Fehr, R., Fulmer, A., Awtrey, E., & Miller, J. A. (2017). The grateful workplace: A multilevel model of gratitude in organizations. *Academy of Management Review, 42,* 361–381.

Gino, F., & Pierce, L. (2010). Robin Hood under the hood: Wealth-based discrimination in illicit customer help. *Organization Science, 21,* 1176–1194.

Goetz, J. L., Keltner, D., & Simon-Thomas, E. (2010). Compassion: An evolutionary analysis and empirical review. *Psychological Bulletin, 136,* 351–374.

Greenbaum, R., Bonner, J., Gray, T., & Mawritz, M. (2019). Moral emotions: A review and research agenda for management scholarship. *Journal of Organizational Behaviour, 4,* 95–114.

Klotz, A. C., & Bolino, M. C. (2013). Citizenship and counterproductive work behavior: A moral licensing view. *Academy of Management Review, 38,* 292–306.

Scheffer, J. A., Cameron, C. D., & Inzlicht, M. (2021). Caring is costly: People avoid the cognitive work of compassion. *Journal of Experimental Psychology: General, 151,* 172–196. https://doi.org/10.1037/xge0001073

Tangney, J. P., Stuewig, J., & Mashek, D. J. (2007). Moral emotions and moral behaviour. *Annual Review of Psychology, 58,* 345–372.

Zaki, J. (2014). Empathy: A motivated account. *Psychological Bulletin, 140,* 1608–1647.

REFERENCES

Algoe, S. B. (2012). Find, remind, and bind: The functions of gratitude in everyday relationships. *Social and Personality Psychology Compass, 6,* 455–469.

Andersson, L. M., Giacalone, R. A., & Jurkiewicz, C. L. (2007). On the relationship of hope and gratitude to corporate social responsibility. *Journal of Business Ethics, 70,* 401–409.

Andersson, L. M., & Pearson, C. M. (1999). Tit for tat? The spiralling effect of incivility in the workplace. *Academy of Management Review, 24,* 452–471.

Aquino, K., Lewis, M. U., & Bradfield, M. (1999). Justice constructs, negative affectivity, and employee deviance: A proposed model and empirical test. *Journal of Organizational Behavior, 20*(7), 1073–1091.

Ashkanasy, N. M., & Dorris, A. D. (2017). Emotions in the workplace. *Annual Review of Organizational Psychology and Organizational Behavior, 4,* 67–90.

Aw, S. S. Y., Ilies, R., & de Pater, I. E. (2020). Dispositional empathy, emotional display authenticity, and employee outcomes. *Journal of Applied Psychology, 105,* 1036–1046.

Bandura, A. (1986). *Social foundations of thought and action: A social cognitive theory*. Prentice Hall.

Bandura, A. (1999). Moral disengagement in the perpetration of inhumanities. *Personality and Social Psychology Review, 3*, 193–209.

Barclay, L. J., Skarlicki, D. P., & Pugh, S. D. (2005). Exploring the role of emotions in injustice perceptions and retaliation. *Journal of Applied Psychology, 90*, 629–643.

Barsade, S., Brief, A., & Spataro, S. (2003). The affective revolution in organizational behaviour: The emergence of a paradigm. In J. Greenberg (Ed.), *Organizational behaviour: The state of the science* (pp. 3–52). Lawrence Erlbaum Associates.

Barsade, S. G., & Gibson, D. E. (2007). Why does affect matter in organizations? *Academy of Management Perspectives, 21*, 36–59.

Batson, C. D., Klein, T. R., Highberger, L., & Shaw, L. L. (1995). Immorality from empathy-induced altruism: When compassion and justice conflict. *Journal of Personality and Social Psychology, 68*, 1042–1054.

Batson, C. D., & Shaw, L. L. (1991). Evidence for altruism: Toward a pluralism of prosocial motives. *Psychological Inquiry, 2*, 107–122.

Blau, P. M. (1964). Justice in social exchange. *Sociological Inquiry, 34*(2), 193-206.

Bonner, J. M., Greenbaum, R. L., & Quade, M. J. (2017). Employee unethical behaviour to shame as an indicator of self-image threat and exemplification as a form of self-image protection: The exacerbating role of supervisor bottom-line mentality. *Journal of Applied Psychology, 102*, 1203–1221.

Brief, A. P., & Weiss, H. M. (2002). Affect in the workplace. *Annual Review of Psychology, 53*, 279–307.

Brockner, J., DeWitt, R. L., Grover, S., & Reed, T. (1990). When it is especially important to explain why: Factors affecting the relationship between managers' explanations of a layoff and survivors' reactions to the layoff. *Journal of Experimental Social Psychology, 26*, 389–407.

Bunk, J. A., & Magley, V. J. (2013). The role of appraisals and emotions in understanding experiences of workplace incivility. *Journal of Occupational Health Psychology, 18*(1), 87.

Cameron, C. D. (2017). Compassion collapse: Why we are numb to numbers? *The Oxford Handbook of Compassion Science*, 261–271.

Cameron, C. D., Harris, L. T., & Payne, B. K. (2016). The emotional cost of humanity: Anticipated exhaustion motivates dehumanization of stigmatized targets. *Social Psychological and Personality Science, 7*(2), 105–112.

Cameron, C. D., & Payne, B. K. (2012). The cost of callousness: Regulating compassion influences the moral self-concept. *Psychological Science, 23*, 225–229.

De Cremer, D., & Moore, C. (2020). Toward a better understanding of behavioural ethics in the workplace. *Annual Review of Organizational Psychology and Organizational Behaviour, 7*, 369–393.

DeSteno, D., Bartlett, M. Y., Baumann, J., Williams, L. A., & Dickens, L. (2010). Gratitude as moral sentiment: Emotion-guided cooperation in economic exchange. *Emotion, 10*, 289–293.

Detert, J. R., Treviño, L. K., & Sweitzer, V. L. (2008). Moral disengagement in ethical decision making: A study of antecedents and outcomes. *Journal of Applied Psychology, 93*, 374–391.

DeWall, C. N., Lambert, N. M., Pond, R. S., Kashdan, T. B., & Fincham, F. D. (2012). A grateful heart is a nonviolent heart. *Social Psychological and Personality Science, 3*, 232–240.

Dutton, J. E., Workman, K. M., & Hardin, A. E. (2014). Compassion at work. *Annual Review of Organizational Psychology and Organizational Behavior, 1*, 277–304.

Eisenberg, N., & Miller, P. A. (1987). Empathy, sympathy, and altruism: Empirical and conceptual links. In N. Eisenberg & J. Strayer (Eds.), *Empathy and its development* (pp. 292–316). Cambridge University Press.

Elfenbein, H. A. (2007). Emotion in organizations: A review and theoretical integration. *Academy of Management Annals, 1*, 371–457.

Ellen, B. P., III, Alexander, K. C., Mackey, J. D., McAllister, C. P., & Carson, J. E. (2021). Portrait of a workplace deviant: A clearer picture of the Big Five and Dark Triad as predictors of workplace deviance. *Journal of Applied Psychology, 106*, 1950–1961.

Fehr, R., Fulmer, A., Awtrey, E., & Miller, J. A. (2017). The grateful workplace: A multilevel model of gratitude in organizations. *Academy of Management Review, 42*, 361–381.

Figley, C. R. (1995). Compassion fatigue: Toward a new understanding of the costs of caring. In B. H. Stamm (Ed.), *Secondary traumatic stress: Self-care issues for clinicians, researchers, and educators* (pp. 3–28). Sidran Press.

Ford, M. T., Wang, Y., Jin, J., & Eisenberger, R. (2018). Chronic and episodic anger and gratitude toward the organization: Relationships with organizational and supervisor supportiveness and extrarole behavior. *Journal of Occupational Health Psychology, 23*, 175–187.

Gino, F., & Pierce, L. (2009). Dishonesty in the name of equity. *Psychological Science, 20*, 1153–1160.

Gino, F., & Pierce, L. (2010). Robin Hood under the hood: Wealth-based discrimination in illicit customer help. *Organization Science, 21*, 1176–1194.

Giumetti, G. W., Hatfield, A. L., Scisco, J. L., Schroeder, A. N., Muth, E. R., & Kowalski, R. M. (2013). What a rude e-mail! Examining the differential effects of incivility versus support on mood, energy, engagement, and performance in an online context. *Journal of Occupational Health Psychology, 18*, 297–309.

Goetz, J. L., Keltner, D., & Simon-Thomas, E. (2010). Compassion: An evolutionary analysis and empirical review. *Psychological Bulletin, 136*, 351–374.

Gouldner, A. W. (1960). The norm of reciprocity: A preliminary statement. *American Sociological Review*, 161–178.

Grant, A. M., & Gino, F. (2010). A little thanks goes a long way: Explaining why gratitude expressions motivate prosocial behavior. *Journal of Personality and Social Psychology, 98*(6), 946.

Grant, A. M., & Wrzesniewski, A. (2010). I won't let you down... or will I? Core self-evaluations, other-orientation, anticipated guilt and gratitude, and job performance. *Journal of Applied Psychology, 95*, 108–121.

Greenbaum, R., Bonner, J., Gray, T., & Mawritz, M. (2019). Moral emotions: A review and research agenda for management scholarship. *Journal of Organizational Behaviour, 4*, 95–114.

Haidt, J. (2003). The moral emotions. In R. J. Davison, K. R. Scherer, & H. H. Goldsmith (Eds.), *Handbook of affective sciences* (pp. 852–870). Oxford University Press.

Haidt, J., & Morris, J. P. (2009). Finding the self in self-transcendent emotions. *Proceedings of the National Academy of Sciences, 106*, 7687–7688.

Harvey, P., Martinko, M. J., & Borkowski, N. (2017). Justifying deviant behavior: The role of attributions and moral emotions. *Journal of Business Ethics, 141*, 779–795.

Hershcovis, M. S., & Barling, J. (2010). Towards a multi-foci approach to workplace aggression: A meta-analytic review of outcomes from different perpetrators. *Journal of Organizational Behavior, 31*, 24–44.

Ilies, R., De Pater, I. E., & Judge, T. (2007). Differential affective reactions to negative and positive feedback, and the role of self-esteem. *Journal of Managerial Psychology, 22*, 590–609.

Ilies, R., Guo, Y., Lim, S., Yam, K. C., & Li, X. (2020). Happy but uncivil? Examining when and why positive affect leads to incivility. *Journal of Business Ethics, 165*, 595–614.

Ilies, R., & Judge, T. A. (2002). Understanding the dynamic relationships among personality, mood, and job satisfaction: A field experience sampling study. *Organizational Behaviour and Human Decision Processes, 89*, 1119–1139. https://doi.org/10.1016/S0749-5978(02)00018-3

Ilies, R., & Judge, T. A. (2004). An experience-sampling measure of job satisfaction and its relationships with affectivity, mood at work, job beliefs, and general job satisfaction. *European Journal of Work and Organizational Psychology, 13*, 367–389. https://doi.org/10.1080/13594320444000137

Ilies, R., Peng, A. C., Savani, K., & Dimotakis, N. (2013). Guilty and helpful: An emotion-based reparatory model of voluntary work behavior. *Journal of Applied Psychology, 98*, 1051–1059. https://doi.org/10.1037/a0034162

Ilies, R., Scott, B. A., & Judge, T. A. (2006). The interactive effects of personal traits and experienced states on intraindividual patterns of citizenship behavior. *Academy of Management Journal, 49*, 561–575. https://doi.org/10.5465/AMJ.2006.21794672

Judge, T. A., Ilies, R., & Scott, B. A. (2006). Work-family conflict, hostility, and guilt: Effects on work and family outcomes. *Personnel Psychology, 59*, 779–814.

Kamdar, D., McAllister, D. J., & Turban, D. B. (2006). "All in a day's work": How follower individual differences and justice perceptions predict OCB role definitions and behavior. *Journal of Applied Psychology, 91*, 841–855.

Köllen, T. (2016). Acting out of compassion, egoism, and malice: A Schopenhauerian view on the moral worth of CSR and diversity management practices. *Journal of Business Ethics, 138*(2), 215-229.

Klotz, A. C., & Bolino, M. C. (2013). Citizenship and counterproductive work behavior: A moral licensing view. *Academy of Management Review, 38*, 292–306.

Kouchaki, M., & Desai, S. D. (2015). Anxious, threatened, and also unethical: How anxiety makes individuals feel threatened and commit unethical acts. *Journal of Applied Psychology, 100*, 360–375.

Leary, M. R. (2002). When selves collide: The nature of the self and the dynamics of interpersonal relationships. In A. Tesser, D. A. Stapel, & J. V. Wood (Eds.), *Self and motivation* (pp. 119–145). American Psychological Association.

Lee, H. W., Bradburn, J., Johnson, R. E., Lin, S. H. J., & Chang, C. H. D. (2019). The benefits of receiving gratitude for helpers: A daily investigation of proactive and reactive helping at work. *Journal of Applied Psychology, 104*, 197–213.

Lickel, B., Schmader, T., Curtis, M., Scarnier, M., & Ames, D. R. (2005). Vicarious shame and guilt. *Group Processes & Intergroup Relations, 8*, 145–157.

Lim, S., & Cortina, L. M. (2005). Interpersonal mistreatment in the workplace: The interface and impact of general incivility and sexual harassment. *Journal of Applied Psychology, 90*, 483–496.

Lin, S. H. J., Ma, J., & Johnson, R. E. (2016). When ethical leader behavior breaks bad: How ethical leader behavior can turn abusive via ego depletion and moral licensing. *Journal of Applied Psychology, 101*, 815–830.

Liu, W., Zhu, Y., Chen, S., Zhang, Y., & Qin, F. (2022). Moral decline in the workplace: Unethical pro-organizational behavior, psychological entitlement, and leader gratitude expression. *Ethics and Behavior, 32*, 110–123.

Ma, L. K., Tunney, R. J., & Ferguson, E. (2017). Does gratitude enhance prosociality? A meta-analytic review. *Psychological Bulletin, 143*, 601–635.

Mao, C., Chang, C. H., Johnson, R. E., & Sun, J. (2019). Incivility and employee performance, citizenship, and counterproductive behaviors: Implications of the social context. *Journal of Occupational Health Psychology, 24*, 213–227.

Mawritz, M. B., Mayer, D. M., Hoobler, J. M., Wayne, S. J., & Marinova, S. V. (2012). A trickle-down model of abusive supervision. *Personnel Psychology, 65*(2), 325–357.

McCullough, M. E., Kilpatrick, S. D., Emmons, R. A., & Larson, D. B. (2001). Is gratitude a moral affect? *Psychological Bulletin, 127*, 249–266.

Meier, L. L., & Semmer, N. K. (2013). Lack of reciprocity, narcissism, anger, and instigated workplace incivility: A moderated mediation model. *European Journal of Work and Organizational Psychology, 22*(4), 461–475.

Miller, D. T., & Effron, D. A. (2010). Psychological license: When it is needed and how it functions. In *Advances in experimental social psychology* (Vol. 43, pp. 115–155). Academic Press.

Mitchell, T. R. (2018). A dynamic, inclusive, and affective evolutionary view of organizational behavior. *Annual Review of Organizational Psychology and Organizational Behavior, 5*, 1–19.

Moore, C., Detert, J. R., Trevino, L. K., Baker, V. L., & Mayer, D. M. (2012). Why employees do bad things: Moral disengagement and unethical organizational behavior. *Personnel Psychology, 65*, 1–48.

Moore, C., & Gino, F. (2013). Ethically adrift: How others pull our moral compass from true North, and how we can fix it. *Research in Organizational Behavior, 33*, 53–77.

Morelli, S. A., Lieberman, M. D., & Zaki, J. (2015). The emerging study of positive empathy. *Social and Personality Psychology Compass, 9*, 57–68.

Morris, M. W., & Keltner, D. (2000). How emotions work: The social functions of emotional expression in negotiations. *Research in Organizational Behavior, 22*, 1–50.

Ng, J. W. X., Tong, E. M. W., Sim, D. L. Y., Teo, S. W. Y., Loy, X., & Giesbrecht, T. (2017). Gratitude facilitates private conformity: A test of the social alignment hypothesis. *Emotion, 17*(2), 379–387. https://doi.org/10.1037/emo0000249

Ogunfowora, B. T., Nguyen, V. Q., Steel, P., & Hwang, C. C. (2022). A meta-analytic investigation of the antecedents, theoretical correlates, and consequences of moral disengagement at work. *Journal of Applied Psychology, 107*, 746–775. https://doi.org/10.1037/apl0000912

O'Reilly, J., Aquino, K., & Skarlicki, D. (2016). The lives of others: Third parties' responses to others' injustice. *Journal of Applied Psychology, 101*, 171–189.

Organ, D. W. (1994). Personality and organizational citizenship behavior. *Journal of Management, 20*, 465–478.

Organ, D. W. (2018). Organizational citizenship behavior: Recent trends and developments. *Annual Review of Organizational Psychology and Organizational Behavior, 80*, 295-306.

Pearson, C. M., & Porath, C. L. (2005). On the nature, consequences and remedies of workplace incivility: No time for "nice"? Think again. *Academy of Management Perspectives, 19*(1), 7–18.

Penney, L. M., & Spector, P. E. (2005). Job stress, incivility, and counterproductive work behavior (CWB): The moderating role of negative affectivity. *Journal of Organizational Behavior, 26*, 777–796.

Porath, C. L., & Erez, A. (2007). Does rudeness matter? The effects of rude behavior on task performance and helpfulness. *Academy of Management Journal, 50*, 1181–1197.

Robinson, S. L., & Bennett, R. J. (1995). A typology of deviant workplace behaviors: A multidimensional scaling study. *Academy of Management Journal, 38*(2), 555–572.

Rothschild, Z. K., Landau, M. J., Sullivan, D., & Keefer, L. A. (2012). A dual-motive model of scapegoating: Displacing blame to reduce guilt or increase control. *Journal of Personality and Social Psychology, 102*, 1148–1163.

Scheffer, J. A., Cameron, C. D., & Inzlicht, M. (2022). Caring is costly: People avoid the cognitive work of compassion. *Journal of Experimental Psychology: General, 151*, 172–196. https://doi.org/10.1037/xge0001073

Schilpzand, P., De Pater, I. E., & Erez, A. (2016). Workplace incivility: A review of the literature and agenda for future research. *Journal of Organizational Behaviour, 37*, S57–S88.

Shu, L. L., Gino, F., & Bazerman, M. H. (2011). Dishonest deed, clear conscience: When cheating leads to moral disengagement and motivated forgetting. *Personality and Social Psychology Bulletin, 37*(3), 330–349.

Skarlicki, D. P., Van Jaarsveld, D. D., & Walker, D. D. (2008). Getting even for customer mistreatment: The role of moral identity in the relationship between customer interpersonal injustice and employee sabotage. *Journal of Applied Psychology, 93*, 1335–1347.

Tang, P. M., Ilies, R., Aw, S. S. Y., Lin, K. J., Lee, R., & Trombini, C. (2022). How and when service beneficiaries' gratitude enriches employees' daily lives. *Journal of Applied Psychology, 107*(6), 987–1008. https://doi.org/10.1037/apl0000975

Tang, P. M., Yam, K. C., & Koopman, J. (2020). Feeling proud but guilty? Unpacking the paradoxical nature of unethical pro-organizational behavior. *Organizational Behavior and Human Decision Processes, 160*, 68–86.

Tangney, J. P. (1999). The self-conscious emotions: Shame, guilt, embarrassment, and pride. In T. Dalgleish & M. J. Power (Eds.), *Handbook of cognition and emotion* (pp. 541–568). Wiley.

Tangney, J. P., & Dearing, R. L. (2002). *Shame and guilt.* Guilford Press.

Tangney, J. P., Stuewig, J., & Mashek, D. J. (2007). Moral emotions and moral behaviour. *Annual Review of Psychology, 58,* 345–372.

Taylor, S. G., & Locklear, L. R. (2022). A little rudeness goes a long way. *MIT Sloan Management Review, 63,* 1–6.

Thomson, A. L., & Siegel, J. T. (2017). Elevation: A review of scholarship on a moral and other-praising emotion. *Journal of Positive Psychology, 12,* 628–638.

Umphress, E. E., & Bingham, J. B. (2011). When employees do bad things for good reasons: Examining unethical pro-organizational behaviours. *Organization Science, 22,* 621–640.

Watson, D. (2000). *Mood and temperament.* Guilford Press.

Watson, D., & Clark, L. A. (1994). *The PANAS-X: Manual for the positive and negative affect schedule-expanded form.* University of Iowa.

Watson, D., & Tellegen, A. (1985). Toward a consensual structure of mood. *Psychological Bulletin, 98,* 219–235.

Wayne, S. J., Hoobler, J., Marinova, S. V., & Johnson, M. M. (2008). Abusive behavior: Trickle-down effects beyond the dyad. *Academy of Management Proceedings, 1,* 1–6. https://doi.org/10.5465/ambpp.2008.33622318

Weiss, H. M., & Beal, D. J. (2005). Reflections on Affective Events Theory. In N. M. Ashkanasy, W. J. Zerbe, & C. E. J. Härtel (Eds.), *The effect of affect in organizational settings* (pp. 1–21). Emerald Group.

Weiss, H. W., & Cropanzano, R. (1996). Affective events theory: A theoretical discussion of the structure, causes and consequences of affective experiences at work. *Research in Organizational Behaviour, 18,* 1–74.

Weiss, H. M., Nicholas, J. P., & Daus, C. S. (1999). An examination of the joint effects of affective experiences and job beliefs on job satisfaction and variations in affective experiences over time. *Organizational Behaviour and Human Decision Processes, 78,* 1–24.

Weiss, H. M., Suckow, K., & Cropanzano, R. (1999). Effects of justice conditions on discrete emotions. *Journal of Applied Psychology, 84,* 786–794.

Welbourne, J. L., & Sariol, A. M. (2016). When does incivility lead to counterproductive work behavior? Roles of job involvement, task interdependence, and gender. *Journal of Occupational Health Psychology, 22,* 194–206.

Yam, K. C., Klotz, A. C., He, W., & Reynolds, S. J. (2017). From good soldiers to psychologically entitled: Examining when and why citizenship behavior leads to deviance. *Academy of Management Journal, 60,* 373–396.

Zaki, J. (2014). Empathy: A motivated account. *Psychological Bulletin, 140,* 1608–1647.

Remus Ilies and Sherry Aw

EMOTIONS AT WORK

INTRODUCTION

Since the advent of the "Affective Revolution" in the 1980s (see Barsade et al., 2003), scholars have sought to study the role of emotions and affect in organizations, and in particular the effects of emotions on human behavior and interactions. Prior to 2003, however, researchers in organizational psychology and organizational behavior tended to focus on only one or two levels of analysis (e.g., see Hochschild, 1983; Sutton & Rafaeli, 1988; Weiss & Cropanzano, 1996). This changed following publication of Ashkanasy's (2003a) multilevel theory of emotions. Ashkanasy argued that, rather than being confined to one or two levels of analysis, emotions in fact pervade the whole spectrum of human behavior and interaction in organizations, spanning all levels of organizational analysis. As such, Ashkanasy (2003a, 2003b) was the first to outline how emotion, despite its ephemeral and idiosyncratic nature, is pervasive across all levels of organizational analysis. This new holistic view contrasted with the emotion literature at the time, which tended to focus on the micro- (individual level, e.g., Weiss & Cropanzano, 1996), meso- (group level, e.g., Kelly & Barsade, 2001), and macrolevel (organizational level, e.g., de Rivera, 1992) nature of emotions, rather than recognizing that emotions span all levels of analysis.

Before discussing the Ashkanasy (2003a) model, however, it is instructive to look at a brief history of the advances in studying emotions in the field of organizational psychology. In this context, it is also appropriate to discuss the broad conceptualization of emotions including some of the discrete emotions that are commonly experienced in the workplace. In the next section, an explanation of how employees experience emotions in organizations in terms of the five levels identified by Ashkanasy is given. Finally, based on the Mayer and Salovey (1997) definition of emotional intelligence, the role of emotional intelligence is revisited in the section "Emotional Intelligence as an Integrating Factor," across the five levels of the model.

HISTORICAL BEGINNINGS

As Mastenbroek (2000) points out, the study of the role played by emotion in work settings goes back many centuries. In the 20th century, however, despite early interest (see Brief & Weiss, 2002 for a review of this work), scholars were slow to recognize that emotions play an important role in work settings. As Ashkanasy and Ashton-James (2005) put it, emotions had been "A neglected topic in I/O psychology." This began to change following publication of Hochschild's *The Managed Heart* in 1983, and especially after Ashforth and Humphrey (1995) called for reappraisal of the field. The 1990s saw a marked upsurge of interest resulting in a slew of important books (Ashkanasy, Härtel, et al., 2000; Ashkanasy et al., 2002; Fineman, 1993, 2000; Härtel et al., 2005; Lord et al., 2002; Payne & Cooper, 2001) and special issues of journals (Fisher & Ashkanasy, 2000; Fox & Spector, 2002; Weiss, 2001). A similar rise of interest was also occurring in the behavioral economics and decision-making literature (Loewenstein, 2000). This period in essence involved a shift from neglecting the role of emotions in human thought processes to one of validating the axiomatic role of emotion in organizations (cf. Mumby & Putnam, 1992). This growth of interest in studying emotions in the field of psychology fitted well with the concurrent development of theories of leadership, particularly charismatic and transformational leadership, which inherently encompass emotional components (e.g., see Shamir & Howell, 1999; Ashkanasy & Tse, 2000).

CONCEPTUALIZATION OF EMOTION

Defining Emotion. Although there are inconsistencies surrounding the definition of emotion, a widely accepted definition is the one offered by Fischer et al. (1990), who defined emotion as a "discrete, innate, functional, biosocial action and expression system" (p. 84).

Ashkanasy, Härtel, et al. (2000) subsequently defined emotions as involving endogenous and exogenous inputs to the brain, which result in internal and external manifestations of emotion. Internal manifestations of emotion include the subjective feelings experienced by the individual resulting from emotion-eliciting stimulus; and external manifestations include pupil dilation, sweating, respiration rate, facial expression, and posture. Emotions can also be considered either as a temporally varying *state* (Level 1 in the model) or as a more stable disposition or *trait* (Level 2) (Zelenski & Larsen, 2000).

Measuring Emotion.   Dasborough et al. (2008) point out that, owing to the various manifestations of emotions, methods of measuring emotions vary widely. Measures include self-report questionnaires (e.g., Positive and Negative Affect Schedule or PANAS, see Watson et al., 1988); physiological responses (e.g., heartbeat, sweat glands, blood pressure, and respiration); real-time measures of emotions (e.g., using daily diary data, see Weiss et al., 1999; or experiential sampling methods, see Beal, 2015); and retrospective reports of emotion (Schwarz & Sudman, 1994), although scholars question the validity of the latter (see Barrett, 1997; Robinson & Clore, 2002).

It is also important to raise the issue that scholars often use the term *emotion* interchangeably with *affect, mood,* and *feelings.* As Dasborough and her colleagues (2008) point out, scholars need to be cognizant of the distinctions among these terms. Frijda (1986) makes the distinction between emotion and mood by explaining that moods are more pervasive than emotions but are generally experienced with less intensity. Moreover, Watson and Tellegen (1985) differentiate emotions and moods from affect by proposing the "circumplex model of affect," where discrete emotions can be plotted around the circumplex defined in terms of orthogonal dimensions of positive and negative affect (e.g., high positive and low negative affect represents happiness). Note, however, that the circumplex model of affect has been subjected to some revisions in its representation of affect. For example, Russell and Carroll (1999) argue that the circumplex comprises two different dimensions: arousal (high vs. low) and valence (positive vs. negative)—although Ashkanasy (2003a) later argued that the models are, in fact, equivalent.

Moreover, Damasio (1999) differentiates between primary emotions, which are emotions that evolved for survival, and secondary emotions (e.g., guilt), which are responses to primary emotions, arising from complex cognitive processing involving the neocortex, and which develop progressively over the lifetime of an individual. This distinction is based on the evolutionary theory of emotion, which asserts that emotions—such as fear—activate the autonomic and endocrine systems (e.g., increase heartbeat and respiration) to deal with threats from the environment (and thus offer survival advantages).

Researchers have developed various models of emotions in the attempt to capture the nuances of human emotion. These include Lazarus and Folkman's (1984) primary and secondary appraisal model; and the dimensional approach, which consists of factor-analytic attempts to identify the minimum number of dimensions that account for the greatest amount of variance in emotion. Most dimensional models in the end comprise only two dimensions, however. These include Russell's (1980) circumplex model of affect (i.e., valence and arousal), Watson and Tellegen's (1985) model (i.e., positive affect and negative affect), and Thayer's (1989) model (i.e., energetic vs. tense arousal).

An alternative approach is categorical, where all emotions are assumed to derive from a limited set of universal and innate basic emotions, which typically include fear, anger, disgust, sadness, surprise, and happiness (Ekman, 1999). These categories are innate, reflex-like modules that involve unique behavioral, neural, and physiological patterns. Although scholars (e.g., see Panksepp, 1992) debate the number of categories and the labels for those categories, Ekman (1992) argues that the categorical model has garnered empirical evidence from cross-cultural (Russell, 1994), developmental (Ekman, 1999), neural (Panksepp, 1992), and physiological studies (Ekman, 1992) spanning four decades.

Dimensional Versus Discrete Emotions. While organizational scholars had traditionally sought to examine the role of positive and negative affectivity in the workplace, Gooty et al. (2009) argue that scholars should pay more attention to the role of discrete emotions in organizational behavior. Gibson (2008) argued that discrete emotions are reflected in "emotion scripts" (p. 263) employed by organizational members. Fisher (2019) outlined a comprehensive summary of the role played by discrete emotions in organizational settings, focusing in particular on six discrete emotion sets: (a) pride; (b) interest; (c) gratitude; (d) affection, love, admiration, respect, and compassion; (e) guilt; and (f) anger.

The case against adopting the dimensional approach was made by Lazarus (2001), who argued that the dimensional approach is too simplistic and instead proposed the *appraisal-centered approach* for emotions at work (see also Lazarus & Folkman, 1984). In particular, Lazarus suggested that there are 15 discrete emotions commonly experienced in the workplace (i.e., happiness, pride, relief, hope, love, gratitude, compassion, anger, anxiety, fright, guilt, shame, sadness, envy, and jealousy) and that there are distinct relational meanings underlying each emotion.

The fundamental premise of the appraisal approach is that emotional reactions are the result of evaluating each event in the workplace that is perceived with respect to its significance for one's well-being. For instance, Weiss et al. (1999) argue that anger results from perceptions of unfairness (e.g., lack of concern for employees from management), which communicates that the person lacks social significance (see also Pillutla & Murnighan, 1996). Moreover, people vary in which types of goals are at the top of their goal hierarchy. In this regard, Vogel et al. (1959) argue that important sources of happiness or joy in organizational settings are career advancement, income, praise, and pleasing social relationships at work. In view of this, Ashkanasy (2003a) structured his five-level model in terms of a discrete rather than a dimensional view of emotions as outlined next.

THE FIVE-LEVEL MODEL OF EMOTION IN ORGANIZATIONS

In response to an emerging impetus for organizational researchers to adopt a more multilevel approach to their research (e.g., Dansereau et al., 1999), Ashkanasy (2003a) developed a model of emotion in organizations that includes five levels of analysis: (a) within-person temporal variations, (b) between-person individual differences, (c) interpersonal interactions, (d) group, and (e) organization-wide. In the following sections, each of these levels is discussed in turn. Figure 1 presents a summary of the model. Finally, interrelationships across the five levels are discussed, including the idea that emotional intelligence plays an integrating role across the levels of the model.

450 • EMOTIONS AT WORK

Level	Descriptor	Theories	Concepts
1	Within-person 	Affective Events Theory	• State (vs. trait) affect • Frequency vs. intensity • Peaks and ends • Mood vs. emotion • Discrete emotions • Affect-driven behavior • Judgment-driven behavior • Affective events
2	Between-persons	Trait affectivity	• Positive affect • Negative affect
		Emotional intelligence	• Perceiving emotions • Assimilating emotions in thought processes • Understanding emotion • Managing emotion in self and others
3	Interpersonal interactions	Emotional labor	• Displayed vs. felt emotions • Display norms • Surface vs. deep acting
		Emotional regulation	• Intrinsic vs. extrinsic regulation • Resource dependence vs. independence • Co-regulation
4	Groups and teams 	Leadership theory Leader-member exchange Emotional contagion	• Leading with emotional labor • Group affective tone • Emotionally intelligent groups
5	Organization-wide 	Climate and culture	• Emotional climate vs. culture • Organizational policies • Shared assumptions • Healthy organizational climate

Figure 1. Emotion at five levels of organizational analysis.

Level 1: Within-Person Temporal Variations in Emotion.

Emotions and affective states are dynamic in nature. This is because emotions can quickly change from day to day and even from moment to moment. In the context of organizational research, this variability is captured in Affective Events Theory (AET; Weiss & Cropanzano, 1996). Within this theory, the authors assert that work events determine employees' emotional states moment-by-moment throughout the workday. The consequential moods and emotions then result in one of two forms of behavior: (a) *affect-driven* behaviors that result as a direct consequence of the affective response; versus (b) *judgment-driven* behaviors that derive from the formation of long-term attitudes (e.g., job satisfaction and affective commitment) in response to the affect induced by the triggering event. Moreover, AET highlights the importance of accumulation of state (as opposed to trait) effect and affective episodes (Weiss & Beal, 2005). That is, emotions tend to be determined more by the *frequency* of affective events, rather than the *intensity* of major events in the workplace (Fisher, 2000). This suggests that employees should be more capable of handling one-off affective incidents than ongoing affect-inducing hassles.

Fredrickson (2000) asserts further that the experience of affective episodes is determined respectively by "peaks and ends," namely, (a) the most intense experience (i.e., the "peak") and (b) the experience at the end of the episode (i.e., the "end"). In this case, if an employee were to experience difficulties at work, they may look back on the setbacks in a positive light if the episode concludes in a positive manner.

In Level 1, within-person variation in emotion includes state affect (i.e., momentary affective experiences), discrete emotions, and mood. Studies demonstrate that in general, positive mood is associated with positive outcomes in workplace settings, including more prosocial behaviors at work (Williams & Shiaw, 1999) and improved performance (Wright & Staw, 1999). Despite the many benefits of positive mood in organizations, for some tasks however, positive mood may inhibit performance (George & Brief, 1996a). This is because high performance often requires effort and motivation to meet challenging goals (cf. Locke & Latham, 1990)—and it is unlikely that positive mood feelings occur in such conditions. Negative mood effects are less straightforward than for positive mood (George & Brief, 1996b) and usually have stronger effects (Dasborough, 2006). For example, Rusting and DeHart (2000) point out that people in a negative mood are often motivated to change their mood to a positive one and thus they are likely to display more helping behavior and work more productively. Nonetheless, and as Pelled and Xin (1999) found, people are less satisfied with their jobs and have high turnover intentions when in negative moods. Kampf et al. (2020) showed further that emotions and moods can change dynamically in organizational settings, depending on personal and contextual factors.

In summary, AET highlights the significance of "affective events" in the workplace and the influence of such events on the emotional reactions of individuals and in turn, their attitudes and behaviors. Thus, the AET model provides a heretofore-unappreciated explanation of why people behave as they do in organizations. In addition, mood constitutes an important source of within-person variability with positive and negative mood having differential effects in the workplace depending on the task and the employee's choice of behavior.

Level 2: Between-Person Individual Differences.   This level concerns personal traits and long-lasting attitudes, such as affective commitment (i.e., an emotionally driven liking and attachment to the organization, see Meyer & Allen, 1991) and job satisfaction (i.e., an attitude of contentment involving facets of the job such as pay, conditions, and supervision, see Spector, 1997). In the following paragraphs, the focus is on two trait-like variables: (a) trait affectivity and (b) emotional intelligence.

452 • EMOTIONS AT WORK

Trait Affectivity. This refers to an individual's tendency to experience a negative or positive affective state, and thus represents a personal disposition (Watson & Tellegen, 1985). Although the effect of trait affectivity on personal outcomes in organizational settings appears in general to be small (see Fox & Spector, 2000; Staw & Barsade, 1993), in cases where an employee experiences chronic negative affect, s/he is likely to experience job burnout in the form of emotional exhaustion (Cordes & Dougherty, 1993; Maslach et al., 2000). Other research (e.g., see Cooper & Williams, 1994) shows that maintenance of positive affect in workplace settings enhances the mental well-being of employees. In another study, Leki and Wilkowski (2017) studied trait anger and neuroticism, and found that trait anger is a particularly strong predictor of employee anger in workplace settings.

Emotional Intelligence. Defined by Mayer and Salovey (1997) as an ability to perceive emotions and to use this information to facilitate thought, as well as to understand emotions and to manage emotions in self and others, emotional intelligence has received much attention in the popular press (e.g., Goleman, 1995) and in the practitioner literature (e.g., Cooper & Sawaf, 1997). Popularized through Goleman's *New York Times* best seller, *Emotional Intelligence: Why It Can Matter More Than IQ*, the construct nevertheless remains controversial (e.g., see Antonakis et al., 2009). Despite this controversy, however, meta-analytic findings (Joseph & Newman, 2010; Miao et al., 2016, 2017a, 2017b, 2017c, 2018a, 2018b; O'Boyle et al., 2011; Schlaerth et al., 2013) consistently support relationships between emotional intelligence and key organizational attitudinal, leadership, and performance outcomes. MacCann et al. (2020) found meta-analytic evidence that emotional intelligence links to academic performance. In view of the centrality of this variable, it is revisited in more detail later in this article in a separate section, proposing that it plays an integrative role across the levels of analysis.

Level 3: Interpersonal/Dyadic Interactions.
This level relates to how employees perceive and communicate emotions in dyadic interactions at work. Extending back to James (1884) and Darwin (1872/1985), expression of emotions has been central to our understanding of how humans relate in everyday life. In the context of the modern workplace, Hochschild (1983) introduced the idea of *emotional labor*, which she defines as "management of feeling to create a publicly observable facial and bodily display" (p. 7). Hochschild distinguished in particular between *surface acting* (i.e., when an individual outwardly displays the appropriate emotions required for the job without changing their internal feelings) and *deep acting* (i.e., the individual changes their internal feelings to align with organizational expectations, which produces more genuine emotional displays). Humphrey et al. (2008) subsequently extended this notion to the concept of "leading with emotional labor" (see also Ashkanasy & Humphrey, 2011; Lewis, 2000).

Based on the work of Gross (1998), Troth et al. (2018) introduced the related idea of *interpersonal emotional regulation*. In this regard, Gross defines emotional regulation as the process by which individuals influence which emotions they have (i.e., when and how they experience and express these emotions). Gross and Thompson (2007) assert that the regulation of emotions can be a conscious, effortful, and controlled process as well as being unconscious, effortless, and automatic. Examples of emotion regulation include increasing, maintaining, or decreasing emotion, which is dependent on the individual's goals. Within the Troth et al.

formulation, emotional regulation can have either an intrinsic or an extrinsic focus, and can be response dependent or independent. Individuals seek to regulate the emotion of others via emotional labor or emotional intelligence. They can also work with others in what Troth and her colleagues refer to as *emotional co-regulation*, where both parties in the dyad seek cooperatively to regulate both their own emotions and the emotions of the other member of the dyad.

Martin et al. (1998) demonstrated the ubiquitous nature of emotional labor in retail and service organizations. In this regard, service providers are expected to display positive emotional expressions (e.g., retail workers should always smile at customers) while employees in enforcement industries are expected to display negative emotions (e.g., debt collectors should express anger toward consumers). These organizations embody strongly sanctioned norms regarding the appropriate display of emotion (Sutton & Rafaeli, 1988) that are embedded in the organizational culture, recruitment strategies, job descriptions, employee socialization, and policies relating to rewards (Fineman, 2001; Humphrey, 2000; Ozcelik, 2013).

Owing to these norms, employees who engage in surface acting are likely to experience detrimental health effects. Research (e.g., see Kammeyer-Mueller et al., 2013) shows that the experience of emotional dissonance is much greater for surface rather than deep acting. This is because individuals who engage in such emotional labor tend to experience greater emotional exhaustion (Morris & Feldman, 1996) and can develop various physical illnesses, including hypertension and cancer (Grandey, 2000; Mann, 2003; Schaubroeck & Jones, 2000).

Level 4: Groups and Teams. At Level 4, Ashkanasy (2003a) addresses emotions in groups and teams, which Schermerhorn et al. (2001) define as "a collection of two or more people who work with one another regularly to achieve common goals" (p. 174), including leadership (i.e., as a team property). In the workplace, consideration of the team level of analysis embraces concepts such as team cohesiveness, group affective tone, and emotional contagion. Moreover, emotions displayed within group situations play a vital role for group effectiveness and satisfaction (George & King, 2007).

According to De Dreu et al. (2001), the emotional states of group members interact to affect all members of the group, albeit in different ways. Van Kleef et al. (2017, p. 156) note in this regard that "Groups are natural breeding grounds for emotions." Similarly, Kelly and Barsade (2001) argue that individual-level affective experiences combine to form the affective composition of the group through implicit and explicit group convergence processes (i.e., emotional contagion, entrainment, and modelling). The resulting emotional exchanges in turn present implications for group cohesion and performance (De Jong et al., 2014). In this instance, emotion acts as an essential element in the formation and maintenance of groups with the expression of positive emotions strengthening social ties in organizational workgroups (Lawler, 1992) and negative emotions tending to weaken these ties (De Jong et al., 2014).

In addition to the role of moods and feelings of team members in shaping group cohesion, there is also evidence that emotions play a role in shaping leaders' relationships with group members. That is, organizational leaders are largely responsible for communicating, expressing, and managing emotions of team members (see Graen & Uhl-Bien, 1995) via "emotional contagion," which Hatfield et al. (1994) define as a process whereby one individual's emotions converge with emotions expressed by others via mimicking of facial expressions, body language, and tone of voice. Consistent with this idea, Barsade (2002, p. 664) found that emotions "ripple" though groups via contagion. Sy et al. (2005) found similarly that leaders' positive mood states led to a more positive affective tone in the group. Tee et al. (2013) subsequently found that emotional contagion also works in the opposite direction, where leaders can "catch" members' emotional states, which in turn affects the leader's behavior.

In line with these findings, George (2000) argues that leaders need to regulate their own emotions if they are to influence effectively the emotions of their team members. In addition, Ashkanasy and Humphrey (2011) argue that leaders need to practice "leading with emotional labor" (p. 363). This involves leaders engaging in appropriate emotional expression (via genuine expressions, deep acting, or surface acting) to model the emotions suited to the situation, which is then picked up by group members (Dasborough et al., 2009), and ultimately back to the leaders (cf. Tee et al., 2013).

The foregoing discussion on the need for leaders to manage the emotions of group members effectively raises the idea that a critical element of good leadership is the leader's emotional intelligence. In support of this idea, Pescosolido (2002) found that effective leaders are more adept at dealing with workplace events involving strong emotions and consequently develop greater team harmony and cohesion within the team. In this discussion of emotional intelligence in the context of groups, it is possible for group members to be more emotionally astute, which results in an "emotionally intelligent group" (Druskat & Wolff, 2001).

In summary, Level 4 represents a "meso-level" variable (cf. House et al., 1995), in that it bridges the individual (Levels 1 and 2) and interpersonal (Level 3) processes, together with aspects of an organization's culture and climate (Level 5).

Level 5: Organization-Wide. As opposed to the lower levels of Ashkanasy's (2003a) multilevel model, where managers are able to recognize employees' felt emotions (e.g., whether employees feel confident about reaching their work goals), organizational leaders are less able to ascertain members' emotions across a whole organization. Instead, they must rely on the nebulous concept of "emotional climate," which De Rivera (1992) defines as "an objective group phenomenon that can be palpably sensed—as when one enters a party or city and feels an attitude of gaiety or depression, openness or fear" (p. 197; for more on this concept, see Ashkanasy, Wilderom, et al., 2000). In this regard, Ashkanasy et al. (2020) define affective climate in terms of the collective mood of organizational members toward their work, coworkers, management, and the organization as a whole.

Ashkanasy and Härtel (2014) also differentiate organizational-level emotional climate from "emotional culture," where organizational members' beliefs, values, norms, symbols, actions, language patterns, and shared assumptions play a determinant role (cf. Schein, 1985). In fact, even the broader conceptualizations of organizational climate and culture rely on emotional underpinnings (Ashkanasy & Härtel, 2014; Beyer & Nino, 2001; Fineman, 2001; Hochschild, 1983; Van Maan & Kunda, 1989). In support of this idea, Schein (1985) states that the assumptions embedded in the organizational culture are associated with deeply felt emotions by organizational members. De Rivera (1992) states that the objective markers of emotional climate in organizations are determined more so in the social structures and patterns of behavior that are manifested in the organization (i.e., felt emotion) rather than observing the emotional expressions of individuals (i.e., displayed emotion). This is because individuals are more sensitive to these cues, which then shape the attitudes and behaviors of organizational members.

Another point in respect to the organizational level (at Level 5) is the role of organizational policies in creating "healthy organizations." Cooper and Williams (1994) assert that a healthy organization is one that reduces negative emotional events for its employees, such as enforcing more reasonable emotional labor demands in the workplace. In addition, management places a high priority on implementing policies that contribute toward employee well-being while also focusing on the attainment of organizational goals. That is, there is a strong connection between organizational policies and the emotional well-being of employees (Härtel et al., 2002). In addition, Ashkanasy and Härtel (2014) emphasize the necessity for a *healthy emotional climate*, typified by the creation and maintenance of positive emotions throughout the entire organization.

In summary, organizational climate and organizational culture include emotional elements at their core. As such, it is the responsibility of managers to foster a positive emotional climate, which is required for the creation of healthy work environments and the promotion of employee well-being.

INTEGRATING THE FIVE LEVELS

An important aspect of the Ashkanasy (2003a) five-level model is that it emphasizes cross-level effects (e.g., see Dasborough et al., 2009). To illustrate this, Figure 2 presents the five-level model as a set of concentric circles similar to Schein's (1985) "onion" model of culture, where each layer encompasses the lower-level layers. Thus, organizational members' temporally varying emotional states exist at the core of the model, which is enclosed in the members' emotional properties, and so on until the outer layer, which represents culture/climate across the whole organization.

The depiction of the model presented in Figure 2 also illustrates how processes at each level cross over to other levels. For example, leadership, which essentially represents a group-level phenomenon (Level 4), crosses over to individual differences such as emotional intelligence (Level 2) and emotional labor (Level 3). As Schein (1985) argues, leaders act to shape organizational culture and climate (Level 5) and as sources of affective events (Level 1). In this regard, Dasborough and her colleagues point out, "What goes around, comes around" (p. 571). Thus, what a leader does at one level is ultimately reflected in variability at the other four levels (see also Ashkanasy & Humphrey, 2014). For example, members of a group where a leader is perceived to be unfair are likely to experience negative emotions, resulting in poor team performance ratings and a loss of top management's confidence in the leader. Emotional intelligence (at Level 2) can also act as an integrating factor across the levels, discussed in the section "Emotional Intelligence as an Integrating Factor." Similar arguments can be made to establish the full set of interconnections represented in Figure 2.

Emotional Intelligence as an Integrating Factor. In this section, the concept of emotional intelligence is revisited. This variable was initially proposed as a Level 2 factor in the Ashkanasy (2003a) model, but it may also be seen as a key integrating factor across all levels of the model. This is consistent with the view expressed by Jordan et al. (2002), who propose

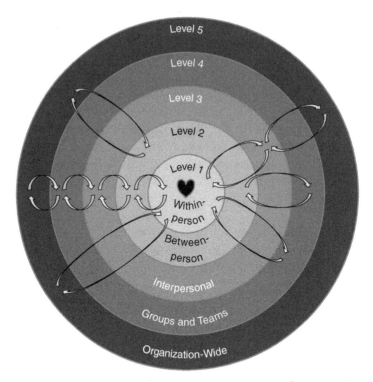

Figure 2. The five-level model of emotions in organizations (the onion diagram).

that, compared with their high emotional intelligence compatriots, employees who are low in emotional intelligence are more likely to experience negative emotional reactions to job insecurity and adopt negative emotion-focused coping strategies (e.g., withdrawal, self-blame).

While controversy exists regarding the conceptualization of emotional intelligence (see Antonakis et al., 2009; Landy, 2005), the evidence that emotions are necessary for developing social relationships (and distinct from the idea of "social intelligence", Gardner, 2011) seems incontrovertible. Nonetheless, it is important to clarify the construct.

In this regard, Ashkanasy and Daus (2005) identified three "streams" or approaches to emotional intelligence. Stream 1 is based on the original "four-branch model" of emotional intelligence set out by Mayer and Salovey (1997). The four "branches" (or abilities) are: (a) recognition of emotions in both self and others (e.g., from other people's nonverbal expressions); (b) use of emotions in facilitating cognition; (c) understanding emotions (i.e., qualities, causes, and consequences of emotions); and (d) managing emotions in self and others (e.g., ability to create and maintain positive affective states in oneself; Mayer & Salovey, 1997).

In the Stream 1 model, these abilities are measured using performance-based IQ-style tests (e.g., Mayer-Salovey-Caruso Emotional Intelligence Test [MSCEIT]: Mayer et al., 2002; the Geneva Emotional Competence Test [GECo]: Schlegel & Mortillaro, 2018). Stream 2 approaches use the same Mayer-Salovey (1997) definition of emotional intelligence (i.e., ability-based approaches), but measure the construct using self- or peer-report measures (e.g., Jordan et al., 2002; Schutte et al., 1998; Wong & Law, 2002).

Conversely, Stream 3 models are based on so-called "mixed" models of emotional intelligence that view the construct as comprising a concoction of noncognitive traits, behavioral dispositions, and motivational variables that are linked to successful coping with environmental demands (Petrides & Furnham, 2000). Such approaches measure emotional intelligence using self-report questionnaires using a mixture of personality-type items and behavioral preferences. This approach is not endorsed by researchers such as Daus and Ashkanasy (2003), however, because it does not appear to differ markedly from traditional personality models. While the Stream 3 models do show up well in meta-analytic studies (MacCann et al., 2020; Miao et al., 2016, 2017a, 2017b, 2017c, 2018a, 2018b), this may be largely attributable to this overlap. Nonetheless, and as Ashkanasy and Daus (2005) acknowledge, these models may be useful in organizational development interventions (i.e., as a measure of emotional competency rather than a purely emotional intelligence measure).

The central argument here is that emotional intelligence has an impact within and across each level of the Ashkanasy (2003a) model. For instance, at the within-person level, emotional intelligence contributes to how employees appraise events (Jordan et al., 2002) and how emotions are regulated (Siemer et al., 2007). Moreover, the ability to regulate and to accumulate positive affect can lead to positive attitudes (e.g., job satisfaction and affective commitment) and improved work performance (see Wright et al., 1993; Wright & Cropanzano, 1998). At the between-person level, individual differences in the management of negative emotions (i.e., trait affectivity) can predict burnout over the long term (e.g., Bakker & Schaufeli, 2000). At the interpersonal level, the ability to recognize emotions accurately in dyadic interactions is essential to effective communication (Mehu et al., 2012; Mortillaro et al., 2013). At the group level, emotionally intelligent leaders engage in emotional labor to model the appropriate display of emotions to team members, who subsequently adopt the emotions through emotional contagion (Dasborough et al., 2009; Tee et al., 2013). In addition, and as Côté et al. (2010) demonstrate, emotional intelligence contributes to effective leadership in the context of work groups. Ashkanasy and Tse (2000) note further that emotionally intelligent leaders form positive and constructive relationships with their subordinates and motivate the team to perform above expectations.

These findings highlight the importance of emotional intelligence for employees and leaders in workplace settings across all levels of the Ashkanasy (2003a) model—which also has practical implications for managers. That is, managers should be encouraged to participate in emotional intelligence workshops that build their ability to read emotional and affective signs in their employees. For instance, if managers were to become more sensitive to the real attitudes of employees in relation to the work they carry out, they can more readily implement remedial actions to rectify any issues associated with the employee's work performance. In addition, managers could build their ability to "read" the signs of a negative organizational climate, which would in turn enable them to develop interventions to address the sources of the negative emotional climate.

CONCLUSIONS

The study of emotions in organizations entered the mainstream of organizational psychology following the publication of Hochschild's (1983) *The Managed Heart*. This interest has led to the understanding that emotions are manifested internally (i.e., subjective feelings experienced by an individual) and externally (i.e., facial expressions, body language). Moreover, scholars have devised various models relating to the conceptualization of emotions, which include the dimensional approach (e.g., emotions are represented by the dimensions of valence and arousal; Russell & Carroll, 1999) and the categorical approach (i.e., emotions can be categorized into a set of universal and innate basic emotions). It is arguable in particular that emotions are pervasive in the workplace and that emotional intelligence is an important concept that links across the levels. For instance, organizational members need to engage in emotional regulation techniques (e.g., emotional labor) to be successful in their work, particularly in the service industries. Finally, the cross-level effects of emotions and especially emotional intelligence have potential to lead to far-reaching and significant consequences relating to the overall effectiveness of the organization and the well-being of organizational members.

FURTHER READING

Ashkanasy, N. M., & Dorris, A. D. (2017). Emotion in the workplace. *Annual Review of Organizational Psychology and Organizational Behavior, 4,* 67–90.
Yang, L.-Q., Cropanzano, R. S., Martinez-Tur, V., & Daus, C. A. (Eds.). (2020). *The Cambridge handbook of workplace affect.* Cambridge University Press.
Zietsma, C., Toubiana, M., Voronov, M., & Roberts, A. (2019). *Emotions in organization theory.* Cambridge University Press.

REFERENCES

Antonakis, J., Ashkanasy, N. M., & Dasborough, M. T. (2009). Does leadership need emotional intelligence? *The Leadership Quarterly, 20,* 247–261.
Ashforth, B. E., & Humphrey, R. H. (1995). Emotion in the workplace: A reappraisal. *Human Relations, 48,* 97–125.
Ashkanasy, N. M. (2003a). Emotions in organizations: A multilevel perspective. In F. Dansereau & F. J. Yammarino (Eds.), *Research in multi-level issues* (Vol. 2, pp. 9–54). Elsevier Science.
Ashkanasy, N. M. (2003b). Emotions at multiple levels: An integration. In F. Dansereau & F. J. Yammarino (Eds.), *Research in multi-level issues* (Vol. 2, pp. 71–81). Elsevier Science.
Ashkanasy, N. M., & Ashton-James, C. E. (2005). Emotion in organizations: A neglected topic in I/O psychology, but with a bright future. In G. P. Hodgkinson & J. K. Ford (Eds.), *International review of industrial and organizational psychology* (Vol. 20, pp. 221–268). Wiley.
Ashkanasy, N. M., & Daus, C. S. (2005). Rumors of the death of emotional intelligence in organizational behavior are vastly exaggerated. *Journal of Organizational Behavior, 26,* 441–452.
Ashkanasy, N. M., & Härtel, C. E. J. (2014). Emotional climate and culture: The good, the bad, and the ugly. In B. Schneider & K. Barbera (Eds.), *The Oxford handbook of organizational culture and climate* (pp. 136–152). Oxford University Press.
Ashkanasy, N. M., & Humphrey, R. H. (2011). A multi-level view of leadership and emotions: Leading with emotional labor. In A. Bryman, D. Collinson, K. Grint, B. Jackson, & M. Uhl-Bien (Eds.), *Sage handbook of leadership* (pp. 363–377). SAGE.
Ashkanasy, N. M., & Humphrey, R. H. (2014). Leadership and emotion: A multi-level perspective. In D. V. Day (Ed.), *The Oxford handbook of leadership and organizations* (pp. 780–801). Oxford University Press.

Ashkanasy, N. M., & Tse, B. (2000). Transformational leadership as management of emotion. In N. M. Ashkanasy, C. E. J. Härtel, & W. J. Zerbe (Eds.), *Emotions in the workplace: Research, theory, and practice* (pp. 221–235). Quorum Books.

Ashkanasy, N. M., Härtel, C. E. J., & Bialkowski, A. (2020). Affective climate and organization-level emotion management. In L.-Q. Yang, R. S. Cropanzano, V. Martinez-Tur, & C. A. Daus (Eds.), *The Cambridge handbook of workplace affect* (pp. 375–385). Cambridge University Press.

Ashkanasy, N. M., Härtel, C. E. J., & Zerbe, W. J. (2000). Emotions in the workplace: Research, theory, and practice. In N. M. Ashkanasy, C. E. J. Härtel, & W. J. Zerbe (Eds.), *Emotions in the workplace: Research, theory, and practice* (pp. 3–18). Quorum Books.

Ashkanasy, N. M., Wilderom, C. P. M., & Peterson, M. F. (2000). Introduction. In N. M. Ashkanasy, C. Wilderom, & M. Peterson (Eds.), *Handbook of organizational culture and climate* (pp. 1–18). SAGE.

Ashkanasy, N. M., Zerbe, W. J., & Härtel, C. E. J. (Eds.). (2002). *Managing emotions in the workplace.* M. E. Sharpe.

Bakker, A. B., & Schaufeli, W. B. (2000). Burnout contagion processes among teachers. *Journal of Applied Social Psychology, 30,* 2289–2308.

Barrett, L. F. (1997). The relationships among momentary emotion experiences, personality descriptions, and retrospective ratings of emotion. *Personality and Social Psychology Bulletin, 23,* 1100–1110.

Barsade, S. G. (2002). The ripple effect: Emotional contagion and its influence on group behavior. *Administrative Science Quarterly, 47,* 644–675.

Barsade, S. G., Brief, A. P., & Spataro, S. E. (2003). The affective revolution in organizational behavior: The emergence of a paradigm. In J. Greenberg (Ed.), *Organizational behavior: A management challenge* (pp. 3–52). Lawrence Erlbaum Associates.

Beal, D. J. (2015). ESM 2.0: State of the art and future potential of experience sampling methods in organizational research. *Annual Review of Organizational Psychology and Organizational Behavior, 2,* 383–407.

Beyer, J., & Nino, D. (2001). Culture as a source, expression, and reinforcer of emotions in organizations. In R. L. Payne & C. L. Cooper (Eds.), *Emotions at work: Theory, research, and applications for management* (pp. 173–197). Wiley.

Brief, A. P., & Weiss, H. M. (2002). Organizational behavior: Affect in the workplace. *Annual Review of Psychology, 53,* 279–307.

Cooper, C. L., & Williams, S. (1994). *Creating healthy work organizations.* Wiley.

Cooper, R. K., & Sawaf, A. (1997). *Executive EQ: Emotional intelligence in business.* Orion Business.

Cordes, C. L., & Dougherty, T. W. (1993). A review and an integration of research on job burnout. *Academy of Management Review, 18,* 621–656.

Côté, S., Lopes, P. N., Salovey, P., & Miners, C. T. H. (2010). Emotional intelligence and leadership emergence in small groups. *The Leadership Quarterly, 21,* 496–508.

Damasio, A. R. (1999). *The feeling of what happens: Body and emotion in the making of consciousness.* Harcourt Brace.

Dansereau, F., Yammarino, F. J., & Kohles, J. C. (1999). Multiple levels of analysis from a longitudinal perspective: Some implications for theory building. *Academy of Management Review, 24,* 346–357.

Darwin, C. R. (1872/1985). *The expression of emotions in man and animals.* University of Chicago Press.

Dasborough, M. T. (2006). Cognitive asymmetry in employee emotional reactions to leadership behaviors. *The Leadership Quarterly, 17,* 163–178.

Dasborough, M. T., Ashkanasy, N. M., Tee, E. Y., & Herman, H. M. (2009). What goes around comes around: How meso-level negative emotional contagion can ultimately determine organizational attitudes toward leaders. *The Leadership Quarterly, 20,* 571–585.

Dasborough, M. T., Sinclair, M., Russell-Bennett, R., & Tombs, A. (2008). Measuring emotion: Methodological issues and alternatives. In N. M. Ashkanasy & C. L. Cooper (Eds.), *Research companion to emotion in organizations* (pp. 197–208). Edward Elgar.

Daus, C. S., & Ashkanasy, N. M. (2003). Will the real emotional intelligence please stand up? On deconstructing the emotional intelligence "debate." *The Industrial–Organizational Psychologist, 41*(2), 69–72.

Daus, C. S., Dasborough, M. T., Jordan, P. J., & Ashkanasy, N. M. (2012). We are all mad in Wonderland: An organizational culture framework for emotions and emotional intelligence research. In N. M. Ashkanasy, C. E. J. Härtel, & W. J. Zerbe (Eds.), *Research on emotion in organizations* (Vol. 8, pp. 375–399). Emerald Publishing.

De Dreu, C. K. W., West, M. A., Fischer, A. H., & MacCurtain, S. (2001). In R. L. Payne & C. L. Cooper (Eds.), *Emotions at work: Theory, research, and applications for management* (pp. 199–217). Wiley.

De Jong, J. P., Curşeu, P. L., & Leenders, R. T. A. (2014). When do bad apples not spoil the barrel? Negative relationships in teams, team performance, and buffering mechanisms. *Journal of Applied Psychology, 99*, 514–522.

De Rivera, J. (1992). Emotional climate: Social structure and emotional dynamics. In K. T. Strongman (Ed.), *International review of studies on emotion* (Vol. 2, pp. 197–218). Wiley.

Druskat, V. U., & Wolff, S. B. (2001). Group emotional intelligence and its influence on group effectiveness. In C. Cherness & D. Goleman (Eds.), *The emotionally intelligent workplace: How to select for, measure, and improve emotional intelligence in individuals, groups and organizations* (pp. 132–155). Wiley.

Ekman, P. (1992). An argument for basic emotions. *Cognition & Emotion, 6*, 169–200.

Ekman, P. (1999). Basic emotions. In T. Dalgleish & T. Power (Eds.), *Handbook of cognition and emotion* (pp. 45–60). Wiley.

Fineman, S. (Ed.). (1993). *Emotion in organizations*. SAGE.

Fineman, S. (Ed.). (2000). *Emotion in organizations* (2nd ed.). SAGE.

Fineman, S. (2001). Emotions and organizational control. In R. L. Payne & C. L. Cooper (Eds.), *Emotions at work: Theory, research, and applications for management* (pp. 219–240). Wiley.

Fischer, K. W., Shaver, P. R., & Carnochan, P. (1990). How emotions develop and how they organize development. *Cognition and Emotion, 4*, 81–127.

Fisher, C. D. (2019). Emotions in organizations. In M. A. Hitt (Ed.), *Oxford research encyclopedia of business and management* (pp. 1–40). Oxford University Press. https://oxfordre.com/business/view/10.1093/acrefore/9780190224851.001.0001/acref-9780190224851-e-160

Fisher, C. D. (2000). Affect and performance: A within-person analysis. In L. N. Dosier & J. B. Keys (Eds.), *Academy of Management best paper proceedings* (CD-ROM). Academy of Management.

Fisher, C. D., & Ashkanasy, N. M. (2000). The emerging role of emotions in work life: An introduction. *Journal of Organizational Behavior, 21*, 123–129.

Fox, S., & Spector, P. (2000). Relations of emotional intelligence, practical intelligence, general intelligence, and trait affectivity with interview outcomes: It's not all just "G." *Journal of Organizational Behavior, 21*, 203–220.

Fox, S., & Spector, P. (2002). Emotions in the workplace: The neglected side of organizational life introduction. *Human Resource Management Review, 12*, 167–171.

Fredrickson, B. L. (2000). Extracting meaning from past affective experiences: The importance of peaks, ends, and specific emotions. *Cognition & Emotion, 14*, 577–606.

Frijda, N. H. (1986). *The emotions*. Cambridge University Press.

Gardner, H. (2011). *Frames of mind: The theory of multiple intelligences* (3rd ed.). Basic Books.

George, J. M. (2000). Emotions and leadership: The role of emotional intelligence. *Human Relations, 53*, 1027–1055.

George, J. M., & Brief, A. P. (1996a). Motivational agendas in the workplace: The effects of feelings on focus of attention and work motivation. *Research in Organizational Behavior, 18*, 75–109.

George, J. M., & Brief, A. P. (1996b). Negative affectivity and coping with job loss. *Academy of Management Review, 21*, 7–9.

George, J. M., & King, E. B. (2007). Potential pitfalls of affect convergence in teams: Functions and dysfunctions of group affective tone. In E. A. Mannix, M. A. Neale, & C. P. Anderson (Eds.), *Research on managing groups and teams* (Vol. 10, pp. 97–124). Emerald Publishing.

Gibson, D. E. (2008). Emotion scripts in organizations: A multi-level model. In N. M. Ashkanasy & C. L. Cooper (Eds.), *Research companion to emotion in organizations* (pp. 263–283). Edward Elgar.

Goleman, D. (1995). *Emotional intelligence: Why it can matter more than IQ.* Bantam.

Gooty, J., Gavin, M., & Ashkanasy, N. M. (2009). Emotions research in OB: The challenges that lie ahead. *Journal of Organizational Behavior, 30,* 833–838.

Graen, G. B., & Uhl-Bien, M. (1995). Development of leader-member exchange (LMX) theory of leadership over 25 years: Applying a multi-level multi-domain perspective. *The Leadership Quarterly, 6,* 219–247.

Grandey, A. (2000). Emotion regulation in the workplace: A new way to conceptualize emotional labor. *Journal of Occupational Health Psychology, 5,* 95–110.

Gross, J. J. (1998). The emerging field of emotion regulation: An integrative review. *Review of General Psychology, 2,* 271–299.

Gross, J. J., & Thompson, R. A. (2007). Emotion regulation: Conceptual foundations. In J. J. Gross (Ed.), *Handbook of emotion regulation* (pp. 3–24). Guilford Press.

Härtel, C. E. J., Hsu, A. C. F., & Boyle, M. V. (2002). A conceptual examination of the causal sequences of emotional labor, emotional dissonance and emotional exhaustion: The argument for the role of contextual and provider characteristics. In N. M. Ashkanasy, W. J. Zerbe, & C. E. J. Härtel (Eds.), *Managing emotions in the workplace.* M. E. Sharpe.

Härtel, C. E. J., Zerbe, W. J., & Ashkanasy, N. M. (Eds.). (2005). *Emotions in organizational behavior.* Lawrence Erlbaum Associates.

Hatfield, E., Cacioppo, J. T., & Rapson, R. L. (1994). *Emotional contagion.* Cambridge University Press.

Hochschild, A. R. (1983). *The managed heart: Commercialization of human feeling.* University of California Press.

House, R., Rousseau, D. M., & Thomas-Hunt, M. (1995). The meso paradigm: A framework for the integration of micro and macro organizational behavior. In B. Staw (Ed.), *Research in organizational behavior* (Vol. 17, pp. 71–114). JAI Press.

Humphrey, R. H. (2000). The importance of job characteristics to emotional displays. In N. M. Ashkanasy, C. E. J. Härtel, & W. J. Zerbe (Eds.), *Emotions in the workplace: Theory, research, and practice* (pp. 236–249). Quorum Books.

Humphrey, R. H., Pollack, J. M., & Hawver, T. H. (2008). Leading with emotional labor. *Journal of Managerial Psychology, 23,* 151–168.

James, W. (1884). What is an emotion? *Mind, 9,* 188–205.

Jordan, P. J., Ashkanasy, N. M., & Härtel, C. E. J. (2002). Emotional intelligence as a moderator of emotional and behavioral reactions to job insecurity. *Academy of Management Review, 27,* 361–372.

Jordan, P. J., Ashkanasy, N. M., Härtel, C. E. J., & Hooper, G. S. (2002). Workgroup emotional intelligence: Scale development and relationship to team process effectiveness and goal focus. *Human Resource Management Review, 12,* 173–194.

Joseph, D. L., & Newman, D. A. (2010). Emotional intelligence: An integrative meta-analysis and cascading model. *Journal of Applied Psychology, 95,* 54–78.

Kammeyer-Mueller, J. D., Rubenstein, A. L., Long, D. M., Odio, M. A., Buckman, B. R., Zhang, Y., & Halvorsen-Ganepola, M. D. (2013). A meta-analytic structural model of dispositional affectivity and emotional labor. *Personnel Psychology, 66,* 47–90.

Kampf, P. H., Hernández, A., & González-Romá, V. (2020). Antecedents and consequences of workplace mood variability over time: A weekly study over a three-month period. *Journal of Occupational and Organizational Psychology.* Advance online publication. https://doi.org/10.1111/joop.12329

Kelly, J. R., & Barsade, S. G. (2001). Mood and emotions in small groups and work teams. *Organizational Behavior and Human Decision Processes, 86,* 99–130.

Landy, F. J. (2005). Some historical and scientific issues related to research on emotional intelligence. *Journal of Organizational Behavior, 26,* 411–424.

Lawler, E. J. (1992). Affective attachment to nested groups: A choice-process theory. *American Sociological Review, 57,* 327–339.

Lazarus, R. S. (1991). *Emotion and adaptation.* Oxford University Press.

Lazarus, R. S. (2001). Relational meaning and discrete emotions. In K. R. Scherer, A. Schorr, & T. Johnstone (Eds.), *Appraisal processes in emotion* (pp. 37–67). Oxford University Press.

Lazarus, R. S., & Folkman, S. (1984). *Stress, appraisal, and coping.* Springer.

Leki, E. F., & Wilkowski, B. M. (2017). Trait anger, neuroticism, and the hostile reaction to provocation: Examining the hierarchical organization of affective traits in context. *Motivation & Emotion, 41,* 713–729.

Lewis, K. M. (2000). When leaders display emotion: How followers respond to negative emotional expression of male and female leaders. *Journal of Organizational Behavior, 21,* 221–234.

Locke, E. A., & Latham, G. P. (1990). *A theory of goal setting and task performance.* Prentice Hall.

Loewenstein, G. (2000). Emotions in economic theory and economic behavior. *American Economic Review, 90,* 426–432.

Lord, R. G., Klimoski, R. J., & Kanfer, R. (Eds.). (2002). *Emotions in the workplace: Understanding the structure and role of emotions in organizational behavior.* Pfeiffer.

MacCann, C., Jiang, Y., Brown, L. E., Double, K. S., Bucich, M., & Minbashian, A. (2020). Emotional intelligence predicts academic performance: A meta-analysis. *Psychological Bulletin, 146,* 150–186.

Mann, S. (2003). *Hiding what we feel, faking what we don't: Understanding the role of your emotions at work.* Pavilion Books.

Martin, J., Knopoff, K., & Beckman, C. (1998). An alternative to bureaucratic impersonality and emotional labor: Bounded emotionality at The Body Shop. *Administrative Science Quarterly, 43,* 429–469.

Maslach, C., Schaufeli, W. B., & Leiter, M. P. (2000). Job burnout. *Annual Review of Psychology, 52,* 397–422.

Mastenbroek, W. (2000). *Organizational behavior as emotion management.* In N. M. Ashkanasy, C. E. J. Härtel, & W. J. Zerbe (Eds.), *Emotions in the workplace: Research, theory, and practice* (pp. 19–35). Quorum Books.

Mayer, J., & Salovey, P. (1997). What is emotional intelligence? In P. Salovey & D. Sluyter (Eds.), *Emotional development and emotional intelligence: Implications for educators* (pp. 3–31). Basic Books.

Mayer, J. D., Salovey, P., & Caruso, D. (2002). *Mayer-Salovey Caruso Emotional Intelligence Test (MSCEIT): User's manual.* Multi-Health Systems.

Mehu, M., Mortillaro, M., Bänziger, T., & Scherer, K. R. (2012). Reliable facial muscle activation enhances recognizability and credibility of emotional expression. *Emotion, 12,* 701–715.

Meyer, J. P., & Allen, N. J. (1991). A three-component conceptualization of organizational commitment. *Human Resource Management Review, 1,* 61–98.

Miao, C., Humphrey, R. H., & Qian, S. (2016). Leader emotional intelligence and subordinate job satisfaction: A meta-analysis of main, mediator, and moderator effects. *Personality and Individual Differences, 102,* 13–24.

Miao, C., Humphrey, R. H., & Qian, S. (2017a). Are the emotionally intelligent good citizens or counterproductive? A meta-analysis of emotional intelligence and its relationships with organizational citizenship behavior and counterproductive work behavior. *Personality and Individual Differences, 116,* 144–156.

Miao, C., Humphrey, R. H., & Qian, S. (2017b). A meta-analysis of emotional intelligence and work attitudes. *Journal of Occupational and Organizational Psychology, 90,* 177–202.

Miao, C., Humphrey, R. H., & Qian, S. (2017c). A meta-analysis of emotional intelligence effects on job satisfaction mediated by job resources, and a test of moderators. *Personality and Individual Differences, 116,* 281–288.

Miao, C., Humphrey, R. H., & Qian, S. (2018a). A cross-cultural meta-analysis of how leader emotional intelligence influences subordinate task performance and organizational citizenship behavior. *Journal of World Business, 53*, 463–474.

Miao, C., Humphrey, R. H., & Qian, S. (2018b). Emotional intelligence and authentic leadership: A meta-analysis. *Leadership & Organization Development Journal, 39*, 679–690.

Morris, J. A., & Feldman, D. C. (1996). The dimensions, antecedents, and consequences of emotional labor. *Academy of Management Review, 21*, 986–1010.

Mortillaro, M., Mehu, M., & Scherer, K. R. (2013). The evolutionary origin of multimodal synchronization and emotional expression. In E. Altenmüller, S. Schmidt, & E. Zimmermann (Eds.), *Evolution of emotional communication: From sounds in nonhuman mammals to speech and music in man* (pp. 3–25). Oxford University Press.

Mumby, D. K., & Putnam, L. A. (1992). The politics of emotion: A feminist reading of bounded rationality. *Academy of Management Review, 17*, 465–486.

O'Boyle, E. H., Humphrey, R. H., Pollack, J. M., Hawver, T. H., & Story, P. A. (2011). The relation between emotional intelligence and job performance: A meta-analysis. *Journal of Organizational Behavior, 32*, 788–818.

Ozcelik, H. (2013). An empirical analysis of surface acting in intra-organizational relationships. *Journal of Organizational Behavior, 34*, 291–309.

Panksepp, J. (1992). A critical role for "affective neuroscience" in resolving what is basic about basic emotions. *Psychological Review, 99*, 554–560.

Payne R. L., & Cooper, C. (Eds.). (2001). *Emotions at work: Theory, research, and applications for management*. Wiley.

Pelled, L. H., & Xin, K. R. (1999). Down and out: An investigation of the relationship between mood and employee withdrawal behavior. *Journal of Management, 25*, 875–895.

Pescosolido, A. T. (2002). Emergent leaders as managers of group emotion. *The Leadership Quarterly, 13*, 583–599.

Petrides, K., & Furnham, A. (2000). On the dimensional structure of emotional intelligence. *Personality and Individual Differences, 29*, 313–320.

Pillutla, M. M., & Murnighan, J. K. (1996). Unfairness, anger, and spite: Emotional rejections of ultimatum offers. *Organizational Behavior and Human Decision Processes, 68*, 208–224.

Robinson, M. D., & Clore, G. L. (2002). Belief and feeling: Evidence for an accessibility model of emotional self-report. *Psychological Bulletin, 128*, 934–960.

Russell, J. A. (1980). A circumplex model of affect. *Journal of Personality and Social Psychology, 39*, 1161.

Russell, J. A. (1994). Is there universal recognition of emotion from facial expression? A review of the cross-cultural studies. *Psychological Bulletin, 115*, 102–141.

Russell, J. A., & Carroll, J. M. (1999). On the bipolarity of positive and negative affect. *Psychological Bulletin, 125*, 3–30.

Rusting, C. L., & DeHart, T. (2000). Retrieving positive memories to regulate negative mood: Consequences for mood-congruent memory. *Journal of Personality and Social Psychology, 78*, 737–752.

Schaubroeck, J., & Jones, J. R. (2000). Antecedents of workplace emotional labor dimensions and moderators of their effects on physical symptoms. *Journal of Organizational Behavior, 21*, 163–183.

Schein, E. H. (1985). *Organizational culture and leadership*. Jossey-Bass.

Schermerhorn, R. R., Jr., Hunt, J. G., & Osborn, R. N. (2001). *Organizational behavior* (7th ed.). Wiley.

Schlaerth, A., Ensari, N., & Christian, J. (2013). A meta-analytical review of the relationship between emotional intelligence and leaders' constructive conflict management. *Group Processes & Intergroup Relations, 16*, 126–136.

Schlegel, K., & Mortillaro, M. (2018). The Geneva Emotional Competence Test (GECo): An ability measure of workplace emotional intelligence. *Journal of Applied Psychology, 104*, 559–580.

Schutte, N. S., Malouff, J. M., Hall, L. E., Haggerty, D. J., Cooper, J. T., Golden, C. J., & Dornheim, L. (1998). Development and validation of a measure of emotional intelligence. *Personality and Individual Differences*, 25, 167–177.

Schwarz, N., & Sudman, S. (1994). *Autobiographical memory and the validity of retrospective reports*. Springer.

Shamir, B., & Howell, J. (1999). Organizational and contextual influences on the emergence and effectiveness of charismatic leadership. *The Leadership Quarterly*, 10, 257–284.

Siemer, M., Mauss, I., & Gross, J. J. (2007). Same situation–Different emotions: How appraisals shape our emotions. *Emotion*, 7, 592–600.

Spector, P. E. (1997). *Job satisfaction: Application, assessment, causes and consequences*. SAGE.

Staw, B. M., & Barsade, S. G. (1993). Affect and managerial performance: A test of the sadder-but-wiser vs. happier-and-smarter hypotheses. *Administrative Science Quarterly*, 38, 304–328.

Sutton, R. I., & Rafaeli, A. (1988). Untangling the relationship between displayed emotions and organizational sales: The case of convenience stores. *Academy of Management Journal*, 31, 461–487.

Sy, T., Côté, S., & Saavedra, R. (2005). The contagious leader: Impact of the leader's mood on the mood of group members, group affective tone, and group processes. *Journal of Applied Psychology*, 90, 295–305.

Tee, E. Y. J., Ashkanasy, N. M., & Paulsen, N. (2013). The influence of follower mood on leader mood and task performance: An affective, follower-centric perspective of leadership. *The Leadership Quarterly*, 24, 496–515.

Thayer, R. E. (1989). *The biopsychology of mood and arousal*. Oxford University Press.

Troth, A. C., Lawrence, S. A., Jordan, P. J., & Ashkanasy, N. M. (2018). Interpersonal emotion regulation in the workplace: A conceptual and operational review and future research agenda. *International Journal of Management Reviews*, 20, 523–543.

Van Kleef, G. A., Heerdink, M. W., & Homan, A. C. (2017). Emotional influence in groups: The dynamic nexus of affect, cognition, and behavior. *Current Opinion in Psychology*, 17, 156–161.

Van Maanen, J., & Kunda, G. (1989). "Real feelings": Emotional expression and organizational culture. *Research in Organizational Behavior*, 11, 43–103.

Vogel, W., Raymond, S., & Lazarus, R. S. (1959). Intrinsic motivation and psychological stress. *Journal of Abnormal and Social Psychology*, 58, 225–233.

Watson, D., & Tellegen, A. (1985). Toward a consensual structure of mood. *Psychological Bulletin*, 98, 219–235.

Watson, D., Clark, L. A., & Tellegen, A. (1988). Development and validation of brief measures of positive and negative affect: The PANAS scales. *Journal of Personality and Social Psychology*, 54, 1063–1070.

Weiss, H. M. (2001). Introductory comments [Special Issue on Emotions in the Workplace]. *Organizational Behavior and Human Decision Processes*, 86, 1–2.

Weiss, H. M., & Beal, D. J. (2005). Reflections on affective events theory. In N. M. Ashkanasy, W. J. Zerbe, & C. E. J. Härtel (Eds.), *Research on emotion in organizations* (Vol. 1, pp. 1–21). Elsevier Science.

Weiss, H. M., & Cropanzano, R. (1996). Affective events theory: A theoretical discussion of the structure, causes and consequences of affective experiences at work. *Research in Organizational Behavior*, 18, 1–74.

Weiss, H. M., Nicholas, J. P., & Daus, C. S. (1999). An examination of the joint effects of affective experiences and job beliefs on job satisfaction and variations in affective experiences over time. *Organizational Behavior and Human Decision Processes*, 78, 1–24.

Weiss, H. M., Suckow, K., & Cropanzano, R. (1999). Effects of justice conditions on discrete emotions. *Journal of Applied Psychology*, 84, 786–794.

Williams, S., & Shiaw, W. T. (1999). Mood and organizational citizenship behavior: The effects of positive affect on employee organizational citizenship behavior intentions. *Journal of Psychology*, 133, 656–668.

Wong, C. S., & Law, K. S. (2002). The effects of leader and follower emotional intelligence on performance and attitude: An exploratory study. *The Leadership Quarterly*, 13, 243–274.

Wright, T. A., & Cropanzano, R. (1998). Emotional exhaustion as a predictor of job performance and voluntary turnover. *Journal of Applied Psychology, 83*, 486–493.

Wright, T. A., & Staw, B. M. (1999). Affect and favorable work outcomes: Two longitudinal tests of the happy-productive worker thesis. *Journal of Organizational Behavior, 20*, 1–13.

Wright, T. A., Bonett, D. G., & Sweeney, D. A. (1993). Mental health and work performance: Results of a longitudinal field study. *Journal of Occupational and Organizational Psychology, 66*, 277–284.

Zelenski, J. M., & Larsen, R. J. (2000). The distribution of basic emotions in everyday life: A state and trait perspective from experience sampling data. *Journal of Research in Personality, 34*, 178–197.

Neal M. Ashkanasy and Agata Bialkowski

PERSON–ENVIRONMENT FIT FROM AN ORGANIZATIONAL PSYCHOLOGY PERSPECTIVE

INTRODUCTION

Individuals' fit or misfit with their environment is one of the most fundamental psychological experiences in organizational life. Those who experience fit with the environment usually have high levels of job satisfaction, organizational commitment, overall performance, motivation, well-being, and desire to remain in such an environment (Kristof-Brown et al., 2005). Those who experience misfit with the environment tend to feel uncomfortable, stressful, and exhausted and desire to escape or change the situation (Chi et al., 2020; Tong et al., 2015; Wheeler et al., 2005). These experiences are examples of person–environment (PE) fit and misfit. PE fit is broadly defined as the degree of congruence or match between a person and the environment (e.g., Edwards et al., 1998; Holland, 1997; Kristof, 1996; Schneider, 1987). The concept of PE fit is complex and multidimensional. For example, one often says "fit with something" or "someone" because the two are similar. One also says "fit" because what one has compensates for what another does not have. The former type of fit is called supplementary fit, and the latter type of fit is called complementary fit (Kristof, 1996). As another example, a person can fit with the characteristics of an organization or of a job. The former is called person–organization (PO) fit, and the latter is called person–job (PJ) fit (Cable & DeRue, 2002; Edwards, 1991; Kristof, 1996).

This article introduces the concept of PE fit by explaining its theoretical foundations, its various conceptualizations, and their relationships. It then reviews theoretical and empirical work on the outcomes of PE fit, the dynamic perspective of PE fit, how individuals address PE misfit, and the role of organizational practices on PE fit. Table 1 provides the list of acronyms used in this article.

THEORETICAL FOUNDATIONS

The basic idea of PE fit has a long history. For example, it can be traced back to the mid-20th century when Lewin (1951) proposed field theory. This theory states that human behavior is a function of the person and the environment. Beginning with this perspective, researchers integrated the factors of both persons and environments and argued that human behavior results from the interaction between that person and an organization. This is called the

Table 1. List of Acronyms

Acronym	Meaning
PE fit	Person–environment fit
ASA theory	Attraction–selection–attrition theory
TWA	Theory of work adjustment
PV fit	Person–vocation fit
PO fit	Person–organization fit
PG fit	Person–group fit
PP fit	Person–person fit
PJ fit	Person–job fit
DA fit	Demands–abilities fit
NS fit	Needs–supplies fit
OCB	Organizational citizenship behavior
PS fit	Person–supervisor fit
POQ	Perceived over-qualification
HR	Human resources

Note: The list is in the order of appearance.

interactionist theory of behavior (Chatman, 1989; Muchinsky & Monahan, 1987), which asserts that neither personal characteristics nor the situation alone adequately explains the variance in behavioral and attitudinal variables. Instead, the interaction between personal and situational variables accounts for the greatest variance (Turban & Keon, 1993). Another theoretical framework that is closely related to PE fit, especially PO fit, is the attraction–selection–attrition (ASA) theory (Schneider, 1987). The ASA framework states that people are attracted to organizations with similar characteristics, are selected if they fit the organization's characteristics, and leave the organization if their personality and values no longer fit the organization's characteristics (Schneider, 1987; Schneider et al., 2001).

Other theoretical frameworks are relevant to individual careers and vocations. Holland's vocational fit theory (1985) is closely related to a person's fit with their vocation or occupation (person–vocation fit or PV fit). The vocational fit theory states that individuals prefer and choose vocations that are similar to their personalities (Holland, 1985). The theory of work adjustment (TWA) is the classic career theory that captures a more temporal and dynamic nature of fitting into a work environment. The TWA emphasizes the process through which individuals attempt to obtain and maintain fit with their environments. The fit fluctuates over time due to changes in the individual and the environment (Dawis et al., 1968). Individuals change themselves or their environments to achieve fit, and environments or jobs may change over time, resulting in changes in fit between the individual and the environment (Bradley et al., 2002).

CONCEPTUALIZATIONS OF PERSON–ENVIRONMENT FIT

Different Forms of PE Fit.   There are different forms of PE fit in terms of the relationship between the characteristics of the person and the environment. PE fit can be conceptualized as complementary and supplementary (Muchinsky & Monahan, 1987). Supplementary fit exists when the characteristics of a person and an environment are similar to each other (Cable & Edwards, 2004). In other words, supplementary fit is based on similarity. On the contrary, complementary fit exists when the characteristics of a person and an environment provide what the other wants (Cable & Edwards, 2004). Complementary fit can be achieved when an individual's characteristics meet an environment's demands (i.e., demands–abilities fit, DA fit) or when the characteristics of an environment fulfill an individual's needs (i.e., needs–supplies fit, NS fit; Kristof, 1996; Muchinsky & Monahan, 1987).

These different forms of PE fit are also related to how PE misfit is understood. PE misfit can be understood simply as the lack of fit, but the nature of PE misfit differs according to the form of PE fit. For supplementary fit, misfit is conceptualized as dissimilarity between the characteristics of the person and the environment. For complementary fit, including DA fit and NS fit, PE misfit can be conceptualized as the excess or deficiency of the person or the environment against the other (Edwards, 2008a).

Different Dimensions of PE Fit.   Individuals have various characteristics, ranging from values and personality to knowledge and skills. Individuals are also surrounded by the different aspects or dimensions of the environment simultaneously, such as a vocation, an organization, a group/team, a person (e.g., a supervisor), and a job. Therefore, PE fit can occur with different targets, in terms of what aspects of the environment correspond with the individual's characteristics or the target into which the person fits. Person–vocation (PV) fit occurs when there is a match between individual characteristics (e.g., values, personality, knowledge, and skills) and the characteristics of one's vocational environment (Kristof, 1996; Ostroff, 2012). PO fit occurs when there is a match between individual characteristics (e.g., values and personality) and the organization's characteristics (e.g., organizational culture; Kristof, 1996). Person–group (PG) fit occurs when the characteristics of a person are similar to or compatible with those of the group (Kristof, 1996; Seong et al., 2015). Person–person (PP) fit occurs when there is a match between two individuals (e.g., supervisors and subordinates; Muchinsky & Monahan, 1987). Lastly, PJ fit occurs when an individual's knowledge, skills, and abilities (KSAs) meet the job's requirements (i.e., DA fit) or when the individual's needs are satisfied by the supplies from the job (i.e., NS fit; Kristof-Brown et al., 2005).

Objective and Subjective PE Fit.   Theoretically, the characteristics of the person and environment and the resultant PE fit can be conceptualized objectively as actual characteristics. In this case, the objective level of PE fit is determined by comparing the actual characteristics of the person with those of the environment. The person, environment, and PE fit can also be conceptualized subjectively as a focal person's perceptions of these characteristics. In this case, subjective PE fit is the judgment that a person fits well in their environment (Cable & DeRue, 2002). These objective and subjective characteristics are theorized as being causally related (Ostroff, 2012). The objective characteristics of a person and environment will each influence the subjective perceptions of the person and environment, respectively. The PE fit, which is determined objectively, will influence the subjective experience of PE fit. Furthermore, the subjective experience of PE fit is influenced by not only objective PE fit but also subjective perceptions of the person and environment. Reflecting these relationships, Edwards and colleagues (2006) theorized that three ways of experiencing PE fit, namely *atomistic* (perceptions of the person and environment as separate entities), *molecular* (the perceived discrepancy between the person and environment), and *molar* (the perceived similarity, match, or fit between the person and environment), sequentially occur as a subjective experience of fit. However, their empirical results showed that the relationships among the approaches deviate from the theoretical logic.

Direct and Indirect Assessments of PE Fit. The more empirical question about PE fit is how to measure it. PE fit can be assessed directly as a subjective experience of whether individuals perceive fit with the environment. PE fit can also be assessed indirectly by comparing the characteristics of the person and the environment. Direct assessment of the subjective experience of PE fit is rather simple, often using a Likert scale that asks the degree to which a person feels fit. A low level of PE fit measured in this way can be interpreted as PE misfit. An indirect assessment of PE fit that can be applied at both the objective and subjective levels is more complex because several patterns exist in how a person and their environment are compared. For example, when the characteristics of the person and environment are assessed by degree (e.g., high, middle, or low), PE fit can occur in which the characteristics of the person and the environment are both high, both middle, or both low. PE misfit can be understood as a situation in which the person's characteristics exceed those of the environment (e.g., overqualification in the job; Erdogan & Bauer, 2020), the characteristics of the environment being less than what the person needs (e.g., supplies from the environment do not fulfill the person's needs), the environment's characteristics exceeding what the person needs (e.g., abundant environmental resources compared with the person's needs), and the person's characteristics being less than what the environment requires (e.g., the lack of skills to perform a job).

CONSEQUENCES OF PERSON–ENVIRONMENT FIT

How PE Fit Influences Individual Outcomes. Theoretically, not only the degree of PE fit but also the characteristics of the person and environment can influence individual outcomes. These influences can be best understood using the following mathematical equation, usually called the polynomial regression equation (Edwards & Parry, 1993; Van Vianen, 2018).

$$Z = b_0 + b_1 P + b_2 E + b_3 P^2 + b_4 PE + b_5 E^2$$

In this equation, P refers to the person, E refers to the environment, and Z refers to the individual outcome being predicted. The regression coefficients (denoted as $b_1, b_2, b_3, b_4,$ and b_5) represent distinct effects from P and E, the quadratic for each (P^2 and E^2), and their interaction $(P \times E)$. The direct effects on individual outcomes by the person and the environment are represented by b_1P and b_2E. The influences of various natures of PE fit and misfit on individual outcomes, including the effect of fit—where the characteristics of the person and the environment are both high, both middle, or both low—are understood by the higher-order terms b_4PE, b_3P^2, and b_5E^2. This way of capturing the effects of the person's and environment's characteristics and of PE fit can be applied both at the objective and the subjective levels using indirect measures.

The three-dimensional surface plot in Figure 1 illustrates a theoretically idealized fit effect for the person (P) and the environment (E) on the outcome (Z) (Edwards & Cable, 2009; Van Vianen, 2018). The congruence line in the figure represents optimal fit when P value and E value are the same (both high and both low). As the figure shows, the value of Z is the highest and the surface should be flat along the congruence line. The incongruence line in the figure represents misfit when (a) P value is high and E value is low and (b) P value is low and E value is high. As the figure shows, the surface should be curved along the incongruence line and the value of Z decreases when E value is lower than P value (the right side of the figure) or when E value is higher than P value (the left side of the figure).

Van Vianen (2018) reviewed studies on PJ fit and PO fit that used polynomial regression with surface plot analyses and concluded that the relationships among the person, the environment, PE fit, and individual outcomes are more complex than the symmetrical

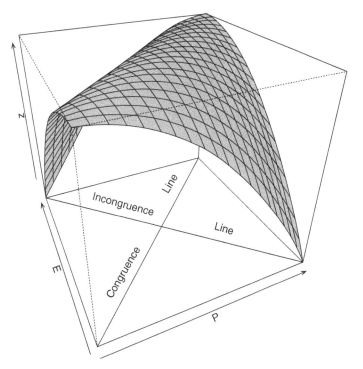

Figure 1. Surface plot representing the fit–outcome relationship.
Note: P refers to the person, E refers to the environment, and Z refers to the individual outcome.
Source: The data used for this figure is based on Edwards (2008b).

relationship that PE fit models propose. First, not only the PE fit but also the person and the environment can independently influence individual outcomes, with the effects of organizational attributes being greater than those of personal attributes. Second, although the effects of PE fit occur at all levels (e.g., high–high, middle–middle, low–low), PE fit at higher levels of an attribute generally produces better outcomes than PE fit at lower levels. Third, the two types of PE misfit—deficiency and excess—both produce negative consequences, with the negative influence of deficiency being stronger than that of excess. Excess can be as beneficial as fit, depending on the fit attributes.

The Relationship Between Subjective and Objective PE Fit.   Subjective PE fit is a more proximal predictor of various individual outcomes (Andela & van der Doef, 2019; Kristof-Brown et al., 2005). Additionally, subjective PE fit is considered to mediate the relationship between objective PE fit and individual outcomes (Judge & Cable, 1997; Kristof, 1996; Yu, 2009). This is because individual attitudes and behaviors are more influenced by what the individual perceives than by the objective characteristics of a person and the environment (Caplan, 1987). Empirical studies have shown that subjective PE fit or PE fit with direct measures is a stronger predictor of certain outcomes, such as job attitudes, than objective PE fit or PE fit with indirect measures is (Judge & Cable, 1997; Leung & Chaturvedi, 2011), although common method variance might have an influence when a direct measure is used (Kristof-Brown & Guay, 2011).

Outcomes of Different Dimensions of PE Fit.   Several meta-analytic studies have summarized the effects of different dimensions of PE fit on various employee outcomes (Arthur et al., 2006; Hoffman & Woehr, 2006; Kristof-Brown et al., 2005; Oh et al., 2014; Verquer et al., 2003). PO fit and PJ fit have been investigated most frequently (Kristof-Brown et al., 2005). Research shows that PO fit and PJ fit are likely to have positive effects on individuals' attitudes, well-being, and work-related performance. For example, PO fit and PJ fit increase commitment and satisfaction and decrease stress (Andela & van der Doef, 2019; Cable & DeRue, 2002; Chen et al., 2016; Edwards et al., 1998; Gabriel et al., 2014; Gregory et al., 2010; Greguras & Diefendorff, 2009; Saks & Ashforth, 1997). PO fit and PJ fit also have positive influences on various performance constructs such as overall job performance, task performance, organizational citizenship behavior (OCB), and innovative work behavior (Afsar et al., 2015, Farzaneh et al., 2014; Vogel & Feldman, 2009). Hamstra and colleagues (2019) found that the positive effect of employees' perceived PO fit on in-role performance evaluations was stronger when the supervisor's perceived PO fit was high rather than low. Further, PO fit and PJ fit are negatively related to turnover intention and actual turnover (Andela & van der Doef, 2019; Boon & Biron, 2016; Liu et al., 2010).

Scholars have shown that a high level of PV fit increases employees' job performance and their subjective career success, and it also decreases employees' turnover intention (Nye et al., 2012, 2017; Vogel & Feldman, 2009). The empirical findings are less clear regarding its relationship with job satisfaction. Some studies have shown that PV fit positively influences job satisfaction (Feij et al., 1999; Swaney & Prediger, 1985), while early meta-analytic studies have suggested that PV fit has a weak relationship with satisfaction (Tranberg et al., 1993; Tsabari et al., 2005). Consistent with these findings, Wille and colleagues (2014) demonstrated that although individuals' interest–occupation congruence remained relatively stable across a 15-year time interval, their congruence was not associated with job satisfaction.

Research on PG fit has shown that PG fit is related to a variety of positive outcomes such as job performance, individual performance, and turnover intention (Chuang et al., 2016; Kristof-Brown et al., 2005; Oh et al., 2014). Seong and Kristof-Brown (2012) examined three types of PG fit—value-based, personality-based, and abilities-based—and found that PG value fit is significantly related to commitment to one's team, PG personality fit is significantly related to voice behaviors, and PG ability fit is significantly related to knowledge sharing. Seong and Choi (2014) examined PG goal fit and PG ability fit, and found that only PG goal fit had a significant effect on group performance. Seong et al. (2015) found that overall PG fit perception was significantly associated with group performance. Similarly, De Cooman and colleagues (2016) found that PG fit is significantly related to team effectiveness, and they examined the mediating role of team cohesion.

Van Vianen and colleagues (2011) found that employees' PS fit perceptions are both directly and indirectly (through commitment to the supervisor) related to organizational commitment. Astakhova (2016) compared the effects of PS fit between the United States and Japan and found that perceived PS fit was directly and indirectly (mediated by perceived PO fit) related to affective organizational commitment in Japan but only indirectly related in the United States. Additionally, research has shown that PS fit is negatively related to work-related strain and turnover intention, and positively related to job satisfaction (Klaic et al., 2018; Tak, 2011). Marstand and colleagues (2017) found that when a leader's fulfillment of employees' work values (i.e., the complementary PS fit) is high, the leader-member exchange quality tends to be higher, which can increase task performance and OCB. Xu and colleagues (2019) demonstrated that when supervisor–employee congruence in proactive personality is high, employees tend to perceive high levels of psychological safety, which facilitates their engagement in voice behavior.

The effects of PE fit differ by national culture. Oh et al. (2014) meta-analytically examined the relationships among PJ fit, PO fit, PG fit, and PS fit and organizational commitment, job satisfaction, intent to quit, and job performance in East Asia, Europe, and North America. Their findings suggest that the effects of rational fit (PO fit and PJ fit) are stronger in North America and, to a lesser extent, Europe than in East Asia. Contrarily, the effects of relational fit (PG fit and PS fit) are stronger in East Asia than in North America. Their findings highlight that in collectivist and high-power-distance (vs. individualist and low-power-distance) cultures, relational (vs. rational) fit is more salient in influencing employees' perceptions about their work environments. The results are less clear concerning job performance.

Simultaneous Effects of Multiple Dimensions of PE Fit.

Given that individuals are simultaneously nested within multiple aspects of an environment (Chuang et al., 2016; Edwards & Billsberry, 2010; Jansen & Kristof-Brown, 2006), researchers have examined the simultaneous effects of multiple dimensions of PE fit, both theoretically and empirically. Theoretically, different dimensions of PE fit will influence individual outcomes in both additive and interactive ways. Different dimensions of PE fit have additive effects on outcomes, but the relative importance of a particular dimension of PE fit may differ according to the outcomes (Chuang et al., 2016; Jansen & Kristof-Brown, 2006). Different levels of PE fit influence outcomes interactively through buffering or spillover effects (Chuang et al., 2016; Jansen & Kristof-Brown, 2006).

Empirical evidence of this "nested" or "holistic" view of PE fit is being accumulated. Using an experimental policy-capturing study, Kristof-Brown and colleagues (2002) found that the perceptions of PO, PJ, and PG fit have not only separate effects on work satisfaction but also interactive effects. Chuang et al. (2016) found that PJ, PO, PG, and PS fit perceptions are related, but each of them can be perceived as distinct. Specifically, the relative importance of each fit perception differed strongly by outcome variables, such that PG fit explained the greatest amount of variance in in-role behavior, PJ fit explained the greatest amount of variance in job satisfaction, PO fit explained the greatest amount of variance in turnover intention, and PG fit explained the greatest amount of variance in OCB.

Lauver and Kristof-Brown (2001) showed that PO fit has a more significant influence on turnover intentions than PJ fit does, but there is no difference in their relative influence on job-focused satisfaction. Contrarily, Tak (2011) found that PJ fit is associated more strongly with turnover intention than PO or PS fit is. Choi and Yoo (2005) also showed that PJ fit has a stronger correlation with turnover intention than PO fit does. Andela and van der Doef (2019) found that PJ fit and PO fit are more strongly associated with work-related outcomes (i.e., burnout, job satisfaction, and turnover intention) than PG fit and PS fit are.

Using a sample of participants in a 12-week internship program, Resick and colleagues (2007) found that interns' PO fit was more strongly associated with satisfaction when they experienced low NS fit, whereas PO fit was less critical for satisfaction when the interns' NS fit was high. In addition, PO fit was more strongly linked to job-choice intentions for interns who experienced a low level of DA fit. Chi et al. (2020) focused on the context of newcomer adjustment and found that newcomers' PG fit alleviated the positive effects of initial NS misfit on subsequent actual turnover. In addition, newcomers' fit within a specific interpersonal relationship (i.e., person–mentor fit) buffered the negative effects of initial DA misfit on subsequent task performance.

To summarize, there is substantial evidence showing that different dimensions of PE fit have substantial benefits for individuals, teams, and organizations. These findings also suggest that each dimension of PE fit not only has a relatively different effect on the outcomes, but also drives the outcomes nested with other types of PE fit in interactive ways.

THE DYNAMIC PERSPECTIVE OF PE FIT

While past research on PE fit tended to study PE fit in a rather static way (DeRue & Morgeson, 2007; Jansen & Shipp, 2013), PE fit is an inherently dynamic phenomenon because organizational life is more volatile than stable, and characteristics of the person and work environment change (Caplan, 1983; Jansen & Kristof-Brown, 2006; Sekiguchi, 2004b; Shipp & Jansen, 2011). In response to this view, an emerging body of research has focused on within-person changes in PE fit and has examined how and why fit changes over time. DeRue and Morgeson (2007) examined how PE fit dynamically changes over time in a team context and found that value-based person–team fit is usually stable over time, whereas the overall mean of PJ fit decreases over time. Jansen and Shipp (2013) proposed a temporal theory of fit and highlighted the effect of psychological time on fit perceptions. They argued that individuals' current fit cannot be viewed in isolation but that past fit and anticipated fit must also be considered. They proposed that individuals' past fit and anticipated fit influence their current fit, which ultimately affects work-related outcomes. Consistent with these ideas, an interview-based study conducted by Jansen and Shipp (2019) demonstrated that individuals' current fit depends on what they recollect and forecast. On the other hand, Vleugels and colleagues (2018) discussed that the fluctuations of fit perceptions should be explained by what is going on at that moment, rather than by prior changes in PE fit perceptions. Another study, by Boon and Biron (2016), showed that PO fit and PJ fit influence each other over time, supporting the idea that different types of PE fit can affect each other over time.

Prior research has identified factors that increase or decrease PE fit. Bayl-Smith and Griffin (2018) found that career initiative activities and job change negotiation behaviors lead to an increase in individuals' DA fit over time but only when one's work style fit is high. Sylva et al. (2019) found that increases in one's career initiative over time are related to increases in one's perceived DA fit over time. Lu and colleagues (2014) found that work engagement is positively related to changes in DA fit through changes in physical job crafting and is positively related to changes in NS fit through changes in relational job crafting.

A growing number of studies have examined how changes in PE fit relate to changes in work-related affect and behavior (e.g., job satisfaction, organizational commitment, and job performance). Gabriel et al. (2014) found that changes in perceived PJ fit are positively related to changes in job satisfaction. Kim et al. (2020) also showed that change in PJ fit predicts increases in affective organizational commitment and job satisfaction. Other studies have suggested that changes in PE fit may have relatively small temporal impacts on these desirable outcomes. Vleugels et al. (2018) showed that changes in PE fit have no temporal impacts on work-related affect and work performance but are only momentarily associated with changes in them. Similarly, Ghetta and colleagues (2020) found that changes in PE fit are related to neither simultaneous change in job satisfaction nor subsequent job satisfaction.

To conclude, there is accumulating evidence that PE fit changes over time, such that individuals' current fit can be influenced by past fit, anticipated fit, or what is going on at that moment. These findings also suggest that work adjustment behaviors (e.g., career initiative activities) potentially contribute to the change in PE fit. Consequently, changes in PE fit have shown to influence the changes in individuals' attitudes and behaviors.

RESPONSES TO PERSON–ENVIRONMENT MISFIT

Because PE fit is inherently dynamic, individuals experience misfit in some aspects of their working environment when changes occur to the environment or the individuals themselves. Indeed, scholars have demonstrated that misfit is prevalent in most work situations and could happen at any point in one's career (Wheeler et al., 2005, 2007). Contrary to PE fit, PE misfit is often presumed to be an uncomfortable and stressful experience with uniformly negative outcomes (e.g., Edwards & Shipp, 2007; Sacco & Schmitt, 2005). Therefore, when individuals perceive PE misfit, they may be motivated to resolve it (Kristof-Brown & Billsberry, 2013).

Because the research on PE fit has shown that good fit is negatively related to turnover intention, it is assumed that employees who perceive misfit are expected to leave the organization (Schneider, 1987; Wheeler et al., 2005). However, a growing body of research has challenged this perspective by demonstrating that misfit may not always result in turnover (Kristof-Brown et al., 2005). Wheeler et al. (2005) suggested that employees who experience misfit would leave an organization only if other promising work opportunities exist. A poor labor market and unacceptable outside alternatives often hinder employees' voluntary turnover. The empirical study by Wheeler et al. (2007) indicated that although misfit would decrease employees' job satisfaction, it might not result in increased turnover intention if employees perceive few available job alternatives.

To further elaborate on the individuals' responses to misfit, Follmer and colleagues (2018) conducted a qualitative study and identified three strategies with which individuals respond to PE misfit. The resolution approach (leaving or making adjustments to oneself or the environment) is aimed at fixing the problem stemming from the misfit, while the relief approach (surface-level behavior change, buffering misfit with fit, or framing misfit as short-term) is aimed at reducing the pain of misfit and making the person more comfortable. These two strategies represent the positive end of a response continuum. When these strategies fail, the resignation approach (distancing oneself from work or taking pride in one's misfit), which represents the negative end of the response continuum, tends to be employed.

Several studies have examined the proactive responses to misfit. Simmering et al. (2003) found that when employees with high conscientiousness perceived autonomy misfit between them and their organization, they were more likely to engage in developmental activities, which can provide them with increased autonomy at work and subsequently lead to better fit. Devloo and colleagues (2011) showed that managerial employees who hold an incremental implicit person theory (i.e., the belief that individuals' characteristics and competences are malleable) exhibit proactive feedback-seeking behavior when they observe incongruent demands and abilities. Vogel et al. (2016) found that employees who engage in job crafting (i.e., making changes in their tasks or relationships at work) and employees who have leisure activities (e.g., exercise, community involvement, and personal hobbies) can maintain higher levels of engagement despite the perceptions of misfit in the workplace.

One type of misfit that has been paid much attention is over-qualification, which refers to the situation where an individual's qualifications (e.g., education and experience) exceed the job requirements (Erdogan & Bauer, 2020). On the one hand, previous research has shown that perceived over-qualification (POQ) is associated with negative outcomes including lower job satisfaction, organizational commitment, and psychological well-being (Alfes et al., 2016; Fine & Nevo, 2008; Harari et al., 2017; Johnson & Johnson, 1996, 2000); lower extra-role behaviors (Erdogan et al., 2020); counterproductive work behaviors (Liu et al., 2015; Luksyte et al., 2011); and withdrawal behaviors, such as active job search behavior and voluntary turnover behavior (Erdogan & Bauer, 2009; Maynard & Parfyonova, 2013; Wu & Chi, 2020). On the other hand, scholars demonstrated that POQ can lead to positive outcomes. For example, POQ has been shown to be positively related to supervisor-related performance (Erdogan & Bauer, 2009; Fine & Nevo, 2008). In addition, POQ is positively associated with employees' proactive behaviors (Zhang et al., 2016), and can influence OCB and creativity under certain circumstances (Hu et al., 2015; Lin et al., 2017; Luksyte et al., 2020; Luksyte & Spitzmueller, 2016).

To summarize, although misfit is often regarded as a stressful experience and associated with negative outcomes, individuals' responses to misfit are complicated. Misfit does not completely cause employees to quit the job, especially under uncertain conditions of the labor market. In order to cope with the stressful situation resulting from the misfit, employees tend to take action to adapt to the environment.

THE ROLE OF ORGANIZATIONAL PRACTICES ON PERSON–ENVIRONMENT FIT

Organizational practices such as human resources (HR) practices play important roles in determining the degree of PE fit, both objectively and subjectively. For example, during organizational entry, recruitment and selection practices are usually aimed at creating a good fit between a person and the organization or job (Chuang & Sackett, 2005; Dineen & Noe, 2009; Sekiguchi, 2004a). These practices interact with the individual's job-search behavior and job-choice decisions based on fit perceptions (Cable & Judge, 1994, 1996; Yu, 2014). After organizational entry, organizational socialization tactics and training and development practices help newcomers to develop PE fit with various aspects of the organization (Cable & Parsons, 2001; Chao et al., 1994; Cooper-Thomas et al., 2004; Kim et al., 2005; Riordan et al., 2001; Sekiguchi, 2006; Yu & Davis, 2016).

Recruitment. PE fit is critical within the recruitment context from the companies' perspective, as well as within the job-search context from the job seekers' perspective (Chapman et al., 2005; Uggerslev et al., 2012). Most research on fit in the recruitment context focuses on PO fit and, to a lesser extent, PJ fit. Carless (2005) found that perceived PO and PJ fit influenced organizational attractiveness at different stages of the hiring process and that organizational attractiveness mediated the relationship between PO and PJ fit and intention to accept a job offer. In experimental studies using a Web-based recruitment context, Dineen and colleagues (2002) found that objective PO fit was positively related to organizational attractiveness, and Dineen and Noe (2009) found that applicant pool PO and DA fit became greater when fit information was customized. Roberson et al. (2005) found that detailed recruitment messages led to enhanced PO fit perception, which, in turn, increased intention to apply to the organization.

Yu (2014) showed that experiencing PO fit as values congruence during the recruitment process perpetuates certain expectations about one's future work environments and employer relationships, which in turn have a positive impact on organizational attraction. Furthermore, Swider et al. (2015) found significant initial differentiation in PO fit perceptions across recruiting organizations at the start of the recruitment process and that the extent of differentiation in these PO fit perceptions increased throughout the recruitment process, predicting future job choice. Vanderstukken and colleagues (2019) showed that job seekers' perceived PO fit was influenced by not only the focal organization's characteristics but also industry characteristics. In the internship context, Sekiguchi et al. (2020) found that NS fit mediated the relationship between the characteristics of the internship and organizational attractiveness.

Selection. One of the major purposes of employee selection is to find the best person to fit various aspects of the organization. In this regard, PJ fit—especially the match between job demands and an individual's abilities, or DA fit—and PO fit are the most salient in the selection context, from employers' perspective (Anderson & Ostroff, 1997; Kristof-Brown, 2000; Werbel & Gililland, 1999). Adkins et al. (1994) found that work value congruence between applicants and recruiters was significantly related to recruiters' judgments of the applicant's fit and general employability. Cable and Judge (1997) further demonstrated a strong positive relationship between recruiters' perceptions of the applicant's PO fit and hiring. Higgins and Judge (2004) showed that interviewers assess applicant fit and that job applicants use influence tactics to influence the interviewers' applicant-fit perceptions. A meta-analytic study found a moderate to strong relationship between PJ fit and PO fit and intention to hire (Kristof-Brown et al., 2005).

Several studies examined the roles of PO fit and PJ fit in the selection process simultaneously. Sekiguchi (2007) proposed that the characteristics of the positions influence the relative importance of PJ and PO fit in selection, such that PJ fit will be more important when the organization emphasizes transactional psychological contracts and general human capital, whereas PO fit will be more important when the organization emphasizes relational psychological contracts and firm-specific human capital. Chuang and Sackett (2005) found that PJ fit was more important during first interviews, whereas PO fit became more important in subsequent interviews. Nolan and colleagues (2016) found that practitioners consider PO fit more important when they expect to work closely with new hires and PJ fit more important when they do not expect to work closely with them. Sekiguchi and Huber (2011) found that when decision makers weigh PO fit and PJ fit in assessing job candidates, they weighed PO fit more heavily for permanent positions but weighed PJ fit more heavily for hiring fixed-term contracts and knowledge-intensive positions.

Socialization and Other Practices.   Research has shown that individuals' personal values become more similar to those of their organizations during the socialization process (Chatman, 1991; Kim et al., 2005; Ostroff & Rothausen, 1997). Chatman (1991) found that objective PO fit, assessed after hiring, was correlated with socialization activities, which in turn predicted positive change in PO fit. Saks and Ashforth (1997) proposed that the differences between fit perceptions formed before organizational entry and those made after joining an organization are primarily attributable to the socialization process. Cooper-Thomas et al. (2004) found that within several months after organizational entry, individuals' perceived PO fit became more similar to their objective PO fit. Cable and Parsons (2001) found that organizations using institutionalized socialization tactics (sequential, fixed, serial, and PE fit investiture tactics) improved newcomers' levels of perceived PO fit. Likewise, Riordan et al. (2001) found that institutionalized socialization tactics were positively related to post-entry perceptions of PJ fit. A meta-analysis conducted by Saks et al. (2007) found that institutionalized socialization tactics positively influenced perceived PO fit and PJ fit.

Employees can also play an important role in the socialization process by seeking information and networking with insiders to increase PE fit (Ashford & Black, 1996; Bauer & Green, 1998; Griffin et al., 2000; Morrison, 1993; Wanberg & Kammeyer-Mueller, 2000). Kim et al. (2005) demonstrated that the relationship between socialization tactics and perceived fit was influenced by the degree to which employees took a proactive role in their new organizations. Specifically, if employees proactively developed strong relationships with their supervisors (PS fit), it replaced the effect of institutional socialization tactics on perceived PO fit. Through a 6-month longitudinal study, Deng and Yao (2020) found a reciprocal causal relationship between proactive socialization behaviors and student–university fit (PO fit), in which some dimensions of proactive socialization behavior influenced subsequent PO fit, which in turn influenced those proactive socialization behaviors.

Previous research has also examined how other HR practices such as training and development impact PO fit. Autry and Wheeler (2005) found a positive relationship between formal training and long-term employees' PS fit and PO fit. Kooij and colleagues (2017) examined the effects of a job crafting training intervention using an experimental field study and found that participating in the intervention led to job crafting among older workers, which was positively associated with DA fit and NS fit. Mostafa and Gould-Williams (2014) found that high-performance HR practices such as training and development were perceived as major factors that facilitated employees' PO fit, which subsequently influenced job satisfaction and OCB. Similarly, Kilroy et al. (2017) found that high-involvement work practices (e.g., development practices) were positively related to perceived PO fit, which in turn decreased employees' emotional exhaustion and depersonalization.

CONCLUSION

PE fit is one of the most fundamental psychological experiences in organizational life. It involves the basic question of how the relationship between a person and an environment in an organizational context influences various individual outcomes. Research on PE fit has evolved from a static view to a dynamic, simultaneous, and multidimensional view. Because the concept of PE fit is broad and even elusive, there still are many challenges to understanding this concept more deeply. For example, it is related to various theories, forms, dimensions, and measures and empirical analyses. Organizational psychologists' continuing efforts to research PE fit will contribute to a deeper understanding of organizational life.

FURTHER READING

Barrick, M. R., & Parks-Leduc, L. (2019). Selection for fit. *Annual Review of Organizational Psychology and Organizational Behavior*, 6, 171–193.

Edwards, J. R. (2008). Person–environment fit in organizations: An assessment of theoretical progress. *Academy of Management Annals*, 2(1), 167–230.

Kristof-Brown, A., & Guay, R. P. (2011). Person–environment fit. In S. Zedeck (Ed.), *APA handbook of industrial and organizational psychology: Vol. 3. Maintaining, expanding, and contracting the organization* (pp. 3–50). APA Handbooks in Psychology. American Psychological Association.

Kristof-Brown, A. L., Zimmerman, R. D., & Johnson, E. C. (2005). Consequences of individual's fit at work: A meta-analysis of person–job, person–organization person–group, and person–supervisor fit. *Personnel Psychology*, 58, 281–342.

Ostroff, C. (2012). Person-environment fit in organizational settings. In S. W. J. Kozlowski (Ed.), *The Oxford handbook of organizational psychology* (Vol. 1, pp. 373–408). Oxford Library of Psychology. Oxford University Press.

Ostroff, C., & Judge, T. A. (Eds.). (2007). *Perspectives on organizational fit*. Erlbaum.

Van Vianen, A. E. (2018). Person–environment fit: A review of its basic tenets. *Annual Review of Organizational Psychology and Organizational Behavior*, 5, 75–101.

REFERENCES

Adkins, C. L., Russell, C. J., & Werbel, J. D. (1994). Judgments of fit in the selection process: The role of work value congruence. *Personnel Psychology, 47*(3), 605–623.

Afsar, B., Badir, Y., & Khan, M. M. (2015). Person–job fit, person–organization fit and innovative work behavior: The mediating role of innovation trust. *The Journal of High Technology Management Research, 26*(2), 105–116.

Alfes, K., Shantz, A., & van Baalen, S. (2016). Reducing perceptions of overqualification and its impact on job satisfaction: The dual roles of interpersonal relationships at work. *Human Resource Management Journal, 26*(1), 84–101.

Andela, M., & van der Doef, M. (2019). A comprehensive assessment of the person–environment fit dimensions and their relationships with work-related outcomes. *Journal of Career Development, 46*(5), 567–582.

Anderson, N., & Ostroff, C. (1997). Selection as socialization. *International Handbook of Selection and Assessment, 13*, 413–440.

Arthur, W., Jr., Bell, S. T., Villado, A. J., & Doverspike, D. (2006). The use of person-organization fit in employment decision making: An assessment of its criterion-related validity. *Journal of Applied Psychology, 91*(4), 786–801.

Ashford, S. J., & Black, J. S. (1996). Proactivity during organizational entry: The role of desire for control. *Journal of Applied Psychology, 81*(2), 199–214.

Astakhova, M. N. (2016). Explaining the effects of perceived person-supervisor fit and person-organization fit on organizational commitment in the US and Japan. *Journal of Business Research, 69*(2), 956–963.

Autry, C. W., & Wheeler, A. R. (2005). Post-hire human resource management practices and person-organization fit: A study of blue-collar employees. *Journal of Managerial Issues, 17*(1), 58–75.

Bauer, T. N., & Green, S. G. (1998). Testing the combined effects of newcomer information seeking and manager behavior on socialization. *Journal of Applied Psychology, 83*(1), 72–83.

Bayl-Smith, P. H., & Griffin, B. (2018). Maintenance of DA fit through work adjustment behaviors: The moderating effect of work style fit. *Journal of Vocational Behavior, 106*, 209–219.

Boon, C., & Biron, M. (2016). Temporal issues in person–organization fit, person–job fit and turnover: The role of leader–member exchange. *Human Relations, 69*(12), 2177–2200.

Bradley, J. C., Arthur, P. B., & George, J. M. (2002). More than the Big Five: Personality and careers. In D. C. Feldman (Ed.), *Work careers: A developmental approach* (pp. 27–62). Jossey-Bass.

Bretz, R. D., Rynes, S. L., & Gerhart, B. (1993). Recruiter perceptions of applicant fit: Implications for individual career preparation and job search behavior. *Journal of Vocational Behavior, 43*(3), 310–327.

Cable, D. M., & DeRue, D. S. (2002). The convergent and discriminant validity of subjective fit perceptions. *Journal of Applied Psychology, 87*(5), 875–884.

Cable, D. M., & Edwards, J. R. (2004). Complementary and supplementary fit: A theoretical and empirical integration. *Journal of Applied Psychology, 89*(5), 822–834.

Cable, D. M., & Judge, T. A. (1994). Pay preferences and job search decisions: A person-organization fit perspective. *Personnel Psychology, 47*(2), 317–348.

Cable, D. M., & Judge, T. A. (1996). Person–organization fit, job choice decisions, and organizational entry. *Organizational Behavior and Human Decision Processes, 67*(3), 294–311.

Cable, D. M., & Judge, T. A. (1997). Interviewers' perceptions of person–organization fit and organizational selection decisions. *Journal of Applied Psychology, 82*(4), 546–561.

Cable, D. M., & Parsons, C. K. (2001). Socialization tactics and person-organization fit. *Personnel Psychology, 54*(1), 1–23.

Caplan, R. D. (1983). Person-environment fit: Past, present, and future. In C. L. Cooper (Ed.), *Stress research* (pp. 35–78). Wiley.

Caplan, R. D. (1987). Person–environment fit theory and organizations: Commensurate dimensions, time perspectives, and mechanisms. *Journal of Vocational Behavior, 31*, 248–267.

Carless, S. A. (2005). Person–job fit versus person–organization fit as predictors of organizational attraction and job acceptance intentions: A longitudinal study. *Journal of Occupational and Organizational Psychology, 78*(3), 411–429.

Chao, G. T., O'Leary-Kelly, A. M., Wolf, S., Klein, H. J., & Gardner, P. D. (1994). Organizational socialization: Its content and consequences. *Journal of Applied Psychology, 79*(5), 730–743.

Chapman, D. S., Uggerslev, K. L., Carroll, S. A., Piasentin, K. A., & Jones, D. A. (2005). Applicant attraction to organizations and job choice: A meta-analytic review of the correlates of recruiting outcomes. *Journal of Applied Psychology, 90*(5), 928–944.

Chatman, J. A. (1989). Improving interactional organizational research: A model of person-organization fit. *Academy of Management Review, 14*(3), 333–349.

Chatman, J. A. (1991). Matching people and organizations: Selection and socialization in public accounting firms. *Administrative Science Quarterly, 36*(3), 459–484.

Chen, P., Sparrow, P., & Cooper, C. (2016). The relationship between person-organization fit and job satisfaction. *Journal of Managerial Psychology, 31*(5), 946–959.

Chi, N. W., Fang, L. C., Shen, C. T., & Fan, H. L. (2020). Detrimental effects of newcomer person–job misfit on actual turnover and performance: The buffering role of multidimensional person–environment fit. *Applied Psychology, 69*(4), 1361–1395.

Choi, M. O., & Yoo, T. Y. (2005). The effects of person-organization, person-job, and person-supervisor fit on organization commitment, job satisfaction, and turnover intention: The focus on interaction effects among three types of fit. *Korean Journal of Industrial and Organizational Psychology, 18*(1), 139–162.

Chuang, A., & Sackett, P. R. (2005). The perceived importance of person-job fit and person-organization fit between and within interview stages. *Social Behavior and Personality: An International Journal, 33*(3), 209–226.

Chuang, A., Shen, C. T., & Judge, T. A. (2016). Development of a multidimensional instrument of person–environment fit: The Perceived Person–Environment Fit Scale (PPEFS). *Applied Psychology, 65*(1), 66–98.

Cooper-Thomas, H. D., Van Vianen, A., & Anderson, N. (2004). Changes in person–organization fit: The impact of socialization tactics on perceived and actual P–O fit. *European Journal of Work and Organizational Psychology, 13*(1), 52–78.

Dawis, R. V., Lofquist, L. H., & Weiss, D. J. (1968). A theory of work adjustment: A revision. *Minnesota Studies in Vocational Rehabilitation, 23*, 1–14.

De Cooman, R., Vantilborgh, T., Bal, M., & Lub, X. (2016). Creating inclusive teams through perceptions of supplementary and complementary person–team fit: Examining the relationship between person–team fit and team effectiveness. *Group & Organization Management, 41*(3), 310–342.

Deng, Y., & Yao, X. (2020). Person-environment fit and proactive socialization: Reciprocal relationships in an academic environment. *Journal of Vocational Behavior, 120*, 103446.

DeRue, D. S., & Morgeson, F. P. (2007). Stability and change in person-team and person-role fit over time: The effects of growth satisfaction, performance, and general self-efficacy. *Journal of Applied Psychology, 92*(5), 1242–1253.

Devloo, T., Anseel, F., & De Beuckelaer, A. (2011). Do managers use feedback seeking as a strategy to regulate demands–abilities misfit? The moderating role of implicit person theory. *Journal of Business and Psychology, 26*(4), 453–465.

Dineen, B. R., Ash, S. R., & Noe, R. A. (2002). A web of applicant attraction: Person-organization fit in the context of Web-based recruitment. *Journal of Applied Psychology, 87*(4), 723–734.

Dineen, B. R., & Noe, R. A. (2009). Effects of customization on application decisions and applicant pool characteristics in a Web-based recruitment context. *Journal of Applied Psychology, 94*(1), 224–234.

Edwards, J. A., & Billsberry, J. (2010). Testing a multidimensional theory of person-environment fit. *Journal of Managerial Issues, 22*(4), 476–493.

Edwards, J. R. (1991). Person–job fit: A conceptual integration, literature on review and methodological critique. *International Review of Industrial and Organizational Psychology, 6*, 283–357.

Edwards, J. R. (2008a). Person–environment fit in organizations: An assessment of theoretical progress. *Academy of Management Annals, 2*(1), 167–230.

Edwards, J. R. (2008b). Polynomial regression and response surface methodology. In C. Ostroff & T. A. Judge (Eds.), *Perspectives on organizational fit* (pp. 361–372). Lawrence Erlbaum.

Edwards, J. R., & Cable, D. M. (2009). The value of value congruence. *Journal of Applied Psychology, 94*(3), 654–677.

Edwards, J. R., Cable, D. M., Williamson, I. O., Lambert, L. S., & Shipp, A. J. (2006). The phenomenology of fit: Linking the person and environment to the subjective experience of person-environment fit. *Journal of Applied Psychology, 91*(4), 802–827.

Edwards, J. R., Caplan, R. D., & Van Harrison, R. (1998). Person-environment fit theory. *Theories of Organizational Stress, 28*, 28–67.

Edwards, J. R., & Parry, M. E. (1993). On the use of polynomial regression equations as an alternative to difference scores in organizational research. *Academy of Management Journal, 36*, 1577–1613.

Edwards, J. R., & Shipp, A. J. (2007). The relationship between person–environment fit and outcomes: An integrative theoretical framework. In C. Ostroff & T. A. Judge (Eds.), *Perspectives on organizational fit* (pp. 209–258). Erlbaum.

Erdogan, B., & Bauer, T. N. (2009). Perceived overqualification and its outcomes: The moderating role of empowerment. *Journal of Applied Psychology, 94*(2), 557–565.

Erdogan, B., & Bauer, T. N. (2020). Overqualification at work: A review and synthesis of the literature. *Annual Review of Organizational Psychology and Organizational Behavior, 8*, 259–283.

Erdogan, B., Karaeminogullari, A., Bauer, T. N., & Ellis, A. M. (2020). Perceived overqualification at work: Implications for extra-role behaviors and advice network centrality. *Journal of Management, 46*(4), 583–606.

Farzaneh, J., Farashah, A. D., & Kazemi, M. (2014). The impact of person-job fit and person-organization fit on OCB. *Personnel Review, 43*(5), 672–691.

Feij, J. A., Van Der Velde, M. E., Taris, R., & Taris, T. W. (1999). The development of person–vocation fit: A longitudinal study among young employees. *International Journal of Selection and Assessment, 7*(1), 12–25.

Fine, S., & Nevo, B. (2008). Too smart for their own good? A study of perceived cognitive overqualification in the workforce. *The International Journal of Human Resource Management, 19*(2), 346–355.

Follmer, E. H., Talbot, D. L., Kristof-Brown, A. L., Astrove, S. L., & Billsberry, J. (2018). Resolution, relief, and resignation: A qualitative study of responses to misfit at work. *Academy of Management Journal, 61*(2), 440–465.

Gabriel, A. S., Diefendorff, J. M., Chandler, M. M., Moran, C. M., & Greguras, G. J. (2014). The dynamic relationships of work affect and job satisfaction with perceptions of fit. *Personnel Psychology, 67*(2), 389–420.

Ghetta, A., Hirschi, A., Wang, M., Rossier, J., & Herrmann, A. (2020). Birds of a feather flock together: How congruence between worker and occupational personality relates to job satisfaction over time. *Journal of Vocational Behavior, 119*, 103412.

Gregory, B. T., Albritton, M. D., & Osmonbekov, T. (2010). The mediating role of psychological empowerment on the relationships between P–O fit, job satisfaction, and in-role performance. *Journal of Business and Psychology, 25*(4), 639–647.

Greguras, G. J., & Diefendorff, J. M. (2009). Different fits satisfy different needs: Linking person-environment fit to employee commitment and performance using self-determination theory. *Journal of Applied Psychology, 94*(2), 465–477.

Griffin, A. E., Colella, A., & Goparaju, S. (2000). Newcomer and organizational socialization tactics: An interactionist perspective. *Human Resource Management Review, 10*(4), 453–474.

Hamstra, M. R., Van Vianen, A. E., & Koen, J. (2019). Does employee perceived person-organization fit promote performance? The moderating role of supervisor perceived person-organization fit. *European Journal of Work and Organizational Psychology*, 28(5), 594–601.

Harari, M. B., Manapragada, A., & Viswesvaran, C. (2017). Who thinks they're a big fish in a small pond and why does it matter? A meta-analysis of perceived overqualification. *Journal of Vocational Behavior, 102*, 28–47.

Higgins, C. A., & Judge, T. A. (2004). The effect of applicant influence tactics on recruiter perceptions of fit and hiring recommendations: A field study. *Journal of Applied Psychology*, 89(4), 622–632.

Hoffman, B. J., & Woehr, D. J. (2006). A quantitative review of the relationship between person–organization fit and behavioral outcomes. *Journal of Vocational Behavior*, 68(3), 389–399.

Holland, J. L. (1985). *Making vocational decisions* (2nd ed.). Prentice Hall.

Holland, J. L. (1997). *Making vocational choices: A theory of vocational personalities and work environments* (3rd ed.). Psychological Assessment Resources.

Hu, J., Erdogan, B., Bauer, T. N., Jiang, K., Liu, S., & Li, Y. (2015). There are lots of big fish in this pond: The role of peer overqualification on task significance, perceived fit, and performance for overqualified employees. *Journal of Applied Psychology*, 100(4), 1228–1238.

Jansen, K. J., & Kristof-Brown, A. (2006). Toward a multidimensional theory of person-environment fit. *Journal of Managerial Issues*, 18(2), 193–212.

Jansen, K. J., & Shipp, A. J. (2013). A review and agenda for incorporating time in fit research. In A. L. Kristof-Brown & J. Billsberry (Eds.), *Organizational fit: Key issues and new directions* (pp. 195–221). Wiley-Blackwell.

Jansen, K. J., & Shipp, A. J. (2019). Fitting as a temporal sensemaking process: Shifting trajectories and stable themes. *Human Relations*, 72(7), 1154–1186.

Johnson, G. J., & Johnson, W. R. (1996). Perceived overqualification and psychological well-being. *The Journal of Social Psychology*, 136(4), 435–445.

Johnson, G. J., & Johnson, W. R. (2000). Perceived overqualification and dimensions of job satisfaction: A longitudinal analysis. *Journal of Psychology*, 134(5), 537–555.

Judge, T. A., & Cable, D. M. (1997). Applicant personality, organizational culture, and organization attraction. *Personnel Psychology*, 50(2), 359–394.

Kilroy, S., Flood, P. C., Bosak, J., & Chênevert, D. (2017). Perceptions of high-involvement work practices, person-organization fit, and burnout: A time-lagged study of health care employees. *Human Resource Management*, 56(5), 821–835.

Kim, T. Y., Cable, D. M., & Kim, S. P. (2005). Socialization tactics, employee proactivity, and person-organization fit. *Journal of Applied Psychology*, 90(2), 232–241.

Kim, T. Y., Schuh, S. C., & Cai, Y. (2020). Person or job? Change in person–job fit and its impact on employee work attitudes over time. *Journal of Management Studies*, 57(2), 287–313.

Klaic, A., Burtscher, M. J., & Jonas, K. (2018). Person-supervisor fit, needs-supplies fit, and team fit as mediators of the relationship between dual-focused transformational leadership and well-being in scientific teams. *European Journal of Work and Organizational Psychology*, 27(5), 669–682.

Kooij, D. T., van Woerkom, M., Wilkenloh, J., Dorenbosch, L., & Denissen, J. J. (2017). Job crafting towards strengths and interests: The effects of a job crafting intervention on person–job fit and the role of age. *Journal of Applied Psychology*, 102(6), 971–981.

Kristof, A. L. (1996). Person-organization fit: An integrative review of its conceptualizations, measurement, and implications. *Personnel Psychology*, 49, 1–49.

Kristof-Brown, A. L. (2000). Perceived applicant fit: Distinguishing between recruiters' perceptions of person–job and person–organization fit. *Personnel Psychology*, 53 (3), 643–671.

Kristof-Brown, A. L., & Billsberry, J. (2013). Fit for the future. In A. Kristof-Brown & J. Billsberry (Eds.), *Organizational fit: Key issues and new directions* (pp. 1–18). Wiley.

Kristof-Brown, A. L., & Guay, R. P. (2011). Person-environment fit. In S. Zedeck (Ed.), *APA handbook of industrial and organizational psychology* (Vol. 3, pp. 3–50). APA.

Kristof-Brown, A. L., Jansen, K. J., & Colbert, A. E. (2002). A policy-capturing study of the simultaneous effects of fit with jobs, groups, and organizations. *Journal of Applied Psychology, 87*(5), 985–993.

Kristof-Brown, A. L., Zimmerman, R. D., & Johnson, E. C. (2005). Consequences of individual's fit at work: A meta-analysis of person-job, person-organization person-group, and person-supervisor fit. *Personnel Psychology, 58*, 281–342.

Lauver, K. J., & Kristof-Brown, A. (2001). Distinguishing between employees' perceptions of person–job and person–organization fit. *Journal of Vocational Behavior, 59*(3), 454–470.

Leung, A., & Chaturvedi, S. (2011). Linking the fits, fitting the links: Connecting different types of PO fit to attitudinal outcomes. *Journal of Vocational Behavior, 79*(2), 391–402.

Lewin, K. (1951). *Field theory in social science.* Harper & Row.

Lin, B., Law, K. S., & Zhou, J. (2017). Why is underemployment related to creativity and OCB? A task-crafting explanation of the curvilinear moderated relations. *Academy of Management Journal, 60*(1), 156–177.

Liu, B., Liu, J., & Hu, J. (2010). Person-organization fit, job satisfaction, and turnover intention: An empirical study in the Chinese public sector. *Social Behavior and Personality: An International Journal, 38*(5), 615–625.

Liu, S., Luksyte, A., Zhou, L., Shi, J., & Wang, M. (2015). Overqualification and counterproductive work behaviors: Examining a moderated mediation model. *Journal of Organizational Behavior, 36*(2), 250–271.

Lu, C. Q., Wang, H. J., Lu, J. J., Du, D. Y., & Bakker, A. B. (2014). Does work engagement increase person–job fit? The role of job crafting and job insecurity. *Journal of Vocational Behavior, 84*(2), 142–152.

Luksyte, A., Bauer, T. N., Debus, M. E., Erdogan, B., & Wu, C. H. (2020). Perceived overqualification and collectivism orientation: Implications for work and nonwork outcomes. *Journal of Management.* https://doi.org/10.1177/0149206320948602

Luksyte, A., & Spitzmueller, C. (2016). When are overqualified employees creative? It depends on contextual factors. *Journal of Organizational Behavior, 37*(5), 635–653.

Luksyte, A., Spitzmueller, C., & Maynard, D. C. (2011). Why do overqualified incumbents deviate? Examining multiple mediators. *Journal of Occupational Health Psychology, 16*(3), 279–296.

Marstand, A. F., Martin, R., & Epitropaki, O. (2017). Complementary person-supervisor fit: An investigation of supplies-values (SV) fit, leader-member exchange (LMX) and work outcomes. *The Leadership Quarterly, 28*(3), 418–437.

Maynard, D. C., & Parfyonova, N. M. (2013). Perceived overqualification and withdrawal behaviours: Examining the roles of job attitudes and work values. *Journal of Occupational and Organizational Psychology, 86*(3), 435–455.

Morrison, E. W. (1993). Newcomer information seeking: Exploring types, modes, sources, and outcomes. *Academy of Management Journal, 36*(3), 557–589.

Mostafa, A. M. S., & Gould-Williams, J. S. (2014). Testing the mediation effect of person–organization fit on the relationship between high performance HR practices and employee outcomes in the Egyptian public sector. *The International Journal of Human Resource Management, 25*(2), 276–292.

Muchinsky, P. M., & Monahan, C. J. (1987). What is person-environment congruence? Supplementary versus complementary models of fit. *Journal of Vocational Behavior, 31*(3), 268–277.

Nolan, K. P., Langhammer, K., & Salter, N. P. (2016). Evaluating fit in employee selection: Beliefs about how, when, and why. *Consulting Psychology Journal: Practice and Research, 68*(3), 222–251.

Nye, C. D., Su, R., Rounds, J., & Drasgow, F. (2012). Vocational interests and performance: A quantitative summary of over 60 years of research. *Perspectives on Psychological Science, 7*(4), 384–403.

Nye, C. D., Su, R., Rounds, J., & Drasgow, F. (2017). Interest congruence and performance: Revisiting recent meta-analytic findings. *Journal of Vocational Behavior, 98*, 138–151.

Oh, I. S., Guay, R. P., Kim, K., Harold, C. M., Lee, J. H., Heo, C. G., & Shin, K. H. (2014). Fit happens globally: A meta-analytic comparison of the relationships of person–environment fit dimensions with work attitudes and performance across East Asia, Europe, and North America. *Personnel Psychology, 67*(1), 99–152.

Ostroff, C. (2012). Person-environment fit in organizational settings. In S. W. J. Kozlowski (Ed.), *Handbook of organizational psychology* (pp. 373–408). Oxford University Press.

Ostroff, C., & Rothausen, T. J. (1997). The moderating effect of tenure in person–environment fit: A field study in educational organizations. *Journal of Occupational and Organizational Psychology, 70*(2), 173–188.

Resick, C. J., Baltes, B. B., & Shantz, C. W. (2007). Person-organization fit and work-related attitudes and decisions: Examining interactive effects with job fit and conscientiousness. *Journal of Applied Psychology, 92*(5), 1446–1455.

Riordan, C. M., Weatherly E. W., Vandenberg R. J., & Self, R. M. (2001). The effects of pre-entry experiences and socialization tactics on newcomer attitudes and turnover. *Journal of Managerial Issues, 13*(2), 159–176.

Roberson, Q. M., Collins, C. J., & Oreg, S. (2005). The effects of recruitment message specificity on applicant attraction to organizations. *Journal of Business and Psychology, 19*(3), 319–339.

Sacco, J. M., & Schmitt, N. (2005). A dynamic multilevel model of demographic diversity and misfit effects. *Journal of Applied Psychology, 90*(2), 203–231.

Saks, A. M., & Ashforth, B. E. (1997). Organizational socialization: Making sense of the past and present as a prologue for the future. *Journal of Vocational Behavior, 51*(2), 234–279.

Saks, A. M., Uggerslev, K. L., & Fassina, N. E. (2007). Socialization tactics and newcomer adjustment: A meta-analytic review and test of a model. *Journal of Vocational Behavior, 70*(3), 413–446.

Schneider, B. (1987). The people make the place. *Personnel Psychology, 40*, 437–454.

Schneider, B., Smith, D. B., & Paul, M. C. (2001). P–E fit and the attraction–selection–attrition model of organizational functioning: Introduction and overview. In M. Erez, U. Kleinbeck, & H. Thierry (Eds.), *Work motivation in the context of a globalizing economy* (pp. 231–246). Erlbaum.

Sekiguchi, T. (2004a). Person-organization fit and person-job fit in employee selection: A review of the literature. *Osaka Keidai Ronshu, 54* (6), 179–196.

Sekiguchi, T. (2004b). Toward a dynamic model of person-environment fit. *Osaka Keidai Ronshu, 55*(1), 177–190.

Sekiguchi, T. (2006). How organizations promote person-environment fit: Using the case of Japanese firms to illustrate institutional and cultural influences. *Asia Pacific Journal of Management, 23*, 47–69.

Sekiguchi, T. (2007). A contingency perspective of the importance of PJ fit and PO fit in employee selection. *Journal of Managerial Psychology, 22*, 118–131.

Sekiguchi, T., & Huber, V. L. (2011). The use of person-organization fit and person-job fit information in making selection decisions. *Organizational Behavior and Human Decision Processes, 116*, 203–216.

Sekiguchi, T., Mitate, Y., & Yang, Y. (2020). Internship experience and organizational attractiveness: Does realistic job fit matter? *Academy of Management Best Paper Proceedings, 1*, 14720.

Seong, J. Y., & Choi, J. N. (2014). Effects of group-level fit on group conflict and performance: The initiating role of leader positive affect. *Group & Organization Management, 39*(2), 190–212.

Seong, J. Y., & Kristof-Brown, A. L. (2012). Testing multidimensional models of person-group fit. *Journal of Managerial Psychology, 27*(6), 536–556.

Seong, J. Y., Kristof-Brown, A. L., Park, W. W., Hong, D. S., & Shin, Y. (2015). Person-group fit: Diversity antecedents, proximal outcomes, and performance at the group level. *Journal of Management, 41*(4), 1184–1213.

Simmering, M. J., Colquitt, J. A., Noe, R. A., & Porter, C. O. (2003). Conscientiousness, autonomy fit, and development: A longitudinal study. *Journal of Applied Psychology, 88*(5), 954–963.

Shipp, A. J., & Jansen, K. J. (2011). Reinterpreting time in fit theory: Crafting and recrafting narratives of fit in medias res. *Academy of Management Review, 36*(1), 76–101.

Swaney, K., & Prediger, D. (1985). The relationship between interest-occupation congruence and job satisfaction. *Journal of Vocational Behavior, 26*(1), 13–24.

Swider, B. W., Zimmerman, R. D., & Barrick, M. R. (2015). Searching for the right fit: Development of applicant person-organization fit perceptions during the recruitment process. *Journal of Applied Psychology*, *100*(3), 880–893.

Sylva, H., Mol, S. T., Den Hartog, D. N., & Dorenbosch, L. (2019). Person-job fit and proactive career behaviour: A dynamic approach. *European Journal of Work and Organizational Psychology*, *28*(5), 631–645.

Tak, J. (2011). Relationships between various person–environment fit types and employee withdrawal behavior: A longitudinal study. *Journal of Vocational Behavior*, *78*(2), 315–320.

Tong, J., Wang, L., & Peng, K. (2015). From person-environment misfit to job burnout: Theoretical extensions. *Journal of Managerial Psychology*, *30*, 169–182.

Tranberg, M., Slane, S., & Ekeberg, S. E. (1993). The relation between interest congruence and satisfaction: A metaanalysis. *Journal of Vocational Behavior*, *42*(3), 253–264.

Tsabari, O., Tziner, A., & Meir, E. I. (2005). Updated meta-analysis on the relationship between congruence and satisfaction. *Journal of Career Assessment*, *13*(2), 216–232.

Turban, D. B., & Keon, T. L. (1993). Organizational attractiveness: An interactionist perspective. *Journal of Applied Psychology*, *78*(2), 184–193.

Uggerslev, K. L., Fassina, N. E., & Kraichy, D. (2012). Recruiting through the stages: A meta-analytic test of predictors of applicant attraction at different stages of the recruiting process. *Personnel Psychology*, *65*(3), 597–660.

Van Vianen, A. E. (2018). Person–environment fit: A review of its basic tenets. *Annual Review of Organizational Psychology and Organizational Behavior*, *5*, 75–101.

Van Vianen, A. E., Shen, C. T., & Chuang, A. (2011). Person–organization and person–supervisor fits: Employee commitments in a Chinese context. *Journal of Organizational Behavior*, *32*(6), 906–926.

Vanderstukken, A., Proost, K., & Van Den Broeck, A. (2019). Subjective PO fit in recruitment: Is it always really "O"? Organizational values may be industry values, depending on temporal distance. *European Journal of Work and Organizational Psychology*, *28*(5), 602–615.

Verquer, M. L., Beehr, T. A., & Wagner, S. H. (2003). A meta-analysis of relations between person–organization fit and work attitudes. *Journal of Vocational Behavior*, *63*(3), 473–489.

Vleugels, W., De Cooman, R., Verbruggen, M., & Solinger, O. (2018). Understanding dynamic change in perceptions of person-environment fit: An exploration of competing theoretical perspectives. *Journal of Organizational Behavior*, *39*(9), 1066–1080.

Vogel, R. M., & Feldman, D. C. (2009). Integrating the levels of person-environment fit: The roles of vocational fit and group fit. *Journal of Vocational Behavior*, *75*(1), 68–81.

Vogel, R. M., Rodell, J. B., & Lynch, J. W. (2016). Engaged and productive misfits: How job crafting and leisure activity mitigate the negative effects of value incongruence. *Academy of Management Journal*, *59*(5), 1561–1584.

Wanberg, C. R., & Kammeyer-Mueller, J. D. (2000). Predictors and outcomes of proactivity in the socialization process. *Journal of Applied Psychology*, *85*(3), 373–385.

Werbel, J. D., & Gilliland, S. W. (1999). Person–environment fit in the selection process. In G. R. Ferris (Ed.), *Research in personnel and human resource management* (Vol. 17, pp. 209–243). JAI Press.

Wheeler, A. R., Buckley, M. R., Halbesleben, J. R., Brouer, R. L., & Ferris, G. R. (2005), "The elusive criterion of fit" revisited: Toward an integrative theory of multidimensional fit. In J. Martocchio (Ed.), *Research in personnel and human resource management* (Vol. 24, pp. 265–304). JAI Press.

Wheeler, A. R., Gallagher, V. C., Brouer, R. L., & Sablynski, C. J. (2007). When person–organization (mis) fit and (dis)satisfaction lead to turnover: The moderating role of perceived job mobility. *Journal of Managerial Psychology*, *22*(2), 203–219.

Wille, B., Tracey, T. J., Feys, M., & De Fruyt, F. (2014). A longitudinal and multi-method examination of interest–occupation congruence within and across time. *Journal of Vocational Behavior*, *84*(1), 59–73.

Wu, I. H., & Chi, N. W. (2020). The journey to leave: Understanding the roles of perceived ease of movement, proactive personality, and person–organization fit in overqualified employees' job searching process. *Journal of Organizational Behavior, 41*(9), 851–870.

Xu, M., Qin, X., Dust, S. B., & DiRenzo, M. S. (2019). Supervisor-subordinate proactive personality congruence and psychological safety: A signaling theory approach to employee voice behavior. *The Leadership Quarterly, 30*(4), 440–453.

Yu, K. Y. T. (2009). Affective influences in person–environment fit theory: Exploring the role of affect as both cause and outcome of PE fit. *Journal of Applied Psychology, 94*(5), 1210–1226.

Yu, K. Y. T. (2014). Person–organization fit effects on organizational attraction: A test of an expectations-based model. *Organizational Behavior and Human Decision Processes, 124*(1), 75–94.

Yu, K. Y. T., & Davis, H. M. (2016). Autonomy's impact on newcomer proactive behaviour and socialization: A needs–supplies fit perspective. *Journal of Occupational and Organizational Psychology, 89*(1), 172–197.

Zhang, M. J., Law, K. S., & Lin, B. (2016). You think you are big fish in a small pond? Perceived overqualification, goal orientations, and proactivity at work. *Journal of Organizational Behavior, 37*(1), 61–84.

Tomoki Sekiguchi and Yunyue Yang

POLITICAL SKILL AT WORK AND IN CAREERS

INTRODUCTION

Recent awareness of the interpersonal nature of work and careers suggests that interpersonal skills may be important predictors of getting ahead and getting along, as well as enjoying job and career satisfaction. Both scholars and professionals believe relationship and communication skills are highly important factors for success at work (Klein, DeRouin, & Salas, 2006). For instance, social skill "helps individuals put a gloss on their performance that ensures a higher rating" (Pfeffer, 2009, p. 68). Hogan and Shelton (1998, p. 135) suggested that "social skill allows one to achieve his or her interpersonal goals just as hand-eye coordination allows one to hit a tennis ball accurately." In addition, employer cybervetting (i.e., the extraction of job applicant online information for assessing candidates' reputation, connections, and value alignments), is becoming more and more popular. Cognizant of online available information suggesting applicants with "red flags" will not be hired, workers need social skills to create a favorable public professional image (Berkelaar, Scacco, & Birdsell, 2015).

With the social nature of work and careers given increased attention (Fugate, Kinicki, & Ashforth, 2004), psychological research applied to work, organizations, and careers witnessed a proliferation of social effectiveness constructs since the 2000s (Semadar, Robins, & Ferris, 2006). One of these social effectiveness constructs is political skill (Ferris et al., 2005, 2007), conceptualized as the ability to effectively enhance one's personal and organizational objectives in vocational life (Blickle, Frieder, & Ferris, 2018). Compared to other social effectiveness constructs (such as emotional intelligence, leadership self-efficacy, and self-monitoring), researchers have found political skill to be the strongest predictor of job performance with incremental validity above and beyond other social effectiveness constructs (Semadar et al., 2006). In addition, Blickle, Kramer et al. (2011) examined the predictive effectiveness of political skill in combination with cognitive intelligence (general mental ability; GMA) and the Big Five personality traits in both a cross-sectional and a predictive study design with a one-year time interval. Both studies found incremental validity of political skill in the prediction of job performance above and beyond GMA and the Big Five personality traits.

Moreover, political skill has attracted a great deal of attention from various organizational, leadership, and career researchers, and it has been investigated in a broad range of empirical studies across many different nations and cultures with consistent results (Vigoda-Gadot & Drory, 2016). Despite its recent development, five meta-analyses already have been conducted to assess the predictors, consequences, and moderators of political skill at work and in careers (Bedi & Skowronski, 2014; Bing, Davison, Minor, Novicevic, & Frink, 2011; Jacobson & Viswesvaran, 2017; Munyon, Summers, Thompson, & Ferris, 2015; Ng, Eby, Sorensen, & Feldman, 2005). These meta-analytic results combined outcomes across numerous studies and samples, providing a strong empirical basis for the assertion that the results are valid and replicable (Schmidt & Oh, 2016).

This article will provide a brief overview of the main theoretical concepts and empirical findings with a special focus on newly emerging trends. The following themes have been identified: (a) construct specification; (b) measurement of political skill; (c) antecedents of political skill; (d) workplace and career outcomes of political skill; (e) political skill and stress management; (f) political skill in leadership roles; (g) political skill and (dark) personalities; (h) political skill, social media, and reputation formation; and, finally, (i) implications for practice.

CONSTRUCT SPECIFICATION

Definition of Political Skill. The construct of political skill (Ferris et al., 2005, 2007) does not imply politicking, but derives its name from the political perspective on organizations and careers (e.g., Inkson, 2004; Mintzberg, 1983; Pfeffer, 1981; Silvester & Wyatt, 2018). Political behavior is the power struggle that concerns who gets what, as well as when and how the person gets it (Lasswell, 1936), and it can take place at all hierarchical levels and in all types of organizations (Vigoda-Gadot, 2003). Viewed through the lens of politics, Inkson (2004) suggested that vocational careers can be seen as political campaigns, involving contact hunting, self-promotion, and impression management. Pfeffer (2010) argued that to be successful in organizations, individuals must understand political dynamics and complex power structures. Moreover, Mintzberg (1983) reasoned that political skill referred to the exercise of influence through building coalitions, negotiation, and persuasion. Ferris et al. (2007, p. 331) defined political skill as "the ability to effectively understand others at work, and use such knowledge to influence others to act in ways that enhance one's personal and/or organizational objectives."

Political skill combines four interrelated, yet distinct, key dimensions (Ferris et al., 2005): politically skilled individuals observe and understand cues from their social environment (social astuteness); they subtly influence others around them (interpersonal influence), build and maintain useful relationships (networking ability), and are, or are at least perceived as being, authentic and honest (apparent sincerity). Taken together, political skill is a construct of social effectiveness consisting of cognitive, affective, as well as behavioral components (Ferris et al., 2007).

McAllister, Ellen, and Ferris (2018) have developed a three-stage cascading model of social influence. The first stage refers to opportunity recognition, that is, the process of recognizing new and potentially successful opportunities for social influence. The second stage deals with opportunity evaluation which addresses the viability of executing the available opportunities for influence. The third stage focuses on opportunity capitalization, namely, the style with which influence behavior is socially implemented. The social astuteness and networking ability dimensions of political skill are suggested to be critical in the opportunity recognition stage, whereas the interpersonal influence and apparent sincerity facets are argued to be critical in the opportunity capitalization stage of social influence. Political will (i.e., the degree and direction of self-serving and benevolent strategic influence goals; Blickle, Schütte, & Wihler, 2018; Kapoutsis, Papalexandris, Treadway, & Bentley, 2017) is thought to be critical in the opportunity evaluation stage. Wihler, Blickle, Ellen, Hochwarter, and Ferris (2017) found empirical support for the opportunity recognition function of the social astuteness facet and for the opportunity capitalization function of the interpersonal influence dimension. Future empirical research should address the opportunity recognition and opportunity capitalization functions of networking ability and apparent sincerity, respectively.

Measurement of Political Skill. During the course of its development, different operationalizations of the political skill construct have been introduced. Although two scales measure political skill one-dimensionally (Ferris et al., 1999; Ferris, Witt, & Hochwarter, 2001), by far the most widely used scale with the broadest validation evidence is the multi-dimensional political skill inventory (PSI; Ferris et al., 2005). The PSI comprises 18 Likert-type scaled items to capture the four key dimensions of political skill, which in turn serve as indicators for the higher-order political skill factor (Ferris et al., 2008). In its nomological network, the PSI relates to other social effectiveness constructs (e.g., self-monitoring, emotional intelligence), personality (e.g., conscientiousness), or other akin constructs (e.g., political savvy), while still providing a unique contribution (Banister & Meriac, 2015; Ferris et al., 2005; Munyon et al., 2015; Semadar et al., 2006).

Hogan and Shelton (1998, p. 136) noted that "social skill is a judgement about an actor's performance rendered by observers regardless of what an actor may intend; that is, social skill is in the eyes of the observer not in the intentions of the actor." Indeed, there usually is a moderate degree of empirical convergence between self- and observer ratings of political skill (Ferris et al., 2008). Self-ratings of political skill can be interpreted as identity (i.e., how people see themselves and how their actions are motivated), but other-ratings of political skill represent a person's reputation (i.e., how other people perceive that person's behavior; Hogan & Blickle, 2018). Therefore, self-rated political skill should be associated with internal outcomes, such as well-being. On the other hand, other-rated political skill should be associated with criteria related to behavior observed and evaluated by others, such as performance. Correspondingly, Meurs, Gallagher, and Perrewé (2010) argued that self- and other-ratings of political skill measure unique yet overlapping facets of the same construct. They assert that self-ratings of political skill reflect self-perceptions of control, confidence, and efficacy, whereas other-ratings indicate the target's interpersonal abilities, resource control, and reputation. In line with this suggestion, Meurs et al. (2010) found that high self-rated political skill neutralized the relation between interpersonal conflict and emotional burnout and supervisor-rated political skill buffered the effects of work conflict on job performance. In addition, Blickle et al. (2011) reported that other-ratings of political skill were positive predictors of job performance in a multi-source investigation both in cross-sectional and longitudinal designs.

The PSI has been implemented in a broad range of countries and cultures, such as Brazil (Zellars, Perrewé, Rossi, Tepper, & Ferris, 2008), French-speaking Canada (Bonnelly & Senechal, 2018), China (Shi & Chen, 2012), Germany (Ferris et al., 2008), India (Kalra, Agnihotri, Chaker, Singh, & Das, 2017), Iran (Mokhtari, Safaia, & Zarandi, 2018), Israel (Vigoda-Gadot & Meisler, 2010), Italy (Chiesa, Van Der Heijden, Mazzetti, Mariani, & Guglielmi, 2019), Japan (Kimura, 2013), Pakistan (Khan, Ma, Sadick, & Ibn Musah, 2018), and Spain (Garcia-Chas, Neira-Fontela, Varela-Neira, & Curto-Rodriguez, 2019). Regarding cross-cultural equivalence, Lvina et al. (2012) showed that the PSI was largely invariant across American, Chinese, German, Russian, and Turkish samples. In all samples, the respective translated PSI version showed good model fit as well as invariant factor loadings. Exceptions from measurement invariance, that is, differing latent factor means throughout the different samples, could be explained by cultural differences (uncertainty avoidance and low-to-high context communication), thereby providing support for the universal and stable structure of the PSI (Lvina et al., 2012).

Antecedents of Political Skill.   When asking the question of nature or nurture, Ferris et al. (2007) proposed that political skill had both dispositional and developmental antecedents that could be arranged into five categories. Table 1 presents these five categories and how they associate with political skill dimensions, as proposed by Ferris et al. (2007). Perceptiveness as the first theme refers to an individual's capacity to be observant of social cues in their environment, helping to build a broader database used to understand and influence others. Specifically, Ferris et al. (2007) expected conscientiousness and self-monitoring to signal high perceptiveness and, thus, to enable higher political skill through higher social astuteness, as supported by empirical findings (Ferris et al., 2005). A recent addition to the category of perceptiveness was made by Momm et al. (2015), who identified the ability to accurately recognize other's emotions from human faces and voices as a further antecedent of political skill.

As the second theme, control refers to an individual's self-efficacy, which enables politically skilled individuals to act with self-confidence, knowing that their efforts are likely to be successful (Ferris et al., 2007). Self-efficacy correlated both with composite political skill and with the interpersonal influence dimension (Ferris et al., 2008). Affability, the third antecedent category, refers to an individual's orientation toward other people in terms of extraversion (Ferris et al., 2008; Kolodinsky, Hochwarter, & Ferris, 2004; Liu et al., 2007), positive affectivity (Kolodinsky et al., 2004), humility, and affability (Smith, Plowman, Duchon, & Quinn, 2009).

Active influence refers to an individual's action-proneness, which is captured by constructs like proactive personality (Liu et al., 2007; Thompson, 2005) and self-motivation (Smith et al., 2009). When considering that an active interest in influencing others could result in manipulative tendencies, dark personality should be considered as an additional antecedent. Accordingly, Templer (2018) suggested that those with "toxic" personalities get ahead at work via political skill. Finally, the development and application of political skill is argued to be grounded in political will (i.e., an individual's "motivation to engage in strategic,

Table 1. Dispositional and Developmental Antecedents of Political Skill

Antecedent Theme	Construct	Positively Correlated With	Source
Perceptiveness	Self-monitoring	Social astuteness	Ferris et al. (2005)
	Conscientiousness	Social astuteness	Ferris et al. (2005)
	Emotion recognition ability	Composite political skill	Momm et al. (2015)
Control	Self-efficacy	Composite political skill	Ferris et al. (2008)
		Interpersonal influence	Ferris et al. (2008)
Affability	Extraversion	Composite political skill	Kolodinsky et al. (2004)
		Interpersonal influence	Ferris et al. (2008); Liu et al. (2007)
		Social astuteness	Ferris et al. (2008); Liu et al. (2007)
		Networking ability	Ferris et al. (2008); Liu et al. (2007)
	Positive affectivity	Composite political skill	Kolodinsky et al. (2004)
	Humility	Composite political skill	Smith et al. (2009)
Active influence	Proactive personality	Composite political skill	Liu et al. (2007)
		Networking ability	Thompson (2005)
	Self-motivation	Composite political skill	Smith et al. (2009)
	Dark personality	Composite political skill	Templer (2018)
	Political will	Composite political skill	Kapoutsis et al. (2017)
Developmental experience	Received mentoring	Composite political skill	Ferris et al. (2008)
	Social astuteness		
	Networking ability		
	Apparent sincerity		
	On-the job learning	Composite political skill	Oerder et al. (2014)

goal-directed, behavior that advances the personal agenda and objectives of the actor that inherently involves the risk of relational or reputational capital," Treadway, 2012, p. 533; Kapoutsis et al., 2017).

As opposed to the dispositional characteristics that figure prominently in the first four themes, developmental experience refers to learning processes. In line with the notion that the primary function of a mentor is to help their protégé navigate organizational politics (Ferris et al., 2007), the amount of received mentoring was found to be favorable for the development of political skill (Ferris et al., 2008). Another important driver of political skill development is on-the-job learning. Oerder, Blickle, and Summers (2014) found that targets' (higher) hierarchical position and time involvement in political behavior predicted political skill increases, showing that political skill can be developed beyond formal training and mentoring.

WORKPLACE AND CAREER OUTCOMES

A major reason why political skill sparked so much scholarly interest is its relevance for workplace and career outcomes above and beyond previously established predictors, such as personality and intelligence (Munyon et al., 2015). Moreover, political skill sheds light on what is important in the workplace next to fulfilling core task duties, such as how social influence (attempts) and informal processes affect personal and organizational results. To date, many studies have investigated the direct, indirect, and moderation of political skill's relationships with work outcomes and/or how political skill itself is a moderator of other predictors' association with outcomes. Ultimately, high political skill and high perceived performance should result in higher interpersonal power and occupational status (Dietl, Meurs, & Blickle, 2017; Ferris, Ellen, McAllister, & Maher, 2019; Treadway et al., 2013). A model of political skill's direct and moderating relations is portrayed in Figure 1.

Political Skill as Predictor. Political skill has been linked to various aspects of job performance. Along with the initial validation, Ferris et al. (2005) showed a positive association

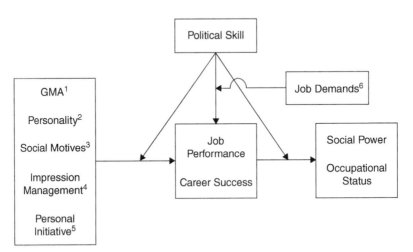

Figure 1. Overview of the direct and moderated relations of political skill at work based on primary studies ([1]Ferris, Witt, & Hochwarter, 2001; [2]Blickle et al., 2008; Blickle et al., 2010; Blickle et al., 2013; Meurs, Perrewé, & Ferris, 2011; Witt & Ferris, 2003; [3]Blickle, Fröhlich et al., 2011; [4]Blickle et al., 2012; Dietl, Meurs, & Blickle, 2017; Harris et al., 2007; Kolodinsky et al., 2007; Treadway et al., 2007; Treadway et al., 2013; [5]Wihler et al., 2017; [6]Blickle et al., 2009; Blickle, John et al., 2012; Gansen-Ammann et al., 2017).

of the PSI with annual performance ratings. In other studies, even after controlling for the typical predictors (i.e., GMA and personality) of job performance, political skill explained significant incremental variance (Bing et al., 2011; Blickle, Kramer et al., 2011; Munyon et al., 2015). When compared with other social effectiveness constructs (i.e., emotional intelligence, self-monitoring, and self-efficacy), political skill was not only the strongest predictor of individual job performance, but it also explained incremental variance beyond them (Semadar et al., 2006). In addition, political skill has predicted managerial effectiveness over traditional measures of managerial skill (Snell, Tonidandel, Braddy, & Fleenor, 2014).

Besides task performance, job performance also consists of what is referred to as contextual performance (i.e., cooperation with and support of colleagues), job dedication, and effort (Conway, 1999). Both contextual performance and related constructs like organizational citizenship behavior (OCB) are just as vital for individual and organizational success as is task performance (Ferris, Witt, & Hochwarter, 2001; Hogan & Shelton, 1998). Blickle, Kramer et al. (2011) found that political skill positively predicted an important aspect of contextual performance, namely, interpersonal facilitation (i.e., the amount of cooperative and helpful behavior toward coworkers; van Scotter & Motowidlo, 1996). Likewise, political skill has related to OCB directed toward individuals (Jawahar, Meurs, Ferris, & Hochwarter, 2008). These direct relations of political skill with task and contextual performance were meta-analytically supported (Bing et al., 2011; Munyon et al., 2015).

Much less research has focused on non-linear relations of political skill. In their field study of supervisor-colleague triads, Zettler and Lang (2015) found inverted U-shaped relations to varying dimensions of job performance, with intermediate levels of political skill resulting in the best performance ratings. Gansen-Ammann et al. (2017) also expected and found non-linear relationships. Specifically, depending on job demands, political skill showed exponential and asymptotic slopes, when looking at managers' performance ratings.

For career outcomes, Ng et al. (2005) meta-analytically showed that political knowledge and skill positively related to both career success and career satisfaction. Similarly, the meta-analysis of Munyon et al. (2015) found that political skill was associated with overall career success (i.e., career satisfaction, income, and position).

Despite the increasing importance of work teams, little research has looked at political behavior in and around teams (Vigoda-Gadot & Vashdi, 2012). However, due to its positive associations with individual performance and career outcomes, it should not be surprising that political skill also plays a role in a team's performance (Lvina, Maher, & Harris, 2017). Going beyond the individual level, Lvina et al. (2018) investigated team-level political skill. After changing the item's perspective from, e.g., "at work" to "in my team," they explored the team's political skill strength as a product of the mean and standard deviation (reversed), so that higher scores (high mean, low standard deviation) would signal higher strength (Lvina et al., 2018). Teams high in political skill showed higher effectiveness in terms of subjective and objective team performance. More research is needed on political skill at the team level, since the investigation of teams offers various new perspectives (e.g., within-team political behavior, inter-team political behavior, team roles, and different types of teams).

Political Skill as Moderator. When predicting workplace outcomes, political skill not only presents direct associations, but has also served as a moderator. Socioanalytic theory posits that in order to translate a person's identity (e.g., their aspirations) into reputation (e.g., how their performance is perceived by others), individuals need social skill (Hogan & Blickle, 2018; Hogan & Shelton, 1998). Accordingly, research suggests that political skill serves as a catalyst when looking at the relation between various employee characteristics and workplace outcomes. Ferris et al. (2001) found that the association between GMA and job performance was strengthened under high levels of social skill. Further, political skill has interacted with the personality traits of extraversion (Blickle, Wendel, & Ferris, 2010), conscientiousness (Blickle et al., 2008; Witt & Ferris, 2003), agreeableness (Blickle et al., 2008), and trait sincerity (Meurs, Perrewé, & Ferris, 2011). Regarding the socioanalytic motives to get along and to get ahead (Hogan & Shelton, 1998), political skill was the moderating variable that helped individuals to higher job performance ratings (Blickle, Fröhlich et al., 2011).

People aim to build a certain reputation at work (Hogan & Blickle, 2018), and, with this aim, they employ impression management strategies. It is not hard to imagine that the success of such behaviors depends on the individual's level of political skill. Better recognition and understanding of social cues should result in an increased ability to exert influence over others and to seem sincere in doing so. Thus, the intended image to be perceived as a better performer should be more clearly conveyed. Indeed, supervisors felt more manipulated by their subordinate's ingratiation behaviors when those subordinates possessed weak political skill (Treadway, Ferris, Duke, Adams, & Thatcher, 2007). This finding implies that employees with high political skill, while making use of the same amount of ingratiation as their less politically skilled co-workers, come across as less manipulative, and are likely seen as better (contextual) performers (Treadway et al., 2007). Moreover, Harris, Kacmar, Zivnuska, and Shaw (2007) showed that the advantage of the combination of impression management with high political skill for favorable supervisor ratings also holds true for further influence tactics, such as intimidation, exemplification, self-promotion, and supplication. In addition, political skill not only moderated the relation between the tactic of rationality and supervisor ratings, but also directly related to the use of rationality (Kolodinsky, Treadway, & Ferris, 2007). Even with a long-term perspective, political skill seems to steer impression management behaviors into the right direction. Blickle, Diekmann, Schneider, Kalthöfer, and Summers (2012) showed that those individuals who were high on political skill and who employed modesty as an impression management tactic (e.g., understatement of own accomplishments or talents) were most satisfied with their career 3 years later, and also reported higher achieved hierarchical ranks.

Finally, Wihler, Blickle, Ellen, Hochwarter, and Ferris (2017) suggested that political skill would be essential for recognizing and capitalizing on opportunities at work. In the first part of their moderated mediation model, social astuteness moderated the relation between organizational climate for personal initiative and an employee's personal initiative. In the second part of their model, interpersonal influence moderated the relation between personal initiative and job performance (Wihler et al., 2017). Hence, the cognitive part of political skill (social astuteness) is needed to discern what opportunities the situation holds and to choose the appropriate behavior (personal initiative). The behavioral part (interpersonal influence) is subsequently responsible for those efforts to be perceived and valued (job performance).

Interactions of Political Skill with Job Demands. Not only does political skill play a role as a predictor of work and career outcomes and as a moderator of the relationship that other predictors have with outcomes, a meta-analysis by Munyon et al. (2015) suggested that there are moderators of the political skill–work outcome association. One important set of moderators are job demands that favor the use of political skill. Empirical evidence supports this contention, as relations of political skill with task and contextual performance have been strengthened when interpersonal demands are increased (Bing et al., 2011; Blickle et al., 2009; Blickle, John et al., 2012).

Holland (1997) elaborated six occupational job types, namely, realistic, investigative, artistic, social, conventional, and enterprising jobs. Based on this theory of vocational job characteristics, Gansen-Ammann et al. (2017) recently investigated the role of political skill in enterprising vocational contexts. Enterprising job characteristics entail influencing others (e.g., customers, co-workers, or subordinates), dealing with risk, leading a group, and negotiating. Enterprising work environments encourage people to influence others to attain organizational or personal goals and to view the world in terms of money, power, and status (Holland, 1997).

In their study, Gansen-Ammann et al. (2017) found that a manager's political skill under high enterprising demands related to an exponential increase in performance ratings. In contrast, under low enterprising demands there was an asymptotic relationship of political skill with performance, such that increases beyond the mean in political skill resulted in minimal improvements. Additionally, Solga, Betz, Düsenberg, and Ostermann (2015) found that when high problem-solving negotiation strategy in salary negotiations of expatriates with their company was combined with high political skill, it resulted in higher additional annual net benefits for the expatriates. In sum, in line with previous theory-based empirical research (Blickle et al., 2009) and meta-analytic findings (Bing et al., 2011), political skill seems to develop its full impact under enterprising job demands.

Mediating Variables. Even though the majority of research attends to the (workplace) outcomes of political skill, some studies have identified potential processes through which political skill might affect those workplace outcomes. Among them, Liu et al. (2007) found that the relation between political skill and performance was mediated by reputation (i.e., an individual's success at developing a favorable image in the eye of others). This result was supported by a meta-analysis (Munyon et al., 2015), which also found self-efficacy to be another mediator in the political skill–performance relation. For career outcomes, Blickle, Schneider, Liu, and Ferris (2011) found that reputation also functioned as a mediating variable in the prediction of career satisfaction and hierarchical position by political skill. In sum, part of the effect of political skill on workplace criteria can be explained through the favorable social situations politically skilled individuals create and through the confidence they feel by having control of their actions and resulting outcomes.

Political Skill and Stress Management. Besides being relevant for job performance and career success, research suggests that political skill also has impact on psychological well-being. Across three samples, Brouer, Ferris, Hochwarter, Laird, and Gilmore (2006) found that political skill buffered the negative relation between the perception of organizational politics and the severity of depressive symptoms. Similarly, political skill was found to counterbalance various job-related stressors, such as role conflict (Jawahar, Stone, & Kisamore, 2007; Perrewé et al., 2004), role overload (Perrewé et al., 2005), political decision-making

(Gallagher & Laird, 2008), social stressors (Harvey, Harris, Harris, & Wheeler, 2007), abusive supervision (Harvey, Stoner, Hochwarter, & Kacmar, 2007), job tension (Hochwarter et al., 2007), perceived entitlement behavior by others (Hochwarter, Summers, Thompson, Perrewé, & Ferris, 2010), conflict (Meurs et al., 2010), perceived politics (Rosen & Levy, 2013), and workplace ostracism (Wu, Yim, Kwan, & Zhang, 2012).

Additionally, a recent study (Carnes, 2017) reported that high political skill buffers role conflict and role overload in the work–family interface. A person experiences role conflict when the demands of different significant role senders are not compatible with one another. In a sample of full-time employed married couples, Carnes (2017) found that husband role conflict at work negatively predicted wife marital satisfaction when husband political skill was low, but not when his political skill was high. Role overload occurs when a person feels they have too many responsibilities compared to given time, abilities, or other limiting factors. Husband marital satisfaction was lower in that study when the wife role overload at work was high and her political skill was low. This evidence suggests political skill to have an impact on psychological well-being above and beyond the work context.

The overarching interpretation of these findings suggests that being well-equipped with work-related social skill attenuates the negative relation of different stressors with strains (e.g., reduced performance and satisfaction, psychological and physiological afflictions) at work and beyond. To date, less is known about the mechanisms through which individuals with high political skill perceive these stressors. It is conceivable that politically skilled employees differ in their appraisal (interpretation of stressors as less threatening) from their less politically skilled peers, that they cope with them differently due to heightened self-efficacy according to Munyon et al. (2015), or that both explanations have validity.

Political Skill in Leadership Roles.   Since leadership is inherently a social influence process, a notable part of leadership roles involves getting things done by other people. Thus, in essence, the leadership role represents enterprising job demands (Blickle et al., 2009). Although formal power sources (e.g., position power, coercive power) are valuable to exert this influence, the role of personal power (e.g., persuasiveness) may outshine the power sources (Yukl & Falbe, 1991), since they concern counseling, persuading, explaining, and suggesting rather than ordering, criticizing, or coercing subordinates (Hogan & Shelton, 1998).

On that note, political skill should help leaders to better fulfill their roles. Indeed, politically skilled leaders exhibited a higher leadership effectiveness (Douglas & Ammeter, 2004), led better performing teams (Ahearn, Ferris, Hochwarter, Douglas, & Ammeter, 2004), and had followers with higher job satisfaction (Treadway et al., 2004). When looking at potential mediating variables, Ewen et al. (2013) found that the link between political skill and leader effectiveness as well as follower satisfaction was explained by the application of both transformational and transactional leadership styles. Wihler, Frieder, Blickle, Oerder, and Schütte (2016) reported that politically skilled managers are better able to both identify visions that resonate with their subordinates and articulate such visions convincingly, such that employees are inspired and mobilized into purposeful action. Dietl and Reb (2019) also suggested that political skill strengthened the relation between a leader's self-regulated attention (a facet of mindfulness) and as how authentic they are perceived by their followers, which, in turn, positively related to leader effectiveness. Again, these findings demonstrated that political skill helps to translate certain motives (e.g., self-awareness) into positively evaluated action (e.g., leader authenticity).

In addition, politically skilled leaders understand that the way to the follower's heart is through demonstrating concern and respect (Frieder, Ferris, Perrewé, Wihler, & Brooks, 2019). Further, political skill has been shown to be especially favorable for leaders when they also possessed high position power (Blickle et al., 2013), in that their subordinates were more satisfied with their jobs when their supervisors initiated more structure and showed more consideration. Similarly, leaders showed more initiating structure, as rated by their followers, when they were politically skilled and motivated to get ahead (Ewen et al., 2014). Moreover, the creativity facet of the personality trait of openness to experience was translated into leader charisma and subsequent leader effectiveness when combined with high political skill (Blickle, Meurs, Wihler, Ewen, & Peiseler, 2014). Overall, political skill seems to foster both leader performance and affective outcomes (e.g., follower satisfaction). Additionally, it strengthens the relations between several leader characteristics and leadership effectiveness criteria, in such a way that the leader's intentions are translated into effective action.

Previous research has neglected a developmental perspective on leader activities in organizational politics (Solga, Witzki, & Blickle, 2015). Using semi-structured interviews with 38 leaders in U.K.-based high-tech and consumer goods organizations at different seniority levels, Doldor (2017) developed and explored a three-stage model of political maturation from politically naïve to politically mature mindsets, cognitive scripts, and social skills. According to Doldor (2017), at the first stage, junior managers develop awareness of organizational politics. They learn to read the political landscape, understand individual motives, map out conflicting agendas, read the informal power web, and identify key stakeholders. At the second stage, they build strong interpersonal relationships with key stakeholders, extend their social networks, and try to find common ground among competing agendas and interests. At the third stage, the level of proficiency, they have the ability to adapt their influence behaviors to different individuals and situations with a high degree of versatility and authenticity (i.e., they feel genuine and consistent with their personal values when using political skill). Future research should test these developmental hypotheses in large samples with quantitative research designs, which allow for rigorous analytical hypothesis testing.

EMERGING AREAS IN POLITICAL SKILL RESEARCH

Political Skill and Dark Personalities.   A research topic that attracted increasing attention since the 2000s is that of the so-called dark personalities and their impact in the workplace (LeBreton, Shiverdecker, & Grimaldi, 2018; O'Boyle, Forsyth, Banks, & McDaniel, 2012; Smith & Lilienfeld, 2013). Even though they are deemed as "toxic" and counterproductive (O'Boyle et al., 2012; Templer, 2018), studies often find individuals with those traits at higher positions in organizations (Landay, Harms, & Credé, 2018). However, it has yet been scarcely investigated how or under which circumstances this happens. One solution to the mystery may be to consider the level of social skill "dark" employees exhibit at work.

Schütte et al. (2018) and Blickle and Schütte (2017) proposed and tested that the positive relation of fearless dominance (i.e., a facet of trait psychopathy that entails fearlessness, stress resilience, and getting social attention; Lilienfeld, Watts, Francis Smith, Berg, & Latzman, 2015) with counterproductive work behavior would be buffered by high levels of the interpersonal influence facet of political skill. This dimension of political skill reflects an ability to adapt one's behavior in subtle, sophisticated, and situationally effective ways. Individuals with this ability should be better suited to package and present their interpersonal style in a manner that allows them to get ahead without being perceived as acrimonious and entirely self-centered. As expected, these employees showed better task and contextual performance. Schütte et al. (2018) concluded that the capacity for directing social interactions skillfully serves as an "antidote" for dark personality traits.

Templer (2018) suggested that dark personality traits (i.e., low honesty-humility; Spain, Harms, & LeBreton, 2014) may even function as an antecedent of political skill, in so far as "dark" employees try to translate their desire to manipulate others into a reputation for high political skill. Indeed, when their supervisors perceived them as politically skilled, individuals low in honesty-humility indirectly received better ratings of task and team performance (Templer, 2018). This result corroborates findings that other-assessment of political skill mediated recommendations for promotion to a middle-management position and receiving venture capital funding (Huang, Frideger, & Pearce, 2013). This is in line with socioanalytic personality theory's (Hogan & Shelton, 1998) suggestion that personality traits with a disposition toward selfishness, treachery, and deceit can coexist with good social skill. Thus, political skill can be an antidote for dark personality traits and it can create a protective façade that camouflages the successful enactment of dark personality traits in the workplace.

Political Skill, Social Media, and Reputation Formation. So far, research concerning political skill has primarily focused on in-person social interactions (e.g., employee–supervisor interactions, team work at the workplace). However, social media is rapidly increasing the channels and opportunities of interaction. Some organizations check applicants' social media profiles (i.e., cybervetting; Berkelaar et al., 2015), technology mediates communication (Blacksmith, Willford, & Behrend, 2016; Henttonen & Blomqvist, 2005), and coworkers often interact via social media (Schmidt, 2016). As one of the first to investigate the impact of political skill in the social media age, Zivnuska, Carlson, Carlson, Harris, and Harris (2019) found that employees high in political skill were better both in using private social media in order to enhance their mood, and in using social media to enhance their vocational network. Although that study indicates that highly politically skilled individuals use social media more effectively, Burtăverde, Avram, and Vlăsceanu (2019) found that high political skill was associated with avoidance of social media (i.e., use of Facebook). One reason the authors note is that those high in political skill may prefer in-person interaction over virtual contact due to their heightened perceived self-efficacy in those situations.

However, activities in social media should contribute to individual reputation formation and enhance its effects. "Reputation is a perceptual identity formed from the collective perceptions of others, which is reflective of the complex combination of salient personal characteristics and accomplishments, demonstrated behavior, and intended images presented over some period of time as observed directly and/or reported from secondary sources, which reduces ambiguity about expected future behavior" (Zinko, Ferris, Blass, & Laird, 2007, p. 165).

The effects of a positive reputation at work involve more discretion to act, increased power, improved objective job performance, enhanced job performance evaluations, and higher income. Other long-term consequences of a positive reputation include career success, higher subjective well-being, and improved career and life satisfaction (Ferris et al., 2014).

IMPLICATIONS FOR PRACTICE

As described in the section "Measurement of Political Skill," the PSI has demonstrated broad and valuable evidence of construct and criterion validity. Furthermore, political skill has been associated with employee income, hierarchical position, and career satisfaction. In addition, political skill attenuates the negative influence of social stressors on job satisfaction and somatic well-being. However, some jobs require more political skill than others. For example, enterprising job demands moderate the relation between political skill and job performance, such that political skill is more predictive in jobs with higher enterprising demands. Nevertheless, the PSI can be recommended for selection regardless of job type, because political skill is an important resource in successfully coping with stress both at work and in the family. Thus, the PSI meets the necessary conditions to be used as an assessment tool in personnel selection.

Given the belief among organizational decision-makers and in the legal system that job applicants fake their responses on self-reported assessment devices (Dilchert, Ones, Viswesvaran, & Deller, 2006), the consequences of potential response distortion was addressed in several studies. In a within-subjects experimental design with employees, Blickle, von Below, and Johannen (2011) found that self-reports of higher political skill indeed increased under job application conditions. However, criterion validity (i.e., the PSI–job performance relation) was positive, and was not statistically different between the non-job application and the job-application conditions. Additionally, Blickle and Schnitzler (2010), using an employee sample in a between-subjects design that experimentally varied job-application versus honest responding, found that construct and criterion validity were the same under both conditions. These results show that the relation between PSI scores and performance criteria is not critically distorted by impression management. In sum, these findings support the applicability of the PSI to practical personnel decision-making.

Given the various positive workplace and career outcomes of political skill, practitioners may be interested in whether and how this skill could be trained. One way to purposely develop employee political skill would be by establishing mentoring programs. Ferris et al. (2008) found that the amount of received mentoring positively predicted a person's social astuteness, networking ability, and apparent sincerity about 2 years later. Oerder et al. (2014) identified contextual factors that promoted changes in political skill levels. In an investigation of work council members, they found that higher positions (with heightened responsibilities) and the amount of formal time involvement predicted an increase in the networking ability dimension (Oerder et al., 2014). However, although it is generally agreed that political skill can be learned (Ferris et al., 2007, 2008; Oerder et al., 2014; Roberts, 2006), a comprehensive training for political skill has yet to be developed and empirically tested (see Solga et al., 2015 for some useful training tools).

CONCLUSION

Political skill is an established concept of social skill that not only values the relevance of social interaction at work, but also takes into account the political perspective on organizations and careers. In addition, over the course of its broad international use, the political skill inventory (PSI) has continuously proved its construct and criterion validity. Political skill is not only directly related to various positive work and career outcomes, but it also interacts with other important workplace factors (e.g., personality and situational characteristics). Besides its role in the prediction of traditional work criteria (e.g., job performance), political skill seems to be a promising candidate in the investigation of recent work developments and trends, such as new communication technologies and social media.

FURTHER READING

Blickle, G., Frieder, R., & Ferris, G. R. (2018). Political skill. In D. S. Ones, N. R. Anderson, H. K. Sinangil, & C. Viswesvaran (Eds.), *The SAGE handbook of industrial, work & organizational psychology: Personnel psychology and employee performance* (pp. 299–319). Los Angeles, CA: SAGE.

Ferris, G. R., Ellen, B. P., McAllister, C. P., & Maher, L. P. (2019). Reorganizing organizational politics research: A review of the literature and identification of future research directions. *Annual Review of Organizational Psychology and Organizational Behavior, 6,* 299–323. http://dx.doi.org/10.1146/annurev-orgpsych-012218-015221

Ferris, G. R., & Treadway, D. C. (Eds.). (2012). *Politics in organizations: Theory and research considerations.* SIOP Organizational Frontiers Series. London, U.K.: Routledge.

Vigoda-Gadot, E., & Drory, A. (Eds.). (2016). *Handbook of organizational politics: Looking back and to the future* (2d ed.). Northampton, MA: Edward Elgar.

REFERENCES

Ahearn, K. K., Ferris, G. R., Hochwarter, W. A., Douglas, C., & Ammeter, A. P. (2004). Leader political skill and team performance. *Journal of Management, 30,* 309–327. http://dx.doi.org/10.1016/j.jm.2003.01.004

Banister, C. M., & Meriac, J. P. (2015). Political skill and work attitudes: A comparison of multiple social effectiveness constructs. *The Journal of Psychology, 149,* 775–795. http://dx.doi.org/10.1080/00223980.2014.979127

Bedi, A., & Skowronski, M. (2014). Political skill at work: Good or bad? Understanding its predictors and consequences. *SAM Advanced Management Journal, 79,* 39–47.

Berkelaar, B. L., Scacco, J. M., & Birdsell, J. L. (2015). The worker as politician: How online information and electoral heuristics shape personnel selection and careers. *New Media & Society, 17,* 1377–1396. http://dx.doi.org/10.1177/1461444814525739

Bing, M. N., Davison, H. K., Minor, I., Novicevic, M. M., & Frink, D. D. (2011). The prediction of task and contextual performance by political skill: A meta-analysis and moderator test. *Journal of Vocational Behavior, 79,* 563–577. http://dx.doi.org/10.1016/j.jvb.2011.02.006

Blacksmith, N., Willford, J., & Behrend, T. (2016). Technology in the employment interview. A meta-analysis and future research agenda. *Personnel Assessment and Decisions, 2,* 12–20. http://dx.doi.org/10.25035/pad.2016.002

Blickle, G., Diekmann, C., Schneider, P. B., Kalthöfer, Y., & Summers, J. K. (2012). When modesty wins: Impression management through modesty, political skill, and career success—a two-study investigation. *European Journal of Work and Organizational Psychology, 21,* 899–922. http://dx.doi.org/10.1080/1359432X.2011.603900

Blickle, G., Frieder, R., & Ferris, G. R. (2018). Political skill. In D. S. Ones, N. R. Anderson, H. K. Sinangil, & C. Viswesvaran (Eds.), *The SAGE handbook of industrial, work & organizational psychology: Personnel psychology and employee performance* (pp. 299–319). Los Angeles, CA: SAGE.

Blickle, G., Fröhlich, J. K., Ehlert, S., Pirner, K., Dietl, E., Hanes, T. J., & Ferris, G. R. (2011). Socioanalytic theory and work behavior: Roles of work values and political skill in job performance and promotability assessment. *Journal of Vocational Behavior, 78*, 136–148. http://dx.doi.org/10.1016/j.jvb.2010.05.010

Blickle, G., John, J., Ferris, G. R., Momm, T., Liu, Y., Haag, R.,…, Oerder, K. (2012). Fit of political skill to the work context: A two-study investigation. *Applied Psychology, 61*, 295–322. https://doi.org/10.1111/j.1464-0597.2011.00469.x

Blickle, G., Kane-Frieder, R. E., Oerder, K., Wihler, A., Below, A. von, Schütte, N.,…, Ferris, G. R. (2013). Leader behaviors as mediators of the leader characteristics—follower satisfaction relationship. *Group & Organization Management, 38*, 601–629. http://dx.doi.org/10.1177/1059601113503183

Blickle, G., Kramer, J., Schneider, P. B., Meurs, J. A., Ferris, G. R., Mierke, J.,…, Momm, T. D. (2011). Role of political skill in job performance prediction beyond general mental ability and personality in cross-sectional and predictive studies. *Journal of Applied Social Psychology, 41*, 488–514. https://doi.org/10.1111/j.1559-1816.2010.00723.x

Blickle, G., Kramer, J., Zettler, I., Momm, T., Summers, J. K., Munyon, T. P., & Ferris, G. R. (2009). Job demands as a moderator of the political skill-job performance relationship. *Career Development International, 14*, 333–350. http://dx.doi.org/10.1108/13620430910979835

Blickle, G., Meurs, J. A., Wihler, A., Ewen, C., & Peiseler, A. K. (2014). Leader inquisitiveness, political skill, and follower attributions of leader charisma and effectiveness: Test of a moderated mediation model. *International Journal of Selection and Assessment, 22*, 272–285. http://dx.doi.org/10.1111/ijsa.12076

Blickle, G., Meurs, J. A., Zettler, I., Solga, J., Noethen, D., Kramer, J., & Ferris, G. R. (2008). Personality, political skill, and job performance. *Journal of Vocational Behavior, 72*, 377–387. http://dx.doi.org/10.1016/j.jvb.2007.11.008

Blickle, G., Schneider, P. B., Liu, Y., & Ferris, G. R. (2011). A predictive investigation of reputation as mediator of the political-skill/career-success relationship. *Journal of Applied Social Psychology, 41*, 3026–3048. https://doi.org/10.1111/j.1559-1816.2011.00862.x

Blickle, G., & Schnitzler, A. (2010). Is the political skill inventory fit for personnel selection? An experimental field study. *International Journal of Selection and Assessment, 18*, 155–165. https://doi.org/10.1111/j.1468-2389.2010.00497.x

Blickle, G., & Schütte, N. (2017). Trait psychopathy, task performance, and counterproductive work behavior directed toward the organization. *Personality and Individual Differences, 109*, 225–231. http://dx.doi.org/10.1016/j.paid.2017.01.006

Blickle, G., Schütte, N., & Wihler, A. (2018). Political will, work values, and objective career success: A novel approach—The trait-reputation-identity model. *Journal of Vocational Behavior, 107*, 42–56. http://dx.doi.org/10.1016/j.jvb.2018.03.002

Blickle, G., von Below, A., & Johannen, A. (2011). Self-ratings of political skill in job application: A within- and between-subjects field experiment. *International Journal of Selection and Assessment, 19*, 98–104. https://doi.org/10.1111/j.1468-2389.2010.00537.x

Blickle, G., Wendel, S., & Ferris, G. R. (2010). Political skill as moderator of personality—Job performance relationships in socioanalytic theory: Test of the getting ahead motive in automobile sales. *Journal of Vocational Behavior, 76*, 326–335. http://dx.doi.org/10.1016/j.jvb.2009.10.005

Bonnelly, L. B., & Senechal, C. (2018). Validation of the inventory of political skills in a population of school principals. *Psychologie du Travail et des Organizations, 24*, 109–125. http://dx.doi.org/10.1016/j.pto.2017.08.007

Brouer, R. L., Ferris, G. R., Hochwarter, W. A., Laird, M. D., & Gilmore, D. D. (2006). The strain-related reactions to perceptions of organizational politics as a workplace stressor: Political skill as a neutralizer.

In E. Vigoda-Gadot & A. Drory (Eds.), *Handbook of organizational politics* (pp. 187–206). Northampton, MA: Edward Elgar.

Burtăverde, V., Avram, E., & Vlăsceanu, S. (2019). Not using social media. A socioanalytic perspective. *Computers in Human Behavior, 101*, 276–285. http://dx.doi.org/10.1016/j.chb.2019.07.030

Carnes, A. M. (2017). Bringing work stress home: The impact of role conflict and role overload on spousal marital satisfaction. *Journal of Occupational and Organizational Psychology, 90*, 153–176. http://dx.doi.org/10.1111/joop.12163

Chiesa, R., Van Der Heijden, B. I. J. M., Mazzetti, G., Mariani, M. G., & Guglielmi, D. (2019). "It is all in the game!": The role of political skill for perceived employability enhancement. *Journal of Career Development.* http://dx.doi.org/10.1177/0894845319832666

Conway, J. M. (1999). Distinguishing contextual form task performance for managerial jobs. *Journal of Applied Psychology, 84*, 3–13. http://dx.doi.org/10.1037/0021-9010.84.1.3

Dietl, E., Meurs, J. A., & Blickle, G. (2017). Do they know how hard I work? Investigating how implicit-explicit achievement orientation, reputation, and political skill affect occupational status. *European Journal of Work and Organizational Psychology, 26*, 120–132. https://www.tandfonline.com/doi/abs/10.1080/1359432X.2016.1225040?journalCode=pewo20

Dietl, E., & Reb, J. (2019). A self-regulation model of leader authenticity based on mindful self-regulated attention and political skill. *Human Relations.* https://doi.org/10.1177/0018726719888260

Dilchert, S., Ones, D. S., Viswesvaran, C., & Deller, J. (2006). Response distortion in personality measurement: Born to deceive, yet capable of providing valid self-assessments? *Psychology Science, 48*, 209–225.

Doldor, E. (2017). From politically naïve to politically mature: Conceptualizing leaders' political maturation journey. *British Journal of Management, 28*, 666–686. http://dx.doi.org/10.1111/1467-8551.12219

Douglas, C., & Ammeter, A. P. (2004). An examination of leader political skill and its effect on ratings of leader effectiveness. *The Leadership Quarterly, 15*, 537–550. http://dx.doi.org/10.1016/j.leaqua.2004.05.006

Ewen, C., Wihler, A., Blickle, G., Oerder, K., Ellen, B. P., Douglas, C., & Ferris, G. R. (2013). Further specification of the leader political skill–leadership effectiveness relationships: Transformational and transactional leader behavior as mediators. *The Leadership Quarterly, 24*, 516–533. http://dx.doi.org/10.1016/j.leaqua.2013.03.006

Ewen, C., Wihler, A., Frieder, R. E., Blickle, G., Hogan, R., & Ferris, G. R. (2014). Leader advancement motive, political skill, leader behavior, and effectiveness: A moderated mediation extension of socioanalytic theory. *Human Performance, 27*, 373–392. http://dx.doi.org/10.1080/08959285.2014.956174

Ferris, G. R., Berkson, H. M., Kaplan, D. M., Gilmore, D. C., Buckley, M. R., Hochwarter, W. A., & Witt, L. A. (1999). Development and initial validation of the political skill inventory. Paper presented at the 59th Annual National Meeting of the Academy of Management, Chicago.

Ferris, G. R., Blickle, G., Schneider, P. B., Kramer, J., Zettler, I., Solga, J.,…, Meurs, J. A. (2008). Political skill construct and criterion-related validation: A two-study investigation. *Journal of Managerial Psychology, 23*, 744–771. https://www.emerald.com/insight/content/doi/10.1108/02683940810896321/full/html

Ferris, G. R., Ellen, B. P., McAllister, C. P., & Maher, L. P. (2019). Reorganizing organizational politics research: A review of the literature and identification of future research directions. *Annual Review of Organizational Psychology and Organizational Behavior, 6*, 299–323. http://dx.doi.org/10.1146/annurev-orgpsych-012218-015221

Ferris, G. R., Harris, J. N., Russell, Z. A., Ellen, B. P., Martinez, A. D., & Blass, F. R. (2014). The role of reputation in the organizational sciences: A multilevel review, construct assessment, and research directions. *Research in Personnel and Human Resources Management, 32*, 241–303.

Ferris, G. R., Treadway, D. C., Kolodinsky, R. W., Hochwarter, W. A., Kacmar, C. J., Douglas, C., & Frink, D. D. (2005). Development and validation of the political skill inventory. *Journal of Management, 31*, 126–152. http://dx.doi.org/10.1177/0149206304271386

Ferris, G. R., Treadway, D. C., Perrewé, P. L., Brouer, R. L., Douglas, C., & Lux, S. (2007). Political skill in organizations. *Journal of Management, 33*, 290–320. http://dx.doi.org/10.1177/0149206307300813

Ferris, G. R., Witt, L. A., & Hochwarter, W. A. (2001). Interaction of social skill and general mental ability on job performance and salary. *Journal of Applied Psychology, 86*, 1075–1082. http://dx.doi.org/10.1037/0021-9010.86.6.1075

Frieder, R. E., Ferris, G. R., Perrewé, P. L., Wihler, A., & Brooks, C. D. (2019). Extending the meta-theoretical framework of the social/political influence to leadership: Political skill effects on situational appraisals, responses, and evaluations by others. *Personnel Psychology*. http://dx.doi.org/10.1111/peps.12336

Fugate, M., Kinicki, A. J., & Ashforth, B. E. (2004). Employability: A psycho-social construct, its dimensions, and applications. *Journal of Vocational Behavior, 65*, 14–38. http://dx.doi.org/10.1016/j.jvb.2003.10.005

Gallagher, V. C., & Laird, M. D. (2008). The combined effect of political skill and political decision making on job satisfaction. *Journal of Applied Social Psychology, 38*, 2336–2360. https://doi.org/10.1111/j.1559-1816.2008.00394.x

Gansen-Ammann, D.-N., Meurs, J. A., Wihler, A., & Blickle, G. (2017). Political skill and manager Performance: Exponential and asymptotic relationships due to differing levels of enterprising job demands. *Group & Organization Management*. http://dx.doi.org/10.1177/1059601117747487

Garcia-Chas, R., Neira-Fontela, E., Varela-Neira, C., & Curto-Rodriguez, E. (2019). The effect of political skill on work role performance and intention to leave: A moderated mediation model. *Journal of Leadership & Organizational Studies, 26*, 98–110. http://dx.doi.org/10.1177/1548051818774547

Harris, K. J., Kacmar, K. M., Zivnuska, S., & Shaw, J. D. (2007). The impact of political skill on impression management effectiveness. *Journal of Applied Psychology, 92*, 278–285. http://dx.doi.org/10.1037/0021-9010.92.1.278

Harvey, P., Harris, R. B., Harris, K. J., & Wheeler, A. R. (2007). Attenuating the effects of social stress: The impact of political skill. *Journal of Occupational Health Psychology, 12*, 105–115. http://dx.doi.org/10.1037/1076-8998.12.2.105

Harvey, P., Stoner, J., Hochwarter, W., & Kacmar, C. (2007). Coping with abusive supervision: The neutralizing effects of ingratiation and positive affect on negative employee outcomes. *The Leadership Quarterly, 18*, 264–280. http://dx.doi.org/10.1016/j.leaqua.2007.03.008

Henttonen, K., & Blomqvist, K. (2005). Managing distance in a global virtual team. The evolution of trust through technology-mediated relational communication. *Strategic Change, 14*, 107–119. http://dx.doi.org/10.1002/jsc.714

Hochwarter, W. A., Ferris, G. R., Gavin, M. B., Perrewé, P. L., Hall, A. T., & Frink, D. D. (2007). Political skill as neutralizer of felt accountability—Job tension effects on job performance ratings: A longitudinal investigation. *Organizational Behavior and Human Decision Processes, 102*, 226–239. http://dx.doi.org/10.1016/j.obhdp.2006.09.003

Hochwarter, W. A., Summers, J. K., Thompson, K. W., Perrewé, P. L., & Ferris, G. R. (2010). Strain reactions to perceived entitlement behavior by others as a contextual stressor: Moderating role of political skill in three samples. *Journal of Occupational Health Psychology, 15*, 388–398. http://dx.doi.org/10.1037/a0020523

Hogan, R., & Blickle, G. (2018). Socioanalytic theory: Basic concepts, supporting evidences, and practical implications. In V. Zeigler-Hill & T. K. Shackelford (Eds.), *The SAGE handbook of personality and individual differences* (pp. 110–129). Thousand Oaks, CA: SAGE.

Hogan, R., & Shelton, D. (1998). A socioanalytic perspective on job performance. *Human Performance, 11*, 129–144. http://dx.doi.org/10.1080/08959285.1998.9668028

Holland, J. L. (1997). *Making vocational choices: A theory of vocational personalities and work environments* (3d ed.). Englewood Cliffs, NJ: Prentice-Hall.

Huang, L., Frideger, M., & Pearce, J. L. (2013). Political skill: Explaining the effects of nonnative accent on managerial hiring and entrepreneurial investment decisions. *Journal of Applied Psychology, 98*, 1005–1017. http://dx.doi.org/10.1037/a0034125

Inkson, K. (2004). Images of career: Nine key metaphors. *Journal of Vocational Behavior, 65*, 96–111. http://dx.doi.org/10.1016/S0001-8791(03)00053-8

Jacobson, R. K., & Viswesvaran, C. (2017). A reliability generalization study of the political skill inventory. *SAGE Open, 7*, 1–17. http://dx.doi.org/10.1177/2158244017706714

Jawahar, I. M., Meurs, J. A., Ferris, G. R., & Hochwarter, W. A. (2008). Self-efficacy and political skill as comparative predictors of task and contextual performance: A two-study constructive replication. *Human Performance, 21*, 138–157. http://dx.doi.org/10.1080/08959280801917685

Jawahar, I. M., Stone, T. H., & Kisamore, J. L. (2007). Role conflict and burnout: The direct and moderating effects of political skill and perceived organizational support on burnout dimensions. *International Journal of Stress Management, 14*, 142–159. http://dx.doi.org/10.1037/1072-5245.14.2.142

Kalra, A., Agnihotri, R., Chaker, N. N., Singh, R. K., & Das, B. K. (2017). Connect within to connect outside: Effect of salespeople's political skill on relationship performance. *Journal of Personal Selling & Sales Management, 37*, 332–348. http://dx.doi.org/10.1080/08853134.2017.1391100

Kapoutsis, I., Papalexandris, A., Treadway, D. C., & Bentley, J. (2017). Measuring political will in organizations: Theoretical construct development and empirical validation. *Journal of Management, 43*, 2252–2280. http://dx.doi.org/10.1177/0149206314566460

Khan, H. S., Ma, Z., Abubakari Sadick, M. & Ibn Musah, A.-A. (2018). Investigating the role of psychological contract breach, political skill and work ethic on perceived politics and job attitudes relationships. A case of higher education in Pakistan. *Sustainability, 10*, 4737. http://dx.doi.org/10.3390/su10124737

Kimura, T. (2013). The moderating effect of political skill and leader-member exchange on the relationship between organizational politics and affective commitment. *Journal of Business Ethics, 116*, 587–599. http://dx.doi.org/10.1007/s10551-012-1497-x

Klein, C., DeRouin, R. E., & Salas, E. (2006). Uncovering workplace interpersonal skills: A review, framework, and research agenda. In G. P. Hodgkinson & J. K. Ford (Eds.), *International review of industrial and organizational psychology 2006* (pp. 79–126). Hoboken, NJ: Wiley.

Kolodinsky, R. W., Hochwarter, W. A., & Ferris, G. R. (2004). Nonlinearity in the relationship between political skill and work outcomes: Convergent evidence from three studies. *Journal of Vocational Behavior, 65*, 294–308. http://dx.doi.org/10.1016/j.jvb.2003.08.002

Kolodinsky, R. W., Treadway, D. C., & Ferris, G. R. (2007). Political skill and influence effectiveness: Testing portions of an expanded Ferris and Judge (1991) model. *Human Relations, 60*, 1747–1777. http://dx.doi.org/10.1177/0018726707084913

Landay, K., Harms, P. D., & Credé, M. (2018). Shall we serve the dark lords? A meta-analytic review of psychopathy and leadership. *Journal of Applied Psychology.* http://dx.doi.org/10.1037/apl0000357

Lasswell, H. (1936). *Who gets what, when, and how?* New York, NY: McGraw-Hill.

LeBreton, J. M., Shiverdecker, L. K., & Grimaldi, E. M. (2018). The dark triad and workplace behaviour. *Annual Review of Organizational Psychology and Organizational Behavior, 5*, 387–414. http://dx.doi.org/10.1146/annurev-orgpsych-032117-104451

Lilienfeld, S. O., Watts, A. L., Francis Smith, S., Berg, J. M., & Latzman, R. D. (2015). Psychopathy deconstructed and reconstructed: Identifying and assembling the personality building blocks of Cleckley's chimera. *Journal of Personality, 83*, 593–610. http://dx.doi.org/10.1111/jopy.12118

Liu, Y., Ferris, G. R., Zinko, R., Perrewé, P. L., Weitz, B., & Xu, J. (2007). Dispositional antecedents and outcomes of political skill in organizations: A four-study investigation with convergence. *Journal of Vocational Behavior, 71*, 146–165. http://dx.doi.org/10.1016/j.jvb.2007.04.003

Lvina, E., Johns, G., Treadway, D. C., Blickle, G., Liu, Y., Liu, J.,…, Ferris, G. R. (2012). Measure invariance of the political skill inventory (PSI) across five cultures. *International Journal of Cross Cultural Management*, *12*, 171–191. https://doi.org/10.1177/1470595812439870

Lvina, E., Johns, G., & Vandenberghe, C. (2018). Team political skill composition as a determinant of team cohesiveness and performance. *Journal of Management*, *44*, 1001–1028. http://dx.doi.org/10.1177/0149206315598371

Lvina, E., Maher, L. P., & Harris, J. N. (2017). Political skill, trust, and efficacy in teams. *Journal of Leadership & Organizational Studies*, *24*, 95–105. http://dx.doi.org/10.1177/1548051816657984

McAllister, C. P., Ellen, B. P., & Ferris, G. R. (2018). Social influence opportunity recognition, evaluation, and capitalization: Increased theoretical specification through political skill's dimensional dynamics. *Journal of Management*, *44*, 1926–1952. http://dx.doi.org/10.1177/0149206316633747

Meurs, J. A., Gallagher, V. C., & Perrewé, P. L. (2010). The role of political skill in the stressor–outcome relationship: Differential predictions for self- and other-reports of political skill. *Journal of Vocational Behavior*, *76*, 520–533. http://dx.doi.org/10.1016/j.jvb.2010.01.005

Meurs, J. A., Perrewé, P. L., & Ferris, G. R. (2011). Political skill as moderator of the trait sincerity–task performance relationship: A socioanalytic, narrow trait perspective. *Human Performance*, *24*, 119–134. http://dx.doi.org/10.1080/08959285.2011.554469

Mintzberg, H. (1983). *Power in and around organizations*. Englewood Cliffs, NJ: Prentice Hall.

Mintzberg, H. (1985). The organization as a political arena. *Journal of Management Studies*, *22*, 133–154.

Mokhtari, R., Safaia, A. M., & Zarandi, H. P. (2018). The factors affecting the formation of political behavior in Iranian sport ministry and federations. *Annals of Applied Sport Science*, *6*, 95–104. http://dx.doi.org/10.29252/aassjournal.6.2.95

Momm, T., Blickle, G., Liu, Y., Wihler, A., Kholin, M., & Menges, J. I. (2015). It pays to have an eye for emotions: Emotion recognition ability indirectly predicts annual income. *Journal of Organizational Behavior*, *36*(1), 147–163. http://dx.doi.org/10.1002/job.1975

Munyon, T. P., Summers, J. K., Thompson, K. M., & Ferris, G. R. (2015). Political skill and work outcomes: A theoretical extension, meta-analytic investigation, and agenda for the future. *Personnel Psychology*, *68*, 143–184. http://dx.doi.org/10.1111/peps.12066

Ng, T. W. H., Eby, L., Sorensen, K. L., & Feldman, D. C. (2005). Predictors of objective and subjective career success: A meta-analysis. *Personnel Psychology*, *58*, 367–408. https://doi.org/10.1111/j.1744-6570.2005.00515.x

O'Boyle, E. H., Forsyth, D. R., Banks, G. C., & McDaniel, M. A. (2012). A meta-analysis of the Dark Triad and work behavior: A social exchange perspective. *Journal of Applied Psychology*, *97*, 557–579. http://dx.doi.org/10.1037/a0025679

Oerder, K., Blickle, G., & Summers, J. (2014). How work context and age shape political skill. *Journal of Managerial Psychology*, *29*, 582–599. http://dx.doi.org/10.1108/JMP-01-2013-0004

Perrewé, P. L., Zellars, K. L., Ferris, G. R., Rossi, A. M., Kacmar, C. J., & Ralston, D. A. (2004). Neutralizing job stressors: Political skill as an antidote to the dysfunctional consequences of role conflict. *Academy of Management Journal*, *47*, 141–152. http://dx.doi.org/10.5465/20159566

Perrewé, P. L., Zellars, K. L., Rossi, A. M., Ferris, G. R., Kacmar, C. J., Liu, Y.,…, Hochwarter, W. A. (2005). Political skill: An antidote in the role overload-strain relationship. *Journal of Occupational Health Psychology*, *10*, 239–250. http://dx.doi.org/10.1037/1076-8998.10.3.239

Pfeffer, J. (1981). *Power in organizations*. Cambridge, MA: Ballinger.

Pfeffer, J. (2009). Low grades for performance reviews. *Bloomberg Businessweek*, July 23. https://www.bloomberg.com/news/articles/2009-07-23/low-grades-for-performance-reviews

Pfeffer, J. (2010). *Power. Why some people have it and others don't*. New York, NY: Harper Business.

Roberts, B. W. (2006). Personality development and organizational behavior. *Research in Organizational Behavior*, *27*, 1–40. http://dx.doi.org/10.1016/S0191-3085(06)27001-1

Rosen, C. C., & Levy, P. E. (2013). Stresses, swaps, and skill: An investigation of the psychological dynamics that relate work politics to employee performance. *Human Performance, 26,* 44–65. http://dx.doi.org /10.1080/08959285.2012.736901

Schmidt, F. L., & Oh, I.-S. (2016). The crisis of confidence in research findings in psychology: Is lack of replication the real problem? Or is it something else? *Archives of Scientific Psychology, 4,* 32–37. http:// dx.doi.org/10.1037/arc0000029

Schmidt, G. B. (2016). How social media can impact the organizational political process. In E. Vigoda-Gadot & A. Drory (Eds.), *Handbook of organizational politics: Looking back and to the future* (2d ed., pp. 148–171). Northampton, MA: Edward Elgar.

Schütte, N., Blickle, G., Frieder, R. E., Wihler, A., Schnitzler, F., Heupel, J., & Zettler, I. (2018). The role of interpersonal influence in counterbalancing psychopathic personality trait facets at work. *Journal of Management, 44,* 225–231. https://doi.org/10.1177/0149206315607967

Semadar, A., Robins, G., & Ferris, G. R. (2006). Comparing the validity of multiple social effectiveness constructs in the prediction of managerial job performance. *Journal of Organizational Behavior, 27,* 443–461. http://dx.doi.org/10.1002/job.385

Shi, J., & Chen, Z. (2012). Psychometric properties of a Chinese translation of the political skill inventory. *Psychological Reports, 110,* 233–246. https://www.ncbi.nlm.nih.gov/pubmed/22489389

Silvester, J., & Wyatt, M. (2018). Political effectiveness at work. In D. S. Ones, N. R. Anderson, H. K. Sinangil, & C. Viswesvaran (Eds.), *The SAGE handbook of industrial, work & organizational psychology: Personnel psychology and employee performance* (pp. 228–247). Los Angeles, CA: SAGE.

Smith, A. D., Plowman, D. A., Duchon, D., & Quinn, A. M. (2009). A qualitative study of high-reputation plant managers: Political skill and successful outcomes. *Journal of Operations Management, 27,* 428–443. http://dx.doi.org/10.1016/j.jom.2009.01.003

Smith, S. F., & Lilienfeld, S. O. (2013). Psychopathy in the workplace: The knowns and unknowns. *Aggression and Violent Behavior, 18,* 204–218. http://dx.doi.org/10.1016/j.avb.2012.11.007

Snell, S. J., Tonidandel, S., Braddy, P. W., & Fleenor, J. W. (2014). The relative importance of political skill dimensions for predicting managerial effectiveness. *European Journal of Work and Organizational Psychology, 23,* 915–929. http://dx.doi.org/10.1080/1359432X.2013.817557

Solga, J., Witzki, A., & Blickle, G. (2015). Power and interpersonal influence in successful project management. In M. Wastian, L. von Rosenstiel, M. A. West & I. Braumandl (Eds.), *Applied psychology for project managers. A practitioner's guide to successful project management* (pp. 129–146). New York, NY: Springer.

Solga, M., Betz, J., Düsenberg, M., & Ostermann, H. (2015). Political skill in job negotiations: A two-study constructive replication. *International Journal of Conflict Management, 26,* 2–24. http://dx.doi .org/10.1108/IJCMA-02-2012-0022

Spain, S. M., Harms, P., & LeBreton, J. M. (2014). The dark side of personality at work. *Journal of Organizational Behavior, 35,* 41–60. http://dx.doi.org/10.1002/job.1894

Templer, K. J. (2018). Dark personality, job performance ratings, and the role of political skill: An indication of why toxic people may get ahead at work. *Personality and Individual Differences, 124,* 209–214. http:// dx.doi.org/10.1016/j.paid.2017.11.030

Thompson, J. A. (2005). Proactive personality and job performance: A social capital perspective. *The Journal of Applied Psychology, 90,* 1011–1017. http://dx.doi.org/10.1037/0021-9010.90.5.1011

Treadway, D. C. (2012). Political will in organizations. In G. R. Ferris & D. C. Treadway (Eds.), *Politics in organizations: Theory and research considerations* (pp. 529–554). SIOP Organizational Frontiers Series. London, U.K.: Routledge.

Treadway, D. C., Breland, J. W., Williams, L. M., Cho, J., Yang, J., & Ferris, G. R. (2013). Social influence and interpersonal power in organizations. *Journal of Management, 39,* 1529–1553. http://dx.doi .org/10.1177/0149206311410887

Treadway, D. C., Ferris, G. R., Duke, A. B., Adams, G. L., & Thatcher, J. B. (2007). The moderating role of subordinate political skill on supervisors' impressions of subordinate ingratiation and ratings of subordinate interpersonal facilitation. *The Journal of Applied Psychology, 92*, 848–855. http://dx.doi.org/10.1037/0021-9010.92.3.848

Treadway, D. C., Hochwarter, W. A., Ferris, G. R., Kacmar, C. J., Douglas, C., Ammeter, A. P., & Buckley, M. R. (2004). Leader political skill and employee reactions. *The Leadership Quarterly, 15*, 493–513. http://dx.doi.org/10.1016/j.leaqua.2004.05.004

Van Scotter, J. R., & Motowidlo, S. J. (1996). Interpersonal facilitation and job dedication as separate facets of contextual performance. *Journal of Applied Psychology, 81*, 525–531. http://dx.doi.org/10.1037/0021-9010.81.5.525

Vigoda-Gadot, E. (2003). *Developments in organizational politics: How political dynamics affect employee performance in modern work sites.* Cheltenham, U.K.: Edgar Elgar.

Vigoda-Gadot, E., & Drory, A. (Eds.). (2016). *Handbook of organizational politics: Looking back and to the future* (2d ed.). Northampton, MA: Edward Elgar.

Vigoda-Gadot, E., & Meisler, G. (2010). Emotions in management and the management of emotions: The impact of emotional intelligence and organizational politics on public sector employees. *Public Administration Review, 70*, 72–86. https://doi.org/10.1111/j.1540-6210.2009.02112.x

Vigoda-Gadot, E., & Vashdi, D. R. (2012). Politics in and around teams: Toward a team-level conceptualization of organizational politics. In G. R. Ferris & D. C. Treadway (Eds.), *Politics in organizations: Theory and research considerations* (pp. 287–322). SIOP Organizational Frontiers Series. London, U.K.: Routledge.

Wihler, A., Blickle, G., Ellen, B. P., Hochwarter, W. A., & Ferris, G. R. (2017). Personal initiative and job performance evaluations: Role of political skill in opportunity recognition and capitalization. *Journal of Management, 43*, 1388–1420. http://dx.doi.org/10.1177/0149206314552451

Wihler, A., Frieder, R., Blickle, G., Oerder, K., & Schütte, N. (2016). Political skill, leadership, and performance: The role of vision identification and articulation. In E. Vigoda-Gadot & A. Drory (Eds.), *Handbook of organizational politics: Looking back and to the future* (pp. 59–94). Cheltenham, U.K.: Edward Elgar.

Witt, L. A., & Ferris, G. R. (2003). Social skill as moderator of the conscientiousness-performance relationship: Convergent results across four studies. *The Journal of Applied Psychology, 88*, 809–821. http://dx.doi.org/10.1037/0021-9010.88.5.809

Wu, L.-Z., Yim, F. H.-K., Kwan, H. K., & Zhang, X. (2012). Coping with workplace ostracism: The roles of ingratiation and political skill in employee psychological distress. *Journal of Management Studies, 49*, 178–199. https://doi.org/10.1111/j.1467-6486.2011.01017.x

Yukl, G., & Falbe, C. M. (1991). Importance of different power sources in downward and lateral relations. *Journal of Applied Psychology, 76*, 416–423. http://dx.doi.org/10.1037/0021-9010.76.3.416

Zellars, K. L., Perrewé, P. L., Rossi, A. M., Tepper, B. J., & Ferris, G. R. (2008). Moderating effects of political skill, perceived control, and job-related self-efficacy on the relationship between negative affectivity and physiological strain. *Journal of Organizational Behavior, 29*, 549–571. http://dx.doi.org/10.1002/job.484

Zettler, I., & Lang, J. W. B. (2015). Employees' political skill and job performance: An inverted U-shaped relation? *Applied Psychology, 64*, 541–577. http://dx.doi.org/10.1111/apps.12018

Zinko, R., Ferris, G. R., Blass, F. R., & Laird, M. D. (2007). Toward a theory of reputation in organizations. In J. J. Martocchio (Ed.), *Research in personnel and human resources management* (Vol. 26, pp. 163–204). Oxford, U.K.: Elsevier.

Zivnuska, S., Carlson, D. S., Carlson, J. R., Harris, R. B., & Harris, K. J. (2019). Investigating the impacts of regulatory focus and political skill within a social media context. *Computers in Human Behavior, 91*, 151–156. https://doi.org/10.1016/j.chb.2018.09.030

Iris Kranefeld, Gerhard Blickle, and James A. Meurs

DARK PERSONALITIES IN THE WORKPLACE

INTRODUCTION

Spurred on, perhaps, by numerous scandals revealed in organizational contexts in the last decade, ranging from fraud to sexual harassment in the workplace, dark personalities have become a topic of considerable interest (Schyns, 2015). People with dark personalities are often considered to possess one or more of the Dark Triad traits of narcissism, Machiavellianism, and psychopathy (Paulhus & Williams, 2002). The expression of dark personality traits can do considerable damage in organizational contexts (e.g., LeBreton, Shiverdecker, & Grimaldi, 2018).

Dark personalities in organizations can be found occupying positions ranging from lower-level rank-and-file employee to CEO. However, some authors have argued that dark personalities are more prevalent in leadership positions than can be assumed based on their prevalence in the general population (Babiak, Neumann, & Hare, 2010; Boddy, 2011a). This can be problematic, given that leaders are charged with authority over others and have the power to exert influence on organizational functioning.[1] As such, those in higher organizational positions can be quite a destructive force (see Magee & Galinsky, 2008), making the study of leader dark personality highly relevant. Indeed, most research into dark personalities has been conducted with or about leaders (see Braun, 2017; LeBreton et al., 2018; Spain, Harms, & LeBreton, 2014). A substantial part of this research focuses on leader emergence (e.g., Nevicka, De Hoogh, Van Vianen, Beersma, & McIlwain, 2011; see also a recent meta-analysis by Landay, Harms, & Credé, 2019) or leader performance (e.g., Judge, LePine, & Rich, 2006). Therefore, the following review mainly focuses on research of leader dark traits, but the little available knowledge about followers with dark personality traits is also discussed. First, the term *dark personalities* is defined; then, for each of the Dark Triad traits, the available literature is reviewed. Finally, suggestions for ways of dealing with dark personality employees are made, and areas for future research are highlighted.

DARK PERSONALITIES: DEFINITIONS

While different definitions of dark personalities exist (e.g., Moshagen, Hilbig, & Zettler, 2018; Spain et al., 2014), the most commonly used theoretical framework is the Dark Triad (Paulhus & Williams, 2002). The *Dark Triad* comprises the traits narcissism, Machiavellianism, and psychopathy. All three of these traits have in common that individuals who score highly in each of these areas lack empathy (Paulhus, 2014)—that is, they are interested mainly in themselves and tend to pursue their self-interest at the expense of others. According to Paulhus and Williams (2002), narcissism, Machiavellianism, and psychopathy all refer to "a socially malevolent character with behavior tendencies toward self-promotion, emotional coldness, duplicity, and aggressiveness" (p. 557). At the same time, each trait has specific features that differentiate it from the others. Importantly, most research on the role of narcissism, Machiavellianism, and psychopathy in organizations focuses on the personality *trait* rather than the *disorder*. That is, narcissism, Machiavellianism, and psychopathy are usually not operationalized as clinical conditions but are assessed as individual difference factors that are normally distributed in the population (e.g., Campbell & Foster, 2007).

Narcissism is characterized by a strong sense of entitlement (e.g., Raskin & Terry, 1988). Sedikides and Campbell (2017) nicely summarized narcissism as a "self-absorbed, self-aggrandizing, vanity-prone, arrogant, dominant, and manipulative interpersonal orientation. Narcissists are preoccupied with their own sense of specialness and importance, and with fantasies of power, beauty, and acclaim. They manifest low levels of empathy, shame, or guilt, while boasting about their ability, thinking of themselves as exceptional or unique, demanding adulation, lashing out at rivals, and not shying away from interpersonal, business, or political brawls" (p. 400). Morf and Rhodewalt (2001) argued that narcissists' self-concept can be "grandiose yet vulnerable" due to their "chronic goal of obtaining continuous external self-affirmation" (p. 177). Clinical psychology, and more recently, social and personality psychology research suggests that narcissists come in two types: vulnerable and grandiose. Grandiose narcissism is related to disagreeableness and extraversion (Paulhus, 2001), whereas vulnerable narcissism is related to disagreeableness and neuroticism (Miller et al., 2018). This differentiation between grandiose and vulnerable narcissism (e.g., Wink, 1991) can be important in the workplace.

Machiavellianism has been defined as "a strategy of social conduct that involves manipulating others for personal gain" (Christie & Geis, 1970, p. 285) and is characterized by a focus on instrumentality, a cynical disregard for morality, a focus on self-interest, the tendency to distrust others, and a willingness to engage in manipulation (e.g., Dahling, Whitaker, & Levy 2009; Jones & Paulhus, 2009). Machiavellians happily use whatever means available to achieve their goals (e.g., Belschak, Den Hartog, & De Hoogh, 2018), and they typically enjoy and excel in strategic behaviors. In fact, in studies that compare the three Dark Triad traits, Machiavellianism is most often regarded as linked to strategic action and goal-oriented manipulation (see Schyns, Wisse, & Sanders, 2019). Although some scholars distinguish several dimensions of Machiavellianism (e.g., distrust, desire for status and control, and amoral manipulation; see Dahling et al., 2009), most organizational research applies the composite score of Machiavellian tendencies. Notably, Machiavellianism has a substantial environment component, which suggests that Machiavellianism may—in part—denote a person's adjustment to the environment (Vernon, Villani, Vickers, & Harris, 2008).

Possibly the darkest of the Dark Triad traits is *psychopathy* (Paulhus, 2014), as psychopaths often appear to act impulsively and irresponsibly, lacking guilt and behavioral control, and displaying antisocial behavior. Research into psychopathy took off after Cleckley (1941) provided a description of clinical psychopathy and offered a list of 16 defining characteristics. His work served as a basis for models that emphasize two core areas of dysfunction of psychopaths: one pointing to diminished affective experience (i.e., callousness, lack of empathy, anxiety, and feelings of guilt) and one pointing to behavioral deviance and deficits in self-control (i.e., impulsivity, antisocial behavior). Competing conceptualizations of psychopathy exist, some of them suggesting a unitary construct, whereas others imply a multi-dimensional nature (Lilienfeld, Watts, Smith, Berg, & Latzman, 2014; Smith & Lilienfeld, 2013). More recently, models distinguishing three- and four-dimensions have been offered for summarizing psychopathic characteristics (disinhibition, boldness, and meanness in Patrick & Drislane, 2015; Patrick, Fowles, & Krueger, 2009; interpersonal manipulation, criminal tendencies, erratic lifestyle, and callous affect in Williams, Paulhus, & Hare, 2007). Some psychopaths can be perceived as charismatic due to their impression management skills (Babiak et al., 2010;

but see Lilienfeld, Watts, Smith, & Latzman, 2018), and they tend to focus on short-term goals and instant gratification (e.g., Jones & Paulhus, 2014; Levenson, Kiehl, & Fitzpatrick, 1995). While the bulk of research relates to psychopathy in clinical terms, already in 1941, Cleckley described psychopaths in the workplace (for a more recent overview see Smith & Lilienfeld, 2013).

Dark Triad personality traits have been studied in multiple contexts. Here, the focus is on research into Dark Triad personality in the workplace. For each of the three traits, the main findings in the light of the extant literature are discussed. Given the definition of the respective traits, it may come as no surprise that individuals high in those traits are found to have a detrimental impact on other employees and organizational functioning (e.g., LeBreton et al., 2018). More specifically, Machiavellianism has modest negative effects and psychopathy has low but substantial negative effects in multisource studies (O'Boyle, Forsyth, Banks, & McDaniel, 2012). It should be noted that, in monosource studies, the negative effects of Dark Triad traits can be overblown (see Blickle, Schütte, & Genau, 2018).

Yet, some research also suggests that the three traits have an adaptive side and that people and organizations may actually sometimes benefit from having these traits.

DARK PERSONALITY IN THE WORKPLACE

Narcissism.   In terms of organizational behavior research, narcissism is the Dark Triad personality trait that has been on the agenda most often. This may be the case because the assessment of narcissism (e.g., the often administered Narcissistic Personality Inventory; Raskin & Terry, 1988) typically contains aspects of leadership, making the concept particularly relevant in organizational research. Within narcissism, it is grandiose narcissism that research in organizational behavior tends to focus on. In the following, the focus is on research into narcissism and leader selection and emergence, narcissism and leadership, CEO narcissism, and narcissism and employee behavior.

Narcissism, Workplace Behavior, Leader Selection and Emergence.   Campbell and Campbell (2009) argued that narcissists strive to achieve leadership positions. Indeed, it seems that narcissists are successful in their endeavors to achieve leadership positions. For example, Brunell, Gentry, Campbell, Hoffman, Kuhnert, and DeMarree (2008) indicated that narcissists are rated highly on leadership criteria in assessment centers similar to manager selection tools (Study 3). Paulhus, Westlake, Calvez, and Harms (2013) argued that in a Western context, narcissism is linked to success in job interviews, as narcissists show the type of behaviors expected in this context—specifically, self-promotion.

More generally, studies have shown that narcissism is positively related to leadership emergence (Nevicka et al., 2011; Ong, Roberts, Arthur, Woodman, & Akehurst, 2016), that is, narcissists are more likely than their less narcissistic counterparts to be considered by their peers to be a group's leader or to be leader-like. However, this phenomenon seems to be time-sensitive: With longer acquaintance, the relationship between peer-rated leadership and narcissism decreases and eventually turns negative (Ong et al., 2016). This is in line with Campbell's (2005) *chocolate cake model* of narcissism. As Campbell, Hoffman, Campbell, and Marchisio (2011, p. 271) put it: "Relationships with narcissistic individuals are like eating chocolate cake. They are appealing and exciting, and initially far better than relationships with non-narcissists. Over time, however, these exciting leaders/workers/partners turn out to be dishonest, controlling, and not concerned with your interests. In the same way, chocolate cake makes you feel sluggish, depressed, and unhealthy 20 min after you eat it." Thus, while narcissists tend to emerge as leaders in non-acquainted groups, positive perceptions do not hold when group members start to know the narcissistic individual better.

Narcissism and Leadership. So, what happens when narcissists get into leadership positions? Braun, Aydin, Frey, and Peus (2018) found in a series of five field and experimental studies that leader narcissism relates positively to followers' negative emotions (malicious envy), which in turn mediates the positive relation between leader narcissism and leader-targeted counter-productive work behavior (CWB).

In terms of leader effectiveness, Grijalva, Harms, Newman, Gaddis, and Fraley (2015) found in a meta-analytic review that narcissism is related to self-rated leader effectiveness but not to other-rated leader effectiveness. Using the HDS Bold scale (Hogan & Hogan, 2009), they found a curvilinear relationship between narcissism and supervisor-reported leader effectiveness. These results should be interpreted with care, though, as Grijalva et al. (2015, p. 20) noted about the HDS Bold scale, that "High scorers on the Bold scale are described as overly self-confident, arrogant, and having inflated feelings of self-worth (HDS technical manual; Hogan & Hogan, 2009)." This measurement contains positive aspects of narcissism (similar to the Narcissistic Personality Inventory), which could explain the results found.

However, Wisse and Sleebos (2016) found that of the three Dark Triad traits, narcissism—as compared to the other two dark traits—had the lowest correlation with follower-rated abusive supervision. This is somewhat surprising, given how self-centered and dismissive of others narcissists are. Therefore, recent research (Braun, Schyns, Zheng, & Lord, 2019; Koch, Schyns, & Vollmer, 2018) looked deeper into the relationship between narcissism and abusive supervision, arguing that a differentiation between different aspects of narcissism will shed further light on this relationship. Both studies consider grandiose and vulnerable sub-dimensions of narcissism. Grandiose or overt narcissism is described as arrogant, assertive, and aggressive, while vulnerable or covert narcissism is described as shy, insecure, and shame-ridden (Ronningstam, 2009). Both types of narcissists are "preoccupied with self-enhancing fantasies and strivings and hyperreactive to oversights or unfulfilled expectations from others" (Ronningstam, 2009, p. 113). However, the vulnerable type is more prone to self-criticism and feelings of guilt (Ronningstam, 2009) and more prone to abusive supervision (Koch et al., 2018).

CEO Narcissism. Studying leadership on a more strategic level, O'Reilly, Doerr, Caldwell, and Chatman (2014) found that CEO narcissism is related to higher compensation packages and a bigger difference between their own and their team members' salaries. At the same time, companies run by narcissistic CEOs are involved in more and longer lawsuits (O'Reilly et al., 2018). Narcissism does not predict CEO performance positively (Chatterjee & Hambrick, 2007; Resick, Whitman, Weingarden, & Hiller, 2009). However, narcissists have inflated self-views that lead them to self-report positive performance (e.g., Campbell et al., 2011). Chatterjee and Hambrick (2007) found that CEO narcissism is related to more extreme and fluctuating company performance. It is also related to more strategic dynamism and to number and size of acquisitions, meaning that narcissistic CEOs take more risks, which might or might not work out positively for the organization they work for. Chatterjee and Pollock (2017) argued that narcissistic CEOs have a higher need for acclaim and dominance, leading to a pursuit of media celebrity status as well as the overshadowing of others. They propose that narcissistic CEOs create their own environments, which leads to more risk taking. Chatterjee and Hambrick (2011) showed that social praise through media influenced narcissistic CEOs' risk taking. Thus, there seems to be a vicious cycle between narcissistic CEOs' risk taking and media attention: narcissistic CEOs strive for media praise, which, when successful, reinforces their risk taking.

In sum, narcissists can emerge as leaders, particularly when others do not know them well. They do not perform better than others; they may be prone to abusive supervision (depending on the type of narcissism), and they may put their organizations' functioning at risk (e.g., with prolonged law suits). In terms of direct abuse of followers, initial evidence suggests that vulnerable dimensions of narcissism may be particularly relevant and require further attention in future research.

Narcissism and Employee Behavior. Generally, narcissists show more counter-productive work behavior than non-narcissists (Grijalva & Newman, 2015; O'Boyle et al., 2012). This is particularly the case for entitlement and exploitative aspects of narcissism. This research shows that narcissism is relevant not only in the context of leadership, but also more widely in terms of employee organizational behavior. A recent theory paper on follower Dark Triad personality argued that narcissistic followers will engage in strategic behaviors such as (a) over-claiming their contribution (Goncalo, Francis, & Kim, 2010), (b) showing behavior to promote themselves (e.g., "public" Organizational Citizenship Behavior; Spain et al., 2014), (c) becoming aggressive after negative feedback and devaluing the feedback source (Thomaes & Bushman, 2011; Schyns et al., 2019). That means that narcissists are problematic not only in leadership positions but more generally in the workplace.

Machiavellianism.
Unlike psychopathy and narcissism, Machiavellianism is typically studied in healthy populations and organizations and less so in a clinical context. Kessler, Bandelli, Spector, Borman, Nelson, and Penney (2010) defined *organizational Machiavellianism* more specifically as "the belief in the use of manipulation, as necessary, to achieve one's desired ends in the context of the work environment" (p. 1871). In the following, a review of research into (a) Machiavellianism and leader selection and emergence, (b) Machiavellianism and leadership, and (c) Machiavellianism and employee behavior are provided.

Machiavellianism and Leader Selection and Emergence. The term *Machiavellianism* derives from Niccolo Machiavelli, an Italian diplomat and strategist who wrote *The Prince*, a notoriously influential book on the accumulation and leverage of political power. As such, it would seem that Machiavellianism and leader selection and emergence are closely related. Moreover, it has been argued that power, wealth, and admiration are particularly appealing for people high in Dark Triad traits—Machiavellians being no exception (see Kajonus, Persson, & Jonason, 2015; Lee, Ashton, Wiltshire, Bourdage, Visser, & Gallucci, 2013; McHoskey, 1999).

The fact that people are more likely to acquire something if they really want it increases the chances that Machiavellians actually identify leadership opportunities and actively work toward obtaining those positions. As a case in point, research has shown that individuals higher in Machiavellianism are more willing to be dishonest during job interviews, arguably to land the desired job (Fletcher, 1990; Lopes & Fletcher, 2004). Interestingly, direct evidence on the relationship between Machiavellianism and leader selection and emergence is far from abundant. In one experimental study, Gleason, Seaman, and Hollander (1978) showed that people with medium levels of Machiavellianism were more likely to be selected as leaders than people with low or high levels of Machiavellianism. Moreover, Spurk, Keller, and Hirschi (2016) found that Machiavellianism positively predicted the acquisition of a leadership position.

Machiavellianism and Leadership. Some studies have linked leader Machiavellianism to abusive supervision. For instance, Kiazad, Restubog, Zagenczyk, Kiewitz, and Tang (2010) found that supervisor Machiavellianism was positively associated with subordinate perceptions of abusive supervision, and that this effect was mediated by subordinate perceptions of authoritarian leadership behavior. In a similar vein, Wisse and Sleebos (2016) investigated the role of the Dark Triad traits in leaders and the perception of abusive supervision in 225 work teams and found that leader Machiavellianism was positively related to abusive supervision in work teams, but only when leaders perceived their position power to be high rather than low. Thus, possessing power amplifies the behavioral consequences of Machiavellian predispositions in leaders. Sendjana, Pekerti, Härtel, Hirst, and Butarbutar (2016) used self-rated, observational, and cognitive reasoning data to investigate the role of Machiavellianism in the relationships between authentic leadership on the one hand and moral reasoning and action on the other hand. They found that leader Machiavellianism reverses the positive effects of both moral reasoning on authentic leadership and of authentic leadership on moral actions. This finding suggests that leaders who understand the difference between what is right and what is wrong will more likely turn into an authentic leader if they are low on Machiavellianism. Moreover, just because a leader is perceived to be authentic, it does not necessarily mean that he or she will engage in moral action. Indeed, if the leader scores high on Machiavellianism that is more unlikely to happen. Notably, Machiavellians are considered to be adaptable and may invest in pro-organizational activities if they see this as beneficial to themselves (Den Hartog & Belschak, 2012). Therefore, Machiavellian leaders can sometimes also successfully exert ethical leadership behaviors. A recent study by Kwak and Shim (2017) revealed that Machiavellian supervisors' ethical leader behaviors were perceived to be genuine by subordinate employees (perhaps because they are able to lie more successfully, see DePaulo & Rosenthal, 1979). Moreover, the effects of Machiavellian supervisors' ethical leader behaviors were intensified in case of higher, versus lower, employee power distance orientation (Kwak & Shim, 2017).

Leaders with Machiavellian traits may have a deleterious impact on employee well-being and attitudes. This shows, for instance, from a study that found that leaders' Machiavellianism was related to lower subordinate career satisfaction and higher subordinate emotional exhaustion (Volmer, Koch, & Göritz, 2016). Den Hartog and Belschak (2012) found that the positive effects of ethical leadership behavior on employee work engagement were suppressed when leaders were comparatively high on Machiavellianism. Moreover, Belschak, Muhammad, and Den Hartog (2016) found that leader Machiavellianism was significantly correlated with employees' lack of trust and their engagement in counterproductive work behavior.

Machiavellianism and Employee Behavior. The effects of Machiavellianism in employees have been studied more extensively than those of narcissistic and psychopathic employees. These studies indicate that Machiavellian employees have a higher overall tendency to engage in unethical behavior (Belschak et al., 2016; Castille, Buckner, & Thoroughgood, 2018), counterproductive work behaviors (Dahling et al., 2009; O'Boyle et al., 2012), and bullying at work (Pilch & Turska, 2015). The relationship between Machiavellianism and job performance is predominantly negative but small (O'Boyle et al., 2012). Machiavellianism in employees has also been associated with an increased use of both hard influence tactics (e.g., threats and attempts at manipulation; also see Farmer, Maslyn, Fedor, & Goodman, 1997) and soft influence tactics (e.g., ingratiation, offering to exchange a favor, and compromise; see Jonason, Slomski, & Partyka, 2012). Employee Machiavellianism has been negatively related to leader ratings of employee innovative behavior (Wisse, Barelds, & Rietzschel, 2015). Furthermore, Machiavellian employees oftentimes have negative affective experiences in the workplace (Heisler & Gemmill, 1977). Their negative feelings, however, may be contingent on the traits of their interaction partners. Employee Machiavellianism was found to be only significantly negatively related to employee trust and positively related to employee stress when they had leaders with higher levels of Machiavellianism (Belschak et al., 2016).

Notably, Machiavellian employees may also use abusive means to get their way if they feel they can safely do so, and if they perceive that it helps them to achieve their goals (see Schyns et al., 2019). At the same time, they may behave quite positively and pro-socially if they believe that such behavior will further their self-interest. This focus on self-interest for instance may also explain why there is a positive relationship between Machiavellianism and self-related work commitment (career commitment), and a negative relationship between Machiavellianism and other-related work commitment (organizational, supervisor, and team commitment; Becker & O'Hair, 2007; Zettler, Friedrich, & Hilbig, 2011). Relatedly, transformational leadership may mitigate negative effects of employee Machiavellianism. Belschak, Den Hartog, and Kalshoven (2015) found that transformational leadership moderates the relationship between employee Machiavellianism and challenging organizational citizenship behavior. When leaders were low transformational, employee Machiavellianism was negatively related to challenging organizational citizenship behavior (e.g., contributing ideas, taking initiative, voicing opinions, etc.). However, when transformational leadership was high, this effect was muted, arguably because transformational leaders emphasize the importance of new missions and organizational change, which may appeal to Machiavellian employees' self-interested goal orientation and thus stimulate pro-social behavior. Belschak et al. (2018) also showed that employee Machiavellianism is related to reduced helping behavior, increased knowledge hiding, and emotional manipulation, but only when ethical leadership is low. Such increases in organizationally undesirable behaviors of Machiavellian employees do not occur when ethical leadership is high. Ethical leadership dampens Machiavellian employees' tendency to engage in unethical behavior (Ruiz-Palomino & Linuesa-Langreo, 2018). Abusive supervision, in contrast, strengthens Machiavellian employees' tendency to engage in unethical behavior (Greenbaum, Hill, Mawritz, & Quade, 2017). Apparently, Machiavellian employees adjust their behavior to the circumstances.

Psychopathy. Psychopathy is commonly seen as a multi-dimensional construct (Miller & Lynam, 2012), sometimes described as primary and secondary psychopathy, where factor 1 includes affective-interpersonal traits (e.g., guiltlessness, lack of empathy), and factor 2 concerns the lack of behavioral control (e.g., impulsivity, irresponsibility; Lilienfeld et al., 2015; Smith & Lilienfeld, 2013). The dual-pathway model of psychopathy proposes two general deficiencies: first, a lack of fear and social inhibition, and second, deficient emotional and behavioral control (Fowles & Dindo, 2009). According to this model, psychopathy is a developmental outcome with particular risks for individuals and their surroundings when low levels of fear and behavioral discontrol come together. The triarchic model of psychopathy further distinguishes between the three factors: disinhibition, boldness, and meanness (Patrick & Drislane, 2015: Patrick et al., 2009). Behavioral expressions of psychopathy predict deceitful actions even when the risk of punishment is high and when it requires intentional lies (Jones & Paulhus, 2017).

The following summary of studies is specifically concerned with what has been termed psychopathy in a corporate or organizational context, namely, corporate psychopathy (Boddy, 2015; Smith & Lilienfeld, 2013). Scholars have argued that, in a business setting, psychopathic traits may fulfill at least some adaptive functions, especially for the individual who possesses them (Smith & Lilienfeld, 2013). However, while employees with psychopathic traits appear to be successful members of the corporation on the outside, they can pose significant risks to organizational functioning, particularly when they climb the organizational ladder toward influential leadership roles. These risks are rooted in psychopaths' love of money and status in combination with their immorality (Glenn, Koleva, Iyer, Graham, & Ditto, 2010) and their propensity to make unethical decisions (Stevens, Deuling, & Armenakis, 2012). Notably, research into corporate psychopathy often targets the finance and banking industry, suggesting that key players' psychopathy may have contributed to the global financial crisis (Boddy, 2011b, 2015).

Psychopathy and Leadership. Insights into leader psychopathy come from Babiak et al. (2010), who ran a study of 203 corporate professionals selected for a management development program. Managers' psychopathy was studied in relation to ratings obtained from 360-degree assessments and performance evaluations for these professionals. Psychopathy related positively to others' perceptions of charisma/presentational style, but negatively to responsibility/performance. No significant correlations between total psychopathy scores and perceived leadership skills (decision-making, problem-solving, resolving issues without direction, integrity) occurred. The authors speculated that, while the selected professionals may not have been skilled leaders per se, certain psychopathic characteristics could have enabled individuals with high levels of psychopathy to manipulate decision-makers into recommending them for participation in the management development program. However, as Lilienfeld, Waldman, Landfield, Watts, Rubenzer, and Faschingbauer (2012, p. 490) pointed out, the results of this study need to be further replicated due to some methodological issues, notably "the PCL-R ratings in this study were conducted by a single individual who was not blind to other information about participants, including information potentially relevant to criterion ratings."

Later studies suggested that psychopathic individuals lack the skills and characteristics that are typically required for effective leadership. Westerlaken and Woods (2013) surveyed 115 students with management experience. They included self-rating measures of the Full Range of Leadership Model (transformational, transactional, and laissez-faire leadership) and the Self-Report Psychopathy Scale-Revised. The total psychopathy score correlated negatively with transformational leadership—especially with the individualized consideration dimension—but positively with laissez-faire leadership. However, the single source design limits the implications of this finding to some extent. No significant relationship between psychopathy and transactional leadership occurred. In sum, these results point to psychopaths' lack of the active and supportive functions necessary to lead others.

A number of studies focused on the relationships between leaders' psychopathy and outcomes for their followers. Boddy (2011a) conducted a monosource survey of 346 Australian senior white-collar workers, asking them to identify and measure the behaviors of their managers, clustering the rated managers into three groups: Corporate Psychopaths (with clear indications of psychopathic traits), Dysfunctional Managers (with some indications of psychopathic traits), and Normal Managers (no indications of psychopathy). Instances of bullying and unfair supervisory treatment were higher for the group of Corporate Psychopaths. However, psychopathic traits were rated by employees, not focal managers. In a similar vein, Mathieu, Neumann, Hare, and Babiak (2014) explored the relationships between followers' perceptions of their leaders' psychopathy and followers' self-reported psychological distress, work-family conflict, and job satisfaction in two samples. In the first sample, leaders' psychopathy predicted followers' job satisfaction directly and through work-family conflict, but it did not predict followers' psychological distress. Followers of psychopathic leaders were more likely to experience work-family conflict and less likely to be satisfied in their jobs. In the second sample, leaders' psychopathy predicted both followers' work-family conflict and psychological distress positively, and job satisfaction negatively. However, an indirect effect on job satisfaction occurred through psychological distress in this sample. The authors concluded that the differences in results may originate from different sample characteristics (e.g., sample size, private and public sectors), but that overall leaders' psychopathy posed significant risks to employee well-being and satisfaction (Mathieu et al., 2014). In addition, it should be noted that both studies employed single-source ratings of psychopathy and outcome variables that may have inflated relationships.

Further evidence of contextual factors that shape the adaptiveness (or maladaptiveness) of psychopathy for leadership stems from the political realm (Lilienfeld et al., 2012). The study assessed psychopathy trait estimates for 42 U.S. presidents along with historical surveys of presidential leadership and indicators of presidential performance. For this purpose, 121 presidential experts assessed personality traits, which were subsequently mapped onto larger factors underlying psychopathy. The two factors Fearless Dominance (FD) and Impulsive Antisociality (IA) proved most predictive. However, while FD related positively to ratings and indicators of presidential performance (e.g., leadership, persuasiveness, crisis management), IA remained largely unassociated with performance, but it related positively to undesirable perceptions of presidential behavior and character (e.g., tolerating unethical behavior in subordinates, negative character). It therefore appears that in the context of political leadership at least some of the boldness and dominance characteristics that go along with psychopathy can fulfill adaptive functions (Lilienfeld et al., 2012).

A notably new lens on the relationships between psychopathic leaders and their followers illuminates the current understanding of psychopathy in organizations. Barelds, Wisse, Sanders, and Laurijssen (2018) conducted two studies to test the relationship between leaders' psychopathy and their self-serving behavior as well as the moderating role of follower traits for this relationship. Specifically, the authors argued that the likelihood that psychopathic leaders would engage in more self-serving behavior vis-à-vis followers who have low self-esteem stems from those followers' own compliant tendencies, as well as from the psychopathic leaders' competencies in recognizing vulnerability and their willingness to take advantage of that. One experimental study and one multi-source field survey supported this prediction. Psychopathic leaders' expression of their callous traits appears at least in part to be a matter of context, in particular the attributes that followers bring into the relationship.

Blickle et al. (2018) found similarly that context variables influence psychopathic managers' behavior. Specifically, high levels of ascendency prospects as well as prospects for income increases moderated the relationship between psychopathy and consideration. Under both environmental conditions, psychopathic managers showed less considerate leadership toward their followers.

Psychopathy and Employee Behavior. While a number of studies focused on leaders' psychopathy, its potential negative influence on organizational functioning is clearly not limited to the upper echelons of leadership. A meta-analysis of the Dark Triad traits found that psychopathy related significantly but at a very low level negatively to the quality of employees' job performance and positively to CWB (O'Boyle et al., 2012). Again, contextual moderators played a role in these relationships. Employees' authority weakened the positive relationship between psychopathy and CWB, potentially suggesting that these individuals were better able to control their antagonistic tendencies. The results also concur with a recent conceptual framework of Dark Triad traits and CWB, which highlighted the role of mediators and moderators of this relationship (Cohen, 2016). The suggested moderating factors include individual levels of political skills, similarly to O'Boyle et al.'s (2012) conceptualization of authority as a regulating factor of trait expression, as well as organizational factors (transparency, policies, culture/climate), which perform similar functions at higher levels of control (Cohen, 2016). Mediating mechanisms concern the extent to which the individual perceives political opportunities within their organization as well as a personal sense of accountability for their actions in the organization.

Jonason et al. (2012) showed that psychopathy coincided with employees' use of hard influence tactics (i.e., threatening others, manipulating) in a sample of 419 employees who rated their own psychopathy and use of influence tactics. Similarly, when Jonason, Wee, and Li (2015) assessed mechanisms through which Dark Triad traits influenced job satisfaction, they found that individuals with high levels of psychopathic traits were more likely to perceive situations at work as competitive. Interestingly, when Jones (2014) assessed tendencies to engage financial misbehavior of working adults with Dark Triad traits, he also found that psychopathy was the sole predictor of objectively measured continued risky gambling at the expense of others. Ragatz, Fremouw, and Baker (2012) demonstrated that white-collar offenders scored higher on psychopathic traits compared with non-white-collar offenders.

In sum, these results suggest that psychopathy may in fact be the darkest of the Dark Triad traits in terms of predicting undesirable attitudes and behaviors at work. It is less clear, however, how psychopaths manage to climb organizational ladders when their behaviors are likely to harm and damage their surroundings. While one line of reasoning suggests that psychopaths manipulate others into seeing them as successful, and that their dark sides only become apparent later on (Babiak & Hare, 2006), current evidence is somewhat contradictory. Spurk et al. (2016) surveyed 934 German-speaking working adults with the *Dirty Dozen measure* (Jonason & Webster, 2010), and assessed objective career success (monthly salary before taxes, leadership position) as well as subjective career satisfaction. Psychopathy scores related negatively to both objective and subjective indicators of career success, while narcissism predicted salary positively, and Machiavellianism was positively related to leadership position and career satisfaction. While the cross-sectional nature of the study restricts causal interpretation, it appears worthwhile for future research to explore whether psychopathy may indeed prevent long-term career progression.

HOW TO DEAL WITH DARK TRIAD PERSONALITIES IN THE WORKPLACE

Considering that the Dark Triad comprises personality traits, it is perhaps most promising to investigate conditions under which individuals high in Dark Triad traits are less likely to show behaviors associated with those traits (in the sense of trait expression, Christiansen & Tett, 2008). For example, initial insights suggest that leader humility counterbalances some of the negative employee outcomes. When followers saw their narcissistic leaders as humble, narcissism related positively to perceived leader effectiveness, follower job engagement, and follower job performance (Owens, Wallace, & Waldman, 2015). Cohen (2016) considered organizational conditions under which Dark Triad personalities are less strongly correlated to counterproductive work behavior, such as perceived accountability, organizational transparency, organizational policies, and organizational culture/climate. Padilla, Hogan, and Kaiser (2007) suggested that Dark leadership may be more likely to emerge in environments that can be characterized by instability, perceived threat, the endorsement of collectivistic and high-power distance values, and absence of checks and balances and institutionalization. In a similar vein, Nevicka et al. (2011) investigated leadership emergence and performance of narcissistic individuals in reward independent versus interdependent student teams playing a computer simulated game. Narcissistic individuals were generally more likely to emerge as leaders. However, when team success was rewarded interdependently, narcissistic individuals' performance was even higher than in the independent reward condition. Narcissists appear to be keen on contributing to team success when this gives them positive reinforcement within the team. Blickle et al. (2018) point to the relevance of making adaptions in incentive structures to affect the behavioral expression of psychopathy. Schyns et al. (2019) further argue that certain leadership styles, the degree of leader power, as well as leader traits (e.g., if they are similar or not to their Dark Triad followers) and values can facilitate or hinder the expression of their followers' dark traits. All this research shows boundary conditions under which Dark Triad traits might be more or less likely to translate into Dark Triad behaviors.

Another approach to the issue is to prevent individuals with high levels of Dark Triad traits from entering an organization and exerting their negative influence over others. In their book, provocatively titled *Snakes in Suits*, Babiak and Hare (2006) suggest a number of practical strategies that may stop psychopaths from entering an organization or rising up to management levels. In early hiring and selection stages, they recommend particular diligence. If managers are well trained in interview techniques, they are less likely to give psychopathic candidates control of the process. Structured interviews, work samples, and focus on actions and feelings can help to spot inconsistencies between the tales of success and integrity the candidate may seek to present and the possibly bleak reality. Checking the facts (e.g., speaking with previous colleagues or employers) can be a time-consuming, but purposeful endeavor. Once they have entered the organization, psychopathic individuals can be difficult to identify. Babiak and Hare (2006) list a number of "red flags" and provide recommendations to avoid coworkers colluding with the individual and causing harm to the employer or other colleagues.

Similarly, Braun (2017) recommended incorporating background checks and objective measures of previous performance into the selection process to avoid hiring or promoting narcissistic leaders. She also suggested the use of 360-degree feedback to better understand if and when issues with narcissistic leaders arise. Kwak and Shim (2017) recommended ethical leadership to weaken Dark Triad trait expression and to promote desirable employee work behaviors, including voice. Thus, organizations should pay particular attention to their selection processes and, if they already have employees with high levels of Dark Triad traits in their organization, try to contain their behavior by setting boundaries and preventing the development of environments that are conducive to Dark Triad behavior.

AREAS FOR FUTURE RESEARCH

Very often, the Dark Triad personality traits are assessed using short one-dimensional instruments such as the Dirty Dozen (Jonason & Webster, 2010) or the Short Dark Triad (Jones & Paulhus, 2014), although all Dark Triad traits are essentially multidimensional (see e.g., Back, Küfner, Dufner, Gerlach, Rauthmann, & Denissen, 2013; Dahling et al, 2009; Patrick & Drislane, 2015). One of the issues with these short measures is that the three traits are more strongly related than theoretically assumed (Maples, Lamkin, & Miller, 2014), making it more difficult to draw conclusions about differential effects. Other research focuses on one of the traits without taking into consideration the others, although some studies now control for other aspects of the Dark Triad (e.g., Koch et al., 2018; Wisse & Sleebos, 2016). Overall, more research is needed to better understand the different predictive value of each of the three Dark Triad traits.

Research into narcissism in particular found that subdimensions of the concept are relevant in order to better predict the behaviors narcissists show. While most research to date focuses on grandiose narcissism, the few studies that differentiate between grandiose and vulnerable dimensions find marked differences. It would be interesting to see how far similar results emerge for subdimensions of Machiavellianism and psychopathy. For example, Miller, Dir, Gentile, Wilson, Pryor, and Campbell (2010) argue for a vulnerable Dark Triad. According to these authors, the vulnerable Dark Triad consists of vulnerable narcissism, Factor 2 psychopathy, and borderline personality disorder. More research is needed to better understand the differences between more extraverted and more introverted/disinhibited (Miller et al., 2010) types of Dark Triad personality traits.

OUTLOOK

In conclusion, this article has reviewed literature on the Dark Triad personality traits in the workplace, clearly showing the damage that individuals high in those traits can do to others and to their organizations. There is a clear need for organizations to avoid hiring or at least containing the behavior of individuals high in Dark Triad personality traits to prevent the harm they can cause to organizational members and effective functioning.

FURTHER READING

Belschak, F. D., Den Hartog, D. N., & Kalshoven, K. (2015). Leading Machiavellians: How to translate Machiavellians' selfishness into pro-organizational behavior. *Journal of Management, 41*(7), 1934–1956.

Braun, S. (2017). Leader narcissism and outcomes in organizations: A review at multiple levels of analysis and implications for future research. *Frontiers in Psychology*, 8, 773. https://doi.org/10.3389/fpsyg.2017.00773

Campbell, W. K., Hoffman, B. J., Campbell, S. M., & Marchisio, G. (2011). Narcissism in organizational contexts. *Human Resource Management Review, 21*(4), 268–284. https://doi.org/10.1016/j.hrmr.2010.10.007

Cohen, A. 2016. Are they among us? A conceptual framework of the relationship between the Dark Triad personality and counterproductive work behaviors (CWBs). *Human Resource Management Review, 26*(1), 69–85. https://doi.org/10.1016/j.hrmr.2015.07.003

Landay, K., Harms, P. D., & Credé, M. (2019). Shall we serve the dark lords? A meta-analytic review of psychopathy and leadership. *Journal of Applied Psychology, 104*(1), 183–196. https://dx.doi.org/10.1037/apl0000357

LeBreton, J. M., Shiverdecker, L. K., & Grimaldi, E. M. (2018). The Dark Triad and workplace behavior. *Annual Review of Organizational Psychology and Organizational Behavior*, 5, 387–414. https://doi.org/10.1146/annurev-orgpsych-032117-104451

O'Boyle, E. J., Forsyth, D. R., Banks, G. C., & McDaniel, M. A. (2012). A meta-analysis of the Dark Triad and work behavior: A social exchange perspective. *Journal of Applied Psychology, 97*(3), 557–579. https://doi.org/10.1037/a0025679

Paulhus, D. L., & Williams, K. M. (2002). The Dark Triad of personality: Narcissism, Machiavellianism, and psychopathy. *Journal of Research in Personality, 36*(6), 556–563. https://doi.org/10.1016/S0092-6566(02)00505-6

Schyns, B., Wisse, B., & Sanders, S. (2019). Shady strategic behavior: Recognizing strategic behavior of Dark Triad followers. *Academy of Management Perspectives, 33*(2), 234–249. https://doi.org/10.5465/amp.2017.0005

Spain, S. M., Harms, P. D., & LeBreton, J. M. (2014). The dark side of personality at work. *Journal of Organizational Behavior*, 35, S41–S60.

REFERENCES

Antonakis, J., & Day, D. V. (Eds.). (2017). *The nature of leadership*. Thousand Oaks: SAGE.

Antonakis, J., & Day, D. V. (2018). *The nature of leadership* (3rd ed.). Thousand Oaks, CA: SAGE.

Babiak, P., & Hare, R. D. (2006). *Snakes in suits*. New York, NY: HarperCollins.

Babiak, P., Neumann, C. S., & Hare, R. D. (2010). Corporate psychopathy: Talking the walk. *Behavioral Sciences & The Law, 28*, 174–193. https://doi.org/10.1002/bsl.925

Back, M. D., Küfner, A. C., Dufner, M., Gerlach, T. M., Rauthmann, J. F., & Denissen, J. J. (2013). Narcissistic admiration and rivalry: Disentangling the bright and dark sides of narcissism. *Journal of Personality and Social Psychology, 105*(6), 1013–1037. https://doi.org/10.1037/a0034431

Barelds, D. P. H., Wisse, B., Sanders, S., & Laurijssen, M. (2018). No regard for those who need it: The moderating role of follower self-esteem in the relationship between leader psychopathy and leader self-serving behavior. *Frontiers in Psychology, 9*: 1281. https://doi.org/10.3389/fpsyg.2018.01281

Becker, J. A., & O'Hair, D.H. (2007). Machiavellians' motives in organizational citizenship behavior. *Journal of Applied Communication Research, 35*(3), 246–267. https://doi.org/10.1080/00909880701434232

Belschak, F. D., Den Hartog, D. N., & De Hoogh, A. H. (2018). Angels and demons: The effect of ethical leadership on Machiavellian employees' work behaviors. *Frontiers in Psychology, 9*, 1082. https://doi.org/10.3389/fpsyg.2018.01082

Belschak, F. D., Den Hartog, D. N., & Kalshoven, K. (2015). Leading Machiavellians: How to translate Machiavellians' selfishness into pro-organizational behavior. *Journal of Management, 41*(7), 1934–1956. https://doi.org/10.1177/0149206313484513

Belschak, F. D., Muhammad, R. S., & Den Hartog, D. N. (2016). Birds of a feather can butt heads: When Machiavellian employees work with Machiavellian leaders. *Journal of Business Ethics, 151*(3), 613–626. https://doi.org/10.1007/s10551-016-3251-2

Blickle, G., Schütte, N., & Genau, H. A. (2018). Manager psychopathy, trait activation, and job performance: A multi-source study. *European Journal of Work and Organizational Psychology, 2*(4), 450–461. https://doi.org/10.1080/1359432X.2018.1475354

Boddy, C. R. (2011a). Corporate psychopaths, bullying and unfair supervision in the workplace. *Journal of Business Ethics, 100*(3), 367–379. https://doi.org/10.1007/s10551-010-0689-5

Boddy, C. R. (2011b). The corporate psychopaths theory of the global financial crisis. *Journal of Business Ethics, 102*(2), 255–259, https://doi.org/10.1007/s10551-011-0810-4

Boddy, C. R. (2015). Organizational psychopaths: a ten year update. *Management Decision, 53*, 2407–2432. https://doi.org/10.3389/fpsyg.2018.01082

Braun, S. (2017). Leader narcissism and outcomes in organizations: A review at multiple levels of analysis and implications for future research. *Frontiers in Psychology, 8*, 773. https://doi.org/10.3389/fpsyg.2017.00773

Braun, S., Aydin, N., Frey, D., & Peus, C. (2018). Leader narcissism predicts malicious envy and supervisor-targeted counterproductive work behavior: Evidence from field and experimental research. *Journal of Business Ethics, 151*(3), 725–741. https://doi.org/10.1007/s10551-016-3224-5

Braun, S., Schyns, B., Zheng, Y., & Lord, R.G. (2019). *Vulnerable narcissists in leadership? A bifactor model of narcissism and abusive supervision intent*. Annual Meeting of the Academy of Management, Boston, MA.

Brunell, A. B., Gentry, W. A., Campbell, W. K., Hoffman, B. J., Kuhnert, K. W., & DeMarree, K. G. (2008). Leader emergence: The case of the narcissistic leader. *Personality and Social Psychology Bulletin, 34*(12), 1663–1676. https://doi.org/10.1177/0146167208324101

Campbell, W. K. (2005). *When you love a man who loves himself: How to deal with a one-way relationship*. Chicago, IL: Sourcebooks Casablanca.

Campbell, W. K., & Campbell, S. M. (2009). On the self-regulatory dynamics created by the peculiar benefits and costs of narcissism: A contextual reinforcement model and examination of leadership. *Self and Identity, 8*(2–3), 214–232. https://doi.org/10.1080/15298860802505129

Campbell, W. K., & Foster, J. D. (2007). The narcissistic self: Background, an extended agency model, and ongoing controversies. In C. Sedikides & S. J. Spencer (Eds.), *Frontiers of social psychology. The self* (pp. 115–138). New York, NY: Psychology Press.

Campbell, W. K., Hoffman, B. J., Campbell, S. M., & Marchisio, G. (2011). Narcissism in organizational contexts. *Human Resource Management Review, 21*(4), 268–284. https://doi.org/10.1016/j.hrmr.2010.10.007

Castille, C. M., Buckner, J. E., & Thoroughgood, C. N. (2018). Prosocial citizens without a moral compass? Examining the relationship between Machiavellianism and unethical pro-organizational behavior. *Journal of Business Ethics, 149*(4), 919–930. https://doi.org/10.1007/s10551-016-3079-9

Christiansen, N. D., & Tett, R. P. (2008). Toward a better understanding of the role of situations in linking personality, work behavior, and job performance. *Industrial and Organizational Psychology, 1*(3), 312–316. https://doi.org/10.1111/j.1754-9434.2008.00054.x

Christie, R., & Geis, F. L. (1970). *Studies in Machiavellianism.* New York, NY: Academic Press.

Chatterjee, A., & Hambrick, D. C. (2007). It's all about me: Narcissistic chief executive officers and their effects on company strategy and performance. *Administrative Science Quarterly, 52*(3), 351–386. https://doi.org/10.2189/asqu.52.3.351

Chatterjee, A., & Hambrick, D. C. (2011). Executive personality, capability cues, and risk taking: How narcissistic CEOs react to their successes and stumbles. *Administrative Science Quarterly, 56*(2), 202–237. https://doi.org/10.1177/0001839211427534

Chatterjee, A., & Pollock, T. G. (2017). Master of puppets: How narcissistic CEOs construct their professional worlds. *Academy of Management Review, 42*(4), 703–725. https://doi.org/10.5465/amr.2015.0224

Cleckley, H. (1941). *The mask of sanity; an attempt to reinterpret the so-called psychopathic personality.* Oxford, U.K.: Mosby.

Cohen, A. (2016). Are they among us? A conceptual framework of the relationship between the Dark Triad personality and counterproductive work behaviors (CWBs). *Human Resource Management Review, 26*(1), 69–85. https://doi.org/10.1016/j.hrmr.2015.07.003

Dahling, J. J., Whitaker, B. G., & Levy, P. E. (2009). The development and validation of a new Machiavellianism scale. *Journal of Management, 35*(2), 219–257. https://doi.org/10.1177/0149206308318618

Den Hartog, D. N., & Belschak, F. D. (2012). Work engagement and Machiavellianism in the ethical leadership process. *Journal of Business Ethics, 107*(1), 35–47. https://doi.org/10.1007/s10551-012-1296-4

DePaulo, B. M., & Rosenthal, R. (1979). Telling lies. *Journal of Personality and Social Psychology, 37*(10), 1713–1722.

Farmer, S. M., Maslyn, J. M., Fedor, D. B., & Goodman, J. S. (1997). Putting upward influence strategies in context. *Journal of Organizational Behavior, 18*(1), 17–42. https://doi.org/10.1002/(SICI)1099-1379(199701)18:1%3C17::AID-JOB785%3E3.0.CO;2-9

Fletcher, C. (1990). The relationships between candidate personality, self-presentation strategies, and interviewer assessments in selection interviews: An empirical study. *Human Relations, 43*(8), 739–749. https://doi.org/10.1177/001872679004300803

Foster, J. D., & Campbell, W. K. (2007). Are there such things as "narcissists" in social psychology? A taximetrics analysis of the Narcissistic Personality Inventory. *Personality and Individual Differences, 43*(6), 1321–1332. https://doi.org/10.1016/j.paid.2007.04.003

Fowles, D. C., & Dhindo, L. (2009). Temperament and psychopathy: A dual-pathway model. *Current Directions in Psychological Science, 18*(3), 179–183. https://doi.org/10.1111/j.1467-8721.2009.01632.x

Gleason, J. M., Seaman, F. J., & Hollander, E. P. (1978). Emergent leadership processes as a function of task structure and Machiavellianism. *Social Behavior and Personality: An International Journal, 6*(1), 33–36. https://doi.org/10.2224/sbp.1978.6.1.33

Glenn, A. L., Koliva, S., Iyer, R., Graham, J., & Ditto, P. H. (2010). Moral identity in psychopathy. *Judgment and Decision Making, 5*(7), 497–505. https://escholarship.org/uc/item/5b6767j5

Goncalo, J. A., Flynn, F. J., & Kim, S. H. (2010). Are two narcissists better than one? The link between narcissism, perceived creativity, and creative performance. *Personality and Social Psychology Bulletin*, 36(11), 1484–1495. https://doi.org/10.1177/0146167210385109

Greenbaum, R. L., Hill, A., Mawritz, M. B., & Quade, M. J. (2017). Employee Machiavellianism to unethical behavior: The role of abusive supervision as a trait activator. *Journal of Management*, 43(2), 585–609. https://doi.org/10.1177/0149206314535434

Grijalva, E., Harms, P. D., Newman, D. A., Gaddis, B. H., & Fraley, R. C. (2015). Narcissism and leadership: A meta-analytic review of linear and nonlinear relationships. *Personnel Psychology*, 68(1), 1–47.

Grijalva, E., & Newman, D. A. (2015). Narcissism and counterproductive work behavior (CWB). *Applied Psychology: An International Review*, 64(1), 93–126.

Heisler, W. J., & Gemmill, G. R. (1977). Machiavellianism, job satisfaction, job strain, and upward mobility: Some cross-organizational evidence. *Psychological Reports*, 41(2), 592–594. https://doi.org/10.2466/pr0.1977.41.2.592

Hogan, R., & Hogan, J. (2009). *Hogan development survey manual* (2nd ed.). Tulsa, OK: Hogan Assessment Systems.

Jonason, P. K., Slomski, S., & Partyka, J. (2012). The Dark Triad at work: How toxic employees get their way. *Personality and Individual Differences*, 52(3), 449–453. https://doi.org/10.1016/j.paid.2011.11.008

Jonason, P. K., Wee, S., & Li, N. P. (2015). Competition, autonomy, and prestige: Mechanisms through which the Dark Triad predict job satisfaction. *Personality and Individual Differences*, 72, 112–116. https://doi.org/10.1016/j.paid.2014.08.026

Jonason, P. K., & Webster, G. D. (2010). The dirty dozen: A concise measure of the Dark Triad. *Psychological Assessment*, 22(2), 420–432. https://doi.org/10.1037/a0019265

Jones, D. N. (2014). Risk in the face of retribution: Psychopathic individuals persist in financial misbehavior among the Dark Triad. *Personality and Individual Differences*, 67, 109–113. https://doi.org/10.1016/j.paid.2014.01.030

Jones, D. N., & Paulhus, D. L. (2009). Machiavellianism. In M. R. Leary & R. H. Hoyle (Eds.), *Handbook of individual differences in social behavior* (pp. 93–108). New York, NY: Guilford Press.

Jones, D. N., & Paulhus, D. L. (2014). Introducing the short Dark Triad (SD3): A brief measure of dark personality traits. *Assessment*, 21(1), 28–41. https://doi.org/10.1177/1073191113514105

Jones, D. N., & Paulhus, D. L. (2017). Duplicity among the Dark Triad: Three faces of deceit. *Journal of Personality and Social Psychology*, 113(2), 329–342. https://doi.org/10.1037/pspp0000139

Judge, T. A., LePine, J. A., & Rich, B. L. (2006). Loving yourself abundantly: Relationship of the narcissistic personality to self-and other perceptions of workplace deviance, leadership, and task and contextual performance. *Journal of Applied Psychology*, 91(4), 762–776. https://doi.org/10.1037/0021-9010.91.4.762

Kajonius, P. J., Persson, B. N., & Jonason, P. K. (2015). Hedonism, achievement, and power: Universal values that characterize the Dark Triad. *Personality and Individual Differences*, 77, 173–178. https://doi.org/10.1016/j.paid.2014.12.055

Kessler, S. R., Bandelli, A. C., Spector, P. E., Borman, W. C., Nelson, C. E., & Penney, L. M. (2010). Re-examining Machiavelli: A three-dimensional model of Machiavellianism in the workplace. *Journal of Applied Social Psychology*, 40, 1868–1896. https://doi.org/10.1111/j.1559-1816.2010.00643.x

Kiazad, K., Restubog, S. L. D., Zagenczyk, T. J., Kiewitz, C., & Tang, R. L. (2010). In pursuit of power: The role of authoritarian leadership in the relationship between supervisors' Machiavellianism and subordinates' perceptions of abusive supervisory behavior. *Journal of Research in Personality*, 44(4), 512–519. https://doi.org/10.1016/j.jrp.2010.06.004

Koch, I., Schyns, B., & Vollmer, J. (2018). *Narcissistic leaders' different social strategies and abusive supervision.* Paper presented at the IWP conference, Sheffield, 2017.

Kwak, W. J., & Shim, J. H. (2017). Effects of Machiavellian ethical leadership and employee power distance on employee voice. *Social Behavior and Personality: An International Journal, 45*(9), 1485–1498. https://doi.org/10.2224/sbp.5896

Landay, K., & Harms, P. D., & Credé, M. (2019). Shall we serve the dark lords? A meta-analytic review of psychopathy and leadership. *Journal of Applied Psychology, 10*(4), 183–196.

LeBreton, J. M., Shiverdecker, L. K., & Grimaldi, E. M. (2018). The Dark Triad and workplace behavior. *Annual Review of Organizational Psychology and Organizational Behavior, 5*, 387–414. https://doi.org/10.1146/annurev-orgpsych-032117-104451

Lee, K., Ashton, M. C., Wiltshire, J., Bourdage, J. S., Visser, B. A., & Gallucci, A. (2013). Sex, power, and money: Prediction from the Dark Triad and honesty–humility. *European Journal of Personality, 27*(2), 169–184. https://doi.org/10.1002/per.1860

Levenson, M. R., Kiehl, K. A., & Fitzpatrick, C. (1995). Assessing psychopathic attributes in a noninstitutionalized population. *Journal of Personality and Social Psychology, 68*(1), 151–158. https://doi.org/10.1037//0022-3514.68.1.151

Lilienfeld, S. O., Watts, A. K., Smith, S. F., & Latzman, R. D. (2018). Boldness. Conceptual and methodological issues. In C. J. Patrick (Ed.), *Handbook of psychopathy* (2nd ed., pp. 165–186). New York, NY: Guilford Press.

Lilienfeld, S. O., Watts, A. L., Francis Smith, S., Berg, J. M., & Latzman, R. D. (2015). Psychopathy deconstructed and reconstructed: Identifying and assembling the personality building blocks of Cleckley's chimera. *Journal of Personality, 83*(6), 593–610.

Lilienfeld, S. O., Watts, A. L., Smith, S. F., Berg, J. M., & Latzman, R. D. (2015). Psychopathy deconstructed and reconstructed: Identifying and assembling the personality building blocks of Cleckley's chimera. *Journal of Personality, 83*(6), 593–610.

Lilienfeld, S. O., Waldman, I. D., Landfield, K., Watts, A. L., Rubenzer, S., & Faschingbauer, T. R. (2012). Fearless dominance and the U.S. presidency: Implications of psychopathic personality traits for successful and unsuccessful political leadership. *Journal of Personality and Social Psychology, 103*(3), 489–505. https://doi.org/10.1037/a0029392

Lopes, J., & Fletcher, C. (2004). Fairness of impression management in employment interviews: A cross-country study of the role of equity and Machiavellianism. *Social Behavior and Personality: An International Journal, 32*(8), 747–768. https://doi.org/10.2224/sbp.2004.32.8.747

Magee, J. C., & Galinsky, A. D. (2008). Social hierarchy: The self-reinforcing nature of power and status. *Academy of Management Annals, 2*(1), 351–398.

Maples, J. L., Lamkin, J., & Miller, J. D. (2014). A test of two brief measures of the Dark Triad: The dirty dozen and short Dark Triad. *Psychological Assessment, 26*(1), 326–331. https://doi.org/10.1037/a0035084

Mathieu, C., Neumann, C. S., Hare, R. D., & Babiak, P. (2014). A dark side of leadership: Corporate psychopathy and its influence on employee well-being and job satisfaction. *Personality and Individual Differences, 59*, 83–88. https://doi.org/10.1016/j.paid.2013.11.010

McHoskey, J. W. (1999). Machiavellianism, intrinsic versus extrinsic goals, and social interest: A self-determination theory analysis. *Motivation and Emotion, 23*(4), 267–283. https://doi.org/10.1023/A:1021338809469

Miller, J. D., Dir, A., Gentile, B., Wilson, L., Pryor, L. R., & Campbell, W. K. (2010). Searching for a vulnerable Dark Triad: Comparing factor 2 psychopathy, vulnerable narcissism, and borderline personality disorder. *Journal of Personality, 78*(5), 1529–1564. https://doi.org.10.1111/j.1467-6494.2010.00660.x

Miller, J. D., & Lynam, D. R. (2012). An examination of the Psychopathic Personality Inventory's nomological network: A meta-analytic review. *Personality Disorders: Theory, Research, and Treatment, 3*(3), 305–326.

Miller, J. D., Lynam, D. R., Vize, C., Crowe, M., Sleep, C., Maples-Keller, J. L., . . . Campbell, W. K. (2018). Vulnerable narcissism is (mostly) a disorder of neuroticism. *Journal of Personality, 86*(2), 186–199. https://doi.org/10.1111/jopy.12303

Morf, C. C., & Rhodewalt, F. (2001). Unraveling the paradoxes of narcissism: A dynamic self-regulatory processing model. *Psychological Inquiry, 12*(4), 177–196. https://doi.org/10.1207/S15327965PLI1204_1

Moshagen, M., Hilbig, B. E., & Zettler, I. (2018). The dark core of personality. *Psychological Review, 125*(5), 656–688. https://psycnet.apa.org/doiLanding?doi=10.1037%2Frev0000111

Nevicka, B., De Hoogh, A. H., Van Vianen, A. E., Beersma, B., & McIlwain, D. (2011). All I need is a stage to shine: Narcissists' leader emergence and performance. *The Leadership Quarterly, 22*(5), 910–925. https://doi.org/10.1016/j.leaqua.2011.07.011

O'Boyle, E. J., Forsyth, D. R., Banks, G. C., & McDaniel, M. A. (2012). A meta-analysis of the Dark Triad and work behavior: A social exchange perspective. *Journal of Applied Psychology, 97*, 557–579. https://doi.org/10.1037/a0025679

O'Reilly, C. A., III, Doerr, B., Caldwell, D. F., & Chatman, J. A. (2014). Narcissistic CEOs and executive compensation. *The Leadership Quarterly, 25*(2), 218–231. https://doi.org/10.1016/j.leaqua.2013.08.002

O'Reilly, C. A., III, Doerr, B., & Chatman, J. A. (2018). "See you in court": How CEO narcissism increases firms' vulnerability to lawsuits. *The Leadership Quarterly, 29*(3), 365–378. https://doi.org/10.1016/j.leaqua.2017.08.001

Ong, C. W., Roberts, R., Arthur, C. A., Woodman, T., & Akehurst, S. (2016). The leader ship is sinking: A temporal investigation of narcissistic leadership. *Journal of Personality, 84*(2), 237–247. https://doi.org/10.1111/jopy.12155

Owens, B. P., Wallace, A. S., & Waldman, D. A. (2015). Leader narcissism and follower outcomes: The counterbalancing effect of leader humility. *Journal of Applied Psychology, 100*(4), 1203–1213.

Padilla, A., Hogan, R., & Kaiser, R. B. (2007). The toxic triangle: Destructive leaders, susceptible followers, and conducive environments. *The Leadership Quarterly, 18*(3), 176–194. https://doi.org/10.1016/j.leaqua.2007.03.001

Patrick, C. J., & Drislane, L. E. (2015). Triarchic model of psychopathy: Origins, operationalizations, and observed linkages with personality and general psychopathology. *Journal of Personality, 83*(6), 627–643.

Patrick, C. J., Fowles, D. C., & Krueger, R. F. (2009). Triarchic conceptualization of psychopathy: Developmental origins of disinhibition, boldness, and meanness. *Development and Psychopathology, 21*(3), 913–938. https://doi.org.10.1017/S0954579409000492

Paulhus, D. L. (2001). Normal narcissism: Two minimalist accounts. *Psychological Inquiry, 12*, 228–230. https://doi.org/10.3389/fpsyg.2017.01600

Paulhus, D. L. (2014). Toward a taxonomy of dark personalities. *Current Directions in Psychological Science, 23*(6), 421–426. https://doi.org/10.1177/0963721414547737

Paulhus, D. L., Westlake, B. G., Calvez, S. S., & Harms, P. D. (2013). Self-presentation style in job interviews: The role of personality and culture. *Journal of Applied Social Psychology, 43*(10), 2042–2059. https://doi.org/10.1111/jasp.12157

Paulhus, D. L., & Williams, K. M. (2002). The Dark Triad of personality: Narcissism, Machiavellianism, and psychopathy. *Journal of Research in Personality, 36*(6), 556–563. https://doi.org/10.1016/S0092-6566(02)00505-6

Pilch, I., & Turska, E. (2015). Relationships between Machiavellianism, organizational culture, and workplace bullying: Emotional abuse from the target's and the perpetrator's perspective. *Journal of Business Ethics, 128*(1), 83–93. https://doi.org/10.1007/s10551-014-2081-3

Ragatz, L. L., Fremouw, W., & Baker, E. (2012). The psychological profile of white-collar offenders: Demographics, criminal thinking, psychopathic traits, and psychopathology. *Criminal Justice and Behavior, 39*(7), 978–997. https://doi.org/10.1177/0093854812437846

Raskin, R., & Terry, H. (1988). A principal-components analysis of the Narcissistic Personality Inventory and further evidence of its construct validity. *Journal of Personality and Social Psychology, 54*(5), 890–902.

Resick, C. J., Whitman, D. S., Weingarden, S. M., & Hiller, N. J. (2009). The bright-side and the dark-side of CEO personality: examining core self-evaluations, narcissism, transformational leadership, and strategic influence. *Journal of Applied Psychology, 94*(6), 1365–1381. https://doi.org/10.1037/a0016238

Ronningstam, E. (2009). Narcissistic personality disorder: Facing DSM-V. *Psychiatric Annals, 39*(3), 111–121. https://doi.org/10.3928/00485713-20090301-09

Ruiz-Palomino, P., & Linuesa-Langreo, J. (2018). Implications of person–situation interactions for Machiavellians' unethical tendencies: The buffering role of managerial ethical leadership. *European Management Journal, 36*(2), 243–253. https://doi.org/10.1016/j.emj.2018.01.004

Schyns, B. (2015). Dark personality in the workplace: Introduction to the special issue. *Applied Psychology: An International Review, 64*(1), 1–14. https://doi.org/10.1111/apps.12041

Schyns, B., Wisse, B., & Sanders, S. (2019). Shady strategic behavior: Recognizing strategic behavior of Dark Triad followers. *Academy of Management Perspectives, 33*(2), 234–249. https://doi.org/10.5465/amp .2017.0005

Sedikides, C., & Campbell, W. K. (2017). Narcissistic force meets systemic resistance: The energy clash model. *Perspectives on Psychological Science, 12*(3), 400–421. https://doi.org/10.1177/1745691617692105

Sendjaya, S., Pekerti, A., Härtel, C., Hirst, G., & Butarbutar, I. (2016). Are authentic leaders always moral? The role of Machiavellianism in the relationship between authentic leadership and morality. *Journal of Business Ethics, 133*(1), 125–139. https://doi.org/10.1007/s10551-014-2351-0

Smith, S. F., & Lilienfeld, S. O. (2013). Psychopathy in the workplace: The knowns and unknowns. *Aggression and Violent Behavior, 18*(2), 204–218. https://doi.org/10.1016/j.avb.2012.11.007

Spain, S. M., Harms, P. D., & LeBreton, J. M. (2014). The dark side of personality at work. *Journal of Organizational Behavior, 35*(S1), S41–S60.

Spurk, D., Keller, A. C., & Hirschi, A. (2016). Do bad guys get ahead or fall behind? Relationships of the Dark Triad of personality with objective and subjective career success. *Social Psychological and Personality Science, 7*(2), 113–121.

Stevens, G., Deuling, J., & Armenakis, A. (2012). Successful psychopaths: Are they unethical decision-makers and why? *Journal of Business Ethics, 105*(2), 139–149. https://doi.org/10.1007/s10551-011-0963-1

Thomaes, S., & Bushman, B. J. (2011). Mirror, mirror, on the wall, who's the most aggressive of them all? Narcissism, self-esteem, and aggression. In P. R. Shaver & M. Mikulincer (Eds.), *Human aggression and violence: Causes, manifestations, and consequences. Herzilya series on personality and social psychology* (pp. 203–219). Washington, DC: American Psychological Association.

Vernon, P. A., Villani, V. C., Vickers, L. C., & Harris, J. A. (2008). A behavioral genetic investigation of the Dark Triad and the Big 5. *Personality and Individual Differences, 44*(2), 445–452. https://doi.org/10 .1016/j.paid.2007.09.007

Volmer, J., Koch, I. K., & Göritz, A. S. (2016). The bright and dark sides of leaders' Dark Triad traits: Effects on subordinates' career success and well-being. *Personality and Individual Differences, 101*, 413–418. https://doi.org/10.1016/j.paid.2016.06.046

Westerlaken, K. M., & Woods, P. R. (2013). The relationship between psychopathy and the full range leadership model. *Personality and Individual Differences, 54*(1), 41–46. https://doi.org/10.1016/j.paid.2012 .08.026

Williams, K. M., Paulhus, D. L., & Hare, R. D. (2007). Capturing the four-factor structure of psychopathy in college students via self-report. *Journal of Personality Assessment, 88*(2), 205–219. https://doi.org/10 .1080/00223890701268074

Wink, P. (1991). Two faces of narcissism. *Journal of Personality and Social Psychology, 61*(4), 590–597.

Wisse, B., Barelds, D. P., & Rietzschel, E. F. (2015). How innovative is your employee? The role of employee and supervisor Dark Triad personality traits in supervisor perceptions of employee innovative behavior. *Personality and Individual Differences, 82,* 158–162. https://doi.org/10.1016/j.paid.2015.03.020

Wisse, B., & Sleebos, E. (2016). When the dark ones gain power: Perceived position power strengthens the effect of supervisor Machiavellianism on abusive supervision in work teams. *Personality and Individual Differences, 99,* 122–126. https://doi.org/10.1016/j.paid.2016.05.019

Zettler, I., Friedrich, N., & Hilbig, B. E. (2011). Dissecting work commitment: The role of Machiavellianism. *Career Development International, 16*(1), 20–35. https://doi.org/10.1108/13620431111107793

NOTE

1. We define leadership as conceptually distinctive and complementary to management. Leaders are individuals in organizations who "influence others through formal or informal contextually rooted and goal-influencing processes" (Antonakis & Day, 2017, p. 5). Leaders influence others through the power, which can be justified by their position (i.e., management), but also by other means such as identification or expertise.

Birgit Schyns, Susanne Braun, and Barbara Wisse

Diversity in Organizations

DIVERSITY IN THE WORKPLACE

INTRODUCTION

Since the 1990s, diversity in the workplace has not only become an important topic of scientific debate but also transformed organizational practice (Zanoni & Janssens, 2003). From its conceptual origins in North America (Bendl, Hanappi-Egger, & Hofmann, 2012; Mensi-Klarbach, 2018), diversity and its management within organizations have spread across the world in a range of contexts (Bendl, Bleijenbergh, Henttonen, & Mills, 2015). Scholars in many countries have worked to establish a differentiated and nuanced academic discourse on diversity in organizations by introducing diversity-oriented journals[1] and implementing standing working groups and divisions as well as conference streams at major management conferences (e.g., Academy of Management (AOM), European Group of Organization Studies (EGOS), European Academy of Management (EURAM), and British Academy of Management (BAM)). Regarding organizational practice, multinational, national, and local enterprises have implemented diversity management strategies and practices over the last three decades. Rapid demographic change over recent years has also made this an increasingly important concept for European companies (Claes, 2018; Klarsfeld, Booysen, Ng, Roper, & Tatli, 2015).

• 529

This article provides an introduction to diversity in the workplace by offering a summary of key concepts and highlighting various contributions, debates, and controversies in the field. The aim is to give an initial overview of diversity in the workplace for those readers unfamiliar with the topic but who wish to learn more. Thus the text is based on basic literature in the field with suggestions for further reading offered at the end. In the section "Diversity" (following this introduction), we provide some definitions of the term *diversity* from alternative epistemological perspectives (i.e., a difference-oriented essentialist perspective versus a more constructionist perspective) and highlight the pros and cons of more or less precise definitions of diversity. Within this article, diversity is understood as a performative feature that is constantly done rather than fixed over time. Accordingly, the section "From Doing Gender to Doing Diversity" introduces a "doing" perspective on diversity along with a discussion of how diversity and difference are theoretically conceptualized in scholarly discourse and enacted in organizational practice. The section "Diversity Management and Inclusion" provides a definition of two major terms in the field of diversity at the workplace, namely, *diversity management* and *inclusion*, clarifying their meanings and discussing the differences between the two concepts. In the section "Diversity Management and Inclusion: The Business Case Versus the Moral Rationale" we discuss two alternative ways of legitimizing diversity management in organizations (i.e., by moral or business reasoning). Building on this distinction, we critically examine how the motives for implementing diversity management impact how it is carried out and whether or not this fosters inclusion. The article concludes with a brief overview of diversity research and its various approaches as well as the future directions of both diversity research and practice.

Before presenting diversity and its definitions, as authors, we would first like to highlight our academic embeddedness in order to help the reader contextualize our perspectives on diversity at the workplace: despite our generational differences, we are all white, European women, trained in management and organization studies, and working at the Department of Management (more precisely, at the Institute of Gender and Diversity in Organizations) of the Vienna University of Economics and Business (WU Vienna). We therefore adopt more of a *management* perspective on diversity in the workplace, rather than a psychological or sociological perspective. Consequently, the focus within this article is on diversity issues relevant to organizational perspectives and research on diversity in organizations, rather than the presentation of detailed theories and empirical results on how different diversity dimensions affect the workplace. Nonetheless, important research results from the fields of psychology, sociology, and gender studies inform how we present the introductory perspectives on diversity in the workplace.

DIVERSITY

Although *diversity* has become a term popular with academics, policymakers, practitioners, and the general public, its definition is complex and is influenced by the context in which it is applied and interpreted by different actors (Point & Singh, 2003; Prasad, Pringle, & Konrad, 2006).

Generally speaking, diversity refers to the differences between individuals (Hanappi-Egger, 2012) or, more precisely, "the *collective amount of differences among members within a social unit*" (emphasis in the original) (Harrison & Sin, 2006, p. 196). This very open definition of diversity provokes additional questions: what are these differences, how can they be measured, and are they important? There have been various attempts to categorize differences, each offering a distinct definition of diversity. Within this article, we present *four ways of grasping differences/diversity* and discuss their similarities and disparities.

Diversity Definitions. The first of these has been articulated by Harrison, Price, and Bell (1998), who distinguished two levels of heterogeneity. *Surface-level diversity* encompasses those dimensions that are visible, biological, and reflected in physical features such as age, sex, or race/ethnicity. The authors assume that these dimensions can be easily observed, measured, and converted into variables, and that observers can reach clear social consensus on these characteristics. By contrast, *deep-level diversity* concentrates on the values, beliefs, and attitudes of individuals. This type of diversity is not directly visible but can be observed over time through verbal and non-verbal interaction. Harrison et al. (1998) assumed that individuals initially assess others based on (dis)similarity of surface-level demographics; these first impressions are only replaced over time, once individuals get to know each other's deep-level dimensions. The authors thereby underline the importance of the first impression, which is mainly determined by visible characteristics.

A second definition of diversity is the "four layers of diversity" by Gardenswartz and Rowe (2003). This concept distinguishes between the core layer *personality*,[2] which is surrounded by *internal dimensions, external dimensions,* and *organizational dimensions.* Hence, the model highlights the personality of individuals, shaped over time and consisting of various character traits. The internal dimensions, which are assumed to be fixed characteristics, are classified as gender, age, ethnicity/race, sexual orientation, and physical ability. External dimensions are not fixed and not conclusive, encompassing factors such as geographic location, income, or religion. The fourth and outer layer refers to organizational dimensions (i.e., characteristics determined by the working context of a person) and includes dimensions such as work content, functional level, or division/department/unit (Gardenswartz & Rowe, 2003). Figure 1 shows how the four layers of the diversity model build on one another. This definition of diversity by Gardenswartz and Rowe (2003) is especially popular for teaching purposes and with practitioners and counselors due to its comparative simplicity and the integration of the working context into the definition. Here it is important to point out that the idea of a conclusive list of fixed internal dimensions has been contested. Some people argue, for example, that sexual orientation (e.g., coming out later in life), (dis)abilities (in the case of accidents or illness), or skin color (e.g., Michael Jackson) are not fixed but may in fact change over a person's lifetime.

The third definition of diversity stems from Litvin's (1997) demonstration that management and organizational behavior textbooks generally distinguish between *primary* and *secondary* dimensions of diversity. Primary diversity dimensions include age, ethnicity, gender, physical attributes/abilities, race, and sexual orientation, thus resonating with Gardenswartz and Rowe's (2003) inner dimensions. These are also assumed to be permanent core characteristics that influence an individual's behavior and attitude and, therefore, define who we are. Regarding secondary diversity dimensions, there is no conclusive list. Rather, these are described as changeable and, to a certain extent, under the control of individuals—for

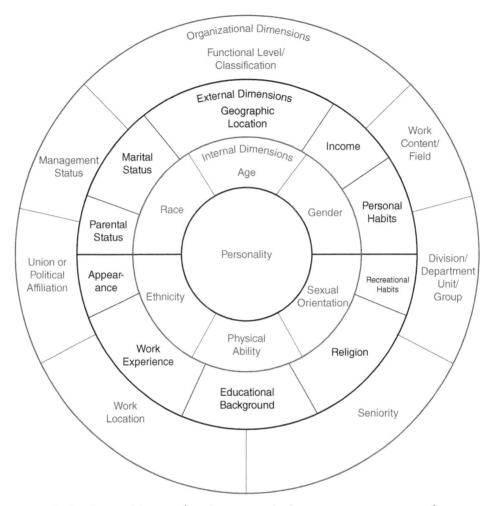

Figure 1. The four layers of diversity (Gardenswartz, Cherbosque, & Rowe, 2010, p. 77).

example, the dimensions income, educational background, parental status, or religion (Litvin, 2006). Such characteristics correlate with the outer dimensions in the four layers model of Gardenswartz and Rowe (2003). It is notable that both concepts view religion as a changeable dimension, implying a rather secular view of religious diversity.

The fourth definition of diversity, rather more normative than the *how* and *what* perspectives presented above, is based on the legal view of diversity as laid out in European Union (EU) anti-discrimination legislation from 1999. This legislation combats discrimination along the following six diversity dimensions: age, ethnicity/race, disability, sex/gender, religion/belief, and sexual orientation (Danowitz & Claes, 2012). This conclusive list, also known as the "Big 6" diversity dimensions (see Bendl, Fleischmann, & Walenta, 2008), is adopted by many European companies when addressing diversity (Hanappi-Egger, 2012). However, the EU regulation has been criticized for ignoring some highly relevant differences such as social class, which remain unprotected and thus open to discrimination (Prasad, Pringle, & Konrad, 2006).

In summary, it can be said that there is no single commonly agreed upon definition of diversity that is able to capture all relevant differences between individuals (Prasad et al., 2006).

Table 1 shows that the four concepts of diversity share some common ideas. These are important to highlight when talking about diversity in the workplace:

- All presented diversity definitions concentrate on differences between individuals.
- Some definitions portray dimensions as a mix of those that are fixed (i.e., determined by biology) and others that can be influenced by individuals. The fixed dimensions seem to be measurable while personality, or deep-level diversity, is harder to define and measure.
- The Big 6 have been the object of much discrimination in organizations across time and place. These dimensions coincide with the inner dimensions of the four layers model, and also the primary dimensions described by Litvin (1997), except for religion and belief, which is covered in the EU regulation but defined as an external/secondary dimension in the two other concepts.
- Job-related diversity such as education and experience are relevant to any discussion of diversity in the workplace.

Critique of Diversity Definitions. The critique of diversity and its definitions is rooted in two alternative approaches to difference, namely, the *essentialist* and the *constructionist* per-

Table 1. Overview of Distinct Categorizations of Diversity

Harrison et al. (1998)	*Gardenswartz/Rowe (2003)*	*Litvin (1997)*	*EU antidiscrimination (1999)*
– **Surface-level dimensions:** visible (age, gender, skin color, ethnicity…) versus – **Deep-level dimensions:** invisible (beliefs, attitudes, values…)	– **Personality** (Values, beliefs…) – **Internal dimensions** (= gender, sexual orientation, race/ethnicity, disability, age = BIG 6 without religion) – **External dimensions** (religion, education, geographic location…) – **Organizational dimensions** (employment, management status…)	– **Primary diversity dimensions** (= inner dimensions + personality) versus – **Secondary diversity dimensions** (income, education, parental status…)	– **Big 6 diversity dimensions:** Age, ethnicity, gender, race, religion, sexual orientation

spectives (Hearn & Louvrier, 2015). The *essentialist perspective* assumes that people have a fixed inner "essence" that cannot be changed (Hanappi-Egger, 2012). It considers given differences to be matters of fact, which stem from biology and determine social behavior and skills. Physical and mental characteristics are ascribed to certain groups based on their seemingly given, and thus neutral, similarities or differences (Hanappi-Egger, 2012; Hearn & Louvrier, 2015). This essentialist conception of differences developed historically in Western philosophical thinking from an understanding of nature and biology (Litvin, 1997). Starting with Plato, the focus of research on nature was to classify not only plants and animals but also humans into groups (e.g., ethnic) according to their natural and true inner "essence." Selected physical characteristics were combined with valued and generalized descriptions of personality and customs to realize this classification. Until the middle of the 19th century, the essentialist idea that groups of humans were determined by their "essence" of physical characteristics, values, and personality was dominant (Litvin, 1997).

Thus, diversity definitions that focus on the supposed influence of natural and permanent dimensions on individual behavior and values are based on the essentialist notion of differences. Diversity definitions such as the Big 6, as well as a comparison of definitions given by management textbooks (Litvin, 1997), show that employees are often classified as homogenous groups based on primary diversity dimensions such as age, gender, or sexual orientation. These are presented as the main determinants of individual identity, while the groups formed by these categories are assumed to be homogenous, sharing the same interests and needs. Yet any view of these categorizations as "natural," and thus immutable, neglects the influence of cultural norms, institutions, power relations, and intersectionality (Litvin, 1997), as well as the notion that natural and biological perspectives are themselves constructions.

The *constructionist perspective* considers differences as arising through interactions with others and not internal to individuals. Here, differences and their meanings are seen as constructed by the social context and neither determined by biology nor viewed as matters of fact. The power relations of specific contexts will largely determine how these differences are socially constructed and whether they are viewed as positive or negative (Hearn & Louvrier, 2015). Phrases like "systemically excluded" or "historically disadvantaged" (Prasad et al., 2006, pp. 3f.) express the idea that power, as well as its rewards and resources, is unequally distributed between groups. Power relations are shaped by historical and structural contexts, which can prove to be highly stable (Prasad et al., 2006). The constructionist perspective assumes that differences are not "innocent" but determine the distribution of positions in society; that is, they form the basis for the (re)production and change of social order (Hearn & Louvrier, 2015). In other words, the social construction of diversity dimensions within a specific historical and institutional context influences the prominence and relevance of differences between individuals. Thus, demographic categories are not understood as rooted in essential, unchangeable, and natural characteristics (Litvin, 1997) but rather in dimensions that are constantly being renegotiated by society.

FROM DOING GENDER TO DOING DIVERSITY

The theory known as *social constructionism* (Berger & Luckmann, 1966) represents the epistemological basis for considering diversity dimensions as socially constructed. Under this model, the meaning, notion, or connotation of, for example, gender, age, or disability is constructed and produced by the members of a social system which, in turn, constitutes its member. In other words, age, gender, and disability represent an invention, artifice, or concept of that society, evolving out of the interaction of its members over time based on their social, legal, political, and economic conditions as well as their hierarchy and power relations. The later theory of post-structuralism (Foucault, 1978) claims that those individual person-bound approaches are influenced by collective discourses based on a "societal power-knowledge complex." This complex—the hierarchical relationship of power and knowledge—extends beyond individuals to create time-specific and locally bound socially and politically legitimated perspectives of reality. As such, subjective, multiple, and relative constructions of diversity dimensions such as gender, age, sexual orientation, ethnicity, or (dis)abilities are not more or less "true," only more or less informed (Pringle & Booysen, 2018).

Doing Gender. The constructionist perspective shifted the focus of inquiry to the question of how gender, ethnicity, disability, sexual orientation, or age, and so on, are enacted in context. By the late 1980s, West and Zimmerman (1987) had already introduced the concept of "doing gender" to reveal and analyze the interrelated (power) processes that create notions of gender. In this approach, the focus lies on the gendered and gendering actions of persons who are part of the system:

> [D]oing gender involves a complex of perceptual, interactional, and micropolitical activities that cast particular pursuits as expressions of manly and womanly "natures." Rather than conceiving of gender as an individual characteristic, we conceived of it as an emergent property of social situations: both an outcome of and a rationale for various social arrangements and a means of justifying one of the most fundamental divisions of society. We suggested that examining how gender is accomplished could reveal the mechanisms by which power is exercised and inequality is produced.
> (West & Fenstermaker, 1995, p. 9)

Doing Difference. As the approach of doing gender only focuses on one diversity dimension, West and Fenstermaker (1995) extended the concept as "doing difference" in order to take account of other dimensions. Figure 2 shows how various diversity dimensions can interplay and overlap, in this case for Black, working-class women.

Figure 2 shows that not all women are oppressed by gender, race, and social class to the same extent but that their oppression depends on the specific interplay of the three selected diversity dimensions. The next section discusses this interplay, termed *intersectionality*. The group of women of color "do" their identity along the intersection of construction and reproduction processes of race, class, and gender. If additional diversity dimensions such as age or family status were introduced to the figure, the outcome would be even closer to reality, opening up space for discussion of which political and organizational measures could be taken to create more empowering than discriminative and marginalizing contexts for Black women.

The prevailing scholarly convention is that all diversity dimensions are constructed. At the same time, the concepts of "doing age," "doing ethnicity," or "doing gender" operate in different

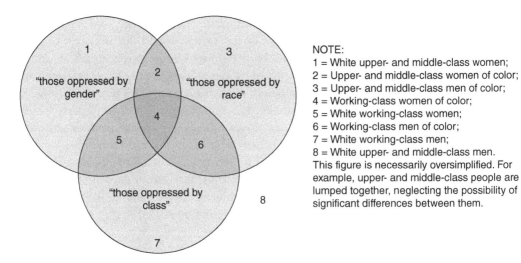

Figure 2. Oppressed people (see West & Fenstermaker, 1995, p. 14).

ways, as the various diversity dimensions may have different functions and may be valued differently in various contexts. For example, Bendl, Eberherr, and Schmidt (2015) have demonstrated that age or marital status is rated differently for men and women in the executive search selection process.

Intersectionality. The various diversity dimensions also reinforce each other contextually in terms of upgrading and downgrading. For instance, age has a higher value in some cultures than in others; a young man may be valued differently in the United States than he would be in Japan. Gender may also become more or less relevant depending on whether the individual is a local national or a foreigner. This perspective of the interrelation between different diversity dimensions is based on the concept of intersectionality, which was introduced by Crenshaw (1989, 1991). Focusing on the living conditions of Black women in the United States, Crenshaw (1989, p. 140) demonstrated that a "single-axis framework erases Black women in the conceptualization, identification, and remediation of race and sex discrimination by limiting inquiry to the experiences of otherwise-privileged members of the group." She proposes the use of intersectional analyses in order to grasp discrimination, marginalization, and exclusion processes more fully in their multidimensionality. Such an intersectional perspective enables us to articulate not only the interaction of racism and patriarchy but all diversity dimensions, offering a way to mediate the tensions between assertions of multiple identities and the ongoing necessity of group politics (see Crenshaw, 1991). Furthermore, to better deal with the complexity of intersectional analysis, McCall (2005) introduced the three approaches of *intra-*, *inter-*, and *anti-categorical complexity*. The first of these, the intra-categorical approach, focuses on the inner heterogeneity of a diversity dimension by exploring the diversity among so-called group members (e.g., differences among women). The inter-categorical approach considers the interplay between the various categories (e.g., an older disabled women, a young Black man . . .). Finally, the anti-categorical approach proceeds from the assumption that individuals are embedded in a number of social relations and subject positions. This helps to open up the categorical continuum by asking how and why dimensions gain relevance and in which contexts (e.g., organizational measures directed at certain needs such as flexible working arrangements rather than focusing on groups such as women). Such a disclosure of static and stereotypical actualizations of diversity dimensions represents the first step in overcoming discrimination, marginalization, and exclusion processes.

In line with the aforementioned concepts, Acker (1992) showed that relations of gender are produced simultaneously at different levels in organizations, namely, the individual-mental level, the structural level, the symbolic level, or the level of action. One can argue that the same applies for all other diversity dimensions. Doing diversity at the individual, structural, symbolic, and action level influences how ethnicity, age, sexual orientation, and so on, are constructed, perceived, and reproduced and vice versa. In order to grasp the intersectional perspectives of different diversity dimensions, Acker (2006) introduced the concept of *inequality regimes*, which she considers all organizations to have. These are defined as "loosely interrelated practices, processes, actions, and meanings that result in and maintain class, gender, and racial inequalities within particular organizations; [. . .] they also tend to be fluid and changing. These regimes are linked to inequality in the surrounding society, its politics, history, and culture" (Acker, 2006, p. 443). The concept of inequality regimes goes one step further than the previously discussed concepts by considering class as the central dimension, influencing the reproduction of other diversity dimensions. Before Acker's 2006 paper, the dimension of class had largely been neglected in organization discourse.

DIVERSITY IN THE WORKPLACE

In this section, the presented theoretical perspectives are linked to the meaning of diversity in the workplace. Clearly, diversity is highly relevant in the work context, where individuals can be considered to constitute a social unit. Returning to the definition of diversity formulated by Harrison and Sin (2006, p. 196) as "the *collective amount of differences among members within a social unit*" (emphasis in the original), we are reminded that diversity is not a characteristic of individuals but of groups. An individual considered in isolation cannot be said to show any features of diversity. At the same time, a social unit is not diverse per se, but rather can only be considered diverse "with respect to one or more specific features of its members" (Harrison & Klein, 2007, p. 1200). As already discussed, dimensions of diversity only become relevant or visible through social interaction. Here, a further aspect must be clarified when discussing diversity in social units such as organizational teams or organizations, namely, the way in which diversity is conceptualized. Harrison and Klein (2007) argue that researchers and practitioners can adopt three different approaches to difference, regardless of the diversity category being considered. First, the diversity construct of *separation* describes a social unit in which members differ in their values or attitudes, their experiences, knowledge, gender, age, and so on. These differences serve to divide the unit into subgroups of individuals who share some feature(s). Differences in the sense of separation potentially lead to conflicts and misunderstandings. Therefore, the adoption of a "separation view" on diversity anticipates potential sources of conflict. Second, the diversity construct of *variety* describes differences between unit members in a more positive sense by focusing on the different experiences, knowledge, or information that is valuable for the social unit. This perspective of diversity reflects what Cox and Blake (1991) coined "the value-in-diversity hypothesis," assuming that diversity brings potential benefits to organizational processes. *Disparity*, the third construct, refers to the vertical differences between members of a social unit, namely, disparities in status or pay as well as, and more importantly, power. Power disparity can foster an organizational or team climate in which less powerful individuals become reluctant to speak up or voice their opinions, thereby denying the full potential of differences in the sense of "value in diversity." This limits the positive benefits of diversity and, more generally, helps to reinforce structural inequalities (or even inequality regimes) in organizations (Harrison & Klein, 2007).

The adopted approach to diversity will influence the ensuing expectations regarding diversity as well as the way in which it is handled. Under the disparity perspective, our attention will turn to the organizational hierarchy by considering the distribution of power as well as potential inequality regimes; that is, the focus is on how individuals are assigned to various positions and departments in managerial, middle, and lower positions. Under the separation perspective, organizations target the level of differences in such dimensions as age, gender, or ethnicity in the workforce and aim to minimize potential conflicts. Viewing diversity from the perspective of variety, on the other hand, means trying to increase diversity as a source of value. All these questions regarding how best to deal with diversity can be subsumed under *diversity management*, a concept discussed in the following section.

DIVERSITY MANAGEMENT AND INCLUSION

As the term indicates, *diversity management* is a management concept that focuses on how to deal with diversity within an organization. Three main premises underlie diversity management: (a) diversity permeates the entire workforce and, consequently, also organizations; (b) diversity can be difficult to handle in cases where excessive differences cause conflicts among employees; and (c) if handled well, diversity can help to improve organizational performance by increasing creativity, fostering innovation, and thus delivering better results (at least for some tasks). Knippenberg and Haslam (2003) call this the *diversity dividend*. Following these premises, Cox (1994), one of the leading U.S. diversity scholars, offered the following definition at the early stage of diversity management practice and research: "By managing diversity I mean planning and implementing organizational systems and practices to manage people so that the potential advantages of diversity are maximized while its potential disadvantages are minimized" (Cox, 1994, p. 15).

Similarly, the definition of diversity management formulated by British academics Kandola and Fullerton (1998) underpins the premise of "value in diversity" (that diversity in work groups enhances the effectiveness of workers) while pointing out that diversity in the workforce must be consciously acknowledged:

The basic concept of managing diversity accepts that the workforce consists of a diverse population of people. The diversity consists of visible and non-visible differences which will include factors such as sex, age, background, race, disability and work style. It is founded on the premise that harnessing these differences will create a productive environment in which everybody feels valued, where their talents are being fully utilized and in which organizational goals are met.
(Kandola & Fullerton, 1998, p. 8)

Both definitions emphasize the notion of "value in diversity," which implies that diversity is basically beneficial for organizations only if managed well. This has several implications (Kirton & Greene, 2005).

First, diversity of people in the sense of a range of individual characteristics is a thing of value that should be recognized, exploited, and rewarded (Liff, 1997). Organizations should enable employees to realize their full potential by being true to themselves, rather than living up to a narrowly defined norm to which all employees are expected to conform.

Second, the "value in diversity" perspective encompasses all individual differences that potentially contribute to an organization's goals. This goes beyond protected diversity dimensions such as gender, age, or disability to include personal traits such as work style (Kandola & Fullerton, 1998). More importantly, diversity management in this sense focuses on individuals and their characteristics rather than on (protected) groups (Kirton & Greene, 2005).

Third, diversity management can help an organization to meet its goals. This is clearly a management concept that focuses on utilizing diversity among the workforce to boost organizational performance. Some scholars argue that the main difference between equal opportunities and diversity management is that the former pursues the goal of social justice while employing, in part, the business rationale as a means to this end, whereas the latter focuses on business ends using diversity as a means (Kaler, 2001; Noon & Ogbonna, 2001).

Under these definitions of diversity management, an organization is encouraged to think about diversity and how to make best use of it. The management team will (re)define organizational structures, practices, and processes (such as recruitment, promotion, work group formation, training, alternative work arrangements, etc.) to better accommodate the needs of diversity under the premise of organizational effectiveness.

Over the last few decades, the term *inclusion* has gained in importance so that, frequently, researchers and practitioners now talk about diversity *and* inclusion. Thus, the following question has to be answered: What is inclusion and in which way does it go beyond diversity management?

Inclusion. Inclusion has been defined as "the degree to which an employee perceives that s/he is an esteemed member of the work group through experiencing treatment that satisfies his or her needs for belongingness and uniqueness" (Shore et al., 2011, p. 1265). Clearly, the basic human need for a sense of uniqueness, as well as a sense of belongingness, conspires to create a climate of inclusion. Shore et al. (2011) provide the framework shown in Table 2 to help understand inclusion.

The clear focus here is the individual perception. A sense of inclusion depends on whether or not the individual feels valued as a unique person who belongs to the work group/organization. Only then, individuals will be able to realize their full potential and thus contribute to improved group performance. In contrast to the concept of assimilation, whereby individuals are urged to conform to norms such as dress codes, habitus, and group language (e.g., management team), inclusion describes an environment in which individuals can exhibit different styles of work, thought, language, and so on. Hewlin (2009) talks about "facades of conformity," when employees are required to suppress their individual values and selves to create the appearance of organizational belongingness. In contrast to this maintenance of

540 • DIVERSITY IN THE WORKPLACE

Table 2. Inclusion Framework

	Degree of belongingness	
	Low	*High*
Degree of uniqueness — Low	**Exclusion** Individual is not treated as an organizational insider with unique value in the work group but there are other employees or groups who are insiders.	**Assimilation** Individual is treated as an insider in the work group when they conform to organizational/dominant culture norms and downplay uniqueness.
Degree of uniqueness — High	**Differentiation** Individual is not treated as an organizational insider in the work group but their unique characteristics are seen as valuable and required for group/organization success.	**Inclusion** Individual is not treated as an organizational insider in the work group but their unique characteristics are seen as valuable and required for group/organization success.

Source: Adapted from Shore et al. (2011, p. 1266).

dominant norms, inclusive organizations view diversity as a resource from which the whole organization can learn and benefit (Ely & Thomas, 2001; Shore et al., 2011). Inclusion may also mean that while individuals perceive themselves to be highly unique, their degree of uniqueness in the organizational context is construed as low: they see themselves as belonging to the "cultural organizational norm," although here the norm is explicit rather than implicit.

Accordingly, an organization seeking to foster inclusion goes beyond diversity management in not merely allowing diversity to permeate the organization (via recruitment, promotion, etc.) but by aiming to create a work climate that values all employees as unique individuals. The inclusive organization regards all employees as important and as insiders. This climate of inclusion is thought to enable the full potential of a diverse workforce to be realized (Mor-Barak, 2011).

From Diversity Management to Inclusion. Studies have shown that implementing structures which "embed accountability, authority, and expertise (affirmative action plans, diversity committees and taskforces, diversity managers and departments) are the most effective means of increasing the proportions of white women, Black women, and Black men in private sector management" (Kalev, Dobbin, & Kelly, 2006, p. 611). Thus, diversity can be increased within an organization by a modification of organizational structures and practices (i.e., through diversity management). However, this does not always result in a climate of inclusion. Research indicates that diversity training designed to reduce cognitive biases toward minorities is rather ineffective (Kalev et al., 2006). Moreover, reforms of personnel practices that are "designed to control managerial bias lead to resistance and tend to backfire" (Dobbin, Schrage, & Kalev, 2015, p. 1034). In these cases, it seems that the overall value of diversity is not universally comprehended. Individuals receiving preferential treatment or making use of certain workplace accommodations may be singled out and stigmatized (Cunningham, 2001; Eaton, 2003). In turn, this reduces their feeling of belongingness and hinders them from unfolding their full potential (Sabharwal, 2014). To prevent such negative repercussions, inclusion goes one step further than diversity management in not merely modifying structures, processes, and practices but also ensuring that the organizational climate is adapted in such a way that the establishment of diversity measures does not engender exclusion. Hence, inclusion means not only increasing diversity in the organizations but also making use of diversity to create a learning organization (Dass & Parker, 1999).

DIVERSITY MANAGEMENT AND INCLUSION: THE BUSINESS CASE VERSUS THE MORAL RATIONALE

One of the major criticisms of diversity management is that it constitutes "an instrument or tool that uses people's diversity as means of achieving economic end goals" (Lorbiecki & Jack, 2000, p. 23). Indeed, the premise of the economic value of diversity is dominant in the definition of both diversity management and inclusion. Yet if the roots of diversity management are considered, it becomes apparent that they lie in the U.S. civil rights movement which began in the 1950s. At that time, and in the following decades, civil activists focused on combating discrimination against minorities in society and the workplace (Mensi-Klarbach, 2018). The most prominent tool to develop out of this political movement was "affirmative action" (AA), which grants preferential treatment to historically disadvantaged groups such as ethnic minorities and women. Under affirmative action, all companies seeking government contracts had to issue an AA plan outlining how they intended to increase the numbers of ethnic minorities and women in their workforce (Dobbin, Sutton, Meyer, & Scott, 1993). While affirmative action was highly effective, it also provoked resistance due to allegations of reverse discrimination against white males (Thomas, 1990). Growing opposition and a change in the political climate in the 1980s, following the election of Ronald Reagan as U.S. president, transformed the country's basic economic philosophy toward profit maximization, thereby reducing the legal and political support for affirmative action. Consequently, AA officers were required to explain how their practices improved and professionalized personnel practices and, as such, contributed to overall organizational effectiveness (Dobbin et al., 1993). They began to adopt the business case rationale to legitimize their activities and diversity work. Supported by a report by Johnston and Packer (1987), *Workforce 2000*, which predicted a fundamental change in the composition of the American workforce by the end of the millennium, the concept of diversity management evolved and spread as an indispensable tool to make companies better prepared to meet the future challenges of diversity (Kelly & Dobbin, 1998).

In this way, diversity management can be seen as derived from affirmative action in the United States, where the primary goal was self-legitimation, at a time when political and legal support for AA was fading. As Lowery (1995, p. 150) states: "corporate executives found diversity a lot easier to swallow than affirmative action, and much easier to sell to a predominantly white workforce." Similarly, economic reasoning has been used across Europe under the rubric of diversity management in order to support existing (gender) equality measures (Singh & Point, 2004). Some scholars argue that measures benefiting disadvantaged or minority groups have remained unchanged under this new reasoning, and that the rhetoric of diversity management has merely been added to local discourses (Heres & Benschop, 2010). Others, however, claim that the economic or business case rationale is not merely a rhetorical device

542 • DIVERSITY IN THE WORKPLACE

to support equality measures, but it does actually exert a considerable influence on the "kinds" of diversity with which an organization must deal. For example, "diverse individuals" whose diversity does not lead to increased performance are not considered "valuable" by the organization. This may create a hierarchy between "beneficial" and "undiverted and unaccepted diversity" (Lorbiecki & Jack, 2000). A further threat to diversity from the business case perspective is that if diversity management does not in fact lead to improved business performance, this could serve as a justification for discrimination. Indeed, some scholars argue that a lack of evidence for the business case serves to foster discrimination (Hansen, 2004). Accordingly, critical scholars call for a more reflexive understanding of diversity management, one that goes beyond the business case rationale to include the moral case in order to promote anti-discrimination measures and equal opportunities, irrespective of economic benefit (Kirton & Greene, 2005; Litvin, 2006; Lorbiecki & Jack, 2000).

Hence, diversity research plays an important role in helping to inform organizational practices and an understanding of how to increase diversity, how diversity takes effect, and how diversity management functions. Not only does research inform and define the way diversity is conceptualized (see Booysen et al., 2018), it also highlights empirical phenomena and thus the way diversity is perceived. In the next section, we turn our attention to various research perspectives on diversity, with a discussion of their implications and future directions for research. While the focus of this section is on mainstream and critical diversity research, it is necessary to stress that especially comparative studies are relevant for a nuanced understanding of diversity. While most of the research on diversity started in the United States and Canada, more and more research is currently conducted in Europe (Klarsfeld, Ng, Booysen, Castro Christiansen, & Kuvaas, 2016). The findings point to the relevance of national and cultural contexts for both understanding and conceptualizing diversity and for the implementation of diversity management.[3]

RESEARCH PERSPECTIVES ON DIVERSITY

Research on diversity in the workplace can be broadly divided into two streams reflecting the essentialist and constructionist dichotomy described above. This can also be described as the mainstream versus the critical literature on diversity (e.g., Ahonen, Tienari, Meriläinen, & Pullen, 2014; Dick & Cassell, 2002; Özbilgin & Tatli, 2011).[4]

Mainstream diversity literature is shaped in particular by a positivist research tradition (Ahonen et al., 2014) based on "the natural scientific model of causal analysis of independent and dependent variables [. . .]" (Knights & Omanović, 2015, p. 85). In this view, research is mainly concerned with determining the value of diversity by calculating its effects on, for example, firm or team performance (i.e., the business case) (Ahonen et al., 2014; Knights & Omanović, 2015). The understanding of difference and diversity is rooted in the essentialist perspective, along with the assumption that diversity has a positive influence on firm performance if managed appropriately (variety perspective). Research is largely conducted using quantitative methods so that differences between individuals can be assessed by transforming them into operational and measurable variables (Knights & Omanović, 2015). Diversity is viewed as a neutral and individual phenomenon, which should be exploited to improve team and company performance (Ahonen et al., 2014). The role of the researcher is seen as objective; that is, researchers are outside observers of "natural" diversity phenomena and should avoid any direct involvement (Prasad et al., 2006). Within a positivist epistemology, research questions are derived from gaps in the existing literature, which are not challenged but taken as starting points (Knights & Omanović, 2015).

Research questions within this stream of study are typically concerned with the business case and thus the financial benefit of diversity in organizations and, frequently, diversity in top management teams. While some scholars focus on the effects of individual diversity dimensions such as functional background (e.g., Buyl, Boone, Hendriks, & Matthyssens, 2011; Cannella, Park, & Lee, 2008), gender (e.g., Campbell & Mínguez-Vera, 2008; Dwyer, Richard, & Chadwick, 2003), or gender combined with ethnicity (e.g., Carter, Simkins, & Simpson, 2003; Erhardt, Werbel, & Shrader, 2003), others try to assess a "total" amount of diversity by incorporating a number of attributes into one diversity index (see Harrison & Klein, 2007, pp. 1215f.). While a wealth of research has been conducted on diversity and its outputs, results remain inconclusive or even contradictory. Meta-analyses aimed at illuminating the theoretical link between diversity and performance (e.g., Bell, Villado, Lukasik, & Briggs, 2011; van Dijk, van Engen, & van Knippenberg, 2012) have also been met with limited success. One of the major problems facing researchers is that the direction of the assumed causal relationship is unclear: does increased diversity lead to better performance or do better performing teams/ organizations seek greater diversity (see Kirsch, 2018)? Another problem lies in the theoretical assumptions underpinning any causal relation (and which reflect some of the theoretical positions discussed in the previous sections): Do researchers conceptualize diversity as disparity, variety, or difference? Do researchers assume diversity categories as fixed and easily observable or as fluid and constructed through interaction (Harrison & Klein, 2007; Kirsch, 2018)? In general, studies have indicated both positive and negative effects. Accordingly, the answer to the question of whether or not diversity is beneficial is that it all depends on the context!

Within the stream of *critical diversity research*, diversity is not seen as a phenomenon that can be evaluated quantitatively and causal relationships between diversity and performance are considered unimportant, or even rejected (Ahonen et al., 2014). Differences are understood as socially constructed and, consequently, not at all neutral or naturally given. Studies in this research stream view the (historic) context as crucial (Knights & Omanović, 2015). Researchers are not assumed to be objective and external observers of the diversity phenomena they are investigating; instead, they are guided by their personal values and perceptions (Prasad et al., 2006). Critical diversity research is motivated by a "quest for social justice" (moral case) (Ahonen et al., 2014, p. 274) so that research activities focus on criticizing existing social problems of inequality while also providing starting points for potential improvements (disparity perspective). This stream of research is dominated by qualitative research methods (Ahonen et al., 2014).

Research questions in the critical tradition typically concentrate on how the diversity discourse and diversity dimensions are constructed, as well as on how an emphasis on single categories can be replaced by intersectional approaches. Hence, two areas of interest within this field are the analysis and critique of the diversity discourse and the dominance of the business case as "common sense" (Ahonen et al., 2014; Litvin, 2006; Noon, 2007), as well as the mapping of actors and their viewpoints within the diversity discourse (Özbilgin & Tatli, 2011). Studies typically include the question of power distribution along different categories of differences and their relational (micro, meso, and macro) perspectives.

Table 3 presents the two identified streams of research. It should be noted that these do not constitute two clearly separable research strands but rather can be understood as a continuum between two poles. Indeed, it can be difficult to assign individual studies/articles to one of these groups if, as is sometimes the case, researchers do not state their assumptions clearly (see Knights & Omanović, 2015).

Furthermore, the highest ranked and most prestigious management journals tend to publish articles following a mainstream perspective on diversity and thus influence the diversity discourse in this direction (Ahonen et al., 2014). Critical diversity studies are more commonly found in critical journals in the field of management studies. In general, it can be said that the mainstream diversity literature is dominant in the United States, whereas critical diversity literature is more prominent in Europe, Australia, and New Zealand.

As much of the mainstream diversity research investigates economic effects of diversity and diversity management, it can be useful and is often used to create awareness among corporations for the need to care about diversity beyond pure ethical reasoning. Also, mainstream diversity research has widened our understanding of the conditions under which diversity can be economically beneficial. Critical diversity research, on the other hand, has constantly pointed to reasons, reproduction, and dangers of inequality. It has proven of particular relevance to pinpoint diversity and, more importantly, inequality from the affected individuals' point of view. This certainly has led to a more thorough understanding and danger of (re)producing inequality within organizations, even if there is a focus on diversity management.

Table 3. Continuum of Diversity Research

	Mainstream diversity research	**DIVERSITY RESEARCH**	*Critical diversity research*
View on differences	Differences are neutral and given by nature		Differences are socially constructed in a (historic) context
Research focus	Calculating effects of diversity		Understanding and ultimately changing inequalities
Role of researcher	Objective observer		Cannot be objective and is involved in the researched phenomenon
Dominant method	Quantitative approaches		Qualitative inquiry
Examples of research topics	Business case for diversity, effect of diversity dimensions on several performance indicators		Diversity discourse, arguments and actors within the diversity discourse

Summing up, both research streams have contributed to a wider understanding of diversity and diversity management, the more mainstream in highlighting the potential benefits of diversity and conditions to leverage these benefits; critical diversity research showed that focusing too much on benefits of diversity might increase, or at least reproduce, inequalities and harm certain groups within disadvantaged groups.

CONCLUSION

In the course of this article we set out to give an overview of definitions, categorizations, and concepts of diversity and difference in the workplace. We have pointed out the existence of distinct ways of understanding diversity and how these distinctions imply alternative ways of dealing with diversity in organizations. Furthermore, the two concepts of diversity management and inclusion were discussed, showing that inclusion goes beyond diversity management in requiring a diversity climate that takes a positive view of differences and the uniqueness of an organization's members. Here it is important to reiterate that a program of diversity management which exploits diversity for overall (economic) goals (i.e., the business case perspective) potentially obscures the moral claims of anti-discrimination and equal opportunities.

As business scholars at a university of economics, the authors believe that the economic and political neo-liberal movement of recent decades has affected the understanding and application of diversity and its management. Companies increasingly favor the business case for diversity, moving beyond the "Big 6" historically disadvantaged groups to promote diversity as any difference with a positive financial impact. Conversely, emphasis on the economic bottom line is one reason why some diversity groups, such as the disabled, are ignored. This not only creates tensions but also functions as a potential "acid test" of whether diversity management is developing toward a pure management concept, thereby disregarding its historical and ethical roots. If this pathway is pursued, diversity and its management will be unable to contribute to solving societal problems by utilizing the best "diverse" people. Furthermore, this will mean a move away from the establishment of equal opportunities, the dismantling of discriminatory practices, and the securing of workplaces and employment for all people in a diverse society.

Future challenges in this regard concern demographic shifts, in particular our aging societies as birthrates continue to decrease. Also, the waves of migration in recent years have created a problem with integration. How will refugees who have suffered traumatic experiences, for example, be able to fit the profiles that organizations codify for their ideal employees? This only underlines the issue of organizations' societal responsibilities with regard to diversity beyond the business case, as well as the particular form of diversity management which can contribute to this debate/challenge. As authors, we believe that continuous critical diversity research is needed to promote a diversity discourse aiming to achieve the best results for organizations *and* society at large. Diversity in the workplace is a source of many opportunities as well as many challenges. Taking these seriously is not only a matter of rational business thinking, but also of social responsibility. Ideally, diversity management and inclusion can serve both of these ends.

FURTHER READING

Bell, M. (2007). *Diversity in organizations*. Mason, OH: Thomson South-Western.

Boogaard, B., & Roggeband, C. (2010). Paradoxes of intersectionality: Theorizing inequality in the Dutch police force through structure and agency. *Organization, 17*(1), 53–75.

Brooks, A. K., & Edwards, K. (2009). Allies in the workplace: Including LGBT in HRD. *Advances in Developing Human Resources, 11*(1), 136–149.

Cox, T. H., & Blake, S. (1991). Managing cultural diversity: Implications for organizational competitiveness. *Academy of Management Executive, 5*(3), 45–56.

Diedrich, A., Eriksson-Zetterquist, U., & Styhre, A. (2011). Sorting people out: The uses of one-dimensional classificatory schemes in a multi-dimensional world. *Culture and Organization, 17*(4), 271–292.

Hayes-Thomas, R. (2017). *Managing workplace diversity and inclusion. A psychological perspective*. New York, NY: Routledge.

Marfelt, M. M. (2016). Grounded intersectionality: Key tensions, a methodological framework, and implications for diversity research. *Equality, Diversity and Inclusion: An International Journal, 35*(1), 31–47.

Mensi-Klarbach, H., & Risberg, A. (Eds.). (2018). *Diversity in organizations. Concepts and practices*. 2nd ed. Houndsmill, U.K.: Palgrave Macmillan.

Mor Barak, M. E. (2017). *Managing diversity. Toward a globally inclusive workplace*. 4th ed. Thousand Oaks, CA: SAGE.

Ng, E. S., & Stephenson, J. (2015). Individuals, teams, and organizational benefits of managing diversity. In R. Bendl, I. Bleijenbergh, E. Henttonen, & A. J. Mills (Eds.), *The Oxford handbook of diversity in organizations* (pp. 235–254). Oxford, U.K.: Oxford University Press.

Oswick, C., & Noon, M. (2014). Discourses of diversity, equality and inclusion: Trenchant formulations or transient fashions? *British Journal of Management, 25*(1), 23–39.

Roberson, Q. M. (2006). Disentangling the meanings of diversity and inclusion in organizations. *Group & Organization Management, 31*(2), 212–236.

Syed, J., & Özbilgin, M. (2009). A relational framework for international transfer of diversity management practices. *International Journal of Human Resource Management, 20*(12), 2435–2453.

Zanoni, P., Janssens, M., Benschop, Y., & Nkomo, S. (2010). Guest editorial: Unpacking diversity, grasping inequality: Rethinking difference through critical perspectives. *Organization, 17*(1), 9–29.

REFERENCES

Acker, J. (1992). Gendering organizational theory. In A. Mills & P. Tancred (Eds.), *Gendering organizational analysis* (pp. 248–260). Oxford, U.K.: SAGE.

Acker, J. (2006). Inequality regimes. Gender, class, and race in organizations. *Gender & Society, 20*(4), 441–464.

Ahonen, P., Tienari, J., Meriläinen, S., & Pullen, A. (2014). Hidden contexts and invisible power relations: A Foucauldian reading of diversity research. *Human Relations, 67*(3), 263–286.

Bell, S. T., Villado, A. J., Lukasik, M. A., Belau, L., & Briggs, A. L. (2011). Getting specific about demographic diversity variable and team performance relationships: A meta-analysis. *Journal of Management, 37*(3), 709–743.

Bendl, R., Bleijenbergh, I., Henttonen, E., & Mills, A. J. (2015). Introduction: Mapping the field of diversity in organizations. In R. Bendl, I. Bleijenbergh, E. Henttonen & A. J. Mills (Eds.), *The Oxford handbook of diversity in organizations* (pp. 1–11). Oxford, U.K.: Oxford University Press.

Bendl, R., Fleischmann, A., & Walenta, C. (2008). Diversity management discourse meets queer theory. *Gender in Management: An International Journal, 23*(6), 382–394.

Bendl, R., Hanappi-Egger, E., & Hofmann, R. (2012). Diversität und Diversitätsmanagement: Ein vielschichtiges Thema. In R. Bendl, E. Hanappi-Egger, & R. Hofmann (Eds.), *Diversität und Diversitätsmanagement* (pp. 11–21). Wien, Austria: Facultas.

Bendl, R., Eberherr, H., & Schmidt, A. (2015). Inclusion and exclusion processes in the executive search business: An intersectional approach. In A. Broadbridge & S. Fielden (Eds.), *Handbook of gendered careers in management. Getting in, getting on, getting out* (pp. 194–207). Cheltenham, U.K.: Edward Elgar.

Berger, P. L., & Luckmann, T. (1966). *The social construction of reality.* New York, NY: Anchor.

Booysen, L., Bendl, R., & Pringle, J. (2018). (Eds.). *Handbook of research methods on diversity management, equality and inclusion at work.* Cheltenham, U.K.: Edward Elgar.

Buyl, T., Boone, C., Hendriks, W., & Matthyssens, P. (2011). Top management team functional diversity and firm performance: The moderating role of CEO characteristics. *Journal of Management Studies, 48*(1), 151–177.

Campbell, K., & Mínguez-Vera, A. (2008). Gender diversity in the boardroom and firm financial performance. *Journal of Business Ethics, 83*(3), 435–451.

Cannella, A. A., Park, J.-H., & Lee, H.-U. (2008). Top management team functional background diversity and firm performance: Examining the roles of team member colocation and environmental uncertainty. *Academy of Management Journal, 51*(4), 768–784.

Carter, D. A., Simkins, B. J., & Simpson, W. G. (2003). Corporate governance, board diversity, and firm value. *Financial Review, 38*(1), 33–53.

Claes, M.T. (2018). Diversity in Europe: Its development and contours. In H. Mensi-Klarbach & A. Risberg (Eds.), *Diversity in organizations. Concepts and practices.* 2nd ed. Houndmills, U.K.: Palgrave Macmillan.

Cox, T. (1994). *Cultural diversity in organizations: Theory, research and practice.* Oakland, CA: Berrett-Koehler Publishers.

Crenshaw, K. (1989). Demarginalizing the intersection of race and sex: A black feminist critique of antidiscrimination doctrine, feminist theory and antiracist politics. *University of Chicago Legal Forum, 140*(1), 139–167.

Crenshaw, K. (1991). Mapping the margins: Intersectionality, identity politics, and violence against women of color. *Stanford Law Review, 43*(6), 1241–1299. https://dx.doi.org/10.2307/1229039

Cunningham, K. (2001). Father time: Flexible work arrangements and the law firm's failure of the family. *Stanford Law Review, 53,* 967–1008.

Danowitz, M. A., & Claes, M.-T. (2012). Diversity in Europe: Its development and contours. In M. A. Danowitz, E. Hanappi-Egger, & H. Mensi-Klarbach (Eds.), *Diversity in organizations: Concepts and practices* (pp. 33–62). Houndmills, U.K.: Palgrave Macmillan.

Danowitz, M. A., Hanappi-Egger, E., & Mensi-Klarbach, H. (2012). *Diversity in organizations: Concepts and practices.* Houndmills, U.K.: Palgrave Macmillan.

Dass, P., & Parker, B. (1999). Strategies for managing human resource diversity: From resistance to learning. *The Academy of Management Executive, 13*(2), 68–80. http://www.jstor.org/stable/4165541

Dick, P., & Cassell, C. (2002). Barriers to managing diversity in a UK constabulary: The role of discourse. *Journal of Management Studies, 39*(7), 953–976.

Dobbin, F., Schrage, D., & Kalev, A. (2015). Rage against the iron cage: The varied effects of bureaucratic personnel reforms on diversity. *American Sociological Review, 80*(5), 1014–1044.

Dobbin, F., Sutton, J. R., Meyer, J. W., & Scott, R. (1993). Equal opportunity law and the construction of internal labor markets. *American Journal of Sociology, 99*(2), 396–427. https://www.jstor.org/stable/2781683

Dwyer, S., Richard, O. C., & Chadwick, K. (2003). Gender diversity in management and firm performance: The influence of growth orientation and organizational culture. *Journal of Business Research, 56*(12), 1009–1019.

Eaton, S. C. (2003). If you can use them: Flexibility policies, organizational commitment, and perceived performance. *Industrial Relations, 42,* 145–167.

Ely, R. J., & Thomas, D. A. (2001). Cultural diversity at work: The effects of diversity perspectives on work group processes and outcomes. *Administrative Science Quarterly, 46*(2), 229–273.

Erhardt, N. L., Werbel, J. D., & Shrader, C. B. (2003). Board of director diversity and firm financial performance. *Corporate Governance: An International Review, 11*(2), 102–111.

Foucault, M. (1978). *Dispositive der Macht. Über Sexualität, Wissen und Wahrheit.* Berlin, Germany: Merve Verlag.

Gardenswartz, L., Cherbosque, J., & Rowe, A. (2010). Emotional intelligence and diversity: A model for differences in the workplace. *Journal of Psychological Issues and Organizational Culture, 1*(1), 74–84.

Gardenswartz, L., & Rowe, A. (2003). *Diverse teams at work: Capitalizing on the power of diversity.* Alexandria, VA: Society for Human Resource.

Hanappi-Egger, E. (2012). Theoretical perspectives on diversity in organizations. In M. A. Danowitz, E. Hanappi-Egger, & H. Mensi-Klarbach (Eds.), *Diversity in organizations: Concepts and practices* (pp. 9–31). Houndmills, U.K.: Palgrave Macmillan.

Hansen U. (2004) Gesellschaftliche Verantwortung als Business Case. In U. Schneider, P. Steiner (Eds.) *Betriebswirtschaftslehre und gesellschaftliche Verantwortung* (pp. 59–83). Wiesbaden: Gabler Verlag.

Harrison, D. A., & Klein, K. J. (2007). What's the difference? Diversity constructs as separation, variety, or disparity in organizations. *Academy of Management Review, 32*(4), 1199–1228.

Harrison, D. A., Price, K. H., & Bell, M. P. (1998). Beyond relational demography: Time and the effects of surface-and deep-level diversity on work group cohesion. *Academy of Management Journal, 41*(1), 96–107.

Harrison, D. A., & Sin, H. (2006). What is diversity and how should it be measured. In A. M. Konrad, P. Prasad, & J. K. Pringle (Eds.), *Handbook of workplace diversity* (pp. 191–216). London, U.K.: SAGE.

Hearn, J., & Louvrier, J. (2015). Theories of difference, diversity, and intersectionality. In R. Bendl, I. Bleijenbergh, E. Henttonen, & A. J. Mills (Eds.), *The Oxford handbook of diversity in organizations* (pp. 62–82). Oxford, U.K.: Oxford University Press.

Heres, L., & Benschop, Y. (2010). Taming diversity: An exploratory study on the travel of a management fashion. *Equality, Diversity and Inclusion: An International Journal, 29*(5), 436–457.

Hewlin, P.F. (2009). Wearing the cloak: Antecedents and consequences of creating facades of conformity. *Journal of Applied Psychology, 94,* 727–741.

Hofmann, R. (2012). Gesellschaftstheoretische Grundlagen für einen reflexiven und inklusiven Umgang mit Diversitäten in Organisationen. In R. Bendl, E. Hanappi-Egger, & R. Hofmann (Eds.), *Diversität und Diversitätsmanagement* (pp. 23–51). Wien, Austria: Facultas Verlags- und Buchhandels AG.

Johnston, W., & Packer, A. (1987). *Workforce 2000: Work and Workers for the 21st Century.* New York, NY: The Hudson Institute.

Kaler, J. (2001). Diversity, equality, morality. In *Equality, diversity and disadvantage in employment* (pp. 51–64). London, U.K.: Palgrave Macmillan.

Kalev, A., Dobbin, F., & Kelly, E. (2006). Best practices of best guesses? Assessing the efficacy of corporate affirmative action and diversity policies. *American Sociological Review, 71*(4), 589–617.

Kandola, R., & Fullerton, J. (1998). *Managing the mosaic: Diversity in action.* London, U.K.: Institute of Personnel and Development.

Kelly, E., & Dobbin, F. (1998). How affirmative action became diversity management: Employer response to antidiscrimination law, 1961 to 1996. *American Behavioral Scientist, 41*(7), 960–984.

Kirsch, A. (2018). The gender composition of corporate boards: A review and research agenda. *The Leadership Quarterly, 29*(2), 346–364.

Kirton, G., Greene, A.-M. (2005). *The dynamics of managing diversity. A critical approach.* 2nd ed. Oxford, U.K.: Elsevier.

Klarsfeld, A., Booysen, L., Ng, E., Roper I., & Tatli, A. (2015). *International handbook on diversity management at work: Country perspectives on diversity and equal treatment.* 2nd ed. London, U.K.: Edward Elgar.

Klarsfeld, A., Ng, E., Booysen, L., Castro Christiansen, L., & Kuvaas, B. (2016). Comparative equality and diversity: Main findings and research gaps. *Cross Cultural & Strategic Management*, 23(3), 394–412.

Klein, K. J., & Harrison, D. A. (2007). On the diversity of diversity: Tidy logic, messier realities. *Academy of Management Perspectives*, 21(4), 26–33.

Knights, D., & Omanović, V. (2015). Rethinking diversity in organizations and society. In R. Bendl, I. Bleijenbergh, E. Henttonen, & A. J. Mills (Eds.), *The Oxford handbook of diversity in organizations* (pp. 83–108). Oxford, U.K.: Oxford University Press.

Liff, S. (1997). Two routes to managing diversity: Individual differences or social group characteristics. *Employee relations*, 19(1), 11–26.

Litvin, D. R. (1997). The discourse of diversity: From biology to management. *Organization*, 4(2), 187–209.

Litvin, D. R. (2006). Making space for a better case. In A. M. Konrad, P. Prasad, & J. K. Pringle (Eds.), *Handbook of workplace diversity* (pp. 75–94). London, U.K.: SAGE.

Lorbiecki, A., & Jack, G. (2000). Critical turns in the evolution of diversity management. *British Journal of Management*, 11(Special Issue), 17–31.

Lowery, M. (1995). The war on equal opportunity. *Black Enterprise*, 27(7), 148–154.

McCall, L. (2005). The complexity of intersectionality. *Signs*, 30(3), 1771–1800.

Mensi-Klarbach, H. (2018). Historical developments and different rationales. In H. Mensi-Klarbach & A. Risberg (Eds.), *Diversity in organizations. Concepts and practices* (pp. 67–92). 2nd ed. Houndmills, U.K.: Palgrave Macmillan.

Mor-Barak, M. E. (2011). *Managing diversity: Toward a globally inclusive workplace*. Thousand Oaks, CA: SAGE.

Noon, M. (2007). The fatal flaws of diversity and the business case for ethnic minorities. *Work, Employment and Society*, 21(4), 773–784.

Noon, M., & Ogbonna, E. (2001). Introduction: The key analytical themes. In *Equality, diversity and disadvantage in employment* (pp. 1–14). London, U.K.: Palgrave Macmillan.

Özbilgin, M., & Tatli, A. (2011). Mapping out the field of equality and diversity: Rise of individualism and voluntarism. *Human Relations*, 64(9), 1229–1253.

Point, S., & Singh, V. (2003). Defining and dimensionalising diversity: Evidence from corporate websites across Europe. *European Management Journal*, 21(6), 750–761.

Prasad, P., Pringle, J. K., & Konrad, A. M. (2006). Examining the contours of workplace diversity—Concepts, contexts and challenges. In A. M. Konrad, P. Prasad, & J. K. Pringle (Eds.), *Handbook of workplace diversity* (pp. 1–22). London, U.K.: SAGE.

Pringle, J. K., & Booysen, L. (2018). Contextualizing the EDI research agenda in the larger social sciences research landscape. In L. Booysen, R. Bendl, & J. Pringle (Eds.), *Handbook of research methods on diversity management, equality and inclusion at work* (pp. 19–35). Cheltenham, U.K.: Edward Elgar.

Qin, J., Muenjohn, N., & Chhetri, P. (2014). A review of diversity conceptualizations: Variety, trends, and a framework. *Human Resource Development Review*, 13(2), 133–157.

Sabharwal, M. (2014). Is diversity management sufficient? Organizational inclusion to further performance. *Public Personnel Management*, 43(2), 197–217.

Shore, L. M., Randel, A. E., Chung, B. G., Dean, M. A., Holcombe Ehrhard, K., & Singh, G. (2011). Inclusion and diversity in work groups: A review and model for future research. *Journal of Management*, 37(4), 1262–1289.

Singh, V., & Point, S. (2004). Strategic responses by European companies to the diversity challenge: An online comparison. *Long Range Planning*, 37(4), 295–318.

Thomas, R. R. (1990). From affirmative action to affirming diversity. *Harvard Business Review*, 1, 107–117.

Van Dijk, H., Van Engen, M. L., & Van Knippenberg, D. (2012). Defying conventional wisdom: A meta-analytical examination of the differences between demographic and job-related diversity relationships with performance. *Organizational Behavior and Human Decision Processes*, 119(1), 38–53.

van Knippenberg, D. A. A. N., & Haslam, S. A. (2003). Realizing the diversity dividend: Exploring the subtle interplay between identity, ideology, and reality. In S. A. Haslam, D. van Knippenberg, M. J. Platow, & N. Ellemers (Eds.), *Social identity at work: Developing theory of organizational practice* (pp. 61–77). New York, NY: Psychology Press.

West, C., & Fenstermaker, S. (1995). Doing difference. *Gender and Society, 9*(1), 8–37.

West, C., & Zimmerman, D. H. (1987). Doing gender. *Gender and Society, 1*(2), 125–151.

Zanoni, P., & Janssens, M. (2003). Deconstructing difference: The rhetoric of human resource managers' diversity discourses. *Organization Studies, 25*(1), 55–74.

NOTES

1. E.g., *Equality, Diversity and Inclusion: An International Journal* (*EDI*) and *Zeitschrift für Diversitätsforschung und -management* (ZDfm).
2. Personality refers to traits and stable characteristics of an individual that are viewed as determining particular consistencies in the manner in which that person behaves in any given situation and over time; internal dimensions, external dimensions, and organizational dimensions influence one's personality.
3. For an international overview, see Klarsfeld et al. (2015, 2016).
4. For further reflections on diversity research see Knights and Omanović (2015) or Prasad et al. (2006).

Regine Bendl, Astrid Hainzl, and Heike Mensi-Klarbach

INDIVIDUAL DIFFERENCES AT WORK

INTRODUCTION

Every manager knows that, in the workplace, some people are more engaged, happy, and productive than others. Some go absent a lot and others very rarely. Some work happily in teams, others not. It has been argued and demonstrated that the most productive workers achieve roughly two and a half times the output of the least productive.

The cost of hiring someone who is unproductive and destructive is considerable. Equally, knowing what to look for in those who turn out to be happy and productive is very important. The central questions are what to look for and how to measure it.

People differ on several different factors relevant in the workplace:

Ability: Ability refers to the extent to which a person can efficiently carry out multiple processes. Ability may refer to psychomotor and co-ordination skills or other very specific abilities associated with particular jobs.

Creativity: Creativity has, and no doubt will continue to be, variously defined. At the heart of most definitions, however, is the concept that creativity leads to, or is manifest in, the production of ideas and/or products that are both novel and useful. That is, an idea might be new, but not at all useful, or practical but not new. The essence of the idea is that real, genuine creativity is marked by new thinking that has real applications. Some individuals clearly have the aptitude to be creative in the arts, sciences, or business.

Demographic factors: Demographic factors include sex, age, social class, education, and ethnicity. There are considerable, but highly sensitive and disputed, data that link these factors to success at work. In some places it is illegal to base selection decisions on some of these factors (e.g., ethnicity or religion) and policies differ from country to country.

Intelligence: Intelligence is the individual's capacity for abstract and critical thinking. Few doubt the effect of general intelligence on performance at work. The more complex and sophisticated the job, the more a person needs high intelligence to perform at it well.

Motivation: Like intelligence, motivation is a multidimensional abstract concept that refers to the drive to engage in some actions. It is notoriously difficult to measure, partly because people cannot or will not talk about the things that motivate them. Motivation is often measured by values, such as how much people want recognition or power, or the opportunity to be altruistic at work.

Personality: Personality is all the fundamental traits or characteristics of the person (or of people generally) that endure over time and that account for consistent patterns of responses to everyday situations. Personality traits supposedly account for the what, why, and how of human functioning.

Style: The concept of style in psychology can be traced back a century. It seems that the concept of cognitive style preceded others, like learning style. The concept of style is particularly attractive to many people, more so than trait, at least in popular and applied rather than academic circles, partly because it implies ease of change. One adopts a style that is easy to modify. Applied psychologists in educational, clinical, and work settings have embraced the concept of style and this has led in turn to a profusion of styles (coping style, thinking style) and measures.

Strength: The original conceptualization of strengths meant psychological processes or mechanisms that define virtues. They are not the opposite of a desirable trait (a counterexample is steadfast and flexible, which are opposites but are both commonly seen as desirable). Strengths are however seen to be trait-like in that they are habitual patterns that are relatively stable over time. Some strengths are absent in some individuals. They tend to be nurtured by societal norms and institutions.

A NOTE ON CULTURAL DIFFERENCES

The majority of the research reported here has been published in English (the de facto language of science) and is based on Western data. This always raises the question whether the findings can be replicated across different national and corporate cultures. Certainly, there is a very considerable literature on the measurement and structure of personality, which is assessed in up to 50 different languages. The results show surprisingly few differences.

However, it is quite possible that work is arranged in very different ways in different cultures depending on technology, teamwork, and how outcomes are measured and rewarded. This could mean that individual differences impact differently from culture to culture. We know that many Western cultures are highly individualistic, while many Eastern cultures are more collectivistic. Thus, individual differences relating to teamwork could well play a much more important role in work outcomes in collectivistic cultures.

ANALYZING MULTIPLE VARIABLES

In this area, different concepts are related, and when looking at the effect of personality and work outcomes, it is essential that one consider several factors and how they interact. More important is longitudinal analysis. For example, Furnham and Cheng (2017) measured parental social status (at birth), childhood intelligence and self-esteem (at age 10), locus of control (at age 16), psychological distress (age 30), educational qualifications (age 34), current occupation, weekly net income, house ownership status, and number of rooms in the home (all measured at age 38). Furnham and Cheng showed that childhood intelligence, locus of control, education, and occupation were all independent predictors of adult financial status for both men and women. Financial status is a good outcome variable. Parental social status and psychological distress were also significant predictors of the outcome variable for men, but not for women.

It is well known that many factors contribute to a person's happiness and success at work. While ability, motivation, and personality play a part, several other factors are also implicated. The best research involves looking at these salient factors, over time, with solid outcome measures of work behavior. The challenge for the researcher lies not so much in analyzing and modeling the data, but in finding it in the first place.

INTELLIGENCE AT WORK

Intelligence is a good predictor of success in complex work (Furnham, 2008). By definition, those who are most able to deal with complexity and are most efficient at information storage and processing are in the best position to succeed in "high-powered" jobs.

Perhaps the best summary of the role of intelligence at work was by Goddfredson (1994), in collaboration with 50 of the world's experts on intelligence:

> IQ is strongly related, probably more so than any other single measurable human trait, to many important educational, occupational, economic, and social outcomes. Its relation to the welfare and performance of individuals is very strong in some arenas in life (education, military training), moderate but robust in others (social competence), and modest but consistent in others (law-abidingness). Whatever IQ tests measure, it is of great practical and social importance.
> A high IQ is an advantage in life because virtually all activities require some reasoning and decision-making. Conversely, a low IQ is often a disadvantage, especially in disorganized environments. Of course, a high IQ no more guarantees success than a low IQ guarantees failure in life. There are many exceptions, but the odds for success in our society greatly favor individuals with higher IQs.
> The practical advantages of having a higher IQ increase as life settings become more complex (novel, ambiguous, changing, unpredictable, or multifaceted). For example, a high IQ is generally necessary to perform well in highly complex or fluid jobs (the professions, management), it is a considerable advantage in moderately complex jobs (crafts, clerical and police work), but it provides less advantage in

settings that require only routine decision-making or simple problem-solving (unskilled work).

Differences in intelligence certainly are not the only factor affecting performance in education, training, and highly complex jobs (no one claims they are), but intelligence is often the most important. When individuals have already been selected for high (or low) intelligence and so do not differ as much in IQ as in graduate school (or special education), other influences on performance loom larger in comparison.

Certain personality traits, special talents, aptitudes, physical capabilities, experience, and the like are important (sometimes essential) for successful performance in many jobs, but they have narrower (or unknown) applicability or "transferability" across tasks and settings compared with general intelligence. Some scholars choose to refer to these other human traits as other "intelligences."

There have been a number of important meta-analyses of studies on the relationship between intelligence and work outcomes (Schmitt & Hunter, 1998, 2004). In the past quarter-century, a large and compelling literature has shown that intelligence is a good predictor of both job performance and training proficiency at work (Dragow, 2003). Extensive meta-analytic reviews have shown that intelligence was a good predictor of job performance, but particularly in complex jobs. Although debated, researchers suggest the correlation between intelligence and job performance is around $r = 0.50$ (Schmidt & Hunter, 1998, 2004). The central question is what other factors, such as personality or social/emotional intelligence (sometimes called "social skills"), account for the rest of the variance. But referring to g or general intelligence, Dragow (2003) was forced to conclude, "For understanding performance in the workplace, and especially task performance and training performance, g is the key. . . . g accounts for an overwhelming proportion of the explained variance when predicting training and job performance" (p. 126).

THE TAXONOMY OF PERSONALITY

Personality dimensions are behavioral dispositions in the sense that they correlate with determination and drive, to affect social behavior.

Personality dimensions are relatively stable over time and manifest consistently and coherently over varying social situations. To understand personality's functions, the personality of a person can, and must, be decomposed into its specific and fundamental parts, elements, and building blocks, as well as be combined into an organized whole system.

Though there remain some disputes among trait psychologists, it is perhaps fair to say that most personality psychologists accept the five-factor (Big Five) model.

Figure 1 depicts some current personality models. While there are many other theories and models, some well-established and commercially well-used, like the Myers-Brigg Type Inventory (MBTI), the academic literature has been dominated by the Big Five model and various relatively similar tests of varying length to measure the traits (Furnham, 2008). Suffice it to say, the Big Five model has dominated personality research for the last 20 years.

The Big Five dimensions are set out in Table 1.

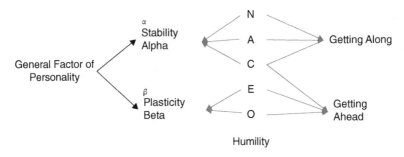

Figure 1. The one-, two-, and five-factor descriptions of personality.

Table 1. The Big Five Traits: Characteristics of High, Average, and Low Levels

High	Average	Low
1. *Neuroticism* Sensitive, emotional, and prone to experience feelings that are upsetting.	Generally calm and able to deal with stress, but sometimes experiences feelings of guilt, anger, or sadness.	Secure, hardy, and generally relaxed, even under stressful conditions.
2. *Extraversion* Extraverted, outgoing, active, and high-spirited. Prefers to be around people most of the time.	Moderate in activity and enthusiasm. Enjoys the company of others but also values privacy.	Introverted, reserved, and serious. Prefers to be alone or with a few close friends.
3. *Openness to experience* Open to new experiences. Has broad interests and is very imaginative.	Practical but willing to consider new ways of doing things. Seeks a balance between the old and the new.	Down-to-earth, practical, traditional, and pretty much set in their ways.
4. *Agreeableness* Compassionate, good-natured, and eager to cooperate and avoid conflict.	Generally warm, trusting, and agreeable, but can sometimes be stubborn and competitive.	Hardheaded, skeptical, proud, and competitive. Tends to express anger directly.
5. *Conscientiousness* Conscientious and well organized. Has high standards and always strives to achieve goals.	Dependable and moderately well organized. Generally has clear goals but is able to set work aside.	Easygoing, not very well organized, and sometimes careless. Prefers not to make plans.

Table 2 sets out the five factors of personality, using adjectives, Q-sort items, positive benefits, and negative costs that define each personality trait. Others have considered personality from an evolutionary perspective. Nettle (2006) noted that his "trade-off" evolutionary account of traits may be useful partly because it is hypothesis-generating: for example, Neuroticism may facilitate performance on particular perceptual motor tasks, highly Open people may be either particularly culturally embraced or marginalized, Conscientious people are slow to respond to affordances in the local environment, or Agreeable people often may be regarded as "suckers" or victims of exploitative individuals.

There have been as many speculations as studies that have investigated the relationship between the Big Five dimensions and different work outcomes (Judge & Locke, 1992; Judge, Martocchio, & Thoresen, 1997; Judge, Higgins, Thoresen, & Barrick, 1999). The work goes back to World War I and the requirement for the military to fit people to the job. Because of

Table 2. Positive and Negative Consequences of Each Big Five Trait

| Factor | Factor Definers | | Positive Benefits | Negative Costs |
	Adjectives	Q-Sort Items		
Extraversion	Active Assertive Energetic Enthusiastic Outgoing Talkative	Talkative Skilled in play, humor Rapid personal tempo Facially, gesturally expressive Behaves assertively Gregarious	Big social networks Relationship and mating success Explorer of opportunities Happiness	Accidents and risk-taking Impulsivity and poor decision-making Relationship instability
Neuroticism	Anxious Self-pitying Tense Touchy Unstable Worrying	Thin-skinned Brittle ego defenses Self-defeating Basically anxious Concerned with adequacy Fluctuating moods	Hyper vigilance Achievement-striving Emotional sensitivity Competitiveness	Poor mental health Stress sensitivity Poor physical health
Openness	Artistic Curious Imaginative Insightful Original Wide interests	Wide range of interests Introspective Unusual thought processes Values intellectual matters Judges in unconventional terms Aesthetically reactive	Social Attractiveness Creativity Flexibility Change-orientated	Mental illness Social exclusion Bizarre belief system and lifestyle
Agreeableness	Appreciative Forgiving Generous Kind Sympathetic Trusting	Not critical, skeptical Behaves in a giving way Sympathetic, considerate Arouses liking Warm, compassionate Basically trustful	Psychological mindedness Social networks Strong relationships Valued group member	Vulnerable to exploitation Failure to maximize personal advantages Too conflict-avoidant Low assertiveness
Conscientiousness	Efficient Organized Planning ability Reliable Responsible Thorough	Dependable, responsible Productive Able to delay gratification Not self-indulgent Behaves ethically Has high aspirational level	Long-term planning Longer life expectancy Good citizenship Dependable and dutiful team member	Obsessionality and perfectionism Rigidity with poor flexibility Slow to respond

the multitude of tests used and the unreliability of the outcome variable, it is difficult to interpret these early studies. However, over the past 30 years, agreement about what to measure, the development of better tests, and the use of multivariate analysis have resulted in several good studies that allow for some conclusions to be drawn.

Table 3 presents some of these hypotheses (Furnham, 2018a). This is not a meta-analysis, although ideally in time one will be done. Three points about the table are noteworthy. First, the strongest and most consistent personality correlate of work-related behavior is Conscientiousness. The second most consistent predictor is Neuroticism (low Adjustment). Third, Extraversion seems to be related to both positive and negative work outcomes.

To understand the mechanisms and processes by which the traits have an impact on work outcomes, it is important to examine each trait.

Extraversion. Extraversion is a dimension that ranges from very high (extraverts) to very low (introverts), although most of us are ambiverts. Extraverts are seen as more likeable, interesting, and popular; introverts are more honest, stable, and reliable. Extraverts are attracted to "people jobs," such as sales and the service industry, and they do well.

Extraverts are less distracted than introverts. Their world is ever more busy, noisy, and distracting. Introverts are only distracted by people, noise, or stimulants of any kind and are less comfortable, less efficient, and less helpful in the noisy world of work.

Introverts take longer to retrieve information, longer to marshal their ideas and thoughts, and longer to respond to the demands of the world around them.

Extraverts respond better to carrots and care less about sticks, while introverts are less motivated by rewards and more sensitive to, and inhibited by, threats of punishments. Perhaps, therefore, extraverts are easier to manage. They are certainly easier to read.

There have always been serious known disadvantages of being a (strong) extravert. The first is accidents. Extraverts are risk takers. They drive fast and choose risky recreational activities. They trade off accuracy for speed. They are prone to all sorts of gaffes, preferring to speak before they think. The second disadvantage of extraversion is criminality. Extraverts are social and impulsive. They are excitement-seekers interested in novel experiences, which often leads them to be poorer learners than introverts at many tasks, including the acquisition of general social rules. They are difficult to train, naughty, and rebellious. They are more likely than introverts to become delinquents or criminals, though it does depend on the nature of the criminal activity. Finally, extraverts have some difficulty with learning. Extraverts do well at primary school but less well at university. The idea of sitting in a quiet room for hours learning complicated, abstract ideas just does not suit the extravert.

Thus, it is clear that:

- Reward enhances the performance of extraverts more than introverts, whereas punishment impairs the performance of introverts more than extraverts.
- Introverts are more susceptible than extraverts to distraction.
- Introverts are more affected than extraverts by response competition.
- Introverts take longer than extraverts to retrieve information from long-term or permanent memory storage, especially nondominant information.
- Introverts have higher response criteria than extraverts.
- Extraverts show better retention-test performance than introverts at short retention intervals, but the opposite holds at long retention intervals.

Table 3. Possible Relationships Between Personality Traits and Work Outcomes

	Positive				Negative			
	Creativity	Engagement	Productivity	Promotion	Absenteeism	Accidents	Derailment	Turnover
N	+	--	--	-	+++	+	+	+
E	+	+		++	+	+++	+	+
O	+++						+	+
A		+		-	-		-	-
C		+++	+++	+++	---	-	-	-

Notes: N = Neuroticism; E = Extraversion; O = Openness; A = Agreeableness; C = Conscientiousness.

Neuroticism. Neuroticism is also called "negative affectivity" or "poor emotional adjustment." It is based on activation thresholds in the sympathetic nervous system or visceral brain (fight-or-flight response).

Neurotic persons have a low activation threshold. When confronted with stressors or anxiety, they experience negative emotions. The manifestations can range from physiological changes in heart rate, increased blood pressure, cold hands, sweating, and muscular tension to feelings of apprehension and nervousness, to the full effects of fear and anxiety.

In contrast, emotionally stable peers have a much higher activation threshold, and they experience negative affect only when confronted by major stressors. Such individuals tend to be calm even in situations that could be described as anxiety-inducing or pressure-laden. They are stable, not moody; robust, not vulnerable; hardy, not overly sensitive.

Neuroticism is most clearly described in three disorders: generalized anxiety disorder, panic disorder, and phobias. Specific disorders detailed to overlap with Neuroticism include agoraphobia, social phobia, obsessive-compulsive disorder, and post-traumatic stress disorder.

Many higher-order theories of personality describe and measure Neuroticism at the domain level, but also at the facet level, although there is very little agreement in the description of the facets. For instance, the Eysenck Personality Profiler (EPP) labels six N (neuroticism) facets: inferiority, unhappiness, anxiety, dependence, hypochondria, and obsessiveness; the HEXACO model labels four facets: fearfulness, anxiety, dependence, and sentimentality; and the Multidimensional Personality Questionnaire (MPQ) labels three facets: stress reaction, alienation, and aggression.

Even the name of the domain changes: for the EPP it is Neuroticism, in the HEXACO it is Emotionality, and for the MPQ it is Negative Emotional Temperament. This indicates subtle but important differences in the conceptualization of Neuroticism.

People who score high on Neuroticism are prone to anxiety, depression, and psychosomatic illness and hence higher levels of stress at work. However, they are very vigilant and are able to pick up the emotional tones around them better than stable individuals. Those who score very high on Neuroticism tend to be problematic at work. They tend to have higher rates of absenteeism and to be gloomier and more negative (Furnham, 2008).

Agreeableness. Agreeableness is associated with being altruistic, appreciative, compliant, trusting, and tender-minded. Agreeable individuals are generous, kind, sympathetic, and warm. Agreeableness facets include easy to live with, sensitive, caring, likes people, and no hostility. Other suggested facets for Agreeableness have been labeled forgiveness, gentleness, flexibility, patience, and altruism versus antagonism.

To some extent, Agreeableness seems less related to many education, health, and work outcomes. Also, doubt has been expressed about whether Agreeableness is a trait (as opposed to a social desirability or social-relational concept). Furthermore, it is often seen to be a disadvantage to be high in Agreeableness, as managers have to be "tough with poor performers."

A review by Tobin and Gadke (2015) provided a short section on theoretical accounts of Agreeableness that suggested it can be seen in terms of "the regulatory process of effortful control," which can easily be identified in children and which is highly predictive. The authors summarized their findings.

- Friendship: Agreeable people are more likely to be identified as friends, to be less victimized, and overall to have fewer risk factors as identified by friends.
- Cooperativeness and competitiveness: Agreeable people across all age groups are more cooperative.
- Helping: Agreeable people are more likely to help others whom they know, even to the point of potentially risking their lives.
- Conflict resolution: Agreeable people are more likely to use constructive conflict-resolution tactics and are less likely to use destructive tactics.
- Aggression: Agreeableness is inversely related to both aggressive thoughts and aggressive behaviors.
- Prejudice: Agreeableness is linked to more positive reactions to others, including when the others are considered targets of prejudice.

Studies on Agreeableness in children have demonstrated that it predicts academic performance and social competence. Agreeableness is often highly valued in the workplace. People like to work with others who are helpful, kind, and empathetic. Agreeable people tend to be liked and valued. However, the workplace is often a competitive environment with a "win–lose" philosophy, where those who are more disagreeable, egocentric, and tough-minded do best.

Openness to Experience. Openness to Experience is often shown as the strongest correlate of ability, particularly creativity and intelligence. Openness is associated with having a vivid imagination and an active fantasy life, with a deep appreciation for art and beauty, with a receptivity to one's own and other's emotions, with a willingness to try new experiences, with intellectual curiosity, and with a readiness to examine political, social and religious values. People high in Openness have been shown to be unconventional, questioning, and emotionally literate. Other personality theories and systems have described Openness as Intellect or Culture and had different ideas about the facets of the super-factor or domain. The facets include aesthetic appreciation, inquisitiveness, creativity, and unconventionality. While there is confusion and disagreement about the facets of Openness, there seems to be agreement that it is a stable trait that reflects intellectual curiosity, imaginativeness, and inquisitiveness.

Those interested in personality correlates of educational, health, and occupational outcomes have tended to show that, of the Big Five traits, Neuroticism and Conscientiousness account for most of the variance, with Openness being related to very specific issues like aesthetic preferences or leisure pursuits. In most individual difference studies, personality traits are the predictor variables and some salient beliefs or behaviors the criterion variables. One relevant theory is Cattell's (1987) investment theory, which suggests personality and fluid intelligence contribute to the development of crystallized intelligence. One research question is: What are the early determinants, including intelligence, of Openness in adulthood? Few studies have examined this because of the difficulty of obtaining longitudinal data, although there are some recent exceptions (Furnham & Cheng, 2015).

There is an extensive literature on Openness. Many studies are concerned with the extent to which Openness is related to cognitive ability. Studies have used different measures of both

Openness and intelligence, but they have tended to show a significant positive correlation (Chamorro-Premuzic, Moutafi, & Furnham, 2005; DeYoung, Quilty, Peterson, & Gray, 2014).

Gow, Whiteman, Pattie, and Deary (2005) found that intelligence measured in childhood and late adulthood was significantly correlated with Intellect (Openness), but that when the association in old age was controlled for childhood intelligence, it fell to almost zero. Their conclusion was that intelligence and Openness in adulthood are related through the lifelong stable trait of intelligence.

Studies on the relationship between Openness and work outcomes suggest it correlates most with creative and complex work. Further, as with all the traits, those extremely high or low in Openness can be very problematic.

Conscientiousness. Conscientiousness is associated with being efficient, organized, reliable, and responsible. Conscientious individuals are achievement oriented, competent, dependable, and productive. Employers value the trait and attempt to shape and encourage it because it is associated with being organized, reliable, and hard-working.

Students who are more Conscientious earn university grades higher than their intelligence scores would predict.

Consistent findings from correlational studies show a very small, but significant, positive association between Conscientiousness and educational achievement and occupational prestige. There is also some evidence to suggest sex differences in Conscientiousness, which have been used to explain why females outperform males in school grades despite the evidence of very small differences in intelligence between the sexes (Furnham, 2008).

The taxonomists of Conscientiousness argue that it has eight distinguishable but related parts:

1. *Industriousness*: This is about working hard, always putting in an effort, and frequently exceeding expectations. Industrious people push themselves (and others) very hard to succeed.
2. *Perfectionism*: This is aiming for high quality, no mistakes, and no rejected work. It is about being detail-oriented and striving always to be the best.
3. *Tidiness*: This is a strong preference for order, regularity, and an everything-in-its-place philosophy. Conscientious people have a strong aversion to disorder and mess. They like things correctly filed and tasks completed.
4. *Procrastination Refrainment*: Truly conscientious people are not easily distracted and do not have difficulty getting started. They don't put off unpleasant tasks, starting only the easy ones. They go to work at once: they prioritize and spend their time and effort wisely.
5. *Control Preference*: This should not be confused with being a control freak. Control preference is about being purposeful, thoughtful, and decisive. It is also about understanding the role of authority. The opposite is rushed, rash, impulsive behavior.
6. *Caution*: The Conscientious person is careful to avoid mistakes, to get their facts right, and to think ahead. They think before they speak, and they choose their words carefully.
7. *Task Planning*: The Conscientious person is deliberate. They carefully devise a plan, a schedule, and a considered path. They stick to the plan and require others to do so, too. They like to work out efficient routines and to stick to them.

8. *Perseverance*: The Conscientious individual deals well with frustrations and setbacks. They don't give up easily, they don't avoid responsibility, and they don't lose interest. They are calm under pressure.

Of all the traits, Consciousness is most closely associated with success at work.

CHANGE OVER TIME

There is considerable debate about the stability of personality over time. The debate about continuity versus change revolves around a number of issues: the reliability and validity of personality tests (to account in part for measurement error), the moderator variables considered (i.e., sex, education, and ethnicity), the age at which people are measured (i.e., adolescence, adulthood, old age), the time span that shows most change and stability, how change is measured (such as mean level change, rank order, ipsative change), the stability of the environment, and what, if anything, leads to change.

There is evidence of both stability and change. Personality seems most stable between the ages of 30 and 60 years. There are modest increases in emotional stability and Agreeableness over this period, with Extraversion and Neuroticism showing least change (both with a slight decline) and Conscientiousness showing most change (an increase).

There is also a debate about whether intelligence can change. People holding an entity theory of intelligence believe that intelligence levels remain constant over a person's lifetime regardless of their education, effort, and experience gained. They argue that anybody can learn new things (skills, knowledge), but their underlying intelligence level essentially never changes. They are fixed-mindset people.

By contrast, incremental theorists believe that intelligence can be increased and cultivated over a lifetime through hard work and continued learning. Fixed-mindset theorists tend not to increase their level of effort in educational and work environments because they do not believe they can improve their performance. Incremental theorists, however, tend to acknowledge the importance of effort when approaching a learning task.

In personality theory, there has been debate between those who argue that people do change (considerably and significantly over time) and those who suggest they do not. The debate centered on the plaster hypothesis versus the plastic hypothesis, with the former's advocates suggesting that personality traits change very little over time, and the latter's proponents arguing that significant, systematic, and explicable changes can and do occur.

Over the years, the plaster hypothesis (of little or no change) has been replaced by the plasticity hypothesis (of possible change). Many trait theorists recognize that traits can and do change over time, although there remains debate about which traits change least and most, why, and by how much.

A related topic of considerable academic debate has some proponents arguing that people can sustainably increase their intelligence, and others arguing that people cannot. Thus, Kuszewski (2011) concluded: "Fluid intelligence is trainable. The training and subsequent gains are dose-dependent, meaning, the more you train, the more you gain. Anyone can increase their cognitive ability, no matter what your starting point is. The effect can be gained by training on tasks that don't resemble the test questions" (p. 2).

It is obvious that, over time, certain aspects of individuals change as they age. We know that fluid intelligence scores start declining in the 20s, and they show steep declines after age 40 years because the speed of processing information declines. On the other hand, crystalized intelligence (knowledge accumulation) increases until the late 70s. Thus, an airline pilot might have to retire at 55, while lawyers can keep working successfully into their late 70s.

PERSONALITY AND WORK SUCCESS: ORGANIZATIONAL LEVEL, PROMOTION HISTORY, AND SALARY

There is a great deal of piecemeal research on personality and work success going back over 80 years. Yet, studies have shown that being high on Conscientiousness and low on Neuroticism are the two best predictors of success at work.

A central question is how to measure success at work, which is the dependent variable in these studies. Essentially, success at work can be measured either objectively or subjectively.

Subjective measurement refers to self-assessment, which takes two approaches. The first is a personal overall rating or a specific personal rating of success at work. The second approach is subjective reporting, such as reporting one's salary, promotion speed, and so on. The issue here is the reliability and accuracy of the reports, which could be distorted for a number of reasons, such as poor memory or social desirability. Furthermore, issues of hubris and humility mean that some people deliberately over- or underreport their general success at work.

Objective measurement uses various criteria that are markers of occupational success, such as salary, rank, job title, speed of promotion, and supervisor ratings. These data can be obtained from company records or manager reports. Considerations include what markers are available and which markers to choose, because they may be only modestly correlated.

There are essentially three problems associated with these variables. The first problem is the difficulty of making comparisons across jobs, organizations, or sectors, which means study results might not replicate.

The second problem is differences between countries and time periods. For example, the salary of a highly successful person from a developing country may be a third of the salary of somebody with identical criteria (even working in the same organization) in a developed country. While there may be ways of correcting for this, again the issue is comparability and replication.

The third problem is that, in times of growth (which may be specific to a sector, or region, or product), people are likely to be paid more than in times of stagnation. Thus, there may be Bull and Bear market results.

There is no doubt that researchers would prefer a range of work-related outcome variables. Inevitably, it is better to have a range of objective and subjective variables that may be combined into meaningful scores, such as "speed of progress," reward packages, and 360 ratings by others.

The literature in this area has addressed a number of issues (Furnham, 2017, 2018a), and three of them are discussed here.

First, are people at different levels of an organization different in their personality profile? Several studies have compared people at different organizational levels, from supervisor level, through management and senior management, to chief executive. The assumption is that differences between the levels are associated with being at that level. Thus, if there is a linear relationship between intelligence or trait Conscientiousness at the various levels, it is because this trait was a major factor in why people were promoted. The questions are whether, when, and how the person's profile is, in some way, responsible for their level. For example, because Conscientious people are more reliable, responsible, and productive, and less Neurotic people are less stress prone, these traits lead to greater productivity, which is rewarded by promotion or appointment to senior levels. On the other hand, it is possible that personality and motivation may change as a person moves up the levels in an organization and learns to become better organized and less stressed. While the studies in the area inevitably give equivocal results, it seems that more senior people tend to be more Extraverted and Conscientious and less Agreeable and Neurotic. They also appear to be brighter and more intrinsically motivated.

Second, is there evidence that personality profile is related to both the speed and number of promotions at work? It is possible to conduct either a retrospective or a prospective study to determine how long it takes people to get promoted to middle or senior management within any organization as well as between organizations in the same sector. Of course, many factors are related to promotion, but they can be taken into account. Studies have looked at the speed of climbing "the greasy pole" of the corporate ladder (Furnham, Crump, & Ritchie, 2013)

Third, is personality linked to salary? Many factors dictate a person's salary. These include the type of job they do (bankers tend to get paid more than bar staff; doctors more than dustmen) as well as their seniority and age. However, it is possible to take many confounding factors into account and to demonstrate that indeed personality is related to personal wealth as a function of salary.

The central question for the researcher is to describe and explain the mechanism and process whereby personality traits are related to various aspects of work success. For most researchers, personality is related to various specific behaviors that directly impact on work productivity:

- *Personality and lifestyle* addresses diet and personal habits, including exercise. Thus, traits influence mental and physical health, which affect such things as efficiency and absenteeism, which affect productivity at work.
- *Personality and risk-taking* includes things outside work, such as driving habits and hobbies, but also risk-taking in the workplace.
- *Personality and stress* includes the extent to which people cause and experience personal stress, which can have many consequences.
- *Personality and social support* includes a person's ability to establish personal bonds and support networks and to succeed on teams.

However, there are other factors like job motivation, intelligence, and demographic factors that need to be examined. In an example of this research, Furnham and Cheng (2017) tested 4,537 British adults where they had data on parental social class (at birth), cognitive ability (at age 11), educational qualifications (at age 33), and personality traits (at age 50), as well as current marital status, occupational prestige, and salary/wage earning level (all measured at age 54). The investigators showed that parental social class, childhood cognitive ability, personality traits (Extraversion, emotional stability, Conscientiousness, and Openness), being married positively, being divorced or separated negatively, education, and occupation, as well as gender, were all significantly associated with adult earning ability. They noted that effect size for the relationship between intelligence and income was moderate. Overall, they showed that childhood cognitive ability, the personality traits Conscientiousness and Openness, educational qualifications, and occupational prestige were significant and independent predictors of adult earning ability, accounting for 30% of the total variance. There was also a gender effect on the outcome variable.

Multivariate, longitudinal research with a valid measure of work success will yield the best understanding of the consequences of individual differences in the workplace.

HIGH-FLYERS

There is a great deal of interest in identifying talented "high-flyers" who will be particularly successful at work. Many organizations are very committed to finding and recruiting these people, for obvious benefit to both the individual and the company as a whole.

There have been many attempts over the years to develop models and measures of high-flyers or talented people who succeed in organizations. The idea is to identify the abilities, motives, and traits that are, in most organizations, clearly linked to occupational success (Silzer & Church, 2009; Spreitzer, McCall, & Mahoney, 1997).

MacRae and Furnham (2014) developed the High Potential Traits Indicator (HPTI), a measure of personality traits directly relevant to workplace behaviors as well as thoughts and perceptions of the self and others at work. The HPTI can be used to investigate which personality traits in the workplace might predict career success and thus predict high potential.

Six scientifically validated personality traits are measured by the HPTI:

Conscientiousness—planning, organization, strong work ethic, achievement drive.
Openness/Curiosity—openness to new information, adopting new approaches.
Approach to Risk—willingness to confront difficult situations as well as ability to thrive during adversity, to solve difficult problems, and to have difficult conversations.
Stress Reactivity—resilience to the impact of stressors, not overly worried about others' judgment.
Tolerance of Ambiguity—ability to tolerate ambiguous situations and information, to make use of mixed information, and to cope (and thrive) with ambivalence.
Competitiveness—need to achieve, drive to exceed one's own or another's performance, desire for control.

Teodorescu, Furnham, and Macrae (2017) used the HPTI to investigate associations between personality traits and measures of career success, in a sample of 383 employed individuals. Results indicated HPTI personality traits relate to subjective and objective measures of success, with Conscientiousness being the strongest predictor.

PERSONALITY DISORDERS AT WORK

Over the past 15 to 20 years, there has been great interest in the relationship between dark-side traits (personality disorders) and work failure. Psychiatrists and psychologists share some simple assumptions with respect to personality. Both argue for the stability of personality. The *Diagnostic and Statistical Manual of Mental Disorders* (DSM) addresses stability with phrases like "enduring pattern," "inflexible and pervasive," and "stable and of long duration." DSM also specifies that the pattern of behavior is not a function of drug usage or some other medical condition. Furthermore, the personality pattern is not a manifestation or consequence of another mental disorder. The DSM is careful to point out that some personality disorders look like other disorders (e.g., anxiety disorder, mood disorder, psychosis, substance-related disorder, etc.), but personality disorders have unique features.

One of the most important ways to differentiate personal style from personality disorder is flexibility. There are lots of difficult people at work, but there are relatively few whose rigid, maladaptive behaviors mean they continually have disruptive, troubled lives. It is their inflexible, repetitive, and poor stress-coping responses that are marks of disorder.

Personality disorders influence the sense of self—the way people think and feel about themselves and how other people see them. The disorders often powerfully influence interpersonal relations at work. The antisocial, obsessive-compulsive, passive-aggressive, and dependent types are particularly problematic in the workplace. People with personality disorders have difficulty expressing and understanding emotions. It is the intensity with which they express them and their variability that makes them odd. More importantly, they often have serious problems with self-control.

The greatest progress in this area occurred when the Hogans developed the Hogan Development Survey (HDS; Hogan & Hogan, 1997). Their idea was to use the categories of the personality disorders but to conceive of "dark-side" tendencies rather than disorders. (For comparison of HDS and DSM-IV categories, see Table 4.)

The dysfunctional dispositions reflect distorted beliefs about others that emerge when people encounter stress or stop considering how their actions affect others. Over time, the dispositions may become associated with a person's reputation and can impede job performance and career success.

The personality disorders make a good "select out" checklist: that is, things to look for at assessment that you do not want. The tremendous interest in the Dark Triad (Machiavellianism, narcissism, and psychopathy) has seen an explosion of studies on the dark-side factors in the workplace (Paulhus & Williams, 2002).

Research in this area has revealed three consistent findings (Furnham, 2010, 2014).

The first is that, paradoxically, some of the dark-side traits are implicated in (temporary and specific) management success. Thus, the "naughtiness" of the antisocial mischievous type, the boldness and self-confidence of the arrogant narcissist, the colorful emotionality of the

Table 4. The DSM-IV Personality Disorders and the Hogan Development Survey (HDS) Compared

| DSM Label | Theme | PROFILE | | HDS | |
		Scale	Theme	Scale	Theme
Borderline	Inappropriate anger; unstable and intense relationships alternating between idealization and devaluation	Unstable relationships	Flighty; inconsistent; forms intense, albeit sudden, enthusiasms and disenchantments for people or projects	Excitable	Moody and hard to please; intense but short-lived enthusiasm for people, projects, or things
Paranoid	Distrustful and suspicious of others; others' motives are interpreted as malevolent	Argumentative	Suspicious of others; sensitive to criticism; expects to be mistreated	Skeptical	Cynical, distrustful, and doubts other's true intentions
Avoidant	Social inhibition; feelings of inadequacy and hypersensitivity to criticism or rejection	Fear of failure	Dread of being criticized or rejected; tends to be excessively cautious; unable to make decisions	Cautious	Reluctant to take risks for fear of being rejected or negatively evaluated
Schizoid	Emotionally cold and detached from social relationships; indifferent to praise and criticism	Interpersonal insensitivity	Aloof; cold; imperceptive; ignores social feedback	Reserved	Aloof, detached, and uncommunicative; lacks interest in, or awareness of, the feelings of others
Passive-Aggressive	Passive resistance to adequate social and occupational performance; irritated when asked to do something he/she does not want to	Passive-aggressive	Sociable, but resists others through procrastination and stubbornness	Leisurely	Independent; ignores people's requests and becomes irritated or argumentative if they persist
Narcissistic	Arrogant and haughty behaviors or attitudes; grandiose sense of self-importance and entitlement	Arrogance	Self-absorbed; typically loyal only to himself/herself and his/her own best interests	Bold	Unusually self-confident; feelings of grandiosity and entitlement; overvaluation of his/her capabilities

Table 4. Continued

Antisocial	Disregard for the truth; impulsivity and failure to plan; failure to conform with social norms	Untrustworthiness	Impulsive; dishonest; selfish; motivated by pleasure; ignores the rights of others	Mischievous	Enjoys risk-taking and testing limits; needs excitement; manipulative, deceitful, cunning, and exploitative
Histrionic	Excessive emotionality and attention-seeking; self-dramatizing, theatrical, and exaggerated emotional expression	Attention-seeking	Motivated by a need for attention and a desire to be in the spotlight	Colorful	Expressive, animated, and dramatic; wants to be noticed and needs to be the center of attention
Schizotypal	Odd beliefs or magical thinking; behavior or speech that is odd, eccentric, or peculiar	No common sense	Unusual or eccentric attitudes; exhibits poor judgment relative to education and intelligence	Imaginative	Acting and thinking in creative and sometimes odd or unusual ways
Obsessive-Compulsive	Preoccupations with orderliness, rules, perfectionism, and control; overly conscientious and inflexible	Perfectionism	Methodical; meticulous; attends so closely to details that he/she may have trouble with priorities	Diligent	Meticulous, precise, and perfectionistic; inflexible about rules and procedures; critical of others' performance
Dependent	Difficulty making everyday decisions without excessive advice and reassurance; difficulty expressing disagreement out of fear of loss of support or approval	Dependency	Demand for constant reassurance, support, and encouragement from others	Dutiful	Eager to please and reliant on others for support and guidance; reluctant to take independent action or go against popular opinion

histrionic type, and the quirky imaginativeness of the schizotypal type may in fact help them ascend in the organization.

The second finding refers to the curvilinearity or optimality of the traits. That is, at high levels these traits are nearly always "dangerous" and are associated with derailment and failure, but at moderate levels they may even be beneficial.

Third, some dark-side traits are nearly always associated with lack of success at work. Thus Cautious/Avoidant and Reserved/Schizoid people rarely do very well at work except in highly technical jobs where they work on their own. Their low social skills and inability to charm and persuade others mean that they very rarely occupy positions of power and influence.

CONCLUSION

Does it matter who you are at work? The answer is, "Profoundly yes, and a great deal." In the workplace, personality traits are proactive, reactive, and evocative. They determine the jobs we seek and how we react to them. Further, every individual evokes in others a whole range of responses, which may be highly positive or negative, thus affecting the whole work environment.

On the basis of our ability, traits, and values, we are attracted to different jobs in different organizations (Furnham & Palaiou, 2017). Our personality plays a big part in how we react to situations at work. Thus, the identical situation may be regarded as fun by some people, as challenging by others, and as stressful by many. In addition, personality, styles, and values have an evocative function: they determine how people react to us. Extraverts are more sociable at work and neurotics are more stressed; coworkers may be attracted to the outgoing and optimistic extravert while shunning the anxious and depressed neurotic.

However, three important caveats need to be considered. The first is that personality traits are only one factor determining behavior at work. Other important factors, such as ability and motivation, are equally and sometimes more important at determining work outcomes than traits. Second, while nearly all researchers in this area have looked at the relative power of different traits, traits tend to interact, which is more difficult to describe and explain. It is the total personality profile that needs to be taken into account to properly understand how personality factors work. Third, workplaces are dynamic and complex and there are many different facets to a work outcome. Thus, some personality traits might more strongly relate to some work behaviors rather than to others.

Furthermore, it should never be forgotten that most people work in teams and are neither dependent nor independent at work but are interdependent. Work outcomes are a function of group interaction and dynamics, which are a product of the individual differences of all the members.

REFERENCES

Cattell, R. B. (1987). *Intelligence: Its structure, growth and action*. Oxford, UK: Elsevier.

Chamorro-Premuzic, T., Moutafi, J., & Furnham, A. (2005). The relationship between personality traits, subjectively-assessed and fluid intelligence. *Personality and Individual Differences, 38*(7), 1517–1528. https://doi.org/10.1016/j.paid.2004.09.018

DeYoung, C. G., Quilty, L. C., Peterson, J. B., & Gray, J. R. (2014). Openness to experience, intellect, and cognitive ability. *Journal of Personality Assessment, 96*(1), 46–52. https://doi.org/10.1080/00223891.2013.806327

Dragow, F. (2003). Intelligence and the workplace. In W. Borman, D. Ilgen, & R. Klimozki (Eds.), *Handbook of psychology* (Vol. 12, pp. 107–130). New York, NY: Wiley.

Furnham, A. (2008). *Personality and intelligence at work*. London, UK: Routledge.

Furnham, A. (2010). *The elephant in the boardroom: The psychology of leadership derailment*. Bracknell, UK: Palgrave Macmillan.

Furnham, A. (2014). *Bullies and backstabbers*. London, UK: Bloomsbury.

Furnham, A. (2017). Does it matter who we are? Personality at work. In N. Chmiel, F. Fraccaroli, & M. Sverke (Eds.), *An introduction to work and organisational psychology* (pp. 317–334). New York, NY: Wiley.

Furnham, A. (2018a). Personality and occupational success. In V. Zeigler-Hill & T. K. Shackelford (Eds.), *The SAGE handbook of personality and individual differences* (pp. 537–551). New York, NY: SAGE.

Furnham, A. (2018b). The great divide: Academic vs practitioner criteria for psychometric test choice. *Journal of Personality Assessment, 100*, 498–506.

Furnham, A., & Cheng, H. (2015). The stability and change of malaise scores over 27 years: Findings from a nationally representative sample. *Personality and Individual Differences, 79*, 30–34. https://doi.org/10.1016/j.paid.2015.01.027

Furnham, A., & Cheng, H. (2017). Childhood cognitive ability predicts adult financial well-being. *Journal of Intelligence, 5*(2), 11. https://doi.org/10.3390/jintelligence5020011

Furnham, A., Crump, J., & Ritchie, W. (2013). What it takes: Ability, demographic, bright and dark side trait correlates of years to promotion. *Personality and Individual Differences, 55*(8), 952–956. https://doi.org/10.1016/j.paid.2013.07.469

Furnham, A., & Palaiou, K. (2017). Applicant attraction to organizations and job choice. In J. Passmore, E. Salas, C. Semedo, & H. Goodstein (Eds.), *The Wiley Blackwell handbook of the psychology of recruitment, selection and team dynamics* (pp. 74–86). New York, NY: Wiley.

Gottfredson, L. (1994, December 13). Mainstream science on intelligence: An editorial with 52 signatories, history, and bibliography. *Wall Street Journal*. https://citeseerx.ist.psu.edu/viewdoc/download?doi=10.1.1.366.7808&rep=rep1&type=pdf

Gow, A. J., Whiteman, M. C., Pattie, A., & Deary, I. J. (2005). Goldberg's "IPIP" Big-Five factor markers: Internal consistency and concurrent validation in Scotland. *Personality and Individual Differences, 39*(2), 317–329. https://doi.org/10.1016/j.paid.2005.01.011

Hogan, R., & Hogan, J. (1997). *Hogan Development Survey manual*. Tulsa, OK: Hogan Assessment Centres.

Ihsan, Z., & Furnham, A. (2018). The new technologies in personality assessment: A review. *Consulting Psychology Journal: Practice and Research, 70*(2), 147–166.

Judge, T. A., Higgins, C. A., Thoresen, C. J., & Barrick, M. R. (1999). The Big Five personality traits, general mental ability, and career success across the lifespan. *Personnel Psychology, 52*(3), 621–652.

Judge, T. A., & Locke, E. A. (1992). *The effect of dysfunctional thought processes on subjective well-being and job satisfaction*. CAHRS Working Paper Series, New York APA.

Judge, T. A., Martocchio, J. J., & Thoresen, C. J. (1997). Five-factor model of personality and employee absence. *Journal of Applied Psychology, 82*(5), 745–755.

Kuszewski, A. (2011). You can increase your intelligence: 5 ways to maximize your cognitive potential. *Scientific American, 7*, 1–8. https://blogs.scientificamerican.com/guest-blog/you-can-increase-your-intelligence-5-ways-to-maximize-your-cognitive-potential/

Macrae, I., & Furnham, A. (2014). *High potential: How to spot, manage and develop talented people at work*. London: Bloomsbury.

Nettle, D. (2006). The evolution of personality variation in humans and other animals. *American Psychologist, 61*(6), 622–631. https://doi.org/10.1037/0003-066X.61.6.622

O'Boyle, E. H., Forsyth, D. R., Banks, G. C., & McDaniel, M. A. (2012). A meta-analysis of the Dark Triad and work behaviour: A social exchange perspective. *Journal of Applied Psychology, 97,* 557–579.

Palaiou, K., Zarola, A., & Furnham, A. (2016). The dark side of personality predicts positive and negative work attitudes. *Personality and Individual Differences, 88,* 12–16.

Paulhus, D. L., & Williams, K. M. (2002). The Dark Triad of personality: Narcissism, Machiavellianism, and psychopathy. *Journal of Research in Personality, 36*(6), 556–563. https://doi.org/10.1016/S0092-6566(02)00505-6

Schmidt, F. L., & Hunter, J. E. (1998). The validity and utility of selection methods in personnel psychology: Practical and theoretical implications of 85 years of research findings. *Psychological Bulletin, 124,* 262–274.

Schmidt, F., & Hunter, J. (2004). General mental ability in the world of work. *Journal of Personality and Social Psychology, 86,* 162–173.

Seligman, M. (2007). *What you can change . . . and what you can't.* London, UK: Nicholas Brearley.

Silzer, R., & Church, A. H. (2009). The pearls and perils of identifying potential. *Industrial and Organizational Psychology, 2*(4), 377–412. https://doi.org/10.1111/j.1754-9434.2009.01163.x

Snyderman, M., & Rothman, S. (1987). Survey of expert opinion on intelligence and aptitude testing. *American Psychologist, 42*(2), 137–144. https://doi.org/10.1037/0003-066X.42.2.137

Spreitzer, G. M., McCall, M. W., & Mahoney, J. D. (1997). Early identification of international executive potential. *Journal of Applied Psychology, 82*(1), 6–29. https://doi.org/10.1037/0021-9010.82.1.6

Teodorescu, A., Furnham, A., & Macrae, I. (2017). Trait correlates of success at work. *International Journal of Selection and Assessment, 25,* 36–42. https://doi.org/10.1111/ijsa.12158

Tobin, R., & Gadke, D. (2015). Agreeableness. *International encyclopedia of the social and behavioural sciences* (Vol. 1, pp. 463–470). Cambridge: Cambridge University Press. https://doi.org/10.1016/B978-0-08-097086-8.25044-7

Adrian Furnham

GENDER IN ORGANIZATIONS

The workplace is historically—but not necessarily permanently—gendered. Some gains in women's workplace representation were reversed by the conditions of the COVID-19 pandemic, which involved workforce reductions in industry sectors dominated by women (e.g., retail, restaurants) and a collapse of childcare centers and schools. Well before (and continuing during) the pandemic, however, some industry sector gender differences have prevailed in the workforce; for instance, men comprise 94% of construction, maintenance, and natural resources occupations, and 83% of architecture and engineering occupations; women, in contrast, comprise 74% of all teaching and librarian occupations, 72% of all administrative occupations, and 85% of healthcare support occupations (U.S. Bureau of Labor Statistics, 2022). Such gender disparities will remain in many industries until changes are made to solve them. Other occupations, such as some in business, social science, legal, arts and media, and sales have much more equitable rates of men and women (U.S. Bureau of Labor Statistics, 2022).[1]

To that end, the beginning of this article reviews the theoretical perspectives that have been brought to bear on these gendered patterns. The following section articulates the intersections of gender with stages of employment. The final section describes strategies that can reduce these historical patterns of inequity at work.

THEORIES OF GENDER IN ORGANIZATIONS

There are a number of theories that provide a context for understanding gender dynamics in organizations. This section focuses on six dominant social explanations regarding the status of men and women at work: (a) social learning theory (Bandura, 1977), (b) social role theory (Eagly, 1987), (c) role congruence theory (Eagly & Karau, 2002), (d) lack of fit model (Heilman & Caleo, 2018), (e) ambivalent sexism theory (Glick & Fiske, 1996), and (f) stereotype content model (Fiske et al., 2002). Each of these theories can be used alone, or in tandem, to better comprehend the different realities that women and men tend to experience in the workplace.

Social Learning Theory. Bandura (1977) introduced social learning theory to explain how individuals learn different social behaviors and described four main components. First, he suggested that individuals process information by observing their environment or watching others. Employees may look around to see what their coworkers are doing. Second, he proposed that individuals must engage in cognitive behaviors to retain the information they have observed. Not only do employees watch their coworkers, but they remember those actions. Third, he argued that individuals reproduce or imitate the behaviors they have seen, particularly mimicking same-sex individuals. Just as little girls (boys) may want to have baby dolls (carpentry sets) if they see their mothers (fathers) taking care of babies (building things), women and men look to the workforce to see what exemplars exist there as (same-sex) role models. Fourth and finally, he suggested that there must be motivational factors for the behavior to be learned and performed. For instance, individuals might decide what sorts of behaviors to pursue based on the reinforcements they see others receive (or experience themselves). If men observe male coworkers receiving praise for being decisive and punitive, they may decide to mimic such behavior. Similarly, if women observe female coworkers receiving praise for helping others, they may follow suit. Finally, Bandura suggested that despite the fact that individuals may not necessarily have the opportunity to practice all the behaviors they see their same-sex role models perform, they still engage in observational learning (see Bandura, 2008) and are able to later rely upon the information they have earlier observed. For instance, when men and women begin their professional careers, they may designate work tasks—such that women take notes (e.g., like secretaries) and men present in meetings (e.g., like leaders)—because those are the behaviors they have observed in others.

Social Role Theory. Introduced by Eagly (1987), social role theory suggests that gender differences arise from the differential distribution of men and women in societal roles. In this division of labor, men tend to be the breadwinners and assume jobs that require physical strength, leadership, and assertiveness, while women tend to be homemakers and stay-at-home caretakers, and to hold caretaking positions. Said differently, the jobs predominantly held by men in our society often require *agency*, or skills such as leading, making decisions, and working independently (Bakan, 1966). In contrast, the jobs predominantly held by women in our society often require *communality*, or skills such as caring, empathizing, helping, and including (Bakan, 1966).

As men and women engage in different sets of behaviors, they gain more opportunities to become skilled in their respective roles. Men are able to practice leading more, and women are able to practice caring more. It is not surprising that others form stereotypes about the genders and act on them. That is, if an employer is trying to hire someone to be compassionate, they may give an edge to a female (versus male) employee, given that the employer sees so many more women in positions displaying compassion. If an employer is hiring a manager, however, the employer may not observe many examples of women leading; hence, they may believe that women are not able to lead as well and hire a man. In this way, gender stereotypes become self-fulfilling prophecies, ultimately further exacerbating inequities in the distribution of men and women into societal roles (see Wisniewski, 2022); unfortunately, greater accolades, power, salary, and opportunities come with the positions that men (versus women) hold.

Role Congruity Theory.   Grounded in social role theory, role congruity theory (Eagly & Karau, 2002) further explains gender differences in organizations and why women occupy few leadership roles. Importantly, this theory suggests that the greater the incongruities between a person's perceived characteristics and a job role, the lower the perceptions of effectiveness in the role. Thus, women who are expected to be caring, indecisive, and emotional would face incongruence if employed in a masculine job role (e.g., leader, manager), thereby resulting in negative evaluations of their effectiveness. This incongruity leads to two forms of prejudice (Eagly & Karau, 2002). First, women (versus men) are perceived less favorably when they occupy leadership roles (e.g., Gupta et al., 2018). Second, when evaluating behaviors that are consistent with the role of a leader, women (versus men) are evaluated more poorly. Thus, women are viewed to be far less suitable for leadership positions than are men, and when women finally do occupy such positions, they also are not evaluated favorably.

In sum, role incongruity theory reveals that attitudes toward female leaders or potential leaders are just not as positive as they are toward male leaders. A study conducted across five decades reveals that these attitudes translate to a strong preference for male versus female bosses at all data timepoints collected (Simmons, 2001). As such, it may be much more difficult for women to become and achieve success in leadership roles. Such unequal representation found across leadership roles is often referred to as the "glass ceiling" phenomenon, or the presence of a barrier that prohibits women from being promoted to the very top leadership positions (Federal Glass Ceiling Commission, 1995). Researchers also have described the presence of a "glass cliff," a phenomenon in which women are more likely to be put in leadership positions of poor performing companies, whereas men are more likely to be put in leadership positions of high performing companies (Ryan & Haslam, 2005). As a whole, there is a significant amount of evidence supporting role congruity theory. Importantly, when evaluating what types of women were seen as leaders by a group of all women, Schock et al. (2019) found that women who tempered their agency with communal actions were viewed more favorably. Essentially, women who were viewed more successfully were trying to emphasize characteristics that would be more congruent with the job role.

Lack of Fit Model. Very similar to role congruity theory is Heilman's (1983) lack of fit theory, which suggests that gender discrimination is a significant contributor to the gender inequalities that continue to persist in the workplace. More specifically, when there is a misalignment between gender stereotypes and gender-typed positions, gender discrimination results. For instance, consider a misalignment associated with women's stereotypical attributes (e.g., nurturing, communal) and what is required in a male-typed position or field (top management, construction worker). Having a woman apply for such a position results in perceptions of a lack of fit, thereby resulting in discrimination (Heilman, 1983). The lack of fit model is heavily rooted in traditional gender stereotypes and is similar to social role theory in that both theories are based on the idea that women are perceived to be communal and relationship-oriented and men are perceived to be agentic, bold, and aggressive (Haines et al., 2016).

The lack of fit model predicts differential effects for men and women in different contexts. Men do not typically want to enter the fields in which women are heavily employed (e.g., secretaries, nurses, house cleaners, grade school teachers) because these jobs tend to have lower status, prestige, and pay. Yet, if they do enter these fields, men sometimes experience the "glass escalator," meaning they get fast-tracked to higher salaries and promotions (Williams, 1992). In contrast, women who want to be employed in male-dominated occupations (often with higher status, more prestige, and higher pay) are often blocked from doing so because they are perceived not to have the necessary characteristics. There are intervention strategies to increase perceptions of fit, either by reducing the belief that women are not suited for male-typed positions or by preventing the negative performance expectations from influencing evaluative judgments (Heilman & Cao, 2018).

Ambivalent Sexism Theory. Ambivalent sexism theory (Glick & Fiske, 1996) also helps explain gender differences in an organization by describing two complementary ideologies that maintain gender inequities: hostile and benevolent sexism. Hostile sexism involves antipathy toward women who violate traditional gender roles; for instance, female employees who seek being in charge and trying to lead are pejoratively labeled as bossy or viewed to be incompetent. Benevolent sexism involves the positive reactions toward women who maintain traditional gender roles; for example, female employees who exhibit motherly instincts, maintain traditional caretaking roles, maintain an attractive appearance, and are neat (see also Weiss, 2015) are often evaluated favorably. Benevolent sexism is not necessarily problematic at face value and can be framed in positive ways, but these beliefs greatly restrict women's personal and professional opportunities.

Benevolent sexism is made up of three components—paternalism, gender differences, and heterosexuality. With regard to paternalism, men are viewed as the dominant or protective force, whereas women are to be "loved, cherished and protected" (Glick & Fiske, 1996). Gender differences between men and women are rooted in the belief that men are the only gender capable of being strong leaders in a group setting (Glick & Fiske, 1996). The final component, heterosexuality, is important in propagating the idea of men and women's interdependence. While men are responsible for leading in the work sphere, women are responsible for the home sphere. Together these beliefs drive sexist behaviors that maintain the status quo of women's subordinate status to men; for example, beliefs that women should be protected by men may lead decision-makers to withhold important, challenging developmental opportunities from women (King et al., 2012).

Stereotype Content Model. A more recent model related to gender differences in organizations is Fiske et al.'s (2002) stereotype content model. This model proposes that stereotypes in society are based on two primary dimensions, warmth and competence. Warmth is the perceived interpersonal orientation of a person, whereas competence is the extent to which a person is perceived as being capable of completing tasks successfully (Fiske et al., 2002). These two dimensions can be crossed to form four different cells: high warmth-high competence, high warmth-low competence, low warmth-low competence, low warmth-high competence. Where a particular group falls on these dimensions predicts the reactions that others have toward its members. People often feel admiration toward groups that are warm and competent and feel contempt toward groups that are incompetent and cold.

Of course, the crossing of these cells reveals that many groups may be the focus of ambivalent attitudes, and women are one of these groups. On one hand, "traditional" women are perceived to be high on warmth but low on competence. These women are targeted with benevolent sexism, are often revered by men, and are treated with paternalism (Glick & Fiske, 2001). On the other hand, "career" women are perceived to be high on competence but low on warmth, and these women are often targeted with hostile sexism (Glick et al., 1997). As career women also often become mothers, however, the competence ratings often decrease and give way to higher warmth ratings (Cuddy et al., 2004). Since they are seen as incompetent but warm, women tend to be pitied and in need of the paternalistic guidance of men (Cuddy et al., 2008).

Intersectionality Theory. Intersectionality is an understudied but critical construct when considering the impact of gender on organizations (Crenshaw, 2017). We define intersectionality as the combination of distinct demographic characteristics (e.g., gender, ethnicity, religion, disability, gender identity, sexual orientation) which result in creating different workplace outcomes for those who have (versus do not have) these combinations (see Naples, 2019). For instance, individuals with certain intersectional identities may face far more discrimination than others, and this is certainly the case when it comes to gender and race (e.g., Black versus white women). Stereotypes about Black women can be particularly problematic in the workforce; for example, Black women are often stereotyped as being dominant, strong, aggressive, or controlling (Thiem et al., 2019). In contrast, white women are often viewed as being communal, affective, and warm (Rosette et al., 2018), and Asian/Asian American women are often perceived as being innocent, submissive, passive, and obedient (Prasso, 2005). Assumptions about minority women are heightened for women that have high phenotypic racial stereotypicality (Kahn & Davies, 2011). For example, Black women who wear their hair in natural hairstyles are perceived to be more dominant and militant, which may decrease their likelihood of receiving an interview recommendation (Rosette et al., 2018). Many women of color also experience organizational segregation; for example, Black women particularly fill a disproportionate number of lower-level jobs such as home health aides, childcare workers, maids, and cashiers (Entmacher et al., 2014). Not only are these careers often viewed as being undesirable, but these jobs are also among the lowest paying occupations. In fact, there is so much segregation in these occupations, for instance, that nearly half of Black women and Latina scientists reported that they had been mistaken for administrative or custodial staff (see Williams et al., 2015). Women, especially women of color, might be judged differently because of stereotypes which may hinder them from being successful.

Beyond race, gender interacts with other demographic characteristics such as disability. One study reported that one in every four women in the United States have a diagnosed disability, and that just having a disability alone can increase the odds of being discriminated against (Jetha et al., 2020). Some women feel that disclosing disability information can cause employers to discriminate against them, but that not disclosing or requesting accommodations makes their work-life harder, thus creating a "double-edged sword" (Moloney et al., 2019). Some of the stereotypes that are applied to women with disabilities are dependency, passivity, and incompetence, which can lead to these women having to work harder than their average coworker to be seen as "normal" or judged on the same playing field as everyone else (Moloney et al., 2019). Despite the lack of research generally on the intersection of gender and disability, the hindering effects are apparent and encourage further research.

Another understudied intersection is the relationship between gender and age. Some research suggests generational differences in regard to this intersection. It may be far easier for women to navigate organizational settings today than it was in generations past, but even today both young and older women cite their personal experiences with ageism. In fact, burnout for women seems to be bimodal (both those 20–35 and those over 55 reported the highest burnout), whereas burnout for men tends to decrease linearly as they age (Marchand et al., 2018). Young women must shoulder the burden of balancing the start of their careers with beginning their families. Older women are harmed by the compounding of experiences from the sectors of the labor market segmentation in which women participate. That is, women tend to occupy lower-paying, lower-status, more transient occupations. Compounded over time, researchers suggest that these differences may have psychological and physical consequences that are likely to be visible as female employees age (Payne & Doyal, 2010). For example, older women, particularly those in clerical professions, indicated that organizations often avoid hiring them into permanent positions and suggested that appearance continued to matter much more than it should (Handy & Davy, 2007). Indeed, other research suggests that women must contend with their appearance throughout their lifespan more than men; for instance, even something as commonplace as men's gray hair is seen as a sign of authority, while women's gray hair is not (Cecil et al., 2021).

Gender Theories Summary.   In summary, there are many theories that help to build an understanding of the role that gender plays in organizations. Although there are some important differences and contradictions, several important themes can be extracted from a synthesis of these perspectives. First, most of the theories emphasize the presence of gendered expectations, or the idea that people's expectations for male and female employees are different and that these differences are rooted in roles, stereotypes, and/or social learning. Second, many of the theories also consistently describe a potential misalignment between feminine gender roles and some of the most highly valued, esteemed, and well-paying occupations and work-roles. Third, many of the theories also describe scenarios in which women in the

THE INTERSECTIONS OF GENDER WITH STAGES OF EMPLOYMENT

Each of the theories we have discussed provide compelling explanations for why women might face more disadvantages relative to men across all stages of employment. In this section, we particularly consider many of these disadvantages—the setbacks, challenges, biases, and inequities—that women (relative to men) face in the workplace. To do this, we consider the two main stages of a job cycle: the challenges of trying to *secure (or obtain)* and *navigate (or maintain)* a job. With respect to trying to secure a job, we discuss (a) gendered educational gaps and experiences, (b) gender differences in self-promotion, (c) gender-based hiring discrimination, (d) gender differences in letters of recommendations, (e) gender-based pay disparities, (f) gendered negotiation differences. Then, we consider the gendered challenges of navigating the job. Specifically, we discuss (a) gendered leadership positions, (b) gender differences in access to mentors, (c) the three taboo Ms, (d) gender differences in occupational health, and (e) caregiving off-ramps.

Gendered Challenges of Trying to Secure a Job. The expectations of women, together with perceived misalignments for work roles, create meaningful barriers for women's employment. Indeed, the challenges that women encounter begin even before their first job offer.

Gendered Educational Gaps and Experiences. Research has repeatedly shown that women enter and graduate from college at greater rates than men, yet they fall behind in science, technology, engineering, and mathematics (STEM) fields. In a report by the National Center for Science and Engineering Statistics (2021), using data from achievement of undergraduate degrees in 2018, women earned more than half (55%) of social science degrees, leading in the field of psychology (79%), but fell behind in the field of economics (32%; see Table 5-2). Women also led in the field of biology (63%) but fell far behind in other STEM fields: women comprised 42% in mathematics and statistics, 22% of bachelor's degree graduates in engineering, 21% in physics, and 20% in computer science (National Center for Science and Engineering Statistics, 2021). The number of women in STEM is bleak, and if obtaining a STEM degree is a gateway for securing a job in STEM—which are among the top-paying jobs (U.S. Bureau of Labor Statistics, 2021a)—then the gender pay gap will likely persist. This raises the question: Why are women less likely to pursue majors and careers in STEM?

Weeden et al. (2020) suggest four factors that contribute to gender differences in STEM: the academic pipeline, self-assessed ability, view of work and family, and career plans—all of which are influenced by developmental socialization. Consistent with this, Morgan et al. (2013) suggest that the strongest predictor of initial major choice in college is the occupational plans of high school seniors. An increase in the representation of women in STEM requires that women learn about and *want* to pursue STEM early, thereby leading to the development of a strong pipeline. Many girls lose interest in STEM during middle school, suggesting that additional efforts are necessary to increase STEM interest in youth (see Choney, 2018). When nearly 1,200 middle schoolers were asked about their career aspirations, 91% of boys and 74% of girls chose a male-dominated career; however, whereas 26% of boys chose a STEM career, only 12% of girls chose a STEM career, a proportion which is oddly reminiscent of the modern workforce (Shapiro et al., 2015). The external barriers that women cite to pursuing STEM careers include intimidation and sexism by men, the lack of women in STEM (both generally and as role models), the lack of awareness of opportunities, the glass ceiling, and a lack of encouragement from men (Swafford & Anderson, 2020).

Gender Differences in Self-Promotion. As discussed by Mohr (2014), a Hewlett Packard internal report revealed that men would apply for a job even if they were only 60% qualified, whereas women would only apply if they were 100% qualified. In a further exploration of this finding, Mohr (2014) surveyed over 1,000 professionals, asking them, "If you decided not to apply for a job because you didn't meet all the qualifications, why didn't you apply?" Actually, the top response from both men (46%) and women (41%) was that they did not want to waste time and energy; however, the second most common response from women was that they did not want to fail (22%), whereas only 13% of men did not apply for this reason. Findings from these studies may suggest that women are less likely to take risks when it comes to applying for jobs and may be holding themselves back.

Not only are women less likely to apply if they feel they are not qualified, but they are also less likely to self-promote compared to men. The National Bureau of Economic Research observed approximately 14,000 participants (adults and students) and found that men tend to describe their ability and test performance higher on average than women (even though both genders performed comparatively; Exley & Kessler, 2019). This difference has vast implications for self-promotion in the workplace because if men are more likely and willing to speak highly of their abilities, they may be evaluated more positively in hiring contexts. This pattern is also observed in other studies, in which women tend to refrain from self-promotion due to a fear of negative reactions from others (Lindeman et al., 2019). This suggests a potential gap and area of development for women necessary to achieve gender equality in the workplace.

Gender-Based Hiring Discrimination. There are a number of studies that show women face more hiring-related biases than men do. Importantly, these differences still emerge even after performance or evaluation criteria are held constant. Reuben et al. (2014) observed both male and female participants being more likely to favor male candidates over female candidates in hiring decisions, even when task performance was comparable. Similarly, Moss-Racusin et al. (2012) observed that STEM faculty members were more likely to select male undergraduates for a lab manager position (compared to equally qualified female candidates), and offered female candidates lower salaries.

Cues other than gender itself also shortchange women in hiring and promotion decisions. Several studies, for instance, show that obese women are seen as being less suitable for jobs than obese men (Flint et al., 2016) and experience significantly lower callback rates for actual jobs (Campos-Vazquez & Gonzales, 2020). Some evidence suggests that this is particularly true for higher-paying and valued jobs (Li et al., 2021). Importantly, while being thin can carry a benefit in the labor market, other research shows that if women are too attractive, they can also face discrimination on the job market (Johnson et al., 2010).

Additionally, studies have found that agentic traits are often highly valued in employees and leaders—and men are often rated (or perceived to be) higher than women on aspects of agency, including competence, leadership abilities, assertiveness, and independence (Hentschel et al., 2019). Unfortunately, when women do exhibit agency in the hiring process, they are more likely to be perceived negatively. For instance, an experimental study by Tyler and McCullough (2009) found that women are perceived more negatively if their résumés suggest agentic traits rather than communal traits. In sum, a variety of factors (e.g., bias, stereotypes, gender-role congruity) impact hiring decisions.

Gender Differences in Letters of Recommendations. Letters of recommendation are a widely used selection tool that provides information on candidates' prior performance and qualifications (see McCarthy & Goffin, 2001); however, they can be subject to gender biases. For example, letter writers tend to use more doubt raisers when writing letters for women versus men (Madera et al., 2019; Trix & Psenka, 2003). Doubt raisers include four types of linguistic phrases: faint praise (e.g., "This individual tries really hard to be good"); negativity (e.g., "This individual has a somewhat *challenging* personality"); hedging (e.g., "This individual might not be the best but is good"); and irrelevancy (e.g., "This individual did well in a different field"). Doubt raisers are perceived negatively for men and women alike; in fact, even the presence of a single doubt raiser can negatively influence how a letter of recommendation is perceived.

In addition to doubt raisers, letter writers also rely on different sets of words when writing letters for male versus female candidates. For instance, Madera et al. (2009) examined the frequency of agentic terms (e.g., outstanding, excellent, dominant, intelligent) and communal terms (e.g., sympathetic, nurturing, warm, friendly) and found that letters written on behalf of women contained significantly more communal adjectives, whereas letters for men contained significantly more agentic adjectives. In a similar study, letters written for male (versus female) applicants in a healthcare context were two times more likely to include the term "future leader" (Hoffman et al., 2019). Gender stereotypes might explain these observed differences in letters of recommendation. As previously mentioned, females are stereotypically described as being communal because women are often perceived as inherently sympathetic, friendly, and nurturing, whereas men are the opposite (Fiske et al., 2002). Beyond linguistic differences, female candidates are also significantly more likely to have their physical appearance mentioned in their letter of recommendation, which is another important finding in light of what women perceive as roadblocks to their success (Horwood et al., 2021).

Gendered Pay Disparities. Pay disparity is a simple, but powerful, sign of how women and men are treated differently in the workplace. In the United States, women earn approximately 84% of what men earn, based on overall median hourly pay (Barroso & Brown, 2021). Such a pattern has been found across fields in business, humanities, education, medicine, law, mathematics, and computer science (U.S. Census Bureau, 2019). Some of these differences arise from women undervaluing their worth and men overvaluing theirs (e.g., Reuben et al., 2017). Experimental studies demonstrate that women will accept less compensation than men for the same amount of work in the absence of comparison information, and that women will work longer hours than men for the same amount of pay (Major & Konar, 1984).

Gender pay differences also stem from gender disparities in entry-level roles. Kauhanen and Napari (2015) found that women are 36% more likely than males to begin their careers at the bottom or second lowest level of the corporate ladder (e.g., maintenance officer, assistant sales representative, senior cashier, stock bookkeeper). In addition, employers treat male and female candidates differently regardless of their similar employment backgrounds and salary requests. Even when starting the job, women have lower starting salaries, and fewer on average receive the actual salary requested compared to similarly qualified men (Säve-Söderbergh, 2019). This pattern is impacted by stereotypes of men, which are closer to employers' expectations of qualified employees compared to women. Thus, with the same qualifications, men often overvalue themselves, helping them to receive a higher salary, while women have to work harder to prove their competence.

Gendered Negotiation Differences.   The characteristics of men's and women's jobs also differ as a function of their negotiations. A meta-analysis of gender differences in negotiation suggested a small, significant relationship, with men receiving better outcomes (Stuhlmacher & Walters, 1999). A more recent meta-analysis identified specific contexts that reduced gender differences—specifically, when there is low role incongruity, such as when having experienced negotiators, having knowledge of bargain range, and negotiating for another individual (Mazei et al., 2015). These small differences in negotiation outcomes may accumulate and contribute to both the earnings gap and rates of men and women in leadership.

One factor explaining gender negotiation gaps is that men and women have varying success with negotiations. For example, Säve-Söderbergh (2019) observed female candidates being somewhat more likely to negotiate their starting pay, but tending to make slightly lower salary requests (about $85 less per month) compared to males. Gender stereotypes also affect negotiations. With males being perceived as more competitive and agentic, it may be more socially acceptable for them to negotiate for a higher salary, whereas females are often perceived as being more cooperative and communal, stereotypes which make it less socially acceptable to negotiate for a higher salary. This is supported by Bowles et al. (2007), who observed male participants being more willing to work with women who accepted their initial compensation offer than with those who initiated negotiation for higher compensation. Overall, men are more likely than women to receive positive outcomes of negotiation because the process is more consistent with a masculine than a feminine gender role (Bowles et al., 2007).

Gendered Challenges of Navigating the Job.
Once they attain a job, women and men have to navigate the challenges of creating and sustaining work products and social networks that will facilitate their success and well-being. These tasks can be particularly burdensome for women. The "leaky pipeline" and "glass ceiling" are two metaphors commonly used to refer to the fact that women do not make it to the top echelons of organizations. The leaky pipeline reveals that at each ascending level of an organization, more and more women drop out; for instance, a 2021 study by consulting company McKinsey in collaboration with LeanIn.org determined that women hold 47% of the entry-level jobs in organizations but only 24% of C-suite jobs. And, of course, the situation is much dire for women of color, who comprise only 17% of the entry-level jobs (compared to 30% of white women) and only 4% of C-suite positions (relative to 20% for white women; Burns et al., 2021). This data clearly shows the

barriers blocking women (and particularly women of color) from advancement. The glass ceiling metaphor conveys the experience of women who are stuck in the middle levels of organizations, hitting a transparent but powerful barrier to further advancement.

In 2020 alone, the U.S. Equal Employment Opportunity Commission reported receiving over 21,000 sex-based discrimination charges, most of which were submitted by women (Equal Employment Opportunity Commission, 2021). Moreover, a Pew Research Center (Parker & Funk, 2017) survey revealed that 42% of working women in the United Statees reported experiencing discrimination at work compared to 22% of men. Women of color may be doubly burdened by racialized forms of sexism in organizations. For example, in a study across five organizations, women of color reported experiencing more harassment when compared to white women and men generally (Berdahl & Moore 2006). In this section, we briefly describe a variety of factors affecting women while navigating the job—gendered leadership perceptions, access to mentorship, and caregiving responsibilities—that exacerbate the effects of discrimination on women's experiences at work.

Gendered Leadership Perceptions. Another important factor influencing women's advancement in organizations is perceptions of leaders. Typically, women display a transformational leadership style, while men display a transactional and laissez-faire leadership style (Eagly et al., 2003). A transformational leadership style is more democratic and encourages positive change through motivation and nurturing. A transformational leader, for example, will set small goals for their employees and provide feedback as they work toward them. On the other hand, transactional leadership relies on a system of rewards and punishments to motivate followers; for example, transactional leaders will offer bonuses for employees who excel and demote those who do not. However, research has shown that the aspects of leadership that women primarily display are positively related to leaders' effectiveness, whereas the leadership styles that men primarily display are negatively or not related to leaders' effectiveness (Eagly et al., 2003). In other words, many women have the characteristics required of good leaders and engage in effective leadership.

Based on this information, why do we see so few women in higher levels of leadership positions? Part of the problem is that women are not perceived as leaders. A meta-analysis examining masculinity and leadership revealed that people view leaders as being more similar to men than women (Koenig et al., 2011). People more often view leaders as agentic and masculine, aligning more closely with men (Adams & Funk, 2012). Therefore, there are discrepancies in effective leadership and in the perceptions of what a leader is. Although women have the skills to be effective leaders, they are limited by stereotypical social roles. The premise of role congruity theory (Eagly & Karau, 2002) is that women are evaluated less favorably in these leadership roles. Although women have the capacity to be great leaders, society's stereotypes about their social roles limit the leadership roles that women can take on.

Gender Differences in Access to Mentors. Another important factor influencing how women navigate the workplace is mentorship. Mentors can be a good source of knowledge for newcomers and can help them develop in their professional careers. Mentors also connect mentees to more experienced employees and improve their career outcomes (see Allen et al., 2004). Moreover, through mentorship, mentees can create a professional network that can help them find new opportunities to grow and advance in their careers. Although mentorship is a great resource, women have a harder time getting access to mentors than do men (Farkas et al., 2019; see Ibarra, 2019).

Finding male mentors has become especially challenging for women after the rise of the #MeToo Movement, which gave women the platform to speak out against sexual harassment and demand change at work. The movement was successful in that the percentage of women reporting sexual coercion decreased from 25% in 2016 to 16% in 2018 (Johnson et al., 2019). However, not all of the consequences from the #MeToo movement were positive; many men started excluding women, avoiding private meetings, and fearing false allegations (Atwater et al., 2021). Male fear likely caused many women to miss out on valuable networking and mentorship opportunities that could have helped them advance in their careers. This is unfortunate because mentorship may be particularly valuable for women who are navigating unique challenges at the intersection of work and life.

The Three Taboo Ms. There are three often taboo topics—menstruation, maternity, and menopause—that are sometimes restrictive elements to women's careers (Grandey et al., 2019). At each expected career stage, women bear physical challenges that they must navigate, often without any organizational support. For instance, young women beginning their careers often have to deal with menstrual discomforts (e.g., cramping); midcareer women may experience childbirth and have postpartum duties (e.g., breastfeeding); and senior career women have to deal with menopause and its effects (e.g., hot flashes). Although all of these stages are linked to fluctuating hormonal and physical changes, negative stereotypes, and workplace attitudes and behaviors, very little empirical work has been done to more fully address and assist women. Not only do men and women have different biological experiences, but they may experience different physical and mental health outcomes as well.

Gender Differences in Occupational Health. There are various work and family stressors that result in differential health outcomes for men and women. In terms of physical health in 2020, from the years 2016–2020, men, people ages 45–64, and people of Hispanic or Latino origin were most likely to experience fatal occupational injuries (U.S. Bureau of Labor Statistics, 2021c). However, in 2020, nursing assistants and registered nurses (female-dominated careers) experienced the greatest number of days away from work as a result of non-fatal workplace injuries and illness (U.S. Bureau of Labor Statistics, 2021b). Thus, although men were more likely to experience fatal workplace injuries and illnesses, the COVID-19 pandemic has increased the number of non-fatal workplace injuries and illnesses in a greater magnitude for women. This pattern is consistent with broad, paradoxical gender differences in health whereby men have higher rates of mortality and women have higher rates of morbidity across the lifespan.

In terms of mental health, women often experience greater psychological distress than men (e.g., Viertiö et al., 2021). This may be a result of women often experiencing greater work-to-family conflict, having less decision authority in the workplace, being more likely to be a single parent, and having lower self-esteem compared to men (Bilodeau et al., 2020). Another potential factor contributing to mental health difference is the composition of the workplace. A longitudinal study by Milner et al. (2018) reviewed data from 14 annual waves of the Household Income Labour Dynamics in Australia (HILDA), finding that both men and women tend to have better mental health when employed in occupations that are dominated by their respective gender. Interestingly, when men switch to a female-dominated occupation, they experience better mental health outcomes, yet when women switch to a male-dominated occupation, they experience poorer mental health. This finding may have important implications for women switching into traditionally male-dominated STEM careers because they may experience worse mental health.

Specific mental illness conditions appear to vary between genders; for example, women are twice as likely to experience depression (Brody et al., 2018), which is the leading cause of disability internationally (World Health Organization, 2021). Importantly, nearly 80% of people with depression, both men and women, reported difficulty working, doing housework, or engaging in social activities (Brody et al., 2018). There are a number of risk factors for depression, such as family history, brain changes, stress, and hormone levels (Office on Women's Health, 2021). When considering these factors, it is important to consider how women may be uniquely impacted by additional stressors (e.g., caretaking responsibilities, lower pay, hormonal changes) that may not only exacerbate negative mental health outcomes, but also prevent gender equality in the workplace.

Gender Differences in Caregiving Responsibilities. In general, women face challenges at the intersection of work and life that impact their career opportunities and vertical mobility within the organization. Many women, for example, begin their "second shift" after returning home from work by tending to various responsibilities like meal preparation, laundry, and housecleaning, as well as taking care of children and even other family members. In contrast, many men simply do not experience this "second shift" (Hochschild & Machung, 2012). Analysis of data from the American Time Use Survey, a robust time diary study sponsored by the U.S. government, suggests that in an average week, women do approximately 10.8 more hours of unpaid household labor than do men (Krantz-Kent, 2009).

Childcare. Indeed, stereotypes about motherhood can prevent women from being hired or from progressing in their careers. For example, for younger women, there is often an unspoken assumption that they will become mothers, a stereotype which can cause women to be perceived as risk assets for companies (Peterson Gloor et al., 2022). As another example, women with children are perceived as being lower in competence, commitment, achievement striving, dependability, and agentic behaviors compared to women without children, and lower on ratings of anticipated competence and agentic behavior compared to fathers (Heilman & Okimoto, 2008). More generally, parents, regardless of gender, were more likely to be rated lower on job commitment, anticipated achievement, and general dependability than candidates without children (Heilman & Okimoto, 2008). Even when mothers prove to be competent and committed to their work, they are still often perceived as being less warm and more hostile than similar non-mothers (Benard & Corell, 2010). Stereotypes around motherhood often result in employers viewing mothers as being less desirable employees before they even get the chance to express their expectations and desires.

Taking time off of work (either temporarily or permanently) after having a child is perhaps one of the biggest off-ramps for women. Women who choose to stay at work face a double-edged sword by which they are characterized as being a poor parent (Morgenroth & Heilman, 2017). Survey data from the Center for Work-Life Policy found that almost 40% of working women voluntarily left work at some point compared to 24% of working men (Hewlett & Luce, 2005). Women who take maternity leave are typically seen as being less competent at work and ultimately less worthy of organizational rewards compared to women who do not take time off (Hewlett & Luce, 2005). Moreover, women sometimes struggle to get the support they need and expect when they return to work after maternity leave (Botsford Morgan & King, 2012). In contrast, men do not often face the same societal expectations to take time off and are not often questioned on how they will balance fatherhood with their work (Hewlett & Luce, 2005). In their review of research on the intersection between gender and race, Rosette and colleagues (2018) described the ways in which motherhood may be perceived differently at work and at home for white women and women of color. Unique, stereotype-based expectations of white, Black, and Asian mothers, they argued, give rise to different workforce participation rates and wages for these groups of women.

Spousal and Elder Care. In addition to childcare demands, an increasing number of women are bearing the burden of elder or spousal care responsibilities. One out of three women aged 41–55 take time off to care for non-children family members (Hewlett & Luce, 2005). Women may also leave their careers to take care of an ailing spouse. Globally, women outlive men by seven years on average (Population Reference Bureau, 2001). Although this off-ramp is less common, there are still many women who take a leave from their careers to take care of their spouses, experiencing greater strain and less support, compared to men (Brazil et al., 2009). Women are often at a disadvantage in the workplace because they are expected to fulfill these caregiving responsibilities. Many women also face challenges when returning to the workplace after such caregiving demands, and rarely catch up to their counterparts in outcomes such as salary and advancement (Henle et al., 2020; Hewlett, 2002).

Summary of Getting the Job and Maintaining the Job. There are clearly a number of ways in which men and women differ in the advantages (or disadvantages) that may be conferred on them in the workplace. Given that many of these differences have been addressed here, both at the selection and maintenance stages, it is clear that there is a need for organizations to work toward reducing such gender inequities. Strategies for addressing these inequities is discussed in the next section.

REMEDYING GENDER INEQUITIES IN ORGANIZATIONS

After the preceding section's discussion of the current state of gender in organizations, this section transitions to addressing potential remedies for inequities. Ely and Meyerson (2000) summarized four different strategies scholars have adopted for achieving gender equity in the workplace. These strategies are reviewed and updated here, focusing only briefly on the first two because they may be rather short-sighted and problematic when it comes to reducing gender workplace inequities in the long run. The focus, detail, and expansion are on the latter two strategies, helping justify that the best strategy for enacting gender equity in organizations may be a multifaceted approach that addresses the need for both organizational and societal change.

Fix the Woman. The "fix the woman" frame views gender differences to be a result of socialization and focuses on women as the problem that needs fixing. This approach typically involves identifying what women did wrong—whether it was doing too much, not doing enough, or doing nothing at all. This approach suggests that gender equity in organizations requires investing in women's skills, traits, and abilities to bring them up to speed (see Ely & Meyerson, 2000). A very popularized example of this approach was adopted in Sheryl Sandberg's (2013) *Lean In* book. Although the book revealed some excellent insights, one of the bottom-line suggestions was that women needed to assert themselves more, both at home and in the workplace. Clearly, there are some women who might benefit from this message of empowerment; however, there are many people who could benefit simply from mentoring and greater skill acquisition. The notion that women just need to improve themselves—to do things like negotiate better, stand up for themselves, work harder to get the promotion, and put away their fears of success—negates the millions of women who have already done these things and still see themselves on the side of inequity. In fact, this approach leaves the system in place and male standards intact, thereby denying more formidable sources of disadvantage. As Wittenberg-Cox (2014) titled their article, "Stop 'fixing' women and start fixing managers."

Another area of research that highlights women as the problem focuses on the "queen bee" phenomenon, or the idea that female leaders may oppose (rather than support) their female subordinates (see Derks et al., 2016). While some research supports such findings (e.g., Ellemers et al., 2012), other research suggests that this phenomenon does not generalize across women and only emerges in a limited number of contexts (e.g., Paustian-Underdahl et al., 2017). Still other researchers suggest that women actually act more (not less) benevolently toward subordinate women (Arvate et al., 2018; see also Kulik et al., 2016). This latter research suggests that women might more accurately be labeled "regal leaders" (see also Fernandez-Mateo & Kaplan, 2020; Groskop, 2015).

Value the Feminine.   A "value the feminine" strategy realizes that men and women typically excel at different sets of strengths and proposes that these strengths should be equally valued and celebrated (Ely & Meyerson, 2000). Socialization and developmental theories provide a context for understanding the acquisition and reinforcement of differing skill sets, but this strategy suggests that the skills displayed by women are simply not recognized or valued in organizations as much as the skills commonly displayed by men. There is clearly some truth to this perspective, as research shows that when different groups of participants are asked to give their definitions of an excellent leader, an excellent female leader, or an excellent male leader, the descriptions of the excellent leader are more closely tied with the excellent male (versus female) leader (see Schein, 2001). As Ely and Meyerson (2000) suggest, differences that favor men tend to be those that organizations recognize, value, and preserve. It is important to recognize and value the fact that women may make important contributions and have differing viewpoints for organizations in ways that may differ from those of men. However, "valuing the feminine" can also be short-sighted in that it reinforces stereotypes and leaves in place the biased processes that created the gender differences in the first place.

Create Equal Opportunity.   The "create equal opportunity" frame views gender differences to be a result of structural barriers and proposes to resolve these barriers to create gender equity (Ely & Meyerson, 2000). Some examples of structural barriers include differences in hiring, negotiation abilities, and parenting responsibilities. Solutions within this frame often involve organizational policies and the provision of additional accommodations that create equal opportunity (Ely & Meyerson, 2000). We group our policy-led solutions into three categories: diversity and inclusion initiatives, on-the-job support, and family policies.

Diversity and Inclusion Initiatives. Starting with diversity initiatives, organizations can implement policies that support diversity and reduce discrimination. For example, organizations can implement quotas that specify the minimum proportion of females in an organization. Such regulations have been effective for increasing diversity in organizations. For example, Norway implemented a quota specifying that 40% of board members must be female. Over 15 years after this mandate, Norway has observed increases in female board members and female chief executive officers (CEOs) (Wang & Kelan, 2013). Moreover, research suggests that inclusion is necessary to reap the benefits of diversity within an organization (Nishii, 2013). One promising way to increase feelings of inclusion is to improve the quality of supervisor-supervisee relationships (Brimhall et al., 2017). Positive interactions at this level are likely one component contributing to an inclusive workplace environment which includes physical and psychological safety, involvement, feeling respected, feeling like one can affect decisions, authenticity, and promoting diversity (Shore et al., 2018). By focusing on these core areas, organizations can work to develop, improve, and enhance the diversity and inclusion of underrepresented employees.

On-the-Job Support. In addition, organizations can also help increase female representation by reevaluating recruitment and selection practices to be more equitable. Some widely accepted institutional policies to promote equality include placing women in positions with power, providing mentorship programs, instituting equal pay programs and initiatives, mandating sexual harassment trainings, documenting and being transparent with gender equality data, promoting networking opportunities, and creating an equity advisor position (Monroe et al., 2014).

Family Policies. A final avenue toward supporting gender equity is to provide family-friendly, work-related policies. In line with the off-ramps described above, companies can support employees (especially women) by constructing thoughtful policies that empower women with caregiving responsibilities. Indeed, in their consideration of the needs of women across the lifespan, Grandey and colleagues (2019) argued that policies which provide autonomy such as flextime and flexplace may be particularly helpful for women in the transitional phases of life.

Revise Work Culture.
The "revise work culture" frame places the burden of achieving gender equity on organizations (and on society more broadly) by pushing for these institutions to create policies that enable gender equity (Ely & Meyerson, 2000). Solutions in this section are focused on the importance of making broad changes in organizational culture.

Organizational Culture. In her article, Burnford (2019) warns people that existing company culture curtails movement toward gender equity because organizational members have not fully considered how they might be engaged in biases. To work toward a gender-balanced culture, Burnford (2019) suggests specifically asking all leaders to consider (a) if they are vocal supporters of gender balance, (b) their underlying beliefs about gender in their organizations, (c) if they encourage others to talk about gender at work, (d) how they define and reward good leadership, and (e) whether they might be unintentionally reinforcing the idea that women might simply need to be fixed.

Egalitarianism.   Prior to the pandemic, about two-thirds of Americans reported having egalitarian beliefs about men and women working in both the workplace and domestic spheres, a number that has steadily increased since 1977 (Scarborough et al., 2018). This increasing shift in egalitarianism may work to combat gender disparities in future employment trends. For example, Carlson et al. (2021) observed the division of labor becoming even more equal during the pandemic, with more fathers reporting that they equally shared the housework with their partners (from 38% pre-pandemic to 53% post-pandemic). Similarly, Shockley et al. (2021) found that 45% of couples seemed to balance the intense demands in an egalitarian manner; however, wives still shouldered most labor in nearly 37% of couples. Thus, moving toward an egalitarian balance of childcare and household labor may be the best opportunity for changing social roles, expectations, and, ultimately, men's and women's status and power.

Summary of Remedying.   Although Ely and Meyerson (2000) describe four strategies used to tackle gender equity, we find creating equal opportunity and revising work culture to be the most fruitful approaches. In order to successfully lead in achieving gender equality, organizations should consider what they are currently doing to support women within their organizations and how they can improve their diversity-related policies and initiatives. More broadly, it is apparent that a top-down approach that involves restructuring societal culture to promote egalitarianism is necessary to observe meaningful and lasting change. The combination of organizational leadership in gender equity and societal shifts toward egalitarianism will hopefully lead to redefining and shaping the societal expectations and barriers that prevent women from achieving equality in the workplace.

CONCLUSION

Despite more recent progress, male and female employees continue to be bound by a variety of gender normative perceptions, expectations, and behaviors. The current article focused on summarizing the current state of affairs for these individuals, particularly focusing on a number of consistent findings showing that women often have a much harder time entering, navigating, and progressing through the workplace than do their male counterparts. Many people have been holding out for the passage of time to flatten the gender differences that exist between men and women in workplace opportunities, growth, and promotion to leadership positions. This means we have to think about the strategies that we have used up to this point and reconsider those and others we might adopt to make haste and achieve gender parity in organizations. Hopefully, bringing attention to these issues will help.

FURTHER READING

Chawla, N., Gabriel, A. S., O'Leary Kelly, A., & Rosen, C. C. (2021). From #MeToo to #TimesUp: Identifying next steps in sexual harassment research in the organizational sciences. *Journal of Management*, 47(3), 551–566. https://doi.org/10.1177/0149206320980518

Ellemers, N. (2018). Gender stereotypes. *Annual Review of Psychology*, 69(1), 275–298. https://doi.org/10.1146/annurev-psych-122216-011719

Gruber, J., Mendle, J., Lindquist, K. A., Schmader, T., Clark, L. A., Bliss-Moreau, E., Akinola, M., Atlas, L., Barch, D. M., Feldman Barrett, L., Borelli, J. L., Brannon, T. N., Bunge, S. A., Campos, B., Cantlon, J., Carter, R., Carter-Sowell, A. R., Chen, S., Craske, M. G., Cuddy A. J. C., . . . Williams, L. A. (2021). The future of women in psychological science. *Perspectives on Psychological Science*, 16(3), 483–516. https://doi.org/10.1177/1745691620952789

Hoover, A. E., Hack, T., Garcia, A. L., Goodfriend, W., & Habashi, M. M. (2018). Powerless men and agentic women: Gender bias in hiring decisions. *Sex Roles*, 80(11–12), 667–680. https://doi.org/10.1007/s11199-018-0964-y

Koch, A. J., D'Mello, S. D., & Sackett, P. R. (2015). A meta-analysis of gender stereotypes and bias in experimental simulations of employment decision making. *Journal of Applied Psychology*, 100(1), 128–161. https://doi.org/10.1037/a0036734

Padavic, I., Ely, R. J., & Reid, E. M. (2020). Explaining the persistence of gender inequality: The work–family narrative as a social defense against the 24/7 work culture. *Administrative Science Quarterly*, 65(1), 61–111. https://doi.org/10.1177/0001839219832310

Ryan, M. K., Haslam, S. A., Morgenroth, T., Rink, F., Stoker, J., & Peters, K. (2016). Getting on top of the glass cliff: Reviewing a decade of evidence, explanations, and impact. *The Leadership Quarterly*, 27(3), 446–455. https://doi.org/10.1016/j.leaqua.2015.10.008

Silver, E., King, D., & Hebl, M. (2022). Gender inequalities in leadership: Shifting the focus from deficient women to destructive leaders. Special Issue: Prejudice at work: What we understand and what we still need to learn. *Management Decision*. https://doi.org/10.1108/MD-06-2021-0809

Strom, P., Collins, C. J., Avgar, A. C., & Ryan, K. (2021). Drawing the line: How the workplace shapes the naming of sexual harassment. *Personnel Psychology*. https://doi.org/10.1111/peps.12496

REFERENCES

Adams, R. B., & Funk, P. (2012). Beyond the glass ceiling: Does gender matter? *Management Science*, 58(2), 219–235. https://doi.org/10.1287/mnsc.1110.1452

Allen, T. D., Eby, L. T., Poteet, M. L., Lentz, E., & Lima, L. (2004). Career benefits associated with mentoring for proteges: A meta-analysis. *Journal of Applied Psychology*, 89(1), 127–136. https://doi.org/10.1037/0021-9010.89.1.127

Anders, C. (2021). More than 1 million nonbinary adults live in the U.S., a pioneering study finds. *The Washington Post*. https://www.washingtonpost.com/dc-md-va/2021/06/22/first-population-estimate-lgbtq-non-binary-adults-us-is-out-heres-why-that-matters/

Arvate, P. R., Galilea, G. W., & Todescat, I. (2018). The queen bee: A myth? The effect of top-level female leadership on subordinate females. *The Leadership Quarterly*, 29(5), 533–548. https://doi.org/10.1016/j.leaqua.2018.03.002

Atwater, L. E., Sturm, R. E., Taylor, S. N., & Tringale, A. (2021). The era of #MeToo and what managers should do about it. *Business Horizons*, 64(2), 307–318. https://doi.org/10.1016/j.bushor.2020.12.006

Bakan, D. (1966). *The duality of human existence: An essay on psychology and religion*. Rand McNally.

Bandura, A. (1977). *Social learning theory*. General Learning Press.

Bandura, A. (2008). Observational learning. In W. Donsbach (Ed.), *The International encyclopedia of communication*. Wiley Online Library. https://doi.org/10.1002/9781405186407.wbieco004

Barroso, A., & Brown, A. (2021, May 25). *Gender pay gap in U.S. held steady in 2020*. Pew Research Center. https://www.pewresearch.org/fact-tank/2021/05/25/gender-pay-gap-facts/

Benard, S., & Correll, S. J. (2010). Normative discrimination and the motherhood penalty. *Gender & Society*, *24*(5), 616–646. https://doi.org/10.1177/0891243210383142

Berdahl, J. L., Moore, C. (2006). Workplace harassment: double jeopardy for minority women. *Journal of Applied Psychology*. *91*(2), 426-436. https://doi.org/10.1037/0021-9010.91.2.426

Bilodeau, J., Marchand, A., & Demers, A. (2020). Psychological distress inequality between employed men and women: A gendered exposure model. *SSM-Population Health*, *11*, 1–8. https://doi.org/10.1016/j.ssmph.2020.100626

Botsford Morgan, W., & King, E. B. (2012). Mothers' psychological contracts: Does supervisor breach explain intention to leave the organization?. *Human Resource Management*, *51*(5), 629-649. https://doi.org/10.1002/hrm.21492

Bowles, H. R., Babcock, L., & Lai, L. (2007). Social incentives for gender differences in the propensity to initiate negotiations: Sometimes it does hurt to ask. *Organizational Behavior and Human Decision Processes*, *103*(1), 84–103. https://doi.org/10.1016/j.obhdp.2006.09.001

Brazil, K., Thabane, L., Foster, G., & Bédard, M. (2009). Gender differences among Canadian spousal caregivers at the end of life. *Health & Social Care in the Community*, *17*(2), 159–166. https://doi.org/10.1111/j.1365-2524.2008.00813.x

Brimhall, K. C., Mor Barak, M. E., Hurlburt, M., McArdle, J. J., Palinkas, L., & Henwood, B. (2017). Increasing workplace inclusion: The promise of leader-member exchange. *Human Service Organizations: Management, Leadership & Governance*, *41*(3), 222–239. https://doi.org/10.1080/23303131.2016.1251522

Brody, D. J., Pratt, L. A., & Hughes, J. P. (2018, February). Prevalence of depression among adults aged 20 and over: United States, 2013–2016. *National Center for Health Statistics*, *303*, 1–8. https://www.cdc.gov/nchs/data/databriefs/db303.pdf

Burnford, J. (2019, January 29). Is organizational culture holding women back in the workplace?. *Forbes*. https://www.forbes.com/sites/joyburnford/2019/01/29/is-organizational-culture-holding-women-back-in-the-workplace/?sh=3eab257f655a

Burns, T., Huang, J., Krivkovich, A., Rambachan, I., Trkulja, T., & Yee, L. (2021, September 27). *Women in the workplace 2021*. McKinsey & Company. https://www.mckinsey.com/featured-ins%20ights/diversity-and-inclusion/women-in-the-workplace

Campos-Vazquez, R. M., & Gonzalez, E. (2020). Obesity and hiring discrimination. *Economics & Human Biology*, *37*, 1–9. https://doi.org/10.1016/j.ehb.2020.100850

Carlson, D. L., Petts, R., & Pepin, J. R. (2021). Changes in US parents' domestic labor during the early days of the COVID-19 pandemic. *Sociological Inquiry*, *92*(3), 1217–1244. https://doi.org/10.1111/soin.12459

Cecil, V., Pendry, L. F., Salvatore, J., Mycroft, H., & Kurz, T. (2021). Gendered ageism and gray hair: Must older women choose between feeling authentic and looking competent? *Journal of Women & Aging*, *34*(2), 210–225. https://doi.org/10.1080/08952841.2021.1899744

Choney, S. (2018, March 13). Why do girls lose interest in STEM? New research has some answers—and what we can do about it. *Microsoft*. https://news.microsoft.com/features/why-do-girls-lose-interest-in-stem-new-research-has-some-answers-and-what-we-can-do-about-it/

Crenshaw, K. W. (2017). *On intersectionality: Essential writings*. The New Press. https://scholarship.law.columbia.edu/books/255

Cuddy, A. J., Fiske, S. T., & Glick, P. (2004). When professionals become mothers, warmth doesn't cut the ice. *Journal of Social Issues*, *60*(4), 701–718. https://doi.org/10.1111/j.0022-4537.2004.00381.x

Cuddy, A. J. C., Fiske, S. T., & Glick, P. (2008). Warmth and competence as universal dimensions of social perception: The stereotype content model and the BIAS Map. *Advances in Experimental Social Psychology, 40*, 61–149. https://doi.org/10.1016/S0065-2601(07)00002-0

Derks, B., Van Laar, C., & Ellemers, N. (2016). The queen bee phenomenon: Why women leaders distance themselves from junior women. *The Leadership Quarterly, 27*(3), 456–469. https://doi.org/10.1016/j.leaqua.2015.12.007

Eagly, A. H. (1987). *Sex differences in social behavior: A social-role interpretation*. Lawrence Erlbaum Associates. https://doi.org/10.4324/9780203781906

Eagly, A. H., Johannesen-Schmidt, M. C., & Van Engen, M. L. (2003). Transformational, transactional, and laissez-faire leadership styles: A meta-analysis comparing women and men. *Psychological Bulletin, 129*(4), 569. https://doi.org/10.1037/0033-2909.129.4.569

Eagly, A. H., & Karau, S. J. (2002). Role congruity theory of prejudice toward female leaders. *Psychological Review, 109*(3), 573–598. https://doi.org/10.1037//0033-295X.109.3.573

Ellemers, N., Rink, F., Derks, B., & Ryan, M. K. (2012). Women in high places: When and why promoting women into top positions can harm them individually or as a group (and how to prevent this). *Research in Organizational Behavior, 32*, 163–187. https://doi.org/10.1016/j.riob.2012.10.003

Ely, R. J., & Meyerson, D. E. (2000). Theories of gender in organizations: A new approach to organizational analysis and change. *Research in Organizational Behavior, 22*, 103–151. https://doi.org/10.1016/S0191-3085(00)22004-2

Entmacher, J., Frohlich, L., Gallagher Robbins, K., Martin, E., Watson, L. (2014). *Underpaid and overloaded: Women in low-wage jobs* National Women's Law Center. https://nwlc.org/wp-content/uploads/2015/08/final_nwlc_lowwagereport2014.pdf

Equal Employment Opportunity Commission. (2021, February 26). *EEOC releases fiscal year 2020 enforcement and litigation data*. U.S. Equal Employment Opportunity Commission. https://www.eeoc.gov/newsroom/eeoc-releases-fiscal-year-2020-enforcement-and-litigation-data

Exley, C. L., & Kessler, J. B. (2019). *The gender gap in self-promotion*. National Bureau of Economic Research. https://doi.org/10.3386/w26345

Farkas, A. H., Bonifacino, E., Turner, R., Tilstra, S. A., & Corbelli, J. A. (2019). Mentorship of women in academic medicine: A systematic review. *Journal of General Internal Medicine, 34*(7), 1322–1329. https://doi.org/10.1007/s11606-019-04955-2

Federal Glass Ceiling Commission. (1995). *Good for business: Making full use of the nation's human capital*. U.S. Government Printing Office. https://hdl.handle.net/1813/79348

Fernandez-Mateo, I., & Kaplan, S. (2020, January). *The immortal—and false—myth of the workplace Queen Bee*. The Conversation. https://theconversation.com/the-immortal-and-false-myth-of-the-workplace-queen-bee-129680

Fiske, S. T., Cuddy, A. J. C., Glick, P., & Xu, J. (2002). A model of (often mixed) stereotype content: Competence and warmth respectively follow from perceived status and competition. *Journal of Personality and Social Psychology, 82*(6), 878–902. https://doi.org/10.1037/0022-3514.82.6.878

Flint, S. W., Čadek, M., Codreanu, S. C., Ivić, V., Zomer, C., & Gomoiu, A. (2016). Obesity discrimination in the recruitment process: "You're not hired!" *Frontiers in Psychology, 7*(647), 1–9. https://doi.org/10.3389/fpsyg.2016.00647

Glick, P., Diebold, J., Bailey-Werner, B., & Zhu, L. (1997). The two faces of Adam: Ambivalent sexism and polarized attitudes toward women. *Personality and Social Psychology Bulletin, 23*(12), 1323–1334. https://doi.org/10.1177/01461672972312009

Glick, P., & Fiske, S. T. (1996). The ambivalent sexism inventory: Differentiating hostile and benevolent sexism. *Journal of Personality and Social Psychology, 70*(3), 491–512. https://doi.org/10.1037/0022-3514.70.3.491

Glick, P., & Fiske, S. T. (2001). An ambivalent alliance: Hostile and benevolent sexism as complementary justifications for gender inequality. *American Psychologist, 56*(2), 109–118. https://doi.org/10.1037/0003-066X.56.2.109

Grandey, A. A., Gabriel, A. S., & King, E. B. (2019). Tackling taboo topics: A review of the three Ms in working women's lives. *Journal of Management, 46*(1), 7–35. https://doi.org/10.1177/0149206319857144

Groskop, V. (2015, June 8). "Queen Bee syndrome": The myth that keeps working women in their little box. *The Guardian.* https://www.theguardian.com/lifeandstyle/womens-blog/2015/jun/08/queen-bee-syndrome-myth-working-women

Gupta, V. K., Han, S., Mortal, S. C., Silveri, S. D., & Turban, D. B. (2018). Do women CEOs face greater threat of shareholder activism compared to male CEOs? A role congruity perspective. *Journal of Applied Psychology, 103*(2), 228–236. https://doi.org/10.1037/apl0000269

Haines, E. L., Deaux, K., & Lofaro, N. (2016). The times they are a-changing... or are they not? A comparison of gender stereotypes, 1983–2014. *Psychology of Women Quarterly, 40*(3), 353–363. https://doi.org/10.1177%2F0361684316634081

Handy, J., & Davy, D. (2007). Gendered ageism: Older women's experiences of employment agency practices. *Asia Pacific Journal of Human Resources, 45*(1), 85–99. https://doi.org/10.1177/1038411107073606

Heilman, M. E. (1983). Sex bias in work settings: The lack of fit model. *Research in Organizational Behavior, 5*, 269–298.

Heilman, M. E., & Caleo, S. (2018). Combatting gender discrimination: A lack of fit framework. *Group Processes & Intergroup Relations, 21*(5), 725–744. https://doi.org/10.1177/1368430218761587

Heilman, M. E., & Okimoto, T. G. (2008). Motherhood: A potential source of bias in employment decisions. *Journal of Applied Psychology, 93*(1), 189–198. https://doi.org/10.1037/0021-9010.93.1.189

Henle, C. A., Fisher, G. G., McCarthy, J., Prince, M. A., Mattingly, V. P., & Clancy, R. L. (2020). Eldercare and childcare: How does caregiving responsibility affect job discrimination? *Journal of Business and Psychology, 35*, 59–83. https://doi.org/10.1007/s10869-019-09618-x

Hentschel, T., Heilman, M. E., & Peus, C. V. (2019). The multiple dimensions of gender stereotypes: A current look at men's and women's characterizations of others and themselves. *Frontiers in Psychology, 10*, 1–18. https://doi.org/10.3389/fpsyg.2019.00011

Hewlett, S. A., & Luce, C. B. (2005, March). Off-ramps and on-ramps: Keeping talented women on the road to success. *Harvard Business Review.* https://hbr.org/2005/03/off-ramps-and-on-ramps-keeping-talented-women-on-the-road-to-success

Hewlett, S. A. (2002). Executive women and the myth of having it all. *Harvard Business Review, 80*(4), 66–73. https://hbr.org/2002/04/executive-women-and-the-myth-of-having-it-all

Hochschild, A., & Machung, A. (2012). *The second shift: Working families and the revolution at home.* Penguin.

Hoffman, A., Grant, W., McCormick, M., Jezewski, E., Matemavi, P., & Langnas, A. (2019). Gendered differences in letters of recommendation for transplant surgery fellowship applicants. *Journal of Surgical Education, 76*(2), 427–432. https://doi.org/10.1016/j.jsurg.2018.08.021

Horwood, C., McDermott, S., Gennell, T., Pawlik, T. M., Grignol, V. P., & Hughes, T. M. (2021). Letters of recommendation for surgical fellowships—Does gender make a difference? *The American Journal of Surgery, 221*(1), 90–94. https://doi.org/10.1016/j.amjsurg.2020.06.036

Ibarra, H. (2019, August 19). A lack of sponsorship is keeping women from advancing into leadership. *Harvard Business Review.* https://hbr.org/2019/08/a-lack-of-sponsorship-is-keeping-women-from-advancing-into-leadership

Jetha, A., Gignac, M. A., Ibrahim, S., & Martin Ginis, K. A. (2020). Disability and sex/gender intersections in unmet workplace support needs: Findings from a large Canadian survey of workers. *American Journal of Industrial Medicine, 64* (2), 149–161. https://doi.org/10.1002/ajim.23203

Johnson, S. K., Keplinger, K., Kirk, J. F., & Barnes, L. (2019, July 18). Has sexual harassment at work decreased since #MeToo? *Harvard Business Review.* https://hbr.org/2019/07/has-sexual-harassment-at-work-decreased-since-metoo

Johnson, S. K., Podratz, K. E., Dipboye, R. L., & Gibbons, E. (2010). Physical attractiveness biases in ratings of employment suitability: Tracking down the "beauty is beastly" effect. *The Journal of Social Psychology, 150*, 301–318. https://doi.org/10.1080/00224540903365414

Kahn, K. B., & Davies, P. G. (2011). Differentially dangerous? Phenotypic racial stereotypicality increases implicit bias among ingroup and outgroup members. *Group Processes and Intergroup Relations, 14*(4), 569–580. https://doi.org/10.1177/1368430210374609

Kauhanen, A., & Napari, S. (2015). Gender differences in careers. *Annals of Economics and Statistics, 117/118,* 61–88. https://doi.org/10.15609/annaeconstat2009.117-118.61

King, E. B., Botsford, W., Hebl, M. R., Kazama, S., Dawson, J. F., & Perkins, A. (2012). Benevolent sexism at work: Gender differences in the distribution of challenging developmental experiences. *Journal of Management, 38*(6), 1835–1866. https://doi.org/10.1177/0149206310365902

Koenig, A. M., Eagly, A. H., Mitchell, A. A., & Ristikari, T. (2011). Are leader stereotypes masculine? A meta-analysis of three research paradigms. *Psychological Bulletin, 137*(4), 616–642. https://doi.org/10.1037/a0023557

Koval, C. Z., & Rosette, A. S. (2021). The natural hair bias in job recruitment. *Social Psychological and Personality Science, 12*(5), 741–750. https://doi.org/10.1177/1948550620937937

Krantz-Kent, R. (2009). Measuring time spent in unpaid household work: Results from the American Time Use Survey. *Monthly Labor Review, 132,* 46–59. https://www.bls.gov/opub/mlr/2009/07/art3full.pdf

Kulik, C. T., Metz, I., & Gould, J. A. (2016). In the company of women: The well-being consequences of working with (and for) other women. In M. Connerley & J. Wu (Eds.), *Handbook on well-being of working women. International handbooks of quality-of-life* (pp. 189–207). Springer. https://doi.org/10.1007/978-94-017-9897-6_12

Li, P., Xiaozhou, C., Stafford, F., & Ou, J. (2021). Body shape and stable employment opportunity analysis of China's nonagricultural labor market. *SSM-Population Health, 17,* 101014. https://doi.org/10.1016/j.ssmph.2021.101014

Lindeman, M. I., Durik, A. M., & Dooley, M. (2019). Women and self-promotion: A test of three theories. *Psychological Reports, 122*(1), 219–230. https://doi.org/10.1177/0033294118755096

Madera, J. M., Hebl, M. R., Dial, H., Martin, R., & Valian, V. (2019). Raising doubt in letters of recommendation for academia: Gender differences and their impact. *Journal of Business and Psychology, 34*(3), 287–303. https://doi.org/10.1007/s10869-018-9541-1

Madera, J. M., Hebl, M. R., & Martin, R. C. (2009). Gender and letters of recommendation for academia: Agentic and communal differences. *Journal of Applied Psychology, 94*(6), 1591–1599. https://doi.org/10.1037/a0016539

Major, B., & Konar, E. (1984). An investigation of sex differences in pay expectations and their possible causes. *Academy of Management Journal, 27*(4), 777–792. https://doi.org/10.5465/255878

Marchand, A., Blanc, M. E., & Beauregard, N. (2018). Do age and gender contribute to workers' burnout symptoms? *Occupational Medicine, 68*(6), 405–411. https://doi.org/10.1093/occmed/kqy088

Mazei, J., Hüffmeier, J., Freund, P. A., Stuhlmacher, A. F., Bilke, L., & Hertel, G. (2015). A meta-analysis on gender differences in negotiation outcomes and their moderators. *Psychological Bulletin, 141*(1), 85–104. https://doi.org/10.1037/a0038184

McCarthy, J. M., & Goffin, R. D. (2001). Improving the validity of letters of recommendation: An investigation of three standardized reference forms. *Military Psychology, 13*(4), 199–222. https://doi.org/10.1207/S15327876MP1304_2

Milner, A., King, T., LaMontagne, A. D., Bentley, R., & Kavanagh, A. (2018). Men's work, women's work, and mental health: A longitudinal investigation of the relationship between the gender composition of occupations and mental health. *Social Science & Medicine, 204,* 16–22. https://doi.org/10.1016/j.socscimed.2018.03.020

Mohr, T. S. (2014, August 25). Why women don't apply for jobs unless they're 100% qualified. *Harvard Business Review.* https://hbr.org/2014/08/why-women-dont-apply-for-jobs-unless-theyre-100-qualified

Moloney, M. E., Brown, R. L., Ciciurkaite, G., & Foley, S. M. (2019). "Going the extra mile": Disclosure, accommodation, and stigma management among working women with disabilities. *Deviant Behavior, 40*(8), 942–956. https://doi.org/10.1080/01639625.2018.1445445

Monroe, K. R., Choi, J., Howell, E., Lampros-Monroe, C., Trejo, C., & Perez, V. (2014). Gender equality in the ivory tower, and how best to achieve it. *PS: Political Science & Politics, 47*(2), 418–426. https://doi.org/10.1017/S104909651400033X

Morgan, S. L., Gelbgiser, D., & Weeden, K. A. (2013). Feeding the pipeline: Gender, occupational plans, and college major selection. *Social Science Research, 42*(4), 989–1005. https://doi.org/10.1016/j.ssresearch.2013.03.008

Morgenroth, T., & Heilman, M. E. (2017). Should I stay or should I go? Implications of maternity leave choice for perceptions of working mothers. *Journal of Experimental Social Psychology, 72*, 53–56. https://doi.org/10.1016/j.jesp.2017.04.008

Morgenroth, T., & Ryan, M. K. (2021). The effects of gender trouble: An integrative theoretical framework of the perpetuation and disruption of the gender/sex binary. *Perspectives on Psychological Science, 16*(6), 1113–1142. https://doi.org/%2010.1177/1745691620902442

Moss-Racusin, C. A., Dovidio, J. F., Brescoll, V. L., Graham, M. J., & Handelsman, J. (2012). Science faculty's subtle gender biases favor male students. *Proceedings of the National Academy of Sciences, 109*(41), 16474–16479. https://doi.org/10.1073/pnas.1211286109

Naples, N. A., Mauldin, L., & Dillaway, H. (2019). From the guest editors: Gender, disability, and intersectionality. *Gender & Society, 33*(1), 5–18. https://doi.org/10.1177/0891243218813309

National Center for Science and Engineering Statistics. (2021, April 29). *Women, minorities, and persons with disabilities in science and engineering*. National Science Foundation. https://ncses.nsf.gov/pubs/nsf21321/report/field-of-degree-women

Nishii, L. H. (2013). The benefits of climate for inclusion for gender-diverse groups. *Academy of Management Journal, 56*(6), 1754–1774. https://www.jstor.org/stable/43589961

Office on Women's Health. (2021, February 17). *Depression*. Office of the Assistant Secretary for Health. https://www.womenshealth.gov/mental-health/mental-health-conditions/depression

Parker, K., & Funk, C. (2017, December 14). *Gender discrimination comes in many forms for today's working women*. Pew Research Center. https://www.pewresearch.org/fact-tank/2017/12/14/gender-discrimination-comes-in-many-forms-for-todays-working-women/

Paustian-Underdahl, S. C., King, E. B., Rogelberg, S. G., Kulich, C., & Gentry, W. A. (2017). Perceptions of supervisor support: Resolving paradoxical patterns across gender and race. *Journal of Occupational and Organizational Psychology, 90* (3), 436–457. https://doi.org/10.1111/joop.12179

Payne, S., & Doyal, L. (2010). Older women, work, and health. *Occupational Medicine, 60*, 172–177. https://doi.org/10.1093/occmed/kqq030

Peterson Gloor, J. L., Okimoto, T. G., & King, E. B. (2022). "Maybe baby?" The employment risk of potential parenthood. *Journal of Applied Social Psychology, 52*, 623-642. https://doi.org/10.1111/jasp.12799

Population Reference Bureau. (2001, September 1). Around the globe, women outlive men. *PRB*. https://www.prb.org/resources/around-the-globe-women-outlive-men/

Prasso, S. (2005). The Asian mystique: Dragon ladies, geisha girls & our fantasies of the exotic Orient. *Choice Reviews Online, 43*(08), 43–4837. https://doi.org/10.5860/choice.43-4837

Reuben, E., Sapienza, P., & Zingales, L. (2014). How stereotypes impair women's careers in science. *Proceedings of the National Academy of Sciences, 111*(12), 4403–4408. https://doi.org/10.1073/pnas.1314788111

Reuben, E., Wiswall, M., & Zafar, B. (2017). Preferences and biases in educational choices and labor market expectations: Shrinking the black box of gender. *The Economic Journal, 127*(604), 2153–2186. https://doi.org/10.1111/ecoj.12350

Rosette, A. S., de Leon, R. P., Koval, C. Z., & Harrison, D. A. (2018). Intersectionality: Connecting experiences of gender with race at work. *Research in Organizational Behavior, 38*, 1–22. https://doi.org/10.1016/j.riob.2018.12.002

Ryan, M. K., & Haslam, S. A. (2005). The glass cliff: Evidence that women are over-represented in precarious leadership positions. *British Journal of Management, 16*(2), 81–90. https://doi.org/10.1111/j.1467-8551.2005.00433.x

Sandberg, S. (2013). *Lean in: Women, work, and the will to lead*. Random House.

Säve-Söderbergh, J. (2019). Gender gaps in salary negotiations: Salary requests and starting salaries in the field. *Journal of Economic Behavior & Organization, 161*, 35–51. https://doi.org/10.1016/j.jebo.2019.01.019

Scarborough, W. J., Sin, R., & Risman, B. (2018). Attitudes and the stalled gender revolution: Egalitarianism, traditionalism, and ambivalence from 1977 through 2016. *Gender & Society, 33*(2), 173–200. https://doi.org/10.1177/0891243218809604

Schein, V. E. (2001). A global look at psychological barriers to women's progress in management. *Journal of Social Issues, 57*(4), 675–688. https://doi.org/10.1111/0022-4537.00235

Schock, A. K., Gruber, F. M., Scherndl, T., & Ortner, T. M. (2019). Tempering agency with communion increases women's leadership emergence in all-women groups: Evidence for role congruity theory in a field setting. *Leadership Quarterly, 30*(2), 189–198. https://doi.org/10.1016/j.leaqua.2018.08.003

Shapiro, M., Grossman, D., Carter, S., Martin, K., Deyton, P., & Hammer, D. (2015). Middle school girls and the "leaky pipeline" to leadership. *Middle School Journal, 46*(5), 3–13. https://doi.org/10.1080/00940771.2015.11461919

Shockley, K. M., Clark, M. A., Dodd, H., & King, E. B. (2021). Work-family strategies during COVID-19: Examining gender dynamics among dual-earner couples with young children. *Journal of Applied Psychology, 106*(1), 15–28. https://doi.org/10.1037/apl0000857

Shore, L. M., Cleveland, J. N., & Sanchez, D. (2018). Inclusive workplaces: A review and model. *Human Resource Management Review, 28*(2), 176–189. http://dx.doi.org/10.1016/j.hrmr.2017.07.003

Simmons, W. W. (2001, January 11). When it comes to choosing a boss, Americans still prefer men. *Gallup Poll News Service*. https://news.gallup.com/poll/2128/when-comes-choosing-boss-americans-still-prefer-men.aspx

Stuhlmacher, A. F., & Walters, A. E. (1999). Gender differences in negotiation outcome: A meta-analysis. *Personnel Psychology, 52*(3), 653–677. https://doi.org/10.1111/j.1744-6570.1999.tb00175.x

Surawicz, C. M. (2016). Women in leadership: Why so few and what to do about it. *Journal of the American College of Radiology, 13*(12), 1433–1437. https://doi.org/10.1016/j.jacr.2016.08.026

Swafford, M., & Anderson, R. (2020). Addressing the gender gap: Women's perceived barriers to pursuing STEM careers. *Journal of Research in Technical Careers, 4*(1), 61–74. https://doi.org/10.9741/2578-2118.1070

Thiem, K. C., Neel, R., Simpson, A. J., & Todd, A. R. (2019). Are Black women and girls associated with danger? Implicit racial bias at the intersection of target age and gender. *Personality & Social Psychology Bulletin, 45*(10), 1427–1439. https://doi.org/10.1177/0146167219829182

Trix, F., & Psenka, C. (2003). Exploring the color of glass: Letters of recommendation for female and male medical faculty. *Discourse & Society, 14*(2), 191–220. https://doi.org/10.1177/0957926503014002277

Tyler, J. M., & McCullough, J. D. (2009). Violating prescriptive stereotypes on job resumes: A self-presentational perspective. *Management Communication Quarterly, 23*(2), 272–287. https://doi.org/10.1177/0893318909341412

U.S. Bureau of Labor Statistics. (2021a, September 8). *Highest paying occupations: U.S. Bureau of Labor*. https://www.bls.gov/ooh/highest-paying.htm

U.S. Bureau of Labor Statistics. (2021b, November 3). *Employer-reported workplace injuries and illnesses (annual) news release*. https://www.bls.gov/news.release/archives/osh_11032021.htm

U.S. Bureau of Labor Statistics. (2021c, December 16). *Census of fatal occupational injuries summary, 2020*. https://www.bls.gov/news.release/cfoi.nr0.htm

U.S. Bureau of Labor Statistics. (2022, January 20). *Employed persons by detailed occupation, sex, race, and Hispanic or Latino ethnicity*. https://www.bls.gov/cps/cpsaat11.htm

U.S. Census Bureau. (2019). *Occupation by sex and median earnings in the past 12 months (in 2019 inflation-adjusted dollars) for the full-time, year-round civilian employed population 16 years and over.* https://data.census.gov/cedsci/table?q=s2412&tid=ACSST1Y2019.S2412

Viertiö, S., Kiviruusu, O., Piirtola, M., Kaprio, J., Korhonen, T., Marttunen, M., & Suvisaari, J. (2021). Factors contributing to psychological distress in the working population, with a special reference to gender difference. *BMC Public Health, 21*(1), 1–17. https://doi.org/10.1186/s12889-021-10560-y

Wang, M., & Kelan, E. (2013). The gender quota and female leadership: Effects of the Norwegian gender quota on board chairs and CEOs. *Journal of Business Ethics, 117*(3), 449–466. https://doi.org/10.1007/s10551-012-1546-5

Weeden, K. A., Gelbgiser, D., & Morgan, S. L. (2020). Pipeline dreams: Occupational plans and gender differences in STEM major persistence and completion. *Sociology of Education, 93*(4), 297–314. https://doi.org/10.1177/0038040720928484

Weiss, S. (2015, December 22). 7 examples of benevolent sexism that are just as harmful as hostile sexism. *Bustle.* https://www.bustle.com/articles/131418-7-examples-of-benevolent-sexism-that-are-just-as-harmful-as-hostile-sexism

Williams, C. S. (1992). The glass escalator: Hidden advantages for men in the "female" professions. *Social Problems, 39*(3), 253–267. https://www.jstor.org/stable/3096961

Williams, J. C., Phillips, K. W., & Hall, E. V. (2015, March 24). Percent of women who report. . . [Visual or photograph]. *Harvard Business Review.* https://hbr.org/data-visuals/2015/03/percent-of-u-s-women-in-stem-who-report

Wisniewski, M. (2022, March 1). What is the gender wage gap in your state?. *United States Census Bureau.* https://www.census.gov/library/stories/2022/03/what-is-the-gender-wage-gap-in-your-state.html

Wittenberg-Cox, A. (2014, February 12). Stop "fixing" women and start fixing managers. *Harvard Business Review.* https://hbr.org/2014/02/stop-fixing-women-and-start-fixing-managers

World Health Organization. (2021, September 13). *Depression,* https://www.who.int/news-room/fact-sheets/detail/depression

NOTE

1. We have addressed the topic of gender in the workplace as if it were binary because that is the basis of nearly all of the existing organizational science. However, it is critical for future research to explore and improve the experiences of people who identify as gender-fluid, gender non-conforming, transgender, intersex, or any other identity experience (see Morgenroth & Ryan, 2021). As 1.2 million Americans do not identify as a man or a woman, it will be essential to research those who do not benefit from the research on men and women in the workplace (Anders, 2021).

Karyssa Courey, Makai Ruffin, Mikki Hebl, Dillon Stewart, Meridith Townsend, Leilani Seged, Jordyn Williams, Cedric Patterson, Sara Mei, and Eden King

WORK AND ORGANIZATIONAL ISSUES AFFECTING YOUNG WORKERS

Imagine what our world could look like if every single one of these young people were supported and empowered to fulfil their potential?

(UNICEF, n.d.)

Young workers are the future of work. Young people (15- to 24-year-olds) (International Labour Organization [ILO], 2018), by virtue of being inexperienced and at the start of their working lives, are in a different position from the rest of society. Young people's unemployment, underemployment, and economic inactivity have multilevel implications: at the individual level (e.g., hampering young people's knowledge, skills, abilities, and relationships development; lowering well-being; slowing career development, resulting in underemployment and reduced lifetime earnings), at the organizational level (e.g., hampering succession planning of retiring workforces; missing out on new talent), and at the societal level (e.g., exclusion from society, social mobility, underutilization of pockets of the labor force) (Baron, 2008; ILO, 2020b; McQuaid, 2017; Strandh et al., 2014; Thern et al., 2017). Young people's attainment of full and productive employment is therefore a global challenge, reflected particularly in the United Nations Sustainable Development Goal 8: "Promote sustained, inclusive and sustainable economic growth, full and productive employment and decent work for all" (Sustainable Development Solutions Network [SDSN], 2015).

This article reviews, from a psychological perspective, the work and organizational issues affecting young workers. Primarily because of the life stage that they are in, young people differ from the rest of working population in the difficulties they experience in access to work and their work-related motives; the empirical evidence and theoretical explanations for these are reviewed herein. The "Conclusion" highlights the importance of socioeconomic context for understanding and improving young workers' experience of work and areas where psychology can make impactful contributions.

YOUNG PEOPLE'S ACCESS TO WORK

Young people experience unique barriers in access to work in comparison to the rest of the working population. Despite great geographical variation (Searle et al., 2014), on average young people are three times more likely to be unemployed compared to the wider working-age population and a substantial proportion of young people (20% in 2020) globally are not in education, employment, or training (NEET) (Chacaltana & Dasgupta, 2021). Even with employment, working poverty is common experience. For instance, in 2020, 30% of young people worldwide were reported to be in extreme or moderate poverty (ILO, 2020a). Young people's jobs are also at the highest risk of automation, especially for those with vocational training whose occupation-specific skills become obsolete with automation (ILO, 2020a).

Beyond persistently high unemployment rates, a number of global trends in youth employment are evident since the turn of the 21st century (ILO, 2020a), including decreasing youth labor force participation, declining share of youth employment, and increasing enrollment in secondary and tertiary education, leading to higher qualification. Meanwhile there is a global decrease in demand for vocational qualifications (Vogel, 2015), such as apprenticeships, which are perceived as leading to blue-collar work (European Commission, 2021). All together, these labor market trends prolong young people's transition from school into "stable" jobs (with reliable incomes, career opportunities, and social protection) (Lodovici & Semenza, 2012). Persistent gender gaps exist (especially in Arab states and Northern Africa), and informal employment is prevalent (especially in sub-Saharan Africa and Southern Asia) for young workers (ILO, 2020a). Socioeconomic context plays a crucial role in youth employment outcomes. For instance, young people in emerging economies take longer to settle into stable jobs and are more likely to be in informal employment or NEET than counterparts in advanced economies, where school retention and completion rates are higher, and social and legal protections are in place, for example, minimum wage, jobseekers' allowance, and union recognition and/or representation (ILO, 2014; Quintini & Martin, 2014). Depending on the social protections afforded to young people, job insecurity and precarity may further exacerbate young people's barriers to employment through social and financial insecurity, low self-esteem, and lack of meaningful labor market experience (Buzzeo et al., 2016). Not being able to secure stable employment (e.g., long spells of unemployment and/or precarious employment), some young people often struggle in their ability to afford basic living and housing costs and may become reliant on the public welfare systems and/or third-sector organizations such as foodbanks (Buzzeo et al., 2019).

Twenty-first-century labor markets can be insecure and precarious for young entrants (Kalleberg, 2019). Even in the most developed parts of the world, young people's first jobs tend to be in temporary employment and accompanied by low wages, unpaid overtime, and informal work, regardless of the worker's educational attainment (Lodovici & Semenza, 2012). Nonstandard forms of employment (temporary and part-time work, temporary agency work, and working without contracts) are thus highly prevalent among young people (European Foundation for the Improvement of Living Working Conditions[EFILWC], 2013). Although young people report receiving greater social support from peers and supervisors, they also experience more adverse social behavior, for example, bullying and harassment—particularly young women (Turte et al., 2012; Vargas Llave et al., 2017). Moreover, their job quality is discernibly different, with lower levels of work autonomy, longer working time, more irregular working hours, and worse pay levels compared to other age groups in the working population (EFILWC, 2013; Okay-Somerville et al., 2019; Wong & Au-Yeung, 2019).

Extant psychology research on school-to-work transitions highlights several key factors. Family can financially, emotionally, and motivationally support young people's transitions to work. Unemployment and work-related struggles may be part of a generational legacy for young people who, growing up, have had vicarious exposure to long-term unemployment through their parents' experiences (O'Reilly et al., 2015). Particularly for young people who could not rely on the emotional or tangible support of their parents, unemployment further diminishes their scarce social support networks and undermines their success (Bolíbar et al., 2019; Selenko & Pils, 2019). Social class has an impact on young people's access to work (Blustein et al., 2002). Young people from more advantaged backgrounds are also more likely to attain higher and more prestigious education, which also increases likelihood of successful transitions. Moreover, academic satisfaction and the resources offered by educational institution play crucial roles in predicting employability and career success (Okay-Somerville et al., 2020; Presti et al., 2021). Internships and work experience during education are positive factors contributing to employability (Ebner et al., 2021; Shoenfelt et al., 2013), especially if the individual is paid and if the young person is provided with a mentor, has similar opportunities as employees, and is given sufficient time to experience work (O'Higgins & Pinedo, 2018). Career self-management and job search quality also predict positive school-to-work transition outcomes (Bridgstock, 2009; Stremersch et al., 2021).

Theoretically, the difficulties young people experience in access to jobs can be explained by referring to the lifespan career theory perspective, focusing particularly on development of career competencies. The analysis in "Lifespan Career Development Theories" is complemented by concepts from economics and sociology, taking into account the wider context of young people's transitions to work.

Lifespan Career Development Theories. Career transitions are always challenging (Arnold, 1997). From a lifespan career theory perspective, it is part of the developmental process that young people take some time to secure employment, and when they do, these are entry-level jobs that do not necessarily offer most of the intrinsic qualities of work that are associated with "good-quality" work, especially pay, autonomy, and responsibility. This is because young people are in the process of developing career resources that enable them to secure jobs and navigate the world of work (Savickas, 2002, 2006; Super, 1980; Super et al., 1957). Because of differences in chronological age, younger workers have had less time than more senior people to accumulate the necessary career resources required to successfully master employment challenges. For example, young people have less work experience, fewer opportunities to build networks of mentors and peers, and fewer experiences of successful job applications (Akkermans et al., 2013), all of which are predictors of successful education-to-work transitions, as noted previously in "Young People's Access to Work." Hence, young people have less bargaining power to (a) access work and (b) secure jobs that offer crucial intrinsic features conducive to career development, such as autonomy or skill development. Understanding career competency development is crucial in order to explain why young people are in a different situation from the rest of the working population.

Career Competencies. Career competencies refer to "competencies that are relevant for all employees to develop their own career, regardless of the specific job they have" (Kuijpers & Scheerens, 2006, p. 305). Three key career competencies for successfully navigating uncertain labor markets are know-how, know-whom, and know-why (De Fillippi & Arthur, 1994). However, young workers' lack of these career competencies makes them particularly vulnerable to unemployment and underemployment, especially during economic downturns (Bell & Blanchflower, 2011). This vulnerability was most clearly evidenced in the Great Recession of 2008–2009 (Kalleberg, 2019) and COVID-19-related economic downturn (Costa Dias et al., 2020). This section reviews the arguments and evidence explaining the difficulties young people experience in developing career competencies and thus their lack of access to (a) work in general and (b) good-quality work in particular.

Know-How. Know-how refers to career-related knowledge and skills that accumulate over time, and is akin to the notion of human capital (De Fillippi & Arthur, 1994). Human capital theory (Becker, 1964) suggests that the likelihood of securing employment and higher earnings is associated with an individual's accumulated human capital, that is, their stock of knowledge, skills, and abilities. Human capital is an integral component of employability (Forrier et al., 2009; McArdle et al., 2007). Human capital is essentially an economics notion that signals one's productivity at work and therefore their worth in the labor market (Becker, 1964). It is not only proxied by education and qualifications but also by labor market involvement, such as internships, apprenticeships, work experience, and occupational expertise and training (Berntson et al., 2006; Judge et al., 1995; Van der Heijden, 2003). Although, globally, young people's enrollment in secondary and tertiary education, and therefore qualification attainment, has been increasing (ILO, 2020a), they can suffer from an "experience trap" (Mann et al., 2020) because of their limited work-related skills and competencies, which paradoxically can only be gained through work (Pastore, 2018).

Level of education makes a difference to young people's likelihood of unemployment (Organisation for Economic Co-operation and Development [OECD], n.d.). Although subject to significant variation across countries, on average, a higher education degree pays a premium not only in terms of salary but also in quality of opportunities that are available (Green & Henseke, 2021). Regardless of level of education and experience, young people may be faced with age stereotypes and deemed "too young" for certain professions based on age-related stereotypes (North & Fiske, 2012; Posthuma & Campion, 2009). These stereotypical beliefs may have negative implications for young people's access to certain occupations, as well as promotion, training, and performance appraisals at work (Snape & Redman, 2003). These beliefs are concerned with perceived age norms for certain jobs, indicative of shared beliefs about a perceived "correct age" to accumulate the necessary know-how to be competent in certain occupations (Posthuma & Campion, 2009). For example, physicians are often expected to be older than 45 years of age; otherwise, patients wonder, "Is this person really old enough to be my doctor?" (Fowler, 2016).

Relatedly, there is also the common belief that younger workers would be "digital natives" (Prensky, 2001). This belief arises from a refuted brain-structural difference argument. More supported differences in digital literacy, defined as "an individual's ability to use computers to investigate, create and communicate" (Fraillon et al., 2013, p. 17), understand it as a learned skill, developed through education and experience. Favorable attitudes toward new technology might also be influenced by younger people's greater adoption of such technology (e.g., Morris & Venkatesh, 2000). Given the clear role of learning in digital literacy, age alone is a limited predictor. From a know-how perspective, being classified as digital natives does not shield young people from unemployment, underemployment, and economic inactivity, as the evidence above suggests. Technical digital skills are necessary, but not sufficient to perform well in digitized knowledge economies unless accompanied by other digital transferable skills in areas such as information management, collaboration, creativity, critical thinking, and problem-solving (van Laar et al., 2017).

Those young people who take longer to secure stable employment tend to join labor markets with fewer qualifications, and they accumulate less work experience than their counterparts who benefit from on-the-job learning and other forms of skill development (Robalino et al., 2013). Critically, long-term unemployment and underemployment is associated with underutilization and erosion of skills and cognitive decline (De Grip et al., 2008; Green & Zhu, 2010), that is, further degradation of know-how.

Know-Whom. A second career competency relevant for career success is know-whom (Akkermans et al., 2013; De Fillippi & Arthur, 1994), denoting career-related social networks or social capital. Social capital refers to an individual's actual and potential resources that arise from their networks of relationships, and therefore captures an interpersonal dimension of employability (McArdle et al., 2007). Who one knows influences access to and flow of job-related information, and is a predictor of future earnings (Seibert et al., 2001). For example, a study of university graduates reveals personal connections and contacts as the most important factor in securing first post-graduation job (Brennan et al., 2001).

Know-whom is also relevant for young people's employability skills (e.g., communication, proactivity, and teamwork). From a sociological perspective, scrutinizing the skills young people are required to demonstrate reveals an implicit "class" bias, mimicking and favoring the attributes of those from high-status social backgrounds (Brown & Hesketh, 2004). Young people from disadvantaged backgrounds are not necessarily socialized into these skills through upbringing; for example, they have fewer opportunities to vicariously learn from their family or social networks. Hence, young people from disadvantaged or minority backgrounds tend to score lower on these skills and have poorer labor market outcomes (Adams, 2012; ILO, 2020b; Silver, 2007).

Social networks also partially explain the prevalence of underemployment among young migrant workers, arising from the challenges in transferring their social and cultural capital to a new country context. Impoverished local social networks and support affects immigrants' labor market success (Zikic, 2015). Further, strong family or national community networks can constrain their integration into the host country and can negatively affect employment, as these social ties are more likely to be employed in low-skilled, low-paid work (Ryan et al., 2008). These findings graphically demonstrate how social networks may constrain young workers' access into labor markets (Hällsten et al., 2017; Winterheller & Hirt, 2017).

The intertwining of social and human capital was evident in the 2020 U.S. Ivy League admissions scandal, with wealthy elites using bribery to gain admissions to top universities for their children (Jack, 2020). Such behavior resonates with positional conflict theory (Brown, 2000, 2003), a sociological theory that argues that social elites use their greater financial and cultural resources to enhance their credentials (human capital) and thus secure advantages in the labor market. The gaining of prestigious education facilitates access to labor markets (Okay-Somerville et al., 2020). These results confirm a direct and indirect impact of social networks on youth employment.

Combined effects of know-how and know-whom on youth transitions to work also resonate with sources of self-efficacy beliefs, as discussed in Bandura's (1986) social cognitive theory. Mastery experiences contribute toward one's know-how, and know-whom may provide vicarious learning and social persuasion on crucial job search and employability-related skills. According to social cognitive career theory (Lent et al., 1994), self-efficacy beliefs impact our work-related interests, goals, and actions. Self-efficacy has been shown to be negatively associated with likelihood of unemployment during school-to-work transitions (Pinquart et al., 2003). Moreover, experience of unemployment further diminishes young people's self-efficacy beliefs (Mortimer et al., 2016), as it depletes young people's cognitive (De Grip et al., 2008) and social resources (Bolíbar et al., 2019).

Considering the growing inequalities in wealth distribution in the 21st century (Organisation for Economic Co-operation and Development [OECD], 2011), access to work by young people from disadvantaged social backgrounds is hindered by their lack of both know-how and know-whom. By contrast, some young people, by virtue of their family up-bringing and life experiences are "socialized" into labor markets, creating a "rocket pack" of human and social capital that propels them into better employment opportunities.

Know-Why. A third crucial career competency relevant for career success is know-why. This relates to individuals' career-related identity (De Fillippi & Arthur, 1994). Identity is an area of important difference between young people and older people in the labor market, with younger people having fewer opportunities and time to develop strong work-related identities. Without these self-understandings, it is harder to develop clear career goals or decisions about how to move forward their desired futures (Praskova et al., 2015). Although some young people can easily identify labor market opportunities, others engage concurrently in job search and career identity and goal formation processes (Saks & Ashforth, 2002). This latter group's lack of familiarity with labor markets and job opportunities impedes their successful navigation (Turban et al., 2009). Hence, they can struggle to situate themselves in the labor market, as they are still addressing crucial know-why questions, such as "who am I?" and "who do I want to be?" (Holmes, 2013).

A young person's successful transition into both work and adulthood involves significant self-exploration relevant to achieving self-definition and developing their know-why. Arnett (2000) used the concept of "emerging adulthood," which signifies a period of instability and identity exploration. For those at the start of careers, this necessitates opportunities to explore and experience different types of work, and from these experiences have support to make sense of their situation and to construct themselves in a particular way (Ashforth & Schinoff, 2016). Many obstacles can hamper young workers' development of know-why: Some obstacles relate to the social context, including lack of positive career feedback, role models, and/or labor market opportunities (Hu et al., 2017); whereas other impediments are internal, such as career indecision. Particularly in the aftermath of the 2008 Great Financial Crisis and during the COVID-19 pandemic, a sharp decline in the availability of entry-level jobs for young people to provide work exploration and experience has been observed (Gonzalez et al., 2020; ILO, 2020b). Young people's career counseling needs, especially those in less disadvantaged communities (e.g., low- or middle-income economies, or those from socially disadvantaged backgrounds), are often not met effectively to support career decision-making (Maree, 2021). Moreover, visibility of opportunities may decline further as the jobs young people hold are at higher risk from automation (ILO, 2020a). Those who struggle to form career identities because of limited availability or visibility of labor market opportunities can be discouraged in their job search and career behaviors, increasing their likelihood of unemployment or underemployment (Lozano & Rentería, 2021).

Know-why is highly relevant for making forward-leading decisions. Although career-indecision can occur at any age, among young workers it is more associated with underemployment. Paradoxically, difficulties in career-goal formation and pursuit can produce hypervigilance (individuals rushing into any decision), procrastination, or decision avoidance (Callanan & Greenhaus, 1992; Feldman, 2003). This indecision is shown to reduce the amount of career exploration and reconsideration, impeding further processes of identity formation (Laughland-Booÿ et al., 2017). Although indecision may not be necessarily detrimental for career development, enabling individuals to take advantage of unplanned or unexpected career opportunities

(Krumboltz, 1992, 1998; Mitchell et al., 1999), it is deleterious for job search: Indecision can lead to indifference in job search activities (Betz & Voyten, 1997) or to less engaged goal-directed job search behaviors (Okay-Somerville et al., 2020). These haphazard job search activities are associated with loss of earnings, underemployment, and poorer first job attitudes (Feldman & Turnley, 1995; Koen et al., 2010; Okay-Somerville & Scholarios, 2021).

The exploratory process of forming know-why may explain the divergence found in age-related effects on work attitudes and behaviors. A negative relationship between age, and organizational commitment and willingness to leave jobs and organizations (Ng & Feldman, 2010) may reflect younger workers' self- and environment exploration. Extant evidence indicates the value of social support during the first critical 6 months of new organizational entry, helping young workers integrate leading to their subsequent organizational commitment (Nägele & Neuenschwander, 2014). However, the amount of security and social protection offered to young people depends on the institutional context of the country and reveals an intricate tension between young people's need for flexibility to explore labor market opportunities and adapt to the challenges, alongside a desire for stability and predictability required for career-identity development (King, 2003; Modestino et al., 2019).

YOUNG PEOPLE'S WORK MOTIVES

Beyond issues in access to work, meta-analytic evidence shows age-related differences in work motives. Younger workers show higher preference for growth (e.g., related to achievement and mastery) and extrinsic motives (e.g., pay, benefits, and promotion), but lower preference for intrinsic motives (e.g., accomplishment) in comparison to older workers (Kooij et al., 2011). It is helpful to understand differences between younger and older people with the use of life-span theories, or through research on aging. This is in contrast to popular discourse, which focuses on simplistic generational perspectives.

Lifespan Theories of Aging.   According to lifespan theories of aging (Baltes, 1987) people's goals and motives change as they age. For instance, from a socioemotional selectivity theory perspective (e.g., Carstensen et al., 2003), growth and expanding horizons is of greater importance when people are younger, with aging and increasing perceptions of mortality shifting their motivation toward emotional meanings of life. Similarly, according to the motivational theory of lifespan development (Heckhausen et al., 2010), throughout people's lives they face different normative developmental goals: At a young age these normative goals include not only having to find a first job, but also to complete education, become financially independent, move out of family home, find a partner, have a first child, and so on. From a lifespan theory of aging perspective, as young people are at the start of working lives and in transitional stages—for example, from adolescence to young adulthood, and from education to work or further education—personal growth and financial security may be more important motives in work.

Generational Perspectives and Their Limitations.   There is a tendency, particularly among popular media, to discuss young people's work and employment experiences and their work-related values, from a generational perspective. Although evidence suggests age effects on work values (Kooij et al., 2011) and life conditions certainly vary over time (Kontopantelis et al., 2018), conceptualizing these in terms of "generational differences" is unhelpful (Costanza & Finkelstein, 2015; Rudolph et al., 2020; Zacher, 2015). This is not only because the concept of generations is too fuzzy, but also because it stereotypes people into cohorts, offering an overly simplistic picture of the nuanced individual experiences people have. Critically, generational effects are nearly impossible to investigate in a conceptually or methodologically valid way (Costanza et al., 2012; Twenge et al., 2010), rendering the practical and explanatory value of generational concepts limited. There are others who have written extensively on the limitations of generational approaches; this article highlights just a few of the most central issues (e.g., Rudolph & Zacher, 2020; Rudolph et al., 2018, 2020).

First, generation is a fuzzy concept. Whereas biological "age" is a relatively undisputed measure of a person's chronological time from birth, "generation" is a socially constructed term that attempts to capture a cohort of people who supposedly share important experiences at crucial times in their lives (Costanza et al., 2012). Although generational labels are widely familiar, there is no agreement on the birth year ranges they supposedly capture (Campbell et al., 2017; Rudolph et al., 2020). For example, are Millennials born between 1980 and 2000 (Rainer & Rainer, 2011), or 1979 and 1994 (Myers & Sadaghiani, 2010), or 1981 and 1996 (Dimock, 2019)? Similar imprecision arises in other workplace generational studies (e.g., Costanza et al., 2012). In short, there is no consensus about who is part of which generation, and thus it can be argued that as an objective category, generations do not exist (Rudolph et al., 2020). That said, generations do exist as socially constructed categories in peoples' minds and have meaning for how people label themselves and others. As such, they can inform social perceptions and actions, leading to age stereotypes and ageism.

Second, a methodologically valid, informative study of workplace generational differences is nearly impossible to carry out—rendering the informative value of almost any study that attempts to capture a "younger generation's values" almost nil (Rudolph et al., 2020). Not only is the concept of generational cohort fuzzy; comparing cohorts is not useful either as it is impossible to distinguish generational differences from those that arise because of age, stage of career, or time points of when the study was conducted (see Rudolph et al., 2020). Perhaps unsurprisingly, meta-analytical evidence of studies investigating cohort differences conclude that effects can rather be attributed to other factors than generations (Costanza et al., 2012). Even observing work values of a singular age cohort over multiple time points cannot eliminate other effects, for example, career effects, learning, aging effects as people get older over time. The solution—sequential longitudinal cohort studies (i.e., repeatedly sampling cohorts of 20-year-olds each year and observing their work values over time)—is immensely laborious to carry out, which might explain why they are not available.

Like societal norms, economic conditions and political contexts change slowly; in the same way individual work norms might change alongside equally slowly—and concurrently across differently aged people. Thus, someone growing up in the 2000s might have learned different values from someone who grew up in the 1980s, but the older person might have adapted their values in the 2000s, as a function of the time period and their personal and career development. Drawing artificial boundaries between people of different ages in the workplace is not only meaningless for conceptual and methodological reasons; it also obscures the real reasons that might explain why work values might be different for younger and older people at a certain workplace. Thinking in generations may serve to cement age stereotypes, which may further undermine the inclusion of younger people in the workplace.

FUTURE DIRECTIONS FOR PSYCHOLOGY RESEARCHERS

This review has highlighted how young people experience work and employment differently from the rest of the working population. These differences are primarily attributable to young people's developmental stage in terms of lifespan and career. Young people's lack of career competencies makes them vulnerable to adverse socioeconomic conditions, for example, economic downturns. This section highlights potential contributions by psychologists for improving young workers' labor market access and experience.

From a youth employment perspective, the replacement of entry-level jobs by automation reflects an impoverishment in work, with reduced provisions failing to support young people in fostering their autonomy and developing their work skills and attitudes. Automation of much entry-level work may also challenge what is meant by "entry-level" work. Digitization may offer new opportunities favoring knowledge workers, even at entry level. For instance, apprenticeships, although often associated with manual work, are recognized as means for developing digital skills (European Commission, 2021). These types of apprenticeships cover crucial digital skills such as cybersecurity, digital banking, software engineering, and IT consulting (ILO, n.d.). For future cohorts of young people, entry-level work may require more sophisticated skills as more mundane tasks may be automated. This may indicate a more up-skilled start for young people. A crucial area for exploration is therefore the role of "digital skills" in employability and education-to-work transitions. Relatedly, there is scope for more scholarly exploration in job analysis and job design, particularly designing entry-level jobs for the "future of work."

Another job design-related psychology contribution is in young people's underemployment. Young people who are discouraged by their struggles to access work may opt to remain in education (ILO, 2020a), in order to improve their labor market opportunities. For instance, in conjunction with disappearing entry-level opportunities during the COVID-19 pandemic, an increase in educational enrollments was observed, especially in high-income countries (UNESCO, 2021). Yet, even with additional credentials, a successful transition into work is not guaranteed, as many may be judged overqualified, at least in the first few years of their careers (Okay-Somerville & Scholarios, 2014). In addition, these education routes are only available to those who can afford them. In fact, a decline in education enrollment was observed in lower-middle-income countries during the COVID-19 pandemic (UNESCO, 2021). Although research shows considerable direct and indirect organizational dividends from employing overqualified staff (Hu et al., 2017), there are clear financial and psychological implications for workers (Harari et al., 2017). These negative impacts could be restored by improvements in job autonomy (Wu et al., 2015) and safeguarding jobs against autonomy. Alternatively, leader and peer support are also highly relevant for improving job satisfaction (Alfes et al., 2016) and retention. There is extant psychology research on overqualification (e.g., Erdogan et al., 2011, 2020; Lee et al., 2021), which could inform young workers' labor market access and experience.

Although more practical support could be given at all stages of education, further research should focus upstream, to better examine the formation of career identity (Searle et al., 2014) and how it differs across the socioeconomic contexts. This review has shown that these contexts impact youth employment outcomes, especially in the provision of social securities. Indeed, prior study has shown the significance of teachers' inputs, especially in helping children from disadvantaged families better navigate the employment context (St. Clair et al., 2013). Through earlier attention on the acquisition of these skills and ongoing exposure to work experiences throughout secondary education, educators and students could significantly enhance the curriculum and their futures. Thus, there is merit in future longitudinal studies that incorporate earlier career identity and attitude development. Further, university curricula need to be infused with opportunities to develop employability skills and promote work identities. Critically, attention should ensure opportunities to build all three career competencies.

Psychologists offer important perspectives as to why there is such widespread institutional inertia in recognizing and engaging with this increasingly "wicked" problem of youth employment (Carter, 2020)—particularly in supporting young people from socially disadvantaged background. Specifically, research reveals a repulsion from, rather than engagement with, those in poverty (Fiske, 2007) and a pernicious prejudice linked to social class that taints those from lower socioeconomic groups as not only less competent but also less deserving (Durante & Fiske, 2017). Thus, this situation is positioned as dispositional and self-inflicted rather than recognizing the disproportionate large stigma that has to be overcome alongside inadequate access to welfare and key resources. There is increasing recognition of the corrosive consequences of poverty, particularly for self-efficacy and identity (Smith, 2015), but there remains a stubborn inertia to recognizing the clear psychological basis regarding income inequality, anti-immigrant tensions, and intergenerational and class prejudice (Moya & Fiske, 2017).

Viewed through this novel psychological prism, responses to these challenges become very different. Critically, they shift employability away from the individual, to instead reveal its more contextual and relational dimensions, showing a polarizing of outcomes that is not always helpful (Forrier et al., 2018). Through a shift in emphasis, far greater support should be provided for young people to address the specific challenges they face in accessing and accumulating resources. Such provision should recognize the role of parents, whose own experiences can curtail the aspirations and identity formation of young people (Berrington et al., 2016; Ladge & Little, 2019). Further, this perspective indicates the declining value of some resources (Forrier et al., 2018). Applying research insights would change career guidance to focus on vocational pathways and identifying jobs that are more resilient to the encroachment of automation. It would position support toward the development of work identities and career competencies concurrent with a capacity to adapt. Extant research shows the value of such provision, especially for migrant workers (Wehrle et al., 2019; Zikic & Richardson, 2016). Future research could incorporate more attention on the contextual and relational factors, to consider the labor market pull-and-push factors for young people, especially from disadvantaged backgrounds, to provide better insight into why interventions might fail.

CONCLUSION

This article has identified a diverse range of factors relevant for understanding young workers' work and employment experiences. This highlights a multilevel phenomenon. Future research should strive to mimic this multilevel, multifaceted nature of young people's experiences in the labor market. In particular, contextualizing young people's work and employment in its unique socioeconomic and lifespan development conditions would provide what could be far more valuable insight and, through this, the means to better inform policy and practice. Indeed, there is growing recognition of the complexity of the problems, and thus their solution, as shown by the United Nations Global Initiative on Decent Jobs for Youth calling for cooperation between public and private actors, the promotion of partnerships, and especially information exchange to facilitate effective labor market interventions (ILO, 2020a). Psychology is uniquely placed to the inform these interventions.

FURTHER READING

Carter, A. J. (Ed.). (2019). *Young people, employment and work psychology: Interventions and solutions.* Routledge.

Eawop Impact Incubator (n.d.). *Youth work.* https://www.eawopimpact.org/youth-work

Kalleberg, A. L. (2020). Labor market uncertainties and youth labor force experiences: Lessons learned. *The Annals of the American Academy of Political and Social Science, 688*(1), 258–270. https://doi.org/10.1177%2F0002716220913861

McQuaid, R. (2017). *Youth unemployment produces multiple scarring effects.* LSE European Politics and Policy (EUROPP) Blog. http://eprints.lse.ac.uk/69950/1/blogs.lse.ac.uk-Youth%20unemployment%20produces%20multiple%20scarring%20effects.pdf

Okay-Somerville, B. (2021). What can human resource management tell us about sustainable youth employment?. *EAWOP In Practice, 15*(3), 193–206. http://www.eawop.org/ckeditor_assets/attachments/1592/3_what_can_human_resource_management_tell_us.pdf?1638994022

Steiner, R., Hirschi, A., & Akkermans, J. (2021). Many roads lead to Rome: Researching antecedents and outcomes of contemporary school-to-work transitions. *Journal of Career Development*, OnlineFirst. https://doi.org/10.1177%2F08948453211063580

REFERENCES

Adams, A. V. (2012). *The role of skills development in overcoming social disadvantage. UNESCO* [Background Paper prepared]. Education for All Global Monitoring Report. http://citeseerx.ist.psu.edu/viewdoc/download?doi=10.1.1.469.602&rep=rep1&type=pdf

Akkermans, J., Brenninkmeijer, V., Huibers, M., & Blonk, R. W. (2013). Competencies for the contemporary career: Development and preliminary validation of the Career Competencies Questionnaire. *Journal of Career Development, 40*(3), 245–267. https://doi.org/10.1177%2F0894845312467501

Alfes, K., Shantz, A., & van Baalen, S. (2016). Reducing perceptions of overqualification and its impact on job satisfaction: The dual roles of interpersonal relationships at work. *Human Resource Management Journal, 26*(1), 84–101. https://doi.org/10.1111/1748-8583.12094

Arnett, J. J. (2000). Emerging adulthood: A theory of development from the late teens through the twenties. *American Psychologist, 55*(5), 469. https://psycnet.apa.org/doi/10.1037/0003-066X.55.5.469

Arnold, J. (1997). *Managing careers into the 21st century*. SAGE.

Ashforth, B. E., & Schinoff, B. S. (2016). Identity under construction: How individuals come to define themselves in organizations. *Annual Review of Organizational Psychology and Organizational Behavior, 3*, 111–137. https://doi.org/10.1146/annurev-orgpsych-041015-062322

Baltes, P. B. (1987). Theoretical propositions of life-span developmental psychology: On the dynamics between growth and decline. *Developmental Psychology, 23*(5), 611. https://psycnet.apa.org/doi/10.1037/0012-1649.23.5.611

Bandura, A. (1986). *Social foundations of thought and action: A social cognitive theory*. Prentice-Hall.

Baron, S. W. (2008). Street youth, unemployment, and crime: Is it that simple? Using general strain theory to untangle the relationship. *Canadian Journal of Criminology and Criminal Justice, 50*(4), 399–434. https://doi.org/10.3138/cjccj.50.4.399

Becker, G. S. (1964). *Human capital: A theoretical and empirical analysis, with special reference to education*. National Bureau of Economic Research.

Bell, D. N., & Blanchflower, D. G. (2011). Young people and the Great Recession. *Oxford Review of Economic Policy, 27*(2), 241–267. https://doi.org/10.1093/oxrep/grr011

Berntson, E., Sverke, M., & Marklund, S. (2006). Predicting perceived employability: Human capital or labour market opportunities? *Economic and Industrial Democracy, 27*(2), 223–244. https://doi.org/10.1177/0143831x06063098

Berrington, A., Roberts, S., & Tammes, P. (2016). Educational aspirations among UK Young Teenagers: Exploring the role of gender, class and ethnicity. *British Educational Research Journal, 42*(5), 729–755. https://doi.org/10.1002/berj.3235

Betz, N., & Voyten, K. K. (1997). Efficacy and outcome expectations influence career exploration and decidedness. *Career Development Quarterly, 46*(2), 179–189. https://doi.org/10.1002/j.2161-0045.1997.tb01004.x

Blustein, D. L., Chaves, A. P., Diemer, M. A., Gallagher, L. A., Marshall, K. G., Sirin, S., & Bhati, K. S. (2002). Voices of the forgotten half: The role of social class in the school-to-work transition. *Journal of Counseling Psychology, 49*(3), 311–323. https://doi.org/10.1037/0022-0167.49.3.311

Bolíbar, M., Verd, J. M., & Barranco, O. (2019). The downward spiral of youth unemployment: An approach considering social networks and family background. *Work, Employment and Society, 33*(3), 401–421. https://doi.org/10.1177/0950017018822918

Brennan, J., Johnston, B., Little, B., Shah, T., & Woodley, A. (2001). *The employment of UK graduates: Comparisons with Europe and Japan*. Higher Education Funding Council for England. http://oro.open.ac.uk/328/

Bridgstock, R. (2009). The graduate attributes we've overlooked: Enhancing graduate employability through career management skills. *Higher Education Research & Development, 28*(1), 31–44. https://doi.org/10.1080/07294360802444347

Brown, P. (2000). The globalisation of positional competition? *Sociology, 34*(4), 633–653. https://doi.org/10.1177/S0038038500000390

Brown, P. (2003). The opportunity trap: Education and employment in global economy. *European Educational Research Journal, 2*(1), 141–178. https://doi.org/10.2304%2Feerj.2003.2.1.4

Brown, P., & Hesketh, A. (2004). *Mismanagement of talent: Employability and jobs in the knowledge economy*. Oxford University Press.

Buzzeo, J., Byford, M., Martin, A., & Newton, B. (2019). *Experiences of homeless young people in precarious employment*. Institute of Employment Studies.

Buzzeo, J., Marvell, R., Everett, C., & Newton, B. (2016). *Tackling unemployment among disadvantaged young people*. Institute of Employment Studies.

Callanan, G. A., & Greenhaus, J. H. (1992). The career indecision of managers and professionals: An examination of multiple subtypes. *Journal of Vocational Behavior, 41*(3), 212–231. https://doi.org/10.1016/0001-8791(92)90023-S

Campbell, S. M., Twenge, J. M., & Campbell, W. K. (2017). Fuzzy but useful constructs: Making sense of the differences between generations. *Work, Aging and Retirement, 3*(2), 130–139. https://doi.org/10.1093/workar/wax001

Carstensen, L. L., Fung, H. H., & Charles, S. T. (2003). Socioemotional selectivity theory and the regulation of emotion in the second half of life. *Motivation and Emotion, 27*(2), 103–123. https://doi.org/10.1023/A:1024569803230

Carter, A. (2020, June 29–July 3). *The wicked problem of youth employment: Context, issues & ways forward* [Paper Presentation]. The EAWOP/ESRC Small Group Meeting on Young People's Work, Employment and Careers, Glasgow, UK.

Chacaltana, J., & Dasgupta, S. (2021). *Is the future ready for youth? Youth employment policies for evolving labour markets.* International Labour Office. https://www.ilo.org/wcmsp5/groups/public/---ed_emp/documents/publication/wcms_776024.pdf

Costa Dias, M., Joyce, R., & Norris Keiller, A. (2020). *COVID-19 and the career prospects of young people* (Briefing Note 299). Institute for Fiscal Studies (IFS).

Costanza, D. P., Badger, J. M., Fraser, R. L., Severt, J. B., & Gade, P. A. (2012). Generational differences in work-related attitudes: A meta-analysis. *Journal of Business and Psychology, 27*(4), 375–394. http://doi.org/10.1007%2Fs10869-012-9259-4

Costanza, D. P., & Finkelstein, L. M. (2015). Generationally based differences in the workplace: Is there a there there? *Industrial and Organizational Psychology, 8*(3), 308. https://doi.org/10.1017/iop.2015.15

De Fillippi, R. J., & Arthur, M. B. (1994). The boundaryless career: A competency-based perspective. *Journal of Organizational Behavior, 15*(4), 307–324. https://doi.org/10.1002/job.4030150403

De Grip, A., Bosma, H., Willems, D., & van Boxtel, M. (2008). Job-worker mismatch and cognitive decline. *Oxford Economic Papers, 60*(2), 237–253. https://doi.org/10.1093/oep/gpm023

Dimock, M. (2019). Defining generations: Where Millennials end and Generation Z begins. *Pew Research Center, 17*(1), 1–7. http://tony-silva.com/eslefl/miscstudent/downloadpagearticles/defgenerations-pew.pdf

Durante, F., & Fiske, S. T. (2017). How social-class stereotypes maintain inequality. *Current Opinion in Psychology, 18*, 43–48. https://doi.org/10.1016/j.copsyc.2017.07.033

Ebner, K., Soucek, R., & Selenko, E. (2021). Perceived quality of internships and employability perceptions: The mediating role of career-entry worries. *Education + Training, 63*(4), 579–596. https://doi.org/10.1108/ET-02-2020-0037

Erdogan, B., Bauer, T. N., Peiró, J. M., & Truxillo, D. M. (2011). Overqualification theory, research, and practice: Things that matter. *Industrial and Organizational Psychology, 4*(2), 260–267.

Erdogan, B., Karaeminogullari, A., Bauer, T. N., & Ellis, A. M. (2020). Perceived overqualification at work: Implications for extra-role behaviors and advice network centrality. *Journal of Management, 46*(4), 583–606. https://doi.org/10.1177%2F0149206318804331

European Commission. (2021). *Quality and effective apprenticeships and international labour standards on apprenticeships.* [Meeting Report]. European Alliance for Apprenticeships and International Labour Organization joint online event. International Labour Organization. https://ec.europa.eu/social/BlobServlet?docId=23897&langId=en

European Foundation for the Improvement of Living Working Conditions. (2013). Working conditions of young entrants to the labour market. *Ketlib.* http://ketlib.lib.unipi.gr/xmlui/handle/ket/950

Feldman, D. C. (2003). The antecedents and consequences of early career indecision among young adults. *Human Resource Management Review, 13*(3), 499–531. https://doi.org/10.1016/S1053-4822(03)00048-2

Feldman, D. C., & Turnley, W. H. (1995). Underemployment among recent business college graduates. *Journal of Organizational Behavior, 16*(S1), 691–706. https://doi.org/10.1002/job.4030160708

Fiske, S. T. (2007). On prejudice and the brain. *Daedalus, 136*(1), 156–159. https://doi.org/10.1162/daed.2007.136.1.156

Forrier, A., De Cuyper, N., & Akkermans, J. (2018). The winner takes it all, the loser has to fall: Provoking the agency perspective in employability research. *Human Resource Management Journal, 28*(4), 511–523. https://doi.org/10.1111/1748-8583.12206

Forrier, A., Sels, L., & Stynen, D. (2009). Career mobility at the intersection between agent and structure: A conceptual model. *Journal of Occupational and Organizational Psychology, 82*(4), 739–759. https://doi.org/10.1348/096317909x470933

Fowler, C. (2016). Careerealism: When you look too young to be the doctor (or how not to be called Doogie Howser). *Emergency Medicine News, 38*(9), 33. https://doi.org/10.1097/01.EEM.0000499539.24562.b8

Fraillon, J., Schulz, W., & Ainley, J. (2013). *International computer and information literacy study: Assessment framework*. Educational Research Information Center.

Gonzalez, S., Gardiner, D., Bausch, J., Danish, M., Moitra, E., & Yan, L. (2020). *Youth and COVID-19. Impacts on jobs, education, rights and mental well-being: Survey report 2020*. International Labour Organization. https://www.ilo.org/global/topics/youth-employment/publications/WCMS_753026/lang--en/index.htm

Green, F., & Henseke, G. (2021). Europe's evolving graduate labour markets: Supply, demand, underemployment and pay. *Journal for Labour Market Research, 55*(1), 2. https://doi.org/10.1186/s12651-021-00288-y

Green, F., & Zhu, Y. (2010). Overqualification, job dissatisfaction, and increasing dispersion in the returns to graduate education. *Oxford Economic Papers, 62*(4), 740–763. https://doi.org/10.1093/oep/gpq002

Hällsten, M., Edling, C., & Rydgren, J. (2017). Social capital, friendship networks, and youth unemployment. *Social Science Research, 61*, 234–250. https://doi.org/10.1016/j.ssresearch.2016.06.017

Harari, M. B., Manapragada, A., & Viswesvaran, C. (2017). Who thinks they're a big fish in a small pond and why does it matter? A meta-analysis of perceived overqualification. *Journal of Vocational Behavior, 102*, 28–47. https://doi.org/10.1016/j.jvb.2017.06.002

Heckhausen, J., Wrosch, C., & Schulz, R. (2010). A motivational theory of life-span development. *Psychological Review, 117*(1), 32–60. https://psycnet.apa.org/doi/10.1037/a0017668

Holmes, L. (2013). Competing perspectives on graduate employability: Possession, position or process? *Studies in Higher Education, 38*(4), 538–554. https://doi.org/10.1080/03075079.2011.587140

Hu, S., Hood, M., & Creed, P. A. (2017). Negative career feedback and career goal disengagement in young adults: The moderating role of mind-set about work. *Journal of Vocational Behavior, 102*, 63–71. https://doi.org/10.1016/j.jvb.2017.07.006

International Labour Organization. (2014). *Informal employment among youth: Evidence from 20 school-to-work transition surveys*. https://www.ilo.org/wcmsp5/groups/public/---dgreports/---dcomm/documents/publication/wcms_234911.pdf

International Labour Organization. (2018). *The youth employment challenge and the 2030 agenda* [Video]. YouTube. https://www.youtube.com/watch?v=odHxTnN7OLg&t=1s

International Labour Organization. (2020a). *Global employment trends for youth 2020: Technology and the future of jobs*.

International Labour Organization. (2020b). *Preventing exclusion from the labour market: Tackling the COVID-19 youth employment crisis*. https://www.ilo.org/wcmsp5/groups/public/---ed_emp/documents/publication/wcms_746031.pdf

International Labour Organization. (n.d.). *Decent jobs for youth*. https://www.decentjobsforyouth.org/about

Jack, A. (2020, July 22). Unacceptable—Inside the Ivy League admissions scandal. *Financial Times*. https://www.ft.com/content/bbdd0722-e368-4611-982d-60b884fd8682

Judge, T. A., Cable, D. M., Boudreau, J. W., & Bretz, J. R. D. (1995). An empirical investigation of the predictors of executive career success. *Personnel Psychology*, *48*(3), 485–519. https://doi.org/10.1111/j.1744-6570.1995.tb01767.x

Kalleberg, A. L. (2019). Precarious work and young workers in the United States. In L. S. Chancer, M. Sanchez-Jankowski, & C. Trost (Eds.), *Youth, jobs, and the future: Problems and prospects* (pp. 35–54). Oxford University Press.

King, Z. (2003). New or traditional careers? A study of UK graduates' preferences. *Human Resource Management Journal*, *13*(1), 5–26. https://doi.org/10.1111/j.1748-8583.2003.tb00081.x

Koen, J., Klehe, U.-C., Van Vianen, A. E. M., Zikic, J., & Nauta, A. (2010). Job-search strategies and reemployment quality: The impact of career adaptability. *Journal of Vocational Behavior*, *77*(1), 126–139. http://doi.org/10.1016/j.jvb.2010.02.004

Kontopantelis, E., Mamas, M. A., van Marwijk, H., Buchan, I., Ryan, A. M., & Doran, T. (2018). Increasing socioeconomic gap between the young and old: Temporal trends in health and overall deprivation in England by age, sex, urbanity and ethnicity, 2004–2015. *Journal of Epidemiology and Community Health*, *72*(7), 636–644. https://doi.org/10.1136/jech-2017-209895

Kooij, D. T. A. M., De Lange, A. H., Jansen, P. G. W., Kanfer, R., & Dikkers, J. S. E. (2011). Age and work-related motives: Results of a meta-analysis. *Journal of Organizational Behavior*, *32*(2), 197–225. https://doi.org/10.1002/job.665

Krumboltz, J. D. (1992). The wisdom of indecision. *Journal of Vocational Behavior*, *41*(3), 239–244. https://doi.org/10.1016/0001-8791(92)90025-U

Krumboltz, J. D. (1998). Serendipity is not serendipitous. *Journal of Counseling Psychology*, *45*(4), 390–392. https://doi.org/10.1037/0022-0167.45.4.390

Kuijpers, M. A. C. T., & Scheerens, J. (2006). Career competencies for the modern career. *Journal of Career Development*, *32*(4), 303–319. https://doi.org/10.1177/0894845305283006

Ladge, J. J., & Little, L. M. (2019). When expectations become reality: Work-family image management and identity adaptation. *Academy of Management Review*, *44*(1), 126–149. https://doi.org/10.5465/amr.2016.0438

Laughland-Booÿ, J., Newcombe, P., & Skrbiš, Z. (2017). Looking forward: Career identity formation and the temporal orientations of young Australians. *Journal of Vocational Behavior*, *101*, 43–56. https://doi.org/10.1016/j.jvb.2017.04.005

Lee, A., Erdogan, B., Tian, A., Willis, S., & Cao, J. (2021). Perceived overqualification and task performance: Reconciling two opposing pathways. *Journal of Occupational and Organizational Psychology*, *94*(1), 80–106. https://doi.org/10.1111/joop.12323

Lent, R. W., Brown, S. D., & Hackett, G. (1994). Toward a unifying social cognitive theory of career and academic interest, choice, and performance. *Journal of Vocational Behavior*, *45*(1), 79–122. https://doi.org/10.1006/jvbe.1994.1027

Lodovici, M. S., & Semenza, R. (2012). *Precarious work and high-skilled youth in Europe* (Vol. 937). FrancoAngeli.

Lozano, M., & Rentería, E. (2021, March 20). Trends in the length of long-term unemployment in Europe: An approach using working life tables, 2000–2018. *SocArXiv Papers*. https://doi.org/10.31235/osf.io/9c2jp

Mann, A., Denis, V., & Percy, C. (2020). *Career ready? How schools can better prepare young people for working life in the era of COVID-19* [OECD Education Working Papers]. OECDiLibrary. https://doi.org/10.1787/e1503534-en

Maree, J. G. (2021). Innovating and contextualising career counselling for young people during the Covid-19 pandemic. *South African Journal of Psychology, 51*(2), 244–255. https://doi.org/10.1177/0081246321999507

McArdle, S., Waters, L., Briscoe, J. P., & Hall, D. T. T. (2007). Employability during unemployment: Adaptability, career identity and human and social capital. *Journal of Vocational Behavior, 71*(2), 247–264. https://doi.org/10.1016/j.jvb.2007.06.003

McQuaid, R. (2017, February 18). Youth unemployment produces multiple scarring effects. *LSE European Politics and Policy (EUROPP) Blog.*

Mitchell, K. E., Levin, A. S., & Krumboltz, J. D. (1999). Planned happenstance: Constructing unexpected career opportunities. *Journal of Counseling and Development, 77*(2), 115–125. https://doi.org/10.1002/j.1556-6676.1999.tb02431.x

Modestino, A. S., Sugiyama, K., & Ladge, J. (2019). Careers in construction: An examination of the career narratives of young professionals and their emerging career self-concepts. *Journal of Vocational Behavior, 115*, 103306. https://doi.org/10.1016/j.jvb.2019.05.003

Morris, M. G., & Venkatesh, V. (2000). Age differences in technology adoption decisions: Implications for a changing work force. *Personnel Psychology, 53*(2), 375–403. https://doi.org/10.1111/j.1744-6570.2000.tb00206.x

Mortimer, J. T., Kim, M., Staff, J., & Vuolo, M. (2016). Unemployment, parental help, and self-efficacy during the transition to adulthood. *Work and Occupations, 43*(4), 434–465. https://doi.org/10.1177/0730888416656904

Moya, M., & Fiske, S. T. (2017). The social psychology of the Great Recession and social class divides. *Journal of Social Issues, 73*(1), 8–22. https://doi.org/10.1111/josi.12201

Myers, K. K., & Sadaghiani, K. (2010). Millennials in the workplace: A communication perspective on millennials' organizational relationships and performance. *Journal of Business and Psychology, 25*(2), 225–238. https://doi.org/10.1007/s10869-010-9172-7

Nägele, C., & Neuenschwander, M. P. (2014). Adjustment processes and fit perceptions as predictors of organizational commitment and occupational commitment of young workers. *Journal of Vocational Behavior, 85*(3), 385–393. https://doi.org/10.1016/j.jvb.2014.08.011

Ng, T. W. H., & Feldman, D. C. (2010). The relationships of age with job attitudes: A meta-analysis. *Personnel Psychology, 63*(3), 677–718. https://doi.org/10.1111/j.1744-6570.2010.01184.x

North, M. S., & Fiske, S. T. (2012). An inconvenienced youth? Ageism and its potential intergenerational roots. *Psychological Bulletin, 138*(5), 982–987. https://psycnet.apa.org/doi/10.1037/a0027843

O'Higgins, N., & Pinedo, L. (2018). *Interns and outcomes just how effective are internships as a bridge to stable employment?* (ILO Working Papers 994999791602676). International Labour Organization.

Okay-Somerville, B., Allison, I., Luchinskaya, D., & Scholarios, D. (2020, May 19). Disentangling the impact of social disadvantage on "becoming employable": Evidence from STEM student university-to-work transitions. *Studies in Higher Education*, OnlineFirst. https://doi.org/10.1080/03075079.2020.1767052

Okay-Somerville, B., & Scholarios, D. (2014). Coping with career boundaries and boundary-crossing in the graduate labour market. *Career Development International, 19*(6), 668–682. https://doi.org/10.1108/CDI-12-2013-0144

Okay-Somerville, B., & Scholarios, D. (2021). Job search strategies and successful university-to-work transitions in the context of labour market ambiguity. *Journal of Career Development*, OnlineFirst. https://doi.org/10.1177%2F08948453211016058

Okay-Somerville, B., Scholarios, D., & Sosu, E. (2019). Young workers' job satisfaction in Europe. In B. Furåker & K. Håkansson (Eds.), *Work orientations: Theoretical perspectives and empirical findings* (pp. 193–218). Routledge.

O'Reilly, J., Eichhorst, W., Gábos, A., Hadjivassiliou, K., Lain, D., Leschke, J., McGuinness, S., Kureková, L. M., Nazio, T., Ortlieb, R., Russell, H., & Villa, P. (2015). Five characteristics of youth unemployment in Europe: Flexibility, education, migration, family legacies, and EU policy. *SAGE Open, 5*(1), 1–19. https://doi.org/10.1177/2158244015574962

Organisation for Economic Co-operation and Development. (2011). *An overview of growing income inequalities in OECD countries: Main findings.* http://www.i-red.eu/resources/publications-files/oecd-divided -we-stand.pdf

Organisation for Economic Co-operation and Development. (n.d.). Unemployment rates by education level (indicator). *OECD iLibrary.* https://doi.org/10.1787/6183d527-en

Pastore, F. (2018). Why is youth unemployment so high and different across countries? *IZA World of Labor, 420.* https://doi.org/10.15185/izawol.420

Pinquart, M., Juang, L. P., & Silbereisen, R. K. (2003). Self-efficacy and successful school-to-work transition: A longitudinal study. *Journal of Vocational Behavior, 63*(3), 329–346.

Posthuma, R. A., & Campion, M. A. (2009). Age stereotypes in the workplace: Common stereotypes, moderators, and future research directions. *Journal of Management, 35*(1), 158–188. https://doi.org /10.1177/0149206308318617

Praskova, A., Creed, P. A., & Hood, M. (2015). Career identity and the complex mediating relationships between career preparatory actions and career progress markers. *Journal of Vocational Behavior, 87,* 145–153.

Prensky, M. (2001). Digital natives, digital immigrants part 2: Do they really think differently? *On the Horizon, 9*(6), 1–6. https://doi.org/10.1108/10748120110424843

Presti, A. L., Capone, V., Aversano, A., & Akkermans, J. (2021). Career competencies and career success: On the roles of employability activities and academic satisfaction during the school-to-work transition. *Journal of Career Development,* OnlineFirst. https://doi.org/10.1177/0894845321992536

Quintini, G., & Martin, S. (2014). *Same but different: School-to-work transitions in emerging and advanced economies* (OECD Social, Employment and Migration Working Papers No. 154). OECD. https://doi .org/10.1787/5jzbb2t1rcwc-en

Rainer, T. S., & Rainer, J. (2011). *The millennials.* B&H Publishing Group.

Robalino, D., Margolis, D., Rother, F., Newhouse, D., & Lundberg, M. (2013). *Youth employment: A human development agenda for the next decade* (Social Discussion and Labor Development Paper No. 1308). World Bank.

Rudolph, C. W., Rauvola, R. S., Costanza, D. P., & Zacher, H. (2020). Generations and generational differences: Debunking myths in organizational science and practice and paving new paths forward. *Journal of Business and Psychology, 36,* 945–967. https://doi.org/10.1007/s10869-020-09715-2

Rudolph, C. W., Rauvola, R. S., & Zacher, H. (2018). Leadership and generations at work: A critical review. *The Leadership Quarterly, 29*(1), 44–57. https://doi.org/10.1016/j.leaqua.2017.09.004

Rudolph, C. W., & Zacher, H. (2020). COVID-19 and careers: On the futility of generational explanations. *Journal of Vocational Behavior, 119,* 103433. https://doi.org/10.1016/j.jvb.2020.103433

Ryan, L., Sales, R., Tilki, M., & Siara, B. (2008). Social networks, social support and social capital: The experiences of recent Polish migrants in London. *Sociology, 42*(4), 672–690. https://doi.org/10 .1177%2F0038038508091622

Saks, A. M., & Ashforth, B. E. (2002). Is job search related to employment quality? It all depends on the fit. *Journal of Applied Psychology, 87*(4), 646–654. https://doi.org/10.1037/0021-9010.87.4.646

Savickas, M. L. (2002). Career construction: A developmental theory of vocational behavior. In D. Browne (Ed.), *Career choice and development* (4th ed., pp. 149–205). Jossey-Bass.

Savickas, M. L. (2006). *Career construction theory* [Paper presentation]. Proceedings of the AACC 15th Annual National Conference, Sydney, Australia.

Searle, R., Erdogan, B., Peiró, J. M., & Klehe, U. C. (2014). *What we know about youth employment: Research summary and best practices* [SIOP White Paper Series]. Society for Industrial and Organization

Psychology. https://www.siop.org/Portals/84/docs/White%20Papers/Youth%20Employment%20Full%20FINAL.pdf

Seibert, S. E., Kraimer, M. L., & Crant, J. M. (2001). What do proactive people do? A longitudinal model linking proactive personality and career success. *Personnel Psychology, 54*(4), 845–874. https://doi.org/10.1111/j.1744-6570.2001.tb00234.x

Selenko, E., & Pils, K. (2019). The after-effects of youth unemployment: More vulnerable persons are less likely to succeed in Youth Guarantee programmes. *Economic and Industrial Democracy, 40*(2), 282–300. https://doi.org/10.1177/0143831X16653186

Shoenfelt, E., Stone, N., & Kottke, J. (2013). Internships: An established mechanism for increasing employability. *Industrial and Organizational Psychology, 6*(1), 24–27. https://doi.org/10.1111/iops.12004

Silver, H. (2007). *Social exclusion: Comparative analysis of Europe and Middle East youth* (Middle East Youth Initiative Working Paper No. 1). SSRN.

Smith, L. (2015). *Psychology, poverty, and the end of social exclusion: Putting our practice to work.* Teachers College Press.

Snape, E., & Redman, T. (2003). Too old or too young? The impact of perceived age discrimination. *Human Resource Management Journal, 13*(1), 78–89. https://doi.org/10.1111/j.1748-8583.2003.tb00085.x

St. Clair, R., Kintrea, K., & Houston, M. (2013). Silver bullet or red herring? New evidence on the place of aspirations in education. *Oxford Review of Education, 39*(6), 719–738. https://doi.org/10.1080/03054985.2013.854201

Strandh, M., Winefield, A., Nilsson, K., & Hammarström, A. (2014). Unemployment and mental health scarring during the life course. *European Journal of Public Health, 24*(3), 440–445. https://doi.org/10.1093/eurpub/cku005

Stremersch, J., Van Hoye, G., & Van Hooft, E. (2021). How to successfully manage the school-to-work transition: Integrating job search quality in the social cognitive model of career self-management. *Journal of Vocational Behavior, 131*, 103643. https://doi.org/10.1016/j.jvb.2021.103643

Super, D. E. (1980). A life-span, life-space approach to career development. *Journal of Vocational Behavior, 16*, 282–298. https://doi.org/10.1016/0001-8791(80)90056-1

Super, D. E., Crites, J. O., Hummel, R. C., Moser, H. P., Overstreet, P. L., & Warnath, C. F. (1957). *Vocational development: A framework for research.* Teachers College, Bureau of Publications.

Sustainable Development Solutions Network. (2015). *Indicators and a monitoring framework for the Sustainable Development Goals: Launching a data revolution for the SDG.* Jossey-Bass. https://sustainabledevelopment.un.org/content/documents/2013150612-FINAL-SDSN-Indicator-Report1.pdf

Thern, E., de Munter, J., Hemmingsson, T., & Rasmussen, F. (2017). Long-term effects of youth unemployment on mental health: Does an economic crisis make a difference? *Journal of Epidemiology and Community Health, 71*(4), 344–349.

Turban, D. B., Stevens, C. K., & Lee, F. K. (2009). Effects of conscientiousness and extraversion on new labor market entrants' job search: The mediating role of metacognitive activities and positive emotions. *Personnel Psychology, 62*(3), 553–573.

Turte, S. L., Correa, M. E. C., da Luz, A. A., & Fischer, F. M. (2012). Harassment at work? Empowerment and autonomy as coping strategies of young workers. *Work, 41*, 5674–5676. https://doi.org/10.3233/WOR-2012-0916-5674

Twenge, J. M., Campbell, S. M., Hoffman, B. J., & Lance, C. E. (2010). Generational differences in work values: Leisure and extrinsic values increasing, social and intrinsic values decreasing. *Journal of Management, 36*(5), 1117–1142. https://doi.org/10.1177%2F0149206309352246

UNESCO. (2021). *Technical and vocational education and training for disadvantaged youth.* https://unevoc.unesco.org/pub/tvet_for_disadvantaged_youth.pdf

UNICEF. (n.d.). *UNICEF and young people: A generation full of potential and the power to change the world.* https://www.unicef.org/young-people

Van der Heijden, B. I. J. M. (2003). Organisational influences upon the development of occupational expertise throughout the career. *International Journal of Training and Development, 7*(3), 142–165. https://doi .org/10.1111/1468-2419.00178

Van Laar, E., Van Deursen, A. J., Van Dijk, J. A., & De Haan, J. (2017). The relation between 21st-century skills and digital skills: A systematic literature review. *Computers in Human Behavior, 72*, 577–588. https://doi.org/10.1016/j.chb.2017.03.010

Vargas Llave, O., Wilkens, M., & Mullan, J. (2017, December 21). *Working conditions of workers of different ages.* Eurofound. https://www.eurofound.europa.eu/publications/report/2017/working-conditions-of -workers-of-different-ages

Vogel, P. (2015). *Generation jobless?* Palgrave Macmillan.

Wehrle, K., Kira, M., & Klehe, U.-C. (2019). Putting career construction into context: Career adaptability among refugees. *Journal of Vocational Behavior, 111*, 107–124. https://doi.org/10.1016/j.jvb.2018.08.007

Winterheller, J., & Hirt, C. (2017). Career patterns of young highly skilled migrants from Southeast Europe in Austria. *Personnel Review, 46*(2), 222–236. https://doi.org/10.1108/PR-05-2015-0148

Wong, V., & Au-Yeung, T. C. (2019). Autonomous precarity or precarious autonomy? Dilemmas of young workers in Hong Kong. *Economic and Labour Relations Review, 30*(2), 241–261. https://doi.org/10 .1177/1035304619838976

Wu, C.-H., Luksyte, A., & Parker, S. K. (2015). Overqualification and subjective well-being at work: The moderating role of job autonomy and culture. *Social Indicators Research, 121*(3), 917–937. https://doi .org/10.1007/s11205-014-0662-2

Zacher, H. (2015). Using lifespan developmental theory and methods as a viable alternative to the study of generational differences at work. *Industrial and Organizational Psychology, 8*(3), 342–346. https://doi .org/10.1017/iop.2015.47

Zikic, J. (2015). Skilled migrants' career capital as a source of competitive advantage: Implications for strategic HRM. *International Journal of Human Resource Management, 26*(10), 1360–1381. https://doi.org /10.1080/09585192.2014.981199

Zikic, J., & Richardson, J. (2016). What happens when you can't be who you are: Professional identity at the institutional periphery. *Human Relations, 69*(1), 139–168. https://doi.org/10.1177/0018726715580865

Belgin Okay-Somerville, Eva Selenko, and Rosalind H. Searle

AGING WORKFORCE ISSUES FROM A MULTILEVEL APPROACH

INTRODUCTION

The proportion of older workers in the global workforce is increasing because of factors such as the aging of the population in most countries, increased life expectancy, improved healthcare services in developed countries, retirement laws that have raised the retirement age, and the need for additional income (Bloom, 2011; Hertel & Zacher, 2015; Truxillo, Cadiz, & Rineer, 2014). The "graying" trend of the global workforce raises a number of issues around the older workforce (Truxillo, Cadiz, & Hammer, 2015) such as who is considered an older worker; the needs and motivation of older workers; age differences in job attitudes and behaviors; age stereotypes, discrimination, and age diversity management; the societal context for older workers; successful policies and laws regarding late career issues; and preparing the worker and the organization for retirement.

DEFINITIONS

Who Is an Older Worker?   In this article, an older worker is defined as one who is at the later stages in his or her career or approaching retirement age or who remains employed after the standard retirement age. Instead of a specific age or age range—which can vary considerably across jobs and across legal and societal contexts—the term "older worker" generally refers to as those in their late 50s, 60s, and older, who are actively involved in the workforce. This broader definition provides a wider representation of the older-worker population given that there are variations across countries in terms of normal retirement age (e.g., the normal retirement age for an employee entering the labor force in 2014 is 67 in Canada, Israel, Netherlands, Norway, and the United States; 65 in Germany and Turkey; and 63 in France; Organization for Economic Co-operation and Development [OECD], 2015, p. 133) and societal norms about aging (e.g., cultural values concerning getting older and being employed at older ages), and differences in ages across professions and work sectors, as well as individual differences in how people age (e.g., physical and psychological changes by age).

SYSTEMS APPROACH TO DEVELOPMENT AND THE MULTILEVEL CONTEXT FOR OLDER WORKERS

The systems approach to development (Bronfenbrenner & Morris, 1998) posits that human development takes place via the interactions between individuals and their surroundings. As opposed to growing up and developing in isolation, humans interact with the agencies in the immediate environment (e.g., family members, friends, peers in a work group, supervisors, and colleagues) and in broader environments (e.g., society), and these mutual relationships function together to shape people's attitudes and behaviors in life. These relationships occur on a continuous basis throughout life, and individuals contribute to them by their own individual characteristics, while at the same time contextual factors contribute to how they will define themselves and react in certain situations.

Taking the systems approach, this article discusses the issues around the aging workforce from a multilevel perspective. First, it presents the issues at the individual level by describing the within-person changes that occur by age, such as physical, cognitive, and personality changes. Next, the issues at the *organizational context* level are addressed, which arise when older workers interact with their colleagues at work. Age-based changes in work motivation, training motivation, job attitudes, and work performance are summarized. Age stereotyping and discrimination are outlined; and how they emerge and affect older workers' job attitudes and behaviors is reviewed by pointing out relevant theories. Finally, from a broader level, this article discusses the implications of the societal context within which older workers live and work by outlining the recent trends and retirement policies and how they influence the evolving issues around the aging workforce.

INDIVIDUAL CONTEXT FOR OLDER WORKERS: AGE-RELATED CHANGES WITHIN THE PERSON

A number of age-related changes occur within the person that may affect work life. These include the changes in physical and cognitive capacities and personality characteristics. Two lifespan development theories have emerged in the age and workplace literature: selection-optimization-compensation (SOC) theory (Baltes, 1987) and socioemotional selectivity theory (SST; Carstensen, 1995), and are helpful in describing the motivational changes by age.

Physical Changes. Neurophysiological and biological aging occurs slowly and gradually across the lifespan. Sensory capacities, including vision, hearing, and smell, are adversely affected by age, and the impairments become more apparent after middle adulthood (Papalia, Sterns, Feldman, & Camp, 2007). Because of the loss of muscular mass starting around age 30, muscular strength and endurance weaken; and motor functions and coordination slow down, causing a decline in the speed of performance and reaction times (Kaplan, 1993). The reserve capacity of the body's organs tends to decline slowly by age, which may adversely affect coping with physical demands of everyday life (Fries & Crapo, 1981). However, these changes are variable between individuals and may depend on other factors, such as gender, ethnicity, lifestyle choices (e.g., diet, exercise), and genetic or environmental factors (e.g., risk of exposure to toxic materials).

Cognitive Changes. Issues about age-related cognitive changes attempt to understand how different types of cognitive ability change across the adult lifespan. Research differentiates between different types of intelligence or cognitive skills, typically broken down into two broad categories (Cattell, 1943). *Fluid intelligence* addresses the capacity to process novel information and for abstract reasoning, short-term memory, learning, and problem-solving. It tends to peak at young adulthood and decline throughout the lifespan (Schaie, 1996). On the other hand, *crystallized intelligence* includes general knowledge, vocabulary, verbal expressions, and experiences that one gains over one's lifetime. While fluid intelligence tends to decline after young adulthood is reached, crystallized intelligence tends to increase through middle age and beyond (Baltes, 1997; Cattell, 1987). In this respect, a loss-and-growth process occurs over the adult lifespan in experiencing a decline in fluid intelligence while accumulating crystallized intelligence (Ackerman, 2014; Kanfer & Ackerman, 2004; Klein, Dilchert, Ones, & Dages, 2015). It is noteworthy to add that, like physical ability, cognitive ability is influenced by many factors besides age, such as culture and cohort effects (Hertel & Zacher, 2015; Salthouse, 2014).

Changes in Personality Characteristics. Research has challenged the commonly held belief that personality was stable across the lifespan. Investigating 92 longitudinal studies meta-analytically, Roberts and colleagues (2006) supported that individuals demonstrated mean-level changes in most of the Big Five personality traits (Five-Factor Model, FFM; Costa & McCrae, 1992). Specifically, as people aged, they reported higher scores on agreeableness, conscientiousness, emotional stability, and social dominance, while they became less socially vital. Likewise, studies using cross-sectional and longitudinal samples found support for a mean-level increase in agreeableness and conscientiousness (Soto & John, 2012; Specht, Egloff, & Schmukle, 2011), and a decline in neuroticism for older people (Soto, John, Gosling, & Potter, 2011). In addition to Big Five personality traits, meta-analytic findings (Ng & Feldman, 2012) demonstrated that age was not significantly related to proactive personality and generalized self-efficacy in working adults.

LifeSpan Developmental Theories and Motivational Changes.
Lifespan developmental theories approach human development as a continuous process. In this respect, they provide a theoretical background about how people successfully adapt to age-related changes. These theories can also apply to the understanding of work life. The following section summarizes two of these lifespan theories that have emerged in the age and workplace literature and their implications for older worker issues.

Selection-optimization-compensation theory (Baltes & Baltes, 1990).
The SOC model suggests that individuals are motivated to use different strategies to keep functioning successfully by attempting to offset negative consequences of declining abilities and resources due to age. Selection strategies help people choose among alternatives when they are setting life goals. Having limited energy and time motivates individuals to attentively review alternative goals and choose those that align with their needs and resources. Selection strategies include such actions as narrowing down goals and prioritizing them. For example, an older employee may choose to focus on a few projects at a time to preserve time and energy for his or her family. Once goals are selected, optimization takes place by reviewing one's available resource repertoire (e.g., knowledge, skills, and abilities) to optimize his or her performance. For instance, to retain their knowledge of a software program, older professionals may want to practice their skills more often than they used to do. Finally, exerting effort to offset a potentially weak performance due to age-related declines in one's capacity constitutes compensation strategies. For example, hiring a personal assistant to help with administrative work would save an older manager time and energy that he or she could use in other life domains (Baltes, Zhdanova, & Clark, 2011). Research findings support that older workers were more content with their work life (i.e., they reported higher job satisfaction) if they actively performed these SOC strategies (Schmitt, Zacher, & Frese, 2012). Using SOC strategies also increased the work ability of older healthcare employees when job control was high (Weigl, Müller, Hornung, Zacher, & Angerer, 2013); and receiving a SOC training enhanced mental well-being of healthcare employees such as nurses when job control was low (Müller, Heiden, Herbig, Poppe, & Angerer, 2015).

Socioemotional selectivity theory (Carstensen, 1995).
SST posits that the perception of "time left in life" influences individuals' motivation to select goals and adopt a present or future orientation in life. The theory suggests that younger individuals tend to have an expansive perception of time, whereas older individuals have a more restricted future time perception (Carstensen, Isaacowitz, & Charles, 1999). As a result of this difference in time

perspectives, older individuals tend to consider time a more valuable commodity; try to use the present time more wisely; and choose to invest their resources (i.e., energy and time) in emotion-related goals, such as building and maintaining meaningful social relationships. Consequently, spending more time with close family members and friends or mentoring colleagues at work become more meaningful goals for social relatedness. In contrast, having a more open-ended perception of time, younger individuals adopt a future orientation and feel more comfortable pursuing knowledge-related goals, such as gaining job knowledge and participating in training to advance in their careers. As job-related knowledge accumulates over time, this focus on attaining growth tends to decline later in life, and emotional goals are prioritized (e.g., Kanfer & Ackerman, 2004; Truxillo, Cadiz, Rineer, Zaniboni, & Fraccaroli, 2012).

Because they recognize different age-related changes in multiple domains within individuals (e.g., cognitive and physical capacities, personality, perception of remaining time) and how those changes can affect motivation, attitudes, and performance, both the SOC model (Baltes & Baltes, 1990) and SST (Carstensen, 1995) are highly relevant to the workplace literature. The implications of these two theories can be easily adapted to the workplace to develop age-related workplace interventions, including training and mentoring programs, work redesign, age-diverse team building, and supportive work-life HR policies for employees of different ages (Truxillo et al., 2015). Another emerging area that integrates the SOC model and SST is the leadership literature (Zacher, Clark, Anderson, & Ayoko, 2015). Capitalizing on age-based motivational changes, the lifespan models of leadership aim to explain how leader age is related to leadership effectiveness and the role of leader-follower age differences in leader performance.

The sections so far have summarized the individual context within which physical, cognitive, personality, and motivational age-related changes occur. Stepping back to the multilevel approach of aging workforce issues, the next section analyzes how those changes in the individual level may shape the specific workplace context for employees of different ages.

AGE WITHIN THE ORGANIZATIONAL CONTEXT: WORK MOTIVATION, JOB ATTITUDES, AND WORK PERFORMANCE

This section reviews how these age-related changes may translate into workplace by describing changes in work motivation, job attitudes, and work performance.

Changes in Work Motivation.   In line with individual-level age-related changes and lifespan developmental perspectives, Kanfer and Ackerman (2004) offered an integrative framework on work motivation by identifying four main themes that change across the lifespan: loss, growth, reorganization, and exchange. Loss describes the declining capacities in fluid intelligence by age (e.g., abstract reasoning, working memory); whereas growth refers to the improving performance on crystallized intelligence (e.g., general knowledge, verbal comprehension) as one gets older. Reorganization includes age-based changes in the organization and structure of nonability traits (e.g., personality, emotion, and affect). And finally, exchange refers to the changes in one's values, self-concept, affect and emotions, personality, and vocational interests over the life course. The authors proposed that changes in these four themes across adult life influence work motivation. For example, older workers are more likely to use their accumulated job knowledge to compensate the decline in fluid intelligence and to pursue intrinsically motivated tasks that affirm their self-concept. Younger workers tend to focus on growth to advance in their careers and to participate in learning and development activities to gain the job knowledge and skills their jobs require.

Kooij, De Lange, Jansen, Kanfer, and Dikkers (2011) conducted a comprehensive meta-analysis, including 86 studies with a total sample size of 48,447, to examine the relationship between age and various work-related motives, such as growth, security, social, extrinsic, and intrinsic motives. In line with SST (Carstensen, 1995) and Kanfer and Ackerman's (2004) model of age-related work motivation, their results showed that age was significantly and negatively associated with growth motives (e.g., development or advancement at work) and extrinsic work-related motives (e.g., promotion, recognition, compensation, and benefits); whereas it was significantly and positively related to intrinsic work-related motives (e.g., job characteristics related to accomplishment, job enjoyment, and existing skill utilization). Thus, Kooij et al.'s (2011) results supported that older workers were more interested in working on interesting jobs and accomplishing meaningful tasks, exercising autonomy and utilizing skill variety at work, and helping others such as mentoring or coaching.

These age-related shifts in work motivation are also supported by the empirical study of Inceoglu, Segers, and Bartram (2012). Investigating two samples with over 10,000 working adults in the United Kingdom, Inceoglu et al. (2012) demonstrated that what motivates employees at work differed across age groups. For example, jobs that require expansive personal resources (e.g., competition and power) were perceived to be less motivating for older workers than for younger colleagues. In addition, older workers reported higher preference for intrinsically rewarding jobs in which they had autonomy and a chance to help others. Finally, older age groups were less motivated by extrinsic rewards, such as material rewards, career progression, status, and recognition, compared to younger workers.

Changes in training motivation.   Relevant to work motivation, training motivation may also change over one's lifetime. As noted in the section "Cognitive Changes," fluid intelligence that is associated with learning and processing of novel information tends to decrease with age after young adulthood is reached; whereas crystallized intelligence, associated with general knowledge, verbal expressions, and experiences gained over time, tends to increase with age (Baltes, 1997; Cattell, 1987). Also, in line with the lifespan work-motivation theories (e.g., Kanfer & Ackerman, 2004; Baltes & Baltes, 1990; Carstensen, 1995), individuals tend to be more growth oriented and motivated to acquire new job knowledge and skills when they are younger. As they become older and gain job knowledge and status in later stages of life, however, pursuing socioemotional goals becomes more meaningful. As a result of these age-related changes in cognitive capacities and the shift in life goals, a single content, design, and delivery method of training may not be equally attractive or beneficial for younger and older workers (Inceoglu et al., 2012). Thus, despite the common negative stereotype that older workers are less motivated to learn compared to their younger counterparts, research argues that older workers are not less motivated to learn but that they are motivated by different job features (Inceoglu et al., 2012). For example, older workers approached coaching trainings more favorably when they could satisfy generativity motives by acquiring new skills to pass their knowledge on to younger colleagues (Ng & Feldman, 2008).

As examples of training design, research supports that older workers benefit more from self-paced training (Callahan, Kiker, & Cross, 2003) in which they are allowed to adjust their own speed while learning; and they respond better to error-management training (e.g., Carter & Beier, 2010) that encourages trainees to perform errors as they learn.

Implications of the changes in work motivation and training motivation. These findings have important implications that combat the negative stereotypes of the aging workforce by demonstrating that older workers value different work characteristics more than younger colleagues, and thus they are not less motivated (Kanfer & Ackerman, 2004; Ng & Feldman, 2012). In an attempt to evaluate whether common stereotypes about older workers were consistent with the empirical data, Ng and Feldman (2012) conducted a meta-analysis including 418 studies ($N = 208,204$). The results presented no empirical support that older workers had low work motivation. Moreover, there was a positive, though weak, relationship between age and job motivation (.11) and job involvement (.12). Despite the common negative stereotype that older employees have lower ability to learn (Posthuma & Campion, 2009), empirical data (Ng & Feldman, 2012) suggests that age was negatively, yet weakly, related to career development motivation (−.14), learning self-efficacy (−.17), and motivation to learn (−.14). In addition, although age was negatively, yet weakly, related to training motivation (rc = −.05; 95% CI: [−.05, −.05]), no significant relationship was detected between age and training participation (rc = −.04; 95% CI: [−.10, .02]). To conclude, the research evidence points out that the relationship between age and work motives is not necessarily negative, and that the magnitude of the negative relationship is not as strong as it is commonly assumed to be (Ng & Feldman, 2012).

Changes in Job Attitudes. Job attitudes refer to "evaluations of one's job that express one's feelings toward, beliefs about, and attachment to one's job" (Judge & Kammeyer-Mueller, 2012). Meta-analytic findings suggest that older workers generally hold more favorable attitudes toward their jobs, colleagues, and organizations (Ng & Feldman, 2010). Some of the attitudes that were positively associated with age were organizational commitment, organizational identification and loyalty, satisfaction with coworkers and supervisors, interpersonal trust, job satisfaction, and intrinsic work motivation. In line with SST (Carstensen, 1995), the authors argued that older workers tend to pursue meaningful emotion-related goals based on their perception of restricted time in life and try to maximize positive experiences gained "now," leading to having more positive attitudes toward work and work environment, in general.

Examining the changes in personality traits over time can also help determine whether older workers have different job attitudes. In a longitudinal study, Wille, Hofmans, Feys, and De Fruyt (2013) tracked young professionals' personality traits and job attitudes over a 15-year time period and reported significantly higher agreeableness and conscientiousness, and lower neuroticism scores at the end of the study. They also revealed that the changes in these personality traits were correlated with the changes in employees' attitudes regarding their jobs (e.g., job involvement and job satisfaction), thus pointing out the possibility of the maturation of attitudes by age over the lifespan. It is noteworthy that studies investigating the age-job-attitudes link are limited. To understand how age relates to job attitudes, future research should utilize longitudinal study designs, explore curvilinear relationships in addition to the linear examinations between age and attitudes, and investigate whether age-based changes in job attitudes are uniform across cultures (Yaldiz & Truxillo, 2015).

Changes in Work Performance.   Although age relates to most of the job attitudes in a positive way, the relationship between age and work performance is more complex. For example, in terms of the relationship between age and various dimensions of work performance, in their meta-analysis, Ng and Feldman (2008) demonstrated that age was not related to core task performance and found a positive relationship between age and organizational citizenship behaviors, a form of contextual performance. These findings indicate that older workers may attempt to offset the negative consequences of declining fluid intelligence by using improved crystallized intelligence. Taking advantage of their job knowledge, professional expertise, and experience accumulated throughout the years, it would be reasonable for older workers to approach work-related issues on a higher level than younger colleagues with limited job knowledge and experience (Salthouse, 2012).

Salthouse (2012) proposed that age-related cognitive declines may not be necessarily associated with work performance for a number of reasons, such as that individuals do not have to manifest maximum performance at all times in everyday life; there are factors other than cognitive ability (e.g., personality, knowledge, skills, and abilities) that affect success in life; individuals can employ accommodations (e.g., SOC strategies) to counteract potentially negative consequences of cognitive declines on performance; and finally, crystallized intelligence improves in later life. Klein et al.'s (2015) studies on working adult samples from executives and nonexecutives positions provide support to Salthouse's last argument on crystallized intelligence. The authors investigated the relationship between cognitive ability and performance across different age groups, and found that although age was negatively related to general mental ability scores, different relationships were observed when specific ability components were analyzed (i.e., crystallized and fluid intelligence). The findings showed that older employees outperformed their younger counterparts in verbal ability tests, which are associated with crystallized intelligence, whereas, relative to their older colleagues, younger employees had higher scores in the figural and inductive reasoning tests that are associated with fluid intelligence.

As it would be expected that physical changes, such as declining sensory-motor capacities, would leave older workers in a less physically fit position than younger colleagues, Warr, Miles, and Platts (2001) have noted that the implications of physical changes on work performance have not been studied with larger samples or across jobs. For example, research on occupational health and safety has revealed that age was positively related to safety performance, whereas it was negatively related to objective work injuries (e.g., Ng & Feldman, 2008), which was contradictory to what would be expected by declines in sensory-motor capacities. Moreover, it seems that older workers are less likely to be injured at the workplace compared to younger colleagues; however, when they are hurt, their injuries tend to be more serious (Rogers & Wiatrowski, 2005).

In terms of age-based changes in health conditions and their effects on performance, meta-analytic findings (Ng & Feldman, 2012, 2013) revealed that age was positively associated with a few negative health outcomes such as higher blood pressure and cholesterol, although these negative outcomes did not translate into lower work performance (Ng & Feldman, 2008, 2012). In addition, although age was modestly related to these negative health outcomes, older workers' self-reports of subjective health found no correlations between age and physical health and somatic complaints. Finally, in terms of self-reported mental health, including anxiety, low positive mood, depression, negative mood, anger, and irritation, the correlations with age were very weak and negative in direction ($<-.15$), suggesting that these negative outcomes are not associated with age, or to the extent that they are, the relationship is negative. A related concern for the aging workforce is shiftwork (Smith, Folkard, Tucker, & Evans, 2011). Disturbed circadian rhythms as a result of changing sleep-wake hours and their unfavorable associations with sleep problems, fatigue, metabolic disorders, and cardiovascular disease present an increased health risk for older workers, especially those who work night shifts. However, more research is needed to uncover the influence of age-related health conditions on older workers' performance during shift work.

In conclusion, research findings have presented evidence that cognitive, physical, biological, and motivational changes throughout the lifespan have numerous implications for older workers' performance, yet more research is needed to explain the mediating mechanisms (e.g., job and organizational tenure, personality) and boundary conditions (e.g., exercise, dietary habits, job characteristics, and organizational safety climate) before reaching more conclusive results on the age-job performance relationship.

AGE WITHIN THE ORGANIZATIONAL CONTEXT: AGE STEREOTYPING AND DISCRIMINATION AT WORK

With increased workplace age diversity, there is also an increased chance for age discrimination against workers of all ages. This section focuses on organizational contextual issues in terms of the stereotyping and discrimination faced by older workers.

Definitions. Although sometimes used interchangeably, the terms "age stereotyping" and "age discrimination" reflect separate, albeit related, issues. Age stereotyping includes the process by which workers in different age groups are viewed differently. Age stereotypes may be explicit (conscious) or implicit (unconscious) on the part of the observer. However, age stereotyping may not always lead to age discrimination, whereby older people and younger people are treated differently by supervisors or coworkers. Such treatment can involve a number of human resources decisions (e.g., hiring, performance appraisals, access to training) or more subtle versions of discrimination (e.g., social inclusion within a work group).

Age Stereotyping. A number of mechanisms have been proposed to explain stereotyping more broadly, including age stereotyping.

Stereotype content model: Competence and warmth. One theoretical approach that has dominated the stereotyping literature is that by Fiske, Cuddy, Glick, and Xu (2002).

This approach describes two key dimensions of stereotyping—namely, competence and warmth. Specifically, certain subgroups are seen as having different levels of competence and warmth, thus affecting an observer's stereotype of a person. For example, middle-class people are seen as having both high competence and high warmth so that, overall, there is a positive stereotype associated with them. In contrast, older adults are seen as being high in warmth but low in competence (Cuddy & Fiske, 2002), and these findings regarding older adults are said to hold across cultures. However, it is important to note that much of the research on nonworkplace age stereotyping included people who are beyond retirement age (i.e., in their 70s, 80s, and beyond), so that these results may not hold true for people of working age.

Explicit and implicit age stereotypes. A related line of research in understanding stereotypes differentiates between explicit (conscious) and implicit (unconscious) stereotypes (Greenwald & Banaji, 1995). Explicit stereotypes fall within the conscious awareness of the observer, and in that sense, they may be more easily combated than implicit stereotypes, which the observer may have but not be aware of. This makes implicit stereotypes particularly insidious both to detect and to combat. The measurement of such implicit stereotypes is also a challenge, although one dominant approach has been through IATs (implicit association tests; Greenwald, McGhee, & Schwartz, 1998), which are said to tap into unconscious stereotypes by measuring a person's response latencies. Research in the social psychology literature differentiates implicit and explicit stereotypes, whereas most of the workplace age discrimination research to date has focused solely on the effects of explicit stereotypes (Truxillo, Finkelstein, Pytlovany, & Jenkins, 2015).

Stereotypes of older workers: General findings. In addition, research has also examined stereotypes specifically associated with older workers. In a review of the literature, Posthuma and Campion (2009) found that typical older worker stereotypes included their being resistant to change and to technology, costlier because they require higher wages and are closer to retirement, and lower performing. This is similar to other meta-analytic evidence regarding the perceptions of older workers (e.g., Bal, Reiss, Rudolph, & Baltes, 2011; Finkelstein, Burke, & Raju, 1995). Moreover, others have argued that older workers may be deemed overqualified; or, at least, overqualification is used as an excuse for age discrimination (Finkelstein, 2011). It is important to note that other meta-analytic evidence (Ng & Feldman, 2012) suggests that most of these older worker stereotypes are not true, except for perhaps having lower motivation to learn and training motivation. Further, there are also some positive stereotypes of older workers, such as being more conscientious and higher in organizational citizenship behaviors than their younger counterparts, and less neurotic (Bertolino, Truxillo, & Fraccaroli, 2013; Truxillo, McCune, Bertolino, & Fraccaroli, 2012). These positive stereotypes of older workers versus their younger counterparts highlight the complexity of understanding why older workers appear to face greater actual discrimination outcomes (Truxillo et al., 2015) and reemployment times (Wanberg, Kanfer, Hamann, & Zhang, 2015).

Job-age stereotypes. In addition, a line of research has identified that there are job-age stereotypes, or stereotypes that are associated with different jobs and industries. As a frequently cited example, the high-tech industry is generally associated with younger-aged people. The existence of these job-age stereotypes have been found for a number of industries and jobs (Cleveland & Landy, 1983; Gordon & Arvey, 1986), and may be partly due to the representation of various age groups within a particular industry. The job-age stereotype concept is important for understanding how discrimination may take place within organizations, because the match between a person's age group and the job under consideration has been found to lead to discriminatory decisions during hiring processes such as the likelihood of hiring an applicant or an applicant's expected job performance were they to be hired (e.g., Perry, Kulik, & Bourhis, 1996).

Relational demography and faultlines. Relational demography research in organizations examines the effects of demographic differences on worker and organizational outcomes. Much of the relational demography research is based on social identity theory (SIT; Tajfel & Turner, 1979), which posits that people exist in a social world in which their self-image is based on their group memberships. People can associate themselves with certain groups to increase their self-esteem. Conversely, social categorization (Lankau, Riordan, & Thomas, 2005) as an outgroup member can lead to negative self-perceptions and may lead to discrimination against them by ingroup members. Based in SIT and social categorization approaches, relational demography research examines how demographic differences within work groups can affect outcomes such as worker well-being and productivity (Shore, Cleveland, & Goldberg, 2003; Thatcher, 1999). Faultlines research examines how subgroups of workers may form within teams based on multiple demographic differences, such as age and gender (e.g., two subgroups within a team consisting of older males and younger females), which can lead to increased tension and conflict within the group (Thatcher & Patel, 2011, 2012). Notably, faultlines based on age may have less potent negative effects than faultlines based on other demographic characteristics (e.g., gender and race; Thatcher & Patel, 2011).

Finally, it may be worthwhile to mention the issue of generational differences, often touted in the popular press. However, it is noteworthy that little research has examined the issue of discrimination based on generations; this is perhaps because the generational concept is highly confounded with chronological age and also because the notion of generations as a concept has been challenged (e.g., Cadiz, Truxillo, & Fraccaroli, 2015; Costanza & Finkelstein, 2015).

Age Discrimination. There have been a number of reviews on actual discrimination against workers based on their age (e.g., Truxillo et al., 2015; Truxillo, Fraccaroli, Yaldiz, & Zaniboni, 2017). These reviews cite a number of ways that age discrimination may occur in organizations, including in recruitment, selection, training opportunities, performance appraisal, retention, and interpersonal treatment. Meta-analytic research confirms that being older is associated with negative workplace outcomes (e.g., Bal et al., 2011; Finkelstein, Burke, & Raju, 1995). Although such age discrimination has been found to exist, its specific underlying mechanism has not been definitively identified, and perhaps varies on the particular decision and context. For example, demographic differences have been found to have fewer effects over time as workers come to know each other at a deep level, not just by the demographic group with which they are associated (Harrison, Price, Gavin, & Florey, 2002). If this is the case, then age stereotypes may affect workplace decisions when less is known about the employee (e.g., they are a job applicant) than when they have become well known to the observer (e.g., during performance appraisals).

Age Diversity in the Workplace.   This section describes research streams on the social environment faced by workers of different ages. This issue has taken increased attention from researchers as workg roups have grown more age-diverse with different ages working side-by-side. One take-away message of this work is that age diversity may increase some workplace challenges, but if properly managed (e.g., when management fosters a positive age diversity climate for people of all ages), age diversity can strengthen team functioning.

Age Diversity Climate.   Diversity climate research focuses on employees' shared perceptions of how workers from different subgroups are treated within an organization (Avery, McKay, & Wilson, 2007). The age diversity climate literature focuses more specifically on employees' perceptions of how workers in different age groups are treated within an organization. One key finding of the age diversity literature is that, if mishandled, age diversity may lead to negative outcomes (Kunze, Böhm, & Bruch, 2011). In contrast, the research on age diversity climate suggests that a positive age diversity climate can be fostered through positive HR functions that support people of all ages; and that a positive age diversity climate leads to positive outcomes for the organization, such as decreased turnover and improved productivity (Böhm, Kunze, & Bruch, 2014).

Team age diversity.   The effects of age diversity within teams are unclear (Truxillo et al., 2014), perhaps because of the effects of moderators in determining whether age has a positive or negative effect on team processes and performance. For example, demographic diversity in teams may initially hamper team functioning (e.g., Cannon-Bowers & Bowers, 2011), but as noted in the "Age Discrimination" section earlier, increased exposure to other team members over time may reduce negative demographic effects (e.g., Harrison, Price, Gavin, & Florey, 2002). Similarly, age diversity may negatively affect team performance under conditions of low transformational leadership (Kearney & Gerbert, 2009) or under conditions of routine (rather than complex) decision-making (Wegge, Roth, Neubach, Schmidt, & Kanfer, 2008). In short, whether or not age diversity affects team performance is likely to be a function of other situational factors.

Age and leadership.   Much has been made in the popular press of the issue of age differences between supervisors and subordinates, particularly in situations where supervisors are younger than their employees. However, the issue of leadership and age is in need of greater examination (e.g., Truxillo & Burlacu, 2015), although researchers are beginning to tackle the issue of age and leader success (Walter & Scheibe, 2013; Zacher, Clark, Anderson, & Ayoko, 2015). For example, Zacher, Rosing, Henning, and Frese (2011) found that older leaders are more successful if they display generativity (support for future generations; Kanfer & Ackerman, 2004) toward subordinates. Research has also shown differences in how performance feedback may be given to older and younger people (Wang, Burlacu, Truxillo, James, & Yao, 2015), an issue related to leadership in an age-diverse workforce.

Age and knowledge transfer. In an age-diverse workforce, older workers and those who transition to retire can be a knowledge source due to their job-related knowledge, skills, and abilities, and the job experience that they accumulated over years. As aging workers get ready to leave the workforce, transfer of critical knowledge from older generations to younger ones who will remain within the organization becomes important for organizational success (Beazley, Boenisch, & Harden, 2002). However, research on knowledge transfer from older and retiring employees is as yet limited (e.g., Burmeister & Deller, 2016) and issues such as types of knowledge (e.g., procedural versus relational), individual (e.g., personality) and relationship characteristics (e.g., age similarity between the older and younger employees, role of trust), and the contextual factors (e.g., organizational support, positive climate) need to be examined to uncover the antecedents of successful transfer knowledge from older workers.

The sections so far have described the age-related changes that occur within the individual and in the organizational contextual environment that surrounds the aging workforce. Proceeding to a higher-level context, the societal context and its implications on older workforce is reviewed next.

THE SOCIETAL CONTEXT FOR OLDER WORKERS

The individual- and organizational-contextual-level issues discussed in the previous sections are related to some broader and deep changes in the socioeconomic and demographic contexts that have mostly occurred in economically developed countries (e.g., Western Europe, North America, and Japan; Phillips & Siu, 2012). These changing trends in socioeconomic and demographic contexts present a new and challenging broader environment for individuals and organizations in decision-making processes and in setting future goals. The following section reviews these changes in the societal context and explains how they are related to issues around the aging workforce.

Demographic Transitions. There has been a consistent decline in birthrates globally during the last 50 years. According to the statistics, birthrates have declined from around 37 births for every 1,000 people in the population between the years 1950–1955 to 20 births per thousand between the years 2010–2015; and this index is particularly low in Europe and North America, at 11 per 1,000 (Kinsella & He, 2009). A second change has occurred in the life expectancy of people, which has consistently increased over the last century. In Europe and North America in the early 21st century, people who reach age 65 are likely to anticipate an additional life expectancy of around 20 years, whereas this number was around 14 years in 1950 (Kinsella & He, 2009). Taken together, lower birthrates and longer life expectancy lead to overall aging of the population and, consequently, aging of the working population. Although this trend is evident mostly in economically developed countries, the growth of the older population should also become noticeable in developing countries, such as China and Russia, in the future.

These two salient demographic changes have strong repercussions for the labor market. The declining birthrates pose risks for a possible deficit in the number of future workers and for destabilizing the size of the workforce in Western society (Vaupel, 2010). In addition, the imbalanced distribution of older populations in certain geographical areas, the huge asymmetry between labor forces concentrated in developing countries, and the capital concentrated in advanced industrialized countries may reinforce a migration across countries.

In addition to the increased longevity, people also have improved access to healthcare services than they used to in the past. Consequently, people are able to continue working, under certain conditions, even in their advanced ages. Thus, a relatively new segment of the labor market is emerging: actively working retired individuals. These individuals continue working after retirement age, such as in the form of bridge employment (e.g., a job where they work fewer hours or they have less responsibility). This emerging phenomenon of late career issues after traditional retirement age has begun to capture the attention of researchers (Wang, Olson, & Shultz, 2013). "Retirement" no longer necessarily means quitting working for everyone. For example, there are more 60- or 65-year-olds in the workforce than in the past. In addition, motivational differences may exist among those who prefer to stay active in the workforce. That is, people may decide to postpone retirement to remain socially engaged in life or due to extrinsic motivational factors, such as earning money.

New Pension System Rules.   The aging of the population and the relative scarcity of young generations of workers in certain countries can put strong pressure on pension systems, particularly in the Western European countries such as Germany, Italy, and Spain. In addition, the current trend in the "old age dependency ratio"—the relationship between number of people at retirement age relative to the number of people at working age—is alarmingly wide in countries around the world (Phillips & Siu, 2012). Consequently, actions have been taken to change the retirement laws such as increasing the retirement age or eliminating a mandatory retirement age entirely (Baruch, Sayce, & Gregoriou, 2014). Moreover, a switch from a pension plan based on "pay" to a pension plan based on "direct contribution" has been introduced in many countries (OECD, 2013). However, the effectiveness of these policies in improving labor-market participation for older workers differs across countries. For instance, from 2003 to 2013, while Germany realized an increase of more than 23% in the labor market participation of older workers (from 55 to 64 years old), quite stable rates were observed in other countries (Fraccaroli & Deller, 2015), which shows that the capacity of national governments to activate pension reform and policies varies largely. Other factors that affect the effectiveness of these policies include socioeconomic factors, such as the intensity of economic crisis and the level of youth unemployment. Specifically, it is more difficult to intervene in favor of older individuals' participation in the labor market in countries where the economic crisis is stronger and the youth unemployment rate is higher.

New Social Meaning of Late Career and Retirement.   The recent changes in demographics, labor market, and retirement norms have led to some other important changes in the ways people interpret, make decisions, and plan the future, as well as in their transitioning from work to retirement. A process of destandardization and individualization of the life course in the elderly is underway (Sargent, Lee, Martin, & Zikic, 2013). Accordingly, a greater variability is expected between individuals in terms of the sequence of the events that characterize the late career issues and transitioning into retirement (Beehr, 2014). Thus, the importance of chronological age may change in a way that may make it less predictive in defining work activities or career stages for older workers. In addition to chronological age, there are other factors that influence the level of engagement and activity of older workers in work life, such as financial situation and health conditions of individuals. There are also various psychological and psychosocial factors that determine behaviors and choices of older workers, such as needs (e.g., need for achievement), work values (e.g., importance of work in life, work centrality), future time perspective (e.g., level of aspiration), relationships inside the family (e.g., occupational position of the partner, family roles), the quality of the job (e.g., autonomy and opportunity to use competences), and the quality of the organizational life (e.g., providing recognition and opportunity for growth; Shultz & Wang, 2011; Wang & Shi, 2014).

Changing Attitudes Toward Aging.   Attitudes are socially constructed, and they are related to larger cultural norms. Because the "social calendar" of events in the late life course has changed, it is common to see a 68-year-old person still working. Another change is that it may be considered quite anomalous to be retired at age 50—which was a common age of retirement in some sectors in the 1980s. Moreover, the increasing presence of older workers in organizations and society can influence the perceptions about the role of seniority in a society (e.g., the extent that older people may be recognized as sources of wisdom and experience). Similarly, age stereotypes against older workers can be reduced by enhancing intergenerational contact in the workplace, as discussed in the "Age Discrimination" and "Age Diversity Climate" sections earlier (Henry, Zacher, & Desmette, 2015). These changes in attitudes, in turn, may transfer into workplace, for example, by directly or indirectly influencing the quality of team functioning (i.e., intergenerational relationship, capacity to manage differences in age) and the organizational age climate (Kunze & Boehm, 2015).

New Psychological Contracts in Organizations.   A final theme is related to the social changes within organizations, that is, the evolution of psychological contracts around changing organizational demographics. Psychological contracts describe the informal exchanges between employees and employers to define mutual obligations: positive work atmosphere, opportunity to develop competencies, rewards (e.g., obligations of the organization), extra-role behaviors, loyalty, and adaptability (e.g., obligations of employees) (Rousseau, 1995). Psychological contracts are subjective in nature, and they present a system to regulate the social exchanges in organizations. Rousseau (1995) distinguishes two types of psychological contract: transactional and relational. Transactional contracts refer to a more materialist exchange in which the essential elements of the psychological contract are rewards from one side and good performance from the other. In contrast, relational contracts deal more with socioemotional exchanges, such as loyalty and long-term engagement. How the perceptions of the psychological contracts may change by age can be explained by SST (Carstensen, 1995). Since SST posits that as people get older socioemotional goals become more important, relative to younger workers, older workers would prefer a relational psychological contract that is more focused on the job aspects related to the quality of social interactions and positive emotional exchanges. In line with this argument, Bal and Kooij (2011) examined whether age moderated the relationship between work centrality and transactional and relational contracts. Collecting data from a sample of 465 healthcare workers in the Netherlands, they found that, surprisingly, age was negatively related to both types of psychological contract. However, the moderation analyses revealed that for older workers, when work centrality was high, the relational contract was high and the transactional contract was low. In the light of SST, the authors discussed that older workers who perceived their work as central to their identities had a relational investment in their organization; whereas those who did not perceive work as an important aspect of their lives had no relational investment in their organization.

To sum up, demographic changes, such as increased life expectancy; new retirement laws that facilitate a longer working life; more favorable attitudes toward aging and the changing norms about the presence of older workers in the workforce; and, finally, the relational focus of psychological contracts are among the factors that constitute the societal context that surrounds the aging workforce.

CONCLUSION

The global trend of the aging of the workforce is evident and becoming more widespread. Exploring age-related changes pertinent to the within-individual-, organizational-, and societal levels will contribute to our understanding about the older-workers population and to promoting an age-diverse yet more effective workforce.

REFERENCES

Ackerman, P. L. (2014). Adolescent and adult intellectual development. *Current Directions in Psychological Science, 23,* 246–251.

Avery, D. R., McKay, P. F., & Wilson, D. C. (2007). Engaging the aging workforce: The relationship between perceived age similarity, satisfaction with coworkers, and employee engagement. *Journal of Applied Psychology, 92,* 1542–1556.

Bal, A. C., Reiss, A. E. B., Rudolph, C. W., & Baltes, B. (2011). Examining positive and negative perceptions of older workers: A meta-analysis. *Journals of Gerontology, Series B: Psychological Sciences and Social Sciences, 66,* 687–698.

Bal, P. M., & Kooij, D. (2011). The relations between work centrality, psychological contracts, and job attitudes: The influence of age. *European Journal of Work and Organizational Psychology, 20,* 497–523.

Baltes, P. B. (1987). Theoretical propositions of life-span developmental psychology: On the dynamics between growth and decline. *Developmental Psychology, 23,* 611–626.

Baltes, P. B. (1997). On the incomplete architecture of human ontogeny: Selection, optimization, and compensation as foundation of developmental theory. *American Psychologist, 52,* 366–380.

Baltes, P. B., & Baltes, M. M. (1990). Psychological perspectives on successful aging: The model of selective optimization with compensation. In P. B. Baltes & M. M. Baltes (Eds.), *Successful aging: Perspectives from the behavioral sciences* (pp. 1–34). New York: Cambridge University Press.

Baltes, B. B., Zhdanova, L. S., & Clark, M. A. (2011). Examining the relationship between personality, coping strategies, and work-family conflict. *Journal of Business Psychology, 4,* 517–530.

Baruch, Y., Sayce, S., & Gregoriou, A. (2014). Retirement in a global labour market: A call for abolishing the fixed retirement age. *Personnel Review, 43,* 464–482.

Beazley, H., Boenisch, J., & Harden, D. (2002). *Continuity management: Preserving corporate knowledge and productivity when employees leave.* New York: Wiley.

Beehr, T. A. (2014). To retire or not to retire: That is not the question. *Journal of Organizational Behavior, 35*, 1093–1108.

Bertolino, M., Truxillo, D. M., & Fraccaroli, F. (2013). Age effects on perceived personality and job performance. *Journal of Managerial Psychology, 28*(7/8), 867–885.

Bloom, D. E. (2011). 7 billion and counting. *Science, 333*, 562–569.

Böhm, S. A., Kunze, F., & Bruch, H. (2014). Spotlight on age diversity climate: The impact of age-inclusive HR practices on firm-level outcomes. *Personnel Psychology, 67*, 667–704.

Bronfenbrenner, U., & Morris, P. A. (1998). The ecology of developmental processes. In W. Damon (Series Ed.) & R. M. Lerner (Vol. Ed.), *Handbook of child psychology: Vol. 1. Theoretical models of human development* (pp. 993–1028). New York: Wiley.

Burmeister, A., & Deller, J. (2016). Knowledge retention from older and retiring workers: What do we know, and where do we go from here? *Work, Aging, and Retirement, 2*, 87–104.

Cadiz, D. M., Truxillo, D. M., & Fraccaroli, F. (2015). What are the benefits of focusing on generation-based differences and at what cost? *Industrial and Organizational Psychology, 8*, 356–362.

Callahan, J. S., Kiker, D. S., & Cross, T. (2003). Does method matter? A meta-analysis of the effects of training method on older learner training performance. *Journal of Management, 29*, 663–680.

Cannon-Bowers, J. A., & Bowers C. (2011). Team development and functioning. In S. Zedeck (Ed.), *APA Handbook of industrial and organizational psychology* (pp. 597–650). Washington, DC: American Psychological Association.

Carstensen, L. L. (1995). Evidence for a life-span theory of socioemotional selectivity. *Current Directions in Psychological Science, 4*, 151–156.

Carstensen, L. L., Isaacowitz, D. M., & Charles, S. T. (1999). Taking time seriously: A theory of socioemotional selectivity. *American Psychologist, 54*, 165–181.

Carter, M., & Beier, M. E. (2010). The effectiveness of error management training with working-aged adults. *Personnel Psychology, 63*, 641–675.

Cattell, R. B. (1943). The measurement of adult intelligence. *Psychological Bulletin, 40*, 153–193.

Cattell, R. B. (1987). *Intelligence: Its structure, growth, and action*. Amsterdam, The Netherlands: North-Holland.

Cleveland, J. N., & Landy, F. J. (1983). The effects of person and job stereotypes on two personnel decisions. *Journal of Applied Psychology, 68*, 609–619.

Costa, P. T., & McCrae, R. R. (1992). *Revised NEO Personality Inventory (NEO PI-R) and NEO Five-Factor Inventory (NEO-FFI) professional manual*. Lutz, FL: Psychological Assessment Resources.

Costanza, D. P., & Finkelstein, L. M. (2015). Generationally based differences in the workplace: Is there a there there? *Industrial and Organizational Psychology, 8*, 308–323.

Cuddy, A. J., & Fiske, S. T. (2002). Doddering but dear: Process, content, and function in stereotyping of older persons. In T. D. Nelson (Ed.), *Ageism: Stereotyping and prejudice against older persons* (pp. 3–26). Cambridge, MA: MIT Press.

Finkelstein, L. M. (2011). Overqualified as a euphemism for too old? *Industrial and Organizational Psychology, 4*, 250–251.

Finkelstein, L. M., Burke, M. J., & Raju, N. S. (1995). Age discrimination in simulated employment contexts: An integrative analysis. *Journal of Applied Psychology, 80*, 652–663.

Fiske, S. T., Cuddy, A. J., Glick, P., & Xu, J. (2002). A model of (often mixed) stereotype content: competence and warmth respectively follow from perceived status and competition. *Journal of Personality and Social Psychology, 82*, 878–892.

Fraccaroli, F., & Deller, J. (2015). Work, aging, and retirement in Europe: Introduction to the special issue. *Work, Aging and Retirement*. Advance online publication. http://dx.doi.org/10.1093/workar/wav017

Fries, J. F., & Crapo, L. M. (1981). *Vitality and aging*. San Francisco: W. H. Freeman.

Gordon, R. A, & Arvey, R. D. (1986). Perceived and actual ages of workers. *Journal of Vocational Behavior,* 28, 21–28.

Greenwald, A. G., & Banaji, M. R. (1995). Implicit social cognition: Attitudes, self-esteem, and stereotypes. *Psychological Review, 102,* 4–27.

Greenwald, A. G., McGhee, D. E., & Schwartz, J. L. (1998). Measuring individual differences in implicit cognition: The implicit association test. *Journal of Personality and Social Psychology, 74,* 1464–1480.

Harrison, D. A., Price, K. H., Gavin J. H., & Florey, A. T. (2002). Time, teams, and task performance: Changing effects of surface- and deep-level diversity on group functioning. *Academy of Management Journal, 45,* 1029–1045.

Henry, H., Zacher, H., & Desmette, D. (2015). Reducing age bias and turnover intentions by enhancing intergenerational contact quality in the workplace: The role of opportunities for generativity and development. *Work, Aging and Retirement, 1,* 243–253.

Hertel, G., & Zacher, H. (2015). Managing the aging workforce. In C. Viswesvaran, N. Anderson, D. Ones, & H. K. Sinangil (Eds.), *The SAGE handbook of industrial, work, and organizational psychology* (2d ed., Vol. 3, pp. 1–93). New York: SAGE.

Inceoglu, I., Segers, J., & Bartram, D. (2012). Age-related differences in work motivation. *Journal of Occupational and Organizational Psychology, 85,* 300–329.

Judge, T. A., & Kammeyer-Mueller, J. D. (2012). Job attitudes. *Annual Review of Psychology, 63,* 341–367.

Kanfer, R., & Ackerman, P. L. (2004). Aging, work motivation, and adult development. *Academy of Management Review, 29,* 440–458.

Kaplan, P. S. (1993). *The human odyssey: Life-span development.* St. Paul, MN: West Publishing.

Kearney, E., & Gerbert, D. (2009). Managing diversity and enhancing team outcomes: The promise of transformational leadership. *Journal of Applied Psychology, 94,* 77–89.

Kinsella, K., & He, W. (2009). An aging world 2008 (US Census Bureau Report No. P95-09/1). Washington, DC: US Government Printing Office.

Klein, R. M., Dilchert, S., Ones, D. S., & Dages, K. D. (2015). Cognitive predictors and age-based adverse impact among business executives. *Journal of Applied Psychology, 5,* 1497–1510.

Kooij, D. T. A. M., De Lange, A. H., Jansen, P. G. W., Kanfer, R., & Dikkers, J. S. E. (2011). Age and work-related motives: Results of a meta-analysis. *Journal of Organizational Behavior, 32,* 197–225.

Kunze, F., & Boehm (2015). Age diversity and age climate in the workplace. In P. M. Bal, D. T. A. M. Kooij, & D. M. Rousseau (Eds.), *Aging workers and the employee-employer relationship* (pp. 33–35). Cham, Switzerland: Springer International. http://dx.doi.org/10.1007/978-3-319-08007-9_3

Kunze, F., Böhm, S. A., & Bruch, H. (2011). Age diversity, age discrimination climate and performance consequences: A cross organizational study. *Journal of Organizational Behavior, 32,* 264–290.

Lankau, M. J., Riordan, C. M., & Thomas, C. H. (2005). The effects of similarity and liking in formal relationships between mentors and protégés. *Journal of Vocational Behavior, 67,* 252–265.

Müller, A., Heiden, B., Herbig, B., Poppe, F., & Angerer, P. (2015). Improving well-being at work: A randomized controlled intervention based on selection, optimization, and compensation. *Journal of Occupational Health Psychology, 21,* 169–181.

Ng, T. W. H., & Feldman, D. C. (2008). The relationships of age to ten dimensions of job performance. *Journal of Applied Psychology, 93,* 392–423.

Ng, T. W. H., & Feldman, D. C. (2010). The relationships of age with job attitudes: A meta-analysis. *Personnel Psychology, 63,* 677–718.

Ng, T. W. H., & Feldman, D. C. (2012). Evaluating six common stereotypes about older workers with meta-analytical data. *Personnel Psychology, 65,* 821–858.

Ng, T. W. H., & Feldman, D. C. (2013). Employee age and health. *Journal of Vocational Behavior, 83,* 336–345.

Organization for Economic Co-operation and Development (OECD). (2013). *Pensions at a Glance 2013: OECD and G20 Indicators.* OECD Publishing. http://dx.doi.org/10.1787/pension_glance -2013-en

Organization for Economic Co-operation and Development (OECD). (2015). *Pensions at a Glance 2015: OECD and G20 indicators.* Paris: OECD Publishing. http://dx.doi.org/10.1787/pension_glance -2015-en

Papalia, D. E., Sterns, H. L., Feldman, R. D., & Camp, C. J. (2007). *Adult development and aging.* New York: McGraw-Hill.

Perry, E. L., Kulik, C. T., & Bourhis, A. C. (1996). Moderating effects of personal and contextual factors in age discrimination. *Journal of Applied Psychology, 81,* 628–647.

Phillips, D. R., & Siu, O. I. (2012). Global aging and aging workers. In J. W. Hedge & W. C. Borman (Eds.), *The Oxford handbook of work and aging* (pp. 9–32). New York: Oxford University Press.

Posthuma, R. A., & Campion, M. A. (2009). Age stereotypes in the workplace: Common stereotypes, moderators, and future research directions. *Journal of Management, 35,* 158–188.

Roberts, B. W., Walton, K. E., & Viechtbauer, W. (2006). Patterns of mean-level change in personality traits across the life course: A meta-analysis of longitudinal studies. *Psychological Bulletin, 132,* 3–27.

Rogers, E., & Wiatrowski, W. J. (2005). Injuries, illness, and fatalities among older workers. *Monthly Labor Review, 128,* 30–34.

Rousseau, D. (1995). *Psychological contracts in organizations: Understanding written and unwritten agreements.* Thousand Oaks, CA: SAGE.

Salthouse, T. A. (2012). Consequences of age-related cognitive declines. *Annual Review of Psychology, 63,* 201–226.

Salthouse, T. A. (2014). Why are there different age relations in cross-sectional and longitudinal comparisons of cognitive functioning? *Current Directions in Psychological Science, 23,* 252–256.

Sargent, L. D., Lee, M. D., Martin, B., & Zikic, J. (2013). Reiventing retirement: New pathways, new arrangements, new meanings. *Human Relations, 66,* 3–21.

Schaie, K. W. (1996). *Intellectual development in adulthood: The Seattle longitudinal study.* New York: Cambridge University Press.

Schmitt, A., Zacher, H., & Frese, M. (2012). The buffering effect of selection, optimization, and compensation strategy use on the relationship between problem solving demands and occupational well-being: A daily diary study. *Journal of Occupational Health Psychology, 17,* 139–149.

Shore, L. M., Cleveland, J. N., & Goldberg, C. B. (2003). Work attitudes and decisions as a function of manager age and employee age. *Journal of Applied Psychology, 88,* 529–537.

Shultz, K. S., & Wang, M. (2011). Psychological perspectives on the changing nature of retirement. *American Psychologist, 66,* 170–179.

Smith, C. S., Folkard, S., Tucker, P., & Evans, M. S. (2011). Work schedules, health, and safety. In J. C. Quick & L. E. Tetrick (Eds.), *Handbook of occupational health psychology* (pp. 185–204). Washington, DC: American Psychological Association.

Soto, C. J., & John, O. P. (2012). Development of Big Five domains and facets in adulthood: Mean-level age trends and broadly versus narrowly acting mechanisms. *Journal of Personality, 80,* 881–915.

Soto, C. J., John, O. P., Gosling, S. D., & Potter, J. (2011). Age differences in personality traits from 10 to 65: Big Five domains and facets in a large cross-sectional sample. *Journal of Personality and Social Psychology, 100,* 330–348.

Specht, J., Egloff, B., & Schmukle, S. C. (2011). Stability and change of personality across the life course: The impact of age and major life events on mean-level rank-order stability of the Big Five. *Journal of Personality and Social Psychology, 101,* 862–882.

Tajfel, H., & Turner, J. C. (1979). An integrative theory of intergroup conflict. In W. G. Austin & S. Worchel (Eds.), *The social psychology of intergroup relations* (pp. 33–47). Monterey, CA: Brooks-Cole.

Thatcher, S. (1999). The contextual importance of diversity: The impact of relational demography and team diversity on individual performance and satisfaction. *Performance Improvement Quarterly, 12,* 97–112.

Thatcher, S. M., & Patel, P. C. (2012). Group faultlines: A review, integration, and guide to future research. *Journal of Management, 38,* 969–1009.

Thatcher, S. M. B., & Patel, P. C. (2011). Demographic faultlines: A meta-analysis of the literature. *Journal of Applied Psychology, 96,* 1119–1139.

Truxillo, D. M., & Burlacu, G. (2015). Does age matter to LMX and its outcomes? A review and future research directions. In T. Bauer & B. Erdogan (Eds.), *Oxford handbook of leader-member exchange* (pp. 397–411). New York: Oxford University Press.

Truxillo, D. M., Cadiz, D. M., & Hammer, L. B. (2015). Supporting the aging workforce: A research review and recommendations for workplace intervention research. *Annual Review of Organizational Psychology and Organizational Behavior, 2,* 351–381.

Truxillo, D. M., Cadiz, D. M., & Rineer, J. R. (2014). The aging workforce: Implications for human resource management research and practice. In M. A. Hitt, S. E. Jackson, S. Carmona, L. Bierman, C. E. Shalley, & D. Michael (Eds.), *Oxford handbook of strategy implementation.* http://dx.doi.org/10.1093/oxfordhb/9780199935406.013.004

Truxillo, D. M., Cadiz, D. M., Rineer, J. R., Zaniboni, S., & Fraccaroli, F. (2012). A life span perspective on job design: Fitting the job and the worker to promote job satisfaction, engagement, and performance. *Organizational Psychology Review, 2,* 340–360.

Truxillo, D. M., Finkelstein, L., Pytlovany, A., & Jenkins, J. (2015). Age discrimination at work: A review of the research and recommendations for the future. In A. Colella & E. King (Eds.), *The Oxford handbook of workplace discrimination.* New York: Oxford University Press.

Truxillo, D. M., Fraccaroli, F., Yaldiz, L., & Zaniboni, S. (2017). Age discrimination. In J. McCarthy & E. Parry (Eds.), *Handbook of age diversity and work.* London: Palgrave MacMillan.

Truxillo, D. M., McCune, E. A., Bertolino, M., & Fraccaroli, F. (2012). Perceptions of older versus younger workers in terms of big five facets, proactive personality, cognitive ability, and job performance. *Journal of Applied Social Psychology, 42,* 2607–2639.

Vaupel, J. W. (2010). Biodemography of human ageing. *Nature, 464,* 536–542.

Walter, F., & Scheibe, S. (2013). A literature review and emotion-based model of age and leadership: New directions for the trait approach. *Leadership Quarterly, 24,* 882–901.

Wanberg, C. R., Kanfer, R., Hamann, D. J., & Zhang, Z. (2015). Age and reemployment success after job loss: An integrative model and meta-analysis. *Psychological Bulletin.* Advance online publication. http://dx.doi.org/10.1037/bul0000019

Wang, M., Burlacu, G., Truxillo, D. M., James, K., & Yao, X. (2015). Age differences in feedback reactions: The roles of feedback orientation on social awareness and utility. *Journal of Applied Psychology, 100,* 1296–1308.

Wang, M., Olson, D. A., & Shultz, K. S. (2013). *Mid and late career issues: An integrative perspective.* New York: Routledge.

Wang, M., & Shi, J. (2014). Psychological research on retirement. *Annual Review of Psychology, 65,* 209–233.

Warr, P., Miles, A., & Platts, C. (2001). Age and personality in the British population between 16 and 64 years. *Journal of Occupational and Organizational Psychology, 74,* 165–199.

Wegge, J., Roth, C., Neubach, B., Schmidt, K. H., & Kanfer, R. (2008). Age and gender diversity as determinants of performance and health in a public organization: The role of task complexity and group size. *Journal of Applied Psychology, 93,* 1301–1313.

Weigl, M., Müller, A., Hornung, S., Zacher, H., & Angerer, P. (2013). The moderating effects of job control and selection, optimization, and compensation strategies on the age-work ability relationship. *Journal of Organizational Behavior, 34*, 607–628.

Wille, B., Hofmans, J., Feys, M., & De Fruyt, F. (2013). Maturation of work attitudes: Correlated change with Big Five personality traits and reciprocal effects over 15 years. *Journal of Organizational Behavior, 35*, 507–530.

Yaldiz, L. M., & Truxillo, D. M. (2015). Job attitudes and age. In N. A. Pachana (Ed.), *Encyclopedia of geropsychology*. Springer Singapore. http://dx.doi.org/10.1007/978-981-287-080-3_22-1

Zacher, H., Clark, M., Anderson, E. C., & Ayoko, O. B. (2015). A life span perspective on leadership. In P. M. Bal, D. T. A. M. Kooij, & D. M. Rousseau (Eds.), *Aging workers and the employee-employer relationship* (pp. 87–104). Cham, Switzerland: Springer International.

Zacher, H., Rosing, K., Henning, T., & Frese, M. (2011). Establishing the new generation at work: Leader generativity as a moderator of the relationships between leader age, leader-member exchange, and leadership success. *Psychology and Aging, 26*, 241–252.

Lale M. Yaldiz, Franco Fraccaroli, and Donald M. Truxillo

AGEISM IN THE WORKPLACE

INTRODUCTION

In most industrialized nations around the world, the population is aging, and this trend is anticipated to continue well into the future. This demographic change has two primary causes—people are living longer and fertility rates are declining (Kulik, Ryan, Harper, & George, 2014). Consequently, this trend impacts the workforce, in that the average age of workers is increasing, workers are working later into life, and the workplace is becoming more age diverse, with more generations of workers working side by side than ever before. Increased age diversity has positive benefits, but it can also lead to misguided age-related attitudes, biases, and behaviors, which could lead to ageism. For example, age-discrimination claims are increasing in the United States (McCann & Giles, 2002) and there is evidence that it is harder for older people to find work (Wanberg, Kanfer, Hamann, & Zhang, 2016), but this runs counter to the organizational and societal need to retain workers into later years because retirement/pension programs will not support retirees for 30 or 40 years. Traditionally, ageism has been defined as the stigmatization of, and discrimination against, people because they are old (Butler, 1969). This definition may be too restrictive, because the focus is only on older people, and ageism can affect people throughout their working years. Therefore, ageism is approached here from a broader perspective, in that it is defined as the stigmatization of, and discrimination against, people based on their age. However, the focus here is narrowed to ageism in the workplace. Readers interested in broader discussions of ageism should review Bulter (1995), Nelson (2004), and Palmore (1999).

The tripartite model of age bias and ageism (Finkelstein & Farrell, 2007) is utilized here to discuss theories and research related to workplace ageism and to identify gaps in the research that need to be addressed to advance knowledge of ageism in the workplace.

TRIPARTITE APPROACH TO WORKPLACE AGEISM

It is important to start the discussion of workplace ageism by defining key terms. Table 1 provides a definition for each of the important concepts in the review of workplace ageism.

The tripartite approach to age bias (Finkelstein & Farrell, 2007) was selected to organize the review and discussion of workplace ageism research literature because it recognizes the complexities of workplace ageism, in that there are multiple components, including cognitive, affective, and behavioral components, that must be considered. The cognitive component includes beliefs and expectancies about people due to their membership in a particular group (i.e., age stereotypes). The affective component includes attributions or judgments of people as good or bad (i.e., age prejudice). The behavioral component includes the tendency to treat or interact with people in a certain manner because of their group membership (i.e., age discrimination). Research on age and the workplace is reviewed here through the lens of each individual component separately, and gaps in the current knowledge are identified within each of the areas.

COGNITIVE COMPONENT OF WORKPLACE AGEISM: STEREOTYPES

The cognitive component of workplace ageism comprises age-related stereotypes. Age stereotypes have received the greatest research attention of the three components in the workplace literature. The assumption of the literature is that age stereotypes affect workplace interactions and decisions like interpersonal treatment (e.g., Cortina, Magley, Williams, & Langhout, 2001; Einarsen & Skogstad, 1996), who is selected for a particular job (Perry, Kulik, & Bourhis, 1996), who receives training and development opportunities (Maurer & Rafuse, 2001), and who is given challenging job assignments (Shore et al., 2009).

Theoretical Frameworks Relating to Stereotypes.

One useful approach for examining stereotypes is through understanding intergroup categorization. The *social identity perspective*, an integration of *social identity theory* (SIT; Tajfel & Turner, 1979) and *self-categorization theory* (SCT; Turner, Hogg, Oakes, Reicher, & Wetherell, 1987) informs understanding of this cognitive process. SIT indicates that an individual's group membership provides emotional

Table 1. Important Terms and Definitions

Term	Definition
Ageism	The broadest of the terms, it includes bias, stereotyping, prejudice, and discrimination against people based on their age.
Age bias	Evaluative judgments and attitudes made based on a person's age.
Age stereotype	Generalizations made about a person or people based on age-group membership, such as believing that older workers in general are less flexible or are more dependable.
Age prejudice	Preconceived attribution of a person as good or bad based on their age, such as not liking older workers.
Age discrimination	Treating someone differently due to their age, such as in the hiring process.

significance and value, including the perception of ability to maintain or change social status through group membership. Comparisons of intergroup status differences within society result in an emphasis on positive attributions distinguishing one's own group from others. SCT builds on SIT and describes the process through which a meaningful shared identity leads to depersonalization. Social identity becomes defined in terms of one's identified ingroup, and therefore thoughts about "me" are replaced by "we"; perceived similarities within-group are enhanced and outgroup members are seen to be undifferentiated and homogenous (for a review of these theories, see Turner & Reynolds, 2001). In sum, the social identity perspective explains why and how ingroup and outgroup boundaries are established.

Ingroup and outgroup categorizations aid cognitive functioning by facilitating the filtering of the massive amounts of information available for processing. Fiske and Taylor (1984) used the term "cognitive miser" to express the tendency of individuals to rely on the most simple and time-efficient strategies for evaluating information and making decisions. Easily identifiable characteristics, such as race, gender, and age, are utilized during interpersonal interactions as a cognitive shortcut to inform affective and behavioral responses. According to the *continuum model* (Fiske, Lin, & Neuberg, 1999; Fiske & Neuberg, 1990) people are most likely to rely on stereotypes to categorize others when personal characteristics are easily categorizable, when limited cognitive resources (e.g., time pressures) inhibit more complex mental processing, and when motivation to develop an accurate understanding of the other person is lacking.

It is important to note that outgroups are not always negatively evaluated. A framework for understanding the often mixed (positive and negative) attributions is the stereotype content model (SCM; Fiske, Cuddy, Glick, & Xu, 2002). SCM suggests individuals and groups are assessed according to their level of competence (informed by social status, capability) and warmth (informed by outgroup competition, intentions). Stereotypes along these dimensions are assigned according to systematic principles, and the interaction of warmth and competence classifications functions as a form of system justification and to maintain societal status quo. For example, positive warmth attributions operate to appease and pacify non-threatening (low status, incompetent) subordinate outgroups. Conversely, negative attributions of low warmth serve to validate resentment and social exclusion of competitors, while high warmth and high competence attributions substantiate privileges for high-status groups. Fiske and colleagues' (2002) research revealed that older individuals tend to be perceived as warm and incompetent; however, it must be noted that the authors assessed attitudes about the "elderly," which may reflect perceptions about those outside of the workforce. A key element of this model posits that although stereotyping processes are stable over time, the content of stereotypes is susceptible to change and is influenced by context.

Work Outcomes Associated with Age Stereotypes.   Empirical research has identified a variety of stereotypes associated with older workers. In their comprehensive review of the age-stereotype literature, Posthuma and Campion (2009) summarized six major stereotype categories commonly associated with older workers, including having poorer performance, being resistant to change, having lower ability to learn, having shorter tenure, being more costly, and being more dependable. Meta-analytic evidence examining the validity of the older worker stereotypes has generally found these perceptions are untrue, except for older workers' being less willing or likely to participate in training and career development activities (Ng & Feldman, 2012). However, because cognitive categorization is relied on in interpersonal and intergroup interactions, stereotypes remain pervasive and influence relational and decision-making processes affecting older workers. For example, interviewers have been shown to rely on age stereotypes when cognitively distracted (Perry, Kulik, & Bourhis, 1996). In fact, a recent meta-analysis examining perceptions of older workers found medium-sized negative effects of age on selection, advancement, and general evaluations (Bal, Reiss, Rudolph, & Baltes, 2011).

In line with the SCM (Fiske et al., 2002), not all stereotypes of older workers are negative. Indeed, older workers are seen as being more dependable and reliable (Bal et al., 2011; Posthuma & Campion, 2009), more experienced (Finkelstein et al., 2000), more conscientious, having more crystallized intelligence, and being more emotionally stable (Truxillo, McCune, Bertolino, & Fraccaroli, 2012). The research on positive stereotypes of older workers adds a level of complexity as to how age stereotypes may function in the workplace and may be one explanation for why studies find inconsistencies in regard to the lack of endorsement of negative stereotypes (Weiss & Maurer, 2004). In other words, people may have conflicting positive and negative stereotypes associated with older workers, which may affect the way they are viewed in the workplace. Fiske and colleagues (2002) found that older people are viewed as being warm, but are also viewed as being less competent. Warmth may be a positive characteristic in certain circumstances, but competence (or incompetence) may be considered more important in the workplace, which could lead to denial of workplace opportunities (Shore & Goldberg, 2005). Furthermore, despite some negative stereotypes of older working-age adults, they are also seen as high in conscientiousness and organizational citizenship behaviors (e.g., Bertolino, Truxillo, & Fraccaroli, 2013). Research suggests a possible shift in the negative stereotype content for older workers, perhaps reflecting the trend of an aging workforce (Rosen & Jerdee, 1976a, 1976b; Weiss & Maurer, 2004). However, more research is certainly needed before drawing any conclusions.

The decrease in the proportion of younger workers is resulting in a "graying" of the workforce, leading to younger workers' becoming a minority in the workforce, which may result in an increase of younger worker ageism due to negative outgroup biases. Indeed, although most of the age-stereotype research has focused on older workers, younger workers also face negative stereotypes in the workplace (Perry, Hanvongse, & Casoinic, 2013). In general, there has been a lack of research focusing on age stereotypes for younger workers. Nevertheless, the limited research investigating negative stereotypes of younger workers indicates that younger workers are perceived as being less trustworthy (Loretto, Duncan, & White, 2000), as being more apt to "job hop" or as having less loyalty to organizations (Coy, Conlin, & Thornton, 2002), and as being more neurotic and performing less individually focused organizational citizenship behaviors (Truxillo et al., 2012; see also Finkelstein, Ryan, & King, 2013). Continuing research is needed to understand the stereotypes of younger workers and their outcomes.

AFFECTIVE COMPONENT OF WORKPLACE AGEISM: PREJUDICE

Age prejudice is the concept primarily considered in the affective component of the tripartite framework, and it has received the least attention in the bias literature (Finkelstein & Farrell, 2007). Prejudice encompasses people's evaluation of a social object as being good or bad (Kite, Stockdale, Whitley, & Johnson, 2005). Specifically, age prejudice could manifest itself as having a dislike of, feeling uncomfortable with, or even hating someone based on age group membership (Finkelstein & Farrell, 2007). In other words, age prejudice may be linked with people's emotions toward others due to their age.

Theoretical Frameworks Relating to Prejudice. The *similarity-attraction paradigm* (Byrne, 1971) suggests that individuals who share similar visible traits (for example, demographics like age) will infer other similarities exist, including attitudes, beliefs, and personality, and this inference will result in greater attraction to, increased liking of, and more positive beliefs about, each other. Increased attraction and liking is thought to increase shared work and/or nonwork activities (e.g., eating lunch together), possibly leading outgroup members to perceive unfair exclusion. This theory has been supported across a wide range of personal characteristics used in investigating a variety of outcomes at multiple levels of the workplace, including age prejudice at work.

Terror management theory (TMT; Greenberg, Solomon, & Pyszczynski, 1997) has also been applied to age-bias research. TMT states that when thoughts about aging and death are made salient, an individual will seek to mitigate the resulting anxiety by enhancing their self-perception of success according to societal standards associated with literal and/or symbolic immortality. Research has demonstrated that interactions with elderly people may evoke anxiety related to mortality, and in response individuals seek to buffer negative feelings by distancing themselves, and by differentiating older individuals as a dissimilar outgroup (Martens, Greenberg, Schimel, & Landau, 2004). However, empirical studies of TMT in the context of workplace age prejudice have not been forthcoming.

Discussed above, the *stereotype content model* (Fiske et al., 2002) describes cognitive processes of assigning stereotypes for system and behavioral justification. This model also explains the unique intergroup emotional responses (prejudices), resulting from stereotypes, that are related to various behaviors directed at different groups. The contents of outgroup stereotypes along warmth and competence dimensions are associated with distinct affective responses, namely, pity (high in warmth, low in competence), envy (low in warmth, high in competence), admiration (high in warmth and competence), and contempt (low in warmth and competence). The stereotype of older people as warm but incompetent indicates they may receive pity from outgroups and be less respected at work. It is important to point out, however, that many of the stereotypes from this model are based on much older people who are no longer of working age.

Work Outcomes Associated with Prejudice. Rupp, Vodanovich, and Credé (2005, 2006) provide some of the only research examining the affective component of age bias in a workplace context. Rupp and colleagues (2005) argue that there is a lack of research examining prejudice because the measures are more focused on cognitive evaluations and fail to include affective assessments. Rupp and colleagues (2006) found that managers who had higher levels of ageism were more likely to select more punitive recommendations for older workers compared to younger workers who made performance errors. Another study, by Kunze, Böhm, and Bruch (2011), revealed that a perceived age-discrimination climate

BEHAVIORAL COMPONENT OF WORKPLACE AGEISM: DISCRIMINATION

Workplace age discrimination (that is, actual behavior toward persons of a certain age) is a robust line of research (Gordon & Arvey, 2004). Age discrimination can be categorized under the behavioral aspect of age bias and is related to people's tendency to treat others in a particular way due to their membership in a particular age category (Finkelstein & Farrell, 2007). In other words, age discrimination captures behavior toward individuals due to their age-group membership and may lead to adverse workplace conditions based on age. This can play out across many different workplace scenarios, including in the selection processes (hiring), career advancement (promotion), performance appraisals, training and development, and interpersonal treatment (Truxillo, Cadiz, & Rineer, 2014; Truxillo et al., 2015b). Indeed, the amount of age-discrimination claims being filed has been increasing, which suggests that age discrimination remains an important concern in organizations (McCann & Giles, 2002).

Although evidence supports the existence of some relatively common age stereotypes in the workplace, whether the endorsement of the stereotypes leads to ageist behavior is complex and dependent on numerous factors. A modest relationship between stereotypes and discrimination has been observed in social bias research (Fiske, 2004) and age stereotypes and prejudice are recognized antecedents that lead to age discrimination (Finkelstein & Farrell, 2007). However, there is acknowledgment in the workplace ageism literature that contextual factors can enhance or weaken the relationship between age stereotypes, prejudice, and discriminatory behaviors. It is also important to recognize that institutional discrimination may not be based solely on stereotypes, and that a variety of situational, contextual, and societal forces may also be involved with discrimination. However, the general assumption is that age stereotypes affect how individuals interact and may shape age-related organizational policies and procedures, decisions, and treatment of workers (Hedge et al., 2006).

Theoretical Frameworks Relating to Discrimination: Context Matters.

A multitude of theories exist for understanding the effect of social role on human behavior, and specifically for investigating the interaction of age and an employee's role. One overarching framework is role theory (Biddle, 1986). Analogous to actors in a theater, *role theory* explains how social roles dictate what part is to be played (social position) and provide a script directing behavior and behavioral expectations. This theory has been applied across many disciplines and has contributed to development of *social role theory* (Eagly, 1987; Eagly, Wood, & Diekman, 2000). Originally applied to explore behavioral gender differences, social role theory has also been applied to age research within organizations (e.g., Kite et al., 2005). The propositions of this theory echo Biddle's role theory, suggesting that observing people in various social roles informs beliefs and expectations about individuals within groups that tend to hold that role. Put another way, the situational constraints (role-related scripts) influencing behavior are disregarded and the behavioral characteristics associated with particular roles come to be associated with group members acting out that role. These theories suggest stereotypes informed by historical social role dictate interactional behaviors.

A frequently held role for individuals is that of employee. Lawrence (1984) identified perceptions of "career timetables" as a concept that integrates an individual's role as an employee, the workplace context, and age discrimination. Lawrence (1988) argued that because chronological age is a universal human experience, it provides an important structural link between individuals and social systems that informs shared beliefs about the expected social positions, and consequently expected behaviors, for different age groups. A conventional career trajectory is for younger employees to join organizations, gain experience, and consequently move up through the organizational hierarchy over time, resulting in an association between older age and higher status within the workplace. Lawrence (1984) proposed that these *implicit career timelines* impact attitudes, and ultimately work outcomes (see also *implicit leadership theories* and *implicit performance theories*; Lord & Maher, 1991; Engle & Lord, 1997). For example, older employees low in the organizational ranks may be perceived negatively because their status does not align with career timeline expectations. Evaluations of whether the self, or another, is "ahead," "behind," or "on time" are influenced by societal expectations, as well as relational and organizational demography. That is, interpretation may be mitigated or exacerbated depending on comparisons to others of similar age within the team or organization.

Relational demography research investigates the impact of an employee's similarity (or dissimilarity) in relation to the demographic composition of their work-group or within the supervisor/subordinate dyad. *Organizational demography* explores the effects of an employee's similarity (or dissimilarity) in comparison to the demographic composition of the whole organization. Informed by the similarity-attraction paradigm (Byrne, 1971; discussed above), increased attraction and positive attitudes toward similar others is proposed to lead to increased quantity and quality of interactions for ingroup members, and bias against outgroup members, consequently affecting work outcomes, including perceptions of age-discrimination climate (Kunze et al., 2011).

Another approach to examining this phenomenon involves consideration of prototypes within industries or organizations relating to the ideal characteristics a person should possess for a particular job. Prototypes are informed by job characteristics (*job stereotype content*) and characteristics of job incumbents (*person-in-job prototypes*). *Prototype matching* occurs when individuals are evaluated to determine if their attributes match with the expected characteristics (Perry, 1994). Age may interact with job stereotype content or person-in-job prototypes during the matching process and lead to discriminatory behavior. An example is an older worker being overlooked for a technology-related position because technology jobs are generally associated with youth, and/or because the last person in the role was young.

Outcomes Associated with Discrimination.   As noted in the cognitive and affective workplace ageism sections, stereotypes and prejudice influence organizational behavior, including functions and processes related to the human resources function of an organization. Discriminatory outcomes may be observed in behaviors and decisions related to selection (hiring), advancement (promotions), performance appraisals, training and development, and interpersonal interactions. Each of these categories of organizational behavior outcomes is briefly reviewed here, but for a more detailed discussion see Truxillo and colleagues (2014).

Selection. Meta-analytic evidence supports the delayed reemployment of older workers (Wanberg et al., 2016), which is posited to be related to the lower performance stereotype associated with older workers (Goldberg, 2007). Indeed, older job applicants have been shown to have shorter interviews, to receive lower favorability ratings from employers, and to receive fewer job offers than younger job applicants (Bendick, Brown, & Wall, 1999). Meta-analytic results examining simulated employment contexts have demonstrated younger workers to be rated slightly higher in terms of job qualification as compared to older workers across job types, but providing job-relevant information about workers reduced age-related rating differences (Finkelstein et al., 1995). The most recent meta-analytic investigation confirmed the existence of a medium-sized negative relationship between age and selection ($r = -.30$), which included ratings of job qualification, hiring outcomes, and the target's suitability for the job (Bal et al., 2011). Some have criticized this line of research (i.e., Gordon & Arvey, 2004; Landy, 2008) because the laboratory research method used to simulate the selection process does not provide individuating information to the raters, which elicits the use of stereotypes to make decisions. Therefore, in general, older workers may face discrimination in selection contexts, but as the selection context becomes more realistic, the effects may be reduced (Gordon & Arvey, 2004; Landy, 2008).

Truxillo and colleagues (2014) identified additional potential biasing factors in a selection context, including perceptions of older job seekers as being overqualified (Erdogan et al., 2011), and age-related perceptions of differing levels of certain personality traits (Bertolino et al., 2013; Truxillo et al., 2014).

Advancement. In addition to the stereotype of being poor performers, the resistance-to-change stereotype may contribute to older workers' having decreased opportunities for advancement or promotion in the workplace (Shore et al., 2003). Research has found that older workers face a difficult challenge when it comes to upward mobility (Goldberg, 2007). In fact, older workers have been found to receive lower managerial assessments of promotability (Shore et al., 2003), and to receive fewer promotions (Goldberg, Finkelstein, Perry, & Konrad, 2004). Bal and colleagues (2011) meta-analytically confirmed the negative relationship between age and advancement ($r = -.21$). In their analysis, advancement included the target's potential for development, promotion outcomes, and predicted success. A possible confounding variable in this research is that older workers may already hold higher-level positions in the organization, and therefore may not have additional room for upward advancement.

Another concern that is related to advancement but on the opposite side of the spectrum is older workers' greater risk of being laid off or being offered early retirement. For instance, Osborne and McCann (2004) found these biases when they examined forced-ranking performance appraisal systems. Therefore, as people age in the workplace, they may find it more difficult to find advancement opportunities in their organizations and they may be a target for layoffs.

Older workers are not the only workers facing potential discrimination related to advancement decisions. Empirical research has found that younger workers were given fewer responsibilities at work because they were not perceived as trustworthy (Loretto et al., 2000). In addition, there is evidence that younger workers were denied access to promotions because they were perceived as less experienced and lacking the skills (O'Higgins, 2001) or because they needed to "pay their dues" (Lieber, 1999).

Performance Appraisals.   Age discrimination can also be observed in the performance-appraisal process. Saks and Waldman (1998) found that older employees received lower performance assessments than younger workers. Bal and colleagues (2011) found a negative medium effect between age and general evaluations, which incorporated perceptions of overall work performance and performance outcomes. However, the age-related negative perceptions are counter to recent meta-analytic evidence that found that age was largely unrelated to core task performance and positively related to types of organizational citizenship behavior (Ng & Feldman, 2008). Therefore, there seems to be mixed evidence regarding the age-work performance relationship that could stem from a lack of accounting for and investigating contextual variables, such as type of occupation (Salthouse & Maurer, 1996) and job-age stereotypes (Perry et al., 1996) that could attenuate the relationship.

Training and Development.   Age and access to training and development is another outcome examined from an age-discrimination perspective. Perceptions that older workers have a decreased ability to learn and shorter tenure may lead to fewer training and development opportunities (Maurer & Rafuse, 2001). In fact, Maurer and Rafuse (2001) discovered that 55- to 60-year-olds are less likely to receive training than 35- to 44-year-olds. Moreover, empirical research suggests that organizations and managers are less willing to support access to training opportunities for older workers (Shore, Cleveland, & Goldberg, 2003). Additionally, Steiner, Bertolino, Fraccaroli, and Truxillo (2007) found that older workers have the greatest difficulty getting training resources compared to their younger counterparts. Finally, older workers receive less mentoring time and career-related mentoring than younger workers, which can limit their development (Finkelstein, Allen, & Rhoton, 2003).

Interpersonal Interactions.   Reduced or negative interactions have been examined as an outcome of workplace ageism. These interactions can involve dyadic relationships (i.e., supervisor-subordinate, coworker-coworker), group/team relationships, and one's perceived relationship with the organization (i.e., organizational climate). For instance, relational demography research has revealed greater role ambiguity for employees younger or older than their supervisor (Tsui & O'Reilly, 1989), and less frequent communication when employees differ in age from the rest of their work group (Zenger & Lawrence, 1989). Organizational age dissimilarity has also been associated with increased perceptions of a negative age-discrimination climate (Kunze et al., 2011).

Group and team research has examined the development of faultlines (Thatcher & Patel, 2012), where homogeneous subgroups may form within a team, which may impact team dynamics. However, the impact may depend on the task the group/team is facing, in that if the team is not facing an age-related issue or task, an age-related faultline may not develop (Jackson & Joshi, 2011). Moreover, there is evidence that the importance of surface-level characteristics like age is reduced over time when workers are exposed to demographically different team members (Harrison et al., 2002).

Age-related negative interpersonal interactions may manifest as mistreatment behaviors, such as harassment and bullying. For example, younger workers are more likely to face harassment behaviors (Cortina et al., 2001). In addition, Einarsen and Skogstad (1996) found that older workers have a greater likelihood of being the target of bullying than their younger coworkers. Therefore, the literature is mixed regarding age-related exposure to mistreatment behavior.

FUTURE RESEARCH

Although there is a growing amount of literature examining the cognitive, affective, and behavioral components of workplace ageism and its effects on individuals and workplace processes, serious gaps remain in understanding this phenomenon and how to combat it. This section identifies several future research directions.

Defining Age-Group Categories. One challenging issue that clouds current understanding of age stereotypes and resulting discrimination is defining what is meant by "older" and "younger" workers. While some researchers have generally defined an older worker as one in their 50s and above (Truxillo et al., 2015a), this issue is far from settled. Factors that likely affect the definition of different age categories are the particular societal norms, national retirement laws, and norms for a particular profession (Truxillo et al., 2015b).

Discrimination Against Younger Workers. Older workers have been the traditional focus of workplace ageism research, and discrimination against younger workers has received scant attention (Perry et al., 2013). For instance, the popular press often characterize the millennial generation as narcissistic and having a poor work ethic, and younger workers are often seen as "fair game" in terms of criticism. As a recently emerging issue, discrimination against younger workers is deserving of increased research to understand its bases and prevalence.

Additional Outcomes of Workplace Age Discrimination. The workplace age-discrimination literature has focused largely on manifestations like treatment by coworkers, hiring, access to training, and performance appraisals. However, outcomes of workplace age discrimination like worker stress, health, and well-being are deserving of increased attention.

Boundary Conditions. As discussed under the cognitive and affective components of workplace ageism, there are a number of possible antecedents to workplace age discrimination, such as age stereotypes and affective reactions to older workers. However, it is unclear when or how these stereotypes and reactions will lead to actual discriminatory behavior against workers in different age groups. For example, although there are many positive stereotypes of older workers (e.g., Bertolino et al., 2013), there is research evidence that they may fare poorly in many workplace decisions (Bal et al., 2011; Finkelstein et al., 1995).

Age Metastereotypes and Their Effects. Metastereotypes are an individual's belief about what another group thinks about that individual's group, an issue that has only recently been applied to age in the workplace (Finkelstein et al., 2013). For example, younger workers may believe that their older colleagues believe that they are lazy or narcissistic—whether or not these other groups actually believe this to be the case—and this belief may affect younger workers' attitudes and behavior. A recent study (Ryan, King, & Finkelstein, 2015) found that younger workers who were self-conscious about younger age stereotypes also had negative attitudes toward older colleagues and experienced a negative mood. This new line of ageism research—about thinking about what others think of your own age group—shows promise in understanding the effects of age discrimination and how to combat it.

Implicit Age Stereotypes in the Workplace. Most research on workplace ageism has focused on the explicit stereotypes that people have about different age groups, that is, conscious stereotypes. However, research also suggests that unconscious or implicit stereotypes exist; and because of their unconscious nature, they may be more difficult to combat than stereotypes that are in the awareness of the individual. Although implicit stereotypes have been studied for years in the social psychology literature (Fazio & Olson, 2003), implicit age stereotypes have remained unexamined in the workplace literature. However, research into implicit stereotypes at work may lead to a better understanding of, and provide a complete picture of, how ageism emerges in the workplace and how to combat it.

Prescriptive Versus Descriptive Age Stereotypes. The distinction between descriptive and prescriptive age stereotypes is a recent advancement in the age-stereotype literature (North & Fiske, 2013). Descriptive stereotypes, descriptive perceptions of older workers' behaviors, have been the traditional focus of age-stereotype research. However, prescriptive stereotypes are beliefs about behavior older workers should display with regard to the use of social resources (North & Fiske, 2013). It is argued that violation of a prescriptive age stereotype would result in an extremely negative judgment about the violating individual (North & Fiske, 2013). Future research is needed to investigate the effect prescriptive age stereotypes have on individual, group, and organizational outcomes.

Cross-Level Research. Most research within the field of workplace ageism focuses on a phenomenon at a single level, such as between individuals, within teams, or, more rarely, at the organizational level. For instance, studies may measure how individuals perceive each other (e.g., stereotyping research), how age-based subgroups may form within a team (e.g., faultlines research), or how organizational HR policies affect organizational phenomena (e.g., age-diversity climate research). It is relatively rare for research to examine ageism-related phenomena across levels (see research by Böhm and colleagues for exceptions). However, ageism is a phenomenon that affects individuals and is also embedded within teams, professions, organizations, and societies. Therefore, research is needed across levels to better understand the emergence of ageism as a multilevel phenomenon.

Intervention Research. Although little research has examined specific workplace interventions to combat ageism (Truxillo et al., 2015a), existing research suggests fruitful paths forward. For example, HR policies that explicitly support members of all age groups have been shown to have a positive effect on age-diversity climate (Böhm et al., 2014), which may in turn affect productivity and performance. Positive intergenerational contact at work (e.g., Iweins et al., 2013) may improve intergenerational relations. The leveraging of existing workplace age

CONCLUSIONS

Workplace ageism is receiving an extensive amount of research attention. This increased consideration is related to the fact that organizations are facing an increasingly age-diverse workforce, potentially increasing the influence of age-related attitudes, biases, and behaviors at all levels of an organization. The literature on workplace ageism is reviewed here using the tripartite workplace age-bias framework (Finkelstein & Farrell, 2007) to organize the discussion. Several important theories are identified and current research findings are highlighted. Finally, a number of gaps and recent theoretical and empirical advancements in the research are identified that need additional consideration to increase understanding of how to prevent ageism in the workplace for workers of all ages.

REFERENCES

Bal, A. C., Reiss, A. E. B, Rudolph, C. W., & Baltes, B. B. (2011). Examining positive and negative perceptions of older workers: A meta-analysis. *The Journal of Gerontology Series B: Psychological Sciences & Social Sciences, 66,* 687–698.

Bendick, M., Brown, L. E., & Wall, K. (1999). No foot in the door: An experimental study of employment discrimination against older workers. *Journal of Aging and Social Policy, 10,* 5–23.

Bertolino, M., Truxillo, D. M., & Fraccaroli, F. (2013). Age effects on perceived personality and job performance. *Journal of Managerial Psychology, 7/8,* 867–885.

Biddle, B. J. (1986). Recent development in role theory. *Annual Review of Sociology, 12,* 67–92.

Böhm, S. A., Kunze, F., & Bruch, H. (2014). Spotlight on age diversity climate: The impact of age-inclusive HR practices on firm-level outcomes. *Personnel Psychology, 67,* 667–704.

Butler, R. N. (1969). Age-ism: Another form of bigotry. *The Gerontologist, 9,* 243–246.

Butler, R. (1995). Ageism. In G. Maddox (Ed.), *Encyclopedia of aging.* New York: Springer.

Byrne, D. (1971). *The attraction paradigm.* New York: Academic Press.

Collins, M. H., Hair, J. F., & Rocco, T. S. (2009). The older-worker-younger supervisor dyad: A test of the reverse Pygmalion effect. *Human Resource Development Quarterly, 20,* 21–41. http://dx.doi.org/10.1002/hrdq.20006

Cortina, L. M., Magley, V. J., Williams, J. H., & Langhout, R. D. (2001). Incivility in the workplace: Incidence and impact. *Journal of Occupational Health Psychology, 6,* 64–80.

Coy, P., Conlin, M., & Thornton, E. (2002). A lost generation? Young and mid-career job seekers are bearing the brunt of U.S. layoffs. *Business Week, 3806,* 44–46.

Eagly, A. H. (1987). *Sex differences in social behavior: A social-role interpretation.* Hillsdale, NJ: Lawrence Erlbaum Associates.

Eagly, A. H., Wood, W., & Diekman, A. B. (2000). Social role theory of sex differences and similarities: A current appraisal. In T. Eckes & H. Trautner (Eds.), *The Developmental Social Psychology of Gender* (pp.123–174). New York: Psychology Press.

Einarsen, S., & Skogstad, A. (1996). Bullying at work: Epidemiological findings in public and private organizations. *European Journal of Work and Organizational Psychology, 5,* 185–201.

Engle, E. M., & Lord, R. G. (1997). Implicit theories, self-schemas, and leader-member exchange. *Academy of Management Journal, 40,* 988–1010. http://dx.doi.org/10.2307/256956

Erdogan, B., Bauer, T. N., Peiró, J. M., & Truxillo, D. M. (2011). Response: Overqualification theory, research, and practice: Things that matter. *Industrial and Organizational Psychology: Perspectives on Science and Practice, 4*, 260–267.

Fazio, R. H., & Olson, M. A. (2003). Implicit measures in social cognition research: Their meaning and use. *Annual Review of Psychology, 54*(1), 297–327.

Finkelstein, L. M., Allen, T. D., & Rhoton, L. A. (2003). An examination of the role of age in mentoring relationships. *Group & Organization Management, 28*, 249–281.

Finkelstein, L. M., Burke, M. J., & Raju, N. S. (1995). Age discrimination in simulated employment contexts: An integrative analysis. *Journal of Applied Psychology, 80*, 652–663.

Finkelstein, L. M., & Farrell, S. K. (2007). An expanded view of age bias in the workplace. In K. S. Shultz & G. A. Adams (Eds.), *Aging and work in the 21st century* (pp. 73–108). Mahwah, NJ: Lawrence Erlbaum Associates.

Finkelstein, L. M., Higgins, K., & Clancy, M. (2000). Justifications for ratings of old and young job applicants: An exploratory content analysis. *Experimental Aging Research, 26*, 263–283.

Finkelstein, L. M., Ryan, K. M., & King, E. B. (2013). What do the young (old) people think of me? Content and accuracy of age-based metastereotypes. *European Journal of Work and Organizational Psychology, 22*, 633–657.

Fiske, S., & Taylor, S. (1984). *Social cognition*. Reading, MA: Addison-Wesley.

Fiske, S. T. (2004). Stereotyping, prejudice, and discrimination: Social biases. In S. T. Fiske (Ed.), *Social beings: A core motives approach to social psychology* (pp. 397–457). Hoboken, NJ: Wiley.

Fiske, S. T., Cuddy, A. J., Glick, P., & Xu, J. (2002). A model of (often mixed) stereotype content: Competence and warmth respectively follow from perceived status and competition. *Journal of Personality and Social Psychology, 82*(6), 878–902. http://dx.doi.org/10.1037//0022-3514.82.6.878

Fiske, S. T., Lin, M., & Neuberg, S. (1999). The continuum model. In S. Chaiken & Y. Trope (Eds.) *Dual-process Theories in Social Psychology* (pp. 221–254). New York: The Guilford Press.

Fiske, S. T., & Neuberg, S. L. (1990). A continuum of impression formation, from category-based to individuating processes: Influences of information and motivation on attention and interpretation. *Advances in Experimental Social Psychology, 23*, 1–74.

Goldberg, C. (2007). Diversity issues for an aging workforce. In K. S. Shultz & G. A. Adams (Eds.), *Aging and work in the 21st century* (pp. 51–72). Mahwah, NJ: Lawrence Erlbaum Associates.

Goldberg, C., Finkelstein, L., Perry, E., & Konrad, A. (2004). Job and industry fit: The effects of age and gender matches on career progress outcomes. *Journal of Organizational Behavior, 25*, 807–829.

Gordon, R. A., & Arvey, R. D. (2004). Age bias in laboratory and field settings: A meta-analytic investigation. *Journal of Applied Psychology, 34*, 468–492.

Greenberg, J., Solomon, S., & Pyszczynski, T. (1997). Terror management theory of self-esteem and cultural worldviews: Empirical assessments and conceptual refinements. In M. P. Zanna (Ed.), *Advances in experimental social psychology* (pp. 61–139). San Diego, CA: Academic Press.

Harrison, D. A., Price, K. H., Gavin J. H., & Florey, A. T. (2002). Time, teams, and task performance: Changing effects of surface- and deep-level diversity on group functioning. *Academy of Management Journal, 45*, 1029–1045. http://dx.doi.org/10.2307/256901

Hedge, J. W., Borman, W. C., & Lammlein, S. E. (2006). *The aging workforce: Realities, myths, and implications for organizations*. Washington, DC: American Psychological Association.

Iweins, C., Desmette, D., Yzerbyt, V., & Stinglhamber, F. (2013). Ageism at work: The impact of intergenerational contact and organizational multi-age perspective. *European Journal of Work and Organizational Psychology, 22*(3), 331–436. http://dx.doi.org/10.1080/1359432X.2012.748656

Jackson, S. E., & Joshi, A. (2011). Work team diversity. In S. Zedeck (Ed.), *APA handbook of industrial and organizational psychology, Vol. 1* (pp. 651–686). Washington, DC: American Psychological Association.

Kite, M. E., Stockdale, G. D., Whitley, B. E., & Johnson, B. T. (2005). Attitudes toward younger and older adults: An updated meta-analytic review. *Journal of Social Issues, 61,* 241–266. http://dx.doi.org/10.1111/j.1540-4560.2005.00404.x

Kulik, C. T., Ryan, S., Harper, S., & George, G. (2014). Aging populations and management. *Academy of Management Journal, 57,* 929–935.

Kunze, F., & Bruch, H. (2010). Age-based faultlines and perceived productive energy: The moderation of transformational leadership. *Small Group Research, 41,* 593–620. http://dx.doi.org/10.1177/1046496410366307

Kunze, F., Böhm S. A., & Bruch, H. (2011). Age diversity, age discrimination climate and performance consequences—a cross organizational study. *Journal of Organizational Behavior, 32,* 264–290. http://dx.doi.org/10.1002/job.698

Landy, F. J. (2008). Stereotypes, bias, and personnel decisions: Strange and stranger. *Industrial and Organizational Psychology, 1,* 379–392.

Lawrence, B. S. (1984). Age grading: The implicit organizational timetable. *Journal of Organizational Behavior, 5,* 23–35.

Lawrence, B. S. (1988). New wrinkles in the theory of age: Demography, norms, and performance ratings, *Academy of Management Journal, 31,* 309–337.

Lieber, R. (December 19, 1999). First jobs aren't child's play. *Fast Company, 25.* Retrieved from http://www.fastcompany.com/37433/first-jobs-arent-childs-play.

Lord, R. G., & Maher, K. J. (1991). Cognitive theory in industrial and organizational psychology. *Handbook of Industrial and Organizational Psychology, 2,* 1–62.

Loretto, W., Duncan, C., & White, P. J. (2000). Ageism in employment: Controversies, ambiguities and younger people's perceptions. *Ageing and Society, 20,* 279–302.

Martens, A., Greenberg, J., Schimel, J., & Landau, M. J. (2004). Ageism and death: Effects of mortality salience and perceived similarity to elders on reactions to elderly people. *Personality and Social Psychology Bulletin, 30,* 1524–1536. http://dx.doi.org/10.1177/0146167204271185

Maurer, T. J., Barbeite, F., Weiss, E. M., & Lippstreu, M. (2008). New measures of stereotypical beliefs about older workers' ability and desire for development: Exploration among employees age 40 and over. *Journal of Managerial Psychology, 23,* 395–418.

Maurer, T. J., & Rafuse, N. E. (2001). Learning, not litigating: Managing employee development and avoiding claims of age discrimination. *Academy of Management Executive, 15,* 110–121.

McCann, R., & Giles, H. (2002). Ageism in the workplace: A communication perspective. In T. Nelson (Ed.), *Ageism: Stereotyping and prejudice against older persons* (pp. 163–199). Cambridge, MA: MIT Press.

Nelson, T. D. (2004). *Ageism: Stereotyping and prejudice against older persons.* Cambridge, MA: MIT Press.

Ng, T. W. H., & Feldman, D. C. (2008). The relationship of age to ten dimensions of job performance. *Journal of Applied Psychology, 93,* 392–423.

Ng, T. W. H., & Feldman, D. C. (2012). Evaluating six common stereotypes about older workers with meta-analytical data. *Personnel Psychology, 65,* 821–858. http://dx.doi.org/10.1111/peps.12003

North, M. S., & Fiske, S. T. (2013). A prescriptive intergenerational-tension ageism scale: Succession, identity, and consumption (SIC). *Psychological Assessment, 25,* 706–713.

O'Higgins, N. (2001). *Youth unemployment and employment policy: A global perspective.* Geneva, Switzerland: International Labour Office.

O'Reilly, C. A. III, Caldwell, D. F., & Barnett, W. P. (1989). Work group demography, social integration, and turnover. *Administrative Science Quarterly, 34,* 21–37.

Osborne, T., & McCann, L. A. 2004. Forced ranking and age-related employment discrimination. *Human Rights, 31,* 6–9.

Palmore, E. B. (1999). *Ageism: Negative and positive.* New York: Springer Publishing Company.

Perry, E. (1994). A prototype matching approach to understanding the role of applicant gender and age in the evaluation of job applicants. *Journal of Applied Social Psychology, 24*, 1433–1473.

Perry, E. L., Hanvongse, A., & Casoinic, D. A. (2013). Making a case for the existence of generational stereotypes: A literature review and exploratory study. In J. Field, R. J. Burke, & C. L. Cooper (Eds.), *The SAGE handbook of aging, work and society* (pp. 416–442). Thousand Oaks, CA: SAGE.

Perry, E. L., Kulik, C. T., & Bourhis, A. C. (1996). Moderating effects of personal and contextual factors in age discrimination. *Journal of Applied Psychology, 81*, 628–647.

Posthuma, R. A., & Campion, M. A. (2009). Age stereotypes in the workplace: Common stereotypes, moderators, and future research directions. *Journal of Management, 35*, 158–188.

Posthuma, R. A., Wagstaff, M. F., & Campion, M. A. (2012). Age stereotypes and workplace age discrimination. In W. C. Borman & J. W. Hedge (Eds.), *The Oxford handbook of work and aging* (pp. 298–312). New York: Oxford University Press.

Rosen, B., & Jerdee, T. H. (1976a). The influence of age stereotypes on managerial decisions. *Journal of Applied Psychology, 61*, 428–432.

Rosen, B., & Jerdee, T. H. (1976b). The nature of job-related age stereotypes. *Journal of Applied Psychology, 61*, 180–183.

Rupp, D. E., Vodanovich, S. J., & Credé, M. (2005). The multidimensional nature of ageism: Construct validity and group differences. *Journal of Social Psychology, 145*, 335–362.

Rupp, D. E., Vodanovich, S. J., & Credé, M. (2006). Age bias in the workplace: The impact of ageism and causal attributions. *Journal of Applied Social Psychology, 36*, 1337–1364.

Ryan, K. M., King, E. B., & Finkelstein, L. M. (2015). Younger workers' metastereotypes, workplace mood, attitudes, and behaviors. *Journal of Managerial Psychology, 30*(1), 54–70.

Saks, A. M., & Waldman, D. A. (1998). The relationship between age and job performance evaluations for entry-level professionals. *Journal of Organizational Behavior, 19*, 409–419.

Salthouse, T., & Maurer, T. (1996). Aging, job performance, and career development. In J. Birren & K. Schaie (Eds.), *Handbook of the psychology of aging* (4th ed., pp. 353–364). San Diego, CA: Academic Press.

Shore, L. M., Chung-Herrera, B. G., Dean, M. A., Ehrhart, K. H., Jung, D. I., Randel, A. E., et al. (2009). Diversity in organizations: Where are we now and where are we going? *Human Resource Management Review, 19*, 117–133.

Shore, L. M., Cleveland, J. N., & Goldberg, C. B. (2003). Work attitudes and decisions as a function of manager age and employee age. *Journal of Applied Psychology, 88*, 529–537. http://dx.doi.org/10.1037/0021-9010.88.3.529

Shore, L. M., & Goldberg, C. B. (2005). Age discrimination in the workplace. In R. L. Dipboye & A. Colella (Eds.), *Discrimination at work* (pp. 203–225). Mahwah, NJ: Lawrence Erlbaum.

Steiner, D. D., Bertolino, M., Fraccaroli, F., & Truxillo, D. M. (April, 2007). Justice perceptions of organizational practices concerning older employees. Paper presented at the annual meeting of the Society for Industrial and Organizational Psychology, San Francisco, CA.

Tajfel, H., & Turner, J. C. (1979). An integrative theory of intergroup conflict. In W. G. Austin & S. Worchel (Eds.), *The social psychology of intergroup relations* (pp. 33–47). Monterey, CA: Brooks/Cole.

Thatcher, S., & Patel, P. C. (2011). Demographic faultlines: A meta-analysis of the literature. *Journal of Applied Psychology, 96*, 1119. http://dx.doi.org/10.1037/a0024167

Thatcher, S. M., & Patel, P. C. (2012). Group faultlines: A review, integration, and guide to future research. *Journal of Management, 38*, 969–1009. http://dx.doi.org/10.1177/0149206311426187

Truxillo, D. M., Cadiz, D. M., & Hammer, L. (2015a). Supporting the aging workforce: A research review and recommendations for workplace intervention research. *Annual Review of Organizational Psychology and Organizational Behavior, 2*, 351–381.

Truxillo D. M., Cadiz, D. M., & Rineer, J. R. (2014). The aging workforce: Implications for human resource management research and practice. In *Oxford handbooks online*. New York: Oxford University Press. http://dx.doi.org/10.1093/oxfordhb/9780199935406.013.004

Truxillo, D. M., Finkelstein, L. M., Pytlovany, A. C., & Jenkins, J. S. (2015b). Age discrimination at work: A review of the research and recommendations for the future. In A. J. Colella & E. B. King (Eds.), *The Oxford handbook of workplace discrimination*. New York: Oxford University Press. http://dx.doi.org/10.1093/oxfordhb/9780199363643.013.10

Truxillo, D. M., McCune, E. A., Bertolino, M., & Fraccaroli, F. (2012). Perceptions of older versus younger workers in terms of big five facets, proactive personality, cognitive ability, and job performance. *Journal of Applied Social Psychology, 42*, 2607–2639.

Tsui, A., & O'Reilly, C. A. III. (1989). Beyond simple demographic effects: The importance of relational demography in superior-subordinate dyads. *Academy of Management Journal, 32*, 402–423.

Turner, J. C., Hogg, M. A., Oakes, P. J., Reicher, S. D., & Wetherell, M. S. (1987). *Rediscovering the social group: A self-categorization theory*. Oxford: Basil Blackwell.

Turner, J. C., & Reynolds, K. J. (2001). The social identity perspective in intergroup relations: Theories, themes, and controversies. In R. Brown & S. Gaertner (Eds.), *Blackwell handbook of social psychology: Intergroup processes* (pp. 133–152). Oxford: Blackwell Publishers. http://dx.doi.org/10.1002/9780470693421.ch7

Wanberg, C. R., Kanfer, R., Hamann, D. J., & Zhang, Z. (2016). Age and reemployment success after job loss: An integrative model and meta-analysis. *Psychological Bulletin, 142*(4), 400–426.

Weiss, E. M., & Maurer, T. J. (2004). Age discrimination in personnel decisions: A re-examination. *Journal of Applied Social Psychology, 34*, 1551–1562.

Zenger, T. R., & Lawrence, B. S. (1989). Organizational demography: The differential effects of age and tenure distributions on technical communication. *Academy of Management Journal, 32*, 353–376.

David M. Cadiz, Amy C. Pytlovany, and Donald M. Truxillo

SEXUAL ORIENTATION (LGBTQ+) ISSUES IN INDUSTRIAL AND ORGANIZATIONAL PSYCHOLOGY

INTRODUCTION

Over the past few decades, people who identify as lesbian, gay, bisexual, transgender, intersex, or queer (LGBTIQ) have become increasingly visible. Internationally, 7% of adults now describe themselves as attracted to the same sex, 4% as "attracted to both sexes," and 1% describe themselves as "transgender, non-binary/non-conforming/gender-fluid" (Ipsos, 2021). In the United States, 7.1% of adults identify as LGBT (Jones, 2022). Given that many conceal their status, this is likely an underestimate (Pachankis & Bränström, 2019). Thus, some have estimated the actual number ranges from 4% to 20% in the United States (Triana, 2017). This visibility has been accompanied by a shift in attitudes as well as increased attention by organizations that recognize that the inclusion of LGBTIQ workers can favorably impact a company's financial performance (e.g., Dupreelle et al., 2020; Lourenço et al., 2021) and even relate to national-level (i.e., GDP) economic development (Badgett et al., 2019). Although still under-researched, scholars in the areas of industrial/organizational (I/O) psychology and management have shown increased attention to understanding the unique workplace experiences of members of this community (Byington et al., 2021).

Various labels have been used to refer to members of this community. Here the term *sexual and gender minority* (SGM) is used. It should be noted, however, that language evolves over time, and therefore one label may be appropriate in one context but not necessarily in another. Over the past decade, the expression LGBT has become common. Lesbian women and gay men are attracted to the same sex, whereas bisexual people are attracted to both sexes. People who are transgender have a gender identity or expression that does not correspond to their sex assigned at birth. Some communities use the label LGBTIQ to include intersex people (those born with reproductive or sexual anatomy that does not fit the typical definition of female or male) and queers (who consider themselves neither heterosexual nor cisgender). While often combined under a single umbrella and treated as a homogeneous group, each has workplace issues and experiences that are unique to them (Brewster et al., 2012; Corrington et al., 2019, 2020; Sawyer et al., 2016). Furthermore, these identities are not mutually exclusive, nor are they separate from other identity statuses such as age, race, religion, and parenthood (Sawyer et al., 2013). Whenever possible, attention is called to research that has examined differences across SGM identities and research that has examined the intersection of SGMs and other identities.

This article reviews the research on workplace experiences of SGM employees in the I/O psychology and management literatures with a focus on synthesizing and reviewing the research on the types, prevalence, and impact of workplace discriminatory behaviors faced by SGM employees and the strategies used at the individual, interpersonal, organizational, and societal levels shown to mitigate their harmful effects.

WORKPLACE DISCRIMINATION EXPERIENCES FOR SGM EMPLOYEES

Formal Discrimination.   Considerable evidence indicates that people with SGM identities experience formal or more overt types of discrimination in the workplace, including discrimination in hiring and promotion, access to developmental opportunities, and the distribution of resources (Hebl et al., 2002). For example, data collected by the Williams Institute (Sears et al., 2021) found that nearly one-third (29%) of LGB individuals reported experiencing discrimination in the form of not being hired or being fired, being denied pay raises, or being passed over for promotions and other opportunities. People who are transgender or gender nonbinary fair even worse, with nearly half (49%) reporting that they had been discriminated against in workplace hiring/firing decisions. Similarly, in a large-scale survey of U.S. federal employees, who are presumably better protected by LGBTIQ antidiscrimination policies and where seemingly merit-based and objective employment practices are more common, Cech and Rothwell (2020) found that SGM individuals reported poorer experiences, such as being mistreated and more concerned about the transparency of their performance evaluations, than non-SGM individuals. Beyond surveys documenting the prevalence of workplace discrimination, a growing body of research has begun to examine how, why, and under what circumstances formal discrimination toward SGM individuals in the areas of hiring, advancement, and leadership evaluations is more or less likely to occur.

Hiring Decisions.   Hiring decisions typically follow a sequential process wherein (a) job seekers apply to open positions by submitting application materials that are then (b) used by decision-makers to screen applicants to determine who will be invited to take part in follow-up interviews and other selection procedures. Much of the research on discrimination against SGMs has focused on the first "pre-interview" phase of this process. One approach to examining discrimination in the hiring process during the pre-interview phase is the use of correspondence methodology (McFadden, 2020). In this type of study, SGM (vs. non-SGM) status is manipulated on a set of otherwise similar application materials that are then sent to multiple organizations, and reactions from the organization are measured. In a meta-analysis of this type of study, Flage (2020) found that gay men were 39% and lesbian women were 32% less likely to receive a response from an employer. These findings are consistent over time and did not differ when only studies conducted in the previous 10 years were considered.

Other research examining the hiring of SGM individuals has used experimental vignette designs. Consistent with attitudes toward SGM generally (Kite et al., 2021), studies have found that women raters tend to evaluate SGM applicants more favorably in simulated employment settings than men (Everly et al., 2016; Pichler et al., 2010) and that participants with negative attitudes toward lesbian women and gay men rate them less favorably (Horvath & Ryan, 2003; Pichler et al., 2010). Other research finds that stereotypes about SGM individuals and the sex-role stereotyping of occupations are also important. According to implicit inversion theory (Kite & Deaux, 1987), gay men are stereotyped as having feminine characteristics, and lesbian women are stereotyped as having masculine characteristics. Occupations are also characterized along stereotypically gendered lines. Some jobs are viewed as more appropriate for men (e.g., mechanic) and others for women (e.g., nurse; see Hancock et al., 2020). In general, research supports the notion that when there is a match or "fit" between gendered stereotypes associated with SGM identities and the stereotypes of occupations, gay men and lesbian women might not be disadvantaged in hiring decisions. For example, Steffens et al. (2019) found that gay men were rated more hirable for feminine-typed jobs. Clarke and Arnold (2018) found when gay men are viewed as androgenous, no difference was found between the hireability ratings of gay men across gender-typed occupations. Focusing on lesbian women, Niedlich et al. (2015) found that lesbian women engaging in behaviors that cue traditional gender stereotypes are not penalized in terms of competence ratings like heterosexual women who engage in those behaviors. The intersection of stereotypes about SGM individuals and stereotypes about other identity-based groups was also shown to be important. Evidence for this comes from Pedulla (2014), who found that rather than being doubly disadvantaged by their status as both gay and Black, these applicants were evaluated more favorably than the nongay Black applicant. Further research adopting this type of intersectional approach is needed.

Advancement and Leadership Evaluations. Selection for promotion and advancement to leadership positions within organizations among SGMs are accompanied by many of the same issues as hiring into organizations. Data show 48% of LGB respondents (Meyer, 2019) and 49% of transgender and gender-nonbinary respondents reported being denied a promotion based on their SGM status (James et al., 2016). Direct evidence for this type of discrimination comes from a large-scale study of workers in the United Kingdom (Aksoy et al., 2019). Results revealed that gay men and lesbian women were more concentrated in lower-level managerial positions than their heterosexual counterparts even though lesbian women had higher levels of human capital (e.g., education).

Attitudes and stereotypes about SGM individuals along with gendered and job-related stereotypes play a role in promotion and advancement to leadership positions. In the case of leadership positions, stereotypes about leaders also come into play. Generally, leadership is stereotyped along masculine lines (i.e., think manager–think male association; Schein, 1973). In an extension of this phenomenon, Liberman and Golom (2015) found that leadership is also stereotyped as heterosexual. Several studies have tested the possibility that a perceived mismatch between SGM individuals and stereotypes of leaders biases promotion and leadership evaluations. Morton (2017) found that a gay man was evaluated as a less effective leader than a heterosexual leader by participants with high levels of homonegativity. Contrary to their predictions, Pichler and Holmes (2017) found that gay men and lesbian women were rated more promotable than heterosexual workers, a finding they cautiously referred to as a "gay advantage." However, they also found a negative indirect effect of SGM status via participant perceptions of how well the candidate would fit in. The authors suggested that bias against gay men and lesbian women is more likely to occur when decision-makers are prompted to consider how well the candidate fits the work environment. Studies considering the gendered nature of the environment support this assertion (Barrantes & Eaton, 2018; Pellegrini et al., 2020). Contrary to these findings, Fasoli and Hagerty (2020) manipulated SGM status via vocal cues and found that gay-sounding men and lesbian-sounding women were rated lower on leadership suitability than people who sounded heterosexual. These authors note the importance of subtle (vocal cues) versus more explicit indicators of SGM identity commonly used in vignette studies. Looking across the literature in this area, when the person's sexual orientation is made explicit in a vignette, it is more common to see more favorable (or at least not unfavorable) ratings of SGM workers, whereas when sexual orientation is inferred from vocal cues, this study found unfavorable ratings of suitability for leadership positions. One explanation for this is that favorable ratings made when sexual orientation is made explicit might be the result of demand characteristics (people wanting to seem fair and not prejudiced); however, when subtle cues are used, the situation is more ambiguous, making it more likely that stereotypes will bias judgments of SGM individuals.

Interpersonal Discrimination.   Although many states and organizations have enacted laws and policies banning formal types of employment discrimination for SGMs, there are interpersonal forms of discrimination, defined as more subtle and indirect behaviors that occur during interactions with others (Hebl et al., 2002) and can include various forms of heterosexist harassment and genderism (Berdahl, 2007; Konik & Cortina, 2008; Silverschanz et al., 2008). This more subtle and insidious type of discrimination has been conceptualized in various ways and by several disciplines. One of the more prominent paradigms to emerge across disciplines is the concept of microaggressions. Microaggressions, a type of interpersonal discrimination, are unconscious or unintentional day-to-day slights, insults, invalidations, and offensive behaviors that convey a hostile, derogatory message to members of marginalized social groups (Sue, 2010). Although the term first originated in 1978 from Pierce et al., Sue and colleagues (2007) developed a more comprehensive theory of microaggressions targeting racial minorities. The construct has since been expanded to include other social identities, including gender and sexual orientation (Nadal et al., 2010; Sue et al., 2008). Examples of microaggressions targeting people who are SGM include the use of heterosexist/

transphobic terminology, discomfort with or disapproval of SGM identities or experiences (e.g., assuming an SGM individual is being overly sensitive about discrimination), and endorsement of heteronormativity/gender binaries (e.g., dress codes that align with birth sex). Subsequent research showed that these experiences arise in various settings, including the workplace (Nadal et al., 2011) and are shown to be quite ubiquitous and pervasive.

In a U.S. national study of SGM adults, the majority of participants reported experiencing interpersonal discrimination due to their sexual orientation or gender identity (Casey et al., 2019). Fifty-seven percent reported hearing a slur or negative word, and 53% reported experiencing insensitive or offensive comments. In another study by Ellsworth et al. (2020), compared to straight men, gay men, and straight women, lesbian and bisexual women experienced more targeted incivility, including having their competence questioned, being overlooked, and being disrespected. These experiences can also be quite prevalent for transgender and gender-nonconforming individuals. A U.S. national survey found that 71% hid their gender or gender transitioning status to avoid discrimination, 50% reported experiencing harassment, and 45% were repeatedly called by the wrong pronouns on purpose at work (Grant et al., 2011).

Exposure to microaggressions is found to have significant and damaging effects on the target. The minority stress model (Meyer, 1995, 2003) is a theoretical framework used to better understand the impact that chronic exposure to minority stress has on marginalized social groups. The theory posits that due to the frequency and intensity of these experiences, marginalized social groups are at a greater risk of harmful physical and psychological health outcomes. Although much of the research in this area has focused on racial/ethnic minorities (e.g., Keith et al., 2010), those studies examining SGMs have found comparable harmful effects. For example, SGMs exposed to microaggressions have reported increased depression, trauma, and negative emotions, including anger and hopelessness, and lower self-esteem (Nadal, 2018; Nadal et al., 2014, 2016).

Although SGM microaggressions have been studied less often in the I/O psychology and management literatures, research has shown the negative impact of such microaggressions on work-related outcomes. For example, in an experimental study, Hebl et al. (2002) found that job applicants who appeared to be gay or lesbian experienced greater hostility than those assumed to be heterosexual. Velez et al. (2013) found that participants who experienced higher levels of microaggressions reported greater levels of psychological distress and job dissatisfaction. Similarly, Rabelo and Cortina (2014) examined microaggressions in the form of gender policing harassment and heterosexist harassment. Gender policing is a form of "negative treatment for failing to adhere to the traditional norms of one's gender" (Konik & Cortina, 2008, p. 320), whereas heterosexist harassment is "insensitive verbal and symbolic (but nonassaultive) behaviors that convey animosity toward nonheterosexuality" (Silverschanz et al., 2008, p. 180). This study found that SGM employees who experienced gender policing reported lower levels of engagement and job satisfaction and higher levels of exhaustion and threat stress, and those experiencing heterosexist harassment reported lower levels of job satisfaction and higher levels of pressure and threat stress. Consistent with these findings, using a mixed-method approach, Galupo and Resnick (2016) found that most SGM participants described their experience of microaggressions as negatively impacting their mood, sense of well-being, job satisfaction, work productivity, and desire to stay at the organization.

Some studies, and in particular those examining employees who are transgender, have begun to explore the psychological processes that relate microaggressions to outcomes. Research by Thoroughgood et al. (2017) found that transgender employees who perceived being the targets of discrimination reported higher levels of paranoid cognition (an aroused psychological state characterized by a heightened level of hypervigilance, rumination, and sinister attributions) than transgender employees who did not feel discriminated against. The measure of discrimination used in the study included items that reflected microaggressions. Paranoid cognition was found to mediate the relationships between perceived discrimination and workplace outcomes, including job dissatisfaction, emotional exhaustion, and intent to leave the organization. In a replication and extension of these findings, Thoroughgood and colleagues (2020) conducted an experience sampling study of transgender employees that examined the impact of daily exposure to discrimination on paranoid cognition and emotional exhaustion. Like their previous study, the results found that those employees who experienced greater levels of daily discrimination (which included forms of microaggressions) experienced more paranoid cognition, which led to more emotional exhaustion. An additional and interesting finding was that the daily exposure to discrimination less adversely impacted those who reported higher levels of trait mindfulness. That is, employees higher on trait mindfulness were able to interrupt the paranoid cognition process in response to the discrimination exposure, rendering its deleterious effects less impactful on employee psychological well-being.

INDIVIDUAL MITIGATION STRATEGIES

Faced with the likelihood of experiencing these types of formal and informal discrimination, as well as their consequences, people who are sexual and gender minorities (SGMs) look for ways to avoid such interactions. Because some SGM identities are concealable, in an effort to avoid being the direct targets of discrimination, some SGM workers may have the option to decide the degree and conditions under which they voluntarily make their SGM identity status known to others in the workplace. The process of managing the degree and conditions under which a concealable SGM identity might become known (or not) is referred to as identity management, and the choices about making one's SGM identity known are referred to as disclosure decisions (King et al., 2017; Ragins, 2008).

Identity Management.   A common theme from the disclosure literature is that SGM individuals disclose when they hold positive perceptions of their identity and receive positive reactions from others at work. However, managing the SGM identity is an ongoing process that depends on situational cues, specific behavioral responses, and timing rather than a fixed strategy (Jones & King, 2014; King et al., 2008). The dominant frameworks of identity management have viewed the disclosure strategies that SGM individuals employ as existing on a spectrum ranging from very high levels of disclosure and expression to completely concealing their SGM identity (Button, 2004; Chrobot-Mason et al., 2001; King et al., 2017; Lynch & Rodell, 2018). The earliest identity management model by Woods (1993) identified three major identity management strategies adopted by gay men in corporate America: integrating, avoiding, and counterfeiting. Integrating refers to revealing an identity in subtle or overt ways, whereas avoiding and counterfeiting strategies involve an intention to conceal one's identity. A decade later, Woods's work was empirically tested and validated by Button (2004) with lesbian and gay employees. Specifically, Button found that these strategies are adopted by lesbian women and gay men and used in combination with one another.

In their seminal review, Clair et al. (2005) identified three disclosure strategies: signaling, normalizing, and differentiation, where signaling reflects indirect disclosure of identity through the use of symbols and clues (e.g., placing a wedding picture of a same-sex partner at their work desk), normalizing reflects disclosing but deemphasizing the importance of one's SGM identity, and differentiation involves emphasizing the distinctions between one's SGM identity and other non-SGM identities. Subsequently, Jones and King (2014) developed a multilevel identity management model focused on within-person identity management strategies (i.e., across situations within a person). In the career literature, Lidderdale et al. (2007) proposed a comprehensive identity management model based on Social Cognitive Career Theory that highlights the interaction between behavioral, cognition, and contextual influences on the identity management strategies of LGB individuals. Empirical research has found that acceptance cues such as supportive policies and climate (Chrobot-Mason et al., 2001; King et al., 2017), positive reactions from others, and the sexual orientation of the other person (King et al., 2017; Martinez et al., 2017b) influence the type of strategy an SGM individual employs. Fewer studies have directly examined the impact of employing such strategies. One study found that when a counterfeiting strategy (i.e., maintaining a false identity) was adopted, others in the work group were more likely to express their views and include others in decision-making (Chrobot-Mason et al., 2001). In another study, Lynch and Rodell (2018) found that those who employed a revealing/integrative strategy experienced less negative treatment by others; however, assimilating (i.e., associating with the dominant social group) was most effective in cultivating positive reactions from colleagues.

Identity Disclosure. Disclosure is the process of expressing one's personal and distinctive self or other personal information to others (Chaudoir & Fisher, 2010; Phillips et al., 2009). SGM employees are often confronted with the dilemma of disclosing their identity at work. Those who decide to conceal their SGM identity may do so to avoid formal and interpersonal discrimination, but the decision to conceal can also be a "curse," as it may create internal conflict, tension, and anxiety (Ragins, 2008). Further, SGM individuals who feel they are not living as their true selves may experience lower levels of job satisfaction (Martinez et al., 2017b).

The decision to disclose is not a one-off event, it will continue to be a challenge across the career life cycle as SGM individuals navigate their careers, meet and work with new people, enter new workplaces, and change careers. According to Derlega and Grzelak (1979), the disclosure decision depends on whether disclosure is necessary for attaining personal goals. Individuals motivated by approach-oriented goals are driven by the potential for rewards (e.g., better promotion opportunities) or positive psychological states (e.g., feeling positive about their identity) that might result from disclosure; whereas those pursuing avoidance-oriented goals are driven by the potential to avoid punishment (e.g., being excluded from career opportunities) or negative psychological states (e.g., anxiety; Chaudoir & Fisher, 2010). The disclosure decision is complex and multifaceted and requires a cost-benefit analysis of what it means for the person's everyday experience. SGM individuals must assess varying contingencies such as the reactions of others and the likelihood of being discriminated against, rejected, or excluded socially or professionally by others at work (King et al., 2008; Ragins, 2004; Trau & Härtel, 2004). A number of factors have been shown to be related to disclosure decisions.

Factors Related to SGM Identity Disclosure Decisions. Two dominant individual antecedents of identity disclosure decisions that have been examined in the literature are *identity centrality* and *stigma consciousness*. Identity centrality describes the extent to which one's identity is an integral part of one's self-definition (Stryker & Serpe, 1994) and is shown to be associated with negative and positive psychological outcomes (Quinn & Chaudoir, 2009). Studies have shown that those high (vs. low) in identity centrality are more likely to disclose their SGM status (e.g., King et al., 2017; Law et al., 2011), and others have found that this relationship is moderated by individual and contextual factors. For example, Fletcher and Everly (2021) found that the positive impact of SGM identity disclosure on the experience of authenticity at work is higher among those with high (vs. low) identity centrality. Relatedly, Holman and colleagues (2021) found that a supportive workplace climate moderates this relationship such that the decision to disclose tends to be higher for those with high (vs. low) identity centrality when there is a supportive workplace climate. Overall, this research demonstrates that identity centrality influences the decision to disclose one's SGM identity and contributes to a positive work experience for those who do disclose.

Another factor influencing the decision to disclose is the perception that the SGM individual has of their own identity. Steele and colleagues (Steele et al., 2002) proposed that the more a person identifies with their identity group, the more likely they will experience fear and anxiety about being negatively stereotyped and judged by others. Building on this work, Pinel (1999) applied this concept to stigmatized groups and coined the term *stigma consciousness* Stigma consciousness refers to the extent to which an individual belonging to a stigmatized group is anxious about the perceptions of and social interactions with others. Research shows stigma consciousness has detrimental effects on emotions, intentions, behaviors, and performance of those with stigmatized identities (Lewis et al., 2006; Marx et al., 1999; Nouvilas-Pallejà et al., 2018; Pinel, 1999; Pinel & Paulin, 2005). Although the relationship between disclosure and stigma consciousness in the workplace has not been explored extensively, Gates (2014) and King and colleagues (2017) have found that the relationship between stigma consciousness and outness at work was not statistically significant and argued that there might be conditions that moderate this relationship. Other constructs related to stigma consciousness, however, such as internal homophobia and self-stigma, are shown to be negatively associated with disclosure at work (King et al., 2017; Rostosky & Riggle, 2002). In general, research suggests that SGMs' perceptions of their identity and the degree to which they internalize the stereotypes and attitudes others hold toward their identity influence the likelihood of disclosing their SGM identity at work.

In addition to individual factors, social and organizational factors are shown to influence disclosure decisions. In the workplace, SGM individuals monitor the characteristics of their environments for cues that signal potential acceptance or rejection of their SGM identity (Ragins, 2004). Two meta-analyses examining supportive SGM workplace characteristics (Wax et al., 2018; Webster et al., 2018) identified several features of the environment that signal the degree of acceptance for SGM identities, including (a) SGM diversity climate, (b) social interactions, and (c) antidiscrimination policies. This research found that these features work in concert with each other, and each is important but to varying degrees. In particular, workplace diversity climate had the strongest effect on disclosure decisions, while social interactions and SGM antidiscrimination policies were modestly related. An implication of these findings is the recognition that organizations play a critical role in supporting the authentic experience of their SGM individuals that requires leadership support and extensive resources to help build inclusive workplaces for SGM individuals (Trau et al., 2019).

Outcomes of SGM Identity Disclosure. A key topic of interest in the SGM management and I/O psychology literatures is the outcomes resulting from SGM identity disclosure decisions. A central finding from this research is that identity disclosure is positively related to attitudes, including increased job satisfaction (Griffith & Hebl, 2002; Martinez et al., 2017b), organizational commitment (Law et al., 2011; Trau & Hartel, 2007), decreased withdrawal intentions (Ragins et al., 2007), and increased career commitment (Trau & Hartel, 2007). Additionally, studies have also shown that disclosing one's SGM identity is related to more support from coworkers (Griffith & Hebl, 2002), supervisors (Huffman et al., 2008), and workplace networks (Trau, 2015). An interesting and somewhat contradictory finding is the near-zero relationship found in a meta-analysis between disclosure and job satisfaction (Wax et al., 2018). This finding reinforces the need for more fine-grained research into the costs and benefits of disclosure at work. A notable example is a study by King et al. (2008), in which they interviewed both SGM and non-SGM employees and found that an early or immediate disclosure— after the first interaction—is more stressful for SGM individuals and thought to be inappropriate by some non-SGM employees. Hence, research into when, why, and how disclosure may lead to negative outcomes for both SGM and non-SGM individuals will provide helpful insights for theory and practice.

INTERPERSONAL MITIGATION STRATEGIES: SUPPORT, ALLYSHIP, ADVOCACY

Social support broadly refers to instrumental (e.g., advice, information sharing) and socioemotional (e.g., positive regard, empathy, caring) resources provided by others via social interactions. In their meta-analysis reviewing workplace contextual supports for workers who are sexual and gender minorities (SGMs), Webster et al. (2018) found that socially supportive relationships were predictive of favorable attitudes and well-being, and those supportive relationships were relatively more important to these outcomes than either the presence of formal organizational policies or a supportive workplace climate. Examining different sources of support in a sample of LGB workers, Ragins et al. (2007) found that when LGB workers felt supported by their supervisors and coworkers, they were less fearful of disclosing their SGM identities and more likely to be out at work. In a study by Huffman et al. (2008), the researchers found that supervisor support was related to job satisfaction and coworker support was related to life satisfaction. Across these studies, the results highlight the importance of supportive workplace relationships and their impact on organizationally relevant and personal outcomes for SGM individuals.

In addition to these types of social support provided by supervisors and coworkers, other forms of support entail more active efforts to improve the work lives of SGMs by confronting instances of discrimination and opposing unjust workplace practices. One such form of this type of support is allyship. Allies are "individuals who strive to end oppression through supporting and advocating on behalf of the oppressed" (Sabat et al., 2013, p. 481). While allyship is often described as a responsibility of dominant un-oppressed groups, individuals from other marginalized groups can also serve as allies; for example, a gay white man can be an ally to a Black lesbian woman (Ruggs et al., 2015). Moreover, being an ally is considered an identity itself, part of one's internalized self-concept (Washington & Evans, 1991). Ally identity has been theorized and operationalized as a multifaceted construct that includes an individual's (a) knowledge and skills, (b) awareness of oppression, and (c) openness and support directed toward SGMs (Jones et al., 2014).

Predictors of engaging in allyship include having close friendships with SGM individuals, lower prejudicial attitudes, and more favorable attitudes toward SGMs (Fingerhut, 2011). Because being an ally is a central part of one's identity, it can also be motivated by deeply held morals and beliefs about justice (Brooks & Edwards, 2009; Russell, 2011). Indeed, being able to act according to one's values has been described by SGM allies as one of the reasons they engage in allyship (Rostosky et al., 2015). Several factors can operate to inhibit allyship. These include the potential ally's concerns about negative reactions from workers who are SGMs and about generating conflict and backlash from those who are not SGMs (Sabat et al., 2013). Concerns about the negative reactions of the workers who are SGMs are an important consideration, and it is important for allies to understand the needs and wants of the SGM individuals in order to act appropriately. Although how they are enacted in specific situations will differ, in general, SGM individuals want allies to (a) respect and support them, (b) provide them a sense of safety, and (c) stand up for them and speak up if needed to ensure that they are treated fairly (Brooks & Edwards, 2009).

Concerns about conflict and backlash from those who are not SGMs stem mainly from the component of allyship that involves actively supporting and advocating for workers who are SGMs. Actively supporting workers can involve taking proactive steps to support SGMs (e.g., helping to foster an inclusive climate) and confronting specific instances of discrimination as they occur (Gardner & Alanis, 2020). Research on confronting instances of discrimination finds that those who confront actions directed at gay men are not viewed more negatively compared to those who did not confront at all and that the optimal style of confrontation is to "do so in a calm way that identifies the perpetrator as being prejudiced" (Martinez et al., 2017a, p. 81). The notion that standing up to influential organizational members and/or challenging the status quo and confronting instances of discrimination can entail considerable social, job, and career-related risks has been recognized in the construct referred to as oppositional courage (Thoroughgood et al., 2021). In a series of studies, Thoroughgood et al. found that witnessing cisgender coworkers engage in oppositional courage (e.g., confronting discrimination despite risks to themselves) was related to higher job satisfaction and lower emotional exhaustion for transgender workers. In addition, they found that this positive effect operated via improved organization-based self-esteem, especially so for workers whose trans identity was more central to them. Taken together, these studies suggest that individual actions taken by allies can have favorable effects on SGMs.

ORGANIZATIONAL MITIGATION STRATEGIES

In the workplace, contextual cues have a profound impact on the experiences of those with stigmatized identities, including attitudes they have about their identity, colleagues, jobs, and organizations (Ragins, 2004). Among these cues are workplace policies, practices, and climate.

Policies, Practices, Climate.   Many organizations have begun including SGM identities within their nondiscrimination policies, including same-sex partners and transgender-related care in benefit programs, and implementing practices such as SGM-related diversity trainings and employee resource groups. These policies and practices are important ways to signal to SGM workers that the organization is welcoming and inclusive of their identities. They also raise awareness and signal to other employees the kinds of behaviors toward SGM workers that are acceptable and those that are not. Research on the effect of such policies and practices suggests that they have a favorable impact on not just the people who are SGM, but also on non-SGM workers (Pichler et al., 2017). This favorable impact includes better work-related attitudes, less psychological strain, and a greater likelihood of SGM identity disclosure (Webster et al., 2018). An additional benefit of SGM inclusive policies and practices is that they can help foster a favorable diversity climate.

Diversity climate refers to employees' shared perceptions of the policies, practices, and procedures that implicitly and explicitly convey the organization's priority in fostering and maintaining diversity and eliminating discrimination (Gelfand et al., 2005, p. 104). In general, research on SGM individuals has shown that an SGM-supportive workplace climate predicts a range of positive attitudinal and behavioral outcomes for SGM employees (Wax et al., 2018; Webster et al., 2018). Pichler et al. (2017) have argued that it is also the case that SGM-supportive policies and climate improve non-SGM individuals' attitudes toward their organization. This positive spillover occurs because a supportive climate signals organizational goodwill toward all employees. Hence, employees trust that the decisions made by management are fair to all groups in the organization. However, there has been limited research on spillover effects in the SGM literature and, broadly, in the diversity and inclusion literature, and so future research is needed.

While diversity climate, policies, and practices are organizational-level phenomena, they can vary across individuals, teams, units, and geographic locations of the organization. That is, to the extent that SGM-supportive climate, policies, and practices are not consistently applied throughout the organization, they can be fragmented (Pichler et al., 2017; Ragins et al., 2007), even more so for those organizations with dispersed geographical locations (Trau et al., 2018). Although there is a paucity of cross-level empirical research conducted thus far, studies have provided interesting insights on cross-level effects on the experiences of SGM employees. For example, Tilcsik (2011) found that recruiters working in regional areas with non-supportive attitudes and laws toward SGM employees, and those who are employees in organizations emphasizing the importance of stereotypically male heterosexual traits, are more likely to discriminate against male job applicants. In sum, more empirical work is needed to identify the antecedents and consequences of SGM-supportive climates, policies, and practices and their variation and uniformity at the individual, group, and organizational levels.

SOCIETAL MITIGATION STRATEGIES

Workplace issues regarding sexual and gender minorities (SGMs) are influenced by the broader sociocultural and political ecologies in which they are embedded. Sociocultural forces influence and are influenced by individual attitudes toward SGMs and the actions of organizations. These interact with the political environment to result in legal actions that can be aimed at protecting (or denying) the rights of SGMs. The relationships among individuals, organizational actors, and these broader ecologies are reciprocal in the sense that each affects the other. In addition to being shaped by them, individuals and organizations shape social attitudes and the legal environment. Understanding and appreciating this is important for at least two main reasons. First, the presence (or lack thereof) of favorable social attitudes and formal legal protections raises critical ethical concerns when conducting research in this area (Hodson et al., 2018). These include considering the degree to which research participants have disclosed their SGM status, the negative consequences that can result from participants being inadvertently "outed," and making certain robust safeguards for the protection of the participants are in place. Second, societal attitudes and legal protections can play a substantive role in research surrounding SGMs and can directly impact the workplace experiences of SGM employees (Tebbe et al., 2019).

Societal Attitudes.   Across the world, societal attitudes and public opinion on the acceptance of SGMs vary by country and region (Poushter & Kent, 2020). Of the countries surveyed by the Pew Research Center in 2019, those with the most negative attitudes were Nigeria, Indonesia, and Tunisia, with less than 10% of participants reporting that homosexuality should be accepted by society. Those with the most positive attitudes were Sweden, the Netherlands, and Spain, with nearly 90% or more of participants reporting that homosexuality should be accepted (Pew Research Center, 2020). Research has also shown that attitudes have become more favorable over time in many countries. For example, between 2002 and 2019, countries such as South Africa, Turkey, and the United States have had a rise in acceptance of homosexuality by more than 10% (Pew Research Center, 2020). Regarding employment, 93% of those in the United States now agree that "gay people" should have equal employment rights, up from just 56% in 1977 (McCarthy, 2019). Several studies have examined and provided important insights into the factors contributing to this shift in societal attitudes and views toward SGMs in the United States and other countries, including an increase in positive media coverage, more people having close contact relationships with others who are SGMs, and increases in education (see review by Adamczyk & Liao, 2019).

Employment-Related Legislation.   Internationally, both the United Nations Human Rights Council (United Nations, 2011) and the International Labor Organization (International Labor Organization, 2015) have affirmed that "gay rights are human rights" and called for legal protections for people who are SGMs. While it is promising that 124 countries have now decriminalized same-sex relationships, being an SGM is still considered a criminalized identity in 69 countries, with penalties ranging from fines and floggings to imprisonment and even the death penalty. Furthermore, while it is also promising that 81 countries (a more than a fivefold increase since the turn of the 21st century) have instituted some form of protection against discrimination in the workplace for SGMs (ILGA World, 2020), these laws vary widely across countries and provide only an inconsistent set of protections from formal discrimination.

In the United States, SGM individuals have historically faced considerable discrimination; same-sex relationships were not decriminalized at the national level until 2003. Employment discrimination against SGMs has not only long been permitted but was formally codified by a decades-old ban on hiring gay and lesbian employees by any federal agency. This ban, authorized by Executive Order 10450 and signed into law in 1953, was based on the baseless fear that gay and lesbian individuals posed a threat to national security due to their vulnerability to blackmail and the perception that they have weak moral character (Lewis, 2001). This effort to systematically investigate, interrogate, and purge people from the federal workplace due to their sexual orientation contributed to what is known as the "Lavender Scare," a time when institutionalized homophobia was widespread (Johnson, 2004). Although some of the restrictions imposed by this order were eased over time, the ban was only completely revoked in 2017.

Revocation of Executive Order 10450 was part of a growing movement to extend the rights of SGMs generally and with regard to employment. Toward that end, in 2015, the U.S. Supreme Court issued a ruling on *Obergell v Hodges* (2015), which established a nationwide constitutional basis for protecting same-sex couples' marriage and spousal benefits. Adding further protection to broader workplace rights during the Obama era, several executive orders were issued that banned any federal agency, government contractor, or subcontractor from discriminating against SGMs (see Zugelder & Champagne, 2018). In what is one of the more significant developments in creating employment rights for SGM individuals in the United States, the Supreme Court decided that discrimination against SGMs is a type of sex discrimination and therefore illegal under Title VII of the Civil Rights Act of 1964 (*Bostock v. Clayton County*, 2020). Until this landmark ruling, there was only a patchwork of nondiscrimination employment laws that varied across states and counties (Human Rights Campaign, 2022). Although positive strides have been made, some fear that with no federal law explicitly including sexual orientation and gender identity as protected classes, there may be grounds for possible discrimination allowances based on religious doctrines such as the Religious Freedom Restoration Act of 1993 (Oakley, 2020; Saxe, 2020). Given this gap in federal discrimination laws, efforts have been made to pass federal legislation to update the language of Title VII to include sexual orientation and gender identity as protected classes. One bill under consideration in the senate is the Equality Act. Like the research reviewed throughout this article, the social and legal context remains in a dynamic and evolving state. The presence of legal protections such as these impact perceptions of discrimination and support reported by SGM individuals as well as disclosure decisions (Ragins & Cornwell, 2001; Riggle et al., 2010; Tebbe et al., 2019). More important, however, they can raise community awareness and at least reduce certain types of discrimination (Barron & Hebl, 2013).

REFERENCES

Adamczyk, A., & Liao, Y. C. (2019). Examining public opinion about LGBTQ-related issues in the United States and across multiple nations. *Annual Review of Sociology, 45*(1), 401–423.

Aksoy, C. G., Carpenter, C. S., Frank, J., & Huffman, M. L. (2019). Gay glass ceilings: Sexual orientation and workplace authority in the UK. *Journal of Economic Behavior & Organization, 159*, 167–180.

Badgett, M. L., Waaldijk, K., & van der Meulen Rodgers, Y. (2019). The relationship between LGBT inclusion and economic development: Macro-level evidence. *World Development, 120*, 1–14.

Barrantes, R. J., & Eaton, A. A. (2018). Sexual orientation and leadership suitability: How being a gay man affects perceptions of fit in gender-stereotyped positions. *Sex Roles, 79*, 549–564.

Barron, L. G., & Hebl, M. (2013). The force of law: The effects of sexual orientation antidiscrimination legislation on interpersonal discrimination in employment. *Psychology, Public Policy, and Law, 19*, 191–205.

Berdahl, J. L. (2007). Harassment based on sex: Protecting social status in the context of gender hierarchy. *The Academy of Management Review, 32*(2), 641–658.

Bostock v. Clayton County, Ga., No. 17-1618, 590 U.S. (2020). https://www.supremecourt.gov/opinions/19pdf/17-1618_hfci.pdf

Brewster, M. E., Velez, B., DeBlaere, C., & Moradi, B. (2012). Transgender individuals' workplace experiences: The applicability of sexual minority measures and models. *Journal of Counseling Psychology, 59*(1), 60.

Brooks, A. K., & Edwards, K. (2009). Allies in the workplace: Including LGBT in HRD. *Advances in Developing Human Resources, 11*(1), 136–149.

Button, S. B. (2004). Identity management strategies utilized by lesbian and gay employees: A quantitative investigation. *Group & Organization Management, 29*(4), 470–494.

Byington, E. K., Tamm, G. F., & Trau, R. N. (2021). Mapping sexual orientation research in management: A review and research agenda. *Human Resource Management, 60*(1), 31–53.

Casey, L. S., Reisner, S. L., Findling, M. G., Blendon, R., J., Benson, J. M., Sayde, J. M., & Miller, C. (2019). Discrimination in the United States: Experiences of lesbian, gay, bisexual, transgender, and queer Americans. *Health Services Research, 54*, 1454–1466.

Cech, E. A., & Rothwell, W. R. (2020). LGBT workplace inequality in the federal workforce: Intersectional processes, organizational contexts, and turnover considerations. *ILR Review, 73*(1), 25–60.

Chaudoir, S. R., & Fisher, J. D. (2010). The disclosure process model: Understanding disclosure decision making and postdisclosure outcomes among people living with a concealable stigmatized identity. *Psychological Bulletin, 136*, 236–256.

Chrobot-Mason, D., Button, S. B., & DiClementi, J. D. (2001). Sexual identity management strategies: An exploration of antecedents and consequences. *Sex Roles, 45*(5), 321–336.

Clair, J. A., Beatty, J., & MacLean, T. (2005). Out of sight but not out of mind: Managing invisible social identities in the workplace. *Academy of Management Review, 30*, 78–95.

Clarke, H. M., & Arnold, K. A. (2018). The influence of sexual orientation on the perceived fit of male applicants for both male- and female-typed jobs. *Frontiers in Psychology, 9*.

Corrington, A., Hebl, M., Stewart, D., Madera, J., Ng, L., & Williams, J. (2020). Diversity and inclusion of understudied populations: A call to practitioners and researchers. *Consulting Psychology Journal: Practice and Research, 72*(4), 303.

Corrington, A., Nittrouer, C. L., Trump-Steele, R. C., & Hebl, M. (2019). Letting him B: A study on the intersection of gender and sexual orientation in the workplace. *Journal of Vocational Behavior, 113*, 129–142.

Derlega, V. J., & Grzelak, J. (1979). Appropriateness of self-disclosure. In G. J. Chelune (Ed.), *Self-disclosures: Origins, patterns and implications of openness in interpersonal relationships* (pp. 151–176). Jossey-Bass.

Dupreelle, P., Novacek, G., Lindquist, J., Micon, N., Pellas, S., & Testone, G. (2020). *A new LGBTQ workforce has arrived—Inclusive cultures must follow.* Boston Consulting Group. https://www.bcg.com/publications/2020/inclusive-cultures-must-follow-new-lgbtq-workforce

Ellsworth, D., Mendy, A., & Sullivan, G. (2020). *How the LGBTQ+ community fares in the workplace.* McKinsey & Company, June, 23. https://www.mckinsey.com/featured-insights/diversity-and-inclusion/how-the-lgbtq-plus-community-fares-in-the-workplace

Everly, B. A., Unzueta, M. M., & Shih, M. J. (2016). Can being gay provide a boost in the hiring process? Maybe if the boss is female. *Journal of Business and Psychology, 31*(2), 293–306.

Fasoli, F., & Hegarty, P. (2020). A leader doesn't sound lesbian!: The impact of sexual orientation vocal cues on heterosexual persons' first impression and hiring decision. *Psychology of Women Quarterly, 44*(2), 234–255.

Fingerhut, A. W. (2011). Straight allies: What predicts heterosexuals' alliance with the LGBT community? *Journal of Applied Social Psychology, 41*, 2230–2248.

Flage, A. (2020). Discrimination against gays and lesbians in hiring decisions: A meta-analysis. *International Journal of Manpower, 41*(6), 671–691.

Fletcher, L., & Everly, B. A. (2021). Perceived lesbian, gay, bisexual, and transgender (LGBT) supportive practices and the life satisfaction of LGBT employees: The roles of disclosure, authenticity at work, and identity centrality. *Journal of Occupational and Organizational Psychology, 94*(3), 485–508.

Galupo, M. P., & Resnick, C. A. (2016). Experiences of LGBT microaggressions in the workplace: Implications for policy. In T. Köllen (Ed.), *Sexual orientation and transgender issues in organizations* (pp. 271–287). Springer.

Gardner, D. M., & Alanis, J. M. (2020). Together we stand: Ally training for discrimination and harassment reduction. *Industrial and Organizational Psychology: Perspectives on Science and Practice, 13*(2), 196–199.

Gates, T. G. (2014). Assessing the relationship between outness at work and stigma consciousness among LGB workers in the Midwest and the resulting implications for counselors. *Counselling Psychology Quarterly, 27*(3), 264–276.

Gelfand, M. J., Nishii, L., Raver, L., & Schneider, B. (2005). Discrimination in the workplace: An organizational level analysis. In R. L. Dipboye & A. Colella (Eds.), *Psychological and organizational bases of discrimination at work* (pp. 89–116). Lawrence Erlbaum Associates.

Grant, J. M., Mottet, L. A., & Tanis, J. (2011). *Injustice at every turn: A report of the National Transgender Discrimination Survey*. National Gay and Lesbian Task Force. https://www.thetaskforce.org/wp-content/uploads/2019/07/ntds_full.pdf

Griffith, K. H., & Hebl, M. R. (2002). The disclosure dilemma for gay men and lesbians: "Coming out" at work. *Journal of Applied Psychology, 87*(6), 1191.

Hancock, A. J., Clarke, H. M., & Arnold, K. A. (2020). Sexual orientation occupational stereotypes. *Journal of Vocational Behavior, 119*, 103427.

Hebl, M. R., Foster, J. M., Mannix, L. M., & Dovidio, J. F. (2002). Formal and interpersonal discrimination: A field study examination of applicant bias. *Personality and Social Psychological Bulletin, 28*, 815–825.

Hodson, J., Jackson, S., Cukier, W., & Holmes, M. (2018). Between the corporation and the closet: Ethically researching LGBTQ+ identities in the workplace. *Equality, Diversity and Inclusion: An International Journal, 37*(3), 283–297.

Holman, E. G., Ogolsky, B. G., & Oswald, R. F. (2021). Concealment of a sexual minority identity in the workplace: The role of workplace climate and identity centrality. *Journal of Homosexuality, 69*(9), 1–19.

Horvath, M., & Ryan, A. M. (2003). Antecedents and potential moderators of the relationship between attitudes and hiring discrimination on the basis of sexual orientation. *Sex Roles, 48*(3), 115–130.

Huffman, A. H., Watrous-Rodriguez, K. M., & King, E. B. (2008). Supporting a diverse workforce: What type of support is most meaningful for lesbian and gay employees? *Human Resource Management, 47*(2), 237–253.

Human Rights Campaign. (2022). *State maps*. https://www.hrc.org/resources/state-maps

ILGA World. (2020). *ILGA World updates state-sponsored homophobia report*. https://ilga.org/ilga-world-releases-state-sponsored-homophobia-December-2020-update

International Labor Organization. (2015). *LGBT workers entitled to equal rights and benefits at the workplace*. https://www.ilo.org/global/about-the-ilo/how-the-ilo-works/ilo-director-general/statements-and-speeches/WCMS_368652/lang--en/index.htm

Ipsos. (2021). *LGBT+ pride 2021 global survey*. https://www.ipsos.com/en/lgbt-pride-2021-global-survey-points-generation-gap-around-gender-identity-and-sexual-attraction

James, S. E., Herman, J. L., Rankin, S., Keisling, M., Mottet, L., & Anafi, M. (2016). *The report of the 2015 U.S. Transgender Survey*. National Center for Transgender Equality.

Johnson, D. K. (2004). *The lavender scare: The cold war persecution of gays and lesbians in the federal government*. The University of Chicago Press.

Jones, J. M. (2022). LGBT identification in U.S. ticks up to 7.1%. *Gallup News*.

Jones, K. N., Brewster, M. E., & Jones, J. A. (2014). The creation and validation of the LGBT ally identity measure. *Psychology of Sexual Orientation and Gender Diversity, 1*(2), 181–195.

Jones, K. P., & King, E. B. (2014). Managing concealable stigmas at work: A review and multilevel model. *Journal of Management, 40*, 1466–1494.

Keith, V. M., Lincoln, K. D., Taylor, R. J., & Jackson, J. S. (2010). Discriminatory experiences and depressive symptoms among African American women: Do skin tone and mastery matter? *Sex Roles: A Journal of Research, 62*(1–2), 48–59.

King, E. B., Mohr, J. J., Peddie, C. I., Jones, K. P., & Kendra, M. (2017). Predictors of identity management: An exploratory experience-sampling study of lesbian, gay, and bisexual workers. *Journal of Management, 43*(2), 476–502.

King, E. B., Reilly, C., & Hebl, M. R. (2008). The best and worst of times: Dual perspectives of coming out in the workplace. *Group and Organization Management, 33*, 566–601.

Kite, M. E., & Deaux, K. (1987). Gender belief systems: Homosexuality and the implicit inversion theory. *Psychology of Women Quarterly, 11*(1), 83–96.

Kite, M. E., Whitley Jr, B. E., Buxton, K., & Ballas, H. (2021). Gender differences in anti-gay prejudice: Evidence for stability and change. *Sex Roles 85*(11), 721–750.

Konik, J., & Cortina, L. M. (2008). Policing gender at work: Intersections of harassment based on sex and sexuality. *Social Justice Research, 21*(3), 313–337.

Law, C. L., Martinez, L. R., Ruggs, E. N., Hebl, M. R., & Akers, E. (2011). Trans-parency in the workplace: How the experiences of transsexual employees can be improved. *Journal of Vocational Behavior, 79*, 710–723.

Lewis, G. B. (2001). Barriers to security clearances for gay men and lesbians: Fear of blackmail or fear of homosexuals? *Journal of Public Administration Research and Theory, 11*, 539–558.

Lewis, R. L., Derlega, V. J., Clarke, E. G., & Kuang, J. C. (2006). Stigma consciousness, social constraints, and lesbian well-being. *Journal of Counselling Psychology, 53*, 48–56.

Liberman, B. E., & Golom, F. D. (2015). Think manager, think male? Heterosexuals' stereotypes of gay and lesbian managers. *Equality, Diversity and Inclusion: An International Journal, 34*, 566–578.

Lidderdale, M. A., Croteau, J. M., Anderson, M. Z., Tovar-Murray, D., & Davis, J. M. (2007). Building lesbian, gay, and bisexual vocational psychology: A theoretical model of workplace sexual identity management. In K. J. Bieschke, R. M. Perez, & K. A. DeBord (Eds.), *Handbook of counseling and psychotherapy with lesbian, gay, bisexual, and transgender clients* (2nd ed., pp. 245–270). American Psychological Association.

Lourenço, I. C., Di Marco, D., Branco, M. C., Lopes, A. I., Sarquis, R. W., & Soliman, M. T. (2021). The relationship between LGBT executives and firms' value and financial performance. *Journal of Risk and Financial Management, 14*(12), 596.

Lynch, J. W., & Rodell, J. B. (2018). Blend in or stand out? Interpersonal outcomes of managing concealable stigmas at work. *Journal of Applied Psychology, 103*(12), 1307.

Martinez, L. R., Hebl, M. R., Smith, N. A., & Sabat, I. E. (2017a). Standing up and speaking out against prejudice toward gay men in the workplace. *Journal of Vocational Behavior, 103*, 71–85.

Martinez, L. R., Sawyer, K. B., Thoroughgood, C. N., Ruggs, E. N., & Smith, N. (2017b). The importance of being "me": The relation between authentic identity expression and transgender employees' work-related attitudes and experiences. *Journal of Applied Psychology, 102*(2), 215–226.

Marx, D. M., Brown, J. L., & Steele, C. M. (1999). Allport's legacy and the situational press of stereotypes. *Journal of Social Issues, 55*, 491–502.

McCarthy, J. (2019). *Gallup first polled on gay issues in '77. What has changed?* Gallup. https://news.gallup.com/poll/258065/gallup-first-polled-gay-issues-changed.aspx

McFadden, C. (2020). Hiring discrimination against transgender job applicants—Considerations when designing a study. *International Journal of Manpower, 41*(6), 731–752.

Meyer, I. H. (1995). Minority stress and mental health in gay men. *Journal of Health and Social Behavior, 36*(1), 38–56.

Meyer, I. H. (2003). Prejudice, social stress, and mental health in lesbian, gay, and bisexual populations: Conceptual issues and research evidence. *Psychological Bulletin, 129*(5), 674–697.

Meyer, I. H. (2019). Experiences of discrimination among lesbian, gay and bisexual people in the US. UCLA, The Williams Institute. https://escholarship.org/uc/item/3d83j61g

Morton, J. W. (2017). Think leader, think heterosexual male? The perceived leadership effectiveness of gay male leaders. *Canadian Journal of Administrative Sciences, 34*(2), 159–169.

Nadal, K. L. (2018). *Microaggressions and traumatic stress: Theory, research, and clinical practice.* American Psychological Association.

Nadal, K. L., Davidoff, K. C., Davis, L. S., & Wong, Y. (2014). Emotional, behavioral, and cognitive reactions to microaggressions: Transgender perspectives. *Psychology of Sexual Orientation and Gender Diversity, 1*(1), 72–81.

Nadal, K. L., Issa, M. A., Leon, J., Meterko, V., Wideman, M., & Wong, Y. (2011). Sexual orientation microaggressions: "Death by a thousand cuts" for lesbian, gay, and bisexual youth. *Journal of LGBT Youth, 8*(3), 234–259.

Nadal, K. L., Rivera, D. P., & Corpus, M. J. H. (2010). Sexual orientation and transgender microaggressions: Implications for mental health and counseling. In D. W. Sue (Ed.), *Microaggressions and marginality: Manifestation, dynamics, and impact* (pp. 217–240). John Wiley & Sons.

Nadal, K. L., Whitman, C. N., Davis, L. S., Erazo, T., & Davidoff, K. C. (2016). Microaggressions toward lesbian, gay, bisexual, transgender, queer, and genderqueer people: A review of the literature. *The Journal of Sex Research, 53*(4–5), 488–508.

Niedlich, C., Steffens, M. C., Krause, J., Settke, E., & Ebert, I. D. (2015). Ironic effects of sexual minority group membership: Are lesbians less susceptible to invoking negative female stereotypes than heterosexual women? *Archives of Sexual Behavior, 44*(5), 1439–1447.

Nouvilas-Pallejà, E., Silván-Ferrero, P., de Apodaca, M., & Molero, F. (2018). Stigma consciousness and subjective well-being in lesbians and gays. *Journal of Happiness Studies, 19*(4), 1115–1133.

Oakley, C. (2020). What the Supreme Court ruling in *Bostock* means for state legislative efforts. Human Rights Campaign. https://www.hrc.org/news/what-the-supreme-court-ruling-in-bostock-means-for-state-legislative-effort

Obergefell v. Hodges. 576 U.S. (2015). . https://www.supremecourt.gov/opinions/14pdf/14-556_3204.pdf

Pachankis, J. E., & Bränström, R. (2019). How many sexual minorities are hidden? Projecting the size of the global closet with implications for policy and public health. *PLoS ONE, 14*(6), e0218084.

Pedulla, D. S. (2014). The positive consequences of negative stereotypes: Race, sexual orientation, and the job application process. *Social Psychology Quarterly, 77*(1), 75–94.

Pellegrini, V., De Cristofaro, V., Giacomantonio, M., & Salvati, M. (2020). Why are gay leaders perceived as ineffective? The role of the type of organization, sexual prejudice and gender stereotypes. *Personality and Individual Differences, 157*, 109817.

Pew Research Center. (2020). Acceptance of homosexuality over time. https://www.pewresearch.org/global/2020/06/25/global-divide-on-homosexuality-persists/pg_2020-06-25_global-views-homosexuality_a-01/

Phillips, K. W., Rothbard, N. P., & Dumas, T. L. (2009). To disclose or not to disclose? Status distance and self-disclosure in diverse environments. *Academy of Management Review, 34*, 710–732.

Pichler, S., & Holmes, O., IV. (2017). An investigation of fit perceptions and promotability in sexual minority candidates. *Equality, Diversity and Inclusion: An International Journal, 36*(7), 628–646.

Pichler, S., Ruggs, E. N., & Trau, R. N. C. (2017). Worker outcomes of LGBT-supportive policies: A cross-level model. *Equality, Diversity and Inclusion: An International Journal, 36*(1), 17–32.

Pichler, S., Varma, A., & Bruce, T. (2010). Heterosexism in employment decisions: The role of job misfit. *Journal of Applied Social Psychology, 40*(10), 2527–2555.

Pierce, C., Carew, J., Pierce-Gonzalez, D., & Willis, D. (1978). An experiment in racism: TV commercials. In C. Pierce (Ed.), *Television and education* (pp. 62–88). SAGE.

Pinel, E. C. (1999). Stigma consciousness: The psychological legacy of social stereotypes. *Journal of Personality & Social Psychology, 76*, 114–128.

Pinel, E. C., & Paulin, N. (2005). Stigma consciousness at work. *Basic and Applied Social Psychology, 27*, 345–352.

Poushter, J., & Kent, N. (2020). *Views of homosexuality around the world.* Pew Research Center's Global Attitudes Project. https://www.pewresearch.org/global/2020/06/25/global-divide-on-homosexuality-persists/

Quinn, D. M., & Chaudoir, S. R. (2009). Living with a concealable stigmatized identity: The impact of anticipated stigma, centrality, salience, and cultural stigma on psychological distress and health. *Journal of Personality and Social Psychology, 97*, 634–651.

Rabelo, V. C., & Cortina, L. M. (2014). Two sides of the same coin: Gender harassment and heterosexist harassment in LGBQ work lives. *Law and Human Behavior, 38*(4), 378–391.

Ragins, B. R. (2004). Sexual orientation in the workplace: The unique work and career experiences of gay, lesbian and bisexual workers. In *Research in personnel and human resources management* (pp. 35–120). Emerald Group.

Ragins, B. R. (2008). Disclosure disconnects: Antecedents and consequences of disclosing invisible stigmas across life domains. *Academy of Management Review, 33*(1), 194–215.

Ragins, B. R., & Cornwell, J. M. (2001). Pink triangles: Antecedents and consequences of perceived workplace discrimination against gay and lesbian employees. *Journal of Applied Psychology, 86*, 1244–1261.

Ragins, B. R., Singh, R., & Cornwell, J. M. (2007). Making the invisible visible: Fear and disclosure of sexual orientation at work. *Journal of Applied Psychology, 92*(4), 1103–1118.

Riggle, E. D., Rostosky, S. S., & Horne, S. (2010). Does it matter where you live? Nondiscrimination laws and the experiences of LGB residents. *Sexuality Research and Social Policy, 7*(3), 168–175.

Rostosky, S. S., Black, W. W., Riggle, E. D. B., & Rosenkrantz, D. (2015). Positive aspects of being a heterosexual ally to lesbian, gay, bisexual, and transgender (LGBT) people. *American Journal of Orthopsychiatry, 85*, 331338.

Rostosky, S. S., & Riggle, E. D. (2002). "Out" at work: The relation of actor and partner workplace policy and internalized homophobia to disclosure status. *Journal of Counseling Psychology, 49*(4), 411.

Ruggs, E. N., Martinez, L. R., Hebl, M. R., & Law, C. L. (2015). Workplace "trans"-actions: How organizations, coworkers, and individual openness influence perceived gender identity discrimination. *Psychology of Sexual Orientation and Gender Diversity, 2*(4), 404–412.

Russell, G. M. (2011). Motives of heterosexual allies in collective action for equality. *Journal of Social Issues, 67*(2), 376–393.

Sabat, I. E., Martinez, L. R., & Wessel, J. L. (2013). Neo-activism: Engaging allies in modern workplace discrimination reduction. *Industrial and Organizational Psychology: Perspectives on Science and Practice, 6*, 480–485.

Sawyer, K., Salter, N., & Thoroughgood, C. (2013). Studying individual identities is good, but examining intersectionality is better. *Industrial and Organizational Psychology, 6*(1), 80–84.

Sawyer, K., Thoroughgood, C., & Webster, J. R. (2016). Beyond the gender binary: Achieving a more complete understanding of transgender workplace experiences. In T. Kollen (Ed.), *Sexual orientation and transgender issues in organizations—Global perspectives on LBGT workforce diversity* (pp. 21–42). Springer.

Saxe, R. (2020). *SCOTUS must now ensure LGBTQ people are not turned away from taxpayer-funded programs*. American Civil Liberties Union, News and Commentary. https://www.aclu.org/news/lgbtq-rights/scotus-must-now-ensure-lgbtq-people-are-not-turned-away-from-taxpayer-funded-programs/

Schein, V. E. (1973). The relationship between sex role stereotypes and requisite management characteristics. *Journal of Applied Psychology, 57*(2), 95–100.

Sears, B., Mallory, C., Flores, A., & Conron, K. (2021). *LGBTQ people's experiences of workplace discrimination and harassment*. The Williams Institute, UCLA Law School.

Silverschanz, P., Cortina, L. M., Konik, J., & Magley, V. J. (2008). Slurs, snubs, and queer jokes: Incidence and impact of heterosexist harassment in academia. *Sex Roles: A Journal of Research, 58*(3–4), 179–191.

Steele, C. M., Spencer, S. J., & Aronson, J. (2002). Contending with group image: The psychology of stereotype and social identity threat. In M. P. Zanna (Ed.), *Advances in experimental social psychology* (Vol. 34, pp. 379–440). Academic Press.

Steffens, M. C., Niedlich, C., Beschorner, R., & Köhler, M. C. (2019). Do positive and negative stereotypes of gay and heterosexual men affect job-related impressions? *Sex Roles, 80*(9–10), 548–564.

Stryker, S., & Serpe, R. T. (1994). Identity salience and psychological centrality: Equivalent, overlapping and complementary concepts? *Social Psychology Quarterly, 57*, 16–35.

Sue, D. W. (2010). *Microaggressions in everyday life: Race, gender, and sexual orientation*. John Wiley & Sons.

Sue, D. W., Capodilupo, C. M., Nadal, K. L., & Torino, G. C. (2008). Racial microaggressions and the power to define reality. *American Psychologist, 63*(4), 277–279.

Sue, D. W., Capodilupo, C. M., Torino, G. C., Bucceri, J. M., Holder, A. M. B., Nadal, K. L., & Esquilin, M. (2007). Racial microaggressions in everyday life: Implications for clinical practice. *American Psychologist, 62*(4), 271–286.

Tebbe, E. A., Allan, B. A., & Bell, H. L. (2019). Work and well-being in TGNC adults: The moderating effect of workplace protections. *Journal of Counseling Psychology, 66*(1), 1–13.

Thoroughgood, C. N., Sawyer, K. B., & Webster, J. R. (2017). What lies beneath: How paranoid cognition explains the relations between transgender employees' perceptions of discrimination at work and their job attitudes and wellbeing. *Journal of Vocational Behavior, 103*, 99–112.

Thoroughgood, C. N., Sawyer, K. B., & Webster, J. R. (2020). Finding calm in the storm: A daily investigation of how trait mindfulness buffers against paranoid cognition and emotional exhaustion following perceived discrimination at work. *Organizational Behavior and Human Decision Processes, 159*, 49–63.

Thoroughgood, C. N., Sawyer, K. B., & Webster, J. R. (2021). Because you're worth the risks: Acts of oppositional courage as symbolic messages of relational value to transgender employees. *Journal of Applied Psychology, 106*(3), 399–421.

Tilcsik, A. (2011). Pride and prejudice: Employment discrimination against openly gay men in the United States. *American Journal of Sociology, 117*(2), 586–626.

Trau, R. N. (2015). The impact of discriminatory climate perceptions on the composition of intraorganizational developmental networks, psychosocial support, and job and career attitudes of employees with an invisible stigma. *Human Resource Management, 54*(2), 345–366.

Trau, R. N. C., Chuang, Y., Pichler, S., Wang, Y., Lim, A., & Halvorsen, B. (2018). The dynamic recursive process of community influences, LGBT-support policies and practices, and perceived discrimination at work. In S. B. Thomson & G. Grandy (Eds.), *Stigmas, work and organizations* (pp. 71–98). Palgrave Macmillan.

Trau, R. N. C., & Härtel, C. E. J. (2004). One career, two identities: An assessment of gay men's career trajectory. *Career Development International, 9*, 627–637.

Trau, R. N. C., & Härtel, C. E. J. (2007). Contextual factors affecting quality of work life and career attitudes of gay men. *Employee Responsibilities and Rights Journal, 19*(3), 207–219.

Trau, R. N. C., O'Leary, J., & Browne, C. (2019). 7 Myths about coming out at work. In *HBR's 10 must reads on diversity* (pp. 181–187). Harvard Business Review.

Triana, M. (2017). *Managing diversity in organizations: A global perspective.* Routledge.

United Nations. (2011). *The United Nations speaks out.* https://www.ohchr.org/Documents/Issues/Discrimination/LGBT_discrimination.pdf

Velez, B. L., Moradi, B., & Brewster, M. E. (2013). Testing the tenets of minority stress theory in workplace contexts. *Journal of Counseling Psychology, 60*(4), 532–542.

Washington, J., & Evans, N. J. (1991). Becoming an ally. In N. J. Evans & V. A. Wall (Eds.), *Beyond tolerance: Gays, lesbians and bisexuals on campus* (pp. 195–204). American College Personnel Association.

Wax, A., Coletti, K. K., & Ogaz, J. W. (2018). The benefit of full disclosure: A meta-analysis of the implications of coming out at work. *Organizational Psychology Review, 8*(1), 3–30.

Webster, J. R., Adams, G. A., Maranto, C. L., Sawyer, K., & Thoroughgood, C. (2018). Workplace contextual supports for LGBT employees: A review, meta-analysis, and agenda for future research. *Human Resource Management, 57*(1), 193–210.

Woods, J. D. (1993). *The corporate closet: The professional lives of gay men in America.* The Free Press.

Zugelder, M. T., & Champagne, P. J. (2018). A management approach to LGBT employment: Diversity, inclusion and respect. *The Journal of Business Diversity, 18*(1), 40–50.

Jennica Webster and Raymond Trau

DISABILITIES AT WORK

INTRODUCTION

According to the World Report on Disability, 15% of the world's population, or 1 billion people, are affected by a disability of some kind, and around 80% of them are of working age (ILO, 2020). People with disabilities are less often employed than people without disabilities. Statistics indicate that in the United States and Europe, roughly 40% of people with disabilities are employed versus 80% of people without disabilities. These figures may fluctuate slightly per country, partially depending on how the statistics are collected. From the group of people with disabilities that find employment, most are in temporary employment and some have created employment for themselves (self-employment) (Office for National Statistics, 2019).

A disability is any condition that makes it more difficult for a person to do certain activities or interact with the world around them. These conditions, or impairments, may be cognitive, developmental, intellectual, mental, physical, sensory, or a combination of multiple factors. Impairments causing disability may be present from birth or occur during a person's lifetime. The United Nations Convention on the Rights of Persons with Disabilities defines disability as: "long-term physical, mental, intellectual or sensory impairments which in interaction with various barriers may hinder [a person's] full and effective participation in society on an equal basis with others." However, the term *disability* is a contested concept, with different meanings in different communities, who may have adopted different perspectives. The term *disability* may refer to physical or mental attributes that according to some perspectives, particularly the medical community, need to be fixed (the medical model); it may also refer to limitations imposed on people by the constraints of an "able-ist society" (the social model); or the term may serve to refer to the identity of disabled people.

Physiological functional capacity is a measure of an individual's performance level that gauges one's ability to perform the physical tasks of daily life and the ease with which these tasks are performed. This relates to the *International Classification of Functioning, Disability and Health*, as published by the World Health Organization, which is generally known as the ICF model. The International Classification of Functioning, Disability and Health (ICF) is a framework for describing and organizing information on functioning and disability. It provides a standard language and a conceptual basis for the definition and measurement of health and disability. The underlying assumption of the ICF is that a person's Physiological and Cognitive Functional Capacity builds up from birth onwards, and after reaching maturity declines with advancing age to result in frailty, cognitive disorders, or physical disorders, all of which may lead to labeling individuals as disabled. According to this perspective, we all, at some point, will be disabled.

Therefore, the issue is how we, as a society, deal with people with disability in all stages of life, including working age. People with disabilities want to have a job as much as anybody else. They have similar expectations of having a job, like having a purpose in life, social contacts, and so on. However, they are less optimistic about finding a job (cf. Ali et al., 2011). In 2006, the United Nations formulated the Convention on the Rights of Persons with a Disability (CRPD), which was adopted in 2008 by most European countries. According to this treaty, people with disabilities should have a place in the labor market, like everybody else. Many countries around the world have ratified this treaty and have adopted legislation that aims to stimulate the participation of people with disabilities. Laws in various countries (like the Americans with Disability Act in the United States, 2008; and the Equality Act in the United Kingdom, 2010) aim to enforce, protect, and promote the rights of people with disabilities (Equal Employment Opportunity), and as a consequence these laws generally require reasonable accommodation in three aspects of employment:

1. To ensure equal opportunity in the application process;
2. To enable a qualified individual with a disability to perform the essential functions of a job; and
3. To enable an employee with a disability to enjoy equal benefits and privileges of employment.

People with disabilities appear to have more problems in finding employment than people without disabilities (ILO, 2020). What are the reasons behind these differences?

In this article, the various causes of nonparticipation, and the various options that might help remedy this situation, will be discussed (in that particular order).

APPLICATION PROCESS

Hiring new staff starts with the process of recruiting and selection. A first question is whether organizations are also considering hiring people with disabilities, and whether they would pass a selection process. When organizations are looking for staff to recruit, they should (at least vaguely) know for what (kind of) jobs they are hiring, after they have identified vacancies in their organizational processes. Generally, the first step is to describe what kind of jobs are vacant, and what kind of tasks need to be done, in order to describe the qualifications and competencies that new recruits should have. Ideally this should be based on an analysis of the jobs in the organization, and this might be the first step to look at equal employment opportunities (Biddle & Kuthy, 2012). In the next step, organizations try to attract applicants with the desired competencies and qualifications, so they invest in "employer branding" (being an attractive employer). What is displayed in advertisements and how texts are formulated has a significant impact on how the organization is branded (i.e., how they are perceived), and has impact on which groups are encouraged to apply (Henry et al., 2014). At this stage, organizations need to consider whether they would be willing to hire people with disabilities. However, most organizations tend to focus on attracting the most competent and talented people in their recruitment strategy. They often operate under the assumption that "talent is scarce" and needs to be fought over in the labor market. In 1997, McKinsey consultants even coined the term *war on talent* to emphasize that talent is scarce. However, there is another way of focusing on the concept of "talent," and that means that we accept that every person has talents. "Talent" needs to be understood in terms of having the motivation, the skills, and the disposition to fulfill a task (Cascio & Aguinis, 2018). It is essential to understand that those talents can be developed. Individuals may differ with respect to what talents they have, and organizations generally make an assessment of whether it is better to hire people with the desired qualities, or to focus on training people for the job. It is obvious that it is important to know what competencies a job requires, and which capacities are easy, or more difficult, to develop. Selection psychologists are good advisers in this domain (Robertson & Smith, 2001; Storey, 2016).

As indicated in the "Introduction," legislation in most countries requires that organizations have to provide equal opportunities in the application process. This means that organizations need to make a fair assessment of whether an applicant with a disability will be equally capable to perform in a job as a person without a disability. However, the question is whether this always happens or not. When two people apply for a particular job, and they have the same qualifications, but one has a disability, then one needs to assess whether they would be equally capable to perform in that job. Evidently, the outcome of this decision depends on the type of tasks that need to be done, and to what extent the particular disability will have a relevant influence (Biddle & Kuthy, 2012). However, this is not always a clear decision, and the assessment of the selection committee members plays a role. Several studies have indicated that decisions are often biased by various cognitions (Ehrlinger et al., 2016). A frequently occurring bias concerns stereotypes. Stereotypes refer to the way a group of people is viewed by society and have been defined as "shared beliefs about personal attributes, usually personality traits, but often also behaviors, of a group of people" (Leyens et al., 1994, p. 11). It is a description of similar characteristics of a certain group, without passing judgment. Stereotypes need not necessarily have a negative connotation; they can be positive or negative, and can be accurate or inaccurate. However, stereotypes are mostly based on oversimplified group features, and are often deeply rooted (Malos, 2015; Nelissen et al., 2016; Stone & Colella, 1996), and thus easily give the wrong impression. People with a disability are often seen as limited, or hampered in their capacity to execute tasks, and in need of help. Human resources managers often want to protect their organizations from the risks of absence, or production loss, for health reasons (Janssens et al., 2021). The acceptance of people with disabilities in the workplace through colleagues is also influenced by stereotypes (cf. Vornholt et al., 2021). Consequently, people with disabilities have difficulties in finding jobs, and are less frequently employed.

Since not all disabilities are immediately noticeable or visible, this brings up the question of whether, or when, people should disclose their disability. When people request accommodations to be made by their workplace, they will have, at some point, to disclose to their employer the reason for the requested accommodation. This brings up the issue of timing: when should a person disclose his or her disability, in what stage of the application process? Disclosing too early might result in the abovementioned decision biases, and disclosing too late may result in missing the opportunity for applying for accommodations, or even jeopardizing, at an early stage, their relationship with the employer by giving the impression of being dishonest (Dewa et al., 2021).

Open Hiring.   A rather recent development is the approach of "open hiring." The Greyston Bakery (https://www.greyston.org/about/), a nonprofit, social justice enterprise in New York initiated this procedure. Organizations that are open to this method announce a vacancy, and people who are interested in working in this organization can put their name on the vacancy list. By putting their name on the vacancy list, people indicate that they are motivated to work in that organization. Evidently, the assumption is that people decide beforehand whether they want to work in a particular branch of industry—such as a bakery, agriculture or horticulture company, or cleaning business.

People at the top of the list are invited to come and work in the organization and demonstrate what they can do. There is no selection interview, nor does one have to submit a résumé. No questions are asked regarding their history or past. People are given a chance to demonstrate that they are willing and motivated to work and to demonstrate what their capacities are. They will have a contract and salary from day 1 onwards. The new employee's capacities are usually properly mapped out, and the organization might steer the employee toward other jobs within the organization, if these are better suited to their capacities. If needed, these opportunities may also be outside the current organization. The focus is on the employee's personal circumstances, and these organizations usually keep in touch with organizations that can provide support or counseling when needed.

This approach works well for people who, due to their personal history, have difficulties in finding a job (people with a criminal history; people with limited training or education, or with mental health issues; people with no, or few job skills). Generally, the jobs that are open for "open hiring" require low-skilled workers. The organizations involved do not spend money on advertisement and selection and recruitment, but tend to focus their human resources on training, learning and development, and employee support.

This is an example of an approach that aims to overcome stereotypes and selection biases in the hiring process.

WORKPLACE ACCOMMODATIONS

This brings us to the second pillar of legislation on equal qualifications: qualified individuals with a disability should be enabled to perform the essential functions of a job. A first implication is that workplaces should be accessible to all employees, and therefore, some measures must sometimes be taken to allow employees access to the workplace. Evidently, what type of measures is dependent on the type of disability. For example, when someone uses a wheelchair, the disability is obvious, and it means that thresholds need to be removed, and an access ramp constructed so that someone in a wheelchair can enter the building. A person in a wheelchair may be able to do all kinds of tasks, except those in which mobility may lead to some restrictions.

However, with hidden handicaps, it is not always evident what kind of accommodations are required. It requires further examination, and relates to the earlier point of whether the person has disclosed whether accommodations are required or not. Accommodations can be of a wide range, such as adjustments to the physical environment of the workplace, like removing thresholds for wheelchairs, or taking additional measures to facilitate visually or hearing-impaired people. These kinds of accommodations fall within the ergonomic spectrum and require specific tools or measures, like hearing aids (or other relevant technologies). However, in the case of hidden disabilities, such as brain injuries, post-traumatic stress syndrome, or intellectual disability, it is necessary to first assess the (remaining) work capacities, and then decide on the best approach to facilitate people with such issues. Therefore, it is important to be able to assess a person's capacity to work. Unfortunately, only a few instruments are specifically dedicated to assessing a disabled person's capacity to work (see Van Ruitenbeek et al., 2018). Most tests, like neurological tests, are geared toward assessing deficiencies in capacities.

In order to stimulate employers to hire people with disabilities, most governments have instruments (mostly encompassing financial aspects) in place. These instruments can take various forms, such as setting a quota (e.g., 1% of all personnel should be people with disabilities), or subsidizing part of the salary costs for employing people with disabilities. However, even in the situation where quota are applicable and financial penalties are issued to those who do not comply, employers sometimes find it more "convenient" to pay the penalty than employ a person with disabilities. This illustrates that the method of "carrot and stick" is not always successful. Various studies that have looked into the reasons why employers are willing to hire people with disabilities indicate that the personal norms and values of the employer are generally the most important factor when deciding whether to hire someone (Hartnett et al., 2011). Employers with a humanitarian or religiously oriented set of values, or with pro-social values, seem to be more inclined to hire people with disabilities. The same goes for those who strongly believe that all people have the right to participate in society (Copeland et al., 2010). Sometimes other reasons are relevant, like the neighborhood supermarket that wants to include some of the people from the local community. This can also be seen as a form of organizational branding, by trying to appeal to the values and beliefs of the customers.

SHELTERED EMPLOYMENT

An instrument that governments sometimes employ is the option of "sheltered employment." Sheltered work is work performed in a protected work environment or sheltered workshops, also referred to as "work centers," by people with disabilities. The type of work in these organizations is often very basic, and is performed under special supervision. The goal of sheltered work is to provide training, experience, and real-world work skills to those with disabilities in order to prepare them to perform in open-market jobs. Although this is an option for some employees, it is not feasible for all people that are employed in a sheltered work setting. For some employees, the nature of their disability, and thus their remaining level of work capacity, make it an unrealistic perspective to move to the open labor market. Sheltered employment institutions have evolved in very diverse legal contexts, ranging from general business law to the special provisions governing establishments with a therapeutic function (cf. Visier, 1998). As a result, the debate often focuses on which factor should get priority: the production of goods or services, or the therapeutic or social aspects? Related to this is the problem of defining these people's employment status, and what their rights are. Should the money they receive be considered as wages or social security benefits? In sheltered employment, people receive an income, but this is not related to the labor market, and this income can be supplemented with local arrangements. Despite this inherent dualistic component, sheltered employment is the only way to employment and some kind of psychological fulfillment for many people with a severe disability.

CHANGING WORK

From the perspective that employees with a disability should have the opportunity to perform the essential functions of the job that they are hired for, this might imply some adjustment and workplace accommodations. A familiar example of such an adjustment in the environment is a ramp for a wheelchair, or devices that may facilitate visually or hearing-impaired people. However, one could also take this one step further with, for example, small adjustments in the task itself. Consider a person with dyslexic problems. This person may be assisted with a spell checker, or a device that reads out texts. A spell checker, or devices for visually or hearing-impaired people are rather simple examples of "assistive technology." More examples of assistive technology in all kinds of domains can be thought of (cf. Sherry et al., 2017).

However, the accommodation may also imply allowing more time when the job requires reading long texts, or maybe avoiding that long texts have to be read at all. These are examples of small adjustments to the work process itself. Both allowing more time, and organizing work in such way that reading (long) texts can be avoided, may change how tasks are executed. In cases of low levels of literacy, this is often what people try to do themselves. People try to develop personal strategies in order to overcome the consequences of their handicap, or select jobs in which they can avoid situations that are difficult to cope with (people with social anxieties might prefer a job where they can avoid social contacts). This can be seen as a form of "job crafting," where people craft or mold their own job based on their preferences or what they think they are good at (Wrzesniewski & Dutton, 2001). In fact, when people try to mold the boundaries of their job to their own preferences (what job crafting actually is), this implies that tasks are exchanged between colleagues because ultimately someone needs to execute the tasks. Such agreements and exchanges happen a lot in organizations; indeed, this is daily practice in teams. It can also be a way to provide job opportunities for people with disabilities. In fact, the technique of "job carving" is based on this practice (cf. Griffin et al., 2007). The idea is that little pieces are "carved" from existing jobs; these little pieces are generally very simple, unskilled tasks. For example, photocopying or printing, cleaning cars in a garage shop, or washing dishes in a restaurant. The charm of this approach is that it is relatively simple to apply; however, its weakness is that it is nearly impossible to create a new and sustainable job in this way. In order to design a decent and sustainable job, a number of conditions should be met, and these conditions concern not only the financial and judicial aspects, but relate primarily to the psychological and ergonomic criteria (Parker & Wall, 1998; Roe & Zijlstra, 1991) that define the quality of a job. At the very minimum, a job should simply be "do-able" over a long period, and this entails a number of criteria. From an ergonomic point of view, it is clear that the job incumbent should not have to lift a very heavy load, or memorize a lot of different numbers. From a psychological perspective, a job also needs to meet some criteria, varying from having reasonable working times and breaks, to having a clear and meaningful goal or objective in the activities, and having the opportunity to communicate with colleagues (Hacker, 1978; Warr, 1994). A series of very simple activities do not necessarily make a real job, and therefore, this is not a very sustainable solution. Additionally, job incumbents, which see that certain activities have been carved from their jobs, may not be very happy with this approach either, as they generally see those simple activities as providing some "breathing space," and fear that their jobs may increase in intensity and become too demanding.

Nevertheless, this approach points toward a new direction. Workplace accommodations are no longer just focusing on the work environment, but are now also focusing on the jobs themselves. Therefore, the options of "job (re)design" need to be explored.

Work Redesign.   According to Roe and Zijlstra (1991), jobs are, in principle, nothing else than a set of agreements between people on how they divide and organize their work. This is the essence of organizing work, and therefore is the basis of what is called *job design*. This term is mostly used when focusing on jobs for individuals, but if the wider context (physical and social environment) is also incorporated, the term *work design* fits better. Over the years, people have been looking into what are the most effective and optimal ways of organizing work, and thus also what is the best possible design of a job. This way of looking was initiated by Frederic Taylor, and his Scientific Management practices, or even earlier by Adam Smith (1776) and Charles Babbage (1832) (see Parker et al., 2017). What all these practices have in common is that they are geared toward finding the most efficient way to organize work and to perform a job. The underlying criteria have always been efficiency and effectiveness, and thus are economically driven. In the 1920s, with the emergence of the "Human Relations Movement" (see Smith, 1987), a more humanistic aspect of job design became important. It became evident that economic criteria were not sufficient to make people work, that workers had to be motivated, and that their well-being should be taken into consideration. This has initiated a different line of research and practices which studied the contribution of various task characteristics on motivation and well-being. The most prominent theory in this domain is probably the Job Characteristics Model by Hackman and Oldham (1976), which states that five key job characteristics contribute to human motivation and well-being. Later theories have refined this, for instance Warr's Vitamin Model (1987), which also demonstrated the relationship between task characteristics and people's mental health. Some theories have taken a slightly different approach, like Hacker's Theory of Activity (1978), which included the elements of formulating goals for people's actions, and cooperation and communication with colleagues. Hackman and Oldham later agreed that this collectivistic aspect of work was missing in their theory (Hackman & Oldham, 2010). In most cases, work is a group activity because pursuing organizational goals requires collaboration with others. This illustrates that designing jobs has received quite some attention over the years, and that various criteria are to be taken into consideration—varying from economic, to ergonomic (safety), to humanistic criteria (motivation and well-being) (Parker et al., 2017).

However, an aspect that has not been considered thus far is that jobs can be redesigned in order to accommodate people with disabilities. Such an approach to work redesign has been initiated by the Centre of Expertise for Inclusive Organisations (CIAO, 2021). The general observation that initiated the approach is that work has become more intense and more complex in the 21st century. Due to societal and technological changes, work has evolved from manufacturing work (which largely required manual skills) to knowledge-and-service-oriented work which requires all kinds of different skills (often referred to as "21st century skills")—like social skills, communication skills, and cognitive skills such as planning and organization. This development has resulted in increased work demands (cf. Wegman et al., 2018), which has made work more and more difficult. Many jobs in the 21st century require employees to have "high interpersonal skills" and high "problem-solving skills" (Fouarge, 2017). The consequence is that it has become quite difficult for an increasing number of people to meet the current demands of the labor market. Labor economists use the label "distance to the labor market" for this group of people. The term *distance* refers to how long it may take to find new employment when one is out of employment, and is a measure of how important relevant skills and competences are for the labor market. The concept implies that people have a distance to the labor market when their skills and competences are lacking, "outdated," or even obsolete. The group may include people with mental or physical disabilities, chronic health issues, or other issues that put them in a disadvantaged position. It may be clear that these people may have problems finding a job because they do not fit in the current labor market, but it does not mean that they have no capacity to work. Hence, the idea is that jobs could also be redesigned to fit the talents of those people (Mulders & Zijlstra, 2009; Zijlstra et al., 2012), which is a novel approach.

Although this novel approach still aims to support people with disabilities in finding employment, the focus of this intervention is primarily targeting organizations. Whereas previous approaches can be characterized as "supply driven" (i.e., the number of people with a disability that needed to be supported in finding a job), this new approach is more "demand driven" because it aims to address the demand for personnel in organizations. The idea is that, after a thorough analysis of work processes, a proposal is made to redistribute certain activities so that tasks can be designed to suit the capabilities and capacities of a wider and more diverse group, including people with limited capacities. The method that is developed is called "Inclusive Redesign of Work" and is extensively described on CIAO's website (CIAO, 2021). The method, which is actually an intervention strategy for organizations, is based on theoretical notions of "business process redesign" (Earl, 1994) in combination with theories on work (re)design (see Van Ruitenbeek et al., 2013; Zijlstra et al., 2012, 2017). The intervention strategy "Inclusive Redesign of Work" aims to design relatively basic or simple jobs next to those jobs that require complex skills and advanced training. This way so-called entry jobs with different levels of complexity can be created.

Whereas traditional approaches in this domain have focused on supporting people to find a job, this perspective takes the view that the solution for matching problems in the labor market should be found within organizations. It supports the notion that structural solutions should be created for the structural problem of miss-matches in the labor market, rather than finding incidental solutions for singular problems. The structural problem is that work has become too complex, too intensive, and thus too demanding for a large (and growing) part of the workforce. This is a problem for people with limited capacities, but also for people who are currently employed. The incidence of employees with mental health complaints in the workplace, due to this high intensity of work (stress, burnout) is quite high. According to various studies, work pressure, stress, and burnout are currently the most prominent complaints among the workforce. According to the 2020 Workplace Stress survey in the United Kingdom, 79% of employees experience stress at the workplace, which is 18% more than in 2018 (Perkbox, 2020). In addition, the Eurofound Reports on working conditions in Europe report sustained high levels of complaints of work pressure and work intensification among employees in Europe (Eurofound, 2015, 2021). Recent statistics from the Mental Health Foundation indicate that in the United Kingdom one out of seven employees experience mental health issues (women twice as much as men). Most of these complaints concern so-called common mental disorders (referring to anxiety disorders, feelings of depression, and so on) that are generally linked to work-related health issues, such as stress and burnout. In the Netherlands, "mental health issues" are the most frequent reason for work incapacity—they account for 51% of all work incapacity diagnoses (UWV, 2019). Although not direct proof, these statistics are indications that the sustainability of employment for a large group of employees is at risk (Fleuren et al., 2016). The best solution under these circumstances would be to hire more staff; however, this can be problematic due to tight labor market conditions.

An additional aspect is that striving toward more efficiency in organizations has boosted the development of office automation from the 1990s onwards. As a result, many "support staff" were made redundant and replaced by computers, leaving professionals to operate these computers, and consequently, they became responsible for executing their own work and the administration of their own activities. As a result, many professionals complain that they spend an increasing amount of time on administration of things rather than on work for which they were trained and educated. For organizations, the implication is that they are paying high salaries to professionals who, for a significant part of their working time (some estimates suggest between 20% and 40%), spend their time on work for which they are overqualified. This is an inefficiency in itself, and provides organizations with additional reasons to consider alternative options for the staffing issues (attracting and retaining personnel) most organizations are facing.

The "Inclusive Redesign of Work" approach can offer such an alternative: through analyzing the processes in organizations, alternative options for organizing work and distributing tasks and responsibilities can be presented. It allows for creating tasks of different levels of complexity that require different levels of competences, which implies that tasks suited to people with various kinds of limitations or disabilities can also be designed (cf. Zijlstra et al., 2017). At the same time, professionals can focus again on tasks requiring *their* level of skills and competences, which may help to overcome the quantitative and qualitative shortages in the labor market. This strategy has been successfully applied in various branches of industry, like healthcare and elderly care, education, governmental institutions, and so on (examples can be found on CIAO's website). Clearly, this is an interesting business case for organizations, as it allows them to benefit from hiring people with disabilities. This is a promising way forward in helping people with disabilities to find sustainable employment, and according to Henry Ford, it might even be the best way: "If an industrial institution is to fill its whole role, it ought to be possible for a cross-section of its employees to show about the same proportions as a cross-section of society in general" (Ford, 1923).

CONCLUDING REMARKS

People with disabilities are less often employed, although most of them would like to work. Despite laws and regulations that try to give them a comparable position in the labor market, there are various mechanisms in society, in the labor market, and in organizations that put them in a disadvantaged position. In the past, most initiatives to support people with disabilities focused on the individual needs of those people and tried to help them to overcome their shortcomings by providing training, support, and other accommodations. This is necessary but not sufficient, as there are structural aspects in the labor market that keep putting people with a disability in a disadvantaged position. The demands of the labor market have increased, and in fact, the labor market has been moving away from what can be asked of people, resulting in a "labor market that has distanced itself from people." The solution should therefore be found in organizations, and we need to focus on the needs that organizations may have in order to solve some of their human resources-related issues—like having difficulties in finding staff, or high levels of sickness absenteeism in their organization due to mental health issues caused by work pressure and stress. This will require an open outlook from employers and a willingness to consider new approaches to the design of work, and also a certain level of corporate responsibility.

REFERENCES

Ali, M., Schur, L., & Blanck, P. (2011). What types of jobs do people with disabilities want? *Journal of Occupational Rehabilitation, 21*(6), 199–210. https://doi.org/10.1007/s10926-010-9266-0

Americans with Disability Amendments Act of 2008, [42 USCA § 12101 note] (2008), https://www.eeoc.gov/statutes/ada-amendments-act-2008

Babbage, C. (1832). *On the economy of machinery and manufactures.* New York: Cambridge University Press, re-issued 2009.

Biddle, D. A., & Kuthy, J. E. (2012). Using job analysis as the foundation for creating equal employment opportunity in the workplace. In M. A. Wilson, W. Bennett Jr., S. G. Gibson, G. M. Alliger (Eds.), *The handbook of work analysis: Methods, systems, applications and science of work measurement in organizations* (pp. 365–397). Routledge.

Cascio, W. F., & Aguinis, H. (2018). *Applied psychology in talent management.* SAGE.

Center for Inclusive Organisations (CIAO). (2021). CIAO. https://www.inclusiveworkredesign.com/about-us/about-ciao

Copeland, J., Chan, F., Bezyak, J., & Fraser, R. T. (2010). Assessing cognitive and affective reactions of employers toward people with disabilities in the workplace. *Journal of Occupational Rehabilitation, 20*(4), 427–434.

Dewa, C. S., van Weeghel, J., Joosen, M. C. W., Gronholm, P. C., & Brouwers, E. P. M. (2021). Workers' decisions to disclose a mental health issue to managers and the consequences. *Frontiers in Psychiatry, 12.* (online), https://doi.org/10.3389/fpsyt.2021.631032

Earl, M. J. (1994). The new and the old of business process redesign. *Journal of Strategic Information Systems, 3*(1), 5–22.

Ehrlinger, J., Readinger, W. O., & Kim, B. (2016). Decision-making and cognitive biases. In H. Friedman (Ed.), *Encyclopedia of mental health* (2nd ed., pp. 5–12). Academic Press.

Equality Act, UK Public General Acts, 2010 c. 15, Part 2, Chapter 2, Discrimination, Section 15, (2010). https://www.legislation.gov.uk/ukpga/2010/15/section/15

Eurofound. (2015). *Sixth European working conditions survey—overview report.* Publications Office of the European Union.

Eurofound. (2021). *Working conditions and sustainable work: An analysis using the job quality framework.* Publications Office of the European Union.

Fleuren, B. P. I., de Grip, A., Jansen, N. W., Kant, I. J., & Zijlstra, F. R. H. (2016). Critical reflections on the current leading definition of sustainable employability. *Scandinavian Journal of Work, Environment and Health, 42*(3), 34–42. https://doi.org/10.5271/sjweh.3585

Ford, H. (1923). *My life and work.* Doubleday.

Fouarge, D. J. A. G. (2017). *Veranderingen in werk en vaardigheden.* Maastricht University.

Greyston Bakery. (2021). About Greyston. https://www.greyston.org/about/

Griffin, C., Hammis, D., & Geary, T. (2007). *The job developer's handbook: Practical tactics for customized employment.* Paul H. Brookes.

Hacker, W. (1978). *Allgemeine arbeits-und ingenieurpsychologie: Psychische struktur und regulation von arbeitstätigkeiten.* Huber Verlag.

Hackman, J. R., & Oldham, G. R. (1976). Motivation through the design of work: Test of a theory. *Organizational Behavior and Human Performance, 16*(2), 250–279.

Hackman, J. R., & Oldman, G. R. (2010). Not what it was and not what it will be: The future of job design research. *Journal of Organizational Behavior, 31*(2–3), 463–479.

Hartnett, H. P., Stuart, H., Thurman, H., Loy, B., & Batiste, L. C. (2011). Employers' perceptions of the benefits of workplace accommodations: Reasons to hire, retain and promote people with disabilities. *Journal of Vocational Rehabilitation, 34*(1), 17–23. https://doi.org/10.3233/JVR-2010-0530

Henry, A. D., Petkauskos, K., Stanislawzyk, J., & Vogt, J. (2014). Employer-recommended strategies to increase opportunities for people with disabilities. *Journal of Vocational Rehabilitation, 41*(3), 237–248.

ILO. (2020). Disability and work. https://www.ilo.org/global/topics/disability-and-work/lang--en/index.htm

Janssens, K. M. E., van Weeghel, J., Dewa, C., Henderson, C., Mathijssen, J. J. P., Joosen, M. C. W., & Brouwers, E. P. M. (2021). Line managers' hiring intentions regarding people with mental health problems: A cross-sectional study on workplace stigma. *Occupational Environmental Medicine, 78*(8), 593–599. https://doi.org/10.1136/oemed-2020-106955

Leyens, J. P., Yzerbyt, V., & Schadron, G. (1994). *Stereotypes and social cognition.* SAGE.

Malos, S. (2015). Overt stereotype biases and discrimination in the workplace: Why haven't we fixed this by now? *Employee Responsibilities and Rights Journal, 27*(4), 271–280.

Mulders, H., van Ruitenbeek, G., & Zijlstra, F. R. H. (2020). Methode inclusief herontwerp van werk vernieuwd: IHW2.0. *Tijdschrift voor Bedrijfs-en Verzekeringsgeneeskunde, 28*(8), 46–49.

Mulders, H., & Zijlstra, F. R. H. (2009). Taylor revisited: "The right job for a man." Participative work (re)design for special need groups. ILO. https://www.ilo.org/legacy/english/protection/travail/pdf/rdwpaper25c.pdf

Nelissen, P. T., Hülsheger, U. R., van Ruitenbeek, G. M., & Zijlstra, F. R. H. (2016). How and when stereotypes relate to inclusive behavior toward people with disabilities. *International Journal of Human Resource Management, 27*(14), 1610–1625. https://doi.org/10.1080/09585192.2015.1072105

Office for National Statistics. (2019). Disability and employment, UK: 2019. Labour Force Survey. https://www.ons.gov.uk/peoplepopulationandcommunity/healthandsocialcare/disability/bulletins/disabilityandemploymentuk/2019

Parker, S., Morgeson, F., & Johns, G. (2017). One hundred years of work design research: Looking back and looking forward. *Journal of Applied Psychology, 102*(3), 403–420. https://doi.org/10.1037/apl0000106

Parker, S. K., & Wall, T. D. (1998). *Job and work design: Organizing work to promote well-being and effectiveness.* SAGE.

Perkbox. (2020). The 2020 UK workplace stress survey. https://www.perkbox.com/uk/resources/library/2020-workplace-stress-survey

Robertson, I. T., & Smith, M. (2001). Personnel selection. *Journal of Occupational and Organizational Psychology, 74*(4), 441–472.

Roe, R. A., & Zijlstra, F. R. H. (1991). Arbeidsanalyse ten behoeve van (her)ontwerp van functies: een handelingstheoretische invalshoek. In J. A. Algera (Ed.), *Analyse van arbeid vanuit verschillende perspectieven* (pp. 179–243). Swets & Zeitlinger.

Rousseau, D. M. (1977). Technological differences in job characteristics, employee satisfaction, and motivation: A synthesis of job design research and sociotechnical systems theory. *Organizational Behavior and Human Performance, 19*(1), 18–42.

Sherry, M., Ravneberg, B., & Söderström, S. (2017). *Disability, society and assistive technology.* Routledge.

Smith, A. (1776). *An inquiry into the nature and causes of the wealth of Nations.* Republished in 2008 by Oxford University Press.

Smith, J. H. (1987). Elton Mayo and the hidden Hawthorne. *Work, Employment and Society, 1*(1), 107–120.

Stone, D. L., & Colella, A. (1996). A model of factors affecting the treatment of disabled individuals in organizations. *Academy of Management Review, 21*(2), 352–401.

Storey, J. (2016). *Human resource management.* Edward Elgar.

Taylor, F. W. (1919). *The principles of scientific management.* New York, Harper & Brothers.

United Nations General Assembly. (2006). Convention on the Rights of Persons with Disabilities. *General Assembly Resolution, 61*, 106.

UWV. (2019). Arbeidsongeschiktheid: cijfers & context. https://www.volksgezondheidenzorg.info/onderwerp/arbeidsongeschiktheid/cijfers-context/oorzaken#node-arbeidsongeschiktheid-naar-oorzaak-en-wet

Van Ruitenbeek, G. M. C., Mulder, M. J. G. P., Zijlstra, F. R. H., Nijhuis, F. J. N., & Mulders, H. P. G. (2013). Een alternatieve benadering van voor herontwerp van werk. Ervaringen met de methode Inclusief Herontwerp Werkprocessen. *Gedrag & Organisatie, 26*(1), 104–122.

Van Ruitenbeek, G., Zijlstra, F. R. H., & Hülsheger, U. (2018). The development of an instrument to measure the work capability of people with limited work capacity (LWC). *Journal of Occupational Rehabilitation, 29*(1), 163–174. https://doi.org/10.1007/s10926-018-9774-x

Van Ruitenbeek, G. M. C., Zijlstra, F. R. H., & Hülsheger, U. R. (2020). Predicting and assessing work performance of people with disabilities and limitations—a multi-wave, multi-source study. *Journal of Occupational Rehabilitation, 31*, 360–375. https://doi.org/10.1007/s10926-020-09925-8

Visier, L. (1998). Sheltered employment for persons with disabilities. *International Labour Review, 137*(3), 347–365.

Vornholt, K., Uitdewilligen, S., van Ruitenbeek, G., & Zijlstra, F. R. H. (2021). The development and validation of the workplace acceptance scale: Evidence from a sample of workers with disabilities. *Journal of Vocational Rehabilitation, 54*(2), 135–149. https://doi.org/10.3233/JVR-201125

Vornholt, K., Vilotti, P., Muschalla, B., Bauer, J., Colella, A., Zijlstra, F. R. H., Van Ruitenbeek, G., Uitdewilligen, S., & Corbière, M. (2018). Disability and employment—overview and highlights. *European Journal of Work and Organizational Psychology, 27*(1), 40–55. http://dx.doi.org/10.1080/1359432X.2017.1387536

Warr, P. (1987). *Work, unemployment, and mental health.* Clarendon Press.

Warr, P. (1994). A conceptual framework for the study of work and mental health. *Work and Stress, 8*(2), 84–97.

Wegman, L. A., Hoffman, B. J., Carter, N. T., Twenge, J. M., & Guenole, N. (2018). Placing job characteristics in context: Cross-temporal meta-analysis of changes in job characteristics since 1975. *Journal of Management, 44*(1), 352–386.

Wrzesniewski, A., & Dutton, J. E. (2001). Crafting a job: Revisioning employees as active crafters of their work. *Academy of Management Review, 26*, 179–201. https://doi.org/10.1111/hsc.12084

Zijlstra, F. R. H., Mulders, H. P. G., & Nijhuis, F. J. (2012). Inclusieve organisaties—op weg naar duurzame arbeidsparticipatie. *Tijdschrift Voor Arbeidsvraagstukken, 28*(1), 21–29.

Zijlstra, F. R. H., & Nyssen, A.-S. (2017). How do we handle technology? In N. Chmiel, F. Fraccaroli, & M. Sverke (Eds.), *An introduction of work and organizational psychology* (pp. 373–386) (3rd ed.). Wiley-Blackwell.

Zijlstra, F. R. H., van Ruitenbeek, G. M. C., Mulders, H. P. G., & van Lierop, B. (2017). Designing work for inclusiveness. In A. Arenas, D. Di Marco, L. Munduate, & M. C. Euwema (Eds.), *Shaping inclusive workplaces through social dialogue* (pp. 121–137). Springer.

Fred Zijlstra and Henny Mulders

Jobs and Work Systems

JOB AND WORK DESIGN

JOB DESIGN

"It is about a search, too, for daily meaning as well as daily bread, for recognition as well as cash, for astonishment rather than torpor; in short, for a sort of life rather than a Monday through Friday sort of dying" (Terkel, 1974, p. xi).

Billions of people spend most of their waking lives at work, so it is fortunate that work can be a positive feature of living. Obviously, the associated salary helps to pay the bills and provides a means for a certain standard of living. But good work also structures one's time, builds identity, allows for social contact, and enables engagement in meaningful activities (Jahoda, 1982). Nevertheless, although work can serve these important functions, it can also be a threat to people's well-being, cause alienation, and result in burnout. As an extreme example of its negative effects, Chinese and French telecom workers have been reported committing suicide because of work-related issues.

Whether work is beneficial or detrimental is largely dependent upon how it is designed. Work design is defined as the content, structure, and organization of one's task and activities (Parker, 2014). It is mostly studied in terms of job characteristics, such as job autonomy and workload, which are like the building blocks of work design. Meta-analytical results show that

· 683

these job characteristics predict employees' health and well-being, their cognitions and learning, and their attitudes and behavior (Humphrey, Nahrgang, & Morgeson, 2007; Nahrgang, Morgeson, & Hofmann, 2011). There is no doubt that work design is important, so it is not surprising that it has received considerable research attention (Parker, Morgeson, & Johns, 2017).

Throughout the 20th century, several authors developed different job-design models, which have been expanded into various contemporary perspectives. The net effect is that the literature on work design is somewhat fragmented. Rather than providing one overall framework to study the design of jobs—similar to the Big 5 framework in personality, for example—job-design models consider the topic from different angles. This diversity may be an advantage in understanding the complexity of job design, but an overview—let alone on overarching model—is lacking, which inhibits the sharing of knowledge and ultimately our understanding of job design.

Against this background, it is necessary to review the approaches that have dominated the literature around the world and the contemporary models that have emerged from them. This overview reveals the basic principles that guide views on job design: how work is conceptualized, how job characteristics relate to important outcomes, and the roles personal aspects play in job design–outcome relationships.

This article makes several contributions to the literature. First, by providing an overview of important job-design models that have dominated the work-design literature around the globe, the article introduces job-design scholars working in one research tradition to other traditions. Second, the article explicates the most important assumptions about the impact of job design across the different models and brings the assumptions together in one integrative work design (IWD) model. Finally, the article supplies an overview of fruitful avenues for future research that might stimulate future research on the important topic of job design. Although previously it had been argued that "we know all there is to know" about job design (Ambrose & Kulik, 1999), one in three employees in Europe still has a job of poor intrinsic quality (Lorenz & Valeyre, 2005) and different influences put pressure on the quality of jobs (Parker, Holman, & Van den Broeck, 2017). Building on this overall model, different pathways emerge for the rejuvenation of the literature (Parker et al., 2017) and for fostering knowledge on how jobs can be designed so that work brings out the best in people.

HISTORICAL OVERVIEW OF MODELS AROUND THE GLOBE

Job design has a long history. Ever since people organized themselves to hunt and gather for food, or even to build the Aztec temples, people identified activities, tasks, and roles and distributed them among collaborators. The scientific study of work design, however, started with the work of Adam Smith, who described in his book *The Wealth of Nations* how the division of labor could increase productivity. Previously, the timing and location of work fitted seamlessly in with everyday activities, and many industries were characterized by craftsmen, who developed a product from the beginning to the end (Barley & Kunda, 2001). A blacksmith would craft pins starting from iron ore, while a carpenter made cupboards out of trees. But Adam Smith advocated the dissection of labor into different tasks, and the division of these tasks among employees, so that each would repetitively execute small tasks: One employee would cut the metal plate, while another one would polish the pins.

Scientific Management. The principle of the division of labor was further developed into scientific management (Taylor, 2004). Adopting a scientific approach to work in order to increase efficiency, Taylor argued that ideal jobs included single, highly simplified, and specialized activities that were repeated throughout the working day, with little time to waste in between (Campion & Thayer, 1988). Taylor developed his ideas in the realm of the Industrial Revolution, which made it possible to automate many of the activities in people's jobs. Employees were essentially considered parts of the machinery, with the idea they could easily be replaced. While previously employees inherited or chose their trades and learned on the job by trial and error, with Taylorism, employees were selected and trained to execute specific tasks according to prescribed procedures and standards. Supervisors were tasked with monitoring employees' actions, leading to the division between unskilled manual labor and skilled managerial tasks, and to the rewarding of employees according to their performance (e.g., via piecework) so that the goals of the employees (i.e., making money) would be aligned with the goal of the company (i.e., making profit).

Essential principles of Taylorism thus include simplification and specialization, but also the selection and training of employees to achieve a fit between demands of the job and employees' abilities. Because of these principles, efficiency rocketed, and Taylorism was soon also adopted for office jobs. Today, Taylorism still inspires the design of both manufacturing and service jobs in many organizations (Parker et al., 2017).

Despite its positive consequences in terms of productivity, one downside of this mechanical approach to job design was that employee morale dropped. For instance, in the Midvale Steel plant, where Taylorism was implemented, employees experienced mental and physical fatigue and boredom, resulting in sabotage and absenteeism (Walker & Guest, 1952). The negative effects of Taylorism eventually led to the development of several less mechanistic and more motivational work designs, including social and psychological approaches.

Social Approaches to Work. In further exploring the effects of Taylorism, Mayo and his colleagues uncovered the importance of individual attitudes toward work and teams. In the famous "Hawthorne studies," focusing on a team of Western Electric Company workers, Mayo and colleagues aimed to improve employees' working conditions, but they failed to find strong effects of interventions like increasing or decreasing illumination, or shortening or lengthening the working day, on individual employee performance, even though such effects would be expected based on Taylorism. Rather, production went up over the course of the period in which the employees were involved and consulted in the experiment. The free expression of ideas and feelings to the management, and sustained cooperation in teams, increased employee morale and ultimately efficiency. Group norms were shown to have a strong effect on employee attitudes and behavior and were more effective in generating employee productivity than individual rewards, potentially because being part of a group increased feelings of security. In a Taylorism model, people were seen as a part of a machine, but according to Mayo, employees should be regarded as part of a social group.

The focus on groups was further developed into sociotechnical systems theory by human relations scholars at the Tavistock Institute in the United Kingdom (Pasmore, 1995). The scholars aimed to optimize the alignment of technical systems and employees. To make optimal use of the available technology, the scholars were convinced that teams of employees should have the autonomy to organize themselves (without too much supervision) and to manage technological problems and to suggest improvements, thereby breaking with the previous division between manual labor and managerial tasks. Furthermore, rather than advocating specialization, human relations scholars argued that, within the teams, employees should work on a meaningful and relatively broad set of tasks and that team members should be allowed to rotate, so that they would have some variety and become multi-skilled (Pasmore, 1995).

Sociotechnical systems theory gave rise to the use of autonomous working groups, later labeled *self-managing teams*. Several studies provided evidence for the positive effects of autonomous working groups on job satisfaction and performance, but the positive effects were not always found. Some have therefore argued that autonomous work teams need to be implemented with care and may be most effective in uncertain contexts, where individuals can make a difference (Wageman, 1997; Wright & Cordery, 1999).

Herzberg's Two-Factor Theory. Building on the importance of employees' attitudes, the first major model that made an explicit link between job design and employee motivation is the two-factor theory of Herzberg (1968). Herzberg started from Maslow's need pyramid (1954) and argued that, while some job aspects caused job satisfaction, other were responsible for employee dissatisfaction. Satisfaction and dissatisfaction were thus considered independent states, with different antecedents. Dissatisfaction was said to occur when employees feel deprived of their physical, animal needs, due to a lack of "hygiene factors," such as a decent salary, security, safe working conditions, status, good relationships at work, and attention to one's personal life. Satisfaction, in contrast, was said to be intertwined with growth-oriented human needs and is influenced by the availability of motivators like achievement, recognition, responsibility, and growth.

Although Herzberg's model has been criticized and has received little empirical support (Wall & Stephenson, 1970), it has had a vast impact on the literature on job design. First, Herzberg provided the building blocks for the meta-theory underlying job design. In building on the differentiation between basic animal needs and more human, higher order growth needs, Herzberg inspired McGregor (1960) to develop Theory X and Theory Y, two views on humankind that managers may hold that have implications for how jobs should be designed. Theory X assumes that employees are passive and lazy and need to be pushed (i.e., the stick approach to motivation) or pulled (i.e., the carrot approach to motivation) using the principles of Taylorism. In contrast, managers who hold Theory Y see employees as active and growth-oriented human beings who like to interact with their environment. Adopting this theory likely stimulates managers to design highly satisfying and motivational jobs that make optimal use of the interest and energy of employees.

Second, Herzberg was the first to develop a well-defined job-design model and to advocate the empirical study of people's jobs, thereby paving the way for the tradition of job-design research that we know today. Moreover, Herzberg pointed out the importance of a fair wage and good working conditions, similar to Taylorism and social relations at work, as did the human relations movement. In addition, he called for attention to opportunities to learn and develop oneself, which were to be found in the content of the job. As such, Herzberg was arguably the first to advance that the true motivational potential of work is linked to the content of one's job. He further advanced that jobs could become more motivating by job enlargement (i.e., adding additional tasks of similar difficulty) and—most importantly—job enrichment (i.e., by adding more complex task and decision authority). As in the case of autonomous teams, these practices can lead to beneficial outcomes, although the effects ultimately depend on the context and manner in which they are implemented (Axtell & Parker, 2003; Campion, Mumford, Morgeson, & Nahrgang, 2005).

Hackman and Oldham's Job Characteristics Model. Hackman and Oldham followed through on the idea of motivational jobs and exclusively focused on job content in their job characteristics model (JCM; Hackman & Oldham, 1976). Specifically, they argued that the motivating potential of jobs could be determined by assessing the degree of task significance, task identity, and variety, as well as the autonomy and feedback directly from the job. Moving beyond mere job satisfaction, these job characteristics were argued to lead to an expanded set of outcomes of job design, including internal motivation, performance, absenteeism, and turnover. Furthermore, where previous models were silent about the psychological process through which job design may have its impact, Hackman and Oldham proposed three psychological states as mediating mechanism: having knowledge of results, feeling responsible, and experiencing meaningfulness in the job. These states were expected to be influenced by feedback, autonomy, and the combination of task identity, task significance, and variety, respectively. While both autonomy and feedback are essential for jobs to be motivating, as each of the latter aspects relate to the same critical psychological state, task identity, task significance, and variety were considered to be interchangeable, which introduced the possibility that particular job aspects can compensate for each other, so that low task identity wouldn't be problematic when employees experience high levels of variety.

An important contribution from Hackman and Oldham is that they acknowledged the importance of individual differences. They assumed that peoples' skills, knowledge, and ability, as well as general satisfaction with the work context, may impact the strength of the relations between the job characteristics and the critical psychological states, and between the latter and the work outcomes (Oldham, Hackman, & Pearce, 1976). Perhaps the most important moderator in the JCM is peoples' growth-need strength, which is defined as the degree to which employees want to develop in the context of work. Highly growth-oriented employees may benefit more from job enrichment.

In addition to developing the JCM, Hackman and Oldham also contributed to the job-design literature by presenting a measure (Hackman & Oldham, 1976), which spurred empirical research. Meta-analysis supported the basic tenets of the model, showing that motivational characteristics lead to favorable attitudinal and behavioral outcomes, via some of the critical psychological states (Fried & Ferris, 1987; Humphrey et al., 2007; Johns, Xie, & Gang, 1992). However, criticism has been directed at the inclusion of only a limited set of job characteristics, mediating mechanisms, and behavioral outcomes, as well as at the model's focus only on the motivational aspects of work, while ignoring the stressful aspects. Parker, Wall, and Cordery (2001) proposed an elaborated version of the JCM that identified an expanded set of work characteristics (including those more important in contemporary work, such as emotional demands and performance-monitoring demands), elaborated moderators (including, for example, operational uncertainty), and outcomes (including creativity, proactivity, and safety). This model also proposed antecedents of work design.

Karasek's Job Demand Control Model. Karasek (1979) built on the criticisms of the JCM. In his job demand control model, he synthesized the traditions on detrimental aspects of work design (i.e., demands, including workload and role stressors) and the beneficial aspects (i.e., job control, including autonomy and skill variety) mentioned in the literature following the development of the Michigan Model (Caplan, Cobb, French, Harrison, & Pinneau, 1975) and the JCM, respectively. Rather than considering both aspects separately, seeing all structural work aspects as a demand, Karasek argued that job demands and job control have to be examined in combination, as the effects of each may be fundamentally different depending on the level of the other.

Specifically, Karasek built his theory on four types of jobs: Passive jobs are characterized by low demands and low control, while high-strain jobs include high job demands and low job control. Low-strain jobs are characterized by low demands and high job control, while active jobs include both high demands and high job control. These four types of jobs fall along two continua. Low- and high-strain jobs are modeled on a continuum from low strain to high strain, which over time may result in stress and health problems, while passive and active jobs are modeled on a growth-related continuum ranging from low to high activation, fostering motivation, learning, and development. Following up on the assumptions of the Michigan Model, Karasek proposed that job design not only may have short-term effects, but also in the long run, may affect employee personality: Continuous exposure to stressful jobs leads to accumulated strain, which then causes long-term anxiety that inhibits learning. Continuous exposure to active jobs, in contrast, builds experiences of mastery, which then buffers the perception of strain (Theorell & Karasek, 1996).

Apart from an expanded focus on the content of work in terms of job demands and job control, Karasek expanded his model by reintroducing social support, as a beneficial aspect of job design, and more specifically as an antidote to job demands. The role of social relations at work was acknowledged by Herzberg (although only as a hygiene factor) but was not included in the JCM, which continued to dominate the job-design literature in the United States.

Karasek's model spurred research on job stress, as well as on health-related outcomes, such as mortality and cardiovascular diseases (Van der Doef & Maes, 1998). The additive effects of job demands and job control are often found, but more cross-sectionally than over time, which suggests that reciprocal or reversed effects may also occur, with well-being, motivation, and learning also predicting job design (Hausser, Mojzisch, Niesel, & Schulz-Hardt, 2010). Results for the interaction between job demands and job control are limited (Van der Doef & Maes, 1999), even among high-quality studies (de Lange, Taris, Kompier, Houtman, & Bongers, 2003).

Warr's Vitamin Model. Warr (1987) further expanded on the number of job characteristics that may influence people's well-being. Going beyond the design of jobs, per se, Warr examined environmental aspects that may serve as vitamins for people's well-being, in or outside the context of work. Well-being is herein broadly defined, including affective well-being, which is arranged around three axes—pleasure and displeasure, anxiety versus comfort, and depression versus enthusiasm—as well as competence, aspiration, autonomy, and integrated functioning of feeling harmonious. In total, Warr discerned nine different broad environmental factors that affect aspects of well-being, including:

1. Availability of money or a decent salary.
2. Physical security (good working conditions and working material).
3. Environmental clarity (low job insecurity, high role clarity, predictable outcomes, and task feedback).
4. A valued social position associated with, for example, task significance and the possibility to contribute to society.
5. Contact with others or the possibility of having (good) social relations at work, being able to depend on others, and working on a nice team.
6. Variety or having changes in one's task context and social relations.
7. Externally generated goals or a challenging workload, with low levels of role conflict and conflict or competition with others.
8. Opportunity for skill use and acquisition or the potential to apply and extend one's skills.
9. Opportunities for personal control or having autonomy, discretion, and opportunities to participate (Warr, 1987).

Intriguingly, Warr was the first to recognize that these job characteristics are not necessarily linearly related to employee well-being. Some job characteristics, and more specifically money, safety, and a valued social position, are the vitamins C and E. First, they affect employee well-being linearly, but only a certain amount, with their effects plateaus maintaining a constant effect (CE). The other job characteristics, however, are vitamins A and D and affect employee well-being in a curvilinear way: both low and high levels are detrimental, with any addition beyond a certain level leading to decrease in well-being (AD). In assuming these relations, Warr captured the widely held assumption that there can be too much of a good thing (Pierce & Aguinis, 2011). For example, while some amount of workload can be beneficial, too much workload may be detrimental for employees' well-being. Similarly, too much job stimulation may contribute to negative health outcomes (Fried et al., 2013).

Furthermore, in line with Hackman and Oldham, Warr proposed that some employees are more susceptible to the impact of particular job characteristics than others, because their personal values or abilities fit better with particular job characteristics. For example, employees with low preference for independence benefit less from autonomy, while employees having a high tolerance for ambiguity suffer less when their environment provides less clear guidelines (Warr, 1987).

Research has provided some support for the vitamin model, showing that externally generated goals, autonomy, and social support may indeed have curvilinear relations with employee well-being (De Jonge & Schaufeli, 1998; Xie & Johns, 1995), but these results are not always replicated, especially not longitudinally (Mäkikangas, Feldt, & Kinnunen, 2007) or when general, rather than job-related, well-being is assessed (Rydstedt, Ferrie, & Head, 2006). One of the merits of the vitamin model is, however, that it broadened researchers' horizons in terms of which job characteristics could influence employee well-being.

The Job Demands Resources Model of Bakker, Demerouti, and Schaufeli.

The job demands resources model (JD-R model; Bakker, Demerouti, & Sanz-Vergel, 2014; Demerouti, Bakker, Nachreiner, & Schaufeli, 2001) aimed to provide an integrative view of job characteristics. At the core of the model lies the various job characteristics that may impact employees, which can be meaningfully classified as job demands and job resources. Job demands are defined as "those physical, psychological, social, or organizational aspects of the job that require sustained physical and/or psychological (cognitive and emotional) effort or skills and are therefore associated with certain physiological and/or psychological costs" (Bakker & Demerouti, 2007, p. 312). They are not necessarily negative, but turn into job stressors when they exceed workers' capacities, which makes it hard for them to recover. Job resources are defined as the "physical, psychological, social, or organizational aspects of the job that... (1) [are] functional in achieving work goals, (2) reduce job demands and the associated physiological and psychological costs, [or] (3) stimulate personal growth, learning, and development" (Bakker & Demerouti, 2007, p. 312).

Just like the vitamin model, the JD-R model focuses on employee well-being as a crucial outcome. Following the positive psychology movement advocating the balanced study of the bright side of employees' functioning (Seligman & Csikszentmihalyi, 2000) along with the dark side, both negative (i.e., burnout) and positive (i.e., work engagement) aspects of well-being are considered as the crucial pathways through which job demands and job resources relate to a host of other outcomes, including employee physical health and well-being, job satisfaction, organizational commitment, and different types of behaviors, including in-role and extra-role performance, as well as counterproductive behavior (for an overview, see Van den Broeck, Van Ruysseveldt, Vanbelle, & De Witte, 2013).

Job demands are considered the main cause of burnout. In being continuously confronted with job demands, employees can become emotionally exhausted because they put all their energy into the job. Under particular situations, such as when all their effort is in vain, they likely start withdrawing from their job as a means to protect themselves and become cynical, which is part of the burnout response. Job resources can also have a (limited) direct negative relationship with burnout (Schaufeli & Bakker, 2004), but they are most crucial for the development of vigor and dedication, the main components of work engagement. Job demands and job resources are also assumed to interact, so that high levels of resources may attenuate (i.e., buffer) the association between job demands and burnout, while job demands are said to strengthen (i.e., boost) the association between job resources and work engagement.

Within the JD-R model, individual factors are modeled as personal resources, which are defined as malleable lower-order, cognitive-affective personal aspects reflecting a positive belief in oneself or the world (van den Heuvel, Demerouti, Bakker, & Schaufeli, 2010). As in the job characteristics model, personal resources can represent the underlying process through which job resources prevent burnout and foster work engagement (Xanthopoulou, Bakker, Demerouti, & Schaufeli, 2007), moderate, and—more specifically—buffer the health-impairing impact of job demands, as job resources do, and they may serve as antecedents of the job characteristics, preventing the occurrence of job demands and increasing the (perceived) availability of job resources.

Evidence supporting the JD-R model is abundant, but the model is used mostly in the European literature. Job demands and job resources are convincingly shown to relate to burnout and work engagement (Nahrgang et al., 2011), while some evidence is provided for their interactions and the role of personal resources (Van den Broeck et al., 2013).

CONTEMPORARY JOB-DESIGN MODELS

Over the years, various other models have been developed. They may range from slightly different perspectives on job characteristics and their roles in the prediction of employee functioning to more fundamental changes in how we could perceive job design.

For example, some scholars suggested that not all job demands are equal, but need to be differentiated into challenging and hindering job demands. While challenges are obstacles that can be overcome and hold the potential for learning, hindrances are threatening obstacles that drain people's energy and prevent goal achievement (Lepine, Podsakoff, & Lepine, 2005). Some authors suggested that job demands can be either challenging, or hindering, or both, depending on the appraisal of the individual employee (Rodríguez, Kozusnik, & Peiro, 2013; Webster, Beehr, & Christiansen, 2010). Others, in contrast, argued that employees generally categorize particular job demands as challenging (e.g., workload and time pressure) or hindering (e.g., red tape and role conflict), in relatively clear-cut categorizations (Cavanaugh, Boswell, Roehling, & Boudreau, 2000; Van den Broeck, De Cuyper, De Witte, & Vansteenkiste, 2010).

Morgeson and Humphrey (2006) aimed to integrate the various job characteristics that have been examined in the literature and encouraged job-design scholars not only to focus on task characteristics, such as autonomy and variety, and social characteristics, such as social support and interdependence, but also to pick up on the work context and consider ergonomics, equipment use, and work conditions. This call aligns with the observations of Campion and Thayer (1985). They noticed that job-design scholars seem to have specialized in either the biological (e.g., concern with noise and lifting), the ergonomic (e.g., lighting, information input), the motivational (e.g., autonomy, variety), or the mechanistic (e.g., specialization, simplification) job characteristics, while Taylor, for example, considered each of these aspects in designing jobs. The more integrative view may be more beneficial, because motivational job characteristics may also have an impact on biological functioning (e.g., heart disease), and the best results may be achieved when ergonomic and motivational factors are jointly considered. For example, Das, Shikdar, and Winters (2007) found that drill press operators who had the most ergonomic tools and received training were more satisfied and performed better than their counterparts who also could use the ergonomic tools but didn't receive any training.

New developments in the job-design literature also focused on the relations between the job characteristics and outcomes. The Demand-Induced Strain Compensation model (DISC model; de Jonge & Dormann, 2003), for example, further refined job-design theory by qualifying the interaction between job demands and job resources. Specifically, the DISC model assumes that job resources have more potential to buffer the negative effect of job demands on employee well-being when the demands, resources, and outcomes are all physical, cognitive, or emotional. That is, emotional resources, such as social support, may best buffer the impact of emotional demands on emotional stability (Van de Ven, De Jonge, & Vlerick, 2014).

More profound changes in job-design theory have been launched. For example, building on the notions of role conflict and role ambiguity (Kahn et al., 1964), Ilgen and Hollenbeck (1992) argued for the study of work roles, which are generally broader than people's prescribed jobs because they also include emergent and self-imitated tasks. The focus on work roles led to a flourishing literature on role breadth self-efficacy (Parker, 1998), personal initiative (Frese, Garst, & Fay, 2007), and proactive work behavior (Parker, Williams, & Turner, 2006), with the argument being that work design is an especially important facilitator of these outcomes.

The relational perspective of Grant and colleagues is also a novel extension (e.g., Grant, 2007). In this approach, a powerful way to design work is to ensure that employees are connected with those that benefit from the work. Such an approach enhances task significance, and thereby promotes greater prosocial motivation among employees, which in turn benefits employee performance (for a review, see Grant & Parker, 2009).

Another development has been to recognize the role of work design in promoting learning. As Parker (2014, p. 671) argued: "Motivational theories of work design have dominated psychological approaches to work design. However, we need to expand the criterion space beyond motivation, not just by adding extra dependent variables to empirical studies but by exploring when, why, and how work design can help to achieve different purposes." Parker outlined existing theory and research that suggest work design might be a powerful—yet currently rather neglected—intervention for promoting learning outcomes, such as the accelerated acquisition of expert knowledge, as well as for promoting developmental outcomes over the lifespan (such as the development of cognitive complexity, or even moral development).

Nevertheless, despite, or perhaps because of, the different perspectives, the current job-design literature can be fragmented, with different job-design models offering insights to different parts of the puzzle but not necessarily the whole puzzle. To move the job-design literature forward, a more synthesized mental model of the literature has been developed that describes what can already be considered established knowledge and that highlights fruitful ways forward.

THE INTEGRATIVE WORK DESIGN MODEL

Building from the job-design models featured in the literature and the principles they put forward, an integrative work design model can be developed. The model may stimulate scholars to think broadly when studying job design and to develop new areas for research. It may equally assist managers to consider various aspects of people's jobs when assessing the adequateness of the jobs they design. The model includes job characteristics as antecedents, and their possible relations with employee outcomes, including employee well-being, cognitions, attitudes, and behaviors. Finally, personal characteristics are taken into account as intervening variables in these relationships. The core aspects of the integrative work design (IWD) model are outlined in Figure 1.

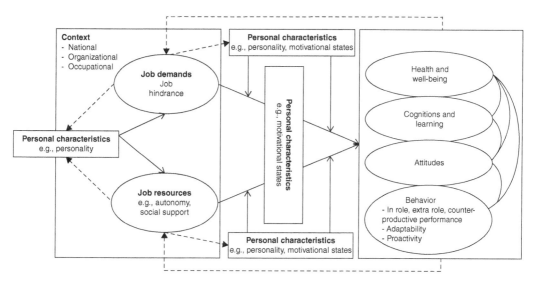

Figure 1. The integrative work design (IWD) model.

JOB CHARACTERISTICS AS ANTECEDENTS

In keeping with the approach of the JD-R, the differentiation between job resources and job demands is maintained as a valuable framework for grouping job characteristics. This approach is not without criticism (Van den Broeck et al., 2013). For example, not all job characteristics can be easily classified as either a job demand or a job resource (e.g., job security could be a resource, while job insecurity could be a demand). However, within the IWD model it is maintained that various positive and negative events are not simply opposite ends of the spectrum (e.g., the absence of aggressive or troublesome patients doesn't necessarily turn patient contacts into positive experiences; Hakanen, Bakker, & Demerouti, 2005). The difference between positive and negative reflects the universal differentiation between the positive and the negative, which is rooted in our neurophysiology and how we appraise each encounter with the environment (Barrett, Mesquita, Ochsner, & Gross, 2007). Negatives typically loom larger than positives and have a stronger impact on negative aspects of employee functioning, while positive aspects are more predictive of positive outcomes (Baumeister, Bratslavsky, Finkenauer, & Vohs, 2001). This suggests that having a mindset that looks at both job demands and job resources allows scholars and managers alike to take a balanced perspective on the beneficial and detrimental characteristics of a job.

Although Warr, as well as the JD-R model, start from the assumption that several job characteristics may have an impact on employee functioning, by far the most empirical attention has been paid to the restricted list of job characteristics proposed by Karasek: autonomy, workload, and social support (Humphrey et al., 2007), and/or the five job characteristics covered in the JCM. To overcome this issue, a broader view on job design seems necessary. People may be inspired by new developments in the job-design literature differentiating between job challenges (e.g., responsibility) and job hindrances (e.g., red tape), as was done in the development of a model including job hindrances, challenges, and resources (Crawford, Lepine, &

Rich, 2010; Van den Broeck et al., 2010). Second, the classification by Campion and Thayer (1985, 1988) may be a source of inspiration to also include job characteristics related to human factors (e.g., equipment) and biological factors (e.g., noise, temperature), along with the mechanical (e.g., repetition) and motivational (e.g., promotion, task significance) job characteristics. Job-design scholars may consider the inclusion of context-specific job-specific hindrances, challenges, and resources, such as student aggression for teachers, number and duration of interventions for firefighters, or having contact with the patients' families for nurses (for an overview, see Van den Broeck et al., 2013).

The study of specific and general job characteristics may also take into account recent developments in the labor market, such as the digital revolution, and the changes in demographics. Few studies have included the consequences of these changes in the study of contemporary jobs, although they have caused dramatic changes in job design (Cordery & Parker, 2012). For example, due to technological advances, jobs have undergone profound changes. While some jobs are disappearing due to automation and digitalization, the remaining jobs—for example, in supporting, maintaining, and repairing technology—have become more analytical and problem-solving in nature. Recent job-design scales therefore include concentration and precision as cognitive or mental demands (Van Veldhoven, Prins, Van der Laken, & Dijkstra, 2016), which may become extremely relevant for older workers who experience a decline in fluid intelligence (Krings, Sczesny, & Kluge, 2011). Due to the technological revolution, employees also become increasingly dependent on technology, leading to techno-stress (Tarafdar, D'Arcy, Turel, & Gupta, 2015). The growing body of research on this issue, however, developed outside of I/O psychology, with the leading publications in information and computer sciences. Similarly, the use of digital technology has made it possible to work from home. This increased the degree to which work-related activities intruded into private life and had implications for job design in terms of autonomy and social support (Allen, Golden, & Shockley, 2015; Gajendran & Harrison, 2007). Research interest on the impact of telework is growing, but—again—mostly as a separate field, rather than as an aspect of job design (Bailey & Kurland, 2002).

Finally, and again in line with the JD-R model and the recent work of Morgeson and Humphrey (2006), job demands and job resources can be found at the level of one's task and job in general—relating to the content of work—but also at the level of the social relations at work (e.g., conflict vs. social support), which includes the social support component of the Karasek model and the call for more research on the role of social influences at work (Grant & Parker, 2009). Apart from the social aspects, attention could also be paid to job characteristics at the team level. In 2012, Hollenbeck, Beersma, and Schouten noted that up to 80% of all Fortune organizations rely on teamwork to achieve their goals. Team characteristics, such as interdependence and team autonomy, have an impact on employee task characteristics, such as autonomy and well-being and performance (Langfred, 2007; Van Mierlo, Rutte, Vermunt, Kompier, & Doorewaard, 2007) and could therefore be taken into account.

Furthermore, scholars may want to go one step further and incorporate aspects at the level of the organization, such as HR-related demands and resources (e.g., strategic impact; De Cooman, Stynen, Van den Broeck, Sels, & De Witte, 2013) and organizational climate (e.g., safety climate; Dollard & Bakker, 2010). Apart from examining the direct impact of these characteristics on employee functioning, job-design scholars could also examine their interplay, in terms of how organizational and team-level variables influence social and task characteristics, as well as how the different levels may buffer, amplify, or boost each other's impact (Parker, Van den Broeck, & Holman, 2017). Furthermore, scholars could examine the interplay between job characteristics through profile analyses (Van den Broeck, De Cuyper, Luyckx, & De Witte, 2012).

THE RELATIONS OF JOB CHARACTERISTICS WITH OUTCOMES

The previous models have outlined that job characteristics may influence employee outcomes in many different ways. While most models assume linear relations, Warr argued for curvilinear relations, where both too little and too much of a job characteristic, such as workload, would lead to lower levels of employee well-being, an assumption that also seems to be implicit in the definition of job demands in the JD-R model. Others have argued that such curvilinear relationships are nothing less than "urban myths," as they are difficult to establish empirically (Taris, 2006). Although the lack of empirical support for curvilinear relations may also be attributable to methodological shortcomings, this challenging statement has encouraged other scholars to argue that not the amount, but the type, of job demands matters for how they relate to employee functioning (Lepine et al., 2005; Van den Broeck et al., 2010). This approach ties in with the appraisal theory (Folkman & Lazarus, 1985), which states that the interpretation of an event as challenging or threatening determines how people react to it. Future studies may follow through on these potential curvilinear or differentiated results.

Moreover, it would be interesting to see more research on the differentiated results of particular job characteristics. While Hackman and Oldham argued that all motivational job characteristics would have an impact on employee motivation, performance, and turnover, other frameworks (e.g., Herzberg's two-factor theory, Karasek's job demand control model, the JD-R, and the DISC model) propose that some job characteristics would be more strongly related to particular outcomes. This is in line with the meta-analysis findings that motivational characteristics may, for example, explain more variance in performance than social characteristics, but the latter seemed to be most important in the prediction of turnover intentions (Humphrey et al., 2007). Furthermore, this meta-analysis showed that work-scheduling autonomy is less predictive of job satisfaction than decision-making autonomy, which shows that it is worthwhile to examine the different effects of different job characteristics.

DIFFERENT OUTCOMES OF JOB DESIGN

Within the job-design literature, different outcomes of job design have been put to the fore. Whereas Taylor mostly focused on performance, most of the motivational and health-oriented job-design models focused on aspects of employee well-being and attitudes. But none of the existing job-design models does full justice to the rich amount of consequences that have been empirically studied. The immediate, that is, individual-level, outcomes of job design are here grouped in terms of health and well-being, cognitions and learning, attitudes, and behaviors (Cordery & Parker, 2012; Humphrey et al., 2007). The IWD model thus goes beyond mere well-being, core task performance, absenteeism, and turnover.

Health and Well-being. First, following through on their importance in job-design models, employee health and well-being have arguably been the most studied outcomes of job design. Meta-analytic results convincingly show that job characteristics like autonomy, feedback, and social support increase employee engagement and prevent employees from feeling anxious, stressed, or burned out (Humphrey et al., 2007; Nahrgang et al., 2011). In line with these results, many countries developed policies that urge employers to take care of the psychosocial risk factors—including mostly quantitative and qualitative demands, job control, and opportunities for skill development—to prevent these outcomes (Formazin et al., 2014).

A policy-oriented focus on the improvement of job design also has the potential to prevent more injuries and somatic health problems related to job design. For example, job characteristics are also important precursors of accidents, injuries, and unsafe behavior (Nahrgang et al., 2011), because high job demands and low job resources might cause employees to routinely violate safety rules (Hansez & Chmiel, 2010). People working in jobs of low quality also have higher risk of stroke and the development of heart disease (Backé, Seidler, Latza, Rossnagel, & Schumann, 2012; Eller et al., 2009). Similar results have been found for the experience of low back pain, pain in the shoulders or knees (Bernal et al., 2015), or obesity (Fried et al., 2013; Kim & Han, 2015). Interestingly, these results are mostly reported in journals featuring biomedical and human factors research (Parker et al., 2017), leaving these far-reaching consequences of job design relatively unnoticed in I/O psychology.

Attitudes. A considerable body of research established the importance of job design for employee attitudes toward work, such as organizational commitment, job involvement, and job satisfaction (Humphrey et al., 2007). Meta-analytic results, for example, show that job demands explain 28% of the variance in job design, while job resources can explain no less than 62% to 85% (Humphrey et al., 2007; Nahrgang et al., 2011). Results are inconclusive whether high levels of job satisfaction should be attributed primarily to good social relations at work or to the motivational characteristics defined by Hackman and Oldham.

Cognitions and Learning. While much attention has been devoted to health and well-being, research interest in cognitions as outcomes of job design has only been emerging recently and is a promising avenue for the future (Parker, 2014). Although more complex jobs may be challenging (Van Veldhoven et al., 2016), in their systematic review, Then et al. (2014) demonstrated that this might also have positive consequences, as high work complexity— together with high job control—has a protective effect against the decline of cognitive functions later in life and dementia. Increasing cognitive demands may thus start a process in which cognitive processes are maintained, if not increased. Similarly, work pressure may reduce daytime intuitive decision making, but enhance analytical thinking (Gordon, Demerouti, Bipp, & Le Blanc, 2015) and foster learning (De Witte, Verhofstadt, & Omey, 2007), as could be expected based on Karasek's model and German action theory (Frese & Zapf, 1994). For example, Holman et al. (2012) showed that blue collar workers in a vehicle manufacturer improved their learning strategies when being allotted job control, while solving complex problems. Similar results were found in a diary study (Niessen, Sonnentag, & Friederike, 2012), where job resources, such as having meaning on one's job, allowed employees to maintain focus and explore new information, which then led to employees' thriving, defined as a combination of learning and high levels of energy.

Behavior.   In the work context, different behaviors are valued, ranging from performance and adaptivity to proactivity (Griffin, Neal, & Parker, 2007). Taylor's primary aim was to design jobs to increase job performance according to the scientific standards he established. Although performance has received less attention throughout the different classic job-design models, it is still considered crucial in job design research. Results are somewhat mixed. While meta-analyses show that a range of job resources (e.g., autonomy, skill or task variety, task significance, feedback) all relate positively to self-rated performance, only autonomy seems to relate to objective performance (Humphrey et al., 2007). Motivational and social factors like autonomy, task identity, feedback from the job, and social support are also important predictors of behaviors like absenteeism, while social aspects of work design, such as social support, feedback from others, and interdependence, prove to be most important for turnover intentions (Humphrey et al., 2007). Job resources like feedback and intrinsically motivating tasks also predict extra role behaviors, such as altruism, courtesy, conscientiousness, and civic virtue, while job demands like role ambiguity, role conflict, and task routinization are negatively related to these behaviors (Podskaoff, Mackenzie, Paine, & Bachrach, 2000).

Job design also affects adaptivity, or the degree to which employees cope well with the ongoing change and adversities in organizations (Griffin et al., 2007). For example, sportsmanship, or tolerating work-related inconveniences without complaining, is fostered when employees find their jobs inherently satisfying and receive feedback, while role problems likely forestall sportsmanship (Podskaoff et al., 2000).

More than just adapting to the rapid changes and the insecurity characterizing the contemporary labor market, employees are also required to proactively anticipate and act upon potential future opportunities (Griffin et al., 2007). Job design had not always been considered essential for employee proactivity (Anderson, De Dreu, & Nijstad, 2004), but recent views see job design—and most importantly autonomy and social support—as an important antecedent (Parker et al., 2006), which is confirmed by meta-analytic results (Tornau & Frese, 2013). Employees in enriched jobs are more inclined to be proactive than employees in jobs characterized by routinization and formalization (Marinova, Peng, Lorinkova, Van Dyne, & Chiaburu, 2015).

Job design is also an important moderator for proactivity, allowing proactive motivations to materialize in proactive behavior (Parker, Bindl, & Strauss, 2010). Meta-analyses, for example, suggest that employees don't need autonomy to generate ideas, but require autonomy for idea implementation (Hammond, Neff, Farr, Schwall, & Zhao, 2011). As for job demands, the relations may be complex: while uncertainty relates negatively to feedback seeking (Anseel, Beatty, Shen, Lievens, & Sackett, 2015), job demands like complexity associate positively with proactive innovation (Hammond et al., 2011). Similar results are found at the within-person level. For example, civil servants are more likely to proactively try to improve procedures and introduce new ways of working when they are challenged by time pressure and situational constraints (Fritz & Sonnentag, 2007). Proactive behavior may also become a challenge in itself, because one has to plan his actions and invest additional hours or effort in the proactive behavior (Podsakoff, Podsakoff, MacKenzie, Maynes, & Spoelma, 2014). Job characteristics like job insecurity may also lead to counterproductive behaviors toward the organization (Van den Broeck et al., 2014) and also toward other employees. For example, Van den Broeck, Baillien, and De Witte (2011) found that job demands like workload are a risk factor for bullying behavior, while job resources like autonomy and supervisory support seem to reduce this risk. However, employees having both high job demands and high job resources were most at risk of becoming bullies at work.

Employee health and well-being, cognitions, attitudes, and behavior are treated as independent elements in the IWD model. They are, however, most likely to influence each other. High levels of well-being have, for example, been shown to relate to commitment and behavioral outcomes (Nahrgang et al., 2011). Moreover, thus far, mostly short-term outcomes at the level of the employee were mentioned, leaving outcomes that evolve only over time or develop at the organizational level unexplored. Job design is, however, also related to several such outcomes, potentially through its impact on well-being, cognitions, attitudes, and behaviors. For example, job design also has an effect on one's self-definition (Parker, Wall, & Jackson, 2016) and careers (Fried, Grant, Levi, Hadani, & Slowik, 2007). Longitudinal studies among more than 2,000 employees show that having high job demands and few opportunities for skill development or social support cause employees to retire early, even above and beyond their impact on mental and physical health (de Wind et al., 2014; de Wind, Geuskens, Ybema, Bongers, & van der Beek, 2015). Job design also leads to the financial success of the organization. High levels of job resources during one's shift, for example, increase the financial returns in the fast food industry, as they contributed to the work engagement of the employees (Xanthopoulou, Bakker, Demerouti, & Schaufeli, 2009). High job resources equally increase the service climate within the hospitality sector, which then associates with customer loyalty (Salanova, Agut, & Peiró, 2005). These outcomes not only may be caused by job characteristics, but also feed into job characteristics (i.e., they have reciprocal relationships), and they may be dependent on employees' personal characteristics.

PERSONAL CHARACTERISTICS

Several of the job-characteristics models have considered the role of personal characteristics within job design. Rightly so, as employee functioning is likely to be a function of both situation (i.e., to be job related) and person factors. Most attention with regard to the role of person factors has been paid to personal resources, which are defined as highly valued aspects, relating to resilience and contributing to individuals' potential to successfully control and influence the environment (Hobfoll, Johnson, Ennis, & Jackson, 2003).

Several personal characteristics have been considered personal resources. Within the JCM, for example, growth-need strength can be seen as a personal resource, as are the critical psychological states of meaning, knowledge of results, and responsibility. Within Warr's vitamin model, employees' values are considered essential to how employees respond to certain contexts, while a host of personal resources have been studied in the realm of the JD-R model, ranging from hope and optimism to the core self-evaluations of self-esteem, generalized self-efficacy, emotional stability, and locus of control (Van den Broeck et al., 2013).

In our view, personal resources may play at least three different roles in the job-design literature. First, they may moderate the impact of job characteristics on employee functioning (i.e., job resources as moderators). Conservation of resources theory (COR), for example, assumes that having resources allows people to cope with demanding circumstances, so that personal resources may buffer the negative consequences (Hobfoll, 1989). In line with this view, employees endowed with self-esteem and optimism were found to experience less psychological distress when confronted with job demands like time pressure (Mäkikangas & Kinnunen, 2003), while customer orientation buffers the association between job demands and burnout (Babakus, Yavas, & Ashill, 2009).

In addition to the buffering effect, job resources can also amplify the positive effects of resourceful job characteristics, as was also mentioned by Hackman and Oldham, as well as by Warr. Again following COR, employees holding high levels of personal resources in a resourceful environment may build resource caravans, which may then lead to low levels of stress and high performance (Hobfoll, 2002). More specifically, personal resources may boost the impact of job resources, because a fit between the personal resources and the job characteristics causes employees to pay more attention to the availability of the job characteristics, but also because they have more adaptive ways to act upon the job characteristics (Kristof-brown, Zimmerman, & Johnson, 2005). For example, employees who aim to develop themselves see more opportunities for development and may make better use of such opportunities, which then increases their well-being (Van den Broeck, Schreurs, Guenter, & van Emmerik, 2015; Van den Broeck, Van Ruysseveldt, Smulders, & De Witte, 2011).

Apart from the relatively straightforward moderating effects, personal resources may also influence the impact of job characteristics in a more complex way. Because of their boosting effect on job resources, personal resources may also enable employees to use their job resources better to offset the negative effects of job demands, leading to a three-way interaction between personal and job resources and job demands. For example, employees having an internal locus of control may make optimal use of the job control at their disposal to attenuate the effects of daily stressors, while for employees having an external locus of control, job control may not be put in practice and in some research actually predicted poorer well-being and health (Meier, Semmer, Elfering, & Jacobshagen, 2008; for a similar study, see Parker & Sprigg, 1999). Considering the curvilinear effects, personal resources may affect the tipping point at which increases in job characteristics stop being positive or even start to have negative consequences, so that employees with a high need for security may appreciate higher levels of role clarity than employees who are more adventurous (Warr, 1987). Overall, personal resources may allow employees to make better use of job resources, while dealing better with job demands, leading to different outcomes for employees working in the same jobs.

A second role of personal resources may be in explaining the relationships between job characteristics and their outcomes (i.e., personal resources as mediators). Hackman and Oldham suggested that the environment could influence employees' psychological states, which then explains why job characteristics affect, for example, employee motivation and performance. According to JD-R scholars, this is true not only for the critical psychological states, but also for various personal resources. An important addition to the assumption is that not only may job resources add to psychological states, but also job demands can be assumed to take away employees' energy and hinder their goal orientation, thereby decreasing employees' personal resources (Hobfoll, 1989). In support of this, research shows that the same psychological resources may indeed explain the effects of both motivational and demanding job characteristics: While job resources lead to high levels of engagement and low levels of burnout through increased satisfaction of Self-Determination Theory's basic needs for autonomy, competence, and relatedness, job demands hinder the experience of basic need satisfaction and therefore lead to higher levels of burnout and more counterproductive behavior (Van den Broeck, Suela, Vander Elst, Fischmann, Iliescu, & De Witte, 2014; Van den Broeck,

Vansteenkiste, De Witte, & Lens, 2008). In exploring the mediating role of personal resources, future research may answer the call for more attention to the processes underpinning the relations between job characteristics and outcomes (Parker et al., 2001).

Finally, personal resources may serve as antecedents of job demands and job resources. This may be because managers provide more favorable job conditions to highly motivated employees (Rousseau, 2001), because such employees craft their job to include more motivational and less demanding characteristics (Wrzesniewski & Dutton, 2001), or because resourceful employees appraise their job situation as more benign or challenging and less threatening (Folkman & Lazarus, 1985).

Notably, thus far, the job-design literature focuses on relatively changeable and positive personal characteristics. However, more stable personal characteristics may also play a role, as they may shape employees' directedness to particular goals and thereby equally serve as antecedents and moderators of job characteristics (Barrick, Mount, & Li, 2013). The personality trait of neuroticism may, for example, cause employees to report higher job demands, while extroverted employees experience more job resources (Bakker et al., 2010). Moreover, recently, it was also shown that job characteristics may change employees' personality (Wu, 2016). A final consideration is that particular personal aspects may also make employees more vulnerable to the negative impact of job demands or make it more difficult to benefit from positive aspects.

CONCLUSION

The job-design literature has a long history and continues to grow. Although some job-design scholars have argued there is nothing left to know about job design, new aspects are still unraveling and many aspects of the nature of job characteristics and their relationship with various outcomes, as well as the role of personal characteristics, remain underexplored. Because job design strongly associates with a host of outcomes and various jobs are still of low quality, job design still deserves scholarly and managerial attention. The integrative work design (IWD) model may assist in the process.

FURTHER READING

Grant, A. M. (2008). The significance of task significance: Job performance effects, relational mechanisms, and boundary conditions. *Journal of Applied Psychology, 93*(1), 108–124. http://dx.doi.org/10.1037/0021-9010.93.1.108

Oldham, G. R., & Fried, Y. (2016). Job design research and theory: Past, present and future. *Organizational Behavior and Human Decision Processes, 136*, 20–35. http://dx.doi.org/10.1016/j.obhdp.2016.05.002

Oldham, G. R., & Hackman, J. R. (2010). Not what it was and not what it will be: The future of job design research. *Journal of Organizational Behavior, 31*(2–3), 463–479. http://dx.doi.org/10.1002/job.678

REFERENCES

Allen, T. D., Golden, T. D., & Shockley, K. M. (2015). How effective is telecommuting? Assessing the status of our scientific findings. *Psychological Science in the Public Interest, 16*(2), 40–68. http://dx.doi.org/10.1177/1529100615593273

Ambrose, M. L., & Kulik, C. (1999). Old friends, new faces: Motivation research in the 1990s. *Journal of Management, 25*(3), 231–292.

Anderson, N., De Dreu, C. K. W., & Nijstad, B. A. (2004). The routinization of innovation research: A constructively critical review of the state-of-the-science. *Journal of Organizational Behavior, 25*(2), 147–173. http://dx.doi.org/10.1002/job.236

Anseel, F., Beatty, A. S., Shen, W., Lievens, F., & Sackett, P. R. (2015). How are we doing after 30 years? A meta-analytic review of the antecedents and outcomes of feedback-seeking behavior. *Journal of Management, 41*(1), 318–348. http://dx.doi.org/10.1177/0149206313484521

Axtell, C. M., & Parker, S. K. (2003). Promoting role breadth self-efficacy through involvement, work redesign and training. *Human Relations, 56*(1), 113–131. http://dx.doi.org/10.1177/0018726703056001452

Babakus, E., Yavas, U., & Ashill, N. J. (2009). The role of customer orientation as a moderator of the job demand–burnout–performance relationship: A surface-level trait perspective. *Journal of Retailing, 85*(4), 480–492. http://dx.doi.org/10.1016/j.jretai.2009.07.001

Backé, E.-M., Seidler, A., Latza, U., Rossnagel, K., & Schumann, B. (2012). The role of psychosocial stress at work for the development of cardiovascular diseases: A systematic review. *International Archives of Occupational and Environmental Health, 85*(1), 67–79. http://dx.doi.org/10.1007/s00420-011-0643-6

Bailey, D. E., & Kurland, N. B. (2002). A review of telework research: Findings, new directions, and lessons for the study of modern work. *Journal of Organizational Behavior, 23*, 383–400. http://dx.doi.org/10.1002/job.144

Bakker, A. B., Boyd, C. M., Dollard, M., Gillespie, N., Winefield, A. H., & Stough, C. (2010). The role of personality in the job demands-resources model: A study of Australian academic staff. *Career Development International, 15*(7), 622–636. http://dx.doi.org/10.1108/13620431011094050

Bakker, A. B., & Demerouti, E. (2007). The job demands-resources model: State of the art. *Journal of Managerial Psychology, 22*(3), 309–328. http://dx.doi.org/10.1108/02683940710733115

Bakker, A. B., Demerouti, E., & Sanz-Vergel, A. I. (2014). Burnout and work engagement: The JD–R approach. *Annual Review of Organizational Psychology and Organizational Behavior, 1*(1), 389–411. http://dx.doi.org/10.1146/annurev-orgpsych-031413-091235

Barley, S. R., & Kunda, G. (2001). Bringing work back in. *Organization Science, 12*(1), 76–95. http://dx.doi.org/10.1287/orsc.12.1.76.10122

Barrett, L. F., Mesquita, B., Ochsner, K. N., & Gross, J. J. (2007). The experience of emotion. *Annual Review of Psychology, 58*, 373–403. http://dx.doi.org/10.1146/annurev.psych.58.110405.085709

Barrick, M. R., Mount, M. K., & Li, N. (2013). The theory of purposeful work behavior: The role of personality, higher-order goals and job characteristics. *Academy of Management Review, 38*(1), 132–153.

Baumeister, R. F., Bratslavsky, E., Finkenauer, C., & Vohs, K. D. (2001). Bad is stronger than good. *Review of General Psychology, 5*(4), 323–370. http://dx.doi.org/10.1037//1089-2680.5.4.323

Bernal, D., Campos-Serna, J., Tobias, A., Vargas-Prada, S., Benavides, F. G., & Serra, C. (2015). Work-related psychosocial risk factors and musculoskeletal disorders in hospital nurses and nursing aides: A systematic review and meta-analysis. *International Journal of Nursing Studies, 52*(2), 635–648. http://dx.doi.org/10.1016/j.ijnurstu.2014.11.003

Campion, M. A., Mumford, T. V., Morgeson, F. P., & Nahrgang, J. D. (2005). Work redesign: Eight obstacles and opportunities. *Human Resource Management, 44*(4), 367–390. http://dx.doi.org/10.1002/hrm.20080

Campion, M. A., & Thayer, P. W. (1985). Development and field evaluation of an interdisciplinary measure of job design. *Journal of Applied Psychology, 70*(1), 29–43. http://dx.doi.org/10.1037/0021-9010.70.1.29

Campion, M. A., & Thayer, P. W. (1988). Job design: Approaches, outcomes and trade-offs. *Organizational Dynamics, 15*(3), 66–79.

Caplan, R. D., Cobb, S., French, J. R. R., Jr., Harrison, R. V., & Pinneau, S. R., Jr. (1975). *Demands and worker health: Main effects and occupational differences.* Washington, DC: U.S. Government Printing Office.

Cavanaugh, M. A., Boswell, W. R., Roehling, M. V., & Boudreau, J. W. (2000). An empirical examination of self-reported work stress among U.S. managers. *Journal of Applied Psychology, 85*(1), 65–74. http://dx.doi.org/10.1037//0021-9010.85.1.65

Cordery, J., & Parker, S. K. (2007). Organization of work. In P. F. Boxall, J. Purcell, & P. M. Wright (Eds.), *Oxford handbook of human resource management* (Vol. 1, pp. 12–13). Oxford: Oxford University Press.

Cordery, J. L., & Parker, S. K. (2012). Job and role design. In S. Kozlowski (Ed.), *Oxford handbook of industrial and organizational psychology* (Vol. 1, pp. 247–284). Oxford: Oxford University Press.

Crawford, E. R., Lepine, J. A., & Rich, B. L. (2010). Linking job demands and resources to employee engagement and burnout: A theoretical extension and meta-analytic test. *The Journal of Applied Psychology, 95*(5), 834–848. http://dx.doi.org/10.1037/a0019364

Das, B., Shikdar, A. A., & Winters, T. (2007). Workstation redesign for a repetitive drill press operation: A combined work design and ergonomics approach. *Human Factors and Ergonomics in Manufacturing, 17*(4), 395–410. http://dx.doi.org/10.1002/hfm

De Cooman, R., Stynen, D., Van den Broeck, A., Sels, L., & De Witte, H. (2013). How job characteristics relate to need satisfaction and autonomous motivation: Implications for work effort. *Journal of Applied Social Psychology, 43*(6), 1342–1352. http://dx.doi.org/10.1111/jasp.12143

De Jonge, J., & Dormann, C. (2003). The DISC model: Demand-induced strain compensation mechanisms in job stress. In M. F. Dollard, H. R. Winefield, & A. H. Winefield (Eds.), *Occupational stress in the service professions* (pp. 43–74). London: Taylor & Francis.

De Jonge, J., & Schaufeli, W. B. (1998). Job characteristics and employee well-being: A test of Warr's vitamin model in health care workers using structural equation modelling. *Journal of Organizational Behavior, 19*(4), 387–407.

de Lange, A. H., Taris, T. W., Kompier, M. A. J., Houtman, I. L. D., & Bongers, P. M. (2003). "The very best of the millennium": Longitudinal research and the demand-control (-support) model. *Journal of Occupational Health Psychology, 8*(4), 282–305. http://dx.doi.org/10.1037/1076-8998.8.4.282

de Wind, A., Geuskens, G. A., Ybema, J. F., Blatter, B. M., Burdorf, A., Bongers, P. M., et al. (2014). Health, job characteristics, skills, and social and financial factors in relation to early retirement—Results from a longitudinal study in the Netherlands. *Scandinavian Journal of Work, Environment & Health, 40*(2), 186–194. http://dx.doi.org/10.5271/sjweh.3393

de Wind, A., Geuskens, G. A., Ybema, J. F., Bongers, P. M., & van der Beek, A. J. (2015). The role of ability, motivation, and opportunity to work in the transition from work to early retirement—Testing and optimizing the Early Retirement Model. *Scandinavian Journal of Work, Environment & Health, 41*(1), 24–35. http://dx.doi.org/10.5271/sjweh.3468

De Witte, H., Verhofstadt, E., & Omey, E. (2007). Testing Karasek's learning and strain hypotheses on young workers in their first job. *Work & Stress, 21*(2), 131–141. http://dx.doi.org/10.1080/02678370701405866

Demerouti, E., Bakker, A. B., Nachreiner, F., & Schaufeli, W. B. (2001). The job demands-resources model of burnout. *Journal of Applied Psychology, 86*(3), 499–512. http://dx.doi.org/10.1108/02683940710733115

Dollard, M. F., & Bakker, A. B. (2010). Psychosocial safety climate as a precursor to conducive work environments, psychological health problems, and employee engagement. *Journal of Occupational and Organizational Psychology, 83*(3), 579–599. http://dx.doi.org/10.1348/096317909X470690

Eller, N. H., Netterstrøm, B., Gyntelberg, F., Kristensen, T. S., Nielsen, F., Steptoe, A., et al. (2009). Work-related psychosocial factors and the development of ischemic heart disease. *Cardiology in Review, 17*(2), 83–97. http://dx.doi.org/10.1097/CRD.0b013e318198c8e9

Folkman, S., & Lazarus, R. S. (1985). If it changes it must be a process: Study of emotion and coping during three stages of a college examination. *Journal of Personality and Social Psychology, 48*(1), 150–170. http://dx.doi.org/10.1037/0022-3514.48.1.150

Formazin, M., Burr, H., Aagestad, C., Tynes, T., Thorsen, S. V., Perkio-Makela, M., et al. (2014). Dimensional comparability of psychosocial working conditions as covered in European monitoring questionnaires. *BMC Public Health, 14*, 1251. http://dx.doi.org/10.1186/1471-2458-14-1251

Frese, M., Garst, H., & Fay, D. (2007). Making things happen: Reciprocal relationships between work characteristics and personal initiative in a four-wave longitudinal structural equation model. *The Journal of Applied Psychology, 92*(4), 1084–1102. http://dx.doi.org/10.1037/0021-9010.92.4.1084

Frese, M., & Zapf, D. (1994). Action as the core of work psychology: A German approach. In H. C. Triandis, M. D. Dunnette, & L. M. Hough (Eds.), *Handbook of industrial and organizational psychology* (Vol. 4, pp. 271–340). Palo Alto, CA: Consulting Psychologists Press.

Fried, Y., & Ferris, G. (1987). The validity of the job characteristics model: A review and meta-analysis. *Personnel Psychology, 40*(2), 287–322. http://dx.doi.org/10.1111/j.1744-6570.1987.tb00605.x

Fried, Y., Grant, A. M., Levi, A. S., Hadani, M., & Slowik, L. H. (2007). Job design in temporal context: A career dynamics perspective. *Journal of Organizational Behavior, 28*(7), 911–927. http://dx.doi.org/10.1002/job

Fried, Y., Laurence, G. A., Shirom, A., Melamed, S., Toker, S., Berliner, S., et al. (2013). The relationship between job enrichment and abdominal obesity: A longitudinal field study of apparently healthy individuals. *Journal of Occupational Health Psychology, 18*(4), 458–468. http://dx.doi.org/10.1037/a0033730

Fritz, C., & Sonnentag, S. (2007). Antecedents of day-level proactive behavior: A look at job stressors and positive affect during the workday. *Journal of Management, 35*(1), 94–111. http://dx.doi.org/10.1177/0149206307308911

Gajendran, R. S., & Harrison, D. A. (2007). The good, the bad, and the unknown about telecommuting: Meta-analysis of psychological mediators and individual consequences. *The Journal of Applied Psychology, 92*(6), 1524–1541. http://dx.doi.org/10.1037/0021-9010.92.6.1524

Gordon, H. J., Demerouti, E., Bipp, T., & Le Blanc, P. M. (2015). The Job Demands and Resources Decision Making (JD-R-DM) model. *European Journal of Work and Organizational Psychology, 24*(1), 44–58. http://dx.doi.org/10.1080/1359432X.2013.842901

Grant, A. M. (2007). Relational job design and the motivation to make a prosocial difference. *Academy of Management Review, 32*(2), 393–417.

Grant, A. M., & Parker, S. K. (2009). Redesigning work design theories: The rise of relational and proactive perspectives. *Academy of Management Annals, 3*(1), 317–375. http://dx.doi.org/10.1080/19416520903047327

Griffin, M. A., Neal, A., & Parker, S. K. (2007). A new model of work role performance: Positive behavior in uncertain and interdependent contexts. *Academy of Management Journal, 50*(2), 327–347.

Hackman, J. R., & Oldham, G. R. (1976). Motivation through the design of work: Test of a theory. *Organizational Behavior and Human Performance, 16*, 250–279.

Hakanen, J. J., Bakker, A. B., & Demerouti, E. (2005). How dentists cope with their job demands and stay engaged: The moderating role of job resources. *European Journal of Oral Sciences, 113*(6), 479–487. http://dx.doi.org/10.1111/j.1600-0722.2005.00250.x

Hammond, M. M., Neff, N. L., Farr, J. L., Schwall, A. R., & Zhao, X. (2011). Predictors of individual-level innovation at work: A meta-analysis. *Psychology of Aesthetics, Creativity, and the Arts, 5*(1), 90–105. http://dx.doi.org/10.1037/a0018556

Hansez, I., & Chmiel, N. (2010). Safety behavior: Job demands, job resources, and perceived management commitment to safety. *Journal of Occupational Health Psychology, 15*(3), 267–278. http://dx.doi.org/10.1037/a0019528

Hausser, J. A., Mojzisch, A., Niesel, M., & Schulz-Hardt, S. (2010). Ten years on: A review of recent research on the Job Demand-Control (-Support) model and psychological well-being. *Work and Stress, 24*(1), 1–35. http://dx.doi.org/10.1080/02678371003683747

Herzberg, F. (1968). One more time: How do you motivate employees? *Harvard Business Review, 48*, 53–62.

Hobfoll, S. E. (1989). Conservation of resources: A new attempt at conceptualizing stress. *American Psychologist, 44*(3), 513–524.

Hobfoll, S. E. (2002). Social and psychological resources and adaptation. *Review of General Psychology, 6*(4), 307–324. http://dx.doi.org/10.1037//1089-2680.6.4.307

Hobfoll, S. E., Johnson, R. J., Ennis, N., & Jackson, A. P. (2003). Resource loss, resource gain, and emotional outcomes among inner city women. *Journal of Personality and Social Psychology, 84*(3), 632–643. http://dx.doi.org/10.1037/0022-3514.84.3.632

Holman, D., Totterdell, P., Axtell, C., Stride, C., Port, R., Svensson, R., & Zibarras, L. (2012). Job design and the employee innovation process: The mediating role of learning strategies. *Journal of Business and Psychology, 27*, 177–191. http://dx.doi.org/10.1007/s10869-011-9242-5

Huang, Y., Xu, S., Hua, J., Zhu, D., Liu, C., Hu, Y., et al. (2015). Association between job strain and risk of incident stroke. *Neurology, 85*, 1–7. http://dx.doi.org/10.1212/WNL.0000000000002098

Humphrey, S. E., Nahrgang, J. D., & Morgeson, F. P. (2007). Integrating motivational, social, and contextual work design features: A meta-analytic summary and theoretical extension of the work design literature. *Journal of Applied Psychology, 92*(5), 1332–1356. http://dx.doi.org/10.1037/0021-9010.92.5.1332

Ilgen, D. R., & Hollenbeck, J. R. (1992). The structure of work: Job design and roles. In M. D. Dunnette & L. M. Hough (Eds.), *Handbook of industrial and organizational psychology* (2d ed., Vol. 2, pp. 165–207). Palo Alto, CA: Consulting Psychologists Press.

Jahoda, M. (1982). *Employment and unemployment: A social-psychological analysis.* Cambridge: Cambridge University Press.

Johns, G., Xie, J. L., & Gang, Y. (1992). Mediating and moderating effects in job design. *Journal of Management, 18*(4), 657–676.

Kahn, R. L., Wolfe, D. M., Quinn, R. P., Snoek, J. D., & Rosenthal, R. A. (1964). *Occupational stress: Studies in role conflict and ambiguity.* New York: John Wiley and Sons.

Karasek, R. A. (1979). Job demands, job decision latitude, and mental strain: Implications for job redesign. *Administrative Science Quarterly, 24*, 285–308.

Kim, T. H., & Han, E. (2015). Impact of body mass on job quality. *Economics and Human Biology, 17*, 75–85. http://dx.doi.org/10.1016/j.ehb.2015.02.003

Krings, F., Sczesny, S., & Kluge, A. (2011). Stereotypical inferences as mediators of age discrimination: The role of competence and warmth. *British Journal of Management, 22*(2), 187–201. http://dx.doi.org/10.1111/j.1467-8551.2010.00721.x

Kristof-Brown, A. L., Zimmerman, R. D., & Johnson, E. C. (2005). Consequences of individuals' fit at work: A meta-analysis of person-job, person-organization, person-group and person-supervisor fit. *Personnel Psychology, 58*, 281–342.

Langfred, C. W. (2007). The downside of self-management: A longitudinal study of the effects of conflict on trust, autonomy and task interdependence in self-managing teams. *The Academy of Management Journal, 50*(4), 885–900.

Lepine, J. A., Podsakoff, N. P., & Lepine, M. A. (2005). A meta-analytic test of the challenge stressor–hindrance stressor framework: An explanation for inconsistent relationships among stressors and performance. *Academy of Management Journal, 48*(5), 764–775.

Lorenz, E., & Valeyre, A. (2005). Organisational innovation, human resource management and labour market structure: A comparison of the EU-15. *The Journal of Industrial Relations, 47*(4), 424–442. http://dx.doi.org/10.1111/j.1472-9296.2005.00183.x

Mäkikangas, A., Feldt, T., & Kinnunen, U. (2007). Warr's scale of job-related affective well-being: A longitudinal examination of its structure and relationships with work characteristics. *Work & Stress, 21*(3), 197–219. http://dx.doi.org/10.1080/02678370701662151

Mäkikangas, A., & Kinnunen, U. (2003). Psychosocial work stressors and well-being: Self-esteem and optimism as moderators in a one-year longitudinal sample. *Personality and Individual Differences, 35,* 537–557.

Marinova, S. V., Peng, C., Lorinkova, N., Van Dyne, L., & Chiaburu, D. (2015). Change-oriented behavior: A meta-analysis of individual and job design predictors. *Journal of Vocational Behavior, 88,* 104–120. http://dx.doi.org/10.1016/j.jvb.2015.02.006

Maslow, A. H. (1954). *Motivation and personality.* New York: Harper & Row.

McGregor, D. (1960). *The human side of enterprise.* New York: McGraw-Hill.

Meier, L. L., Semmer, N. K., Elfering, A., & Jacobshagen, N. (2008). The double meaning of control: Three-way interactions between internal resources, job control, and stressors at work. *Journal of Occupational Health Psychology, 13*(3), 244–258. http://dx.doi.org/10.1037/1076-8998.13.3.244

Morgeson, F. P., & Humphrey, S. E. (2006). The Work Design Questionnaire (WDQ): Developing and validating a comprehensive measure for assessing job design and the nature of work. *Journal of Applied Psychology, 91*(6), 1321–1339. http://dx.doi.org/10.1037/0021-9010.91.6.1321

Nahrgang, J. D., Morgeson, F. P., & Hofmann, D. A. (2011). Safety at work: A meta-analytic investigation of the link between job demands, job resources, burnout, engagement, and safety outcomes. *The Journal of Applied Psychology, 96*(1), 71–94. http://dx.doi.org/10.1037/a0021484

Niessen, C., Sonnentag, S., & Friederike, S. (2012). Thriving at work—A diary study. *Journal of Organizational Behavior, 33,* 468–487. http://dx.doi.org/10.1002/job

Oldham, G. R., Hackman, J. R., & Pearce, J. L. (1976). Conditions under which employees respond positively to enriched work. *Journal of Applied Psychology, 61*(4), 395–403. http://dx.doi.org/10.1037/0021-9010.61.4.395

Parker, S. K. (1998). Enhancing role breadth self-efficacy: The roles of job enrichment and other organizational interventions. *The Journal of Applied Psychology, 83*(6), 835–852. Retrieved from http://www.ncbi.nlm.nih.gov/pubmed/9885197

Parker, S. K. (2014). Beyond motivation: Job and work design for development, health, ambidexterity, and more. *Annual Review of Psychology, 65,* 661–691. http://dx.doi.org/10.1146/annurev-psych-010213-115208

Parker, S. K., Bindl, U. K., & Strauss, K. (2010). Making things happen: A model of proactive motivation. *Journal of Management, 36*(4), 827–856. http://dx.doi.org/10.1177/0149206310363732

Parker, S. K., Holman, D., & Van den Broeck, A. (2017). Work design influences: A synthesis of multi-level factors that affect the design of work. *Academy of Management Annals, 11,* 267–308. http://dx.doi.org/10.5465/annals.2014.0054

Parker, S. K., Morgeson, F. P., & Johns, G. (2017). One hundred years of work design research: Looking back and looking forward. *Journal of Applied Psychology, 102*(3), 403–420.

Parker, S. K., & Sprigg, C. A. (1999). Minimizing strain and maximizing learning: The role of job demands, job conrol, and proactive personality. *Journal of Applied Psychology, 84*(6), 925–939.

Parker, S. K., Wall, T. D., & Cordery, J. L. (2001). Future work design research and practice: Towards an elaborated model of work design. *Journal of Occupational and Organizational Psychology, 74,* 413–440.

Parker, S. K., Wall, T. D., & Jackson, P. R. (2016). "That's Not My Job": Developing flexible employee work orientations. *Academy of Management Journal, 40*(4), 899–929.

Parker, S. K., Williams, H. M., & Turner, N. (2006). Modeling the antecedents of proactive behavior at work. *Journal of Applied Psychology, 91*(3), 636–652. http://dx.doi.org/10.1037/0021-9010.91.3.636

Pasmore, W. A. (1995). Social science transformed: The socio-technical perspective. *Human Relations, 48*(1), 1–21.

Pierce, J. R., & Aguinis, H. (2011). The too-much-of-a-good-thing effect in management. *Journal of Management, 39*(2), 313–338. http://dx.doi.org/10.1177/0149206311410060

Podsakoff, N. P., Podsakoff, P. M., MacKenzie, S. B., Maynes, T. D., & Spoelma, T. M. (2014). Consequences of unit-level organizational citizenship behaviors: A review and recommendations for future research. *Journal of Organizational Behavior, 35*, 87–119.

Podskaoff, P. M., Mackenzie, S. B., Paine, J. B., & Bachrach, D. G. (2000). Organizational citizenship behaviors: A critical review of the theoretical and future research. *Journal of Management, 26*(3), 513–563.

Rodríguez, I., Kozusnik, M. W., & Peiro, J. M. (2013). Development and validation of the Valencia Eustress-Distress Appraisal Scale. *International Journal of Stress Management, 20*(4), 279–308. http://dx.doi.org/10.1037/a0034330

Rousseau, D. M. (2001). Flexibility versus fairness? *Organizational Dynamics, 29*(4), 260–273.

Rydstedt, L. W., Ferrie, J., & Head, J. (2006). Is there support for curvilinear relationships between psychosocial work characteristics and mental well-being? Cross-sectional and long-term data from the Whitehall II study. *Work and Stress, 20*(1), 6–20. http://dx.doi.org/10.1080/02678370600668119

Salanova, M., Agut, S., & Peiró, J. M. (2005). Linking organizational resources and work engagement to employee performance and customer loyalty: The mediation of service climate. *The Journal of Applied Psychology, 90*(6), 1217–1227. http://dx.doi.org/10.1037/0021-9010.90.6.1217

Schaufeli, W. B., & Bakker, A. B. (2004). Job demands, job resources, and their relationship with burnout and engagement: A multi-sample study. *Journal of Organizational Behavior, 25*, 293–315.

Seligman, M. E. P., & Csikszentmihalyi, M. (2000). Positive psychology: An introduction. *American Psychologist, 55*(1), 5–14. http://dx.doi.org/10.1037//0003-066X.55.1.5

Tarafdar, M., D'Arcy, J., Turel, O., & Gupta, A. (2015). The dark side of information technology. *MIT Sloan Management Review, 56*(2), 61–70. Retrieved from http://mitsmr.com/1wD3N7E.

Taris, T. W. (2006). Bricks without clay: On urban myths in occupational health psychology. *Work & Stress, 20*(2), 99–104. http://dx.doi.org/10.1080/02678370600893410

Taylor, F. W. (2004). *Scientific management*. London: Routledge.

Terkel, S. (Ed.). (1974). *Working: People talk about what they do all day and how they feel about what they do*. New York: The New Press.

Then, F. S., Luck, T., Luppa, M., Thinschmidt, M., Deckert, S., Nieuwenhuijsen, K., et al. (2014). Systematic review of the effect of the psychosocial working environment on cognition and dementia. *Occupational and Environmental Medicine, 71*(5), 358–365. http://dx.doi.org/10.1136/oemed-2013-101760

Theorell, T., & Karasek, R. A. (1996). Current issues relating to psychosocial job strain and cardiovascular disease research. *Journal of Occupational Health Psychology, 1*(1), 9–26. http://dx.doi.org/10.1037/1076-8998.1.1.9

Tornau, K., & Frese, M. (2013). Construct clean-up in proactivity research: A meta-analysis on the nomological net of work-related proactivity concepts and their incremental validities. *Applied Psychology: An International Review, 62*(1), 44–96. http://dx.doi.org/10.1111/j.1464-0597.2012.00514.x

Van de Ven, B., De Jonge, J., & Vlerick, P. (2014). Testing the triple-match principle in the technology sector: A two-wave longitudinal panel study. *Applied Psychology, 63*(2), 300–325. http://dx.doi.org/10.1111/j.1464-0597.2012.00523.x

Van den Broeck, A., Baillien, E., & De Witte, H. (2011). Workplace bullying: A perspective from the Job Demands-Resources model. *South African Journal of Industrial Psychology, 37*(2), 1–12. http://dx.doi.org/10.4102/sajip.v37i2.879

Van den Broeck, A., De Cuyper, N., De Witte, H., & Vansteenkiste, M. (2010). Not all job demands are equal: Differentiating job hindrances and job challenges in the Job Demands–Resources model. *European Journal of Work and Organizational Psychology, 19*(6), 735–759. http://dx.doi.org/10.1080/13594320903223839

Van den Broeck, A., De Cuyper, N., Luyckx, K., & De Witte, H. (2012). Employees' job demands–resources profiles, burnout and work engagement: A person-centred examination. *Economic Industrial Democracy, 33*(4), 691–706.

Van den Broeck, A., Schreurs, B., Guenter, H., & van Emmerik, I. H. (2015). Skill utilization and well-being: A cross-level story of day-to-day fluctuations and personal intrinsic values. *Work & Stress, 29*(3), 306–323. http://dx.doi.org/10.1080/02678373.2015.1074955

Van den Broeck, A., Suela, C., Vander Elst, T., Fischmann, G., Iliescu, D., & De Witte, H. (2014). The mediating role of psychological needs in the relation between qualitative job insecurity and counterproductive work behavior. *Career Development International, 19*(5), 526–547. http://dx.doi.org/10.1108/CDI-05-2013-0063

Van den Broeck, A., Van Ruysseveldt, J., Smulders, P., & De Witte, H. (2011). Does an intrinsic work value orientation strengthen the impact of job resources? A perspective from the Job Demands–Resources model. *European Journal of Work and Organizational Psychology, 20*(5), 581–609. http://dx.doi.org/10.1080/13594321003669053

Van den Broeck, A., Van Ruysseveldt, J., Vanbelle, E., & De Witte, H. (2013). The Job Demands–Resources model: Overview and suggestions for future research. In A. B. Bakker (Ed.), *Advances in positive organizational psychology* (Vol. 1, pp. 83–105). Bingley, U.K.: Emerald Group.

Van den Broeck, A., Vansteenkiste, M., De Witte, H., & Lens, W. (2008). Explaining the relationships between job characteristics, burnout, and engagement: The role of basic psychological need satisfaction. *Work & Stress, 22*(3), 277–294. http://dx.doi.org/10.1080/02678370802393672

van den Heuvel, M., Demerouti, E., Bakker, A. B., & Schaufeli, W. B. (2010). Personal resources and work engagement in the face of change. *Contemporary Occupational Health Psychology: Global Perspectives on Research and Practice, 1*, 124–150.

van den Heuvel, M., Demerouti, E., Bakker, A. B., & Schaufeli, W. B. (2013). Adapting to change: The value of change information and meaning-making. *Journal of Vocational Behavior, 83*(1), 11–21. http://dx.doi.org/10.1016/j.jvb.2013.02.004

Van der Doef, M., & Maes, S. (1998). The job demand-control (-support) model and physical health outcomes: A review of the strain and buffer hypotheses. *Psychology & Health, 13*(5), 909–936. http://dx.doi.org/10.1080/08870449808407440

Van der Doef, M., & Maes, S. (1999). The job demand-control (-support) model and psychological well-being: A review of 20 years of empirical research. *Work & Stress, 13*(2), 87–114. http://dx.doi.org/10.1080/026783799296084

Van Mierlo, H., Rutte, C. G., Vermunt, J. K., Kompier, M. A. J., & Doorewaard, J. A. C. M. (2007). A multilevel mediation model of the relationships between team autonomy, individual task design and psychological well-being. *Journal of Occupational and Organizational Psychology, 80*(4), 647–664. http://dx.doi.org/10.1348/096317907X196886

Van Veldhoven, M., Prins, J., Van der Laken, P., & Dijkstra, L. (2016). *Manual QEEW2.0: 42 short scales for survey research on work, well-being and performance.* Amsterdam: SKB.

Wageman, R. (1997). Critical success factors for creating superb teams. *Organizational Dynamics, 26*, 49–61. http://dx.doi.org/10.1016/s0090-2616(97)90027-9

Walker, C. R., & Guest, R. H. (1952). *The man on the assembly line.* Cambridge, MA: Harvard University Press.

Wall, T. D., & Stephenson, G. M. (1970). Herzberg's two-factor theory of job attitudes: A critical evaluation and some fresh evidence. *Industrial Relations Journal, 1*(3), 41–65. http://dx.doi.org/10.1111/j.1468-2338.1970.tb00262.x

Warr, P. (1987). *Work, unemployment, and mental health.* Oxford: Clarendon Press.

Webster, J. R., Beehr, T. A., & Christiansen, N. D. (2010). Toward a better understanding of the effects of hindrance and challenge stressors on work behavior. *Journal of Vocational Behavior, 76*(1), 68–77. http://dx.doi.org/10.1016/j.jvb.2009.06.012

Wright, B. M., & Cordery, J. L. (1999). Production uncertainty as a contextual moderator of employee reactions to job design. *The Journal of Applied Psychology, 84*(3), 456–463. http://dx.doi.org/10.1037/0021-9010.84.3.456

Wrzesniewski, A., & Dutton, J. E. (2001). Crafting a job: Revisioning employees as active crafters of their work. *The Academy of Management Review, 26*(2), 179–201. http://dx.doi.org/10.2307/259118

Wu, C. H. (2016). Personality change via work: A job demand-control model of Big-Five personality changes. *Journal of Vocational Behavior, 92,* 157–166. http://dx.doi.org/10.1016/j.jvb.2015.12.001

Xanthopoulou, D., Bakker, A. B., Demerouti, E., & Schaufeli, W. B. (2007). The role of personal resources in the job demands-resources model. *International Journal of Stress Management, 14*(2), 121–141. http://dx.doi.org/10.1037/1072-5245.14.2.121

Xanthopoulou, D., Bakker, A. B., Demerouti, E., & Schaufeli, W. B. (2009). Work engagement and financial returns: A diary study on the role of job and personal resources. *Journal of Occupational and Organizational Psychology, 82*(1), 183–200. http://dx.doi.org/10.1348/096317908X285633

Xie, J. L., & Johns, G. (1995). Job scope and stress: Can job scope be too high? *Academy of Management Journal, 38*(5), 1288–1309.

Anja Van den Broeck and Sharon K. Parker

JOB CRAFTING

Work design is defined as the content and organization of an individual's tasks, activities, relationships, and responsibilities at work (Parker, 2014). The importance of work design has been established, with work design affecting various individual and organizational outcomes such as job satisfaction, performance, and innovation (see a meta-analysis by Humphrey et al., 2007). However, with technological and economic developments, organizational environments today have become highly uncertain and complex. This has brought about difficulties for organizations to design jobs that fit all employees (Grant & Parker, 2009). Additionally, changes like globalization, downsizing, and an increase in temporary employment highlight the need for workers to be responsible for their own development at work (Grant & Parker, 2009; Lee & Lee, 2018; Tims & Knight, 2019).

Responding to these changes in the contemporary workplace, scholars have proposed the concept of job crafting, defined as self-initiated behaviors that employees take to shape, mold, and change their jobs (Tims & Bakker, 2010; Tims et al., 2012; Wrzesniewski & Dutton, 2001). As a bottom-up approach of work redesign, job crafting has been acknowledged as a major advance in work design theory. Several systematic reviews and meta-analyses have summarized the benefits of job crafting for those who engage in this behavior, such as increased job satisfaction, work engagement, job performance, meaningfulness, and occupational identity (e.g., Lazazzaraa et al., 2020; Lee & Lee, 2018; Rudolph et al., 2017; Zhang & Parker, 2019). This article aims to review job crafting in greater depth by discussing job crafting concepts and measurement and providing an overview of key empirical studies.

DEFINING JOB CRAFTING

Job crafting can be defined at both the individual level and team level. In this section, definitions and constructs of individual job crafting and team job crafting are described, as well as efforts that have been made to integrate two disparate job crafting perspectives.

Individual Job Crafting. The term *job crafting* was first coined by Wrzesniewski and Dutton (2001) who defined it as "the physical and cognitive changes individuals make in the task or relational boundaries of their work" (p. 179). This perspective postulates three types of job crafting. First, *task crafting* includes changing the number, scope, or type of tasks that an individual undertakes at work (e.g., an individual might take on more tasks at work than asked). Second, *relational crafting* includes changing the quality and/or the amount of interaction with others at work (e.g., an employee interacts more with those who are impacted by his/her work). Third, *cognitive crafting* involves altering how employees view or frame their jobs (e.g., teachers might frame their jobs as supporting the development of future generations rather than just imparting knowledge). According to Wrzesniewski and Dutton (2001), the motivation for job crafting emerges from three basic psychological needs: for autonomy, positive self-image, and relatedness. In addition, job crafting behaviors lead to changes in the meaning of work; that is, individuals' understandings of the purpose of their work or what they believe is achieved in the work, as well as changes in the crafter's work identity (i.e., how one defines oneself; Wrzesniewski & Dutton, 2001).

A second and equally popular job crafting perspective was developed by Tims and Bakker (2010), who applied the job demands-resources theory (JD-R; Bakker & Demerouti, 2007) to define job crafting. According to the JD-R theory (Bakker & Demerouti, 2007), employee well-being and effectiveness can be impacted by two working conditions, namely, job demands and job resources. *Job demands* refer to the physical, psychological, social, and organizational aspects of work (e.g., high work pressure, lack of job security) that require sustained physical or psychological effort and lead to physiological and psychological costs. Alternatively, *job resources* refer to the physical, psychological, social, and organizational aspects of work (e.g., autonomy, task significance) that help people achieve work goals, reduce job demands and their impact, or encourage personal growth and development. Based on the JD-R theory, Tims and Bakker (2010) defined job crafting as "the changes that employees may make to balance their job demands and job resources with their personal abilities and preferences" (p. 4). Specifically, Tims and colleagues (2012) proposed four types of job crafting: *increasing structural job resources* (e.g., initiating actions to increase the level of autonomy in one's job), *increasing social job resources* (e.g., asking supervisors for feedback), *increasing challenging job demands* (e.g., volunteering to participate in new projects), and *decreasing hindering job demands* (e.g., reducing the interaction with a demanding customer at work). As of the late 2010s, more research has been undertaken using the Tims and Bakker (2010) perspective of job crafting when compared to the perspective of Wrzesniewski and Dutton (2001), likely because of the prevalence of the JD-R theory (Kooij et al., 2017; Tims & Knight, 2019).

While both job crafting perspectives commonly define job crafting as a bottom-up approach to change the content and structure of work (Lichtenthaler & Fischbach, 2019), there are significant differences between the two perspectives. First, while Wrzesniewski and Dutton (2001) focused on the task and relational boundaries, Tims et al. (2012) focused on job characteristics such as job demands and job resources. Second, while Wrzesniewski and Dutton (2001) considered cognitive crafting as a form of job crafting, Tims and Bakker (2010) highlighted that only actual changes in job characteristics should be included in job crafting, suggesting that job crafting is a behavior rather than a perception. Third, while Tims et al. (2012)

explicitly mentioned making one's job smaller by decreasing hindering job demands, Wrzesniewski and Dutton (2001) only subtly touched upon this aspect when they mention the reduction in the number of tasks (task crafting) and relationships (relationship crafting) as different types of job crafting (Tims & Knight, 2019). Fourth, these perspectives differ in terms of the aims of job crafting, with Wrzesniewski and Dutton (2001) highlighting the importance of job crafting for improving meaning and work identity, with Tims et al. (2012) arguing that the aim of job crafting is to balance the job demands and resources to attain a better person–job fit (Zhang & Parker, 2019).

The differences between the two key job crafting perspectives have led to challenges in the literature, such as a lack of clarity over which behaviors can be classified as job crafting, a lack of consensus over whether cognitive crafting is a form of job crafting, difficulty in differentiating the construct of job crafting from other similar constructs (e.g., personal initiative), and confusion regarding the measurement of job crafting due to the existence of multiple definitions (Zhang & Parker, 2019). Scholars have made efforts to overcome these challenges. To clarify what is job crafting and what is not, Bruning and Campion (2018) defined job crafting as "the changes (structural, cognitive, or social) that individuals make to their jobs with the intention of improving the job for themselves" (p. 500). They highlighted six common characteristics of job crafting based on both perspectives: (a) job crafting is self-targeted and intended to benefit individuals; (b) it involves volitional, conscious, and noticeable change; (c) there should be a noticeable difference in the job post-crafting; (d) it should result in semipermanent or permanent changes; (e) it should bring changes to the job role; and (f) it can be applied to a job with a clear description and specified tasks rather than self-created jobs (Bruning & Campion, 2018).

A further effort of integrating the existing perspectives of job crafting has been made by Zhang and Parker (2019) who introduced a hierarchical model of job crafting. The hierarchical model includes three levels that integrated yet distinguish diverse types of job crafting. The first level is job crafting orientation, indicating that job crafting can either be approach-oriented or avoidance-oriented. Approach-oriented crafting involves active and effortful activities that are directed toward problem-focused and improvement-based goals, leading to the expansion and enrichment of job boundaries (Bruning & Campion, 2018; Zhang & Parker, 2019). For example, an employee may attend more training workshops to acquire new skills. Avoidance crafting, on the other hand, refers to reducing or limiting job boundaries. It helps in evading, reducing, or eliminating certain aspects of one's work (Bruning & Campion, 2018; Zhang & Parker, 2019). For example, an employee might reduce the number of client interactions at work to limit the social boundary of work. The second level differentiates between the forms of job crafting by distinguishing between behavioral and cognitive crafting. Cognitive crafting is self-initiated, self-targeted, intentional, and represents meaningful changes to the job aspects (Wrzesniewski & Dutton, 2001), thus is one type of job crafting (Zhang & Parker, 2019). For example, employees may reframe customer complaints as opportunities for feedback and improvement in performance. Conversely, behavioral crafting refers to making changes to the physical aspects of work such as task or relational boundaries. For example, an employee might avoid participating in projects that require regular travel to maintain his work–life balance. Finally, the third level distinguishes the content of job crafting with respect to the target as changes to job resources or job demands. This hierarchical model is advantageous as it includes all existing types of job crafting, as well as some new types. It also highlights that the most important distinction is the approach versus avoidance crafting as these lead to different outcomes and have different antecedents (Zhang & Parker, 2019).

Team Job Crafting.   The increased use of teams in organizations suggests that most of the tasks that individuals perform at work are in a team setting, making teams a basic unit of work accomplishment (Mäkikangas et al., 2016; Tims et al., 2013). The interdependence between different members of the team in an organization has consequences for individual action. For example, the job crafting behaviors undertaken by an individual may also impact other team members (Tims et al., 2013). With the interdependence of working in a team, individuals can also engage in job crafting as a team (Leana et al., 2009; Tims et al., 2013). Leana et al. (2009) extended Wrzesniewski and Dutton's (2001) perspective to include collaborative crafting which refers to "how employees work together to make physical or cognitive changes to the task and relational boundaries at work" (p.1173). Similarly, Tims et al. (2013) defined team crafting as "the extent to which team members combine their efforts in order to increase structural and social job resources and challenging job demands and decrease their hindering job demands" (p. 432). This may include, for example, deciding together what job resources are required by the team as a whole to achieve their tasks and how these can be collectively mobilized.

Team crafting is not the same as the sum of the individual team members' job crafting. Team job crafting does not imply that all group members need to deal with the same job resources and demands. Instead, it focuses on the collective decisions regarding what and how to craft (Tims et al., 2013) and is more than just simply discussing and setting the team's daily agenda; it aims to bring changes to the psychosocial job characteristics at work. Moreover, team crafting and individual crafting are not mutually exclusive and thus can be undertaken simultaneously by individuals in organizations (Mäkikangas et al., 2017). Research has found that individual job crafting can pave the way for collective job crafting (Mattarelli & Tagliaventi, 2012). Conversely, a positive relationship between team job crafting and individual job crafting also suggests that the team members' beliefs regarding expected behaviors can also influence and guide their individual behaviors (Tims et al., 2013).

MEASURING JOB CRAFTING

Numerous scales for measuring aspects of job crafting have been developed, either based on Wrzesniewski and Dutton's (2001) perspective (e.g., Niessen et al., 2016; Slemp & Vella-Brodrick, 2013), or Tims and Bakker's (2010) perspective (e.g., Nielsen et al., 2017; Petrou et al., 2012; see Table 1). Most of the job crafting scales are multidimensional, with a couple of exceptions (e.g., Bizzi, 2017; Leana et al., 2009). Costantini et al. (2021) highlighted that most of the quantitative research on job crafting has been based on the job demands-resources perspective (Tims & Bakker, 2010).

With progress in the conceptualization of job crafting constructs, some scholars have developed job crafting scales to reflect the approach and avoidance orientation of job crafting behaviors. For example, adopting the job crafting framework proposed by Wrzesniewski and

712 • JOB CRAFTING

Table 1. Job Crafting Scales

Authors	Dimensions and sample items
Leana et al. (2009)	**Individual job crafting** (6 items): e.g., "on your own, change the way you do your job to make it easier for yourself."
Bizzi (2017)	**Job crafting** (task crafting) (8 items): e.g., "I introduced new approaches on my own to improve my work."
Slemp and Vella-Brodrick (2013)	**Task crafting** (5 items): e.g., "change the scope or types of tasks that you complete at work." **Relational crafting** (5 items): e.g., "make friends with people at work who have similar skills or interests." **Cognitive crafting** (5 items): e.g., "remind yourself of the importance of your work for the broader community."
Niessen et al. (2016)	**Task crafting**: e.g., "I undertake or seek for additional tasks." **Relational crafting**: e.g., "I look for opportunities to work together with people whom I get along well with at work." **Cognitive crafting**: e.g., "I find personal meaning in my tasks and responsibilities at work."
Weseler and Niessen (2016)	**Task crafting-extending**: e.g., "I work more intensively on tasks I enjoy." **Task crafting-reducing**: e.g., "I pass on tasks that do not really suit me." **Relational crafting-extending**: e.g., "I invest in relationships with people whom I get along with the best." **Relational crafting-reducing**: e.g., "I communicate less with people who do not fully support my personal work objectives." **Cognitive crafting**: e.g., "I view my tasks and responsibilities as being more than just part of my job."
Bruning and Campion (2018)	**Work role expansion**: e.g., "expand my role by providing opinions on important issues." **Work organization**: e.g., "create structure in my work processes." **Adoption**: e.g., "use new knowledge or technology to enhance communication." **Metacognition**: e.g., "use my thoughts to put myself into a good mood at work." **Work role reduction**: e.g., "find ways to get others to take my place in meetings." **Social expansion**: e.g., "actively initiate positive interactions with others at work." **Withdrawal**: e.g., "work in a way that allows me to avoid others at work."
Bindl et al. (2019)	**Promotion-oriented task crafting**: e.g., "I actively took on more tasks in my work." **Prevention-oriented task crafting**: e.g., "I actively reduced the scope of tasks I worked on." **Promotion-oriented relational crafting**: e.g., "I actively sought to meet new people at work." **Prevention-oriented relational crafting**: e.g., "I changed my work so that I only interacted with people that I felt good about working with."

JOB CRAFTING · 713

Table 1. Continued

Authors	Dimensions and sample items
	Promotion-oriented cognitive crafting: e.g., "I thought about new ways of viewing my overall job."
	Prevention-oriented cognitive crafting: e.g., "I focused my mind on the best parts of my job, while trying to ignore those parts I didn't like."
	Promotion-oriented skill crafting: e.g., "I actively explored new skills to do my overall job."
	Prevention-oriented skill crafting: e.g., "I made sure I stayed on top of knowledge in core areas of my job."
Tims et al. (2012)	**Increasing structural job resources**: e.g., "I try to develop my capabilities." **Increasing social job resources**: e.g., "I ask my supervisor to coach me." **Increasing challenging demands**: e.g., "when an interesting project comes along, I offer myself proactively as project coworker." **Decreasing hindering demands**: e.g., "I make sure that my work is mentally less intense."
Petrou et al. (2012)	**Seeking resources**: e.g., "I ask others for feedback on my job performance." **Seeking challenges**: e.g., "I ask for more tasks if I finish my work." **Reducing demands**: e.g., "I try to ensure that my work is emotionally less intense."
Nielsen et al. (2017)	**Increasing challenging demands**: e.g., "when a new task comes up I sign up for it." **Decreasing social demands**: e.g., "I try to avoid emotionally challenging situations with my customers." **Increasing social job resources**: e.g., "I ask my supervisor whether s/he is satisfied with the work I do." **Increasing quantitative demands**: e.g., "I ask colleagues for their advice." **Decreasing hindrance job demands**: e.g., "I organize my work so I don't get too stressed out."
Leana et al. (2009)	**Collaborative job crafting**: e.g., "decide together with your coworkers to change the way you do your job to make it easier to yourself."
Tims et al. (2013)	**Team crafting increasing job resources and challenging demands**: e.g., "my team asks others for advice." **Team crafting decreasing hindering demands**

Dutton (2001), Bindl et al. (2019) developed a job crafting scale including both promotion and prevention job crafting behaviors.

Scales on team job crafting are less developed than individual job crafting. There are two main team job crafting scales, with one developed by Leana et al. (2009) based on Wrzesniewski and Dutton's (2001) perspective and the other based on the job demands-resources perspective developed by Tims et al. (2013). Table 1 provides an overview of the existing scales of individual and team job crafting.

IMPORTANT INSIGHTS INTO JOB CRAFTING RESEARCH

There have been several systematic reviews (Lazazzaraa et al., 2020; Lee & Lee, 2018; Zhang & Parker, 2019) and meta-analyses (Lichtenthaler & Fischbach, 2019; Rudolph et al., 2017) to synthesize antecedents and outcomes of individual job crafting. Beyond antecedents and outcomes of job crafting that have been systematically reviewed in the literature, studies on job crafting have also provided more insights into job crafting literature.

EMPIRICALLY TESTING THE RELATIONSHIPS OF DIFFERENT JOB CRAFTING CONSTRUCTS

The two different job crafting perspectives and numerous job crafting measures have brought about difficulties in synthesizing the research on the antecedents, outcomes, and mechanisms of job crafting (Zhang & Parker, 2019). Moreover, the use of many different measures and the criteria for adapting them also reduces the chances of moving toward a reliable understanding of the phenomenon itself (Costantini et al., 2021). Therefore, it is important to explore how these job crafting constructs in different measures might be interrelated and whether they are related to any higher-order dimensions (Zhang & Parker, 2019). Scholars have begun to empirically test the interrelationships of job crafting dimensions from different perspectives based on the theoretical integration of job crafting by Zhang and Parker (2019).

One such effort to validate existing behavioral job crafting scales has been made by Costantini et al. (2021). Zhang and Parker (2019) have argued that some job crafting dimensions are reflective while some are formative. Reflective constructs are those in which causality follows from the latent construct to the indicators such that any change to the underlying latent construct causes variation in the indicators. In contrast to this, formative constructs are those that are formed by combining a number of indicators without any assumption of intercorrelation between these items (Coltman et al., 2008). Formative constructs are also defined as aggregate constructs that are composites of the dimensions and form more general concepts (e.g., approach and avoidance crafting or cognitive and behavioral crafting). These constructs are not conceptually or empirically interchangeable. In contrast, reflective or superordinate constructs are defined by their dimensions (e.g., demands crafting and resources crafting) that are conceptually related to one another (Zhang & Parker, 2019). Applying the hierarchical framework of job crafting (Zhang & Parker, 2019), Costantini et al. (2021) proposed four lower-order reflective factors or job crafting behaviors: increasing resources, seeking challenges, decreasing demands, and optimizing demands. Optimizing demands is a new job crafting strategy proposed by Demerouti and Peeters (2018), defined as the active efforts to make work processes more efficient (e.g., to improve the workflow to better manage workload). At the middle level, seeking resources and seeking challenges form the expansion strategies, while decreasing demands and optimizing demands form contraction strategies, which are two second-order formative factors. Finally, at the topmost level, the expansion strategies and contraction strategies together contribute to one third-order formative factor, the behavioral job crafting construct (Costantini et al., 2021). Findings from Costantini et al. (2021) supported the multidimensional hierarchical structure of job crafting proposed by Zhang and Parker (2019). In addition, this paper also revealed that seeking resources, seeking challenges, and optimizing demands were all positively related to overall behavioral job crafting while reducing demands was negatively related to overall behavioral job crafting, reflecting the withdrawal and avoidance nature of reducing demands.

Similarly, building on this work of Costantini et al. (2020), Ebert and Bipp (2021) used multiple measures from both job crafting perspectives. Their findings supported the existence of the higher order of approach and avoidance factors. In addition, the authors found that the approach factor and avoidance factor were not significantly associated, which further supported the distinction between approach crafting and avoidance crafting suggested by Zhang and Parker (2019). Ebert and Bipp (2021) also tested the relationships of job crafting dimensions from different perspectives. Results showed several significant associations, such as between task crafting and increasing structural resources and decreasing hindering demands, and between cognitive crafting and increasing challenging demands and decreasing hindering demands, with the highest correlation $r = .32$ between task crafting and increasing structural resources. However, there were no significant relationships for task crafting and increasing challenging demands, or relational crafting and increasing social resources, which were expected to be significant (Ebert & Bipp, 2021). The authors concluded that the two job crafting perspectives may not share a common underlying core of job crafting and contain their own specific job crafting elements.

Another attempt to explore how divergent theoretical views on job crafting could be integrated has been made by Hu et al. (2020). The authors compared five different job crafting measures from the two theoretical perspectives (Tims & Bakker, 2010; Wrzesniewski & Dutton, 2001). The results suggested that the job crafting measures are largely composed of approach-oriented crafting behaviors. Job crafting behaviors that are targeted to reduce job demands are operationalized inconsistently across different measures. Some measures used items with an active coping component that measure more facilitative forms of avoidance behaviors (e.g., *I make sure that my work is mentally less intense*, in the job crafting scale of Tims et al., 2012), while some measures used more withdrawal-oriented items that are based on the avoidance of the situation or the task itself (e.g., *I pass on tasks that do not really suit me*, in the job crafting measure of Weseler & Niessen, 2016). These differences also led to different outcomes, with active coping crafting positively related to work engagement while withdrawal crafting negatively or nonsignificantly related to work engagement (Hu et al., 2020). Thus, active coping crafting, which is more approach-oriented, could be distinguished from withdrawal crafting. Moreover, measures based on the job demands-resources perspective showed a superior effect on work engagement over measures based on Wrzesniewski and Dutton's (2001) perspective. Similarly, behavioral crafting accounted for more variance in predicting work engagement over cognitive crafting.

While it has been widely acknowledged that job crafting is a multidimensional construct, some researchers have used overall job crafting by aggregating all job crafting dimensions. Zhang and Parker (2019) have cautioned that an aggregated job crafting score could be applied for reflective dimensions, but it is not suitable to aggregate job crafting dimensions that are formative (Zhang & Parker, 2019). Recently, Zampetakis (2022) conducted a study using both general and daily job crafting scales developed by Petrou et al. (2012) to explore whether an overall job crafting score exists. Results supported Zhang and Parker's (2019) argument, and Petrou et al. (2012) cautioned against using aggregated job crafting scores for both a general job crafting scale and daily job crafting scale. Further research is required to explore

NEW FORMS OF JOB CRAFTING

whether composite measures of job crafting exist and whether multiple dimensions of job crafting can be aggregated to provide a single job crafting score.

NEW FORMS OF JOB CRAFTING

Existing job crafting research, no matter which perspective it is based on, predominantly focused on the changes to one's job, the job part of the person–job fit. However, the role of "person" in the person–job fit has been underestimated. To achieve a better person–job fit, scholars have argued that individuals' attributes such as personal strengths and interests should be integrated into job crafting theory and research (Kooij et al., 2017). Based on this argument, Kooij et al. (2017) expanded the job crafting construct by highlighting the motives of job crafting. Specifically, they introduced two new forms of job crafting: *job crafting toward strengths* and *job crafting toward interests*. These two characteristics (strengths and interests) influence and guide the crafting efforts of individuals. Job crafting toward strengths refers to the self-initiated changes that individuals make to their work to better use their strengths (Kooij et al., 2017). For example, a teacher who might be better at teaching smaller groups would prefer to teach students in batches rather than a large number in one go. On the other hand, job crafting toward interests refers to the changing of jobs in such a way that it matches one's interests (Kooij et al., 2017). For example, an employee with an active interest in organizing and planning may actively participate in volunteer initiatives by organizing office programs and events. Expanding on this, Kuijpers et al. (2020) have identified a third goal of job crafting: *job crafting toward development*, defined as "the initiatives that employees take to realize their potential by creating developmental opportunities for themselves" (p. 3). For example, an employee who wishes to improve her communication might seek workshops and training to enhance her skills. These three new job crafting types can be placed into the job crafting hierarchical model (Zhang & Parker, 2019): they are approach-oriented behavioral crafting that aims to increase job resources and challenging demands.

The consideration of job crafting motives is important because job crafting behaviors that look, on the surface, the same in form may lead to different outcomes (Zhang et al., 2021). For example, an employee could proactively take on more tasks in the job to better utilize his/her strengths, to better fit his/her interests, or to develop new skills, which in turn could lead to different outcomes. There has been some empirical evidence regarding the different effects of job crafting with distinct motives. In their intervention study, Kooij et al. (2017) found that both strengths crafting and interests crafting were positively related to a needs–supplies fit because crafting behaviors could better satisfy employees' personal needs. However, only strengths crafting was positively related to a demands–abilities fit, maybe because the interests are not necessarily those that the employees are good at (Kooij et al., 2017). Interests crafting did not improve the fit between the requirements of the job and individuals' abilities.

Regarding well-being and performance, research has shown the unique effects of job crafting behaviors with different motives. Specifically, in a job crafting intervention study, Kuijpers et al. (2020) found that strengths crafting was positively related to three dimensions of work engagement, namely vigor, dedication, and absorption, while interests crafting was only associated with dedication and absorption, and developmental crafting was not significantly related to any dimension of work engagement. Moreover, using two-wave data, Zhang et al.

(2021) showed that both strengths crafting and interests crafting at Time 1 were positively related to Time 2 vitality, an indicator of individuals' sense of enthusiasm, aliveness, and energy (Ryan & Deci, 2008), but only strengths crafting was positively related to Time 2 task performance.

According to studies that have investigated the effects of job crafting with different aims, strengths crafting is the most effective job crafting strategy to improve employees' person–job fit, well-being, and performance. This is because strengths crafting allows individuals to perform at their personal best (Wood et al., 2011) and to focus on tasks that are authentic and energizing to them (Linley, 2008). Interests crafting is beneficial to employees' well-being as it can satisfy individuals' psychological needs (Zhang et al., 2021). However, interests crafting cannot improve employees' task performance, as when the interests are not individuals' strengths it involves experimentation and takes time for employees to perform their interests at their best (Zhang et al., 2021). Developmental crafting might be the most effortful strategy as it focuses on improving one's deficits, hence, it might cost more energy than it gives, which may explain the nonsignificant relationship between developmental crafting and work engagement (Kuijpers et al., 2020).

UNRAVELING THE COMPLICATED EFFECTS OF JOB CRAFTING

A great number of studies have investigated the effects of job crafting. There have been several meta-analyses (e.g., Lichtenthaler & Fischbach, 2019; Rudolph et al., 2017) and systematic reviews (e.g., Lee & Lee, 2018; Zhang & Parker, 2019) to synthesize findings of empirical studies on the effect of job crafting. In general, these meta-analyses and reviews have shown that approach crafting is beneficial to employees' well-being and performance, while avoidance crafting is not related to, or negatively associated with, employees' well-being and performance. This is because approach crafting aims to expand the positive aspects in the job and has a problem-solving focus, while avoidance crafting aims to keep away from the negative aspects in the job and is withdrawal-oriented (Zhang & Parker, 2019).

Recently, some scholars have challenged this idea and shown that approach crafting could have both positive and negative effects on employees' well-being. Using two-wave data, Harju et al. (2021) found that approach crafting was positively related to work engagement via increased job complexity, but it was also associated with increased burnout via increased workload. Bakker and Oerlemans (2019) conducted a diary study and showed that daily approach crafting was positively related to daily work engagement via daily satisfaction of psychological needs, while negatively related to daily work engagement via daily energy depletion. The two studies have shown that approach crafting could lead to both positive and negative outcomes via different mechanisms.

REVEALING THE INFLUENCES OF SOCIAL CONTEXT IN THE JOB CRAFTING PROCESS AND OUTCOMES

A great number of empirical studies have investigated factors that promote job crafting, including individual characteristics such as proactive personality (e.g., Bakker et al., 2012) and job characteristics such as job autonomy (e.g., Petrou et al., 2012). There has been an increasing number of studies investigating how social context influences job crafting as social elements play an important role in influencing employees' behaviors at work (Cai et al., 2019). Conducting a meta-analysis based on 51 empirical job crafting studies, Wang et al. (2020) found that positive leadership styles (e.g., servant leadership and empowering leadership) had the strongest correlation with employee approach crafting, followed by leader–member exchange and coworker support. These social factors were not significantly related to avoidance crafting.

Another emerging trend is to examine how supervisors and coworkers react to employees' job crafting behavior. For example, Fong et al. (2021) specifically investigated how supervisors reacted to employees' avoidance crafting. Conducting a dyadic supervisor–employee study and a vignette study, the authors found that employee avoidance crafting was positively related to a reduction of supervisor support. This relationship was mitigated by employee political skills. Individuals with high political skills could interact with their supervisors more effectively and avoid the negative reactions of supervisors (Fong et al., 2021).

Regarding coworkers' reaction to employee job crafting, Tims and Parker (2020) proposed a conceptual model (see Figure 1 in Tims & Parker, 2020) indicating how coworkers react and influence employee job crafting outcomes. Specifically, coworkers may or may not notice other employees' job crafting behaviors. When they do notice, they will evaluate whether the job crafting behaviors are relevant to them and the positive or negative impact of the job crafting on them, and then attribute a prosocial motive to the job crafter. If the job crafting behaviors have a negative impact on coworkers (e.g., one employee changed the workflow which may hinder the progress of coworkers' work), coworkers are likely to attribute a lack of prosocial motive to the job crafter. In contrast, when coworkers experience a positive impact of one employee's job crafting behaviors (e.g., one employee refined a work method that could be used by other employees), they are likely to attribute a prosocial motive to this job crafter as coworkers are likely to assume that the job crafter intended to benefit them (Tims & Parker, 2020). Employees' attribution of a prosocial motive of the job crafter is important as it affects coworkers' response to the job crafter. When coworkers attribute low prosocial motives to the job crafter, they are likely to show antagonism such as incivility and social undermining to the crafter. In contrast, when coworkers attribute high prosocial motives to the job crafter, they are likely to show more support (Tims & Parker, 2020).

CONSIDERING JOB CRAFTING IN DIFFERENT POPULATIONS AND CONTEXTS

Job crafting has been widely recognized as an effective strategy for employees to create a better job in different populations and occupations (Wrzesniewski & Dutton, 2001). One specific population that can benefit from job crafting is older workers. The proportion of older workers has been increasing worldwide and researchers have paid great attention to factors that help to manage and retain older workers (Kooij et al., 2015). In their book chapter, "Successful Aging at Work: The Role of Job Crafting," Kooij et al. (2015) proposed job crafting as an effective strategy through which older workers can continuously make adjustments to intrapersonal changes during the aging process so that they can maintain a continuous fit with their jobs. The positive effect of job crafting in older workers has been shown in empirical studies. For example, Lichtenthaler and Fischbach (2016) found that approach crafting was positively related to motivation to continue working beyond retirement age through an increased sense of coherence and decreased burnout, while avoidance crafting was negatively related to motivation to continue working beyond retirement age through a decreased sense of coherence and increased burnout. In a daily diary study, Kooij et al. (2020) found that on days older workers engaged in more interest crafting, they had enhanced work engagement and task performance.

One important benefit of job crafting is improved person–job fit (Tims et al., 2012, 2016), and one prevalent person–job misfit in the workplace is overqualification, defined as a situation that individuals' qualification (e.g., education, skills, and work experience) exceeds the job requirements (Erdogan & Bauer, 2021). Overqualification has been linked with a series of negative outcomes such as negative job attitudes, impaired well-being and job performance, turnover intentions, and counterproductive behaviors (Erdogan & Bauer, 2021). Recognizing the important influence of employees in redesigning their jobs, scholars have proposed job crafting as an effective way for employees to address the misfit with the job (e.g., Wu et al., 2015). Empirical research has shown that overqualified employees are more likely to engage in job crafting when they have high organizational identification, and job crafting can lead to positive outcomes such as enhanced well-being, improved task performance, and creativity (Lin et al., 2017; Zhang et al., 2021).

The evolution of digital technology and digital work platforms has seen the emergence of gig employees in many sectors (Goods et al., 2019). Different from traditional jobs, gig employees usually work remotely and more flexibly. However, due to the nature of remote work, gig employees face challenges such as a lack of personal contact and social interactions with task providers, with little to no human resource management support, and concerns about job security and sustainability (Kost et al., 2018; Meijerink & Keegan, 2019). Applying job crafting theories, some scholars have investigated how job crafting can help gig employees to address the challenges in their gig work. Specifically, Mousa et al. (2022) conducted a cross-sectional survey of 279 digital employees and found that individual job crafting was positively related to a sense of organizational inclusion, which in turn led to higher career satisfaction. Similarly, using a two-wave survey design, Wong et al. (2021) showed that gig employees' job crafting at Time 1 was positively related to Time 2 resilience, and subsequently led to higher commitment in the gig economy. Overall, these studies have provided preliminary evidence on the positive effects of job crafting in gig employees.

Investigating the Effect of Cultural Differences on Job Crafting.   Despite positive outcomes of job crafting reported in studies conducted in different countries, scholars have argued that the national context may affect the effectiveness of job crafting as the structure of work design is nested within the culture (Boehnlein & Baum, 2022; Gordon et al., 2015). To provide insights into the effect of cultural differences on the effectiveness of job crafting, drawing on the Global Leadership and Organizational Behavior Effectiveness (GLOBE) framework, Boehnlein and Baum (2022) conducted a meta-analysis to investigate the moderating effect of four cultural practices (i.e., in-group collectivism, future orientation, performance orientation, and uncertainty avoidance) on the relationship between job crafting and performance. Results of the meta-analysis have supported the effects of cultural practices on job crafting effectiveness to some extent, with 16 hypothesized relationships being supported out of 23 testable hypothesized relationships for cultural practices (Boehnlein & Baum, 2022).

Boehnlein and Baum (2022) reported several important findings. First, in line with previous research, collectivism—with a high level of cooperation and social exchange—was found to be beneficial for the effectiveness of job crafting. Employees in collectivistic cultures are more likely to craft their jobs to align with the goals of the workgroup and are more frequently supported by their colleagues during their job crafting process, which in turn leads to the success and effectiveness of job crafting. Second, future orientation was found to be beneficial for job crafting behaviors that aim to increase learning resources and opportunities (i.e., increasing structural resources) as these job crafting behaviors are congruent with future-oriented practices which emphasize future goals and achievements. However, future orientation was found to be detrimental to job crafting behaviors that aim to change the task boundaries (i.e., increasing challenging job demands, task crafting) as these crafting behaviors could occur in an unplanned manner and be intended to satisfy current needs, which goes against a future focus. Similar to future orientation, performance orientation was found to be beneficial for increasing structural resources as improving individual skills and competencies to better complete tasks are congruent with a performance-oriented culture. However, performance orientation was found to be detrimental for increasing challenging demands and task crafting as the results of these behaviors are unpredictable and out of the radar of supervisors, which may lead to decreased performance evaluations. Finally, uncertainty avoidance practices relate to the extent to which the society strives to avoid uncertainty and ambiguity. Thus, as hypothesized, uncertainty avoidance was found to be detrimental to task crafting and increasing challenging demands, which increases the uncertainty of the job (Boehnlein & Baum, 2022).

In sum, the macrolevel of societal cultures can result in the differential effectiveness of distinct job crafting behaviors. More research is needed to replicate these findings and to investigate the effect of cultural differences on unsupported moderated relationships.

INVESTIGATING ANTECEDENTS AND OUTCOMES OF TEAM JOB CRAFTING

With the increasing interest in team processes in organizations, researchers have been inclined toward exploring the antecedents and consequences of team job crafting. Like other team processes, team crafting is also influenced by factors on three levels (Mäkikangas et al., 2017). First, at the individual level, factors such as self-efficacy for teamwork (an individual member's faith in their capabilities particularly in the team setting), positive affect (Mäkikangas et al., 2017), and threat to work-identity integrity (Mattarelli & Tagliaventi, 2012) have been found to positively influence team job crafting. Second, at the team level, factors such as social ties (frequency and closeness of an employee's interaction with peers), discretion in work (or control), interdependence, the strength of ties with peers (Leana et al., 2009), and innovative team climate (e.g., components like vision, participative safety, and support for innovation) (Mäkikangas et al., 2017) have a positive relationship with team job crafting. At the organizational level, factors like the larger work environment and the nature of the work have been argued to influence collaborative job crafting. For example, employees who work in jobs that are unaffected by other coworkers (e.g., tax preparers) would not need to engage in collaborative job crafting (Leana et al., 2009). The role of leadership as an antecedent to team job crafting has also been explored in many studies. Research has shown that supportive supervision

(Leana et al., 2009), connecting leadership (the extent to which leaders encourage collaboration and interpersonal bonding, and seek to foster a good team spirit), charismatic leadership style (marked by encouragement and support to team members) (Luu et al., 2019), and leader humility (Chen et al., 2020) are positively related to collaborative or team level job crafting. Humble leaders are more likely to be open to feedback and may appreciate team members' efforts to be proactive at their jobs and change their team routines such as via crafting (Chen et al., 2020).

Regarding consequences of team crafting, research has shown team crafting contributes to various positive employee attitudes such as job satisfaction and work commitment (Alonso et al., 2019; Leana et al., 2009), individual work engagement (Mäkikangas et al., 2016), and team work engagement (Tims et al., 2013). The positive effect of team crafting is because when employees have the ability to redraw the boundaries of their jobs to fit them better with their needs as an individual or group, it is likely to make them more attached to their jobs and less likely to leave (Leana et al., 2009). Team crafting has also been linked with an improvement in their person–group fit (Cheng et al., 2016).

Research has also shown evidence on the positive relationship between team job crafting and positive behavioral outcomes such as team performance (Mäkikangas et al., 2016; Tims et al., 2013) and individual job performance (Alonso et al., 2019; Cheng et al., 2016), and team creativity (Chen et al., 2020). Since job crafting can help individuals alter what and how tasks are completed and the interpersonal dynamics of the workplace, it can thus influence their work performance (Cheng et al., 2016). In their study on childcare teachers, Leana et al. (2009) found that collaborative job crafting was significantly related to the quality of care provided. Moreover, Leana et al. (2009) found collaborative job crafting was positively related to organizational commitment and quality of care whereas individual job crafting was not related to any of these, supporting the distinctiveness of individual crafting and team crafting.

Regarding the mechanisms of the positive relationships between team job crafting and desirable outcomes, McClelland et al. (2014) found that increased team efficacy, team control, and team interdependence mediated the positive relationships of team job crafting with team-member work engagement and team performance. Luu (2017) found that collaborative job crafting was positively related to team service recovery performance via increased team work engagement. Perceived organizational support (Cheng et al., 2016) and leader–leader exchange (LLX; Chen et al., 2020) have also been found to moderate the relationship between collaborative job crafting and positive outcomes like organizational commitment and team creativity.

While researchers have started to explore team job crafting and its antecedents and consequences, research on this topic is still at a nascent stage. Future research could develop a comprehensive theoretical model explaining team job crafting in organizations.

JOB CRAFTING INTERVENTIONS

The potential benefits of job crafting have led researchers to design job crafting interventions and test their effectiveness. A job crafting intervention is "any intentional activity or method designed to stimulate or develop job crafting behaviors in employees to evaluate its effects on outcomes of interest" (Devotto & Wechsler, 2019, p. 374). Intervention studies are important for multiple reasons such as stronger research designs to test theories, their longitudinal nature, the scope of manipulation of variables of interest, and their ability to demonstrate the possibility of achieving change (Knight et al., 2021).

There has been a steady increase in job crafting intervention studies in recent years (Tims & Knight, 2019). Like the empirical research in job crafting, the majority of intervention studies used the JD-R perspective (Tims & Bakker, 2010) as the theoretical framework (Devotto & Wechsler, 2019; Oprea et al., 2019).

Job crafting interventions include group activities and goal-setting exercises and are usually structured in the following steps. The first step is information dissemination around job crafting. This is followed by job analysis, wherein the participants are instructed to analyze different aspects of their own jobs (e.g., number and frequency of tasks and duties). Next, the participants develop personal job crafting plans and discuss them in groups. These plans include the specific job crafting behaviors and actions they would engage in after the intervention period. Then the participants implement their job crafting action plans at work for around 3 to 4 weeks. Finally, in the evaluation phase, participants share their personal job crafting experiences and discuss their progress (Tims & Knight, 2019).

Most of the job crafting intervention studies have been conducted using a quasiexperimental or experimental design (Devotto & Wechsler, 2019; Oprea et al., 2019) with a comparison between experimental groups (those who were provided with the intervention) and control groups (those who were not given the intervention; e.g., Gordon et al., 2018; Van den Heuvel et al., 2015; Van Wingerden et al., 2017a, 2017b). The job crafting interventions in these studies have been structured to meet both individual and organizational needs (e.g., Van den Heuvel et al., 2015) with some specifically tailoring interventions to meet individual goals of the employees (e.g., Van Wingerden et al., 2017b). The number of participants across these studies is relatively small such that most of these studies have been conducted over a sample of fewer than 100 participants (Devotto & Wechsler, 2019; Oprea et al., 2019). With respect to demographic variables, these studies have been conducted across specific occupational groups and geographical locations, such as healthcare workers, working women, and teachers (for a meta-analysis, see Oprea et al., 2019). These studies have also been dominated by a cultural and economic context since most were conducted in the Netherlands (Tims & Knight, 2019). The intervention design in these studies included different activities such as knowledge dissemination of job crafting strategies and training (e.g., Gordon et al., 2018) and the use of the Michigan Job Crafting Exercise (JCE; Berg et al., 2008) that involves proactive goal-setting (e.g., Van Wingerden et al., 2017a, 2017b), simulation of patient interactions and experience narratives (Gordon et al., 2018), and sharing of personal crafting stories (e.g., Van den Heuvel et al., 2015).

As of the early 2020s, researchers started exploring electronic job crafting intervention (delivering job crafting interventions via e-resources, e.g., online structured learning modules with information and activities to guide individuals to create job crafting plan and engage in job crafting) as a time-efficient, more accessible, and cost-effective alternative to traditional job crafting interventions (Verelst et al., 2021). In addition, most of the job crafting intervention studies have been carried out using one to three training sessions conducted over 1 to 2 months using a longitudinal research design (for a review, see Devotto & Wechsler, 2019).

However, some studies have also been conducted over longer periods and have assessed post-intervention effects after 1 year (e.g., Van Wingerden et al., 2017b).

Job crafting interventions are effective in increasing participants' job crafting behaviors. Most intervention studies have reported an increase in crafting structural, social resources, and challenge demands, crafting to reduce hindrance demands (e.g., Van den Heuvel et al., 2015; Van Wingerden et al., 2017b), an increase in the task (relational and cognitive crafting; Sakuraya et al., 2016), and crafting toward strengths, crafting toward interests, and crafting toward development (Kooij et al., 2017; Kuijpers et al., 2020). In a job crafting intervention meta-analysis, Oprea et al. (2019) found significant effects of job crafting interventions on seeking challenges and reducing demands but not on seeking resources. This reflects the heterogeneity of intervention studies with inconsistent findings on seeking resources, which may be due to different intervention designs and samples.

In this same meta-analysis but looking at the impact of job crafting interventions on positive outcomes, Oprea et al. (2019) found a small but positive effect of job crafting interventions on work engagement and contextual performance but a nonsignificant effect on task performance and adaptive performance. These findings suggest inconsistent results across job crafting intervention studies. In addition, studies have also found that job crafting interventions impact other positive outcomes such as self-efficacy and performance feedback (Van Wingerden et al., 2017b), developmental opportunities, leader–member exchange, less negative affect (Van den Heuvel et al., 2015), and well-being (Gordon et al., 2018).

Despite the increase in job crafting intervention studies, these studies are bound by limitations. First, most of these studies have been conducted without any focus on the situational or conditional factors that could influence the impact of the intervention. For example, Knight et al. (2021) highlighted that previous job crafting intervention studies have not been able to adequately answer the question of under what conditions crafting interventions are more successful. Second, very few studies have focused on the subjective impact of the job crafting interventions as experienced by the participants in their own behaviors. Third, the majority of intervention studies have not been able to adequately provide evidence that the interventions were effective in changing job demands and resources (Tims & Knight, 2019). Fourth, the existing intervention studies have only been conducted across specific samples and countries which makes the generalization of findings difficult (Devotto & Wechsler, 2019; Oprea et al., 2019). Finally, due to the small number of job crafting intervention studies included in the meta-analytic studies, the findings are not conclusive.

CONCLUSION

The job crafting literature does not have a long history, but it continues to grow. Job crafting theories have been established and tested, and a great number of empirical studies have been conducted to investigate antecedents and outcomes of job crafting. However, due to the use of different job crafting theoretical perspectives and multiple measures, important efforts have been made to both conceptually and empirically synthesize distinct job crafting constructs and measurements. Future studies need to follow the new framework of job crafting to contribute to the job crafting literature. Building on literature investigating antecedents and outcomes of job crafting, future research is needed to uncover the complex mechanisms of positive or negative effects of job crafting, social processes that influence job crafting behaviors and outcomes, how job crafting plays a role in future work contexts and for specific populations such as gig workers and mature workers, and processes and mechanisms of team crafting.

REFERENCES

Alonso, C., Fernández-Salinero, S., & Topa, G. (2019). The impact of both individual and collaborative job crafting on Spanish teachers' well-being. *Education Sciences, 9*(2), 74.

Bakker, A. B., & Demerouti, E. (2007). The job demands-resources model: State of the art. *Journal of Managerial Psychology, 22*(3), 309–328.

Bakker, A. B., & Oerlemans, W. G. (2019). Daily job crafting and momentary work engagement: A self-determination and self-regulation perspective. *Journal of Vocational Behavior, 112,* 417–430.

Bakker, A. B., Tims, M., & Derks, D. (2012). Proactive personality and job performance: The role of job crafting and work engagement. *Human Relations, 65*(10), 1359–1378.

Berg, J. M., Dutton, J. E., & Wrzesniewski, A. (2008). *What is job crafting and why does it matter?* Positive Organizational Scholarship. https://positiveorgs.bus.umich.edu/wp-content/uploads/What-is-Job-Crafting-and-Why-Does-it-Matter1.pdf

Bindl, U. K., Unsworth, K. L., Gibson, C. B., & Stride, C. B. (2019). Job crafting revisited: Implications of an extended framework for active changes at work. *Journal of Applied Psychology, 104*(5), 605–628.

Bizzi, L. (2017). Network characteristics: When an individual's job crafting depends on the jobs of others. *Human Relations, 70*(4), 436–460.

Boehnlein, P., & Baum, M. (2022). Does job crafting always lead to employee well-being and performance? Meta-analytical evidence on the moderating role of societal culture. *The International Journal of Human Resource Management, 33*(4), 647–685.

Bruning, P. F., & Campion, M. A. (2018). A role-resource approach-avoidance model of job crafting: A multimethod integration and extension of job crafting theory. *Academy of Management Journal, 61*(2), 499–522.

Cai, Z., Parker, S. K., Chen, Z., & Lam, W. (2019). How does the social context fuel the proactive fire? A multilevel review and theoretical synthesis. *Journal of Organizational Behavior, 40*(2), 209–230.

Chen, C., Feng, J., Liu, X., & Yao, J. (2020). Leader humility, team job crafting and team creativity: The moderating role of leader–leader exchange. *Human Resource Management Journal, 31*(1), 326–340.

Cheng, J.-C., Chen, C.-Y., Teng, H.-Y., & Yen, C.-H. (2016). Tour leaders' job crafting and job outcomes: The moderating role of perceived organizational support. *Tourism Management Perspectives, 20,* 19–29.

Coltman, T., Devinney, T. M., Midgley, D. F., & Venaik, S. (2008). Formative versus reflective measurement models: Two applications of formative measurement. *Journal of Business Research, 61,* 1250–1262.

Costantini, A., Demerouti, E., Ceschi, A., & Sartori, R. (2020). Implementing job crafting behaviors: Exploring the effects of a job crafting intervention based on the theory of planned behavior. *The Journal of Applied Behavioral Science,* 1–36.

Costantini, A., Demerouti, E., Ceschi, A., & Sartori, R. (2021). Evidence on the hierarchical, multidimensional nature of behavioral job crafting. *Applied Psychology, 70*(1), 311–341.

Demerouti, E., & Peeters, M. C. (2018). Transmission of reduction-oriented crafting among colleagues: A diary study on the moderating role of working conditions. *Journal of Occupational and Organizational Psychology, 91*(2), 209–234.

Devotto, R. P., & Wechsler, S. M. (2019). Job crafting interventions: Systematic review. *Trends in Psychology, 27,* 371–383.

Ebert, T., & Bipp, T. (2021). Tomayto, tomahto? An empirical comparison and integration of job crafting perspectives. *European Journal of Psychological Assessment*, 1–13.

Erdogan, B., & Bauer, T. N. (2021). Overqualification at work: A review and synthesis of the literature. *Annual Review of Organizational Psychology and Organizational Behavior, 8*, 259–283.

Fong, C. Y. M., Tims, M., Khapova, S. N., & Beijer, S. (2021). Supervisor reactions to avoidance job crafting: The role of political skill and approach job crafting. *Applied Psychology, 70*(3), 1209–1241.

Goods, C., Veen, A., & Barratt, T. (2019). "Is your gig any good?" Analysing job quality in the Australian platform-based food-delivery sector. *Journal of Industrial Relations, 61*(4), 502–527.

Gordon, H. J., Demeroutia, E., Le Blanc, P. M., Bakker, A. B., Bipp, T., & Verhagen, M. A. (2018). Individual job redesign: Job crafting interventions in healthcare. *Journal of Vocational Behavior, 104*, 98–114.

Gordon, H. J., Demerouti, E., Le Blanc, P. M., & Bipp, T. (2015). Job crafting and performance of Dutch and American health care professionals. *Journal of Personnel Psychology, 14*(4), 192–202.

Grant, A. M., & Parker, K. S. (2009). 7 redesigning work design theories: The rise of relational and proactive perspectives. *Academy of Management Annals, 3*(1), 317–375.

Harju, L. K., Kaltiainen, J., & Hakanen, J. J. (2021). The double-edged sword of job crafting: The effects of job crafting on changes in job demands and employee well-being. *Human Resource Management, 60*(6), 953–968.

Hu, Q., Taris, T. W., Dollard, M. F., & Schaufeli, W. B. (2020). An exploration of the component validity of job crafting. *European Journal of Work and Organizational Psychology, 29*(5), 776–793.

Humphrey, S. E., Nahrgang, J. D., & Morgeson, F. P. (2007). Integrating motivational, social, and contextual work design features: A meta-analytic summary and theoretical extension of the work design literature. *Journal of Applied Psychology, 92*(5), 1332–1356.

Knight, C., Tims, M., Gawke, J., & Parker, S. K. (2021). When do job crafting interventions work? The moderating roles of workload, intervention intensity, and participation. *Journal of Vocational Behavior, 124*, 103522.

Kooij, D. T., Nijssen, H., Bal, P. M., & van der Kruijssen, D. T. (2020). Crafting an interesting job: Stimulating an active role of older workers in enhancing their daily work engagement and job performance. *Work, Aging and Retirement, 6*(3), 165–174.

Kooij, D. T., Tims, M., & Kanfer, R. (2015). Successful aging at work: The role of job crafting. In P. M. Bal, D. T. A. M. Kooij, & D. M. Rousseau (Eds.), *Aging workers and the employee-employer relationship* (pp. 145–161). Springer.

Kooij, D. T., van Woerkom, M., Wilkenloh, J., Dorenbosch, L., & Denissen, J. J. (2017). Job crafting towards strengths and interests: The effects of a job crafting intervention on person–job fit and the role of age. *Journal of Applied Psychology, 102*(6), 971–981.

Kost, D., Fieseler, C., & Wong, S. I. (2018). Finding meaning in a hopeless place? The construction of meaningfulness in digital microwork. *Computers in Human Behavior, 82*, 101–110.

Kuijpers, E., Kooij, D. T., & van Woerkom, M. (2020). Align your job with yourself: The relationship between a job crafting intervention and work engagement, and the role of workload. *Journal of Occupational Health Psychology, 25*(1), 1–16.

Lazazzaraa, A., Tims, M., & Gennaro, D. (2020). The process of reinventing a job: A meta–synthesis of qualitative job crafting research. *Journal of Vocational Behavior, 116*, 103267.

Leana, C., Appelbaum, E., & Shevchuk, I. (2009). Work process and quality of care in early childhood education: The role of job crafting. *Academy of Management Journal, 52*(6), 1169–1192.

Lee, J. Y., & Lee, Y. (2018). Job crafting and performance: Literature review and implications for human resource development. *Human Resource Development Review, 17*(3), 277–313.

Lichtenthaler, P. W., & Fischbach, A. (2016). Job crafting and motivation to continue working beyond retirement age. *Career Development International, 21*(5), 477–497.

Lichtenthaler, P. W., & Fischbach, A. (2019). A meta-analysis on promotion- and prevention-focused job crafting. *European Journal of Work and Organizational Psychology, 28*(1), 30–50.

Lin, B., Law, K. S., & Zhou, J. (2017). Why is underemployment related to creativity and OCB? A task-crafting explanation of the curvilinear moderated relations. *Academy of Management Journal, 60*(1), 156–177.

Linley, P. A. (2008). *Average to A+: Realizing strengths in yourself and others.* CAPP.

Luu, T. T. (2017). Collective job crafting and team service recovery performance: A moderated mediation mechanism. *Marketing Intelligence & Planning, 35*(5), 641–656.

Luu, T. T., Rowley, C., Dinh, C. K., Qian, D., & Le, H. Q. (2019). Team creativity in public healthcare organizations: The roles of charismatic leadership, team job crafting, and collective public service motivation. *Public Performance & Management Review, 42*(6), 1448–1480.

Mäkikangas, A., Aunola, K., Seppälä, P., & Hakanen, J. (2016). Work engagement–team performance relationship: Shared job crafting as a moderator. *Journal of Occupational and Organizational Psychology, 89*(4), 772–790.

Mäkikangas, A., Bakker, A. B., & Schaufeli, W. B. (2017). Antecedents of daily team job crafting. *European Journal of Work and Organizational Psychology, 26*(3), 421–433.

Mattarelli, E., & Tagliaventi, M. R. (2012). How offshore professionals' job dissatisfaction can promote further offshoring: Organizational outcomes of job crafting. *Journal of Management Studies, 52*(5), 585–620.

McClelland, G. P., Leach, D. J., Clegg, C. W., & McGowan, I. (2014). Collaborative crafting in call center teams. *Journal of Occupational and Organizational Psychology, 87*, 464–486.

Meijerink, J., & Keegan, A. (2019). Conceptualizing human resource management in the gig economy: Toward a platform ecosystem perspective. *Journal of Managerial Psychology, 34*(4), 214–232.

Mousa, M., Chaouali, W., & Mahmood, M. (2022). The inclusion of gig employees and their career satisfaction: Do individual and collaborative job crafting play a role? *Public Organization Review, 23*(3), 1055–1068.

Nielsen, K., Antino, M., Sanz-Vergel, A., & Rodríguez-Muñoz, A. (2017). Validating the Job Crafting Questionnaire (JCRQ): A multi-method and multi-sample study. *Work & Stress, 31*(1), 82–99.

Niessen, C., Weseler, D., & Kostova, P. (2016). When and why do individuals craft their jobs? The role of individual motivation and work characteristics for job crafting. *Human Relations, 69*(6), 1287–1313.

Oprea, B. T., Barzin, L., Vîrgă, D., Iliescu, D., & Rusu, A. (2019). Effectiveness of job crafting interventions: A meta-analysis and utility analysis. *European Journal of Work and Organizational Psychology, 28*(6), 723–741.

Parker, S. K. (2014). Beyond motivation: Job and work design for development, health, ambidexterity, and more. *Annual Review of Psychology, 65*, 661–691.

Petrou, P., Demerouti, E., Peeters, M. C., Schaufeli, W. B., & Hetland, J. (2012). Crafting a job on a daily basis: Contextual correlates and the link to work engagement. *Journal of Organizational Behavior, 33*(8), 1120–1141.

Rudolph, C. W., Katza, I. M., Lavigne, K. N., & Zacher, H. (2017). Job crafting: A meta-analysis of relationships with individual differences, job characteristics, and work outcomes. *Journal of Vocational Behavior, 102*, 112–138.

Ryan, R. M., & Deci, E. L. (2008). From ego depletion to vitality: Theory and findings concerning the facilitation of energy available to the self. *Social and Personality Psychology Compass, 2*(2), 702–717.

Sakuraya, A., Shimazu, A., Imamura, K., Namba, K., & Kawakami, N. (2016). Effects of a job crafting intervention program on work engagement among Japanese employees: A pretest–posttest study. *BMC Psychology, 4*(1), 1–9.

Slemp, G. R., & Vella-Brodrick, D. A. (2013). The job crafting questionnaire: A new scale to measure the extent to which employees engage in job crafting. *International Journal of Wellbeing, 3*(2), 126–146.

Tims, M., & Bakker, A. B. (2010). Job crafting: Towards a new model of individual job redesign. *SA Journal of Industrial Psychology, 36*(2), 1–9.

Tims, M., Bakker, A. B., & Derks, D. (2012). Development and validation of the job crafting scale. *Journal of Vocational Behavior, 80*(1), 173–186.

Tims, M., Bakker, A. B., Derks, D., & Van Rhenen, W. (2013). Job crafting at the team and individual level: Implications for work engagement and performance. *Group & Organization Management, 38*(4), 427–454.

Tims, M., Derks, D., & Bakker, A. B. (2016). Job crafting and its relationships with person–job fit and meaningfulness: A three-wave study. *Journal of Vocational Behavior, 92*, 44–53.

Tims, M., & Knight, C. (2019). Job crafting: An individual strategy to develop oneself. In R. J. Burke & A. M. Richardsen (Eds.), *Creating psychologically healthy workplaces* (pp. 152–170). Edward Elgar.

Tims, M., & Parker, S. K. (2020). How coworkers attribute, react to, and shape job crafting. *Organizational Psychology Review, 10*(1), 29–54.

Van den Heuvel, M., Demerouti, E., & Peeters, M. C. (2015). The job crafting intervention: Effects on job resources, self-efficacy, and affective well-being. *Journal of Occupational and Organizational Psychology, 88*, 511–532.

Van Wingerden, J., Bakker, A. B., & Derks, D. (2017a). Fostering employee well-being via a job crafting intervention. *Journal of Vocational Behavior, 100*, 164–174.

Van Wingerden, J., Bakker, A. B., & Derks, D. (2017b). The longitudinal impact of a job crafting intervention. *European Journal of Work and Organizational Psychology, 26*(1), 107–119.

Verelst, L., De Cooman, R., Verbruggen, M., Van Laar, C., & Meeussen, L. (2021). The development and validation of an electronic job crafting intervention: Testing the links with job crafting and person-job fit. *Journal of Occupational and Organizational Psychology, 94*(2), 338–373.

Wang, H., Li, P., & Chen, S. (2020). The impact of social factors on job crafting: A meta-analysis and review. *International Journal of Environmental Research and Public Health, 17*(21), 8016.

Weseler, D., & Niessen, C. (2016). How job crafting relates to task performance. *Journal of Managerial Psychology, 31*(3), 672–685.

Wong, S. I., Kost, D., & Fieseler, C. (2021). From crafting what you do to building resilience for career commitment in the gig economy. *Human Resource Management Journal, 31*(4), 918–935.

Wood, A. M., Linley, P. A., Maltby, J., Kashdan, T. B., & Hurling, R. (2011). Using personal and psychological strengths leads to increases in well-being over time: A longitudinal study and the development of the strengths use questionnaire. *Personality and Individual Differences, 50*(1), 15–19.

Wrzesniewski, A., & Dutton, J. E. (2001). Crafting a job: Revisioning employees as active crafters of their work. *The Academy of Management Review, 26*(2), 179–201.

Wu, C. H., Luksyte, A., & Parker, S. K. (2015). Overqualification and subjective well-being at work: The moderating role of job autonomy and culture. *Social Indicators Research, 121*(3), 917–937.

Zampetakis, L. A. (2022). Does an overall job crafting dimension exist? A multidimensional item response theory analysis. *European Journal of Psychological Assessment, 38*(1), 32–35.

Zhang, F., & Parker, S. K. (2019). Reorienting job crafting research: A hierarchical structure of job crafting concepts and integrative review. *Journal of Organizational Behavior, 40*(2), 126–146.

Zhang, F., Wang, B., Qian, J., & Parker, S. K. (2021). Job crafting towards strengths and job crafting towards interests in overqualified employees: Different outcomes and boundary effects. *Journal of Organizational Behavior, 42*(5), 587–603.

Fangfang Zhang, Sabreen Kaur, and Sharon K. Parker

HUMAN–COMPUTER INTERACTION

INTRODUCTION

Human–computer interaction (HCI) is a multidisciplinary field of research that aims to understand and design the interaction between humans and computers. Originally exclusively concerned with "computers," in the last decade of the 20th century it progressively addressed every form of digital technology.

HCI originates from human factors and ergonomics (HF&E) and cognitive sciences. However, despite the initial cooperation with HF&E scientists, who were and still are primarily focused on studying performance and error issues of "mandatory" uses of technology in specific professional contexts like industry and aviation, HCI researchers soon diverged from these research interests (Grudin, 2005). They inaugurated a new field of inquiry, by exploring "nonexpert" usage of digital devices, in which aspects of interaction like pleasure and fun and the social, organizational, and cultural use of technology (Rogers, 2012) also come to matter. Moreover, since the late 1980s, HCI researchers have progressively adopted approaches, theories, and methods that did not belong to cognitive sciences, rather being specific to other disciplines, like anthropology and sociology.

The landscape of contemporary HCI is thus extremely complex and multifaceted. As our societies have become completely pervaded by the digital, the HCI focus in the third decade of the 21st century covers almost every aspect of people's lives. HCI popular topics currently span from techno-spirituality, human–agent interaction, virtual reality, video games, and wearable devices to sustainability, three-dimensional printing, aging technologies, tangible interaction, speculative design, physical or mental health, and well-being. Moreover, diverse theories, methods, and research traditions coexist within a research field that is increasingly difficult to chart.

Nonetheless, its distinguishing features are evident to HCI researchers. What all these research topics have in common is HCI's interest in understanding what people do in various settings and how they interact with machines in their daily lives, as well as how it is possible to design interactive systems that truly have value to them. HCI has its own precise identity, a well-defined and enormous body of literature, dedicated conferences like CHI (Conference on Human Factors in Computing Systems), and journals like *Human–Computer Interaction* and *ACM Transactions on Computer–Human Interaction* in which to publish. There is a huge community of researchers who draw on a common pool of lenses, approaches, and "philosophies," as well as a distinctive "style" for studying and writing about technology. Even though it may be difficult to identify the essence of contemporary HCI, it is possible to clearly see, in Wittgenstein's terms, a variety of "family resemblances" across the many different studies that are now conducted within HCI—namely, "a complicated network of similarities overlapping and criss-crossing: sometimes overall similarities, sometimes similarities of detail" (Wittgenstein, 1953/1967, PU § 66), which circumscribe a precise field of interest and research.

In the "History of HCI," "Theories of HCI," "Methods of HCI," and "Lines of Research in HCI" sections, the field of HCI is outlined by highlighting its history, the theories it uses, the methods it employs, and some of its lines of research, which may give a snapshot, albeit incomplete, of the evolution of the discipline, as well as of its contemporary landscape.

HISTORY OF HCI

HCI at the Beginning of Computing. HCI can be dated back to when, after World War II, general-purpose electronic computers appeared, and researchers started paying attention to what were called man–machine interfaces. In the 1940s, 1950s, and 1960s, a few pioneers envisioned a world where people could interact with computers in extremely "natural" ways, whereby machines could extend human capabilities by amplifying, for instance, memory and reasoning. For example, in 1945, Vannevar Bush (1945) introduced the MEMEX in his essay "As We May Think," a hypothetical information-processing machine based on microfilm technology that would have expanded the human memory. In 1960, Joseph Carl Robnett Licklider (1960) envisioned "man–computer symbiosis," a subclass of man–computer systems in which human brains and computers were strictly tied together and the functions performed by data-processing machines were meant to be introduced into the thought process itself, improving thinking and problem solving. Likewise, in 1962, Douglas Engelbart (1962) proposed a framework orienting toward the opportunities associated with using digital technologies to augment human intellect and extend human abilities to approach complex problems.

However, at the dawn of computing, the interaction with computers in the "real world" had a completely different form. Grudin (2005) explains that the management of first computers like ENIAC, which was put into operation at the University of Pennsylvania in 1946, required the machine to be manually loaded with programs by setting dials, switches, and cable connections. In the late 1950s and early 1960s, instead, using a computer meant managing programs and data keypunched onto cards or tape: Once the program was loaded in the computer, it ran without interruption until it terminated and produced output (e.g., printed; Grudin, 2012). At that time, the unique figure that operated directly on the computer was the operator, who "loaded and unloaded cards and magnetic or paper tapes, set switches, pushed buttons, read lights, loaded and burst printer paper, and put printouts into distribution bins" (Grudin, 2012, p. 8). Thus, reducing operators' burden, by improving the design of displays and buttons, became an important issue to deal with and a matter for the emerging discipline of HCI. Grudin traces the first HCI publication back to Brian Shackel's article "Ergonomics for a Computer," published in 1959, followed by "Ergonomics in the Design of a Large Digital Computer Console," in 1962 (Shackel, 1997). For this kind of research, which persisted throughout the 1960s and 1970s, interaction with computers was primarily a form of man–machine coupling, whereby HCI scientists needed to identify problems in such coupling and find pragmatic solutions to them, in order to reduce training time, eliminate possible errors, and increase performance. In so doing, they were inspired more by industrial engineering, human factors, and ergonomics (Harrison et al., 2007) than by the early computer scientists' visions of interaction embedded in our everyday lives and as a means for extending the human mind.

HCI During the Spreading of Personal Computing. During the 1980s, the personal computer became popular, and HCI started diverging from HF&E. Grudin (2005) identifies the beginning of this divergence in the emergent attention that HCI was giving to the discretionary use of computers in the early 1980s, when HCI researchers started paying attention to nonexpert users and novices like students and hobbyists. By contrast, HF&E continued to focus on mandatory and bureaucratic use (e.g., in the military, aviation, and telecommunication domains, where small efficiency improvements could yield large benefits over time). In 1983, the first CHI Conference on Human Factors in Computing Systems, which is still the primary scientific venue for HCI, was held in Boston and officially sanctioned HCI as an independent and well-identified research field. In fact, the next year, the Human Factors Society did not cosponsor the conference again, and its researchers were no longer in the conference program committee (Grudin, 2005).

The 1980s inaugurated the so-called classical period of HCI, or first-wave HCI (Bødker, 2006), as there was wide tacit consensus on its focus and objectives, as well as on cognitive sciences as its overarching research paradigm (Rogers, 2012): HCI was conceived as an applied science using the theories and methods of cognitive psychology to understand individual users interacting with computers and drive software development (Carroll, 2003). During the late 1980s, however, some cracks in this unifying paradigm started appearing: Alternative scientific ideas coming from anthropology, sociology, and organizational psychology seeped into HCI theory and practice, and the field became progressively multidisciplinary. HCI focus shifted from studying technology for an individual user at a desktop in an office to including group working and interaction in organizational settings on the basis of ideas like "situated action" and "context" (Bødker, 2006). In this sort of "turn to the social," or "second wave," HCI paid a lot of attention to cooperation and participation, also changing the used methods from controlled laboratory experiments to "in-the-wild" ethnographies and participatory design workshops (Bødker, 2015).

HCI During the Era of Mobile and Ubiquitous Computing.   Starting from the 1990s, the HCI focus has broadened again: The Internet and mobile phones have made it possible to communicate and use digital services everywhere at any time, while myriads of electronic devices collect an unprecedented amount of data. Digital technologies have begun to be used not only in the context of work but also in leisure time, and most of everyday people's actions have become digitally mediated. A new research direction, called ubiquitous computing (Weiser, 1991), proposed a future in which computation is embedded in everyday environments and objects and in which interactions with digital artifacts become completely transparent. HCI's response to these technological advancements, either actual or expected, has yielded the adoption of a variety of new methods and theories, which were brought in to deal with the complexity of novel interaction modalities, no longer relegated to the desktop computers. Aspects that were previously ignored, like emotions, body, experience, meaning, and aesthetics, came thus to the foreground in what has been called the "third paradigm" or the "third wave" of HCI (Bødker, 2006; Harrison et al., 2007). Also, human actors have stepped out of the role of worker and "participate in design as a person who brings her entire life to the design" (Bødker, 2006, p. 7). This significant change in HCI direction has made HCI almost a boundless domain (Barnard et al., 2000), whereby the potential downside of this burgeoning growth is a lack of direction in the field (Rogers, 2012, p. 1).

However, even though the recent history of HCI appears to be characterized by such a paradigm shift, it should be noticed that "older" approaches, like those based on cognitive sciences and human factors, continue to coexist, whereby a new wave of research has not completely replaced another, rather going in parallel and serving different purposes as well as answering different questions (Rogers, 2012).

THEORIES OF HCI

Since its origins, a variety of theories have been introduced into HCI to understand how people behave and to identify their situated needs, as well as to inform and drive the design practice. The evolution of HCI over the years witnessed a constant increase of models, frameworks, and theories, being originally developed by HCI researchers or imported from other fields like psychology, anthropology, and sociology. These theoretical transformations paralleled the evolution of HCI from a discipline with a clear and narrow focus—namely, that of designing systems more efficient and easier to be used—to a much wider problem space (Rogers, 2012).

The HCI theoretical landscape can be described by referring to the different "waves" that have succeeded each other in HCI history and were briefly mentioned in the "History of HCI" section. Each of these waves is characterized by a common epistemology and shared conceptualizations about interaction and the user, and it relies on a common set of research questions, procedures, and methods.

It is possible to identify three main waves in the history of HCI (Bødker, 2006, 2015; Harrison et al., 2007). The first wave builds on the epistemology of the cognitive sciences, being model driven and focused on the "user" as a subject to be studied using rigid guidelines, formal methods, and systematic laboratory testing (Bødker, 2015). It was organized around the metaphor of mind and computer as symmetric information processors (Harrison et al., 2007). This wave characterized HCI during the early era of personal computers, when HCI was focused on designing for a user at a desktop in an office setting, and cognitive psychology was seen as able to inform the design of easy-to-learn and easy-to-use computers (Rogers, 2012).

The second wave represents the "turn to the social" of HCI and focuses on groups working and work settings, as well as on interaction within established communities of practice (Bødker, 2015). It revolves around the ideas of "context" and "situated action" and introduces alternative conceptualizations to those provided by cognitive psychology, like theories taken from anthropology and social sciences (Bødker, 2006), which may better account for the "messy" nature of interaction.

The third wave, instead, widens the HCI focus to the experience and the meaningfulness of interaction (Bødker, 2006). This wave mainly occurs during the affirmation of mobile and ubiquitous computing and highlights the subjective, lived, embodied, and meaning-laden experience of interacting with computers, which can now be embedded in every object of everyday life. Notions of culture, emotion, and reflexivity become central (Rogers, 2012), and the number of theories employed in HCI dramatically increases to account for the whole lives of people, who are now mainly conceptualized as fully humans, rather than merely as "users."

However, these three waves should not be meant as mutually exclusive. First-wave approaches coming from cognitive sciences and information processing continue to coexist with theories attentive to the situated nature of interaction and those focused on the individual's first-person experience, serving different purposes in the field (Grudin, 2005). Therefore, it is not the case of one wave replacing another, but it is needed to see the evolution of HCI through different overlapping epochs, each dominated by different questions, methods, and theories (Rogers, 2012).

First-Wave Theories

Cognitive Theories. In the first wave, HCI almost exclusively relied on the epistemology of cognitive sciences (Carroll, 2003), referring to the computational theory of mind (McCulloch & Pitts, 1943) and the representational theory of mind (Fodor, 1975). These theories see minds and computers sharing fundamental similarities in their working principles: Mind and machine states can be explained by the function that they have, and their operations can be characterized as computations—namely, a series of elementary instructions that imply the manipulation of symbols (Haugeland, 1985). Cognitive processes, like computer processes, are "computations" on representations that have a symbolic nature: This ultimately means that both minds and computers are information-processing units (Fodor, 1983). In this perspective, the mind is conceived as modular, composed of a variety of functions that can be combined in cognitive architectures, as well as be separately studied, which led to the definition of models and theories of specific cognitive abilities, like memory, perception, and communication.

HCI thus became one of the first cognitive science domains, using a variety of cognitive theories of, for example, motor activity, attention, learning, and problem solving, to drive system design (Carroll, 2003). For instance, information-processing theory explains how information is encoded in memory: Short-term memory, for example, can only hold seven (plus or minus two) chunks of information at any one time (Miller, 1956). Likewise, the problem space theory states that the mind is a limited information processor and that people solve problems by searching in a problem space, which comprises the initial problem state, the goal state, and all possible states in between: As the problem space may be huge, heuristics can be employed to move from the initial state to the goal state (Newell & Simon, 1972). In the adaptive character of thought theory, complex cognition arises from an interaction of declarative knowledge, which refers to the fact of the world, and procedural knowledge, which refers to "how to" do a task (Anderson, 1983). For example, people go through three stages when they acquire a skill: First, they learn declarative knowledge about the task (e.g., instructions for driving); second, as task knowledge is repeatedly acted out, it yields production rules within procedural memory; and third, production rules are tuned to speed up performance through practice and actions become automatic (Dix et al., 2003).

By and large, cognitive sciences provided designers and researchers with explanations of users' capabilities and limitations when they interact with a computer, explanations that have been popularized in books like those written by Donald Norman (1988) and Andrew Monk (1984). Principles like "recognition is better than recall" were used to create graphical interfaces helping users in recognizing rather than remembering the commands that they need to interact with a digital artifact, while theories of human memory were employed to identify the best set of icons or labels to use, given people's memory limitations (Rogers, 2012).

Cognitive Models. Another approach adopted during the first wave was to develop cognitive models to explain how people deal with a task specifically thought to explain the interaction with machines. Hutchins et al.'s (1986) and Norman's (1986) ideas that gulfs at the interface need to be bridged by design were among the most influential models of this kind. Norman (1986) explains that when people use something, they face two gulfs: the Gulf of Execution, where they try to figure out how the system operates, and the Gulf of Evaluation, where they try to figure out what happened. The Gulf of Execution is bridged when people easily understand what kinds of operations they can perform on the system, whereas the Gulf of Evaluation is small when the device provides information about its state in a form that is easy to interpret and matches the way the person thinks about the system. Designers should then work toward reducing the two gulfs in order to minimize the cognitive load of the user, and this can be accomplished by designing usable interfaces that match their psychological characteristics.

Second-Wave Theories

Alternative Psychological Theories. During the late 1980s and early 1990s, HCI witnessed a consistent paradigm shift as a reaction against the dominant cognitive paradigm and its underlying information-processing models. Cognitive theories and models were mostly developed to identify single cognitive processes in experimental settings, where they are studied in isolation while subjects are asked to perform well-defined tasks in a controlled environment. Instead, interactions with computers usually happen in a messy environment, where multiple tasks are performed together, and multiple cognitive processes are put into action (Rogers, 2012). HCI researchers then started referring to alternative psychological approaches to the classical cognitive sciences to account for the messiness of the "real world." Ecological psychology, for example, was very influential in informing and driving the design of computer systems, especially with reference to the notion of "affordance," which was originally defined by Gibson (1979) in the attempt to deviate from the classical theories of visual perception. Gibson believed that animals perceive the environment ecologically—that is, they perceive not atoms or particles but what the medium, substances, and surfaces offer them, namely, the affordances. Therefore, affordances "of the environment are what it offers the animal, what it provides or furnishes, either for good or ill" (Gibson, 1979, p. 127). The concept of affordance was then brought to HCI by Donald Norman (1988) to refer to attributes of objects that allow people to know how to use them, assuming that when they are perceptually obvious, they make the interaction with objects easier. However, while real-world objects have real affordances, virtual interfaces have only perceived affordances, which are based on feedback, constraints, and conventions, which designers should also pay attention to (Norman, 1999). The concept of affordance became so popular in HCI that, over the years, a variety of HCI researchers tried to develop a deeper understanding of its use in design. Gaver (1991), for instance, claimed that it is essential to distinguish affordances from perceptual information about them. This allows researchers to consider affordances as properties that can be designed and analyzed in their own terms.

Another example of alternative psychological approaches is distributed cognition theory, which was originally developed by Hutchins on the basis of cognitive ethnographies in contexts like navigation aboard U.S. Navy ships (Hutchins, 1995): The theory "extends the reach of what is considered cognitive beyond the individual to encompass interactions between people and with resources and materials in the environment" (Hollan et al., 2000, p. 175). In this perspective, a "cognitive system" involves not only what is inside people's heads but also the artifacts they use and the environment they are working in, thus challenging the idea of classic cognitive sciences that cognitive processes occur only within individuals' mind. As Rogers (2012) points out, one of the main outcomes of this approach is an explication of the complex interdependencies between people and artifacts in their work activities, which allows researchers to identify the distributed problem-solving processes that emerge during interaction. However, distributed cognition was found difficult to apply to HCI in practice, as it requires extensive fieldwork before being able to come to design decisions for a given work setting (Nardi, 1996).

The Turn to the Social. A focus on situated work activities, carried out by people using computer systems within specific communities, is the real distinguishing feature that characterizes the second wave of HCI. This wave attempted to compensate the gaps left by the first one, which saw cognition as "detached" by real-world contexts and the user interacting alone with a desktop computer, bringing alternative ways of understanding interaction with computers also from sociology and cultural anthropology (Rogers, 2012). This "turn to the social" is best exemplified by the increasing popularity of ethnomethodology as a theory to explain interaction with computers. Ethnomethodology has its roots in the work of Harold Garfinkel, who, in the late 1950s, aimed to redefine the "problem of social order"—that is, how it is maintained and reproduced, despite the fact that it arises from the action of independent individuals. The classic perspective in sociology at that time, represented by Talcott Parsons's structural functionalism, was that social order is achieved through the interiorization of shared rules and norms, which allow for the coordination of social actors' activities. Instead, ethnomethodology suggests that the orderliness displayed by social action arises from within the action itself (Dourish, 2004). It is not imposed from outside, by the interiorization of rules of conduct or social norms; rather, parties to some activity find, within the circumstances of action, the means to render that action meaningful and orderly, making such resources available to others:

> The social world is not orderly because people blindly follow social rules that are imposed on them. Instead, finding the social world orderly and meaningful is a practical problem that people solve, endlessly and unproblematically, as they go about their business. (Dourish, 2004, p. 23)

In HCI, ethnomethodology has been used to inform design especially through fieldwork investigations that may develop an understanding of organizations and work from the "inside," which can be eventually used in the design of technology aimed at supporting work practices (Dourish & Button, 1998).

The attention to the social setting of interaction in the second wave was also testified at that time by Lucy Suchman's (1987) book *Plans and Situated Action*, which was partly grounded in the work of ethnomethodology and soon became extremely popular among HCI researchers. Suchman contests the classic cognitive view that purposeful action is determined by abstract plans located in the actor's head, rather arguing that plans as such neither determine the actual course of action nor adequately reconstruct it. Instead, actors use the resources that a particular occasion provides to construct their action's developing purpose and intelligibility. In other words, action is situated and sensitive to local circumstances and resources: People produce and find evidence for plans in the course of situated action, so whatever plans they may have in mind, they may need to modify them depending on what is happening in that specific situation. Suchman (Suchman et al., 1999) also thought that making sense of a new artifact is an inherently problematic activity and that, however clear, self-evident, or easy to use a machine interface may be, this would never eliminate the need for users' active sense-making. By arguing for detailed observations of the actual work practices of ordinary users instead of the standard user cognitive modeling approaches, Suchman inspired a variety of HCI studies that explored the situated nature of users' interaction with computers, yielding an in-depth exploration of practices that were often achieved through ethnographic investigations (Anderson, 1997).

Third-Wave Theories. The technological transformations that started in the 1990s, like the arrival of the Internet, the mobile phones, and the ubiquitous technologies, expanded the focus of HCI to new horizons other than the context of work. Technologies started pervading almost every aspect of people's lives, and in parallel, the HCI lens has had to change to address the new contexts of interaction, where notions of culture, experience, meaning, and emotion have become prevalent. In the third wave, matters like sense-making, embodiment, behavior change, posthumanism, and multiculturalism have become potential research topics for HCI, and the theoretical tools available to HCI researchers until that moment have started showing their inadequacy. As anything became potentially a matter for HCI (Rogers, 2009), a variety of alternative frameworks, models, and theories continued to be imported and adapted to HCI needs: like somaesthetics theory, which draws attention to the importance of our bodily movements as part of our ways of being, in order to design opportunities for encouraging people to be close to their own bodies (Höök et al., 2016); the legitimate peripheral participation theory, which explains how newcomers become part of a community of practice, to understand how people participate, for instance, in virtual organizations (Rapp, 2020a); the persuasive systems design framework, which highlights underlying postulates behind persuasive systems aimed at changing people's behavior and proposes ways to analyze the persuasion context (Oinas-Kukkonen & Harjumaa, 2009); or the theory of nomadic practices that offers a way for thinking about design that embraces multiplicity and diversity (Wakkary, 2020).

This proliferation of theoretical perspectives makes it almost unfeasible to depict an exhaustive picture of the theoretical landscape that characterizes third-wave HCI research and practice. However, it is possible to highlight a few theoretical directions that are proving to be promising in opening opportunities to see interaction with "computers" in different ways.

Phenomenological Approaches. A first theoretical line that well exemplifies the third wave's new interest in the subjective experience of people interacting with technology and, at the same time, how philosophy entered the HCI discourse is represented by phenomenology. Phenomenology is a philosophical and psychological paradigm that explores phenomena as they appear in our "lifeworld"—namely, the world that we experience in our ordinary life (Fallman, 2011). It takes people's experiences, perceptions, and meanings as its objects of study, in order to recover the natural way through which individuals look at themselves and the world—namely, from a first-person point of view (Gallagher & Zahavi, 2008; Husserl, 1962). In such an approach, meanings may be viewed as actively constructed by the person, so that phenomenology may entail a form of constructivism (Rapp & Tirassa, 2017). Despite phenomenology having been used in HCI since the late 1980s against the cognitivist position (Winograd & Flores, 1986) and to argue in favor of a tool-based approach to design (Ehn, 1988), it came to the foreground when HCI started focusing on the lived, meaning-laden experience of interaction. It was then adopted as a frame to understand social computing and tangible interfaces (Dourish, 2001), to build theories for grounding the interaction with self-tracking devices (Rapp & Tirassa, 2017), and to backdrop the discussion on *embodied interaction*, a new paradigm for interaction design that focuses on the bodily aspects of our interaction with technology (Svanæs, 2013). Phenomenology has thus offered to HCI theoretical tools that explain how people make sense of the world, paving the way for the use of various forms of philosophy to understand the effects of technology on people's experience. In this sense, postphenomenology, which builds on the major phenomenological thinkers and sees interaction with technology in terms of *mediation* (i.e., how it shapes [mediates] our relations to the world; Rosenberger & Verbeek, 2015), also allowed several HCI researchers to identify the multiple effects that specific technological artifacts have on people's experience (Fallman, 2011; Rapp, 2021). In this sense, both phenomenology and postphenomenology have been used to ground and analyze the design of new artifacts (e.g., Wakkary et al., 2018), as well as examine existing applications and projects (e.g., Ohlin & Olsson, 2015).

Social Practices Approaches. An opposite theoretical direction, instead, is represented by the theory of social practices, which gained popularity in HCI in the second decade of the 21st century, so that it has been argued for "a turn to practice" in HCI (Kuutti & Bannon, 2014). Even though there is no unified theory, but rather a diverse set of theories revolving around the notion of practice, a social practice (or simply practice) can be defined as a routinized type of behavior made up of "forms of bodily activities, forms of mental activities, 'things' and their use, a background knowledge in the form of understanding, know-how, states of emotion and motivational knowledge" (Reckwitz, 2002, p. 249). This definition of practice can be further expanded by considering the objects and technological devices involved in the practice itself (Latour, 1992). Social actors reproduce ways of interpreting, knowing how, and wanting (Reckwitz, 2002), but also physically, in the form of patterns of postures and gestures (Bourdieu, 1977). In this sense, social practice theories are essentially nonsubjective, as opposed to phenomenology, since here the individual is only a carrier of collective practices, which are independent from them (Schatzki, 2001): The person may perform such practices, reproducing them over time, even with variations and resistance, but the real agents are the practices themselves. In HCI, these theories have been seen as a way to direct researchers to look beyond isolated interactions between humans and computers (Pierce et al., 2013), challenging the traditional HCI distinction between human and nonhuman, as well as shifting the focus from discrete individual human actors to networks of people and technological artifacts. Social practice theories have been especially used in sustainable HCI, for example, to understand and design for consumption (Rapp et al., 2017), food waste (Ganglbauer et al., 2013), and heating (Kuijer et al., 2013).

"Methodological" Approaches. A last theoretical direction that may exemplify the diversities in approaching theory in the third-wave HCI points to grounded theory. Grounded theory is not a proper theory but a method to develop theories from the analysis of data of a different nature (e.g., interviews, documents, conversations). Originally defined by Glaser and Strauss (1967), grounded theory is engaged in conceptual exploration and theoretical development, implying a continuous exchange between theoretical ideas and subjective understandings grounded on the data (Furniss et al., 2011). To do so, it uses qualitative coding processes heavily by coding data through open codes, in which codes freely describe the characteristics of the data; axial codes, which categorize the previously defined codes; and selective codes, which group the categories in overarching themes. By following this approach, theories emerge directly from the data, through an inductive, rather than a hypothetical-deductive, stance. In its most orthodox version, grounded theory is against the use of extant concepts and theories (Goldkuhl & Cronholm, 2010). Nonetheless, it has been suggested that researchers may simply avoid being stuck on a particular theoretical perspective in ways that may excessively direct their way of looking at the data (Henwood & Pidgeon, 2003). The approach does not necessarily entail the development of a complete theoretical framework but can also be used for defining taxonomies or describing a specific concept in depth (Furniss et al., 2011). Grounded theory allowed HCI researchers to build theoretical models of specific phenomena, like modeling collaboration in virtual teams (Sarker et al., 2001), understanding autonomy experiences in work and leisure contexts (Deterding, 2016), and defining taxonomies of video games (Alharthi et al., 2018).

METHODS OF HCI

HCI always has been concerned with understanding what people do in diverse settings to improve existing technologies or develop new ones. In particular, since the early 1990s, design has been considered central to HCI, with a focus on software design, user-centered design, and interface design (Rogers, 2012).

Traditionally, the technology design process in HCI can be divided into different phases: (a) the understanding of the users' behavior and the identification of their needs (e.g., with reference to a particular task, context, or application domain), in order to define user requirements or identify novel opportunities for design; (b) the design of the solution based on such understanding and the identified requirements using prototypes at different levels of fidelity, which may also imply the direct participation of the users to the design process; and (c) the assessment of the product of the design activity through (possibly multiple) evaluation cycles with users (Benyon, 2013). These phases include a collection of methods that HCI researchers have defined over time, which aim to properly involve the user during the whole design process (Duque et al., 2019).

Methods for Understanding the User. In order to understand the user, HCI researchers have developed a variety of tools, spanning from "formal techniques," which, for example, decompose the user's behavior into smaller tasks, to exploratory methods, such as surveys, semistructured interviews, and ethnographies.

During the first wave, the most popular methods for gaining user requirements were based on cognitive sciences, whereby HCI researchers primarily aimed to design for a single user interacting with a screen-based interface (Rogers, 2012). For instance, low-level modeling techniques such as the keystroke-level model provided predictions of the time that users will take to perform low-level physical tasks (Dix et al., 2003). Task analysis was another popular method allowing the study of the way people perform tasks with existing systems, by decomposing a given activity into subtasks (Dix et al., 2003). These analyses were then used to inform the design of new systems.

When computers became common outside the work environment, many innovative methods, unheard of in the 1970s and 1980s, were imported in and adapted to HCI research (Rogers, 2012), in order to understand people's "situated action." This change in the used methods paralleled the theoretical shifts that were involving HCI at those times, from a paradigm based on the cognitive sciences to the focus on contextual interaction characterizing the second wave (Bødker, 2006).

The emerging need to gain knowledge about the social and organizational forms of people's activities and to fully account for the contextual and situated nature of interaction encouraged the use of ethnographic methods in HCI (Dourish, 2006). Ethnography explores in depth what people do in a specific community, what tools they use, and the values and knowledge they have, attempting to grasp their own understanding of the world through contextual interviews, participant observation, and the analysis of relevant documents (Tedlock, 1991). In HCI, ethnography has been precisely used as a method to understand people in a particular context, by participating in their everyday activities, and to generate implications for the design of novel technologies (Sas et al., 2014). These implications, which were traditionally drawn through requirements gathered using more formal methods like task analysis, were criticized during the second wave for their failure to capture the richness of social and organizational settings (Crabtree et al., 2000). Ethnographic methods precisely emerged to address this limitation (Sas et al., 2014), and starting from the 1990s, they have become widely employed in the initial stages of the design process, as well as to conduct exploratory studies to identify novel opportunities for design.

The third wave, then, brought into HCI new interest in the experiential aspects of interaction to the detriment of the utilitarian ones, which, in turn, fostered the use of qualitative methods to understand the lived and meaning-laden experience of the person (Bødker, 2015). For instance, interpretive phenomenological analysis is a method for conducting and analyzing semistructured interviews that values individual idiosyncrasies and fits well the purpose of understanding people's sense-making, focusing on participants' perceptions of what is important in relation to the phenomenon under study (Smith & Shinebourne, 2012). Likewise, ethnography takes the form of reflexive ethnographies, which entail "confessional" modalities of recounting the fieldwork valuing the subjective experience of the ethnographer, instead of emphasizing objectivity and realism as common in traditional HCI ethnographic works (Rode, 2011), or autoethnographies, in which the first-person experience of the fieldworker is considered essential because it allows researchers and designers to grasp important matters for interaction design from an "internal" point of view (Rapp, 2018).

Methods for Designing the Interaction.　To design interaction between users and machines, HCI employs a variety of prototyping techniques that allow for the rapid development of systems (e.g., Benyon, 2013; Buxton, 2010). For instance, storyboards are graphical "stories" that depict the appearance of the system recounting a possible interaction of a user with it. They do not require computational power as they can be simply designed using paper and pencil. Likewise, the Wizard of Oz technique allows the designers to develop a limited-functionality prototype and then enhance its functionalities during the evaluation by providing the missing features through human intervention (Dix et al., 2003).

HCI researchers also use proactive techniques such as participatory design workshops and cultural probes (Bødker, 2006). In particular, participatory design is a set of practices related to people as active participants to the design activities (Muller, 2002) that were increasingly employed in HCI during the second wave, as well as to empower the users and give voice to marginalized communities (Hope et al., 2019). Other techniques like scenario-based design, which allows researchers to envision uses of a future technology through narrative (or visual) descriptions (Carroll, 1997), and Personas, which are stereotypical representations of possible users of a system (Cooper, 1999), further signal the abandonment of formal analysis and modeling of well-specified tasks characterizing the first wave, in favor of more lightweight methods (Rosson & Carroll, 2002).

Methods for Evaluating the Interaction. A central focus of HCI research is to evaluate systems and interfaces, in order to understand whether they are able to satisfy the user's needs. First-wave evaluation techniques were formal and often conducted in laboratory settings. An example of this kind of evaluation method is Goals, Operators, Methods, and Selection rules (GOMS), a set of models developed by Card et al. (1983) that were used to assess interactive systems and proved to be highly popular during the late 1980s and early 1990s (Rogers, 2012).

Another example refers to one of the traditional goals of HCI, which is to increase the systems' usability (i.e., to design easy-to-use technologies). Usability is a key construct in classical HCI research denoting a desired quality of interactive systems (Tractinsky, 2018). The HCI community has developed a variety of methods to evaluate usability in an interface or system: These span from experimental laboratory studies, where users are taken out of their normal work environment to take part in controlled tests, to field studies, which take the evaluator out into the users' environment to observe the system in action (Dix et al., 2003). Specific techniques like thinking aloud, which is a protocol wherein users are encouraged to verbalize their thoughts, doubts, and experiences while interacting with the interface, are also employed during usability tests (Alhadreti & Mayhew, 2018). Heuristic evaluation is another technique of usability analysis where several expert evaluators are presented with an interface design and asked to comment on it (Nielsen & Molich, 1990).

However, the theoretical shifts characterizing the second and third waves pushed the HCI community to look at evaluation methods that could take more into account the experiential, situated, and messy nature of interaction. At the same time, the emergence of novel technologies offered unprecedented modalities of interaction, which could be hardly assessed by employing the old techniques focused on usability. For instance, the advent of ubiquitous computing made it difficult to employ usability studies, which are task focused, in the sense that they require that users pay attention to and evaluate the interface, which is precisely what the ubiquitous systems are devised to avoid (Harrison et al., 2007). These theoretical and technological shifts, therefore, encouraged a wider adoption of "in-the-wild" evaluation methods, where the interaction with a system is studied in a real context of use, as well as explorative and qualitative techniques, like ethnographies and contextual inquiries, which can better capture the users' meaning-laden experience of interacting with technology in the real world.

However, quantitative, experimental methods did not disappear; rather, they are still widely used by HCI researchers to tackle more specific research questions, either alone or in combination with qualitative methods within mixed-method studies. For example, usability tests have certainly not become obsolete in HCI but have progressively widened their scope. During the third wave, the one who used a technology was mostly no longer conceptualized merely as a "user," an entity defined in terms of their use of a system, thus conveying a utilitarian perspective, but was often acknowledged as fully human, who exceeds the fact of using an artifact. Third-wave HCI researchers also paid more attention to systems' characteristics that do not refer to the improvement of performance and efficiency but deal with "internal" human aspects like experience and enjoyment. In this perspective, usability was redefined in terms of an array of experiential goals (e.g., motivating, aesthetically pleasing, fun) in addition to those focused on efficiency, leading to the definition of the concept of "user experience," an approach that is "about technology that fulfils more than just instrumental needs in a way that acknowledges its use as a subjective, situated, complex and dynamic encounter" (Hassenzahl & Tractinsky, 2006, p. 95). Protocols and tools (e.g., questionnaires) to evaluate usability, therefore, have been redefined accordingly, in order to quantitatively assess the nonutilitarian aspects of user experience (e.g., Vermeeren et al., 2010).

Rigorous quantitative methods are also employed to identify the specific effects that certain technologies may have on people. For example, randomized controlled trials, which are the gold standard of efficacy research in health sciences, may be used as an evaluation method to show whether a technology helped to bring about a change in users' behavior (e.g., Klasnja et al., 2011); controlled experiments, adopting between-subjects or within-subjects designs, for example, are conducted to test hypotheses or figure out which version of a technology has the greatest impact on the users (e.g., Morschheuser et al., 2019); and log analyses, which exploit the behavioral traces left by the users when they interact with a digital artifact, are performed to examine the users' interaction behavior (e.g., Xiao et al., 2020).

Research Through Design Methods.   It remains to say that, in the second decade of the 21st century, the HCI community has also witnessed an increase in the impact of design methods on research, which offered a further means to question and subvert the values that were traditionally embedded in traditional HCI designs and methodologies (Gaver, 2012). In particular, "research through design" has established itself as a "thing-making practice whose objects can offer a critique of the present and reveal alternative futures" (Bardzell et al., 2015, p. 2095). In this approach, design researchers, instead of aiming to produce a marketable prototype, use design methods to produce knowledge and question the status quo (Zimmerman et al., 2007; Zimmerman & Forlizzi, 2008). The design practice becomes a tool to explore and trigger critical reflections on the impact of technology on individuals, organizations, and society, as well as on the design practice itself. With this aim, different approaches and techniques are used. By embodying cultural critique in designs, for instance, critical design (Dunne & Raby, 2001) wants to provoke and encourage people to reflect on designs' participation in sociocultural norms and structures (Bardzell et al., 2012). Reflective design, instead, is a set of design principles and strategies that encourage researchers and users to rethink dominant metaphors and values, by bringing unconscious aspects of experience to conscious awareness (Sengers et al., 2005). Along this trend, design fictions recently emerged as a field of research through design in HCI: This method entails the creation of "fantasy prototypes" embedded in plausible narrative futures, which may not even exist, on the basis of the idea that concept designs can be usefully discussed without necessarily making them (Blythe, 2014). This method has been enacted in the forms of imaginary abstracts and papers (Blythe, 2014), fictional stories, movies, advertisements, and "worlds" (e.g., Blythe, 2017; Coulton et al., 2017; Rapp, 2020c).

LINES OF RESEARCH IN HCI

At the beginning of the third decade of the 21st century, HCI tackles practically every aspect of people's lives, including matters like religion and techno-spirituality, global crises like pandemics or humanmade disasters, food and poverty, the spreading of conspiracy theories on social media, peripheral practices mediated by technology, technologies for sensing context and body signals, self-changing and biointerfaces, robots for helping people with disabilities or the elderly, and virtual, mixed, and augmented reality applications, to name a few. There are no longer taboo subjects that cannot be analyzed by HCI researchers, like sexuality, illness, and death, if they relate to digital technology.

Despite this richness and diversity of current HCI studies, the HCI community has certainly aggregated around some particular research areas, which can be identified by looking at the list of the specialized conferences sponsored by the Association for Computing Machinery Special Interest Group on Computer–Human Interaction (ACM SIGCHI), which is the leading international community of students and professionals interested in research, education, and practical applications of HCI. Among the most popular ones, the International Conference on Intelligent User Interfaces (IUI) intertwines artificial intelligence (AI) and HCI, hosting research on artificial agents, human-centered AI, and intelligent multimodal systems; the UbiComp conference on Ubiquitous Computing focuses on wearable instruments, pervasive technologies, and mobile devices; the conference on Computer-Supported Cooperative Work and Social Computing (CSCW) is the premier venue for research on technologies that affect groups, organizations, communities, and networks; the international conference on Tangible, Embedded, and Embodied Interaction (TEI) revolves around tangible user interfaces, physical interaction design, interactive art and performance, and embodied cognition and perception; the conference on Designing Interactive Systems (DIS) is the arena in which to discuss matters about interactive system design; and the annual symposium on Computer–Human Interaction in Play (CHI PLAY) gathers researchers interested in video games and game-based interaction. Other examples of specialized research areas that have drawn the attention of the HCI community in the 21st century are automotive, the design of interactive systems specifically addressed to children, interactive surfaces and spaces, personalized and adaptive interfaces, collective intelligence, and creativity.

Given the variety of current HCI research, it is not possible to map an exhaustive and detailed picture of its research lines. What is possible is to point out several promising ones that intertwine the individual, social, and organizational levels of the usage of technologies to highlight the theoretical and methodological complexity that HCI is currently facing. The research lines described in the "gameful" interaction, self-tracking and behavior change technologies, and conversational agents subsections may be also of particular interest from the perspective of industrial and organizational psychology. Research on gameful interaction makes it visible that video games are often designed to mirror already existing social structures, such as work and organization ecosystems (Rapp, 2020b), and that many real-world work and organizational practices are now embedded with "game elements" aimed at motivating employees and improving organizational dynamics (Stanculescu et al., 2016). Studies on self-tracking and behavior change technologies point to the pervasive nature of current digital devices, which can be exploited in work and organizational environments to monitor employees, improve their well-being, and potentially modify their behavior. Finally, work on conversational agents exemplifies the increasing interest of HCI for AI technologies, which can be potentially used in organizations to automatize organizational dynamics, profoundly transform customer service, and give rise to new forms of collaboration between men and machines in the context of work.

"Gameful" Interaction. A first line of research revolves around video games, play, and "gameful interaction." As HCI started moving beyond the well-circumscribed context of work, it has had to deal with the emerging leisure practices mediated by technology, among which video game playing is now certainly one of the most relevant. In 2021, there were almost three billion gamers across the globe (Newzoo, 2021), and video games are reshaping the way they spend their time in their daily life (Rapp, 2022). The HCI community has not only designed and developed novel video games and modalities for interacting with them, like affective gaming systems that rely on physiological interaction (e.g., through emotion control), rather than on conventional devices (e.g., joystick; Bersak et al., 2001). It has also explored in depth the individual, social, and organizational dynamics of play: A variety of research highlighted, for example, that people may develop new affective bonds by playing video games or may use them to maintain and rework their existing relations (Rapp, 2018; Vella et al., 2016). Moreover, players may create stable organizational structures to solve complex in-game problems, which entail organizational assimilation dynamics, mentoring practices, hierarchies, and leaderships, which are conditioned by how the games are designed (Rapp, 2018, 2020b).

HCI research has also suggested that video games may yield impacts on players' lives, which reverberate far beyond the well-circumscribed world of the game. Researchers emphasized that video game play may constitute a meaningful activity (Mekler & Hornbæk, 2019) that allows players to reflect on how playing relates to their personal everyday life (Bopp et al., 2016; Zhang et al., 2020), providing benefits on their well-being and mental health (Boldi & Rapp, 2022): for instance, by improving their postwork recovery and reducing work-related stress (Collins & Cox, 2014), by giving them a sense of belonging in times when they may feel alone (Iacovides & Mekler, 2019), or by providing a way to escape from an unwanted reality in moments of crisis (Boldi et al., 2022).

By acknowledging the progressive seeping of gaming into the "real" world, HCI had the opportunity to explore emerging phenomena that intertwine "gameful" and "serious" aspects, engaging in novel design practices that attempt to exploit the "power of games" to affect people's everyday lives. Gamification, for instance, meant as the use of game design elements in nongame environments (Deterding et al., 2011), has established itself as a new design technique that may produce "positive" behavioral and motivational effects on people's health, work, and learning practices. As HCI practitioners and researchers began to embed nongame applications and services with gamelike interaction mechanisms, however, new theoretical and ethical matters arose, as these design techniques have been found, for example, to potentially encourage exploitation in the context of work and organizations (Rapp, 2020b).

Self-Tracking and Behavior Change Technologies. A second line of research is tied to the technological advancements in the miniaturization of sensors and the mining of contextual and personal data: These have recently led to the spread of wearable technologies, which are miniature devices that are worn under, over, or in clothing, and, more generally, of self-tracking devices, which allow people to constantly monitor their own body parameters and activities. In this technological landscape, HCI has been engaged in exploring novel modalities of interaction, which, for example, yield sensory alterations (Karpashevich et al., 2018), communicate enhanced visceral sensations (Neidlinger et al., 2017), or express emotions in an embodied way (Du et al., 2018): These and other prototypes that experiment on the opportunities that wearables have in augmenting people's capabilities of perceiving, feeling, and even remembering can be characterized as forms of body/mind extensions or prostheses, in line with the ideas of pioneers of the early history of computer science (Rapp, 2021).

On the other hand, HCI has explored how wearable and tracking technology may encourage changes in people's behavior or, at least, increase their "self-knowledge." The HCI research areas of "personal informatics" (Li et al., 2010) and "behavior change technologies" (Pinder et al., 2018) precisely exploit the personal data made available by these digital instruments to influence people's behavior subtly or openly in domains as diverse as health, sustainability, work, and safety (e.g., Luo et al., 2018). Alternatively, they may support individuals in becoming more aware of their own daily activities, body parameters, mind states, and habits (Rapp & Tirabeni, 2018; Rooksby et al., 2014). This kind of research has entailed the need to go in depth into the mechanisms that regulate behavior and self-knowledge (Rapp & Tirassa, 2017). Consequently, it has encouraged HCI scholars to engage with a variety of behavioral and psychological theories and to reflect on the theoretical issues arising when models, frameworks, and constructs originally developed in other disciplines are used to inform system design. For instance, HCI designers commonly utilize individual constructs rather than whole theoretical frameworks, because the former translate more easily into features of a behavior change technology. However, in so doing, they might inadvertently design a system based on single constructs, which, nonetheless, do not work independently but only in tandem with others (Hekler et al., 2013).

Moreover, by exploring the mechanisms underlying the modification of behavior, HCI researchers have had the opportunity to encounter a variety of existential, societal, and ethical challenges, which allowed them not only to connect the behavior change domain to other, fundamental aspects of people's life but also to critically reflect on the role of technology when used for this aim. In fact, behavior change technologies may potentially increase efficiency at work and wellness within an organization, promote a healthier society, and even help people make sense of their own existence, the changes that they undertake, and their inner sense of the self (Rapp et al., 2019). In this sense, research of this kind may respond to the recent call for adopting an existential perspective in HCI (Kaptelinin, 2018), connecting the experience of change to relevant existential matters such as illness, aging, and death, which found a place within HCI during "the third wave" (e.g., Gulotta et al., 2016).

However, technologies for modifying behavior may also negatively affect how organizations treat their employees by increasing control in the workplace; motivate people to behave in certain "desirable" ways, which nonetheless are enforced by the designers, possibly resulting in pervasive surveillance and "dataveillance"; and make individuals adhere to dominant values (like a sublimated idea of health; Brynjarsdóttir et al., 2012; Purpura et al., 2011). By reflecting on the potential side effects of behavior change technologies, HCI researchers have potentially unveiled the taken for granted embedded in them (Rapp, 2019). The adoption of a critical lens to look at this kind of technology thus makes apparent the broader critical trend that characterizes so much recent HCI research, which aims to identify the ramifications of the created designs, propose alternative values to the dominant ones, and envision alternate futures (Bardzell et al., 2012; Blythe, 2017).

Conversational Agents. A third line of promising HCI research relates to human–agent interaction, especially with reference to conversational agents. Making it possible to interact with computers through language is certainly one of the greatest ambitions of computer science since Alan Turing's imitation game (Turing, 1950), which was addressed to assess whether a computer can "deceive" a human by making that person believe it to be a human itself. Earlier efforts in creating conversational "interfaces," such as ELIZA in 1966 (Weizenbaum, 1966), which mimicked a Rogerian-style therapist encouraging users to reflect on themselves, and PARRY in 1972 (Colby et al., 1971), which masqueraded as a person with schizophrenia, developed agents that conversed with users by teletype and keyboard. HCI has recently begun to seriously tackle the investigation of how machines can effectively converse with humans, despite the still consistent limitations of the technology. This may be due to the rise in popularity of chatbots and virtual assistants, which are now increasingly adopted by companies to manage customer care relations and improve internal organizational processes, as well as to the availability of cloud-based services of composable AI building blocks, like the IBM Watson Developer Cloud, which can be used to easily develop new chatbots.

HCI researchers have both designed novel forms of conversational interfaces and explored how people react and communicate with prototypes and existing applications. In fact, novel conversation agents have been deployed in the attempt to experiment on key features of human–agent communication, like collaboration (Cranshaw et al., 2017) and empathy (Seering et al., 2020), which allowed HCI researchers to experiment on novel forms of cooperation between humans and agents in work and organizational contexts, explore ways to express and elicit emotional states during the interaction, and investigate how people may ascribe humanness to artificial entities.

This last point is particularly interesting for HCI, because conversational agents entail a diverse way for interacting with machines with respect to traditional interfaces: The computer, here, is no longer a mere "object" to be manipulated but may be seen by the users as a "subject" to which they attribute fundamental characteristics of human beings, like morality, agency, and empathy (Rapp et al., 2021). Empirical HCI research on humanness has mainly tackled speech-based intelligent personal assistants (IPAs), like Siri and Amazon Alexa, which helped to develop further the idea of humanness itself. For instance, it has been highlighted that humanness needs to be considered a multidimensional concept (Doyle et al., 2019) and that users often blur the lines between pairs of categories typically understood as nonoverlapping, like human–machine, when they converse with an IPA (Leahu et al., 2013).

In sum, contemporary HCI has to deal with technological developments that have consistently changed how we interact with computers as well as modified traditional oppositions that have driven design for many years, like those between play and work, inside and outside (the body), and humans and machines. Janlert and Stolterman (2015) have identified four ways through which an interface is traditionally conceptualized: a surface of contact between matching objects, a boundary of an independent object, a means for controlling an object, and a means for expressions and impressions, which all point to the crucial role of "surfaces" in traditional interfaces. They also point out that recent technological advancements may lead to other directions for the development of interactions: "things," that is, technological artifacts that can be interacted with in similar ways to traditional things; "beings," namely, technologies that become behavioral and intelligent; and "fields," in which the user becomes an inhabitant, traveling through a field of interactive forces. The list, nevertheless, cannot be seen as exhaustive, as novel devices like wearables and their progressive miniaturization may lead to further ways of conceiving interaction—for example, in the direction of "organisms," whereby the interface is internalized and the device is designed to perfectly couple the internal dynamics of the person's body, mind, and world (Rapp, 2021).

CONCLUSION

HCI is an interdisciplinary research field that emerged with the rise of the first digital machines to study how people interact with computers and how it is possible to design digital instruments that can satisfy their situated needs. As computers evolved during the 20th and 21st centuries, HCI underwent profound transformations as well: From a discipline based almost exclusively on cognitive sciences, it has opened up to other perspectives and approaches coming from sociology, anthropology, and philosophy. Such transformations brought into HCI a variety of new theories, far beyond the cognitive approaches used in its early history, also expanding the range of methods used by HCI researchers to understand people and design better technologies, from ethnographies to laboratory experiments, from participatory design techniques to design fictions. At the beginning of the third decade of the 21st century, HCI tackles almost whole people's lives, as digital technologies pervade almost every aspect of the everydayness: While HCI shows increasing interest in research areas as diverse as ubiquitous technologies, personalized and adaptive interfaces, computer-supported collaborative practices, and intelligent systems, promising lines of research of particular interest for industrial and organizational psychology can be identified in gameful interaction, self-tracking and behavior change technologies, and conversational agents.

FURTHER READING

Benyon, D. (2013). *Designing interactive systems: A comprehensive guide to HCI, UX and interaction design*. Pearson.

Card, S. K., Moran, T. P., & Newell, A. (1983). *The psychology of human-computer interaction*. Hillsdale Learning Center.

Clark, A. (2004). *Natural born cyborgs*. Oxford University Press.

Dix, A., Finlay, J., Abowd, G. D., & Beale, R. (2003). *Human-computer interaction* (3rd ed.). Pearson Education.

Dourish, P. (2001). *Where the action is: The foundations of embodied interaction*. MIT Press.

Filimowicz, M., & Tzankova, V. (2018a). *New directions in third wave human-computer interaction: Volume 1—Technologies*. Springer International.

Filimowicz, M., & Tzankova, V. (2018b). *New directions in third wave human-computer interaction: Volume 2—Methodologies*. Springer International.

Hutchins, E. (1995). *Cognition in the wild*. MIT Press.

Lazar, J., Feng, J. H., & Hochheiser, H. (2017). *Research methods in human-computer interaction*. Morgan Kaufmann.

Norman, D. A. (2013). *The design of everyday things: Revised and expanded edition.* MIT Press.

Preece, J., Sharp, H., & Rogers, Y. (2015). *Interaction design: Beyond human computer-interaction* (4th ed.). Wiley.

Rogers, Y. (2012). HCI theory: Classical, modern, and contemporary. *Synthesis Lectures on Human-Centered Informatics, 5*(2), 1–129.

Schüll, N. D. (2012). *Addiction by design: Machine gambling in Las Vegas.* Princeton University Press.

Suchman, L. A. (2007). *Human-machine reconfigurations: Plans and situated actions.* Cambridge University Press.

Winograd, T. (1996). *Bringing design to software.* Addison-Wesley.

Winograd, T., & Flores, F. (1986). *Understanding computers and cognition: A new foundation for design.* Addison-Wesley.

REFERENCES

Alhadreti, O., & Mayhew, P. (2018, April). Rethinking thinking aloud: A comparison of three think-aloud protocols [Conference session]. In *Proceedings of the 2018 CHI Conference on Human Factors in Computing Systems (CHI '18)*, Montréal, Canada. https://doi.org/10.1145/3173574.3173618

Alharthi, S. A., Alsaedi, O., Toups, Z. O., Tanenbaum, T. J., & Hammer, J. (2018, April). Playing to wait: A taxonomy of idle games [Conference session]. In *Proceedings of the 2018 CHI Conference on Human Factors in Computing Systems (CHI '18)*, Montréal, Canada. https://doi.org/10.1145/3173574.3174195

Anderson, J. R. (1983). *The architecture of cognition.* Harvard University Press.

Anderson, R. (1997). Work, ethnography, and system design. In A. Kent, J. Williams, & M. Dekker (Eds.), *Encyclopedia of microcomputing* (Vol. 20, pp. 159–183). Marcel Dekker.

Bardzell, J., Bardzell, S., & Hansen, L. K. (2015, April). Immodest proposals: Research through design and knowledge [Conference session]. In *Proceedings of the 33rd Annual ACM Conference on Human Factors in Computing Systems (CHI '15)*, Seoul, Korea. https://doi.org/10.1145/2702123.2702400

Bardzell, S., Bardzell, J., Forlizzi, J., Zimmerman, J., & Antanitis, J. (2012, June). Critical design and critical theory: The challenge of designing for provocation [Conference session]. In *Proceedings of the Designing Interactive Systems Conference (DIS '12)*, Newcastle, UK. https://doi.org/10.1145/2317956.2318001

Barnard, P. J., May, J., Duke, D. J., & Duce, D. A. (2000). Systems interactions and macrotheory. *ACM Transactions on Computer Human Interaction (TOCHI), 7*(2), 222–262. https://doi.org/10.1145/353485.353490

Benyon, D. (2013). *Designing interactive systems: A comprehensive guide to HCI, UX and interaction design.* Pearson.

Bersak, D., McDarby, G., Augenblick, N., McDarby, P., McDonnell, D., McDonald, B., & Karkun, R. (2001, September). Intelligent biofeedback using an immersive competitive environment. In *Paper at the designing ubiquitous computing games workshop at UbiComp* (pp. 1–6), Atlanta, GA.

Blythe, M. (2014, April). Research through design fiction: Narrative in real and imaginary abstracts [Conference session]. In *Proceedings of the SIGCHI Conference on Human Factors in Computing Systems (CHI '14)*, Toronto, Canada. https://doi.org/10.1145/2556288.2557098

Blythe, M. (2017, May). Research fiction: Storytelling, plot and design [Conference session]. In *Proceedings of the 2017 CHI Conference on Human Factors in Computing Systems (CHI '17)*, Denver, CO. https://doi.org/10.1145/3025453.3026023

Bødker, S. (2006, October). When second wave HCI meets third wave challenges [Conference session]. In *Proceedings of the 4th Nordic Conference on Human-Computer Interaction: Changing Roles*, Oslo, Norway.

Bødker, S. (2015). Third-wave HCI, 10 years later—Participation and sharing. *Interactions, 22*(5), 24–31.

Boldi, A., & Rapp, A. (2022). Commercial video games as a resource for mental health: A systematic literature review. *Behaviour & Information Technology, 41*(12), 2654–2690. https://doi.org/10.1080/0144929X.2021.1943524

Boldi, A., Rapp, A., & Tirassa, M. (2022). Playing during a crisis: The impact of commercial video games on the reconfiguration of people's life during the COVID-19 pandemic. *Human–Computer Interaction*, 1–42. https://doi.org/10.1080/07370024.2022.2050725

Bopp, J. A., Mekler, E. D., & Opwis, K. (2016, May). Negative emotion, positive experience? Emotionally moving moments in digital games [Conference session]. In *Proceedings of the 2016 CHI Conference on Human Factors in Computing Systems (CHI '16)*, San Jose, CA. https://doi.org/10.1145/2858036.2858227

Bourdieu, P. (1977). *Outline of a theory of practice* (R. Nice, Trans.). Cambridge University Press.

Brynjarsdóttir, H., Håkansson, M., Pierce, J., Baumer, E., DiSalvo, C., & Sengers, P. (2012, May). Sustainably unpersuaded: How persuasion narrows our vision of sustainability [Conference session]. In *Proceedings of the SIGCHI Conference on Human Factors in Computing Systems*, Austin, TX.

Bush, V. (1945). As we may think. *The Atlantic Monthly, 176*, 101–108.

Buxton, B. (2010). *Sketching user experiences: Getting the design right and the right design*. Morgan Kaufmann.

Card, S. K., Moran, T. P., & Newell, A. (1983). *The psychology of human-computer interaction* (pp. 24–25). Hillsdale Learning Center.

Carroll, J. (1997). Scenario-based design. In M. Helander & T. K. Landauer (Eds.), *Handbook of human computer interaction* (2nd ed., pp. 383–406). North Holland.

Carroll, J. (2003). Introduction: Toward a multidisciplinary science of human-computer interaction. In J. M. Carroll (Ed.), *HCI models, theories and frameworks* (pp. 1–9). Morgan Kaufmann.

Colby, K. M., Weber, S., & Hilf, F. D. (1971). Artificial paranoia. *Artificial Intelligence, 2*(1), 1–25. https://doi.org/10.1016/0004-3702(71)90002-6

Collins, E., & Cox, A. L. (2014). Switch on to games: Can digital games aid post-work recovery? *International Journal of Human-Computer Studies, 72*(8–9), 654–662. https://doi.org/10.1016/j.ijhcs.2013.12.006

Cooper, A. (1999). *The inmates are running the asylum: Why high tech products drive us crazy and how to restore the sanity*. Sams.

Coulton, P., Lindley, J., Sturdee, M., & Stead, M. (2017, March). Design fiction as world building [Conference session]. In *Proceedings of the 3rd Biennial Research Through Design Conference*, Edinburgh, UK.

Crabtree, A., O'Brien, J., Nichols, D., Rouncefield, M., & Twidale, M. (2000). Ethnomethodologically informed ethnography and information systems design. *The Journal of the Association for Information Science and Technology, 51*(7), 666–682.

Cranshaw, J., Elwany, E., Newman, T., Kocielnik, R., Yu, B., Soni, S., Teevan, J., & Monroy-Hernández, A. (2017, May). Calendar.help: Designing a workflow-based scheduling agent with humans in the loop [Conference session]. In *Proceedings of the 2017 CHI Conference on Human Factors in Computing Systems*, Denver, CO. https://doi.org/10.1145/3025453.3025780

Deterding, S. (2016, May). Contextual autonomy support in video game play: A grounded theory [Conference session]. In *Proceedings of the 2016 CHI Conference on Human Factors in Computing Systems (CHI '16)*, San Jose, CA. https://doi.org/10.1145/2858036.2858395

Deterding, S., Dixon, D., Khaled, R., & Nacke, L. (2011, September). From game design elements to gamefulness: Defining "Gamification" [Conference session]. In *Proceedings of the 15th International Academic MindTrek Conference: Envisioning Future Media Environments (MindTrek '11)*, Tampere, Finland.

Dix, A., Finlay, J., Abowd, G. D., & Beale, R. (2003). *Human-computer interaction*. Pearson Education.

Dourish, P. (2001). *Where the action is: The foundations of embodied interaction*. MIT Press.

Dourish, P. (2004). What we talk about when we talk about context. *Personal and Ubiquitous Computing, 8*(1), 19–30.

Dourish, P. (2006, April). Implications for design. In R. Grinter, T. Rodden, P. Aoki, E. Cutrell, R. Jeffries, & G. Olson (Eds.), *Proceedings of the SIGCHI Conference on Human Factors in Computing Systems (CHI '06)*, Montréal, Canada. http://doi.acm.org/10.1145/1124772.1124855

Dourish, P., & Button, G. (1998). On "technomethodology": Foundational relationships between ethnomethodology and system design. *Human–Computer Interaction, 13*(4), 395–432.

Doyle, P. R., Edwards, J., Dumbleton, O., Clark, L., & Cowan, B. R. (2019, October). Mapping perceptions of humanness in intelligent personal assistant interaction [Conference session]. In *Proceedings of the 21st International Conference on Human-Computer Interaction With Mobile Devices and Services (MobileHCI '19)*, Taipei, Taiwan. https://doi.org/10.1145/3338286.3340116

Du, J., Markopoulos, P., Wang, Q., Toeters, M., & Gong, T. (2018, March). ShapeTex: Implementing shape-changing structures in fabric for wearable actuation [Conference session]. In *Proceedings of the Twelfth International Conference on Tangible, Embedded, and Embodied Interaction (TEI '18)*, Stockholm, Sweden. https://doi.org/10.1145/3173225.3173245

Dunne, A., & Raby, F. (2001). *Design noir: The secret life of electronic objects*. Birkh.

Duque, E., Fonseca, G., Vieira, H., Gontijo, G., & Ishitani, L. (2019, October). A systematic literature review on user centered design and participatory design with older people [Conference session]. In *Proceedings of the 18th Brazilian Symposium on Human Factors in Computing Systems (IHC '19)*, Vitória Espírito Santo, Brazil. https://doi.org/10.1145/3357155.3358471

Ehn, P. (1988). *Work-oriented design of computer artifacts*. Arbetlivscentrum.

Engelbart, D. C. (1962). *Augmenting human intellect: A conceptual framework*. Stanford Research Institute.

Fallman, D. (2011, May). The new good: Exploring the potential of philosophy of technology to contribute to human–computer interaction [Conference session]. In *Proceedings of the SIGCHI Conference on Human Factors in Computing Systems (CHI '11)*, Vancouver, BC. https://doi.org/10.1145/1978942.1979099

Fodor, J. (1975). *The language of thought*. Thomas Y. Crowell.

Fodor, J. (1983). *The modularity of mind*. MIT Press.

Furniss, D., Blandford, A., & Curzon, P. (2011, May). Confessions from a grounded theory PhD: Experiences and lessons learnt [Conference session]. In *Proceedings of the SIGCHI Conference on Human Factors in Computing Systems (CHI '11)*, Vancouver, BC. https://doi.org/10.1145/1978942.1978960

Gallagher, S., & Zahavi, D. (2008). *The phenomenological mind*. Routledge.

Ganglbauer, E., Fitzpatrick, G., & Comber, R. (2013). Negotiating food waste: Using a practice lens to inform design. *ACM Transactions on Computer–Human Interaction (TOCHI), 20*(2), 1–25.

Gaver, W. (1991, March). Technology affordances [Conference session]. In *Proceedings of the SIGCHI Conference on Human Factors in Computing Systems (CHI '91)*, New Orleans, LA. https://doi.org/10.1145/108844.108856

Gaver, W. (2012, May). What should we expect from research through design [Conference session]. In *Proceedings of the SIGCHI Conference on Human Factors in Computing Systems*, Austin, TX.

Gibson, J. J. (1979). *The ecological approach to visual perception*. Houghton-Mifflin.

Glaser, B., & Strauss, A. (1967). *Discovery of grounded theory*. Sociological Press.

Goldkuhl, G., & Cronholm, S. (2010). Adding theoretical grounding to grounded theory: Toward multi-grounded theory. *International Journal of Qualitative Methods, 9*(2), 187–205. https://doi.org/10.1177/160940691000900205

Grudin, J. (2005). Three faces of human-computer interaction. *IEEE Annals of the History of Computing, 27*(4), 46–62.

Grudin, J. (2012). A moving target—The evolution of human-computer interaction. In J. Jacko (Ed.), *Human-computer interaction handbook* (3rd ed., pp. xxvii–lxi). Taylor & Francis.

Gulotta, R., Gerritsen, D. B., Kelliher, A., & Forlizzi, J. (2016, June). Engaging with death online: An analysis of systems that support legacy-making, bereavement, and remembrance [Conference session]. In *Proceedings of the 2016 ACM Conference on Designing Interactive Systems*, Brisbane, Australia.

Harrison, S., Tatar, D., & Sengers, P. (2007, April). The three paradigms of HCI [Conference session]. In *Alt. Chi: Session at the SIGCHI Conference on Human Factors in Computing Systems*, San Jose, CA.

Hassenzahl, M., & Tractinsky, N. (2006). User experience—A research agenda. *Behaviour & Information Technology*, 25(2), 91–97.

Haugeland, J. (1985). *Artificial intelligence: The very idea*. MIT Press.

Hekler, E. B., Klasnja, P., Froehlich, J. E., & Buman, M. P. (2013, April). Mind the theoretical gap: Interpreting, using, and developing behavioral theory in HCI research [Conference session]. In *Proceedings of the SIGCHI Conference on Human Factors in Computing Systems (CHI '13)*, Paris, France. https://doi.org/10.1145/2470654.2466452

Henwood, K., & Pidgeon, N. (2003). Grounded theory in psychological research. In P. Camic, J. Rhodes, & L. Yardley (Eds.), *Qualitative research in psychology: Expanding perspectives in methodology and design* (pp. 131–155). American Psychological Association.

Hollan, J., Hutchins, E., & Kirsh, D. (2000). Distributed cognition: Toward a new foundation for human-computer interaction research. *ACM Transactions on Human-Computer Interaction (TOCHI)*, 7(2), 174–196. https://doi.org/10.1145/353485.353487

Höök, K., Jonsson, M. P., Ståhl, A., & Mercurio, J. (2016, May). Somaesthetic appreciation design [Conference session]. In *Proceedings of the 2016 CHI Conference on Human Factors in Computing Systems (CHI '16)*, San Jose, CA. https://doi.org/10.1145/2858036.2858583

Hope, A., D'Ignazio, C., Hoy, J., Michelson, R., Roberts, J., Krontiris, K., & Zuckerman, E. (2019, May). Hackathons as participatory design: Iterating feminist utopias [Conference session]. In *Proceedings of the 2019 CHI Conference on Human Factors in Computing Systems (CHI '19)*, Glasgow, UK. https://doi.org/10.1145/3290605.3300291

Husserl, E. (1962). *Phenomenological psychology: Lectures from the summer semester, 1925*. Martinus Nijhoff.

Hutchins, E. (1995). *Cognition in the wild*. MIT Press.

Hutchins, E., Hollan, J. D., & Norman, D. (1986). Direct manipulation interfaces. In S. Draper & D. Norman (Eds.), *User centred system design* (pp. 87–124). Lawrence Erlbaum Associates.

Iacovides, I., & Mekler, E. D. (2019). The role of gaming during difficult life experiences. In *Proceedings of the 2019 CHI Conference on Human Factors in Computing Systems (CHI '19)* (pp. 1–12), Glasgow, UK.

Janlert, L.-E., & Stolterman, E. (2015). Faceless interaction—A conceptual examination of the notion of interface: Past, present, and future. *Human–Computer Interaction*, 30(6), 507–539. https://doi.org/10.1080/07370024.2014.944313

Kaptelinin, V. (2018, April). Technology and the givens of existence: Toward an existential inquiry framework in HCI research [Conference session]. In *Proceedings of the 2018 CHI Conference on Human Factors in Computing Systems (CHI '18)*, Montréal, Canada.

Karpashevich, P., Hornecker, E., Honauer, M., & Sanches, P. (2018, April). Reinterpreting Schlemmer's triadic ballet: Interactive costume for unthinkable movements [Conference session]. In *Proceedings of the 2018 CHI Conference on Human Factors in Computing Systems (CHI '18)*, Montréal, Canada.

Klasnja, P., Consolvo, S., & Pratt, W. (2011, May). How to evaluate technologies for health behavior change in HCI research [Conference session]. In *Proceedings of the SIGCHI Conference on Human Factors in Computing Systems*, Vancouver, Canada.

Kuijer, L., De Jong, A., & van Eijk, D. (2013). Practices as a unit of design: An exploration of theoretical guidelines in a study on bathing. *ACM Transactions on Computer–Human Interaction (TOCHI)*, 20(4), 1–22.

Kuutti, K., & Bannon, L. J. (2014, April). The turn to practice in HCI: Towards a research agenda [Conference session]. In *Proceedings of the SIGCHI Conference on Human Factors in Computing Systems (CHI '14)*, Toronto, Canada. https://doi.org/10.1145/2556288.2557111

Latour, B. (1992). Where are the missing masses? The sociology of a few mundane artifacts. In W. E. Bijker & J. Law (Eds.), *Shaping technology/building society: Studies sociotechnical change* (pp. 225–258). MIT Press.

Leahu, L., Cohn, M., & March, W. (2013, April). How categories come to matter [Conference session]. In *Proceedings of the SIGCHI Conference on Human Factors in Computing Systems (CHI '13)*, Paris, France. https://doi.org/10.1145/2470654.2466455

Li, I., Dey, A., & Forlizzi, J. (2010, April). A stage-based model of personal informatics systems [Conference session]. In *Proceedings of the SIGCHI Conference on Human Factors in Computing Systems (CHI '10)*, Atlanta, GA. https://doi.org/10.1145/1753326.1753409

Licklider, J. C. R. (1960). Man-computer symbiosis. *Transactions on Human Factors in Electronics, HFE-1*(1), 4–11. https://doi.org/10.1109/THFE2.1960.4503259

Luo, Y., Lee, B., Wohn, D. Y., Rebar, A. L., Conroy, D. E., & Choe, E. K. (2018, April). Time for break: Understanding information workers' sedentary behavior through a break prompting system [Conference session]. In *Proceedings of the 2018 CHI Conference on Human Factors in Computing Systems (CHI '18)*, Montréal, Canada. https://doi.org/10.1145/3173574.3173701

McCulloch, W., & Pitts, W. (1943). A logical calculus of the ideas immanent in nervous activity. *Bulletin of Mathematical Biophysics, 7*, 115–133.

Mekler, E. D., & Hornbæk, K. (2019, May). A framework for the experience of meaning in human-computer interaction [Conference session]. In *Proceedings of the 2019 CHI Conference on Human Factors in Computing Systems (CHI '19)*, Glasgow, UK. https://doi.org/10.1145/3290605.3300455

Miller, G. A. (1956). The magical number seven, plus or minus two: Some limits on our capacity for processing information. *Psychological Review, 63*, 81–97.

Monk, A. (1984). *Fundamentals of human-computer interaction*. Academic Press.

Morschheuser, B., Hamari, J., & Maedche, A. (2019). Cooperation or competition—When do people contribute more? A field experiment on gamification of crowdsourcing. *International Journal of Human-Computer Studies, 127*, 7–24.

Muller, M. J. (2002). Participatory design: The third space in HCI. In J. A. Jacko & A. Sears (Eds.), *The human-computer interaction handbook: Fundamentals, evolving technologies and emerging applications* (pp. 1051–1068). Lawrence Erlbaum Associates.

Nardi, B. A. (1996). *Context and consciousness: Activity theory and human-computer interaction*. MIT Press.

Neidlinger, K., Truong, K. P., Telfair, C., Feijs, L., Dertien, E., & Evers, V. (2017, March). AWElectric: That gave me goosebumps, did you feel it too? [Conference session]. In *Proceedings of the Eleventh International Conference on Tangible, Embedded, and Embodied Interaction (TEI '17)*, Yokohama, Japan. https://doi.org/10.1145/3024969.3025004

Newell, A., & Simon, H. A. (1972). *Human problem solving*. Prentice-Hall.

Newzoo (2021). *Newzoo Global Games Market Report 2021*. https://newzoo.com/insights/trend-reports/newzoo-global-games-market-report-2021-free-version/

Nielsen, J., & Molich, R. (1990, March). Heuristic evaluation of user interfaces [Conference session]. In *Proceedings of the SIGCHI Conference on Human Factors in Computing Systems (CHI '90)*, Seattle, WA. https://doi.org/10.1145/97243.97281

Norman, D. A. (1986). Cognitive engineering. In S. Draper & D. Norman (Eds.), *User centered system design* (pp. 31–61). Lawrence Erlbaum Associates.

Norman, D. A. (1988). *The psychology of everyday things*. Basic Books.

Norman, D. A. (1999). *Affordances, conventions and design: Interactions*. Association for Computing Machinery.

Ohlin, F., & Olsson, C. M. (2015, September). Beyond a utility view of personal informatics: A postphenomenological framework [Conference session]. In *Adjunct Proceedings of the 2015 ACM International Joint Conference on Pervasive and Ubiquitous Computing and Proceedings of the 2015 ACM International Symposium on Wearable Computers (UbiComp/ISWC '15 Adjunct)*, Osaka, Japan. https://doi.org/10.1145/2800835.2800965

Oinas-Kukkonen, H., & Harjumaa, M. (2009). Persuasive systems design: Key issues, process model, and system features. *Communications of the Association for Information Systems, 24*(1), 28.

Pierce, J., Strengers, Y., Sengers, P., & Bødker, S. (2013). Introduction to the special issue on practice-oriented approaches to sustainable HCI. *ACM Transactions on Computer–Human Interaction (TOCHI), 20*(4), 1–8.

Pinder, C., Vermeulen, J., Cowan, B. R., & Beale, R. (2018). Digital behaviour change interventions to break and form habits. *ACM Transactions on Computer–Human Interaction (TOCHI), 25*(3), 1–66.

Purpura, S., Schwanda, V., Williams, K., Stubler, W., & Sengers, P. (2011, May). Fit4Life: The design of a persuasive technology promoting healthy behavior and ideal weight [Conference session]. In *Proceedings of the SIGCHI Conference on Human Factors in Computing Systems (CHI '11)*, Vancouver, Canada. https://doi.org/10.1145/1978942.1979003

Rapp, A. (2018). Social game elements in World of Warcraft: Interpersonal relations, groups and organizations for gamification design. *International Journal of Human–Computer Interaction, 34*(8), 759–773. https://doi.org/10.1080/10447318.2018.1461760

Rapp, A. (2019). Design fictions for behaviour change: Exploring the long-term impacts of technology through the creation of fictional future prototypes. *Behaviour & Information Technology, 38*(3), 244–272. https://doi.org/10.1080/0144929X.2018.1526970

Rapp, A. (2020a, December). A gameful organizational assimilation process: Insights from World of Warcraft for gamification design [Conference session]. In *Proceedings of the ACM on Human-Computer Interaction, 4(CSCW3)*, New York, NY. https://doi.org/10.1145/3434172

Rapp, A. (2020b, July–August). An exploration of World of Warcraft for the gamification of virtual organizations. *Electronic Commerce Research and Applications, 42*, 100985, 1–17. https://doi.org/10.1016/j.elerap.2020.100985

Rapp, A. (2020c). Design fictions for learning: A method for supporting students in reflecting on technology in human-computer interaction courses. *Computers & Education, 145*, 1–18. https://doi.org/10.1016/j.compedu.2019.103725

Rapp, A. (2021). Wearable technologies as extensions: A postphenomenological framework and its design implications. *Human–Computer Interaction*, 1–39. https://doi.org/10.1080/07370024.2021.1927039

Rapp, A. (2022). Time, engagement and video games: How game design elements shape the temporalities of play in massively multiplayer online role-playing games. *Information Systems Journal, 32*(1), 5–32. https://doi.org/10.1111/isj.12328

Rapp, A., Curti, L., & Boldi, A. (2021). The human side of human-chatbot interaction: A systematic literature review of ten years of research on text-based chatbots. *International Journal of Human-Computer Studies, 151*, 102630. https://doi.org/10.1016/j.ijhcs.2021.102630

Rapp, A., Marino, A., Simeoni, R., & Cena, F. (2017). An ethnographic study of packaging-free purchasing: Designing an interactive system to support sustainable social practices. *Behaviour & Information Technology, 36*(11), 1193–1217. https://doi.org/10.1080/0144929X.2017.1365170

Rapp, A., Tirabeni, L. (2018). Personal informatics for sport: Meaning, body, and social relations in amateur and elite athletes. *ACM Transactions on Computer-Human Interaction (TOCHI), 25*(3), 1–30. https://doi.org/10.1145/3196829

Rapp, A., & Tirassa, M. (2017). Know thyself: A theory of the self for personal informatics. *Human–Computer Interaction, 32*(5–6), 335–380. https://doi.org/10.1080/07370024.2017.1285704

Rapp, A., Tirassa, M., & Tirabeni, L. (2019). Rethinking technologies for behavior change: A view from the inside of human change. *ACM Transactions on Computer–Human Interaction (TOCHI), 26*(4), 33. https://doi.org/10.1145/3318142

Reckwitz, A. (2002). Toward a theory of social practices: A development in culturalist theorizing. *European Journal of Social Theory, 5*(2), 243–263. https://doi.org/10.1177/13684310222225432

Rode, J. A. (2011, May). Reflexivity in digital anthropology [Conference session]. In *Proceedings of the SIGCHI Conference on Human Factors in Computing Systems (CHI '11)*, Vancouver, Canada. https://doi .org/10.1145/1978942.1978961

Rogers, Y. (2009, November). The changing face of human-computer interaction in the age of ubiquitous computing [Paper presentation]. In *Symposium of the Austrian HCI and Usability Engineering Group*, Linz, Austria.

Rogers, Y. (2012). *HCI theory: Classical, modern, and contemporary: Synthesis lectures on human-centered informatics*. Morgan & Claypool.

Rooksby, J., Rost, M., Morrison, A., & Chalmers, M. (2014, April). Personal tracking as lived informatics [Conference session]. In *Proceedings of the SIGCHI Conference on Human Factors in Computing Systems*, Toronto, Canada.

Rosenberger, R., & Verbeek, P.-P. (2015). A field guide to postphenomenology. In R. Rosenberger & P.-P. Verbeek (Eds.), *Postphenomenological investigations: Essays on human-technology relations: Postphenomenology and the philosophy of technology* (pp. 9–41). Lexington Books.

Rosson, M. B., & Carroll, J. M. (2002). Scenario-based design. In J. Jacko & A. Sears (Eds.), *The human-computer interaction handbook: Fundamentals, evolving technologies and emerging applications* (pp. 1032–1050). Lawrence Erlbaum Associates.

Sarker, S., Lau, F., & Sahay, S. (2001). Using an adapted grounded theory approach for inductive theory building about virtual team development. *The Data Base for Advances in Information Systems, 32*(1), 38–56. https://doi.org/10.1145/506740.506745

Sas, C., Whittaker, S., Dow, S., Forlizzi, J., & Zimmerman, J. (2014, April). Generating implications for design through design research [Conference session]. In *Proceedings of the SIGCHI Conference on Human Factors in Computing Systems (CHI '14)*, Toronto, Canada. https://doi.org/10.1145/2556288 .2557357

Schatzki, T. R. (2001). Introduction: Practice theory. In T. R. Schatzki, K. Knorr-Cetina, & E. von Savigny (Eds.), *The practice turn in contemporary theory* (pp. 1–14). Routledge.

Seering, J., Luria, M., Ye, C., Kaufman, G., & Hammer, J. (2020, April). It takes a village: Integrating an adaptive chatbot into an online gaming community [Conference session]. In *Proceedings of the 2020 CHI Conference on Human Factors in Computing Systems*, Online. https://doi.org/10.1145/3313831 .3376708

Sengers, P., Boehner, K., David, S., & Kaye, J. (2005, August). Reflective design [Conference session]. In *Proceedings of the Decennial Conference on Critical Computing*, Aarhus Denmark.

Shackel, B. (1997). HCI: Whence and whither? *Journal of ASIS, 48*(11), 970–986.

Smith, J. A., & Shinebourne, P. (2012). *Interpretative phenomenological analysis*. American Psychological Association.

Stanculescu, L. C., Bozzon, A., Sips, R.-J., & Houben, G. (2016, February). Work and play: An experiment in enterprise gamification [Conference session]. In *Proceedings of the 19th ACM Conference on Computer-Supported Cooperative Work and Social Computing*, San Francisco, CA.

Suchman, L., Blomberg, J., Orr, J. E., & Trigg, R. (1999). Reconstructing technologies as social practice. *American Behavioral Scientist, 43*(3), 392–408.

Suchman, L. A. (1987). *Plans and situated actions: The problem of human-machine communication*. Cambridge University Press.

Svanæs, D. (2013). Interaction design for and with the lived body: Some implications of Merleau-Ponty's phenomenology. *ACM Transactions on Computer–Human Interaction (TOCHI), 20*(1), 30. https://doi .org/10.1145/2442106.2442114

Tedlock, B. (1991). From participant observation to the observation of participation: The emergence of narrative ethnography. *Journal of Anthropological Research, 47*(1), 69–94.

Tractinsky, N. (2018). The usability construct: A dead end? *Human–Computer Interaction, 33*(2), 131–177.

Turing, A. M. (1950). Computing machinery and intelligence. *Mind, 49,* 433–460.

Vella, K., Johnson, D., & Mitchell, J. (2016). Playing support: Social connectedness amongst male video-game players. In *Proceedings of the 2016 Annual Symposium on Computer-Human Interaction in Play Companion Extended Abstracts,* Austin, TX (pp. 343–350). ACM. https://doi.org/10.1145/2968120.2987734

Vermeeren, A. P., Law, E. L. C., Roto, V., Obrist, M., Hoonhout, J., & Väänänen-Vainio-Mattila, K. (2010, October). User experience evaluation methods: Current state and development needs [Conference session]. In *Proceedings of the 6th Nordic Conference on Human-Computer Interaction: Extending Boundaries,* Reykjavik, Iceland.

Wakkary, R. (2020). Nomadic practices: A posthuman theory for knowing design. *International Journal of Design, 14*(3), 117.

Wakkary, R., Oogjes, D., Lin, H., & Hauser, S. (2018, April). Philosophers living with the tilting bowl [Conference session]. In *Proceedings of the 2018 CHI Conference on Human Factors in Computing Systems (CHI '18),* Montréal, Canada. https://doi.org/10.1145/3173574.3173668

Weiser, M. (1991). The computer for the 21st century. *Scientific American, 265*(3), 94–104. https://doi.org/10.1038/scientificamerican0991-94

Weizenbaum, J. (1966). ELIZA—A computer program for the study of natural language communication between man and machine. *Communications of the ACM, 9*(1), 36–45. https://doi.org/10.1145/365153.365168

Winograd, T., & Flores, F. (1986). *Understanding computers and cognition: A new foundation for design.* Addison-Wesley.

Wittgenstein, L. (1967). *Philosophical investigations* (G. E. M. Anscombe, Trans.). Blackwell. (Original work published 1953).

Xiao, Z., Zhou, M. X., Chen, W., Yang, H., & Chi, C. (2020, April). If I hear you correctly: Building and evaluating interview chatbots with active listening skills [Conference session]. In *Proceedings of the 2020 CHI Conference on Human Factors in Computing Systems,* Online. https://doi.org/10.1145/3313831.3376131

Zhang, X., Gui, X., Kou, Y., & Li, Y. (2020). Mobile collocated gaming: Collaborative play and meaning-making on a university campus. *Proceedings of the ACM on Human-Computer Interaction, 4*(CSCW2), 1–24. https://doi.org/10.1145/3415213

Zimmerman, J., & Forlizzi, J. (2008). The role of design artifacts in design theory construction. *Artifact: Journal of Design Practice, 2*(1), 41–45.

Zimmerman, J., Forlizzi, J., & Evenson S. (2007, April). Research through design as a method for interaction design research in HCI [Conference session]. In *Proceedings of the SIGCHI Conference on Human Factors in Computing Systems (CHI '07),* San Jose, CA. https://doi.org/10.1145/1240624.1240704

Amon Rapp

TELEWORK AND REMOTE WORK

TOFFLER'S VISION OF TELEWORK IN 1980

COVID-19 forced hundreds of millions of people around the world into teleworking; what used to be voluntary and agreed became a duty. However, the scaling up of telework and remote work to become a "new normal" mode of working was anticipated 50 years ago by a well-known futurist Alvin Toffler (1980) in his book *The Third Wave*. The third wave refers to a postindustrial society after the Agricultural and the Industrial Ages. It is intriguing and inspiring to see how these prophesies have come true in recent years and after the pandemic.

Based on the work by Nilles et al. (1976), Toffler envisioned a new production system that would shift millions of jobs out of the factories and offices into homes and local work centers. One driving force he foresaw was that manufacturing workers would increasingly handle information instead of things; they would become knowledge workers. Second, "smart" technologies such as teleconferencing would enable working in "the electronic cottage" (the name given by Toffler to a new workplace). Toffler saw the motivation, management, and efforts needed in corporate and social reorganization as hindrances to this shift, as well as the inability to handle communication vicariously, especially in nonroutine jobs. In the vision, the following drivers justified the change:

- *The economic trade-off between transportation and telecommunication*: The escalating costs of commuting (e.g., construction of new highways vs. the decreasing costs of telecommuting) as well as the price of energy used in computers. In addition, the reduction of commuting would reduce pollution.
- *Social factors*: Shorter workdays because of less commuting time and value changes in the nuclear family working together as a unit.

Toffler further envisioned that as working at and near the home increased, the consequences would include

- *Community impacts*: Work at home could mean greater community stability—for example, making friendships deeper and making engaging in local politics possible.
- *Environmental impacts*: Reduced energy requirements and energy decentralization—for example, the increased use of solar, wind, and other alternative energy technologies and a decline in pollution because of renewable energy sources and smaller releases of highly concentrated pollutants.
- *Economic impacts*: The electronic, computer, communications, and service industries would flourish, whereas the oil, paper-making, car, and real estate industries would be hurt. Small-scale computer stores and information services and other small firms would spring up.
- *Psychological impacts*: Deepening of face-to-face and emotional relationships in both the home and the neighborhood.

Overall, it was expected that the benefits would include more leisure time, an enhanced work-life balance, and greater work autonomy at the individual level, as well as less traffic congestion and environmental pollution because of reduced commuting at the societal level. People could also work at home part-time and outside the home in dispersed telecenters. To foster these developments, there would be a need to develop new leadership and management patterns. During the last 50 years, the evidence on telework—and remote work overall—has accumulated, showing the partial correctness of the vision, but the nature of reality is more complicated.

WHAT IS TELEWORK AND REMOTE WORK?

There are numerous names used to describe working from a place other than an office or company premises (e.g., Allen et al., 2015). These include: "telecommuting," "telework," "remote work," "home-based work," "flexible work," "distance work," "multilocational work," "mobile work," and even "crowdwork." For historical reasons, there is a slight difference between the "telework" and "remote work" concepts. Their contents are related to the development and use of information and communication technologies (ICTs) and the locations of workplaces. According to the International Labour Organization ([ILO], 2020, p. 6), the basic difference between telework and remote work is that a teleworker uses personal electronic devices in addition to working remotely. Table 1 defines the main types of telework and remote work.

Telework. One form of telework is telecommuting, which involves using communication technologies and refers to work activities conducted outside a main office but related to it (Eurofound & International Labour Office, 2017; Gareis, 2006; Messenger, 2019; Nilles et al., 1976; Olson & Primps, 1984; Toffler, 1980). Telecommuting was first described in *The Telecommunications-Transportation Tradeoff* (Nilles et al., 1976, p. 4), which proposed telecommuting as an alternative to transportation: "it appears probable that many information industry workers could 'telecommute'. That is, they could perform their work by using communication and computer technologies, at locations much closer to their homes than is the case now." The envisioned firms were broken up into satellite offices, where employees could

Table 1. Definitions of the Main Types of Telework and Remote Work

➢ **Remote work** is a work arrangement in which an employee resides and works at a location beyond the local commuting area of the employing organization's worksite (e.g., Mokhtarian, 1991). A remote worker can be self-employed or dependent on an employer.

➢ **Telework** is fully or partially carried out at an alternative location rather than the default place of work, and personal electric devices (i.e., telecommunications) are used to perform the work (e.g., International Labour Organization, 2020). A teleworker can be a self-employed or a dependent worker.

➢ **Home-based telework** occurs at or from home using electronic devices. "Permanent teleworkers" spend more than 90% of their working time from home. "Supplementary teleworkers" or "regular teleworkers" spend one full day per week working at home. "Occasional teleworkers" have worked at/from home at least once in the last 4 weeks (e.g., International Labour Organization, 2020).

➢ **Home-based remote work** is carried out at or from home. Home-based workers do not use electronic devices. They can equally work "permanently," "regularly," and "occasionally."

➢ **Digital online telework** is a form of employment that uses online platforms to enable individuals, teams, and organizations to access other individuals or organizations to solve problems or to provide services in exchange for payment (e.g., Berg et al., 2018).

➢ **A virtual team (VT)** is a group of people who work interdependently with a shared purpose across space, time, and organizational boundaries using technology (e.g., Lipnack & Stamps, 2000).

work remotely when they did not need to be physically present at company headquarters. Telework is fully or partially carried out at an alternative location from the default place of work, and personal electric devices (i.e., telecommunications) are used to perform the work (International Labour Office, 2020, p. 6). The default place of work can be understood as the place or location where the work would typically be expected to be carried out, taking into account the profession and status in employment. What makes telework a unique category is that the work carried out remotely includes the use of personal electronic devices.

Remote Work.   Remote work is a more comprehensive concept and does not require visits to the main workplace or the use of electronic personal devices, leaving open many types and places of work (e.g., Bailey & Kurland, 2002; Gareis, 2006; International Labour Organization, 2020; Korte & Wynne, 1996; Sullivan, 2003; Van der Wielen & Taillieu, 1993), and it can involve mobile work. Mokhtarian (1991, p. 3) suggested one reasonable definition of remote work: *"work done by an individual while at a different location than the person(s) directly supervising and/or paying for it."* Telework and remote work provide the viewpoint of an individual working remotely using or not using ICT to interact and work with others. The use of technologies also links telework to virtual teamwork.

In both telework and remote work, the physical location that a worker uses is the main criterion, and it categorizes basic types of workplace and work (e.g., Eurofound & International Labour Office, 2017; Gareis et al., 2004; International Labour Office, 2020):

> *The home as a workplace* is where a person works full- or part-time. Both independent and dependent workers can do "remote work at and from home"; for example, self-employed people may be engaged in artisanal production or industrial piece-rate production carried out from home. The home is their main workplace. The home is also a place to work remotely for independent self-employed freelancers, entrepreneurs, consultants, plumbers, and so on, who use the home as a base from where they may go to meet partners and customers and communicate with them face to face.
>
> *Home-based teleworkers* work at home as opposed to working from an employer's workplace and are dependent on an employer. They use electronic devices in their work. This work type is further subdivided according to the amount of working time spent at home. "Permanent teleworkers" are those who spend more than 90% of their working time at home. "Supplementary teleworkers" or "regular teleworkers" (International Labour Organization, 2020) are those who spend one full day per week working at home. "Occasional teleworkers" are those who have worked at/from home at least once in the last 4 weeks (International Labour Organization, 2020). The rest of the time they work in the main workplace. In addition, *telework* can be carried out *from home*, visiting other places for work and using a variety of technologies.
>
> *Home-based remote workers* carry out their remote work at and from their home. They do not use electrical devices. They also can work "permanently," "regularly," and "occasionally" both from home and outside.

Mobile Telework and Remote Work.   Mobile tele- and remote workers (Andriessen & Vartiainen, 2006; Gareis et al., 2006) use other places in addition to home for working:

Other workplaces such as a customer's or partner's premises or the company's other premises. Toffler (1980) referred to these kinds of places as "telecottages," that is, co-working spaces such as "hubs," "telework centers," "satellite work centers," and "satellite offices." These are remote from the main office and often close to employees' homes. The first were built up at the beginning of the 1970s in the United States (Nilles et al., 1976) and later in other countries. Other workplaces include locations used to meet clients, partners, or suppliers. These places may include the premises of another party or of the mobile worker's company that are outside the main office. In addition to working with local people, other places are often used for interacting with the home office regarding progress and challenges related to the business.

Third workplaces, such as hotels, cafés, pubs, restaurants, conference venues, and fairs, as well as public areas, such as parks, airport lounges, railway stations, and motorway service stations, are usually for short-term transitional stops. For example, airports may be used for reading documents and emails, working from a laptop, making business calls, and conducting meetings.

Moving places such as cars, trains, taxis, buses, trams, airplanes, ships, bicycles, and other vehicles are common places for tele- and remote workers to conduct their work. Work-related mobility can be divided into commuting (i.e., traveling between a place of residence and a place of work) and traveling for work (e.g., traveling to meet a client).

The *main workplace* (i.e., main office) is a place for a tele- or remote worker to physically visit and work. It is especially a place for meeting superiors and interacting with colleagues and team members both formally and informally.

Those tele- and remote workers who use multiple locations are called mobile multilocational workers (Andriessen & Vartiainen, 2006; Lilischkis, 2003, p. 3) or mobile teleworkers (Hislop & Axtell, 2007, 2009). They are employees who spend some paid working time away from home or away from their main workplace, for example, on business trips, in the field, traveling, or on a customer's premises.

Lilischkis (2003, p. 8) used a still-valid topology based on the dimensions of space and time to profile five types of physically mobile employees. *Space* criteria include (a) the number of locations, (b) the recurrence of locations, (c) whether there is a main workplace to return to, (d) whether the work takes place while moving or at a destination, (e) whether work can take place at fixed locations without changing it, (f) whether there is a limitation of the work area, and (g) the distance between locations. *Time* criteria include (a) the frequency of changing location, (b) the time spent moving between work locations, and (c) the time spent at a certain work location if not moving. The five types of mobile workers are distinguished by an increasing level of detachedness of the workplace from a fixed place (Lilischkis, 2003, p. 3); these include *on-site movers* (e.g., a farmer), who work around a certain area; *pendulums* (e.g., an accountant at home), who work at two different fixed locations; *yo-yos* (e.g., a customer manager), who occasionally go to meet customers away from a fixed location and returning back there; *nomads* (e.g., a sales representative), who work at changing fixed locations; and *carriers* (e.g., a flight attendant), who work on the move transporting goods or people.

Digital Online Telework. In the 2010s, fully *digital* often global *telework* on *online* labor platforms appeared and were detached from any stabilized social and organizational setting. The development of digital working environments, also known as online outsourcing, crowdwork, or online gig platforms employing microproviders (Lehdonvirta et al., 2019), has expanded working locations worldwide. Digital online telework is a form of employment that uses online platforms to enable individuals, teams, and organizations to access other individuals or organizations to solve problems or to provide services in exchange for payment (e.g., Berg et al., 2018). Mandl and Codagnone (2020, p. 180) distinguish between (a) tasks that are entirely traded and delivered online or are traded, monitored, and paid online but the delivery is physical and collocated; and (b) the types of tasks that are traded and the skills required to deliver them, that is, low skills which are mostly routine or manual versus high skills which are mostly cognitive and interactive. Based on these differences, it is possible to distinguish online labor markets that are potentially global from local mobile labor markets. The second dimension distinguishes between the intermediation of tasks embedding a relatively lower or higher skill set.

In digital online telework, work-related social interaction fully occurs in a virtual space, making the global Internet a work platform in addition to a local working location. From the viewpoint of the work organization, having platforms as a virtual space for work is a necessity for teleworkers so they can access knowledge and their clients and collaborate with colleagues if needed. Online, digital, and crowdsourcing platforms as new working environments are varied and numerous, ranging from those based on volunteer work (e.g., Wikipedia) and those exploiting it (e.g., Facebook, Google, and YouTube) to global platforms providing employment services (e.g., Amazon Mechanical Turk) to enterprises using internal social media. Routine microtasks (e.g., translating an advertising slogan from Finnish to English) as well as large innovation projects are carried out on digital working platforms. Online digital teleworkers often work from their homes on different continents. Mobile Internet and cloud services also enable mobile, multilocational telework. People collaborate if needed from their present locations in temporary or permanent virtual teams and communities. One difference from conventional jobs is the fact that this kind of work often involves temporary entrepreneurial freelancing, often without any kind of social protection. Figure 1 shows the trajectory from traditional remote work to home-based and mobile, multilocational telework, and then on to platform-based digital online telework.

Teleworker Often Virtual Team Member. By definition, members of conventional collocated, face-to-face teams are not remote workers as they participate in joint efforts locally and work at fixed locations, although they can also be considered "semimobile" in the sense of moving around their workplace (e.g., a nurse in a hospital). The members of nonconventional teams also work outside their fixed locations. Team members working in different locations and geographically distant from each other make a distributed team. A team becomes virtual when dispersed group members communicate and collaborate with each other via electronic media and do not meet each other face to face. The physical mobility of group members adds a new characteristic to distributed work. Mobile virtual teams are always distributed; however, not all distributed virtual teams are mobile. In conclusion, it can be said that mobile virtual teams are the most complex types of teams to lead and manage because of the changing contexts of individual mobile workers. In each working context, the physical settings, virtual

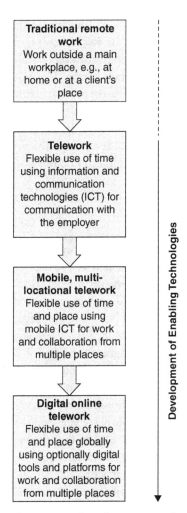

Figure 1. The path from traditional remote work to the concept of mobile, multilocational, and global digital online teleworking.
Source: Modified from Vartiainen and Hyrkkänen (2010, p. 119).

tools, and people who are met vary. The use of various spaces varies, depending on the type of work and the interdependence of the tasks to be done. Remote solo work carried out in solitude at home without virtual connections to others is an extreme and rather rare case. Usually, home-based teleworkers communicate sporadically with superiors and colleagues either virtually or face to face.

PREVALENCE OF TELEWORK, REMOTE, AND DIGITAL ONLINE TELEWORK

Challenges Measuring Telework and Remote Work. Showing the type, incidence, and intensity of telework and remote work (e.g., the number of days, hours of work performed, or changes of places in a particular period) across countries involves some important conceptual challenges because telework and remote work are defined in many ways, resulting in heterogeneity in what is meant by a tele- and remote worker. The current surveys do not always capture features of work on digital platforms due to the work's temporary and transient nature. In addition, platforms are highly protective of their proprietary databases on work and compensation flows, and thus research that uses such data is scarce (Piasna, 2020). Mokhtarian et al. (2005, p. 423) demonstrated how definitions, measurement instruments, sampling, and sometimes vested interests affect the quality and utility even of seemingly objective and "measurable" data. In addition to varying measures, there are substantial limitations in the available global data. Therefore, the evidence shows large differences in the prevalence of telework and remote work—not to speak about mobile and digital online telework—among different continents, countries, professions, and so on.

Prevalence

Europe. The basic trend of shifting to tele- and remote working was quite slow until the corona pandemic starting in 2020. In 2019, approximately 11% of dependent employees in Europe worked from home at least some of the time, which was up from less than 8% in 2008 (Sostero et al., 2020), whereas 35% of the self-employed reported working from home sometimes or usually in 2019 compared to 29% in 2008. Yet just 3.2% of European employees usually worked from home—a share that has remained quite stable since 2008. There were, and still are, large differences among countries, sectors, and occupations: The figures were above 25% in most Northern European countries and below 10% in 15 of the 27 European Union (EU) member states; the numbers were high in information technology (IT) and communication services and low in manufacturing, and high among white-collar IT service occupations and low among sales workers (similar differences have been found in U.S. data (see Wulff Pabilonia & Vernon, 2020). From the viewpoint of mobile work, the Eurofound (2017, p. 62) survey showed that the vast majority of workers in the EU (70%) still had a single regular workplace (particularly employees), while 30% carried out their work in multiple locations (often knowledge workers). Additionally, the proportion of workers with multiple workplaces varied substantially between countries. The figure was larger for self-employed workers, agricultural workers, and managers and was particularly prevalent in the construction, transport, and agriculture sectors. A majority of self-employed workers worked daily on their own premises (72%) but were also quite likely to work on a daily basis at a client's premises (13%), in a car or vehicle (14%), outdoors (13%), or from home (16%). In general, a small proportion of workers reported working in public spaces such as coffee shops and airports: 3% daily, 3% several times a week, and 4% several times a month.

The COVID-19 epidemic dramatically changed the number of those working remotely. The Eurofound survey (Eurofound, 2020a) in April and July 2020 showed that more than a third (37%) of those working in the EU had begun to telework—more than 30% in most member states. The largest proportions of workers who switched to working from home were found in the Nordic and Benelux countries (close to 60% in Finland and above 50% in Luxembourg, the Netherlands, Belgium, and Denmark and 40% or more in Ireland, Sweden, Austria, and Italy).

The United States and Canada. According to a survey collected in 2004 (Wulff Pabilonia & Vernon, 2020), 15% of wage and salary paid workers in the United States reported that they did some work at home, but only 3% of workers worked exclusively at home at least 1 day every 2 weeks. More recently, based on data from a 2017–2018 survey, 25% of wage and salary paid workers did some work at home, and 13% of workers worked exclusively at home at least once every 2 weeks. A U.S. pandemic study (Brynjolfsson et al., 2020), conducted in three waves in April, May, and July 2020, covering a total of 75,000 respondents, showed that about half of those employed were working from home during the pandemic, including 33% who reported they had previously been commuting. The study showed that younger people and employees in knowledge work, including management, professional, and related occupations, were more likely to shift to working from home and were more likely to switch to remote work. In Canada, the pandemic also led to a significant increase in telework. At the beginning of 2021, 32% of Canadian employees ages 15–69 worked most of their hours from home, compared with only 4% in 2016 (Mehdi & Morrissette, 2021).

Elsewhere. Messenger (2019, p. 294; see also Eurofound & International Labour Office, 2017) showed the estimated share of regular teleworkers based on the intensity (i.e., the number of days or hours of telework performed in a particular period) among all employees in a number of regions in the 2010s, including Japan (16%), EU-28 (8%), United States (20%), Argentina (2%), and India (19%). Furthermore, according to a recent survey (Citrix & ANSA Latina) conducted in 2019 in six Latin-American countries (Argentina, Brazil, Chile, Colombia, Peru, and Mexico), up to 45% of the workers surveyed in Colombia claimed to have the possibility to work remotely or from home, whereas only 21% of Peruvian respondents said the same. In Australia, before COVID-19 restrictions, 24% of people with a job were likely to work from home one or more times a week, whereas in February 2021 the count was 41% (Australian Bureau of Statistics, 2021).

Globally Online. In spite of the difficulties getting data for digital online work, some estimations have been made. According to the ILO study (2021), the number of online web-based and location-based (taxi and delivery) labor platforms rose from 142 in 2010 to more than 777 in 2020. A European study covering almost 39,000 Internet users in 16 member states (Pesole et al., 2018) indicated that on average, 10% of the adult population used online platforms for the provision of some type of labor services. Fewer than 8% do this kind of work with some frequency, and fewer than 6% spend a significant amount of time on it (at least 10 hours per week) or earn a significant amount of income (at least 25% of the total). The main platform workers are defined as those who earn 50% or more of their income via platforms and/or work via platforms for more than 20 hours a week. According to Pesole et al. (2018), they account for about 2% of the adult population on average. There are differences between European countries: The United Kingdom has the highest incidence of platform work. Other countries with high relative values are Germany, the Netherlands, Spain, Portugal, and Italy. In contrast, Finland, Sweden, France, Hungary, and Slovakia show very low values compared to the rest.

In the United States, the U.S. Bureau of Labor Statistics (Current Population Survey, 2018) measured electronically mediated work, which it defined as short jobs or tasks that workers find through websites or mobile apps that both connect them with customers and arrange payment for the tasks. In May 2017, there were 1.6 million electronically mediated workers in these kinds of jobs, accounting for 1.0% of total employment. The estimates include all people who did electronically mediated work, whether as their main job, as a second job, or as additional work for pay.

Overall, the number of platform workers is still low, although it is growing, especially due to the pandemic (International Labour Organization, 2021). For example, The Online Labour Index (OLI) produced by Kässi and Lehdonvirta (2018, see also Kässi et al., 2021) showed that in May 2021, the number of starting projects on platforms had increased by 93% from May 2016. The index tracks the daily number of new projects or tasks posted on five major English-speaking online labor platforms. In their recent paper, Kässi et al. (2021) estimated the size of the global online freelance population gathering data from globally relevant online freelance platforms and using public data sources. According to them, there are 163 million freelancer profiles registered on online labor platforms globally. They conclude that online workers represent a nontrivial segment of labor today, but one that is spread thinly across countries and sectors, although it is clearly growing.

DRIVERS AND ENABLERS OF TELEWORK AND REMOTE WORK

Over the past few years, the "natural experiment" of the COVID-19 pandemic has globally challenged ways of working and life in general, and the number of tele- and remote workers has increased swiftly. In their vision, Nilles et al. (1976) considered that increasing knowledge work and smart technologies would drive and enable telework. Telework and remote work can be advantageous for both employers and employees for a number of reasons (Eurofound & International Labour Office, 2017; Messenger, 2019). For instance, these ways of working may reduce the costs of commuting and transportation and urban congestion (e.g., the construction of new highways). They can also be beneficial for environmental reasons—for example, concerning climate change and encouraging society and political decision-makers to favor shifting to new ways of working, which may even potentially spark economic growth in remote regions. Companies—both large and small—are looking for new businesses by utilizing digital tools and platforms and using a dispersed workforce, reducing office space and associated costs, and attracting and retaining qualified workers.

On the individual level, two primary motives have been suggested (Allen et al., 2015) to underlie the desire to telework: productivity and personal life. Productivity motives relate to expectations of increased efficiency, effectiveness, and work performance. Personal-life motives involve the desire to accommodate nonwork needs such as balancing work, family, and leisure. In addition, shorter workdays due to the reduction in time spent commuting and increasing autonomy from management surveillance and the resulting possibility to schedule one's own work inspire and attract people to tele- and remote work. For an employee, teleworking could increase autonomy and self-determination (Deci & Ryan, 2012), provide more dynamic and enriched work contents, and lead to a more flexible integration of work and private life, while for the organization there are benefits such as savings in premises and greater flexibility, as well as more effectiveness, productivity, and innovativeness (e.g., Bailey & Kurland, 2002; Baruck, 2000).

Technologies have been the determinant feature and enabler of telework since Nilles et al. (1976), separating it from other types of remote work. The swift conversion of information into a digital format; the digitalization of tools, products, and services; value-adding processes; working environments; and the adoption of digital business models have gradually changed the nature of work and ways of working in micro-, small-, medium-sized, and large companies both in local regions such as cities and globally on virtual online platforms (Schaffers et al., 2020). On the microlevel, smart technologies—such as wearables using sensors to measure the quality of sleep and health—intrude into the life of individuals or a small group of individuals in a particular social context. On the mesolevel, which falls between the micro- and macrolevels (such as a community, organization, or city), technology takes the form of smart transport systems, service applications, social media, and various applications of the Internet of Things (IoT). At the macrolevel, technology (such as global labor platforms) potentially influences the outcomes of interactions (such as economic transactions or other resource transfer interactions) over a large population. The market, working conditions, and working processes stimulate the work-demand side—that is, what needs to be done and how. Demographic and social changes influence the work-supply side—that is, the kinds of workers who are available and their preferences, competences, and behavior. These changes force and enable organizations to develop new business strategies including increased shares of teleworking and remote work in business and work. The direct consequence of all this is to be found in the growth of distributed work processes, network organizations, the physical mobility of workers, and intensive mediated interaction.

IMPACTS OF TELE-, REMOTE, AND ONLINE DIGITAL WORKING

Overall Impacts. The findings on the impacts of tele- and remote working are somewhat controversial (e.g., Becker & Sims, 2000, Bosch-Sijtsema et al., 2010; Eurofound, 2020b; Felstead et al., 2005; Harrison et al., 2004; Hill et al., 2003, Hislop & Axtell, 2009; Vartiainen & Hyrkkänen, 2010), showing that while companies and employees recognize the benefits of remote working, there are also drawbacks, which are very often experienced on an individual level as an increase in the workload. It has been claimed (Felstead & Henseke, 2015) that while remote working is associated with higher organizational commitment, job satisfaction, and job-related well-being, these benefits come at the cost of work intensification and a greater inability to switch off. Therefore, the impact of changing working contexts—indicating variable job demands in physical, virtual, and social spaces—is critical both to the effectiveness of remote work and to the well-being of teleworkers. For example, increasing telework and remote work during the pandemic in 2020–2021 challenged strongly the traditional open office concept and turned the focus on the home (and other places) as a workplace. A few comparative research findings regarding the effects of telework and remote or digital online work are available globally (Eurofound, 2020b; International Labour Organization, 2021). They focus on working time, the work-life balance, well-being, occupational health, performance, effectiveness, and societal impacts. For example, a comparison of data from Japan, the EU, the United States, Argentina, and India (Messenger, 2019) shows longer hours of work combined with much greater discretion for workers regarding the scheduling of their working time. In Europe (Eurofound & International Labour Office, 2017), non-teleworkers work an average of 42.6 hours per week, while teleworkers work somewhat longer: an average of 44.5 hours per week. They are also more likely to work in the evenings and on weekends than workers who always work in the office. However, there are large variations both within and between countries because of varying operational definitions.

Social and Psychological Impacts. Telework traditionally takes place in a different physical place than usual. Over the years, many advantages and benefits, as well as challenges, shortcomings, and risks to employees, organizations, and society, have been listed (e.g., Bailey & Kurland, 2002; Baruck, 2000; Mann & Holdsworth, 2003; Shamir & Salomon, 1985). An evidence-based review (Eurofound, 2020b) suggests that workers with telework and remote work arrangements report greater autonomy, a better work-life balance, higher productivity, and reduced commuting times. However, instead of achieving only a positive work-life balance, working remotely can lead to the "autonomy paradox" (Mazmanian et al., 2013); that is, autonomy turns from being an asset into a liability resulting in workaholic behavior, higher stress levels, and lower job satisfaction. The work-life balance at home may be disturbed, and interpersonal relations in the workplace loosen, resulting in isolation. The societal and economic divide may increase because of impoverished job contents, for example, in the market for global gig-work. All in all, the demand characteristics of telework and remote and digital online work are influenced not only by the complexity of one organization, its resources, and tasks (Carayon & Zijlstra, 1999) but also by the numerous changing work environments from which the work is potentially executed (Axtell et al., 2008; Hyrkkänen & Vartiainen, 2005, 2007; Vartiainen & Hyrkkänen, 2010). For example, Gajendran and Harrison (2007) in their meta-analysis proposed a model to study individual outcomes of teleworking such as job satisfaction, performance, turnover intentions, role stress, and career prospects. In the model, the telework intensity would be mediated through perceived autonomy, work-family conflict, and the relationship quality with coworkers and supervisors. Next, some empirically based social and psychological outcomes are reported based on the locations that telework and remote workers use. Then, some organizational outcomes are shown.

Home-Based Telework and Remote Work. The most common workplace for teleworkers is home. It is evident that working conditions in peoples' homes vary a lot. As Harrison et al. (2004) noted, blurring the boundaries between work and private life leads to the temporary use of primary working spaces for private purposes and vice versa. The homes of remote workers are often not ideal places to work as they often do not have an appropriate workspace, and as a consequence, work may be conducted, for example, at the kitchen table, which generally must be cleared to make room for paperwork and often presents ergonomic challenges as well (Halford, 2005; Hislop & Axtell, 2009).

Autonomy. The basic dilemma in the discussion of telework at home has been whether it reinforces the individual's autonomy and self-control over work and other, nonwork-related issues (e.g., those relating to the family), which have been seen as factors interfering with and constraining working at home. Already Olson and Primps (1984) found that, depending on the extent to which the organization views the employee as an irreplaceable resource, working at home can either result in increased autonomy and freedom or reduce autonomy through more formal control procedures, the loss of promotion opportunities, and a change in compensation or work status. Indeed, European studies (Eurofound & International Labour Office, 2017) show that tele- and remote workers enjoy a significant degree of more working time autonomy than do their office-based counterparts. In a meta-analysis by Gajendran and Harrison (2007), perceived autonomy was the most influential and extensive conveyor of telecommuting's effects. It fully mediated positive impacts on job satisfaction and partially mediated the impact of supervisors or objective ratings of performance, turnover intent, and role stress.

Work-Nonwork Balance. The family is often considered a counterbalance to work. This is challenged by home-based telework and remote work as work concretely intrudes into the field of recreation. The relationship between telework and remote work and work-life balance can be either positive or negative depending upon certain factors. In a meta-analysis by Gajendran and Harrison (2007), high-intensity telecommuting (more than two and a half days a week) reduced work-family conflicts. Some overviews (Eurofound & International Labour Office, 2017; Messenger, 2019) show positive effects on the work-life balance overall, mainly because of the reduction in commuting time and the autonomy workers have in organizing their working time. However, highly mobile teleworkers seem to have more work-family conflicts when compared to employees doing regular home-based telework or occasional mobile work (Eurofound, 2020b). Women in the EU who telework typically report more positive work-life balance results than do men, and this result appears to be because they work fewer hours than male teleworkers. Teleworkers with small children at home perceive difficulties in doing their jobs at home. In addition, virtual meetings from home at night and during weekends and long working days have led to breakdowns in the work-life balance at home and problems with family members as stress factors.

Social Relations. The geographical distance from colleagues, coworkers, and managers has been seen as a challenge (Felstead et al., 2005). Social isolation has been identified as a key challenge in early studies on teleworkers (Feldman & Gainey, 1997). Telework has been found to be socially isolating, and it could potentially harm chances of promotion. Moreover, the physical absence from the workplace and subsequent reduced social participation with coworkers can result in social stigmatization. According to Halford (2005), the main challenges regarding the organizational relationship are the pressures to prove one's availability to others and the fact that the home working environment undermines office sociability. Reduced social interaction with coworkers results in the loss of opportunities to learn from others. In the meta-analysis by Gajendran and Harrison (2007), high-intensity telecommuting (more than two and a half days a week) harmed relationships with coworkers. Managers also telework, and this may have an influence on subordinate experiences and outcomes. Based on a large data set, Golden and Fromen (2011) found that employees with teleworking managers responded less positively than employees of traditional managers when they considered work experiences such as feedback and workload and outcomes such as job satisfaction and turnover intentions.

Working at home seems to generate some uncertainty and unpredictability concerning employees and their managers. Because of reduced staff interaction, there is a lack of social contact and isolation from the flow of information, support, and help from management and colleagues. A deterioration of the relationship with supervisors may harm promotion prospects. Problems linked to the need for team and managerial support and training, as well as the more nebulous reliance on visual methods of problem-solving, are also described by remote workers who use their home as a workspace. But managers are more concerned with issues of trust and time with respect to mobile workers who work from home. The unpredictability of some of the work causes a particular concern. For example, how would a manager know whether a worker had really encountered a problem that took longer to resolve than expected, or whether the worker was slacking off? O'Neill et al. (2014) found that cyberslacking (i.e., using the Internet for nonwork-related purposes) when working at home is positively related to procrastination and negatively related to honesty, agreeableness, and conscientiousness as personality characteristics. Managers also expressed protective concern for their staff as they worried that workers may be struggling on a work-related issue or struggling with working from home. They were concerned that when working from home, workers may not always receive important information in a timely manner.

Well-Being and Job Satisfaction. The main sources of well-being and job satisfaction at home are the opportunities to concentrate and to exert control over one's own jobs and time (i.e., autonomy). Home-based teleworkers can have uninterrupted time at home to read, plan, schedule, coordinate, prepare, research, and be creative. However, Bailey and Kurland (2002) found little clear evidence of increased general job satisfaction among teleworkers in their review, whereas they did show satisfaction with the freedom and flexibility of working at home. On the other hand, home-based teleworkers in a 16,000-employee study (Bloom et al., 2015) reported improved work satisfaction and a halved attrition rate.

In all, it seems that several variables moderate and mediate well-being and job satisfaction (Allen et al., 2015), such as the amount of telework, interdependence of jobs, work-family conflicts, and coworker relationships. Much seems to depend on the family status of an employee (i.e., whether there are small children or not) (Eurofound, 2020b). Other factors may also play a role. For example, cross-cultural studies (Eurofound & International Labour Office, 2017; Messenger, 2019) show contradictory effects of telework on occupational health and well-being. Only 5.4% of Japanese teleworkers considered a feeling of isolation/alienation to be a disadvantage, whereas in Brazil, the majority of the workers in a company stated that being isolated from their colleagues was the key disadvantage of teleworking (63%).

For home-based teleworkers, the reduced commuting between home and the main workplace reduced stress because of traffic congestion. Owing to remote work with digital technologies, ergonomic issues (e.g., eyestrain and neck pain) are important (Eurofound, 2020b). In a study (Mann & Holdsworth, 2003) comparing home-based teleworkers and office workers, teleworkers reported negative emotions such as loneliness, irritation, worry, and guilt more often than office workers. Teleworkers overall were also found to experience more mental health problems than office workers.

As the explanation to the controversial findings on well-being, Messenger (2019, p. 305) proposes "autonomy," stating: "Those employees who are engaged in telework are happier, healthier and experience less stress if they are given a substantial degree of autonomy regarding where, when and how they work."

Mobile Telework and Remote Work. Mobile multilocational tele- and remote workers outside home use "other places," "third places," and "moving places" as workplaces and possibly return back to home or to a main workplace. The general reasons for moving are production-related (e.g., doing an assignment) or consumption-related (e.g., shopping and holidays) (Hardill & Green, 2003). When moving for work, one important purpose is to meet other people face to face (Breuer & Van Mel, 2003; Brown & O'Hara, 2003; Mark & Su, 2010; Perry et al., 2001). Meeting customers has been one of the reasons for companies to introduce mobile teleworking. The most common hindrances show that problems concerning incompatible and limited working spaces, ICT connections, and access are found in all identified locations, while interruptions are related to most of the identified locations, except the home, and that being an outsider with respect to the work community is common to all places except third places.

Changing Physical Premises.   The main challenge in mobile work is the necessity to repeatedly adapt to changing environments. Mobility and changing contexts are important factors, but common hindrances can be found in all locations and spaces, although some hindrances are unique to certain types of places. What is possible in one space may not be possible in another. After finding an appropriate space, often in an open office, the work environment must be structured to be conducive for work (Bosch-Sijtsema et al., 2010; Brown O'Hara, 2003; Hislop & Axtell, 2009). Challenges associated with new sites include finding appropriate places from which to perform relevant tasks (Bosch-Sijtsema et al., 2010). Additionally, locating the local people who can facilitate the successful completion of the necessary tasks (Mark & Su, 2010) is another challenge. Finding an appropriate space that can accommodate the various work activities, such as creative tasks, can be difficult. This is especially typical in third places. Forlano (2008) notes that in popular cafés, it is often difficult to find an available workplace or table and doing so may require queuing and table-hopping.

Disruptions, Interruptions.   Continually changing environments can be noisy and cause disturbances to those who need to concentrate or need a private place for other reasons. The number of meetings, phone calls, and informal interactions means that the periods of undisturbed time are limited (Bosch-Sijtsema et al., 2010; Hislop & Axtell, 2009; Vartiainen & Hyrkkänen, 2010). The places to work outside the home and the main workplace are quite often public places; therefore, it is significant to note differences between the activities that should be done in private versus those that can be done in public places. Because public places such as trains were not originally designed as work sites, they tend to be noisy and filled with commotion (Breuer & Van Mel, 2003; Forlano, 2008; Lyons et al., 2008). Specific, mainly physical, hindrances are associated with moving places emerging both from internal and external demands. In some cases, mobile workers may feel that their work-related phone calls are disruptive to others (Perry & Brodie, 2006).

Technological Affordances.   The role of technology is critical as the enabler of telework. The corona pandemic led to a rapid increase especially in the use of collaboration technologies needed in meetings. Allen et al. (2015) showed the positive impact of mobile ICT among self-employed home workers. Its use allowed them to leave home without compromising their work availability. This also helped reduce people's feelings of social isolation, although at the same time it created a sense of continuous availability. The connectivity paradox helps explain these findings. Leonardi et al. (2010, p. 99) suggest that connectivity should be viewed as a paradox, as the technologies "that provide the connectivity for teleworkers to successfully conduct work also create the opportunity for perpetual connectivity that raises perceived obstacles to work." The paradox suggests that teleworkers' connectivity to others through communication media facilitates remote work by affording greater social presence, while also negating the benefits of telework by enabling stressful interruptions. Still, the reality is that the technological infrastructure and devices that are needed to enable work are often lacking or insufficient. The main challenges of virtual spaces are limited connections and a lack of Internet access despite the technological improvements in recent years. In addition, behavioral norms limit the possibilities to work. In order to work, it is necessary to take along numerous devices to communicate and collaborate, and missing power sockets are a common nuisance. There may also be restrictions associated with mobile phone usage in some places, such as train carriages or some public locations (Brown & O'Hara, 2003). For example, during short journeys, it may not be practical to set up certain technologies simply due to the time required to do so

(Axtell et al., 2008). The exception to these environments are private cars that offer the needed privacy, thus allowing mobile workers to use their mobile phones quite freely while driving (Laurier, 2004), although the usage is risky because driving and, for example, reading emails simultaneously divides attention into two objects (i.e., dual-task) decreasing driving safely.

Social Relations. From the social perspective, Koroma et al. (2014; Axtell & Hislop, 2008) characterize mobile and multilocational workers as "lonely riders" as they are strangers when visiting their clients or partners, and even when at their main workplace. Mobile workers are alone while traveling and visiting their contacts, thus resulting in a lack of support, challenges in terms of synchronizing with colleagues (perhaps due to different time zones), and sometimes a feeling of being marginalized. The multitude of individuals encountered, the cultural differences, and sometimes dissatisfied or noncommunicative clients can result in pressure and difficulties to complete a work assignment (Vartiainen & Hyrkkänen, 2010). Although the social environment is often rather hectic and there are many other people around, there is a risk of a lack of identification as belonging to a certain group, and the frequent absence of other group members reduces informal interactions, even when a mobile worker is in the main office (Bosch-Sijtsema et al., 2010).

According to Vartiainen and Hyrkkänen (2010), third places such as cafés represent a forum for informal meetings with colleagues or an environment for conducting activities and necessary business activities using laptops and other forms of technology. Often, this work is conducted after official office hours in hotel rooms or restaurants. Forlano (2008) noted that these places, especially cafés, are used as innovative spaces to enhance one's productivity, to collaborate, and to participate in specific work communities and networks. Today, cafés have increasingly become more important and more common as places for both work and social activities. Public and private aspects mix in various manners; for example, on the one hand, cafés are places where people may engage in conversation, but, on the other hand, teleworkers may signal their unavailability by wearing headphones, and private spaces are sometimes found outside in the street. Furthermore, if more permanent social networks were built while working in cafés, informal short discussions could grow into long-term collaboration on work issues. Locally, mobile workers frequently use service stations and other agreed upon rendez-vous points for both informal and formal meetings.

Moving places are rather special workplaces. Public transport throws large numbers of strangers together in enclosed spaces under mutual observation. Cars allow drivers more choice as to the type of social encounters. Felstead et al. (2005, p. 139) name different ways to use the private space of a car. First, it can be used to extend private time—that is, time beyond the scrutiny of others that is used to think, reflect, talk aloud, or express emotions. The second use is to promote varying levels of intimacy between friends and colleagues. The time used in the car can be used in committed social interaction, which otherwise would not be possible. The third use is to connect to the outside world via communication devices.

Privacy. Traveling also provides chances to be alone and to think and reflect. The opportunities to concentrate on reading, writing, using a mobile phone, and consulting documents also increase. Easy access contrarily may reduce the ability to separate work from personal life. Privacy and personal space are missing, and there may be interruptions. Furthermore, a lack of privacy is a limitation, and because confidential tasks can be overheard and/or overseen, they are less likely to be performed (Axtell et al., 2008; Forlano, 2008). Forlano (2008, p. 39) claims that nontraditional work settings are locations of "inconvenience, constraint and specificity" opposite to the anytime, anywhere philosophy and ideology. A train, for example, is a very public physical place. Sustained concentration in a noisy, public space, even under the best conditions, is difficult (Lyons et al., 2008). Consequently, there is a need to take breaks and alternate between business and relaxation (Axtell et al., 2008; Brown & O'Hara, 2003; Lyons et al., 2008). Accordingly, certain precautions are required to guard personal workspace as it is not easy to leave the seat or the specific location even for a short period (Axtell et al., 2008). Consequently, Brown and O'Hara (2003) as well as Forlano (2008) found that the lack of privacy and confidentiality in cafés limits the work activities that can be conducted there. The time spent traveling and waiting at airports is associated with delays and waiting times over which the mobile worker has little control (Breuer & Van Mel, 2003; Perry et al., 2001). Workers can only partially use the available time for their work activities as there is little control over the resources in the environment available to the mobile worker (Perry et al., 2001). In their study of Dutch business travelers, Breuer and Van Mel (2003) found that quiet work environments such as airline lounges may allow more privacy, but they are often too far from the terminal and access is therefore limited.

Tele- and Remote Workers at the Default Place of Work. When returning to the main workplace (e.g., the office), tasks conducted there often require team and managerial support, training on unfamiliar tasks, or joint problem-solving (Halford, 2005). Furthermore, mobile workers usually have an accumulation of work that requires timely attention (Vartiainen & Hyrkkänen, 2010; Venezia & Allee, 2007) as the result of their visits to other places. Golden (2007) suggests that telework also affects those who remain in the office. He found that the prevalence of teleworking was negatively associated with coworker satisfaction, and that this relationship was influenced by the amount of time coworkers teleworked, the extent of face-to-face interactions, and job autonomy. Moreover, a non-teleworker's satisfaction with coworkers was also found to be negatively associated with turnover intentions.

Digital Online Teleworking. There are few studies on the impacts of digital online teleworking. However, there are reasons to expect that most of the impacts are similar to other forms of telework and remote work. An ILO survey of working conditions covering 3,500 gig-workers living in 75 countries around the world and working on five English-speaking microtask platforms (Berg et al., 2018) showed that workers appreciated the ability to set their own schedule and work from home and to supplement their income (International Labour Organization, 2021). Many worked atypical hours: 7 days per week, during the evening and night either in response to task availability, differences in time zones, or because of other commitments. Many women combined platform work with homework, for example, with their children. This may have negative implications on their work-life balance. In the ILO (2021) study, workers in location-based labor platforms mentioned that they had some degree of stress due to their work, which was often related to traffic congestion, insufficient pay, lack of orders or clients, long working hours, the risk of work-related injury, and pressure to drive quickly. One source of stress is that digital online teleworkers mostly lack occupational safety and health protection because of missing labor contracts.

Commuting, Costs, and Performance Impacts

Commuting and environment. In Toffler's visions of telework (1980), working remotely was expected to have an impact on environmental sustainability by reducing traffic congestion, energy consumption, air pollution, and the number of commutes. However, Bailey and Kurland (2002) could not find support for this in their review, claiming that commuting factors did not appear to be the primary motives for teleworking and in many cases were absent altogether. However, in a recent simulation study, Shabanpour et al. (2018) identified the potential for reducing daily vehicle miles and the number of hours traveled (as well as congestion and vehicular emissions) if there are sufficiently large numbers of workers with flexible working times. By referring to earlier studies, Moeckel (2017) emphasizes that the impacts of teleworking on transportation and land use are ambiguous. It has been found that telework may reduce the number of vehicle-kilometers traveled by eliminating commuting trips, though at the same time teleworkers may compensate for the commute-time savings with additional recreational travel and the number of person trips increased slightly on telework days. In addition, some emissions (in particular N_2O and CH_4 emissions) may increase because of added activity at home. Furthermore, workers who only need to visit the office 1 or 2 days a week may decide to move further away from their workplace to enjoy lower housing costs or a larger house, which may offset any travel savings from telecommuting.

Costs. From an employer's point of view, working remotely reduces the need for office premises and transportation and the costs associated with them (Bailey & Kurland, 2002). In addition, companies can reduce their space costs as mobile employees just occasionally visit the main workplace. From a company's viewpoint, "other workplaces" such as satellite and telework offices also usually reduce costs per square meter because of their location away from business centers. From an employee's point of view, building a home office, additional square meters used, furniture, equipment, electricity, and additional media lines create costs. Investing in the communication and collaboration technologies that are needed is neither without its cost; the question is: "Who pays the bill?"

Individual and Organizational Performance. Several studies (e.g., Baruck, 2000; Eurofound & International Labour Office, 2017; Messenger, 2019) indicate generally positive effects of teleworking on individual performance; that is, teleworkers typically perform better than their counterparts working only in the office. This increased productivity has been credited to a number of factors, including working for part of the time that would have been spent commuting, fewer interruptions, being able to work when being most productive, and even being able to work on days when workers would have had to call in sick (Messenger, 2019). However, Bailey and Kurland (2002) observed that mostly self-reported data have been used, and that the positive findings can be explained by increased working hours in telework. A meta-analysis by Gajendran and Harrison (2007) confirmed this conclusion by showing that flextime work schedules had a significant effect on objective measures of performance (productivity) but no effect on self-rated performance. A quasi-experimental study (Bloom et al., 2015) in a Chinese call center, on employees (N = 16,000) who were randomly assigned to work either from home or in the office for 9 months, showed that home working led to a 13% performance increase, of which 9% was from working more minutes per shift (fewer breaks and sick days) and 4% from more calls per minute (attributed to a quieter and more convenient working environment). In another recent study (Golden & Gajendran, 2019), for teleworkers doing complex jobs involving low levels of interdependence and social support, the extent of telework was positively associated with job performance.

Company Benefits. In their meta-analysis, Martin and MacDonnell (2012) found a positive relationship between telework and organizational benefits such as increased productivity, retention, strengthened organizational commitment, and performance. A European study (Eurofound & International Labour Office, 2017) also underlines that for many companies, telework is a way of improving staff retention and recruiting high-skilled professionals. However, missing or weak ICT skills of personnel and technical difficulties may prevent a company from implementing and using telework and remote work. From the viewpoint of third-place owners, the possibility of third-place workspaces may attract new customers, as happens in cafés. The ability to work remotely may also attract and retain certain highly valued employees, thus broadening the workforce pool. However, management control over work performance is lost as the visibility of employees is lower. Employees may commit only weakly to the organization, and there are challenges to renew bases of compensation. Remote management is a challenge as indicators to measure performance may be missing as well as guidelines on how to act. On the other hand, employers' responsibilities based on legislation (e.g., insurance liabilities) may increase. Additionally, protecting confidential information is a challenge. There is no direct control over employees, as tracking them may be unethical. In some cases, protecting company secrets represents a challenge.

LEADING AND MANAGING REMOTE WORKFORCE

General Management Requirements.
Uncertainty and the need for continual change have implications for management strategies. As the law of requisite variety according to Ashby (1958) says, the greater the variety in the environment of a system, the greater the variety that should be within the system to adapt properly to its environment. The changes in workplace strategy and the large-scale shift into the telework and alternative officing have a large effect on the organization, its human resource functions, the required technologies, and employee well-being and performance. Tele- and remote working challenge the social functions of a traditional organization such as socializing, commitment, knowledge sharing, and organizational learning. The challenge is to develop a model for which alternative work options are the norm. This requires a fundamental change of mindset.

The flexibility paradigm (e.g., Skorstad & Ramsdal, 2009) refers to the potential of individual autonomy and to an organization's ability to respond to unexpected occurrences in the environment. Flexible organizing involves temporal flexibility; that is, workers can, or are expected to, begin and end their work according to the situation and the need. One essential question for work motivation is to what extent the choice of working place and time is autonomous. For example, during the COVID-19 pandemic, "forced remote work" started to become the new normal as employees often were not allowed access to their workplaces and were obliged to work remotely. In this sense, it reduced autonomy. Worker-oriented flexibility can help facilitate the coordination of work and other life and can help workers cope in their work. On the other hand, the border between working time and leisure has become obscured as work spills over into leisure and vice versa. Colleagues, superiors, and customers ever more easily contact workers also outside official working hours. The choice of working hours is also affected by international cooperation, which requires, for example, arranging online meetings that require some participants to be available unusually early in the morning or late in the evening. The COVID-19 epidemic created a natural experiment that highlighted the importance of the capability to adapt and overcome abrupt changes in work and its contexts. The studies on telework during the pandemic show that most teleworkers collaborated virtually with their colleagues, managers, and customers during their working days. Therefore, digital competencies are especially needed for remote virtual work. These and similar studies around the globe demonstrate that this "natural experiment" has brought forth unanswered questions on how to anticipate these kinds of situations, organize large numbers of new remote workers and their working conditions, and provide the needed social and virtual support.

Digital technology is the main enabler for tele- and remote work, allowing workers to access information and other people during remote work. Telework requires employees to be equipped with laptop computers and smartphones with wireless access to an information network. It requires them to work from home and at their clients' offices, on the move, in hotels, and it requires that they sometimes come into the office to meet their colleagues and superiors. Electronic communication and collaboration can replace social contact to some degree but not fully. Different technologies for telework are developing. Virtual worlds, one type of virtualization technology, offer a potentially promising solution for the future (Aten, 2020, available in the Oxford Research Encyclopedia of Business [https://doi.org/10.1093/acrefore/9780190224851.013.170]). Virtual world technological affordances that can especially support virtual social collaboration with features such as multiuser voice and chat, persistence, avatars, and three-dimensional environments allow social actions that are associated with successful collaboration.

Baruck (2000; Baruch & Nicholson, 1997) suggested four factors, which need to be present to enable effective teleworking: (a) the telework interface, which needs first, a match between working and the family point of view, and second, the availability of the required physical facilities; (b) a job for which relevant technology is available and achievable without the necessity of a physical presence in the workplace; (c) personal qualities and circumstances, which play a significant role in determining the success of a person in teleworking—not every person can work effectively from home or, at least, not under all circumstances; and (d) a special culture in an organization is needed to enable teleworking to flourish, a culture of the kind in which relationships are built on trust.

What these factors have in common is that they require autonomy, adaptation, and resilience from individuals and flexibility from the organization. Meeting external pressures, new individual, team, and organizational capabilities and competencies are needed and old ones must be updated. One organizational way to adapt is to implement telework.

Practical Leadership Principles. Some general practical principles can be derived for improving human resources and design telework and remote work, even though teleworkers are generally able to autonomously determine and craft their own jobs. Human resource professionals, management, and teleworkers and remote workers themselves should notice the following demands as starting points for improvements:

- *Promote the awareness of telework and remote work-specific challenges and hindrances* to develop practical improvements and solutions to working practices that could positively impact employee engagement and vigor.
- Places outside the main workplace and home are regularly used for work despite the fact that they are busy and crowded. Thus, the ability to use the space for work purposes is restricted because of concerns about privacy, security, and space.
- A continual change in the physical working environment results in a recurrent search for a suitable place to perform the tasks at hand.
- Teleworkers and remote workers must repeatedly solve problems caused by limited working space.
- Mobile multilocational workers remain outsiders in the workplace community when visiting their clients or partners and when at their primary workplace, which results in a lack of support, a challenge synchronizing work-related matters with colleagues (e.g., different time zones), and, perhaps, feelings of marginalization.
- The changed context of work requires *new* communication *competencies* from leaders and self-leadership competencies from employees.
- *Smart mobile devices are not a complete virtual office.* The main challenge related to the use of digital technologies is limited connections and access despite the technological improvements in recent years. *Applicable ICT support is always needed.*

These challenges are fairly easy to solve and, consequently, make the lives of teleworkers and remote workers less complicated, more satisfying, and more productive.

A RESILIENT TELEWORKABLE FUTURE

Before the outbreak of the pandemic, large differences in the telework and remote work intensity between countries were driven by factors such as the organization of work and practices and regulations in common use, as well as management culture. Sostero et al. (2020) estimated that 37% of dependent employment in the EU is currently teleworkable—which is very close to the number of teleworkers indicated in real-time surveys during the COVID-19 crisis. Because of differences in the employment structure, the fraction of teleworkable employment ranges between 33% and 44%. According to Sostera et al. (2020), even starker differences in teleworkability emerge between high- and low-paid workers and white- and blue-collar workers, as well as by gender. Their results suggest that the large expansion of telework since the COVID-19 outbreak has been strongly skewed toward high-paid white-collar employment. Yet, enforced closures of workplaces have likely resulted in many new teleworkers among low- and mid-level clerical and administrative workers who previously had limited access to this working arrangement. In all, it is expected that working from home (WFH) (and other off-office places) will increase. Barrero et al. (2021) suggest five reasons for WFH: better-than-expected experiences, new investments in enabling physical and human capital, diminished stigma, lingering concerns about crowds and contagion risks, and technological innovations that support remote work.

Flexible tele- and remote working arrangements could enable resilience needed for the future. The recent developments in working life have raised discussion about resilience as the future key competence for individuals, teams, organizations, and society at large. An increasing amount of research concerning the changes produced by the corona epidemic has started to identify realistic scenarios and scalable practices anticipating similar external disruptions expected in the future. The key concept in this respect is "resilience."

Giustiniano et al. (2018) define resilience as

> connoting capacities to absorb external shocks and to learn from them, while simultaneously preparing for and responding to external jolts, whether as organizations, teams or individuals. Resilience is claimed to be necessary to protect actors and agencies from shocks, crises, scandals, and business fiascos that generate fear and create dissonance. Resilient people and organizations get knocked down and get up again, ready to learn from events and to be ready for future challenges: The ultimate connotation of resilience. (p. 3)

Resilient individuals are said to bounce back from stressful experiences quickly and efficiently, just as resilient metals bend but do not break (Fredrickson, 2001). Referring to the coping theory (Lazarus & Folkman, 1984), Fredrickson (2001, p. 222) suggests that positive emotions may fuel psychological resilience. Those studying organizational behavior define resilience as the "positive psychological capacity to rebound, to 'bounce back' from adversity, uncertainty, conflict, failure, or even positive change, progress and increased responsibility" (Luthans, 2002, p. 702). The Finnish concept of "sisu" (Lahti, 2019) similarly refers to the enigmatic power that enables individuals to push through unbearable challenges.

The study *of team and organizational resilience* varies considerably depending on the context and disciplinary perspective. West et al. (2009, p. 253) suggest that *team resilience* serves to provide teams with the capacity to bounce back from failure, setbacks, conflicts, or any other threat a team may experience. Giustiniano et al. (2018) mention that resilience can appear in two differentiated ways complementing each other as an adaptive or a reactive response to external jolts and stressors. According to Duchek (2020, p. 215), organizational resilience can be conceptualized as a meta-capability, and inspired by process-based studies, and suggests three successive resilience stages: anticipation, coping, and adaptation. Individual, team, and organizational resilience are interdependent from each other. Building resilience on the individual level can spread within organizational settings and beyond, and collective cultural resilience can make individuals more resilient.

In the future, the development and increase of telework and remote and digital online work will be closely integrated with the development of technologies, expanding 5G bandwidths, and ever-smarter mobile devices. Through the broadband mobile Internet and digital labor platforms, there is access to multiple communication functions including email, the Internet, instant messaging, text messaging, and company networks. It is evident that digitalization changes the working environment; impacts working processes, tasks, and job content; and affects structures and organizations, products, and services in many ways—resulting in the need for partly and completely new competencies, organizing, and ways of working. This development has resulted in various types of present and future jobs—some are hybrid; some are completely new. On the organizational level, there are examples of "all remote" dispersed companies. For example, Choudhury et al. (2020) describe a company without a physical office with 1,000 employees located in more than 60 countries. Their common feature is the multipurpose use of digital technologies, especially those technologies used for communication and collaboration and the search for new knowledge.

FURTHER READING

Allen, T. D., Golden, T. D., & Shockley, K. M. (2015). How effective is telecommuting? Assessing the status of our scientific findings. *Psychological Science in the Public Interest, 16*(2), 40–68.

Charalampous, M., Grant, C. A., Tramontano, C., & Michailidis, E. (2019). Systematically reviewing remote e-workers' well-being at work: A multidimensional approach. *European Journal of Work and Organizational Psychology, 28*(1), 51–73.

Felstead, A., & Henseke, G. (2015). Assessing the growth of remote working and its consequences for effort, well-being and work-life balance. *New Technology, Work and Employment, 32*(2), 195–212.

Golden, T. D., & Fromen, A. (2011). Does it matter where your manager works? Comparing managerial work mode (traditional, telework, virtual) across subordinate work experiences and outcomes. *Human Relations, 64*(11), 1451–1475.

Jachimowicz, J. M., Cunningham, J. L., Staats, B., Gino, F., & Menges, J. I. (2021). Between home and work: Commuting as an opportunity for role transitions. *Organization Science, 32*(1), 64–85.

Kotera, Y., & Vione, K. C. (2020). Psychological impacts of the new ways of working (NWW): A systematic review. *International Journal of Environmental Research and Public Health, 17*(14), 5080.

Leonardi, P. M., Treem, J. W., & Jackson, M. H. (2010). The connectivity paradox: Using technology to both decrease and increase perceptions of distance in distributed work arrangements. *Journal of Applied Communication Research, 38*(1), 85–105.

Mokhtarian, P. L., Salomon, I., & Choo, S. (2005). Measuring the measurable: Why can't we agree on the number of telecommuters in the U.S.? *Quality & Quantity, 39*(4), 423–452.

REFERENCES

Allen, T. D., Golden, T. D., & Shockley, K. M. (2015). How effective is telecommuting? Assessing the status of our scientific findings. *Psychological Science in the Public Interest, 16*(2), 40–68.

Andriessen, J. H. E., & Vartiainen, M. (Eds.). (2006). *Mobile virtual work—A new paradigm.* Springer-Verlag.

Ashby, W. R. (1958). Requisite variety and its implications for the control of complex systems. *Cybernitica, 1,* 83–99.

Australian Bureau of Statistics. (2021, February). *Household impacts of COVID-19 survey.* Abs.gov. https://www.abs.gov.au/statistics/people/people-and-communities/household-impacts-covid-19-survey/feb-2021#data-download

Axtell, C., & Hislop, D. (2008). The lonely life of the mobile engineer? In D. Hislop (Ed.), *Mobility and technology in the workplace* (pp. 105–119). Routledge.

Axtell, C., Hislop, D., & Whittaker, S. (2008). Mobile technologies in mobile spaces: Findings from the context of train travel. *International Journal of Human-Computer Studies, 66*(12), 902–915.

Bailey, D. E., & Kurland, N. B. (2002). A review of telework research: Findings, new directions, and lessons for the study of modern work. *Journal of Organizational Behavior, 23*(4), 383–400.

Barrero, J. M., Bloom, N., & Davis, S. J. (2021). *Why working from home will stick* (BFI Working Paper No. 2020-174). Becker Friedman Institute.

Baruch, Y. (2000). Teleworking: Benefits and pitfalls as perceived by professionals and managers. *New Technology, Work and Employment, 15*(1), 34–49.

Baruch, Y., & Nicholson, N. (1997). Home, sweet work: Requirements for effective home-based working. *Journal of General Management, 23*(2), 15–30.

Becker, F., & Sims, W. (2000). *Managing uncertainty: Integrated portfolio strategies for dynamic organisations.* International Workplace Studies Program, Cornell University.

Berg, J., Furrer, M., Harmon, E., Rani, U., & Silberman, M. S. (2018). *Digital labour platforms and the future of work: Towards decent work in the online world.* International Labour Office.

Bloom, N., Liang, J., Roberts, J., & Ying, Z. J. (2015). Does working from home work? Evidence from a Chinese experiment. *The Quarterly Journal of Economics, 130*(1), 165–218.

Bosch-Sijtsema, P., Ruohomäki, V., & Vartiainen, M. (2010). Multi-locational knowledge workers in the office: Navigation, disturbances and effectiveness. *New Technology, Work and Employment, 25*(3), 183–195.

Breuer, A., & Van Mel, J. (2003). Airport offices: Facilitating nomadic workers. *Facilities, 21*(7–8), 175–179.

Brown, B., & O'Hara, K. (2003). Place as a practical concern of mobile workers. *Environment and Planning A, 35*(9), 1565–1587.

Brynjolfsson, E., Horton, J., Ozimek, A., Rock, D., Sharma, G., & Yi Tu, H. (2020, September 8). *COVID-19 and remote work: An early look at US data.* Squarespace.

Carayon, P., & Zijlstra, F. (1999). Relationship between job control, work pressure and strain: Studies in the USA and in the Netherlands. *Work & Stress, 13*(1), 32–48.

Choudhury, P., Crowston, K., Dahlander, L., Minervini, M. S., & Raghuram, S. (2020). GitLab: Work where you want, when you want. *Journal of Organization Design, 9*(1), 23.

Citrix & ANSA Latina. (2019, October). *Percentage of employees who are allowed to work remotely in selected countries in Latin America as of 2019.* Statista. https://www.statista.com/statistics/1108490/home-office-adoption-latin-america-country/

Current Population Survey. (2018, September). *Electronically mediated work: New questions in the Contingent Worker Supplement.* U.S. Bureau of Labor Statistics. https://www.bls.gov/opub/mlr/2018/article/electronically-mediated-work-new-questions-in-the-contingent-worker-supplement.htm

Deci, E. L., & Ryan, R. M. (2012). Self-determination theory. In P. A. M. Van Lange, A. W. Kruglanski, & E. T. Higgins (Eds.), *Handbook of theories of social psychology* (Vol. 1, pp. 416–437). SAGE.

Duchek, S. (2020). Organizational resilience: A capability-based conceptualization. *Business Research, 13*(1), 215–246.

Eurofound. (2017). *Sixth European working conditions survey—Overview report (2017 update).* Publications Office of the European Union.

Eurofound. (2020a). *Living, working and COVID-19.* Publications Office of the European Union.

Eurofound. (2020b). *Telework and ICT-based mobile work: Flexible working in the digital age.* Publications Office of the European Union.

Eurofound & International Labour Office. (2017). *Working anytime, anywhere: The effects on the world of work.* Publications Office of the European Union; International Labour Office.

Feldman, D. C., & Gainey, T. W. (1997). Patterns of telecommuting and their consequences: Framing the research agenda. *Human Resources Management Review, 7*(4), 369–388.

Felstead, A., & Henseke, G. (2015). Assessing the growth of remote working and its consequences for effort, well-being and work-life balance. *New Technology, Work and Employment, 32*(2), 195–212.

Felstead, A., Jewson, N., & Walters, S. (2005). *Changing places of work.* Palgrave Macmillan.

Forlano, L. (2008). Working on the move: The social and digital ecologies of mobile workplaces. In D. Hislop (Ed.), *Mobility and technology in the workplace* (pp. 28–42). Routledge.

Fredrickson, B. L. (2001). The role of positive emotions in positive psychology: The broaden-and-build theory of positive emotions. *American Psychologist, 56*(3), 218–226.

Gajendran, R. S., & Harrison, D. A. (2007). The good, the bad, and the unknown about telecommuting: Meta-analysis of psychological mediators and individual consequences. *Journal of Applied Psychology, 92*(6), 1524–1541.

Gareis, K. (2006). *New work environments: An overview of available evidence on success factors and impacts* (Empirica Schriftenreihe, Report No. 07/2006). Empirica GmbH.

Gareis, K., Kordey, N., & Müller, S. (2004). *Work in the information society* (BISER Domain Report No. 7). Eurostat. https://www.biser-eu.com/results.htm

Gareis, K., Lilischkis, S., & Mentrup, A. (2006). Mapping the mobile eWorkforce in Europe. In J. H. E. Andriessen & M. Vartiainen (Eds.), *Mobile virtual work—A new paradigm* (pp. 45–69). Springer-Verlag.

Giustiniano, L., Clegg, S. R., Cunha, M. P., & Rego, A. (2018). *Theories of organizational resilience*. Edward Elgar.

Golden, T. D. (2007). Co-workers who telework and the impact on those in the office: Understanding the implications of virtual work for co-worker satisfaction and turnover intentions. *Human Relations, 60*(11), 16–41.

Golden, T. D., & Fromen, A. (2011). Does it matter where your manager works? Comparing managerial work mode (traditional, telework, virtual) across subordinate work experiences and outcomes. *Human Relations, 64*(11), 451–475.

Golden, T. D., & Gajendran, R. (2019). Unpacking the role of a telecommuter's job in their performance: Examining job complexity, problem solving, interdependence, and social support. *Journal of Business and Psychology, 34*(2), 1–15.

Halford, S. (2005). Hybrid workspace: Recapitalizations of work, organization and management. *New Technology, Work and Employment, 20*(1), 19–33.

Hardill, I., & Green, A. (2003). Remote working—Altering the spatial contours of work and home in the new economy. *New Technology, Work and Employment, 18*(3), 212–222.

Harrison, A., Wheeler, P., & Whitehead, D. (2004). *The distributed workplace*. Spon Press.

Hill, E. J., Ferris, M., & Märtinson, V. (2003). Does it matter where you work? A comparison of how three work venues (traditional office, virtual office, and home office) influence aspects of work and personal/family life. *Journal of Vocational Behavior, 63*(2), 220–241.

Hislop, D., & Axtell, C. (2007). The neglect of spatial mobility in contemporary studies of work: The case of telework. *New Technology, Work and Employment, 22*(1), 34–51.

Hislop, D., & Axtell, C. (2009). To infinity and beyond? Workspace and multi-location worker. *New Technology, Work and Employment, 24*(1), 60–75.

Hyrkkänen, U., & Vartiainen, M. (2005). *Mobile work and well-being: Työpoliittinen tutkimus, no. 293*. Työministeriö.

Hyrkkänen, U., & Vartiainen, M. (2007). Hyvinvoinnin haasteet mobiilissa työssä [Well-being challenges in mobile work]. *Työ ja ihminen, 21*(2), 160–172.

International Labour Office. (2020). *Defining and measuring remote work, telework, work at home and home-based work* [Policy brief].

International Labour Office. (2021). *World employment and social outlook 2021: The role of digital labour platforms in transforming the world of work*.

Kässi, O., & Lehdonvirta, V. (2018). Online labour index: Measuring the online gig economy for policy and research. *Technological Forecasting and Social Change, 137*(C), 241–248.

Kässi, O., Lehdonvirta, V., & Stephany, F. (2021). *How many online workers are there in the world? A data-driven assessment*. Open Research Europe. https://doi.org/10.2139/ssrn.3810843

Koroma, J., Hyrkkänen, U., & Vartiainen, M. (2014). Looking for people, places and connections: Hindrances when working in multiple locations—A review. *New Technology, Work and Employment, 29*(2), 139–159.

Korte, W. B., & Wynne, R. (1996). *Telework. Penetration, potential and practice in Europe*. IOS Press.

Lahti, E. (2019). Embodied fortitude: An introduction to the Finnish construct of sisu. *International Journal of Wellbeing, 9*(1), 61–82.

Laurier, E. (2004). Doing office work on the motorway. *Theory, Culture & Society, 21*(4–5), 261–277.

Lazarus, R. S., & Folkman, S. (1984). *Stress appraisal and coping.* Springer.

Lehdonvirta, V., Kässi, O., Hjorth, I., Barnard, H., & Graham, M. (2019). The global platform economy: A new offshoring institution enabling emerging-economy microproviders. *Journal of Management, 45*(2), 567–599.

Leonardi, P. M., Treem, J. W., & Jackson, M. H. (2010). The connectivity paradox: Using technology to both decrease and increase perceptions of distance in distributed work arrangements. *Journal of Applied Communication Research, 38*(1), 85–105.

Lilischkis, S. (2003). *More yo-yos, pendulums and nomads: Trends of mobile and multi-location work in the information society* (STAR Issue Report No. 36). Empirica.

Lipnack, J., & Stamps, J. (2000). *Virtual teams: People working across boundaries with technology.* Wiley & Sons.

Luthans, F. (2002). The need for and meaning of positive organizational behavior. *Journal of Organizational Behavior, 23*(6), 695–706.

Lyons, G., Holley, D., & Jain, J. (2008). The business of train travel. In D. Hislop (Ed.), *Mobility and technology in the workplace* (pp. 74–86). Routledge.

Mandl, I., & Codagnone, C. (2020). The diversity of platform work—Variations in employment and working conditions. In H. Schaffers, M. Vartiainen, & J. Bus (Eds.), *Digital innovation and the future of work* (pp. 177–195). Rivers.

Mann, S., & Holdsworth, L. (2003). The psychological impact of teleworking: Stress, emotion and health. *New Technology, Work and Employment, 18*(3), 156–234.

Mark, G., & Su, N. M. (2010). Making infrastructure visible for nomadic work. *Pervasive and Mobile Computing, 6*(3), 312–323.

Martin, B. H., & MacDonnell, R. (2012). Is telework effective for organizations? A meta-analysis of empirical research on perceptions of telework and organizational outcomes. *Management Research Review, 35*(8), 602–616.

Mazmanian, M., Orlikowski, W. J., & Yates, J. (2013). The autonomy paradox: The implications of mobile email devices for knowledge professionals. *Organization Science, 24*(5), 1337–1357.

Mehdi, T., & Morrissette, R. (2021, April 1). *StatCan COVID-19: Data to insights for a better Canada. Working from home: Productivity and preferences.* Statistics Canada. https://www150.statcan.gc.ca/n1/pub/45-28-0001/2021001/article/00012-eng.htm

Messenger, J. C. (Ed.). (2019). *Telework in the 21st century: An evolutionary perspective.* Edward Elgar.

Moeckel, R. (2017). Working from home: Modeling the impact of telework on transportation and land use. *Transportation Research Procedia, 26,* 207–214.

Mokhtarian, P. L. (1991). *Defining telecommuting* (Research Report No. UCD-ITS-RR-91-04). Institute of Transportation Studies, University of California at Davis.

Mokhtarian, P. L., Salomon, I., & Choo, S. (2005). Measuring the measurable: Why can't we agree on the number of telecommuters in the U.S.? *Quality & Quantity, 39*(4), 423–452.

Nilles, J. M., Carlson, F. G., Gray, P., & Hannemann, G. J. (1976). *The telecommunications-transportation trade-off: Options for tomorrow.* Wiley.

Olson, M. H., & Primps, S. B. (1984). Working at home with computers: Work and nonwork issues. *Journal of Social Issues, 40*(3), 97–112.

O'Neill, T. A., Hambley, L. A., & Bercovich, A. (2014). Prediction of cyberslacking when employees are working away from the office. *Computers in Human Behavior, 34,* 291–298.

Perry, M., & Brodie, J. (2006). Virtually connected, practically mobile. In J. H. E. Andriessen & M. Vartiainen (Eds.), *Mobile virtual work: A new paradigm* (pp. 95–126). Springer.

Perry, M., O'Hara, K., Sellen, A., Brown, B., & Harper, R. (2001). Dealing with mobility: Understanding access anytime, anywhere. *ACM Transactions on Computer-Human Interaction, 8*(4), 323–347.

Pesole, A., Urzì Brancati, C., Fernández-Macías, E., Biagi, F., & González Vázquez, I. (2018). *Platform workers in Europe: Evidence from the COLLEEM survey.* Publications Office of the European Union.

Piasna, A. (2020). *Counting gigs. How can we measure the scale of online platform work* (Working Paper No. 2020.06)? The European Trade Union Institute (ETUI).

Schaffers, H., Vartiainen, M., & Bus, J. (Eds.). (2020). *Digital innovation and the future of work*. River.

Shabanpour, R., Golshani, N., Tayarani, M., Auld, J., & Mohammadian, A. (2018). Analysis of telecommuting behavior and impacts on travel demand and the environment. *Transportation Research Part D: Transport and Environment, 62*, 563–576. https://www.sciencedirect.com/science/journal/13619209

Shamir, B., & Salomon, I. (1985). Work-at-home and the quality of life. *Academy of Management Review, 10*(3), 455–464.

Skorstad, E. J., & Ramsdal, H. (Eds.). (2009). *Flexible organizations and the new working life*. Ashgate.

Sostero, M., Milasi, S., Hurley, J., Fernández-Macías, E., & Bisello, M. (2020). *Teleworkability and the COVID-19 crisis: A new digital divide?* European Commission.

Sullivan, C. (2003). What's in a name? Definitions and conceptualizations of teleworking and homeworking. *New Technology, Work and Employment, 18*(3), 158–165.

Toffler, A. (1980). *The third wave*. William Collins & Sons.

Van der Wielen, J. M. M., & Taillieu, T. C. B. (1993, April 14–17). *Telework: Dispersed organizational activity and new forms of spatial-temporal coordination and control* [Paper presentation]. Sixth European Congress on Work and Organizational Psychology, Alicante, Spain.

Vartiainen, M., & Hyrkkänen, U. (2010). Changing requirements and mental workload factors in mobile multi-locational work. *New Technology, Work and Employment, 25*(2), 117–135.

Venezia, C., & Allee, V. (2007). Supporting mobile worker networks: Components of effective workplaces. *Journal of Corporate Real Estate, 9*(3), 168–182.

West, B. J., Patera, J. L., & Carsten, M. K. (2009). Team level positivity: Investigating positive psychological capacities and team level outcomes. *Journal of Organizational Behavior, 30*(2), 249–267.

Wulff Pabilonia, S., & Vernon, V. (2020). *Telework and time use in the United States* (GLO Discussion Paper No. 546). Global Labor Organization.

Matti Vartiainen

INFORMAL WORK

INTRODUCTION

There has been an increased interest in examining informal work within the domain of organizational sciences and work psychology (Ashford et al., 2018; Bruton et al., 2012; Darbi et al., 2018; Saxena, 2017). This interest has burgeoned in the post-COVID-19 era, as large percentages of the global working population have moved toward informal work arrangements (International Labour Organization [ILO], 2022). It is estimated that over 61% of the world's workers work in the informal economy— engage and operate in informal work (ILO, 2019c). The COVID-19 pandemic acted as a disrupter for the world of work (Carr et al., 2021; ILO, 2022) to further increase these numbers, evidenced by global policy reports such as the World Employment and Social Outlook Trends that estimate that the number of informal workers remains firmly where it was in the pre-COVID era.

The International Labour Organization (ILO) defines *informal work* as paid work outside the regulatory framework, covering about three-quarters of the global workforce (ILO, 2012), particularly concentrated in the developing world (Biles, 2009; Sánchez & Alvarez, 2011).

Informal work is often housed within the informal economy, wherein the latter often lies outside government regulation and taxation. Informal work is characterized, among other things, by the absence of job-related benefits such as medical or unemployment insurance (ILO, 2013). Informal work affects the financing and functioning of the state, as the lack of social-protection contributions derived from informal work may undermine state or government ability to provide social services, especially pensions and other benefits (Hurtado et al., 2017).

Despite the scale of the informal economy, the bulk of psychology research as it relates to *work* pertains to formal *jobs* that are embedded within organizations that are legal entities (Saxena, 2017). This is a serious oversight (Bergman & Jean, 2016); while there has been interest in informal work across broader work and labor disciplines, less attention has been paid to this area in Industrial Organizational (I-O) and work psychology (Saxena, 2017). Broadly speaking, research and policy work in the domain of informal work are conducted under different names and labels in various disciplinary traditions and are adversely affected by terminological overlap (Saxena & Tchagneno, 2023).

This article is a first attempt to summarize the different, often disparate, streams of research that investigate informal work, from an I-O psychological point of view. It provides a nonexhaustive list, acknowledging that many streams and paths of research in the broader discipline of psychology and organizational sciences also approach the idea of working informally. First, this article defines informal work in the broadest possible sense of the term. Next, it provide an overview of streams and areas of research that cater to working informally—albeit under myriad names and labels. Thereafter, themes are drawn that connect across disparate literature to glean commonalities across various forms of informal work. Finally, the article argues for an an urgent need for greater research attention to informal work and issues an appeal that cuts across disciplinary boundaries and concerns broader societal benefit.

INFORMAL WORK

In the broadest sense of the term, informal work refers to work that occurs outside of organizational boundaries (Williams & Nadin, 2012), often relies on personal relationships or contracts (Monteith & Giesbert, 2017), may not have a fixed daily work schedule (Biles, 2009), lies outside of formal employment contracts between an employer and the employee (Godfrey, 2011), often does not provide a fixed income (Danquah et al., 2020), could involve an exchange of goods or services (Godfrey, 2011), and may live in the informal economy (Swider, 2015). An informal worker could work in the formal or the informal sector or lie at the cusp of formal and informal economies, sometimes engaging in transactions that intersect the two realms (Shapland & Heyes, 2017). Each of these concepts is detailed one by one in the following paragraphs.

In thinking about informal work, the image that is most often conjured up is that of someone working *outside* of an organization. This is the ground reality for many who engage in informal work (Godfrey, 2011). For instance, this could be an agricultural worker who works for daily wages (Saxena et al., 2015) or a freelance artist who sells her paintings at a local farmer's market (Alacovska, 2018). Most people who engage in informal work do not go into a typical organizationally embedded "office space" (Tucker, 1993) in pursuit of duties and responsibility that are part of a "job." While the present era of remote work allows one to work virtually, the key distinction between remote formal work and informal work is the attachment to an organization where the former does (in some way, shape, or form) attach itself to an organization, while informal work remains unattached to organizational boundaries.

Thus, one can think about informal work as being fundamentally different from a "posh" job (Brannick et al., 2019; Gloss et al., 2017; Kalleberg & Sorensen, 1979), which is most often tied to an organization (although one can have nonorganizational "jobs" such as the "job" of a nanny, which does not necessarily require "going into" an organization, although it could in some cases be governed or controlled via a service agency [Malson, 2021; Watson et al., 2021], making the service agency the primary employer and the family who seeks caregiving services the client). Thus, informal work is undertaken by the *workers* themselves and has different psychological realities in terms of the constructs that we typically tend to care about in Industrial and Organizational psychology that relate to an employ*ee*. Consequently, those engaged in informal work are best described as *workers* rather than as *employees*. This leads to questions surrounding constructs of interest such as job satisfaction, organizational commitment, turnover intentions, and so on that may not apply in the realm of nonorganizationally driven informal work.

Informal work often appears due to personal contacts or relationships that solicit goods, services, or labor through word of mouth (Alacovska, 2018). A tailor in Indonesia who operates a microbusiness for custom-tailoring school uniforms for the local school in exchange for income or tuition reduction for her children is an example of this. Similarly, a freelance information technology project manager in the United States who receives a small gig from one of her previous contacts to manage a short-term technical project is also engaging in informal work (Mitchell, 2021). In both these examples, there is no one fixed job or income; there is an inherent precariousness involved in these arrangements, which likely flourish due to personal contact, word of mouth, and the skills of the service provider. In the case of the former, taxation and benefit protection are likely not assessed, but very well may be in the latter case.

Due to the nature of work and inconsistencies inherent in the workflow, informal work may not have a fixed work schedule (Abraham & Houseman, 2019). This is closely linked to the ebb and flow of the availability of work and related tasks. In other words, the periods of work may not follow a typical daily or nightly schedule, like that of an office worker who, most typically, works a relatively fixed, approximately 8-hour daily schedule from Monday to Friday (Norouziasl et al., 2020). Thus, informal workers may dedicate their days working for different durations (i.e., they may work for different amounts of time every day, with different start and end times). At one level then, because the informal worker is free from organizational ties, they have increased flexibility to dynamically reassess and shift their working hours and days to accommodate other aspects of their life (Lehdonvirta, 2018). A new mother working in two informal gigs may prioritize her childcare responsibilities and work nights or weekends, after having first fulfilled her responsibilities to her children.

Informal work can also be tied to seasonal work or increased output or demands during certain periods of the year. The ebb and flow of productivity and product demands are tied to extraneous factors in more significant ways in informal work compared to traditional office-going jobs. For instance, a freelance informal worker in finance may have more work at year end (Lehdonvirta, 2018). Similarly, Saxena (2021) found that the work cycles for highly skilled artisans in the informal economy in rural India changed not just in terms of amount of work but also in terms of the nature of work they engaged in. Specifically, highly skilled potters had *greater amounts* of and *more complex and nuanced* work during culturally relevant holiday periods, such as Diwali or Naag Panchami (festivals of great importance to the local population), as opposed to other periods of time.

Informal work lies outside of formal employment contracts between an employer and the employee (Godfrey, 2011). Most informal work occurs *without* the organizational contract that tends to define "jobs" (Brannick et al., 2019, p. 35; Kalleberg & Sorensen, 1979). Informal work arrangements could be borne out of outsourcing (Williams & Nadin, 2012), and sometimes formal organizations also outsource certain tasks in an informal capacity to informal workers, albeit without a contract (Biles, 2009). In most informal economies, informal work relies on word of mouth or a verbal agreement between individuals who are commissioned for work, services, or goods (Mwemezi, 2018). One could imagine a daily-wage construction worker who waits for a pickup in the morning by a contractor who takes him to a building construction site and pays at the end of that day for the number of hours worked (Swider, 2016). Similarly, in the case of a highly skilled artisan weaver who hand-produces her own bamboo weave rug to sell at the local bazar, there is no larger organizational contract (Saxena, 2017).

A downside of this (lack of) arrangement is that informal workers are often left *unprotected* (Williams & Lansky, 2013) and vulnerable to abuse and exploitation (Hurtado et al., 2017). By its very nature, informal work lacks formal protections in terms of benefits, social security, and medical aid through an organized employer. Indeed, informal workers usually have to support themselves when it comes to medical insurance (Hurtado et al., 2017), healthcare (Hurtado et al., 2017), and retirement funds (Oteng et al., 2022). Other important factors absent from the discussion include benefits and legal protections regarding sick leave and associated compensation (Horwood et al., 2019), issues pertaining to termination from employment or the gig (Ergün, 2009), income discrepancies (Bargain & Kwenda, 2014), and formal mechanisms for seeking legal or related recourse in the case of wrongful action by another party (Women in Informal Employment: Globalizing and Organizing [WIEGO], 2020).

This absence of systemic policy and formal benefits, along with the lack of protection, leaves informal workers vulnerable to wage exploitation (WIEGO, 2020), shortfalls in decent work opportunities (Kantor et al., 2006), a lack of voice (Valodia, 2001), and occupational safety and health hazards (Saxena & Burke, 2020). The latter could arise from deliberate exploitation, as observed in some factories in China (Basu & Tzannatos, 2003; ILO, 2015), as well as from factors such as low wages and excessive overtime (Godfrey, 2011), or even inadvertently, as Saxena (2015) noted with regard to rice farming posing an occupational safety hazard for low-income, daily-wage agricultural workers by exposing those informal workers to the communicable disease of Japanese encephalitis (Saxena & Dhole, 2008).

Due to the factors and characteristics previously discussed, income and wage precarity is a core characteristic of informal work. Work tends to vary and is dependent on cycles of work availability (RoyChowdhury, 2021), seasons (Saxena, 2021), ability to make sales (Saxena, 2021), and even on the external market climate, including the local and global economy (Williams & Schneider, 2016). Even highly skilled artisans in the informal economy, while extremely competent producers and makers of beautiful and functionally useful products, cannot always generate sales at their local bazaars. They are then often left struggling financially when their sales are poor (Saxena, 2021). Similarly, a freelance finance advisor or a yoga trainer may not be able to procure enough gigs and may therefore face income shortage when the national economy is lean and the public may not want to invest money in what might be considered more luxury services (Deloitte, 2021). Thus, precariousness is often a characteristic of informal work.

Relatedly, due to the informal nature of work and contracts in informal work, a nonmonetary exchange may be involved in place of monetary income (Godfrey, 2011). For instance, many skilled Native American artisans produce goods and services in exchange for other goods and services that they may not possess the expertise to create themselves. These can involve a range of exchanges, such as collaborating on the production of regalia, beadwork, ceremonial gear, traditionally cooked fried bread, and other items. They may also oversee traditional spiritual ceremonies and so on. A local artist may offer to paint in exchange for home-cooked tiffin (packed) meals by a local freelance cook.

Additionally, when it comes to reskilling or upskilling, informal workers are responsible for their own skill upgrades (Sheikh & Gaurav, 2020), in contrast to organizational employees, for whom organizations often provide required training (Aguinis & Kraiger, 2009) and skill-enhancement workshops (Organisation for Economic Co-operation and Development [OECD], 2012). Increasingly, multilateral organizations (ILO, 2019a; OECD, 2022) and professional bodies (Rudolph et al., 2021; Society for Industrial and Organizational Psychology, 2022) are engaging in discussions about the future of work (Oswald et al., 2019). In this line of conversation, the traditional "job" is becoming obsolete (Lund et al., 2021), and greater numbers of individuals are moving toward informal, freelance, gig, and own-account work (Watson et al., 2021). Even though this has been a longstanding reality for informal workers, extending beyond the present discussions, the onus is increasingly on them to upgrade their skills and ensure that their skills, services, and products align with market demands. In a traditional job, organizations usually assume this responsibility as they strive to stay competitive and adapt to market forces. They assess both the market landscape and the skills of their workforce and then implement necessary training and development programs for their employees (Aguinis & Kraiger, 2009; Kraiger & Ford, 2021). In the world of informal work, where there is organizational structure to track these changes, individual workers *must* spend time, money, and resources to keep pace with the market forces via self-driven and self-initiated skill/product enhancement. One can observe this, for instance, in the case of a handloom weaver who tries to create distinct weaves to match trending fashion cycles (Ponnurajan et al., 2021).

CHARACTERISTICS OF INFORMAL WORK

Due to the scale and widely varying forms of informal work found globally, it is hard to generalize the characteristics of or the themes that govern informal work. However, based on the conceptual review previously articulated in this article, we can identify the following key characteristics of informal work. A caveat here is that the wide-ranging nature and the global scope of informal work necessitate an awareness that these characteristics might not always apply to every form of informal work in existence.

Theme 1: Work Precariousness / Precarious Work.   Work precariousness (Kalleberg, 2009), or lack of stability, is a core feature of informal work. This can manifest in multiple ways. Precarity surrounding income, wages, and earnings is one of the main features of informal work (Williams & Nadin, 2012), and one that makes such workers vulnerable to exploitation (Maiti & Sen, 2010). Due to the lack of protections, informal work is subject to workload precarity (Premji et al., 2014), work-opportunity precarity, and certainly precariousness in terms of earnings. Often, the term *precarious work* or *precarious employment* is used to refer to informal work. A clearer conceptualization is to consider precariousness a core characteristic that *describes* informal work.

Within economics, precariousness is considered multidimensional, referring to poor regulatory protection, low wages, greater employment insecurity, and poor worker or employee control or voice over outcomes that affect them, such as working hours, working conditions, and wages (Campbell & Price, 2016; Standing, 2011). In most cases, informal work displays the previously mentioned characteristics of precariousness, making it uncertain, unpredictable, unsecure, unstable, and risky, and thus undermining the well-being of workers. As a result, workers bear the risks of work, as opposed to organizations or the government (Kalleberg, 2009; Kalleberg & Vallas, 2018). Informal workers also have limited or no social benefits or statuary protections (Williams & Lansky, 2013).

Theme 2: Decent Work Deficits.   Decent work meets "aspirations all people have for their working lives; for work that is productive, delivers a fair income with security and social protection" (ILO, 2020, p. XX). Decent work is a core mandate of the International Labour Organization, which aims to provide better and dignified work and working conditions for all people around the world. Decent work encompasses the notions of human security (Hopner et al., 2021), access to productive work, a fair and stable income, voice, and social protection (Alkire, 2003). It is well known that informal work tends to defy these hallmark indicators of decent and dignified work. Due to often serious decent work deficits, much research and policy attention is directed toward reforming informal work through various programs (Williams et al., 2013) and work-restructuring policies (de Mel et al., 2013; Rosaldo, 2021). The aim is to improve working conditions and promote decent work by facilitating formalization and skill-upgradation programs, which can help eliminate deficiencies in decent work.

It is important to remember that caveats may exist. For instance, in Cameroon, informal to formal restructuring programs were not viewed positively by local informal workers (Saxena & Tchagneno, 2023). Similarly, in India highly skilled workers that were part of the informal economy engaged in intergenerational work that was sustainable (i.e. psychologically sustainable work), culturally and spiritually meaningful, and promoted thriving and positive affect (Saxena, 2021).

Theme 3: Economic Tenuousness and Poverty.   This theme has considerable overlap with the previous categories. However, it deserves its own space, given that it is one of the most conspicuous and influential elements that drives the lived experience of informal workers. Economic tenuousness and income precarity are often core to informal work (Saxena, 2017). Under some circumstances, poverty is a severe outcome of informal work. This threatens global, inclusive sustainable development per the United Nations Sustainable Development Goals 2030 (United Nations, 2022) by exacerbating poverty and undermining poverty alleviation (SDG#1), aggravating hunger and malnutrition (SDG#2), and leading to an inequitable global society (SDG#10). Poverty is a serious stressor and is associated with a wide variety of individual negative consequences (e.g., poor mental and physical health; Lund et al., 2011; Wagstaff, 2002) as well as social (such as greater social unrest; Mood & Jonsson, 2016) and societal adversities (Carroll et al., 2011).

Theme 4: Autonomy. This theme is not addressed as often in the mainstream economics literature. Disciplines such as sociology (Agarwala, 2009) and management (Godfrey, 2011) have acknowledged the availability of high levels of autonomy in informal work. Due to the absence of an organizational hierarchy or a more typical supervisory setup, individuals who work informally govern their own daily schedules, including when, where, and how they want to work (Lehdonvirta, 2018), the levels of effort and persistence (Kanfer, 1990) that they decide to dedicate to work tasks, the quality of the output (Lawler & O'Gara, 1967), and how much they want to extend themselves with regard to work (Muntaner et al., 2010). For instance, a mobile vegetable vendor in Sri Lanka is an informal worker who can choose his days of work, his time of work, and the area where he wants to vend his cart, and these could all change daily.

When viewed from a psychological viewpoint, we now start to see positive characteristics associated with working informally. Per the job-characteristics model, autonomy is a core work characteristic that can support and enhance work satisfaction, intrinsic motivation, and engagement (Hackman & Oldham, 1974).

Theme 5: Global Presence. We often think of informal work as something that occurs in a different part of the world. However, informal work is ubiquitous and is found all over the world, in economically developed regions and developing regions alike (Gërxhani, 2004). While it is true that developing countries bear a greater "burden" from informal work (ILO, 2022), informal work is found in the developed world as well—including in the United States and Europe (Abraham & Houseman, 2019; Williams & Windebank, 2002). The manifestation and terminology of informal work can be different, but it is inherently the same concept. For instance, gig work in the United States, often characterized as freelance work of even a side job, is essentially informal work, similar to that of an artisan weaver in Peru.

Theme 6: Many Names and Labels. An important point that lends itself to much confusion and overlap both in the research and the policy domain is that informal work is known by various names and labels (Williams, 2014) that cross disciplinary boundaries and geographical regions and have different angles of emphasis (Godfrey, 2011). They also govern how policy actions are undertaken by multilateral organizations and national governments. Although it is beyond the scope of this article to go over all the informal work names and labels, we'll examine a few pertinent terms that tend to be used interchangeably with regard to informal work.

Nontraditional Work/Nontraditional Employment. Any job-like engagement or work arrangement that is not a full-time position in a business or organization, that lacks a consistent schedule with regular hours, and that has no explicit contract for employment is referred to as *nontraditional work* or *nontraditional employment* (Murtough & Waite, 2000). It is also characterized by irregular hours, poor legal and social benefits, and no job security, and it is generally not full time and has no contractual protections (Murtough & Waite, 2000).

Gig Economy/Gig Work. This type of work usually takes the form of gig contracting (Watson et al., 2021). It is also known by terms such as *contingent* (Connelley & Gallagher, 2004) and *contract labor* (Agrawal et al., 2015), *temporary work* (Donovan et al., 2016), *just-in-time work-force* (de Stefano, 2015), *on-demand work* (Donovan et al., 2016), *crowdwork* (de Stefano, 2015), and more recently, the *digital economy* (Carlsson, 2004). The terms *gig work* (Tran & Sokas, 2017) and *gig economy* (de Stefando, 2015) were first used in the field of journalism (Brown, 2009). Gig work is a very popular term, particularly in the post-COVID era, and refers to individual "gigs" or short-term projects that (mostly) freelance workers take on, often through digitally enabled tech platforms. These workers provide services to the contracting party in exchange for pay (de Ruyter et al., 2018).

Gig work in the gig economy is generally characterized by flexible, free-moving independent suppliers of services, resources, and goods (Tran & Sokas, 2017). Gig workers tend to move freely from one job (or "gig") to the next, often relying on digital technology–enabled platforms and smartphone app-based connections to connect with purchasers of their services (Kaine & Josserand, 2019; Standing, 2017). Some scholars have argued that gig workers may be viewed as a specific type of worker within the broader category of nonstandard work arrangements, including temporary employees, part-time employees, and contracted employees (Dickson & Lorenz, 2009; Stewart & Stanford, 2017). Gig work often involves irregular hours, and gig workers are usually self-employed and are not tied to an organization or a manager (Kaine & Josserand, 2019). Gig work is also temporary, compensated on a project-by-project basis, and involves flexibility as to where, when, and how work is performed (de Ruyter et al., 2018).

Alternative Work Arrangements. Alternative work arrangement is defined as working as a self-employed freelancer or working for a contract firm that contracts out employees to other companies (Katz & Krueger, 2017). Identified primarily by the flexibility that it affords to workers, it underscores flexibility in the employment relationship, scheduling of work, and where work is accomplished (Spreitzer et al., 2017). In the new world of work, alternative work arrangements are being viewed as the arrangement of choice for high-skill workers, in stark contrast to arrangements for low-skill workers, who struggle to make a living and are beholden to the needs of the organization (Spreitzer et al., 2017). Similar to the other names and labels, it has been recognized that alternative work arrangements are not a single homogeneous group (Goudswaard & Andries, 2002).

As evident, some level of precarity, irregularity, lack of consistency, and a fundamental distinction from traditional "jobs" are essential aspects in defining and understanding all the aforementioned information. These categories of informal work include own account (Chen et al., 1999), microenterprise based (Saxena, 2021), temporary work (Karabchuk & Soboleva, 2020), contingent work (Connelley & Gallagher, 2004), freelance (Storey et al., 2005), and so on. The key point in this section is that although various terms and labels are used, they all fundamentally belong to the broad category of informal work, as they share the common characteristic of being distinct from a job embedded within an organization.

WORK IN THE INFORMAL ECONOMY

Work in the informal economy (Godfrey, 2011) is perhaps the most common *doppelgänger* of informal work; often these terms are used interchangeably (Williams & Nadin, 2012). Work in the informal economy refers strictly to working that occurs within the aegis of the informal economic sector. In addition to having all the characteristics of informal work, the main distinguishing factor is that work in the informal economy lies in the informal economic sector only. The main outcome of this is that it lies outside of governmental regulations or taxation (Godfrey, 2011). By definition, work in the informal economy operates in a realm where it exists, intentionally or unintentionally, beyond formal procedures for taxation and government regulation. It is a much broader term that includes a multitude of forms and formats of work. It can even include illicit and illegal activities like human trafficking (Sharapov, 2017), the drug trade (Webb et al., 2009), and so on.

However, scholars have noted that it is a mistake to think of work in the informal economy as only a safe haven for illicit trade or illegal activities (Saxena & Tchagneno, 2023; Webb et al., 2009). Work in the informal economy represents the most inclusive and diverse category of employment, encompassing the spectrum of traditional, intergenerational, and often ancient-yet-still-thriving forms of work. This includes intergenerational artisans who have honed their craft in the informal economy for centuries, and possibly even millennia (Saxena, 2021), as well as more informal and casual forms of work (e.g., a housemaid or house help in Singapore; Huang & Yeoh, 1996). A key point to note is that the informal economy often acts as a reservoir for the various forms of informal work, each operating within its own self-sustaining ecosystem (Mounia & Mounir, 2021).

WHY STUDY INFORMAL WORK?

This article issues an urgent appeal to the scholarly community to increase our understanding of informal work. This appeal cuts across both scientific and broader societal goals. To have true and complete developmental growth that is inclusive and sustainable and does not leave anyone behind as part of the United Nations' Sustainable Development Goals (UNSDGs 2030; United Nations, 2022), it is imperative that a systematic psychological understanding of informal work is the mainstay of serious research and policy action. Relatedly, to have a full and complete scientific understanding of work and working (Weiss, 2014), the study of informal work cannot be neglected in psychology any further.

This article argues that it is imperative to understand work beyond the confines of jobs and organizations. Instead, we should view work as a fluid and intrinsic human activity that can exist independently and does not have to rely on an organization. Therefore, this article issues an appeal to understand *work* not just in the context of jobs. From a historical standpoint, what is labeled *informal work* has existed for thousands of years (Saxena, 2017, 2021). This is serious, productive, and creative work that is happening and has happened for a long time outside of organizations, where workers are not employees. Two-thirds of the world working in this realm is a testament to this current and historical reality (Hatton, 2015; ILO, 2019c; WIEGO, 2015).

There are many stereotypes and prejudiced assumptions related to informal work (Saxena, 2021; Saxena & Tchagneno, 2023) that, for instance, label informal work as work in the shadow economy (Godfrey, 2011), underground economy (Williams & Nadin, 2012), hidden economy (Williams, 2014), invisible work (Hatton, 2017), undeclared work (Williams et al., 2013), and so on. The International Labour Organization also notes that informal work is characterized by unemployment and underemployment, poor-quality and unproductive jobs, unsafe work, and unsecure income (ILO, 2013). Informal work is also called unproductive (La Porta & Shleifer, 2014), unskilled (Amaral & Quintin, 2006; Hatton, 2017), and incompetent work (ILO, 2013). This article is not arguing against the economic perspective that this work often operates outside of governmental regulation and taxation (Godfrey, 2011). Nor does it deny the presence of occupational safety hazards and deficits of decent work in this context (ILO, 2013).

However, when we adopt a worker-centric perspective, we find that psychological research unravels and debunks many of these myths (e.g., Saxena, 2021). For instance, my own research that explored the lived experience of workers in the informal economy via a non-WEIRD perspective (Henrich et al., 2010), found workers actively involved in the pursuit of highly skilled work. This work not only proved to be productive but also drew upon intergenerational cultural knowledge that had been passed down through generations and shaped their sense of identities and personal narratives. These workers demonstrated a deep intrinsic motivation and expressed their desire to continue working based on their own choices and desires. They did not want to transition to work in low-paying, base-of-the-pyramid (Gutierrez et al., 2019) jobs that were embedded within the industrial economy.

Additional research on informal workers can lead to more intriguing insights that not only debunk economically driven stereotypes and biased attitudes but also answer interesting questions about creativity in the informal sector. Additionally, this research can contribute to a deeper understanding of work experiences in the informal sector and shed light on related issues.

Taking into account the UNSDGs pertaining to decent work (SDG#8), environmental protection (SDG#13), poverty alleviation (SDG#1), and eliminating hunger (SDG#2), focusing on workers in the informal economy can enhance our understanding of the broader world of work. Additionally, this focus can initiate global efforts for sustainable and inclusive development that leave no one behind. In general, policy efforts are aimed at transitioning workers from an informal work setup to formal jobs. While in some cases this may be the ideal course of action, this is not always the most appropriate step for the workers involved. Work is a fundamental part of the human experience. Respecting dignity of labor and all forms of work can lead to unbiased, equitable approaches to creating inclusive, sustainable economies around the world and a more rounded science of work.

FURTHER READING

Bergman, M. E., & Jean, V. A. (2016). Where have all the "workers" gone? A critical analysis of the unrepresentativeness of our samples relative to the labor market in the industrial-organizational psychology literature. *Industrial and Organizational Psychology, 9*(1), 84–113.

Carr, S. C., De Guzman, J. M., Eltyeb, S. M., Furnham, A., MacLachlan, M., Marai, L., & McAuliffe, E. (2012). An introduction to humanitarian work psychology. In S. C. Carr, M. MacLachlan, & A. Furnham (Eds.), *Humanitarian work psychology* (pp. 3–33). Palgrave Macmillan.

International Labour Organization. (2013). The informal economy and decent work: A policy resource guide.

Saxena, M. (2017). Workers in poverty: An insight into informal workers around the world. *Industrial and Organizational Psychology, 10*(3), 376–379.

Saxena, M. (2021). Cultural skills as drivers of decency in decent work: An investigation of skilled workers in the informal economy. *European Journal of Work and Organizational Psychology, 30*(6), 824–836.

REFERENCES

Abraham, K. G., & Houseman, S. N. (2019). Making ends meet: The role of informal work in supplementing Americans' income. *RSF: The Russell Sage Foundation Journal of the Social Sciences, 5*(5), 110–131. https://doi.org/10.7758/RSF.2019.5.5.06

Agarwala, R. (2009). An economic sociology of informal work: The case of India. In Bandelj, N. (Ed.), *Economic sociology of work* (Vol. 18, pp. 315–342). Emerald Group.

Agrawal, A., Horton, J., Lacetera, N., & Lyons, E. (2015). Digitization and the contract labor market: A research agenda. *Economic Analysis of the Digital Economy, 18*, 315–342.

Aguinis, H., & Kraiger, K. (2009). Benefits of training and development for individuals and teams, organizations, and society. *Annual Review of Psychology, 60*(1), 451–474.

Alacovska, A. (2018). Informal creative labour practices: A relational work perspective. *Human Relations, 71*(12), 1563–1589. https://doi.org/10.1177/0018726718754991

Alkire, S. (2003). *A conceptual framework for human security*. CRISE (Department of International Development, University of Oxford). https://ora.ox.ac.uk/objects/uuid:d2907237-2a9f-4ce5-a403-a6254020052d

Amaral, P. S., & Quintin, E. (2006). A competitive model of the informal sector. *Journal of Monetary Economics, 53*(7), 1541–1553. https://doi.org/10.1016/j.jmoneco.2005.07.016

Ashford, S. J., Caza, B. B., & Reid, E. M. (2018). From surviving to thriving in the gig economy: A research agenda for individuals in the new world of work. *Research in Organizational Behavior, 38*, 23–41.

Bargain, O., & Kwenda, P. (2014). The informal sector wage gap: New evidence using quantile estimations on panel data. *Economic Development and Cultural Change, 63*(1), 117–153. https://doi.org/10.1086/677908

Basu, K., & Tzannatos, Z. (2003). The global child labor problem: What do we know and what can we do? *The World Bank Economic Review, 17*(2), 147–173. https://doi.org/10.1093/wber/lhg021

Bergman, M. E., & Jean, V. A. (2016). Where have all the "workers" gone? A critical analysis of the unrepresentativeness of our samples relative to the labor market in the industrial-organizational psychology literature. *Industrial and Organizational Psychology, 9*(1), 84–113. https://doi.org/10.1017/iop.2015.70

Biles, J. J. (2009). Informal work in Latin America: Competing perspectives and recent debates. *Geography Compass, 3*(1), 214–236. https://doi.org/10.1111/j.1749-8198.2008.00188.x

Brannick, M. T., Morgeson, F. P., & Levine, E. L. (2019). *Job and work analysis: Methods, research, and applications for human resource management*. SAGE.

Brown, T. (2009). The gig economy. *Daily Beast*. https://www.thedailybeast.com/the-gig-economy

Bruton, G. D., Ireland, R. D., & Ketchen, D. J., Jr. (2012). Toward a research agenda on the informal economy. *Academy of Management Perspectives, 26*(3), 1–11. https://doi.org/10.5465/amp.2012.0079

Campbell, I., & Price, R. (2016). Precarious work and precarious workers: Towards an improved conceptualisation. *The Economic and Labour Relations Review, 27*(3), 314–332.

Carlsson, B. (2004). The digital economy: What is new and what is not? *Structural Change and Economic Dynamics, 15*(3), 245–264.

Carr, S., Young-Hauser, A., Hodgetts, D., Schmidt, W., Moran, L., Haar, J., Parker, J., Arrowsmith, J., Jones, H., & Alefaio, S. (2021). Research update: How decent wages transform qualities of living—By affording escape from working poverty trap. *Journal of Sustainability Research, 3*(2), 1–15.

Carr, S. C., De Guzman, J. M., Eltyeb, S. M., Furnham, A., MacLachlan, M., Marai, L., & McAuliffe, E. (2012). An introduction to humanitarian work psychology. In S. C. Carr, M. MacLachlan, & A. Furnham (Eds.), *Humanitarian work psychology* (pp. 3–33). Palgrave Macmillan. https://doi.org/10.1057/9781137015228_1

Carroll, P., Casswell, S., Huakau, J., Howden-Chapman, P., & Perry, P. (2011). The widening gap: Perceptions of poverty and income inequalities and implications for health and social outcomes. *Social Policy Journal of New Zealand, 37*, 111–123.

Chen, M., Sebstad, J., & O'Connell, L. (1999). Counting the invisible workforce: The case of homebased workers. *World Development, 27*(3), 603–610. https://doi.org/10.1016/S0305-750X(98)00154-5

Connelly, C. E., & Gallagher, D. G. (2004). Emerging trends in contingent work research. *Journal of Management, 30*(6), 959–983.

Danquah, M., Schotte, S., & Sen, K. (2020). Informal work in sub-Saharan Africa: Dead end or stepping-stone? *IZA Journal of Development and Migration, 12*(1), 1–44. https://doi.org/10.2478/izajodm-2021-0015

Darbi, W. P. K., Hall, C. M., & Knott, P. (2018). The informal sector: A review and agenda for management research. *International Journal of Management Reviews, 20*(2), 301–324. https://doi.org/10.1111/ijmr.12131

de Mel, S., McKenzie, D., & Woodruff, C. (2013). The demand for, and consequences of, formalization among informal firms in Sri Lanka. *American Economic Journal: Applied Economics, 5*(2), 122–150. https://doi.org/10.1257/app.5.2.122

de Ruyter, A., Brown, M., & Burgess, J. (2018). Gig work and the fourth industrial revolution: Conceptual and regulatory challenges. *Journal of International Affairs, 72*(1), 37–50.

De Stefano, V. (2015). The rise of the just-in-time workforce: On-demand work, crowdwork, and labor protection in the gig-economy. *Comparative Labor Law & Policy Journal, 37*(3), 471–504.

Deloitte. (2021). *Global powers of luxury goods 2021: Breakthrough luxury.* https://www2.deloitte.com/content/dam/Deloitte/at/Documents/consumer-business/at-global-powers-of-luxury-goods-2021.pdf

Dickson, K. E., & Lorenz, A. (2009). Psychological empowerment and job satisfaction of temporary and part-time nonstandard workers: A preliminary investigation. *Journal of Behavioral and Applied Management, 10*(2), 166–191.

Donovan, S. A., Bradley, D. H., & Shimabukuru, J. O. (2016). *What does the gig economy mean for workers?* https://ecommons.cornell.edu/handle/1813/79155

Ergün, E. (2009). Bargaining with the devil: Neoliberalization, informal work and workers' resistance in the clothing industry of Turkey. In P. A. Smith, P. A. Stenning, & K. Willis (Eds.), *Social justice and neoliberalism: Global perspectives* (pp. 114–134). Bloomsbury.

Gërxhani, K. (2004). The informal sector in developed and less developed countries: A literature survey. *Public Choice, 120*(3), 267–300. https://doi.org/10.1023/B:PUCH.0000044287.88147.5e

Gloss, A., Carr, S. C., Reichman, W., Abdul-Nasiru, I., & Oesterich, W. T. (2017). From handmaidens to POSH humanitarians: The case for making human capabilities the business of I-O psychology. *Industrial and Organizational Psychology, 10*(3), 329–369. https://doi.org/10.1017/iop.2017.27

Godfrey, P. C. (2011). Toward a theory of the informal economy. *Academy of Management Annals, 5*(1), 231–277. https://doi.org/10.5465/19416520.2011.585818

Goudswaard, A., & Andries, F. (2002). *Employment status and working conditions.* European Foundation for the Improvement of Living and Working Conditions. https://policycommons.net/artifacts/1837282/employment-status-and-working-conditions/2580583/

Gutierrez, I. A., Kumar, K. B., Mahmud, M., Munshi, F., & Nataraj, S. (2019). Transitions between informal and formal employment: Results from a worker survey in Bangladesh. *IZA Journal of Development and Migration, 9*(1), 3. https://doi.org/10.1186/s40176-019-0141-2

Hackman, J. R., & Oldham, G. R. (1974). *The Job Diagnostic Survey: An instrument for the diagnosis of jobs and the evaluation of job redesign projects.* Yale University.

Hatton, E. (2015). Work beyond the bounds: A boundary analysis of the fragmentation of work. *Work, Employment and Society, 29*(6), 1007–1018. https://doi.org/10.1177/0950017014568141

Hatton, E. (2017). Mechanisms of invisibility: Rethinking the concept of invisible work. *Work, Employment and Society, 31*(2), 336–351. https://doi.org/10.1177/0950017016674894

Henrich, J., Heine, S. J., & Norenzayan, A. (2010). The weirdest people in the world? *Behavioral and Brain Sciences, 33*(2–3), 61–83.

Hopner, V., Hodgetts, D., Carr, S., Nelson, N., Chamberlain, K., & Ball, R. (2021). Assembling the psycurity accord in response to the early COVID-19 outbreak in Aotearoa New Zealand. In I. Strasser & M. Dege (Eds.), *The psychology of global crises and crisis politics: Intervention, resistance, decolonization; Palgrave studies in the theory and history of psychology* (pp. 19–42). Palgrave Macmillan.

Horwood, C., Haskins, L., Alfers, L., Masango-Muzindutsi, Z., Dobson, R., & Rollins, N. (2019). A descriptive study to explore working conditions and childcare practices among informal women workers in KwaZulu-Natal, South Africa: Identifying opportunities to support childcare for mothers in informal work. *BMC Pediatrics, 19*(1), 1–11. https://doi.org/10.1186/s12887-019-1737-7

Huang, S., & Yeoh, B. S. A. (1996). Ties that bind: State policy and migrant female domestic helpers in Singapore. *Geoforum, 27*(4), 479–493. https://doi.org/10.1016/S0016-7185(96)00023-1

Hurtado, D. A., Hessel, P., & Avendano, M. (2017). The hidden costs of informal work: Lack of social protection and subjective well-being in Colombia. *International Journal of Public Health, 62*(2), 187–196. https://doi.org/10.1007/s00038-016-0864-2

International Labour Organization. (2012). *World of Work Report 2012.*

International Labour Organization. (2013). *The informal economy and decent work: A policy resource guide.* https://www.ilo.org/emppolicy/pubs/WCMS_212688/lang--en/index.htm

International Labour Organization. (2015). *World report on child labour 2015.* https://www.ilo.org/ipec/Informationresources/WCMS_358969/lang--en/index.htm

International Labour Organization. (2019a). *ILO centenary declaration for the future of work.* https://www.ilo.org/ilc/ILCSessions/108/reports/texts-adopted/WCMS_711674/lang--en/index.htm

International Labour Organization. (2019c). *World employment and social outlook: Trends 2019.* https://www.ilo.org/global/research/global-reports/weso/2019/WCMS_670542/lang--en/index.htm

International Labour Organization. (2020). *World employment and social outlook: Trends 2020.* https://www.ilo.org/wcmsp5/groups/public/---dgreports/---dcomm/---publ/documents/publication/wcms_734455.pdf

International Labour Organization. (2022). *World employment and social outlook: Trends 2022.* https://www.ilo.org/wcmsp5/groups/public/---dgreports/---dcomm/---publ/documents/publication/wcms_834081.pdf

Kaine, S., & Josserand, E. (2019). The organisation and experience of work in the gig economy. *Journal of Industrial Relations, 61*(4), 479–501. https://doi.org/10.1177/0022185619865480

Kalleberg, A. L. (2009). Precarious work, insecure workers: Employment relations in transition. *American Sociological Review, 74*(1), 1–22.

Kalleberg, A. L., & Sorensen, A. B. (1979). The sociology of labor markets. *Annual Review of Sociology, 5,* 351–379.

Kalleberg, A. L., & Vallas, S. P. (2018). Probing precarious work: Theory, research, and politics. *Research in the Sociology of Work, 31*(1), 1–30.

Kanfer, R. (1990). Motivation theory and industrial and organizational psychology. *Handbook of Industrial and Organizational Psychology, 1*(2), 75–130.

Kantor, P., Rani, U., & Unni, J. (2006). Decent work deficits in informal economy: Case of Surat. *Economic and Political Weekly, 41*(21), 2089–2097. https://www.jstor.org/stable/4418264

Karabchuk, T., & Soboleva, N. (2020). Temporary employment, informal work and subjective well-being across Europe: Does labor legislation matter? *Journal of Happiness Studies: An Interdisciplinary Forum on Subjective Well-Being, 21*(5), 1879–1901. https://doi.org/10.1007/s10902-019-00152-4

Katz, L. F., & Krueger, A. B. (2017). The role of unemployment in the rise in alternative work arrangements. *American Economic Review, 107*(5), 388–392. https://doi.org/10.1257/aer.p20171092

Kraiger, K., & Ford, J. (2021). The science of workplace instruction: Learning and development applied to work. *Annual Review of Organizational Psychology and Organizational Behavior, 8,* 45–72. https://doi.org/10.1146/annurev-orgpsych-012420-060109

La Porta, R., & Shleifer, A. (2014). Informality and development. *Journal of Economic Perspectives, 28*(3), 109–126. https://doi.org/10.1257/jep.28.3.109

Lawler, E. E., & O'Gara, P. W. (1967). Effects of inequity produced by underpayment on work output, work quality, and attitudes toward the work. *Journal of Applied Psychology, 51*(5), 403–410. https://psycnet.apa.org/record/1968-01265-001

Lehdonvirta, V. (2018). Flexibility in the gig economy: Managing time on three online piecework platforms. *New Technology, Work and Employment, 33*(1), 13–29. https://doi.org/10.1111/ntwe.12102

Lund, C., De Silva, M., Plagerson, S., Cooper, S., Chisholm, D., Das, J., Knapp, M., & Patel, V. (2011). Poverty and mental disorders: Breaking the cycle in low-income and middle-income countries. *The Lancet, 378*(9801), 1502–1514. https://doi.org/10.1016/S0140-6736(11)60754-X

Lund, S., Madgavkar, A., Manyika, J., Smit, S., Ellingrud, K., Meaney, M., & Robinson, O. (2021). The future of work after COVID-19. *McKinsey Global Institute.* https://www.mckinsey.com/featured-insights/future-of-work/the-future-of-work-after-covid-19

Maiti, D., & Sen, K. (2010). The informal sector in India: A means of exploitation or accumulation? *Journal of South Asian Development, 5*(1), 1–13. https://doi.org/10.1177/097317411000500101

Malson, E. (2021). *Nanny job titles & duties.* U.S. Nanny. https://www.usnanny.org/nanny-industry-job-titles-duties/

Mitchell, H. (2021). How a side hustle can boost performance at your regular job. *The Wall Street Journal.* https://www.wsj.com/articles/how-a-side-hustle-can-boost-your-job-performance-11635533208

Monteith, W., & Giesbert, L. (2017). "When the stomach is full we look for respect": Perceptions of "good work" in the urban informal sectors of three developing countries. *Work, Employment and Society, 31*(5), 816–833. https://doi.org/10.1177/0950017016650606

Mood, C., & Jonsson, J. O. (2016). The social consequences of poverty: An empirical test on longitudinal data. *Social Indicators Research, 127*(2), 633–652. https://doi.org/10.1007/s11205-015-0983-9

Mounia, C., & Mounir, E. K. (2021). Les entreprises formelles sont-elles plus productives que les entreprises informelles? Une étude auprès de microentreprises au Maroc [Are formal firms more productive than informal ones? A study among microenterprises in Morocco]. *African Scientific Journal, 3*(4), 1–28. https://doi.org/10.5281/zenodo.5597043

Muntaner, C., Solar, O., Vanroelen, C., Martínez, J. M., Vergara, M., Santana, V., Castedo, A., Kim, I.-H., & Benach, J. (2010). Unemployment, informal work, precarious employment, child labor, slavery, and health inequalities: Pathways and mechanisms. *International Journal of Health Services, 40*(2), 281–295. https://doi.org/10.2190/HS.40.2.h

Murtough, G., & Waite, M. (2000, October 19). *Unemployment and re-employment of displaced workers* (Working Paper No. 1642). Productivity Commission. http://dx.doi.org/10.2139/ssrn.270781

Mwemezi, B. R. (2018). Administration of agreement practice in the informal construction sector: A case of Goba and Madale, Dar-Es-Salaam. *The International Journal of Construction Engineering and Management, 7*(1), 22.

Norouziasl, S., Jafari, A., & Wang, C. (2020). An agent-based simulation of occupancy schedule in office buildings. *Building and Environment, 186,* 107352. https://doi.org/10.1016/j.buildenv.2020.107352

Organisation for Economic Co-operation and Development. (2012). *Workshop: Skills strategies for inclusive development in India—Accelerating prosperity through policy coherence (New Delhi, India).* https://www.oecd.org/india/workshopskillsstrategiesforinclusivedevelopmentinindiaacceleratingprosperitythroughpolicycoherencenewdelhiindia.htm

Organisation for Economic Co-operation and Development. (2022). *Employment outlook 2022.* https://www.oecd.org/employment-outlook/2022/#take-action

Oswald, F., Behrend, T. S., & Foster, L. (2019). *Workforce readiness and the future of work.* Routledge.

Oteng, S. A., Manful, E., & Akuoko, K. O. (2022). Retiring in the informal economy: Implications for social policy intervention for ageing workers in Ghana. *Ageing International, 47*(3), 415–432. https://doi.org/10.1007/s12126-021-09434-w

Ponnurajan, F., Kandasamy, M., Sengodan, M. L., & Devi, H. (2021). An empirical analysis of constraints faced by the handloom weavers and weaver cooperative societies in Virudhunagar district of Tamil Nadu. *Current Journal of Applied Science and Technology, 40*(45), 34–38. https://doi.org/10.9734/cjast/2021/v40i4531626

Premji, S., Shakya, Y., Spasevski, M., Merolli, J., Athar, S., I. Women, & Precarious Employment Core Research Group. (2014). Precarious work experiences of racialized immigrant woman in Toronto: A community-based study. *Just Labour, 22,* 122–143. https://justlabour.journals.yorku.ca/index.php/justlabour/article/view/8

Rosaldo, M. (2021). Problematizing the "informal sector": 50 years of critique, clarification, qualification, and more critique. *Sociology Compass, 12,* 9–14.

RoyChowdhury, S. (2021). *City of shadows: Slums and informal work in Bangalore.* Cambridge University Press.

Rudolph, C. W., Allan, B., Clark, M., Hertel, G., Hirschi, A., Kunze, F., Shockley, K., Shoss, M., Sonnentag, S., & Zacher, H. (2021). Pandemics: Implications for research and practice in industrial and organizational psychology. *Industrial and Organizational Psychology, 14*(1–2), 1–35.

Sánchez, T. F., & Alvarez, V. O. (2011). *Labor costs, labor informality and income distribution in Colombia and Chile, 1984–2009.* IDRC CRDI. https://idl-bnc-idrc.dspacedirect.org/handle/10625/48642

Saxena, M. (2015). Communicable disease control in South Asia. In I. McWha-Hermann, D. C. Maynard, & M. Berry (Eds.), *Humanitarian work psychology and the global development agenda: Case studies and interventions* (pp. 69–82). Routledge.

Saxena, M. (2017). Workers in poverty: An insight into informal workers around the world. *Industrial and Organizational Psychology, 10*(3), 376–379. http://dx.doi.org/10.1017/iop.2017.29

Saxena, M. (2021). Cultural skills as drivers of decency in decent work: An investigation of skilled workers in the informal economy. *European Journal of Work and Organizational Psychology, 30*(6), 824–836. https://doi.org/10.1080/1359432X.2021.1918760

Saxena, M., & Burke, M. M. (2020). Communicable diseases as occupational hazards for agricultural workers: Using experience sampling methods for promoting public health. *International Perspectives in Psychology: Research, Practice, Consultation, 9,* 127–130. https://doi.org/10.1037/ipp0000129

Saxena, M., Sall, E., Scott, J., Rupp, D., Saari, L., Thompson, L., Osicki, M., & Mallory, D. (2015). News from the SIOP-United Nations team: Exploring work experiences of informal workers and promoting decent work for all. *The Industrial-Organizational Psychologist, 53*(1), 172–175.

Saxena, M., & Tchagneno, C. (2023). Informal work as sustainable work: Pathways to sustainable livelihoods. In S. C. Carr, V. Hopner, & D. Hodgetts, D. (Eds.), *Tackling precarious work* [SIOP New Frontiers Series] (pp. online). Routledge.

Saxena, V., & Dhole, T. N. (2008). Preventive strategies for frequent outbreaks of Japanese encephalitis in Northern India. *Journal of Biosciences, 33*(4), 505–514. https://doi.org/10.1007/s12038-008-0069-9

Shapland, J., & Heyes, J. (2017). How close are formal and informal work? *International Journal of Sociology and Social Policy, 37*(7–8), 374–386. https://doi.org/10.1108/IJSSP-06-2016-0071

Sharapov, K. (2017). Trafficking in human beings and the informal economy. In R. Piotrowicz, C. Rijken, & B. Uhl (Eds.), *Routledge handbook of human trafficking* (pp. 11–18). Routledge.

Sheikh, R. A., & Gaurav, S. (2020). Informal work in India: A tale of two definitions. *The European Journal of Development Research, 32*(4), 1105–1127. https://doi.org/10.1057/s41287-020-00258-z

Society for Industrial and Organizational Psychology. (2022). *Top 10 work trends 2022.* https://www.siop.org/Business-Resources/Top-10-Work-Trends

Spreitzer, G. M., Cameron, L., & Garrett, L. (2017). Alternative work arrangements: Two images of the new world of work. *Annual Review of Organizational Psychology and Organizational Behavior, 4,* 473–499.

Standing, G. (2011). *The precariat: The new dangerous class.* Bloomsbury.

Standing, G. (2017). *Basic income: And how we can make it happen.* Penguin.

Stewart, A., & Stanford, J. (2017). Regulating work in the gig economy: What are the options? *The Economic and Labour Relations Review, 28*(3), 420–437. https://doi.org/10.1177/1035304617722461

Storey, J., Salaman, G., & Platman, K. (2005). Living with enterprise in an enterprise economy: Freelance and contract workers in the media. *Human Relations, 58*(8), 1033–1054. https://doi.org/10.1177/0018726705058502

Swider, S. (2015). Building China: Precarious employment among migrant construction workers. *Work, Employment and Society, 29*(1), 41–59. https://doi.org/10.1177/0950017014526631

Swider, S. (2016). *Building China: Informal work and the new precariat.* Cornell University Press.

Tran, M., & Sokas, R. K. (2017). The gig economy and contingent work: An occupational health assessment. *Journal of Occupational and Environmental Medicine, 59*(4), e63–e66. https://doi.org/10.1097/JOM.0000000000000977

Tucker, J. (1993). Notes from the underground: America's sprawling informal economy. *Policy Review, 65,* 76–80.

United Nations. (2022). *The sustainable development goals report.* https://unstats.un.org/sdgs/report/2022/The-Sustainable-Development-Goals-Report-2022.pdf

Valodia, I. (2001). Economic policy and women's informal work in South Africa. *Development and Change, 32*(5), 871–892. https://doi.org/10.1111/1467-7660.00230

Wagstaff, A. (2002). Poverty and health sector inequalities. *Bulletin of the World Health Organization, 80,* 97–105. https://www.ncbi.nlm.nih.gov/pmc/articles/PMC2567730/

Watson, G. P., Kistler, L. D., Graham, B. A., & Sinclair, R. R. (2021). Looking at the gig picture: Defining gig work and explaining profile differences in gig workers' job demands and resources. *Group & Organization Management, 46*(2), 327–361. https://doi.org/10.1177/1059601121996548

Webb, J. W., Tihanyi, L., Ireland, R. D., & Sirmon, D. G. (2009). You say illegal, I say legitimate: Entrepreneurship in the informal economy. *Academy of Management Review, 34*(3), 492–510. https://doi.org/10.5465/AMR.2009.40632826

Weiss, H. M. (2014). Working as human nature. In J. K. Ford, J. R. Hollenbeck, & A. M. Ryan (Eds.), *The nature of work: Advances in psychological theory, methods, and practice* (pp. 35–47). American Psychological Association. https://doi.org/10.1037/14259-003

Williams, C. C. (2014). Out of the shadows: A classification of economies by the size and character of their informal sector. *Work Employment and Society, 28*(5), 735–753. https://doi.org/10.1177/0950017013501951

Williams, C. C., & Lansky, M. A. (2013). Informal employment in developed and developing economies: Perspectives and policy responses. *International Labour Review, 152*(3–4), 355–380. http://dx.doi.org/10.1111/j.1564-913X.2013.00196.x

Williams, C. C., & Nadin, S. (2012). Work beyond employment: Representations of informal economic activities. *Work, Employment and Society, 26*(2), 1–10. https://doi.org/10.1177/0950017012437006

Williams, C. C., & Schneider, F. (2016). *Measuring the global shadow economy: The prevalence of informal work and labour.* Edward Elgar.

Williams, C. C., & Windebank, J. (2002). The uneven geographies of informal economic activities: A case study of two British cities. *Work Employment and Society, 16*(2), 231–250. https://doi.org/10.1177/095001702400426820

Williams, C. C., Windebank, J., Baric, M., & Nadin, S. (2013). Public policy innovations: The case of undeclared work. *Management Decision, 51*(6), 1161–1175. https://doi.org/10.1108/MD-10-2011-0341

Women in Informal Employment: Globalizing and Organizing. (2015). *Myths & facts about the informal economy and workers in the informal economy.* https://www.wiego.org/sites/default/files/resources/files/WIEGO-Myths-Facts-Informal-Economy.pdf

Women in Informal Employment: Globalizing and Organizing. (2020). *WIEGO briefing note November 2020: Violence and informal work.* https://www.wiego.org/sites/default/files/publications/files/ILC_WIEGO_Briefing%20Note%20Violence%20in%20the%20workplace%20EN%20for%20web.pdf

Mahima Saxena

Interpersonal Relationships, Groups, and Teams

IMPRESSION MANAGEMENT

IMPRESSION MANAGEMENT OVERVIEW

The scientific study of impression management has been underway for nearly a century, beginning with the pleas of experts in sales and marketing who guided their clients on how to best win friends and influence the people around them (e.g., Carnegie, 1936). Since then, numerous social scientists have adopted a Shakespearean assertion that "all the world is a stage, and all the men and women merely players," pursuing a rigorous study of the various ways in which people can influence others' perceptions of them (Goffman, 1959).

Impression management is defined as behaviors that actors use to shape how they are seen by targets (Leary, 1995) and involves trying to create a new, desired image or maintaining and protecting a current image (Tedeschi & Melburg, 1984). Impression management is one of the most pervasive social phenomena that exists because people care a great deal about how they appear to others. Many important outcomes in life are contingent on the impressions individuals make during social interactions, with implications for friendship formation, romantic relationships, career success, and inclusion in groups, as well as one's self-concept and well-being, to name just a few. The research on the topic has primarily focused on the various strategies (i.e., tactics) people use to satisfy their image-related goals and the effectiveness of those strategies. Some researchers use the terms *impression management* and *influence tactics* interchangeably; however, the former term is more about managing others' perceptions while the latter is more about managing others' attitudes and behaviors. Impression management is also sometimes referred to as *self-presentation* and involves an actor, a target audience, and sometimes a third-party observer.

Scholars from sociology, social psychology, and organizational psychology have offered separate yet often overlapping definitions of impression management and self-presentation.

Table 1. Key Impression Management Definitions

Source of Definition	Label	Definition
Arkin (1981)	Self-presentation	The manner in which people plan, adopt, and carry out strategies for managing the impressions they make on others.
Baumeister (1982)	Self-presentation	The use of behavior to communicate some information about oneself to others.
Cialdini and Richardson (1980)	Self-presentation	Influencing one's image in the eyes of observers.
Jellison (1981)	Self-presentation	Creating an impression in other persons that will gain their approval and avoid their disapproval.
Jones and Pittman (1982)	Strategic self-presentation	Features of behavior affected by power augmentation motives designed to elicit or shape others' attributions of the actor's dispositions.
Leary and Kowalski (1990)	Impression management	The process by which individuals attempt to control the impressions others form of them.
Lee et al. (1999)	Self-presentation	Behaviors that are intended to manage the impressions that observers have of actors.
Rosenfeld et al. (1995)	Impression management	The process whereby people seek to influence the image others have of them.
Schlenker (1980)	Impression management	The attempt to control images that are projected in real or imagined social interactions.
Schlenker (1980)	Self-presentation	The attempt to control (self-relevant) images that are projected in real or imagined social interactions.
Schneider (1981)	Impression management	An attempt by one person (actor) to affect another person's (target's) perceptions of them.
Tedeschi and Riess (1981)	Impression management	Any behavior by a person that has the purpose of controlling or manipulating the attributions and impressions formed of that person by others.
Tetlock and Manstead (1985)	Impression management	Behavioral strategies that people use to create desired social images or identities.

These definitions are presented in Table 1. A common thread is that impression management is social and behavioral, involves power augmentation via influence, can be conscious or unconscious, and is strategic in the sense that the actor is attempting to manage others' attributions to create their desired self-image (Jones & Pittman, 1982; Leary & Kowalksi, 1990; Schlenker, 1980; Tedeschi & Riess, 1981).

INTERPRETATIONS OF IMPRESSION MANAGEMENT

Two subtle distinctions have formed in how scholars understand and interpret impression management. The first distinction surrounds the term *self-presentation*. Some scholars suggest that self-presentation is closely related to impression management but is different in that impressions can be managed by means other than the self (e.g., a third party) and self-presentation can be used for goals other than shaping an impression (e.g., information seeking) in others (Schlenker & Pontari, 2000; Schneider, 1981). Other scholars, however, suggest that impression management and self-presentation are one and the same (Leary & Kowalski, 1990; Lee et al., 1999) because they both involve attempts to influence others' rather immediate perceptions, regardless of origin or ultimate goal. Most scholars have adopted the view that they are indeed one and the same because, like perceptions, they involve attributions as actors perform behaviors with the intent of earning specific attributions from their targets (Jones & Pittman, 1982).

A second distinction involves influence tactics, which have been defined as the ways in which individuals influence others to obtain personal benefits or to satisfy goals (Kipnis et al., 1980). Some scholars have lumped influence tactics—which include exchange, persuasion, and other tactics—together with impression management (e.g., Higgins et al., 2003; Wayne & Ferris, 1990). Others have attempted a finer distinction by suggesting that influence tactics are commonly part of the downward influence by leaders, whereas impression management is more universal among actors at all levels (Dubrin, 2011).

Interestingly, scholars have predominantly allowed impression management and influence tactics to develop in separate literatures. This is likely due to differing objectives—impression managers attempt to influence others' attitudes and attributions while influence tacticians attempt to influence others' behavioral outcomes. Influence tactics and impression management are conceptually similar enough to be included together in reviews and summaries of social influence (e.g., Ferris et al., 2002; Higgins et al., 2003), but they are theoretically distinct enough to be kept separate when investigating antecedents and outcomes in primary studies of social influence.

ORIGINS OF IMPRESSION MANAGEMENT RESEARCH

Drawing on symbolic interactionism, the sociologist Erving Goffman wrote about "actors" who performed on "stages" for "audiences," and he believed that self-presentation was not only functional for the individual but also essential for smooth interactions (Goffman, 1959; Leary, 1995). In large part due to Goffman's burnishing the metaphor of the theatrical play, others soon began to take notice of and focus effort on understanding impression management. Subsequently, E. E. Jones, while studying how people view one another (which he called "interpersonal perception"), began to conduct research on flattery. This stream of research led to his influential writing on ingratiation (Jones, 1964). Due to Jones' and Goffman's seminal research, interest in impression management spread to other disciplines, including social psychology (for a review, see Leary, 1995) and organizational psychology (for a review, see Bolino et al., 2016; Dubrin, 2011; Rosenfeld et al., 1995). The combined efforts of these scholars have culminated in more than 25 different types of impression management strategies (Bolino et al., 2008; Lee et al., 1999).

HOW INDIVIDUALS MANAGE IMPRESSIONS

Virtually any behavior can be employed in impression management. The consensus in the literature however, is that favorable impressions are best served by performing positive behaviors, and thus individuals will focus their impression efforts accordingly. For example, individuals are liked for praising others and doing favors for them, are admired for displaying their skills and competencies, and are recognized as exemplars for working hard and volunteering for tough tasks (Bolino & Turnley, 1999; Jones & Pittman, 1982).

One of the surprising findings from the impression management literature is that people sometimes view taking risks—engaging in behaviors that are potentially harmful (Lindell & Hwang, 2008)—as a way to help achieve their social goals (Leary et al., 1994; Martin & Leary, 1999). For example, people might use performance-enhancing drugs, take dietary supplements or engage in extreme dieting, and undergo cosmetic treatments in an effort to be seen in favorable ways (Leary et al., 1994; Martin & Leary, 2001). These behaviors are risky in that they carry the potential for physical harm to those who perform them.

Also surprising is that some people intentionally make impressions that are not favorable in the eyes of others. This often occurs when individuals want to avoid a situation, such as having to perform work they do not wish to perform or having to spend time with someone they do not wish to spend time with. One way that individuals may create negative impressions is through supplication—appearing needy, weak, or incompetent (Becker & Martin, 1995; Jones & Pittman, 1982; Leary, 1995). Here, individuals try to capitalize on the norm of social responsibility, which suggests that targets should feel compelled to provide resources or lend aid to cover for the shortcomings and weaknesses of those who request assistance (Berkowitz & Daniels, 1964). In some situations, this results in supplicants getting extra help or avoiding an undesirable job.

TAXONOMIES OF IMPRESSION MANAGEMENT

Scholars have introduced several key taxonomies of impression management, which are highlighted in Table 2. The taxonomy that has received the most research attention is from Jones and Pittman's (1982) influential chapter on self-presentation. Their taxonomy identified five separate classes (i.e., types) of impression management: ingratiation, where an actor desires to be viewed as likable by flattering, showing interest in, and doing favors for targets; exemplification, which involves an actor seeking to be viewed as dedicated and going the extra mile by volunteering for extra assignments, staying late, and taking work home; supplication, where actors want to be viewed as needy by showing weaknesses or by broadcasting limitations;

Table 2. Key Taxonomies of Management Definitions

Source of Taxonomy	Description	Example
Arkin (1981)	Impression management behavior is either acquisitive (i.e., intended to make a good impression) or protective (i.e., intended to avoid a bad impression).	Acquisitive: Giving a neighbor a hand to appear helpful.
Cialdini (1989)	Indirect impression management (i.e., enhancing one's image by association): boasting, burying, blaring, blurring, burnishing, boosting, blasting, belittling.	Boasting: Drawing attention to your connection to a famous athlete.
Fiske et al. (2007)	Perceived warmth and competence are the two universal dimensions of human social cognition, at both the individual and group levels.	Warmth: Perceived friendliness, trustworthiness; Competence: Perceived ability, creativity.
Gardner and Martinko (1998)	Typology ($2 \times 2 \times 2$) of impression management tactics that are functional or dysfunctional, favorable or unfavorable, and self-focused or other-focused.	Dysfunctional ingratiation: Flattery as seduction intended to secure a reward.
Jones and Pittman (1982)	Five theoretical groupings of common impression management strategies (desired attribution in parentheses): ingratiation (likable), self-promotion (competent), exemplification (dedicated), intimidation (dangerous), supplication (needy).	Ingratiation: Complimenting your boss to elicit the attribute of likable.
Leary and Kowalski (1990)	Impression management is conceptualized as a two-component process of both image motivation (i.e., why to) and image construction (i.e., how to).	Motivation: First-date jitters; Construction: Wearing a flattering outfit.
Tedeschi and Melburg (1984)	Typology (2×2) of impression management tactics that are defensive (i.e., reactive) or assertive (i.e., proactive), and tactical (i.e., short-term) or strategic (i.e., long-term).	Defensive-Tactical: Making excuses after poor performance to avoid blame.
Wayne and Ferris (1990)	Three organizational impression management strategies separated by foci: supervisor, self, and job.	Supervisor focused: Doing personal favors for your supervisor to be seen as friendly.

intimidation, where actors hope to be viewed as threatening by bullying others; and self-promotion, where actors seek to be viewed as competent by touting their personal abilities and accomplishments (Bolino & Turnley, 1999).

In a conceptual paper, Tedeschi and Melburg (1984) explained that impression management can be either tactical (i.e., short term) or strategic (i.e., long term) and assertive (i.e., initiated by the actor) or defensive (i.e., used by the actor to respond to an undesired image). Accordingly, they developed a 2×2 taxonomy that included *tactical-assertive tactics* (e.g., ingratiation, self-promotion), *tactical-defensive tactics* (e.g., apologies, excuses), *strategic-assertive*

802 • IMPRESSION MANAGEMENT

tactics (e.g., trustworthiness, credibility), and *strategic-defensive tactics* (e.g., drug abuse, alcoholism). Given the nature of strategic impression management they identified, researchers have generally focused on the use of assertive and defensive tactical impression management; indeed, Tedeschi and Melburg (1984) classify all five of the behaviors identified by Jones and Pittman (1982) as tactical-assertive forms of impression management.

Other taxonomies were created in an effort to marshal some of the initial research on impression management and to better conceptualize the impression management process. For instance, Arkin (1981) suggested that impression management tactics could be distinguished by their fundamental goal. Acquisitive tactics, such as ingratiation, have a collective aim of making the actor more attractive to others (Jones, 1990; Jones & Pittman, 1982; Rosenfeld et al., 1995). Protective tactics, on the other hand, involve steps taken to repair or prevent a spoiled identity. Making excuses, offering apologies or justifications, and accounts of an event are all part of repairing an image, while self-handicapping and making performance disclaimers are strategies an actor uses in anticipation of a spoiled image (Rosenfeld et al., 1995).

Additionally, Cialdini (1989) noted that impression opportunities existed in managing information about the people and things with which one is simply associated, which he called *indirect tactics*. Cialdini classified indirect tactics as "connection-focused," if one was bringing attention to a personal link with another, or as "other-focused," if one was directing attention to the features and qualities of another. As an example, name dropping is a prototypical connection-focused tactic, as one attempts to impression manage by highlighting a positive link to someone notable (e.g., a celebrity, a company executive).

Still other taxonomies were developed to classify impression management. Leary and Kowalski (1990) argued that impression management is a two-step process, with image motivations preceding image construction. According to these scholars, an individual must become motivated to portray an image—for instance when someone has a damaged image in need of repair. Then, once motivated, the individual must identify a repaired image to portray *and* find a way to contrast it. For example, an individual on a first date who wishes to make a good impression (image motivation) decides to appear lighthearted (desired image) by telling a funny story (image construction). Important to this line of reasoning is that people are not always attuned to how they are perceived and judged by others, and this can determine how motivated someone will become to manage impressions. For example, in some situations people may be oblivious to others' reactions, while in other situations people are acutely aware of others' reactions (Leary & Allen, 2011; Roberts, 2005).

Additionally, Fiske and her colleagues (2002) took the perspective of the perceiver and demonstrated that impressions are formed along two dimensions: warmth, which represents how friendly and kind an actor is, and competence, which represents how skilled and intelligent an actor is (Fiske et al., 2002). Of interest to impression-managing actors, the warmth dimension signals if one intends good or ill to a perceiver, and the competence dimension signals if one is able to act on that intent (Cuddy et al., 2008). This implies that actors should focus on being seen as warm and trusted friends to perceivers before worrying about other types of impressions.

Lastly, some taxonomies were created with a focus on organizations and their members. Wayne and Ferris (1990) categorized impression management as either being job-focused, self-focused, or supervisor-focused. These categories suggested that actors have three different approaches to building a desired image. Bolino et al. (2008) criticized this taxonomy as redundant. For example, supervisor-focused tactics involve doing favors and enhancing others, both of which are included in Jones and Pittman's ingratiation tactic. The measure developed for Wayne and Ferris's taxonomy appears frequently in impression management research (Bolino et al., 2008), but the items included in the measure have apparent face validity concerns. For example, items related to the job-focused ("agree with my supervisor"), self-focused ("be friendly with my supervisor"), and supervisor-focused ("praise my supervisor") categories all focus on one's supervisor and appear to be similar to ingratiation.

Gardner and Martinko (1998) offered a three-dimensional taxonomy of impression management behaviors, which includes the dimensions of functionality, the entity (self or others), and favorability. The purpose of their taxonomy was to draw attention to the effects of dysfunctional impression management, which are image-related behaviors that harm the goals of the organization, and to separate those behaviors from functional impression management, which helps the goals of the organization. For example, ingratiation used as deceit to earn a raise is dysfunctional but ingratiation used as kindness to foster a warm social climate is functional. In other words, the intent of the behavior when combined with its authenticity determines if acts are functional or dysfunctional.

Mohamed et al. (1999) argued that organizations—like individuals—can also manage impressions. These scholars offered a 2 × 2 matrix of organizational impression management that built on the Tedeschi and Melburg (1984) taxonomy; that is, conceptualizing tactics as either direct or indirect and as either assertive or defensive (see Bolino et al., 2008). Direct tactics involve strategies whereby organizations highlight impressive features such as awards and capabilities. In contrast, indirect tactics involve strategies whereby an organization draws attention to highly regarded entities associated with the organization. Assertive tactics are proactive and promote the organization's image in some way. In contrast, defensive tactics are reactive and attempt to ward off a threat to the organization's image.

DISAGREEMENTS ABOUT IMPRESSION MANAGEMENT

Although the literature on impression management has been relatively free of controversy, it is not without its disagreements. Disputes have surfaced in the various literatures on the topic around the following questions: (a) Is impression management unethical? (b) How should impression management be measured? (c) Is impression management the primary underlying mechanism for various psychological phenomena such as cognitive dissonance, prosocial concerns, and moral judgment?

According to Leary (1995), impression management involves controlling how one is perceived by other people. Although not necessarily deceptive or deceitful, impression management is still managed and tactical by nature. Therefore, if targets perceive actors as behaving in an attempt to manage their impressions or the impressions of others, the targets will likely attribute the cause of the behavior to the actors being tactical (Jones, 1990; Roulin & Bourdage, 2017; Vonk, 2002). This has led some scholars to argue that because impression management is managed and purposeful it is manipulative and therefore unethical (Feldman & Klich, 1991; Huber et al., 1989; Jones & Pittman, 1982). However, other scholars have argued that impression management is a normal interpersonal process that helps facilitate a healthy and harmonious social climate (Leary, 1995). Imagine if neighbors withheld exchanging pleasantries because they were untrue, or if spouses avoided being tactical when responding to their significant others' inquiries regarding their appearance. Long (2021) has argued that this disagreement can be settled by taking the perspective of the person targeted with impression management. Assuming no malice on the part of the actor, if the target perceives the impression management behaviors as genuine and authentic then there are fewer ethical concerns than if the behaviors are perceived as deceptive and stemming from ulterior motives. In other words, the eye of the beholder matters most.

Another disagreement has formed surrounding how impression management should be measured. Basically, there are five distinct ways to measure impression management. First is by focus of one's effort, such as self-focused or target-focused (e.g., Wayne & Ferris, 1990). Second is by the strategy employed, such as ingratiation or self-promotion (e.g., Lee et al., 1999). Third is by context, such as job interviews (e.g., Levashina & Campion, 2007) or global culture (Sandal et al., 2014). Fourth is by motivation for managing impressions, such as self-enhancement or prosocial values (e.g., Yun et al., 2007). Fifth is by the personality types that often compel impression management, such as self-monitoring (e.g., Snyder & Gangestad, 1986) and Machiavellianism (e.g., Dahling et al., 2009).

There has been no agreement on the "best" way to measure impression management, but Bolino et al. (2008) suggest that any measure should be validated, with greater effort placed on using more objective measures and less effort placed on using self-reported measures. Moreover, any measure should match researchers' specific purpose for studying impression management. For example, if researchers are interested in the effectiveness of ingratiation they should use a measure that focuses on that tactic. Or, if researchers are interested in the impact of impression management in a job interview they should include a measure that is contextualized to an interview setting.

Scholars also disagree on what source provides the most accurate measure of impression management. Most studies use actors' self-report measures. Bolino and Turnley (1999) argue that these measures are appropriate because actors themselves should be most aware of such behavior and when an actor manages impressions successfully audiences should be less aware that the actor is, in fact, managing impressions. However, Long (2021) has argued that impression management is in the eye of the beholder and is best measured from the perceivers' perspectives since success or failure of an image attempt is determined not by actors but by the targets.

Finally, there is some disagreement around whether impression management is the underlying driver of psychological phenomena such as cognitive dissonance, prosocial concerns, and moral judgment. For instance, Tedeschi et al. (1971) suggested that cognitive dissonance—whereby people resolve inconsistencies between attitudes and behaviors by changing attitudes to match behaviors—was related to people's concerns with appearing inconsistent to others and not to intrapsychic pressures arriving from cognitive inconsistencies. In fact, research by Schlenker et al. (1980) showed that people who had performed behaviors that were inconsistent with their attitudes showed cognitive dissonance primarily when they had reason to think that others would perceive them as inconsistent or immoral for acting in a counter-altitudinal fashion. Similarly, Cialdini (1991) argued that ego—and not altruism—is the primary driver of helping behavior, and Bazerman and Gino (2012) suggest that morality is often guided less by one's moral compass and more by one's desire to be perceived as moral. However, others find it hard to fathom that intrapsychic dissonance, prosocial behaviors, and morality could be explained by interpersonal concerns, as evidenced by the robust and still growing research on the topics as something vastly different from self-presentation (Bazerman & Gino, 2012; Leary, 2011).

ACTORS VERSUS TARGETS

Impression management involves actors and targets (i.e., perceivers, audiences). Most research has focused on the former and their attempts to convey particular impressions. Actors have image-related goals and act out various roles in an effort to satisfy those goals (Schlenker, 1980). Most theory and empirical work has highlighted and investigated how various dispositional and situational variables help determine how, when, and why actors engage in impression management (Bolino et al., 2016; Schlenker & Weigold, 1992).

According to Leary and Bolino (2018), this actor focus can be traced back to Goffman's (1959) dramaturgical approach, which conceptualized impression management as a process by which actors play parts to an audience. However, actors on a stage play their parts irrespective of the audiences' reactions, yet when people manage impressions in everyday life, they are usually involved in interdependent interactions in which audience responses matter in two important and often related ways. First, as a source of information for actors who are sensitive to reactions and will often modify behavior in response to feedback. Second, as a judge—someone who makes inferences and draws conclusions about the actor. Accordingly, to understand how impression management plays out in social settings, one must also consider the targets and how impression management affects them.

TARGET AS A SOURCE OF INFORMATION

Research shows that targets sometime provide feedback to the actor that will help the actor determine whether the desired impression has been achieved or the behaviors intended to draw a desired impression need to be modified (Bozeman & Kacmar, 1997). However, it is not always the case that targets will provide explicit feedback that will allow the actors to accurately determine the success of impression management. The extant work on the topic suggests that there are three reasons that targets may not provide explicit feedback.

First, social norms often discourage expressions of feedback, particularly when the feedback is negative (Larson, 1989; Tesser et al., 1971). Unless the feedback is coming from a formal authority who is providing performance-related constructive feedback, or from close friends and family who have somewhat of a license to offer negative feedback, typically the feedback that actors receive is skewed positively.

Second, feedback may not be provided if the targets are unaware or unconcerned that actors are trying to manage their impressions. According to Leary and Bolino (2018), vigilance represents the attentiveness targets have to actors' impression management. According to these scholars, two factors determine vigilance—the perceived importance of the impression to the actor's outcomes and the perceived costs of drawing incorrect conclusions about the impression. Thus, when actors do not depend on the impressions the actors are making, or when targets will not be penalized for drawing incorrect conclusions about the impressions that an actor is trying to make, vigilance is low and explicit feedback may not be provided to actors.

Third, targets might become so concerned with managing their own image during a social encounter that they do not provide explicit feedback to actors. In any given social encounter, actors and targets often switch roles as they each can be the impression manager and the impression managed. Therefore, when a target observes an actor's behaviors, instead of providing feedback to the actor the target might instead become motivated to construct his or her own image (Baumeister et al., 1989). This would reduce the target's capacity to provide feedback.

TARGET AS A JUDGE

Much of the research on inferences for social behavior has dealt with the factors that influence how perceivers decide, correctly or not, whether to draw correspondent inferences about a target on the basis of the observed actions. Evoking the term *person perception,* Jones and Davis (1965) articulated that a perceiver of another's behavior is like an information processor that tries to make sense of what they have seen (Jones, 1990). Jones and Davis developed correspondent inference theory to explain a person's attributions for others' behavior. They argue that behavior is informative to the extent that it is seen to involve freedom of choice among alternatives, and that inferring an actor's intention, motive, or disposition depends on the consequences of the chosen behavior on the environment. According to their theory, a corresponding inference takes another person's action at face value or as a straightforward extrapolation that links the behavior to the cause, which can be a disposition, intention, or motive (Jones, 1990). Alternatively, noncorresponding inferences could also be drawn, as the behavior could be indicative of something hidden. For example, Amy could infer Jill's polite offer to pick up her dry cleaning to her kind disposition (a corresponding inference) because in Amy's opinion Jill did not have to do that. Conversely, Amy could attribute her polite offer to her flattery and intended seduction (a noncorresponding inference) because Amy thinks that Jill's effort is merely to impress her, perhaps as a ploy for a later request.

Although targets draw some inferences and conclusions in a logical manner (Kelley & Michela, 1980), targets can also be biased. For example, targets—like all individuals—tend to have an overly inflated sense of self-worth. Thus, flattery is often inferred as truth and an indicator of the actor's belief that the target deserves praise (Vonk, 2002). Also, targets tend to infer that behaviors reflect an actor's inner dispositions rather than situational pressures, particularity when the behavior is undesirable. For instance, in a given situation when an actor appears angry a target is likely to infer that the anger stems from the actor's dispositional meanness and not from the urgency of the moment.

IMPRESSION MISMANAGEMENT

Although there are unlimited opportunities for actors to make mistakes when managing impressions and draw bad impressions from targets, scholarly work has pointed to common causes for why actors might make bad impressions unintentionally. According to Steinmetz et al. (2017), actors often make negative impressions due to being overly narcissistic (i.e., self-centered, self-aggrandizing) or failing to take the target's perspective. Actors who fail to take the other person's perspective miss out on understanding what the actor needs in a situation, and actors who are narcissistic do not seem to care about the actor's needs. In both situations, actors run the risk of falling short of their image-related goals.

Other work has also pointed to situations in which actors who are trying to make positive impressions unwittingly make negative impressions. For example, when actors prioritize competence over warmth in new relationships, when actors "humblebrag" by hiding self-promotions behind a curtain of humility, and when actors use backhanded compliments when praising targets.

Scholars who study person perception have found that in new relationships perceivers first look to behaviors that might confer someone's warmth—their kindness, honesty, humility, friendliness, and sincerity. This is because perceivers need to know if those whom they encounter are friend or foe and whether they can be trusted (Cuddy et al., 2008). However, actors are more concerned with appearing competent—displaying intelligence, skills, and abilities that prove they are valuable and desirable to their audiences. Unfortunately for actors, conveying competence over warmth often implies a capable foe—a less than ideal situation for actors concerned with managing favorable impressions (Cuddy et al., 2008).

Humblebragging is when an actor masks a "brag" as a complaint or humility. Most people know that bragging is undesirable in social settings, and to avoid outright bragging actors will attempt to hide their boasts behind a veil. For example, if someone runs their first marathon, instead of posting on social media that they just ran 26.2 miles, a humblebragger might instead post a picture of ice bags on his knees with a caption of "Swollen kneecaps—I guess that's what I deserve for deciding to run my first marathon, on asphalt" in an attempt to be humble and draw sympathy. Notably, researchers have found that these types of humblebrags easily backfire and are obvious to audiences. They have even found that outright bragging is less damaging to one's reputation than humblebragging due to the sneaky nature of the latter (Sezer et al., 2017).

Backhanded compliments are a specific type of impression management whereby actors praise targets ("You played well") but with a criticism ("for a heavyset person"). These acts have two goals for actors: eliciting liking from and conveying status over the target. Although would-be flatterers believe that backhanded compliments will earn them both liking and status, research shows that those who attempt both goals via backhanded compliments are granted neither. In fact, actors who engage in these behaviors not only receive lower liking and status ratings but they actually reduce the motivation of recipients, which harms both parties (Steinmetz et al., 2017).

IMPRESSION MANAGEMENT MISSED

There are also situations where actors miss opportunities to make good impressions. Ego is typically the culprit. When actors focus on displaying their competence or hiding their incompetence they may miss opportunities to be seen in a good light by focusing on the target. One such situation is question-asking. When actors ask targets questions such as "Where do you live?" they are liked by the targets who are pleased by the inquiry (Huang et al., 2017). The effect is amplified when actors ask a follow-up question, like "How long have you lived there?"

These types of additional questions cause targets to perceive actors as being caring and good listeners. However, despite the beneficial effects of asking questions, actors do not anticipate that question-asking increases interpersonal liking. This is likely due to that fact that actors are concerned with establishing their own competence in conversations and neglect asking questions in lieu of telling stories and talking about themselves. Indeed, in most conversations people predominantly share information about themselves and their personal experiences (Dunbar et al., 1997) and thus miss opportunities to make a good impression.

Another situation is advice-seeking, in which actors ask others for assistance, information, advice, or support (Hofmann et al., 2009). Although individuals can garner substantial benefits from seeking advice from others, most individuals are hesitant to do so because they do not want to seem unknowledgeable or incompetent (Morrison & Bies, 1991). However, this fear is misguided, as individuals perceive those who seek advice as more competent (Brooks et al., 2015). Seeking advice boosts the self-confidence of the adviser, which in turn increases their positive perception of the advice seeker (i.e., "She was smart to ask for my advice because I am smart."). Importantly, individuals perceive advice seekers as more competent when the task is difficult rather than easy, when the advice is sought from the individuals directly rather than from others, and when the adviser is an expert rather than nonexpert on the advice being sought.

A final missed opportunity is touch. From an early age, children are taught to "keep their hands to themselves." Later, older youths and adults learn about the role that unsolicited touching plays in sexual harassment. This is for good reason, as inappropriate and illegal touch can be quite damaging to one's reputation for obvious reasons. However, slight and appropriate touch has proven to have image-related benefits for actors. Patrons in automobile dealerships, libraries, and restaurants, as well as college students in a classroom, who experienced tactile contact from an actor all rated the actor higher across various image-related dimensions (Erceau & Guéguen, 2007; for a review, see Gallace & Spence, 2010). Appropriate touching establishes a connection between targets and actors and may lead to targets liking and trusting actors more readily.

FUTURE DIRECTIONS

Although the research on impression management has resulted in a wealth of knowledge about the topic, there are several directions that scholars should pursue in the future. One is a greater focus on the targets and their specific needs. Targets are as involved in the impression management process as actors, and they have their own needs and motivations that must be considered when accounting for the implications of actors' image-related behaviors. Targets—like all individuals—prioritize their own needs and interests (Cuddy et al., 2011; Leary, 2007). An actor might want to appear in a positive light, but targets are less concerned with what the actor wants and are more concerned with what they want. According to research on basic needs and motives, at a deep and often unconscious level targets need attention and approval, status and control of resources, and structure and predictability, and these needs can be satisfied or harmed during the type of social interaction that occurs with impression management (Goffman, 1959; Hogan & Blickle, 2018). Targets will reconcile the information provided by actors during impression management against these needs, and respond by judging the actors' reputations in some positive or negative evaluative way (Long, 2017). Future research should consider these needs in assessing the success or failure of actors' impression management. It could be that actors who are good at satisfying targets' needs are better at impression managing than actors who are not.

Another important direction is continued research on impression management misses—both in terms of missed opportunities for making good impressions and impression management misfires. Actors are typically guided by wanting to make good impressions and not wanting to make bad impressions, but sometimes they are also guided by not wanting to make good impressions (e.g., self-deprecation) and wanting to make bad impressions (e.g., feigning incompetence). This creates unlimited possibilities for impression management misses, and more work is needed here.

A final direction for research is to focus on the damaging behaviors that individuals sometimes engage in when pursuing image-related goals. For example, research shows that out of a fear of looking weak individuals often engage in dangerous behaviors such as drug use and reckless driving (Leary et al., 1994). What other dangerous or risky activities might individuals undertake to avoid looking weak? And what other image concerns besides looking weak drive these types of acts? Perhaps a fear of not seeming like a team player compels individuals to play along with the illicit activities others engage in. More research is needed here to give scholars a better understanding of what negative behaviors can arise from impression management concerns.

REFERENCES

Arkin, R. M. (1981). Self-presentation styles. In J. T. Tedeschi (Ed.), *Impression management theory and social psychological research* (pp. 311–333). Academic Press.

Baumeister, R. F. (1982). A self-presentational view of social phenomena. *Psychological Bulletin, 91,* 3–26. https://doi.org/10.1037/0033-2909.91.1.3

Baumeister, R. F., Tice, D. M., & Hutton, D. G. (1989). Self-presentational motivations and personality differences in self-esteem. *Journal of Personality, 57*(3), 547–579.

Bazerman, M. H., & Gino, F. (2012). Behavioral ethics: Toward a deeper understanding of moral judgment and dishonesty. *Annual Review of Law and Social Science, 8,* 85–104.

Becker, T. E., & Martin, S. L. (1995). Trying to look bad at work: Methods and motives for managing poor impressions in organizations. *Academy of Management Journal, 38,* 174–199. https://doi.org/10.2307/256732

Berkowitz, L., & Daniels, L. R. (1964). Affecting the salience of the social responsibility norm: Effects of past help on the response to dependency relationships. *Journal of Abnormal and Social Psychology, 68*(3), 275–281.

Bolino, M. C., Kacmar, K. M., Turnley, W. H., & Gilstrap, J. B. (2008). A multi-level review of impression management motives and behaviors. *Journal of Management, 34,* 1080–1109. https://doi.org/10.1177/0149206308324325

Bolino, M., Long, D., & Turnley, W. (2016). Impression management in organizations: Critical questions, answers, and areas for future research. *Annual Review of Organizational Psychology and Organizational Behavior, 3,* 377–406. https://doi.org/10.1146/annurev-orgpsych-041015-062337

Bolino, M. C., & Turnley, W. H. (1999). Measuring impression management in organizations: A scale development based on the Jones and Pittman taxonomy. *Organizational Research Methods, 2,* 187–206. https://doi.org/10.1177/109442819922005

Bozeman, D. P., & Kacmar, K. M. (1997). A cybernetic model of impression management processes in organizations. *Organizational Behavior and Human Decision Processes, 69*(1), 9–30.

Brooks, A. W., Gino, F., & Schweitzer, M. E. (2015). Smart people ask for (my) advice: Seeking advice boosts perceptions of competence. *Management Science, 61,* 1421–1435. https://doi.org/10.1287/mnsc.2014.2054

Carnegie, D. (1936). *How to win friends and influence people.* Simon & Schuster.

Cialdini, R. B. (1989). Indirect tactics of image management: Beyond basking. In R. A. Giacalone & P. Rosenfeld (Eds.), *Impression management in the organization* (pp. 45–56). Lawrence Erlbaum.

Cialdini, R. B. (1991). Altruism or egoism? That is (still) the question. *Psychological Inquiry, 2*(2), 124–126.

Cialdini, R. B., & Richardson, K. D. (1980). Two indirect tactics of image management: Basking and blasting. *Journal of Personality and Social Psychology, 39,* 406–415.

Cuddy, A. J., Fiske, S. T., & Glick, P. (2008). Warmth and competence as universal dimensions of social perception: The stereotype content model and the BIAS map. *Advances in Experimental Social Psychology, 40,* 61–149. https://doi.org/10.1016/S0065-2601(07)00002-0

Cuddy, A. J., Glick, P., & Beninger, A. (2011). The dynamics of warmth and competence judgments, and their outcomes in organizations. *Research in Organizational Behavior, 31,* 73–98.

Dahling, J. J., Whitaker, B. G., & Levy, P. E. (2009). The development and validation of a new Machiavellianism Scale. *Journal of Management, 35*(2), 219–257.

Dubrin, A. J. (2011). *Impression management in the workplace: Research, theory, and practice.* Routledge.

Dunbar, R. I., Marriott, A., & Duncan, N. D. (1997). Human conversational behavior. *Human Nature, 8*(3), 231–246.

Erceau, D., & Guéguen, N. (2007). Tactile contact and evaluation of the toucher. *Journal of Social Psychology, 147*(4), 441–444.

Feldman, D. C., & Klich, N. R. (1991). Impression management and career strategies. In R. A. Giacalone & P. Rosenfeld (Eds.), *Applied impression management: How image making affects organizations* (pp. 67–80). SAGE.

Ferris, G. R., Hochwarter, W. A., Douglas, C., Blass, F. R., Kolodinsky, R. W., & Treadway, D. C. (2002). Social influence processes in organizations and human resources systems. In G. R. Ferris & J. J. Martocchio (Eds.), *Research in personnel and human resources management* (Vol. 21, pp. 65–127). JAI Press.

Fiske, S. T., Cuddy, A. J., Glick, P., & Xu, J. (2002). A model of (often mixed) stereotype content: Competence and warmth respectively follow from perceived status and competition. *Journal of Personality and Social Psychology, 82,* 878–902.

Fiske, S. T., Cuddy, A. J., & Glick, P. (2007). Universal dimensions of social cognition: Warmth and competence. *Trends in Cognitive Sciences, 11*(2), 77–83.

Gallace, A., & Spence, C. (2010). The science of interpersonal touch: An overview. *Neuroscience and Biobehavioral Reviews, 34*(2), 246–259.

Gardner, W., & Martinko, M. J. (1998). An organizational perspective of the effects of dysfunctional impression management. In R. W. Griffin, A. O'Leary-Kelly, & J. M. Collins (Eds.), *Dysfunctional behavior in organizations: Non-violent dysfunctional behavior* (pp. 69–125). JAI Press.

Goffman, E. (1959). *The presentation of self in everyday life.* Doubleday.

Higgins, C. A., Judge, T. A., & Ferris, R. G. (2003). Influence tactics and work outcomes: A meta-analysis. *Journal of Organizational Behavior, 24,* 89–106. https://doi.org/10.1002/job.181

Hofmann, D. A., Lei, Z., & Grant, A. M. (2009). Seeking help in the shadow of doubt: The sensemaking processes underlying how nurses decide whom to ask for advice. *Journal of Applied Psychology, 94*(5), Article 12611274.

Hogan, R., & Blickle, G. (2018). Socioanalytic theory: Basic concepts, supporting evidence, and practical implications. In V. Zeigler-Hill & T. K. Shackelford (Eds.), *The science of personality and individual differences: Volume 1. The SAGE handbook of personality and individual differences* (pp. 110–129). SAGE.

Huang, K., Yeomans, M., Brooks, A. W., Minson, J., & Gino, F. (2017). It doesn't hurt to ask: Question-asking increases liking. *Journal of Personality and Social Psychology, 113*(3), 430–452.

Huber, V. L., Latham, G. P., & Locke, E. A. (1989). The management of impressions through goal setting. In R. A. Giacalone & P. Rosenfeld (Eds.), *Impression management in the organization* (pp. 203–217). Lawrence Erlbaum.

Jellison, J. M. (1981). Reconsidering the attitude concept: A behavioristic self-presentation formulation. In J. T. Tedeschi (Ed.), *Impression management theory and social psychological research* (pp. 107–126). Academic Press.

Jones, E. E. (1964). *Ingratiation.* Appleton-Century-Crofts.

Jones, E. E. (1990). *Interpersonal perception.* Freeman.

Jones, E. E., & Davis, K. E. (1965). From acts to dispositions: The attribution process in person perception. In L. Berkowitz (Ed.), *Advances in experimental social psychology* (Vol. 2., pp. 220–266). Academic Press.

Jones, E. E., & Pittman, T. S. (1982). Towards a general theory of strategic self-presentation. In J. Suls (Ed.), *Psychological perspective on the self* (pp. 231–262). Lawrence Erlbaum.

Kelley, H. H., & Michela, J. L. (1980). Attribution theory and research. *Annual Review of Psychology, 31,* 457–501.

Kipnis, D., Schmidt, S. M., & Wilkinson, I. (1980). Intraorganizational influence tactics: Explorations in getting ones way. *Journal of Applied Psychology, 65,* 440–452.

Larson, J. R., Jr. (1989). The dynamic interplay between employees' feedback-seeking strategies and supervisors' delivery of performance feedback. *Academy of Management Review, 14*(3), 408–422.

Leary, M. R. (1995). *Self-presentation: Impression management and interpersonal behavior.* Brown & Benchmark.

Leary, M. R. (2007). Motivational and emotional aspects of the self. *Annual Review of Psychology, 58,* 317–344.

Leary, M. R. (2011). Does impression management have an image problem? In R. M. Arkin (Ed.), *Most underappreciated: 50 prominent social psychologists describe their most unloved work* (pp. 96–100). Oxford University Press.

Leary, M. R., & Allen, A. B. (2011). Personality and persona: Personality processes in self-presentation. *Journal of Personality, 79,* 1191–1218.

Leary, M. R., & Bolino, M. C. (2018). An actor-perceiver model of impression management in organizations. In D. L. Ferris, R. E. Johnson, & C. Sedikides (Eds.), *The self at work: Fundamental theory and research* (pp. 253–272). Routledge.

Leary, M. R., & Kowalski, R. M. (1990). Impression management: A literature review and two-component model. *Psychological Bulletin, 107,* 34–47. https://doi.org/10.1037/0033-2909.107.1.34

Leary, M. R., Tchividijian, L. R., & Kraxberger, B. E. (1994). Self-presentation can be hazardous to your health: Impression management and health risk. *Health Psychology, 13,* 461–470. https://doi.org/10.1037/0278-6133.13.6.461

Lee, S. J., Quigley, B. M., Nesler, M. S., Corbett, A. B., & Tedeschi, J. T. (1999). Development of a self-presentation tactics scale. *Personality and Individual Differences, 26,* 701–722. https://doi.org/10.1016/S0191-8869(98)00178-0

Levashina, J., & Campion, M. A. (2007). Measuring faking in the employment interview: Development and validation of an interview faking behavior scale. *Journal of Applied Psychology, 92*(6), 1638–1656.

Lindell, M. K., & Hwang, S. N. (2008). Households' perceived personal risk and responses in a multihazard environment. *Risk Analysis: An International Journal, 28*(2), 539–556.

Long, D. M. (2017). A method to the martyrdom: Employee exemplification as an impression management strategy. *Organizational Psychology Review, 7*(1), 36–65.

Long, D. M. (2021). Tacticality, authenticity, or both? The ethical paradox of actor ingratiation and target trust reactions. *Journal of Business Ethics, 168,* 847–860.

Martin, K. A., & Leary, M. R. (1999). Would you drink after a stranger? The influence of self-presentational motives on willingness to take a health risk. *Personality and Social Psychology Bulletin, 25*, 1092–1100. https://doi.org/10.1177/01461672992512003

Martin, K. A., & Leary, M. R. (2001). Self-presentational determinants of health risk behavior among college freshmen. *Psychology and Health, 16*, 17–27. https://doi.org/10.1080/08870440108405487

Mohamed, A. A., Gardner, W. L., & Paolillo, J. G. P. (1999). A taxonomy of organizational impression management tactics. *Advances in Competitiveness Research, 7*(1), 108–130.

Morrison, E. W., & Bies, R. J. (1991). Impression management in the feedback-seeking process: A literature review and research agenda. *Academy of Management Review, 16*(3), 522–541.

Roberts, L. M. (2005). Changing faces: Professional image construction in diverse organizational settings. *Academy of Management Review, 30*, 685–711. https://doi.org/10.5465/AMR.2005.18378873

Rosenfeld, P., Giacalone, R. A., & Riordan, C. A. (1995). *Impression management in organizations.* Routledge.

Roulin, N., & Bourdage, J. S. (2017). Once an impression manager, always an impression manager? Antecedents of honest and deceptive impression management use and variability across multiple job interviews. *Frontiers in Psychology, 8*, 1–13.

Sandal, G. M., van de Vijver, F., Bye, H. H., Sam, D. L., Amponsah, B., Cakar, N., Franke, G. H., Ismail, R., Kjellsen, K., Kosic, A., & Leontieva, A. (2014). Intended self-presentation tactics in job interviews: A 10-country study. *Journal of Cross-Cultural Psychology, 45*(6), 939–958.

Schlenker, B. R. (1980). *Impression management: The self-concept, social identity, and interpersonal relations.* Brooks/Cole.

Schlenker, B. R., Forsyth, D. R., Leary, M. R., & Miller, R. S. (1980). Self-presentational analysis of the effects of incentives on attitude change following counterattitudinal behavior. *Journal of Personality and Social Psychology, 39*(4), 553–577.

Schlenker, B. R., & Pontari, B. A. (2000). The strategic control of information: Impression management and self-presentation in daily life. In A. Tesser, R. Felson, & J. Suls (Eds.), *Perspectives on self and identity* (pp. 199–232). American Psychological Association.

Schlenker, B. R., & Weigold, M. F. (1992). Interpersonal processes involving impression regulation and management. *Annual Review of Psychology, 43*, 133–168.

Schneider, D. J. (1981). Tactical self-presentations: Toward a broader conception—Impression management and influence in organizations. In J. T. Tedeschi (Ed.), *Impression management theory and social psychological research* (pp. 23–40). Academic Press.

Sezer, O., Gino, F., & Norton, M. I. (2017). Humblebragging: A distinct—and ineffective—self-presentation strategy. *Journal of Personality and Social Psychology, 114*(1), 52–74.

Snyder, M., & Gangestad, S. (1986). On the nature of self-monitoring: Matters of assessment, matters of validity. *Journal of Personality and Social Psychology, 51*(1), 125–139.

Steinmetz, J., Sezer, O., & Sedikides, C. (2017). Impression mismanagement: People as inept self-presenters. *Social and Personality Psychology Compass, 11*(6), Article e12321.

Tedeschi, J., & Melburg, V. (1984). Impression management and influence in organizations. In S. Bacharach & E. J. Lawler (Eds.), *Research in the sociology of organizations* (Vol. 3, pp. 31–58). JAI Press.

Tedeschi, J. T., & Riess, M. (1981). Identities, the phenomenal self, and laboratory research. In J. T. Tedeschi (Ed.), *Impression management theory and social psychological research* (pp. 3–22). Academic Press.

Tedeschi, J. T., Schlenker, B. R., & Bonoma, T. V. (1971). Cognitive dissonance: Private ratiocination or public spectacle? *American Psychologist, 26*, 685–695.

Tesser, A., Rosen, S., & Tesser, M. (1971). On the reluctance to communicate undesirable messages (the MUM effect): A field study. *Psychological Reports, 29*(2), 651–654.

Tetlock, P. E., & Manstead, A. S. (1985). Impression management versus intrapsychic explanations in social psychology: A useful dichotomy? *Psychological Review, 92*(1), 59–77.

Vonk, R. (1998). The slime effect: Suspicion and dislike of likeable behavior toward superiors. *Journal of Personality and Social Psychology, 74*, 849–864. https://doi.org/10.1037/0022-3514.74.4.849

Vonk, R. (2001). Aversive self-presentations. In R. M. Kowalski (Ed.), *Behaving badly: Aversive interpersonal behaviors* (pp. 79–155). American Psychological Association.

Vonk, R. (2002). Self-serving interpretations of flattery: Why ingratiation works. *Journal of Personality and Social Psychology, 82*, 515–526.

Wayne, S. J., & Ferris, G. R. (1990). Influence tactics, affect, and exchange quality in supervisor-subordinate interactions: A laboratory experiment and field study. *Journal of Applied Psychology, 75*, 487–499. https://dx.doi.org/10.1037/0021-9010.75.5.487

Yun, S., Takeuchi, R., & Liu, W. (2007). Employee self-enhancement motives and job performance behaviors: Investigating the moderating effects of employee role ambiguity and managerial perceptions of employee commitment. *Journal of Applied Psychology, 92*(3), 745–756.

David M. Long

SOCIAL COMPARISON IN ORGANIZATIONS

INTRODUCTION

Social comparison is a basic process that refers to relating one's own characteristics to those of other similar individuals (Buunk & Gibbons, 1997; Wood, 1989). Social comparisons may provide individuals with information that they can use to evaluate, enhance, or improve themselves (e.g., Taylor & Lobel, 1989). Scholars have long recognized the importance of social comparison for human adaptation and survival. As Suls and Wheeler (2000) have noted, theorizing and research on social comparison can be traced to some of the classic contributions to Western philosophy and to pivotal work in social psychology and sociology, including work on the self, adaptation level, reference groups, and social influence (see Buunk & Gibbons, 2007). Nevertheless, it was not until Festinger's (1954) classic paper that the term *social comparison* was introduced. According to Festinger, "There exists, in the human organism, a drive to evaluate his opinions and abilities" (Festinger, 1954, p. 11). As Gilbert et al. (1995) noted, social comparison is phylogenetically very old, biologically very powerful, and recognizable in many species. According to Beach and Tesser (2000), as *Homo sapiens* began to emerge as a distinct species, there was a shift toward more specialization within groups, and this required the ability to assess the domains in which one could specialize, in order to enhance one's status and reproductive opportunities. Social comparison may facilitate such assessment (see Buunk & Mussweiler, 2001).

The work sphere is a major area of life in which people may attain prestige, recognition, and self-esteem, and these features are to an important extent dependent on how one does in comparison with others. Social-comparison processes may therefore especially be manifest in work situations, and may often be difficult to avoid as individuals are usually surrounded by other employees (cf. Goodman & Haisley, 2007; Greenberg et al., 2007). Most individuals will often pay attention to how their colleagues are doing compared to themselves, or will be confronted with such a situation. In modern organizations, employees may compare, for example, their performance, salary, room size, secondary benefits, or career prospects with that of others. One may view that a colleague is doing his or her work better than oneself, that a colleague is neglecting his or her work, that a colleague is promoted to a higher position that one feels they deserved, or that a colleague has a higher or much lower salary than oneself. Some people may just ignore that they are better or worse off than their coworkers, while others may be rather preoccupied with how they are doing in comparison with their coworkers. (e.g., Buunk & Gibbons, 2006). Remarkably, despite the apparent importance of social-comparison processes in organizations, in recent handbooks, organizations and work settings are hardly, if at all, mentioned (e.g., Suls et al., 2020). Interestingly, however, already after World War II the now classic *American Soldier* studies (Stouffer et al., 1949) provided evidence for what was later interpreted as the importance of social comparisons for satisfaction in organizations. For example, Black soldiers from the North of the United States were less satisfied with their situation than Black soldiers from the South, supposedly because both compared themselves with Blacks outside the army, who were considerably worse off in the South.

It must be noted that in organizations—as in other contexts—social comparisons are often seen as unwanted, especially when they result in socially undesirable emotions, such as envy and *Schadenfreude*, that is, the pleasure over the misfortune of another individual (Buckley, 2014). Evidence for the taboo on social comparisons comes from a study by Hoorens et al. (2012), who found that people who make self-superiority claims in which they directly compared themselves with others were disliked more than people who made self-superiority claims without direct comparisons. Although there has been in the 21st century a growing interest of researchers in economy on the effects of social comparison (e.g., Hyll, 2018; Ridge et al., 2017), many of these studies did not assess directly the social comparisons made by employees, but rather made analyses on the group or organizational level. In this article, the focus will be primarily on the psychological research on social comparison in organizations. As described by Greenberg et al. (2007), social-comparison processes are relevant for understanding key areas of organizational inquiry, including organizational justice, performance appraisal, affective behavior, and stress in the workplace. Not all these topics can be discussed here in detail, but most will be dealt with in more or less detail. In the first section, "Uncertainty, Similarity, and the Search for Social-Comparison Information," in line with what Greenberg et al. (2007) noted, the focus is on a crucial subprocess of social comparison—the search for social-comparison information. Special attention is paid to the role of gender differences in the choice of same-versus-opposite-sex comparison targets (see "Social Comparison Among Women and Men"). The second section, "Motives for, and Direction of, Social Comparison," explores how the search for social-comparison information is influenced by the upward-versus-downward direction of social comparison and by the motives for social comparison. In the third section, "Consequences of Social Comparison," the affective-and-motivational consequences of social comparisons, including envy, are related to *identification* and *contrast*, as distinct interpretations of social comparisons. The final section, "The Role of Social-Comparison Orientation," is devoted to the role of individual differences in social-comparison orientation.

UNCERTAINTY, SIMILARITY, AND THE SEARCH FOR SOCIAL-COMPARISON INFORMATION

As has been noted for more than 60 years, people will especially seek out social-comparison information when they are experiencing stress and uncertainty (Schachter, 1959). In line with this classic perspective, a study of 23 companies from South Korea showed that feelings of uncertainty about the self, and a desire to outperform others, motivated individuals to seek comparative information in a wide range of areas (Shin & Sohn, 2015). In the same vein, Brown et al. (2007) found that, among others, role ambiguity was a significant predictor of social comparison with others better off than oneself. Uncertainty seems a rather salient stressor in the nursing profession (e.g., McGrath et al., 1989). Nurses may wonder if they are too involved with patients or not involved enough; they may feel uncertain about how to deal with varying problems with patients, including appeals for help and expressions of anxiety; and they may experience uncertainties about whether they are doing things correctly, which would induce a tendency to compare themselves with others.

Following Festinger (1954), in the social-comparison literature it has been generally assumed that one would compare oneself to *similar others*. The meaning of what constitutes similar others has been heavily debated in the social-comparison literature. It has been suggested, for example, that in this context, similarity should refer primarily to the individual's emotional state (Schachter, 1959), the attribute of comparison, or any form of closeness with the comparison target (cf., Wheeler & Suls, 2020). Field research on the desire to obtain social-comparison information by individuals under stress (e.g., DeVellis et al., 1990; Molleman et al., 1986) generally tends to emphasize *situational* similarity—that is, comparison with others in a similar situation (e.g., with those facing the same stressor). In a study of Dutch registered nurses from various healthcare institutions, the focus was upon this type of similarity (Buunk et al., 1994). This study showed that uncertainty was related to an interest in obtaining social-comparison information, that is, the desire to find out how others in a similar situation responded and reacted. This effect was additional to, and independent of, the effect of emotional exhaustion, an aspect of professional burnout, and a characteristic form of stress. Such information may help in comparing one's interpretations, feelings, and responses with those of others.

It must be noted, however, that when it concerns one's salary, employees may compare their salary with both similar and dissimilar others—that is, with others in the same organization, as well as those in other organizations and with those with different occupations (Sweeney & McFarlin, 2005). As noted by Harris et al. (2008), many studies—though not from a social-comparison perspective—have focused on which referent others use to evaluate one's pay, and have shown that employees may use a variety, and ever-expanding range of referent others in determining their pay satisfaction, including family, friends, neighbors, supervisors, comparison groups within and outside the company, and people with similar versus dissimilar educational backgrounds (for a meta-analysis, see Williams et al., 2006).

Social Comparison Among Women and Men.   Gender similarity is a quite different type of similarity affecting social-comparison tendencies. There is evidence that women tend to compare themselves especially with other women, whereas men tend to compare themselves especially with other men. For instance, Buunk and Van der Laan (2002) presented women with a successful target that was either male or female. Their results showed that women preferred to compare themselves more with the female target than with the male target, and saw the situation of the female target as a more likely potential future for themselves. Studies conducted in the 1970s and 1980s showed that in order to evaluate their performance and their pay, both genders had a pronounced preference for comparisons with others of the same gender over others of the other gender (e.g., Feldman & Ruble, 1981;

Miller, 1984; Suls et al., 1979). Nevertheless, there is evidence that women, more than men, view opposite-sex others as relevant for their self-evaluation, especially in typically male-dominated organizations. For example, Buunk, Carmona, et al. (2011) found that especially in industrial organizations—e.g., the automobile industry in Spain and the appliance sector in the Netherlands—in which there were more male than female employees, women compared themselves more with men even more than their male colleagues compared themselves with one another; whereas this was not the case in public organizations, in both countries, with many female employees (e.g., public libraries). In a similar vein, a study by Steil and Hay (1997), studying a sample of men and women with prestigious, male-dominated careers, showed that women were more likely to make opposite-sex comparisons than men, and that the higher a woman's income became, the more likely she was to compare her situation regarding promotion, compensation, responsibility, and influence in decision-making predominantly with men. For men, the opposite effect was found: the lower their income, the more likely they were to compare themselves with women. Steil and Hay's study is quite relevant, as it has been argued that women in organizations, because of the lack of female leaders, may suffer from a lack of female role models (e.g., Linehan & Scullion, 2008). Steil and Hay's study, however, suggests that this concern is not entirely founded. Ambitious women seem to select their comparison targets not, or not solely, on the basis of sex, but on the basis of the status or income level they aspire to. Therefore, even if there were more female leaders, women may not perceive these women as suitable role models. In addition, Jandeska and Kraimer (2005), for instance, found that female leaders in male-dominated organizations were less inclined to engage in role-modeling behaviors, such as mentoring junior colleagues.

As noted by Sheppard and Aquino (2017), social comparisons between women in organizations are often viewed as resulting more often in conflicts than among men. Sheppard and Aquino argued that especially agentic women will constitute a competitive threat primarily to their female colleagues not only because they will be perceived as competitors for access to organizational resources, but also because of their tendency to self-promote and engage in assertive and dominant behavior. As competition is generally considered as a normal and healthy part of male behavior, third parties will perceive conflict between women as more salient than that of competition among men. Such differences may, of course, change as women are entering more private, originally male-dominated organizations. It seems likely that in organizations with a more or less equal gender distribution, women may focus more on other women as their primary reference standards, whereas men may continue to perceive other men as their primary reference standards (e.g., Buunk, Pollet, et al., 2011; Saad & Gill, 2001). Even more so, with the increasing influx of women in organizations, social comparisons among males may become even more salient and prevalent, as the presence of women tend to make men more aware of their status, and more eager to demonstrate that they can beat other men. For example, an experiment showed that men increased their cooperation in an economic game when observed by women (Iredale et al., 2008), supposedly to impress these women. To conclude, both men and women tend to compare themselves primarily with others of their own gender, but while in male-dominated organizations women tend to compare themselves also with men, in organizations with more women, same-sex others may be more relevant comparison standards for both men and women.

MOTIVES FOR, AND DIRECTION OF, SOCIAL COMPARISON

From the onset of social-comparison research, the preferred direction of comparison when seeking out comparison information has been a central question. That is, under what conditions do people compare themselves with others doing better (upward comparisons), or with others doing worse (downward comparisons)? It has become increasingly clear that the direction of comparison depends to an important extent on the *motive* underlying the comparison. In his original paper, Festinger (1954) made a strong case for the motive of *self-evaluation*, that is, individuals want to find out how well they are doing by comparing themselves with others, particularly with others doing somewhat better than themselves. In organizations, individuals will be concerned with issues like "do I earn enough?," "how well am I performing?," or "how well am I evaluated by my supervisor?" According to classic social-comparison theory, employees will usually not compare their salary with that of the CEO, but instead are more likely to compare it with that of colleagues doing the same type of work who are earning more, and will usually compare their performance with colleagues doing the same type of work who are performing better. However, it now has become clear that individuals in organizations may also compare their contribution to the organization and their salary even with theCEO's, and demand more rewards for their own efforts, especially now salaries have become public in many countries. The second motive is *self-improvement*, a motive already proposed by Brickman and Bulman (1977), among others, who emphasized that people seek social comparisons to improve themselves, which would occur by comparison with others who are performing better (e.g., Buunk, Cohen-Schotanus, & Van Nek, 2007; Suls & Wheeler, 2000; Wood, 1989). Observing a colleague who has proficiency at a task can reveal information about how to improve, and may raise individuals' feelings of self-confidence and self-efficacy (e.g., Blanton et al., 1999). For instance, someone who enters an organization will be particularly interested in how to perform in a competent way and to learn skills that may be valuable for his or her performance—skills that may only be acquired by learning from others who are performing well. The third motive is *self-enhancement*, a motive especially highlighted by the seminal paper by Wills (1981), who emphasized that in situations that imply a decrease in well-being, individuals tend to compare themselves with others who are worse off as a way to improve their well-being, particularly when instrumental action is not possible. According to this line of reasoning, perceiving oneself as better off may boost one's self-esteem, reduce anxiety, and generate the positive effect essential for self-enhancement. In contrast, seeing someone who is better off may deflate the ego and produce a negative effect.

Preferred Comparison Direction. Within organizations, a number of studies have examined the preferred direction of comparison, though the motives for social comparison have received less attention. In general, and in line with Festinger's (1954) original theory, a series of studies in different contexts have shown that upward comparisons in various areas like career progress and performance are, in general, more prevalent than downward comparisons (e.g., Buunk, Zurriaga, et al., 2005; Buunk, Zurriaga, & Peiró, 2010; Carmona et al., 2006; Eddleston, 2009). The direction of social comparison as well as the motives for social comparison will depend, in part, on the level of competitiveness that characterizes an organization. It is usually assumed that competition breeds social comparison and vice versa (García & Tor, 2009). In line with this, Buunk, Carmona, et al. (2011) showed that in Spain, employees working for private industrial organizations—where competition is probably rather salient—made more downward as well as more upward comparisons with respect to their performance, than workers in public organizations. It seems that in organizations with a competitive culture, workers may use downward comparisons to enhance their sense of selves by feeling they are performing better than many of their colleagues, and that in such a context, upward comparisons may stem from a desire for self-evaluation as well as a desire for self-improvement. Workers may look upward to see how they themselves are doing, and to obtain inspiration (e.g., Lockwood & Kunda, 1997) to improve their own performance.

Dimensions of Social Comparison. Studies on social comparisons in organizations, especially those in the economics literature, tend to focus on performance comparisons—in particular, wage comparisons. However, following Tornow (1971), it can be expected that employees may compare themselves at work on many different dimensions. Tornow made a distinction between dimensions described as "inputs," that is, factors that individuals believe make a contribution to the job (e.g., work effort and performance), and dimensions described as "outcomes," that is, factors that individuals believe are derived from the situation and are perceived as worthy (e.g., salary and career opportunities). Basing themselves on the distinction made by Tornow, Buunk, Carmona, et al. (2011) asked employees how often they compared their inputs (i.e., their performance, social skills, work effort), and their outputs (i.e., their salary, work conditions, career opportunities, and capacities) with those of their colleagues. They found that workers from private organizations in Spain (e.g., the automobile and appliance sectors) more often compared themselves with others on their inputs than workers from public organizations (e.g., public libraries), but not on their outputs (Buunk, Carmona, et al., 2011). Spanish women working in private organizations were especially focused on the outcomes-dimension comparison. The explanation for this finding is not directly clear. A very tentative explanation may be that in Spanish society, differences between women and men in aspects such as salary and career opportunities are especially salient in private organizations.

CONSEQUENCES OF SOCIAL COMPARISON

Effects of Comparison Direction. A series of studies have examined the *effects* of social comparison in organizations. In general, there is evidence that both upward-and-downward comparisons may undermine trust in organizations (Dunn et al., 2012). However, the effects of upward-and-downward comparisons are supposed to be different, with upward comparisons resulting more often in dissatisfaction and related variables, and, in line with the theory of Wills (1981), downward comparisons resulting more often in satisfaction and related variables, such as affective commitment (e.g., Brown et al., 2007) and turnover intentions (e.g., Eddleston, 2009). In a study conducted in the United States and Belgium, Harris et al. (2008) found that controlling for gender, age, experience, and education, pay-level satisfaction was in addition to actual, objectively assessed pay, negatively determined by upward social comparisons, that is, the extent to which people thought that others with similar experience and jobs earned, on average, more than they did. In another study, a sample of employees in a U.S. hospitality company were assessed, not according to how well they perceived they did in comparison with others, but instead on how well off they felt they were, objectively compared to their colleagues in the same work unit. It appeared that favorable comparisons with peers in one's work unit on perceived organizational support were positively associated with commitment and retention, whereas unfavorable comparisons were negatively related (Vardaman et al., 2016).

In the same vein, a number of studies, particularly among blue-collar workers, have shown that upward comparisons in the form of pay inequity may be accompanied by occupational stress (McKenna, 1987), and may lead to absenteeism (Dittrich & Carrell, 1979; Hendrix & Spencer, 1989). However, there is evidence for gender differences in this respect. For example, Ataay (2018) found that women who compared themselves with referents at the same level, had relatively lower pay-level satisfaction than men who compared themselves with referents at the same level. Many effects of social comparison have also been established for other dimensions than pay. In a prospective study of two metal factories in the Netherlands, Geurts et al. (1994) asked blue-collar workers how well off they thought they were in comparison to others within the company in terms of 11 different job aspects, such as physical safety, autonomy and freedom, promotion prospects, and social atmosphere. Feeling worse off than others led to more tolerance of absenteeism, and as such to an objectively recorded relatively high number of sick leaves.

The effects of social comparisons are at least as manifest at the highest professional levels. Combining models of Crosby (1976) and Folger (1986), Buunk and Janssen (1992) argued that relative deprivation involves an active cognitive process in which the current situation is evaluated against upward criteria, showing that all criteria distinguished in the models of Folger and Crosby constitute aspects of the same underlying latent construct, including unfavorable social comparisons, strong feelings of entitlement, weak justification of the present situation, and little likelihood of amelioration. In a study of a representative sample of professional men, Buunk and Janssen (1992) found that relative deprivation operationalized in this way correlated strongly with depression in the mid-career group (35–45 years of age), more so than in the early-career group (25–35 years of age), and much more so than in the late-career group (45–55 years of age). Furthermore, although relative deprivation was associated with dissatisfaction in all age groups, it was only during mid-career that it correlated significantly with health complaints. Presumably, younger people still feel they have a chance to attain what they want, whereas older people may have accepted their situation.

Identification and Contrast. The *interpretation* of social-comparison information may influence the effects of social comparison, and may even result in opposite effects of downward and upward comparison than those described. This is indirectly suggested by a number of studies. For example, Foley et al. (2016) showed that although downward social comparison positively impacted job satisfaction, upward social comparison positively affected organizational commitment. In a similar vein, in two samples of customs and police officers, Michinov (2005) found that as officers compared themselves more often with better-off employees, they reported a higher level of job satisfaction as well as fewer health complaints and feelings of emotional exhaustion. Conversely, the more frequently officers compared themselves with less-fortunate employees, the more dissatisfied they were and the more health problems and emotional exhaustion they reported. In line with this, in a study from South Korea, Shin and Sohn (2015) found that downward comparisons, in particular, were associated with a low level of job satisfaction.

To explain this type of seemingly nonobvious findings, Buunk and Ybema (1997) argued—in their identification-contrast model—that in organizations, the effects of social-comparison information depend on whether individuals *identify* or *contrast* themselves with the comparison targets. In the case of identification, employees tend to focus on the actual or potential similarity between themselves and the comparison target, try to recognize features of themselves in the other, and may regard the other's position as similar or attainable for themselves. When employees contrast themselves with a colleague, they tend to regard the other's position as a standard against which they can evaluate themselves. As a consequence, individuals may differ in the extent to which they follow four strategies: upward identification, upward contrast, downward identification, and downward contrast (Buunk, Kuyper, & Van der Zee, 2005; Smith, 2000). In general, upward identification with a successful colleague may enhance one's self-image and evoke positive feelings such as hope and admiration, whereas downward identification with an unsuccessful colleague may lower one's self-image, and may produce feelings of worry and fear (e.g., Collins, 1996; Lockwood, 2002). Conversely, upward contrast with a successful colleague may lower one's self-image and evoke negative feelings such as frustration and resentment, whereas downward contrast may enhance one's self-image and may produce—at least temporarily—feelings of relief and pride.

In general, several studies suggest that the positive effect evoked by upward comparisons (i.e., feeling good when another person is performing well) and the negative effect evoked by downward comparisons (i.e., feeling bad when another person is performing poorly)—both examples of identification—are more prevalent than responses indicating contrast, that is, the negative effect evoked by upward comparisons (i.e., feeling bad when another person is performing well) and the positive effect evoked by downward comparisons (i.e., feeling good when another person is performing poorly) (see Buunk, Zurriaga, & Peiró, 2010; Carmona et al., 2006). However, the occurrence of such feelings seems to depend on a number of variables. First, the *social climate* at work will play a role. A study of physicians from various health centers in Spain showed that when the social climate was perceived as cooperative, individuals tended to interpret social comparisons at work overall in a positive way, deriving positive feelings from upward as well as downward comparisons (Buunk, Zurriaga, et al., 2005). Second, the level of *stress* will affect the interpretation of social comparison, although this depends on the research method used. For example, in an experimental study, Ybema et al. (1996) showed that the more stress individuals facing a loss of work experienced, the more a negative effect was generated, with both an upward-and-downward comparison target. In line with the identification-contrast model, especially in downward comparison, a negative effect was mediated by identification with the downward-comparison other. However, the effects of social comparison may in part depend on the method used. For example, Buunk, Ybema, et al. (2001), who used a survey method, found that nurses experiencing high levels of burnout were reported to derive more positive effects from downward comparisons than nurses with low levels of burnout. Such a downward contrast is in line with Wills's (1981) downward-comparison theory, in which a decrease in well-being will induce one to improve one's well-being by appreciating that he or she is still better off than some others. However, this may be a short-term emotional-coping strategy, and may not be effective in the long run. That is, Carmona et al. (2006) showed that employees who responded more positively to upward comparisons (and not to downward comparisons), and less negatively to downward comparisons, showed a decrease in burnout a year later. Moreover, these effects were independent of the frequency of engaging in upward-and-downward comparisons as such. Third, the *controllability* of the comparison dimension may affect whether contrast or identification occurs. Exposure to a more competent colleague may make contrast with such an individual unavoidable, and may make one feel inferior. A better performance of another who clearly has more experience will be seen as something one can attain oneself, and will evoke more identification. In line with this, in a field experiment among secretaries (Ybema, 1994), participants were confronted with a bogus interview with a successful or an unsuccessful secretary who either spent a lot of effort, or little effort in her job. When the successful experience was attributed to effort, secretaries experienced more positive effects following upward comparison than following downward comparison. This was not the case for subjects who were led to believe that effort could not explain the performance of the comparison target.

Envy and Jealousy as Responses to Upward Comparison.   *Envy*, in particular, is an emotion quite prevalently evoked by social comparisons in organizations (e.g., Fischer et al., 2009). Although in lay language the terms *envy* and *jealousy* are often confused, jealousy and envy are two qualitatively different emotions. Envy occurs when a person lacks another's quality, achievement, or possession, and either desires it or wishes that the other lacked it (Parrott, 1991). Jealousy, in contrast, necessarily occurs in the context of valued relationships. It occurs when a person fears losing, or actually loses, an important relationship due to an actual or imagined rival for the valued person's attention (Dijkstra & Buunk, 1998). The evocation of both jealousy and envy is strongly tied to upward social comparisons (e.g., Van de Ven et al., 2012).

A distinction has been made between *malicious* envy and *benign* envy. Both types of envy appear to motivate individuals to decrease the status gap between themselves and others, but they do so in different ways. Benign envy leads individuals to close the gap by moving themselves up to the level of the other, whereas malicious envy leads individuals to do so by pulling the other down to one's own position, and may result in the emotion of *Schadenfreude* when the envied other experiences some type of misfortune (Van de Ven et al., 2009). Whereas benign envy—which can be viewed as a form of upward identification—stimulates individuals to self-promote and improve the self, for instance, by observational learning and affiliation with a superior other, malicious envy—which can be viewed as a form of upward contrast—may encourage individuals to derogate or even damage rivals.

In general, envy often has negative effects for the organization. In a review of studies on envy in organizations, Duffy et al. (2008) showed that workplace envy is related to lower job satisfaction, less liking for coworkers, lower group performance, higher turnover, higher absence rates, and higher social loafing. A series of experiments by Fischer et al. (2009) showed that envy may have negative effects on performance because envious individuals are less willing to share high-quality information with envied colleagues. Since information exchange is crucial for successful cooperation, group performance may suffer as a consequence. Further illustrating the potentially negative effect of envy for organizations, a study by Gino and Pierce (2009) showed that, in the visible proximity of monetary abundant wealth or wealthy others, individuals are more likely to cheat due to feelings of envy. Indeed, employees who feel their company or employer is extremely rich may more easily engage in unethical behaviors, such as those related to financial fraud, in an attempt to close the monetary gap between themselves and their CEO. Campbell et al. (2017) found that, paradoxically, peers offered more support and tried to more often undermine high performers. Employees seem particularly likely to harm better-performing others in situations accompanied by low expectations of future performance similarity (Lam et al., 2011).

These latter findings are in line with a study by Jia et al. (2016), which did not explicitly address envy, but focused upon what is referred to as the social-comparison bias, that is, the fact that people tend not to recommend higher-performing candidates who have the same strengths as themselves because these candidates can be a threat to their self-esteem. This has a tendency to hinder the effectiveness of employee-referral programs. In a series of studies, Jia et al. (2016) found that supervisors showed this social-comparison bias less, because they were less threatened by it than their subordinates. For example, "a sales team may lose an opportunity to achieve higher team goals if the current team member with the best sales performance refuses to recommend another salesperson who also possesses superior sales skills" (Jia et al., 2016, p. 569). One of their studies showed that employees, but not supervisors, would prefer to recommend someone with similar qualifications as themselves to another department rather than to their own department. They also found that employees would prefer to recommend a candidate with different strengths to their own rather than a candidate who had similar strengths to them. This was particularly true in terms of qualifications, an attribute that people tend to feel especially threatened about.

Even the superiority of another individual with characteristics not related to the requirements of the job, may induce envy and have dire consequences for the individual and the organization. While throughout human history men have competed primarily in the domains of status and physical dominance, women have tended to compete primarily in the domain of physical attractiveness (e.g., Buunk et al., 2020). For example, Buunk, Aan 't Goor, and Castro-Solano (2010) presented participants with a scenario wherein one's satisfying and close relationship with one's supervisor was threatened because a new employee seemed to develop a close relationship with the same supervisor. This was especially true when the supervisor was of one's own gender—women reported more jealousy in response to a physically attractive rival than men, while men reported more jealousy in response to a physically dominant rival than women. These effects were particularly pronounced among those with a dispositional tendency to compare themselves with others. In a similar vein, in an experimental study, women were confronted with either an attractive or an unattractive rival who was interfering with their thus far good relationship with their supervisor. The attractive rival evoked relatively more jealousy and lower career-advancement expectations, especially among women who attributed unfriendliness to the attractive rival (Buunk et al., 2016).

Due to envy and jealousy, the attractiveness of a candidate for a job may also affect his or her chance of being hired, as shown in a study by Luxen and Van de Vijver (2006), among both human resouces professionals and students. First, these authors found evidence for a mate-selection motive when the frequency of interaction between the job applicant and the participant was expected to be high. Under this condition, both men and women showed a preference to hire a highly attractive opposite-sex member over an unattractive opposite-sex other, with men showing this tendency more than women. With respect to same-sex candidates, however, a quite different pattern was found, clearly pointing to social comparison among women: women were less likely to hire a highly attractive female applicant than an unattractive female applicant. The male participants did not show this preference.

THE ROLE OF SOCIAL-COMPARISON ORIENTATION

It has been noted that some of the seemingly contradictory effects of social comparison may in part be due to dispositional differences in the tendency to compare oneself with others (Buunk & Gibbons, 2006). Gibbons and Buunk (1999) proposed the concept of *social-comparison orientation* (SCO) to refer to the personality disposition of individuals who are inclined to base the evaluation of their own characteristics upon comparison with others, and who have a tendency to relate events that happen to others to themselves. A review by Buunk et al. (2019) showed that individuals high in SCO are characterized by an interest in what others think and by a sensitivity to how others behave; they have relatively low intellectual autonomy, and display a high level of neuroticism (two of the Big Five dimensions). Moreover, they have a strong concern with their own motives and feelings, as apparent from substantial correlations of SCO with public and private self-consciousness (see, e.g., Fenigstein et al., 1975). Evidence for the external validity of the scale comes from, among other things, a laboratory experiment showing that individuals high in SCO are more interested in the scores of others after having learned their own score (Gibbons & Buunk, 1999), and also from research among cancer patients showing that patients high in SCO, when given the opportunity, select more information about other patients and respond more strongly to such information (Van der Zee et al., 1998). In organizations, a high SCO is, in general, associated with envy and perceived injustice (e.g., De la Sablonnière et al., 2012). Thau et al. (2007) found that the negative relationship between employee perceptions of justice and supervisory ratings of antisocial behaviors at work was stronger for workers who were high in SCO. According to Thau et al. (2007), individuals high in SCO respond relatively strongly to perceptions of injustice because of their chronic uncertainty about themselves.

In general, there is considerable evidence that the consequences of social comparison are more negative among those high in SCO. In a study of physicians from Spain, Buunk, Zurriaga, et al. (2005) showed that individuals high in SCO tended to interpret social comparisons at work in a relatively negative way. In a study of nurses, Buunk, Zurriaga, and Peiró (2010) found that the frequency of comparisons was a predictor of feelings of burnout 9 to 10 months later, primarily among individuals with a high SCO. Another longitudinal study of nurses by Buunk et al. (2003), examined the effects of social comparison of one's performance (how competently and adequately one felt one was doing one's work) with that of one's colleagues and perceived relative deprivation at work over a period of one year. Relative deprivation had increased particularly among those high in SCO, who a year earlier had (a) more frequently engaged in upward comparisons; (b) more frequently derived positive as well as negative feelings from such comparisons; and (c) more frequently derived negative feelings from downward comparisons. The finding—that deriving a positive as well as a negative effect from upward comparisons, accompanied by an increase in relative deprivation, especially among those high in SCO—suggests that while such individuals may admire someone who is performing better than themselves, such admiration may, at the same time, imply that one realizes that they are doing worse, which may eventually contribute to a sense of relative deprivation. Nevertheless, this study showed that individuals high in SCO tend to make downward comparisons, and this has been confirmed by other studies. For example, in a sample of mental health workers, Buunk et al. (2001) found that individuals with high levels of burnout, but low in SCO, identified themselves more with coworkers who were doing worse and less with coworkers who were doing better. In an experimental study conducted by Buunk, Ybema, et al. (2001), therapists working in a forensic institution were confronted with a bogus interview with someone in the same profession who was either very successful (upward comparison) or very unsuccessful (downward comparison). SCO did not affect the feelings evoked by the upward comparison. However, the higher the level of burnout, the more negative effect was evoked by the description of the downward-comparison target, but only among individuals high in SCO—again an identification effect. In another experimental study, nurses were confronted with a bogus interview with an upward-versus-downward comparison target. The higher individuals were in SCO, the more negative effects they showed following confrontation with the downward-comparison target. The impact on negative effects stayed the same when controlling for positive effects, and vice versa (Buunk, Van der Zee, et al., 2001).

There is only one study that shows that social comparisons *may* have positive effects among those high in SCO in work-related contexts. Buunk, Peiró, and Griffioen (2007) exposed students in their final year of study to a written scenario containing a fictitious interview with a new graduate who was either successful or unsuccessful in the job market. Exposure to the successful target led to a higher degree of inspiration, identification, and proactive career behavior than exposure to the unsuccessful target, especially among students high in SCO. In this study, the fact that high SCO was linked to positive effects rather than negative effects may in part be attributed to the specific type of comparison (i.e., the confrontation with concrete, vivid targets). It is our contention that in this case, those high in SCO tend, in general, to show more assimilation to, and identification with, the comparison target. In contrast, when simply asked how one feels in response to comparison with others, without providing descriptions of such others, contrast effects seem more likely to be evoked among those high in SCO.

CONCLUSION

To conclude, social comparisons seem to be quite prevalent in organizations and may concern various input as well as outcome dimensions, including effort, dedication, performance, salary, appraisal by one's supervisor, and career prospects. Social comparisons may evoke positive and negative emotions, depending on the direction—upward versus downward—and the interpretation of the comparison—identification versus contrast. Other factors include the social climate in the organization, the controllability of the comparison dimension, and individual differences in the tendency to compare oneself with others. Envy and jealousy constitute a specific set of emotions evoked by social comparisons, which may even concern dimensions not directly relevant for job performance, like physical attractiveness, and which may have negative effects for the organization because they may result in not hiring or promoting the most competent colleague for a particular job. In sum, social-comparison processes seem widespread in organizations and deserve due attention from managers and human resources officers.

REFERENCES

Ataay, A. (2018). Effects of referents' gender and hierarchical level on employees' satisfaction with pay. *Social Behavior and Personality: An International Journal, 46*(10), 1623–1636. https://doi-org.proxy-ub.rug.nl/10.2224/sbp.7023

Beach, S. R., & Tesser, A. (2000). Self-evaluation maintenance and evolution: Some speculative notes. In L. Wheeler & J. Suls (Eds.), *Handbook of social comparison: Theory and research* (pp. 123–140). Kluwer Academic.

Blanton, H., Buunk, B. P., Gibbons, F. X., & Kuyper, H. (1999). When better-than-others compare upward: Choice of comparison and comparative evaluation as independent predictors of academic performance. *Journal of Personality and Social Psychology, 76*(3), 420–430. https://doi.org/10.1037/0022–3514.76 .3.420

Brickman, P., & Bulman, R. J. (1977). Pleasure and pain in social comparison. In J. Suls & R. L. Miller (Eds.), *Social comparison processes: Theoretical and empirical perspectives* (pp. 149–186). Hemisphere.

Brown, D. J., Ferris, D. L., Heller, D., & Keeping, L. M. (2007). Antecedents and consequences of the frequency of upward and downward social comparisons at work. *Organizational Behavior and Human Decision Processes, 102*(1), 59–75. https://doi-org.proxy-ub.rug.nl/10.1016/j.obhdp.2006.10.003

Buckley, F. H. (2014). Schadenfreude and laughter. In W. W. van Dijk & J. W. Ouwerkerk (Eds.), *Schadenfreude: Understanding pleasure at the misfortune of others* (pp. 219–226). Cambridge University Press. https://doi-org.proxy-ub.rug.nl/10.1017/CBO9781139084246.018

Buunk, A. P., Aan 't Goor, J., & Castro-Solano, A. (2010). Intrasexual competition at work: Sex differences in the jealousy-evoking effect of rival characteristics in work settings. *Journal of Social and Personal Relationships, 27*(5), 671–684. https://doi-org/10.1177/0265407510368964

Buunk, A. P., Carmona, C., Peiró, J. M., Dijkstra, A., & Dijkstra, P. (2011). Social comparison at work: The role of culture, type of organization and gender. *Crosscultural Communication, 7*(2), 14–21.

Buunk, A. P., Cohen-Schotanus, J., & Van Nek, R. H. (2007). Why and how people engage in social comparison while learning social skills in groups. *Group Dynamics: Theory, Research, and Practice, 11*(3), 140–152. https://doi.org/10.1037/1089–2699.11.3.140

Buunk, A. P., Dijkstra, P. D., Gibbons, F. X., & Krizan, Z. (2019). Individual differences in social comparison: The complex effects of Social Comparison Orientation. In J. Suls, R. L. Collins, & L. Wheeler (Eds.), *Social comparison in judgment and behavior* (pp. 77–105). Oxford University Press.

Buunk, A. P., Dijkstra, P. D., Massar, K., Zurriaga, R., & González-Navarro, P. (2020). Envy and jealousy: The role of intrasexual competition in the workplace. In L. Liu-Qin Yang, R. Cropanzano, C. Daus, & V. Martinez-Tur (Eds.), *The Cambridge handbook of workplace affect* (pp. 440–451). Cambridge University Press.

Buunk, A. P., & Gibbons, F. X. (2006). Social comparison orientation: A new perspective on those who do and those who do not compare with others. In S. Guimond (Ed.), *Social comparison and social psychology: Understanding cognition, intergroup, relationship, and culture* (pp. 15–32). Cambridge University Press.

Buunk, A. P., & Gibbons, F. X. (2007). Social comparison: The end of a theory and the emergence of a field. *Organizational Behavior and Human Decision Process, 102,* 3–21. https://doi.org/10.1016/j.obhdp .2006.09.007

Buunk, A. P., & Gibbons, F. X. (Eds.). (1997). *Health, coping and well-being: Perspectives from social comparison theory* (pp. 359–388). Erlbaum.

Buunk, A. P., & Janssen, P. P. M. (1992). Relative deprivation, career issues, and mental health among men in midlife. *Journal of Vocational Behavior, 40*, 338–350.

Buunk, A. P., Kuyper, H., & Van der Zee, Y. G. (2005). Affective response to social comparison in the classroom. *Basic and Applied Social Psychology, 27*(3), 229–237. https://doi.org/10.1207/s15324834 basp2703_4

Buunk, A. P., & Mussweiler, T. (2001). New directions in social comparison research. *European Journal of Social Psychology, 31*(5), 467–475. https://doi.org/10.1002/ejsp.77

Buunk, A. P., Peiró, J. M., & Griffioen, C. (2007). A positive role model may stimulate career-oriented behavior. *Journal of Applied Social Psychology, 37*(7), 1489–1500. https://doi.org/10.1111/j.1559 –1816.2007.00223.x

Buunk, A. P., Pollet, T. V., Dijkstra, P., & Massar, K. (2011). Intrasexual competition within organizations. In G. Saad (Ed.), *Evolutionary psychology in the business sciences* (pp. 41–70). Springer.

Buunk, A. P., Schaufeli, W. B., & Ybema, J. F. (1994). Burnout, uncertainty, and the desire for social comparison among nurses. *Journal of Applied Social Psychology, 24*(19), 1701–1718. https://doi.org/10.1111 /j.1559–1816.1994.tb01570.x

Buunk, A. P., & Van der Laan, V. (2002). Do women need female role models? Subjective social status and the effects of same-sex and opposite sex comparisons. *Revue Internationale de Psychologie Sociale, 15*(3–4), 129–155.

Buunk, A. P., Van der Zee, K. I., & Van Yperen, N. W. (2001). Neuroticism and social comparison orientation as moderators of affective responses to social comparison at work. *Journal of Personality, 69*(5), 745–763. https://doi.org/10.1111/1467–6494.695162

Buunk, A. P., & Ybema, J. F. (1997). Social comparisons and occupational stress: The identification-contrast model. In A. P. Buunk & F. X. Gibbons (Eds.), *Health, coping and well-being: Perspectives from social comparison theory* (pp. 359–388). Erlbaum.

Buunk, A. P., Ybema, J. F., Gibbons, F. X., & Ipenburg, M. L. (2001). The affective consequences of social comparison as related to professional burnout and social comparison orientation. *European Journal of Social Psychology, 31*(4), 337–351. https://doi.org/10.1002/ejsp.41

Buunk, A. P., Zurriaga, R., González-Navarro, P., & Monzani, L. (2016). Attractive rivals may undermine the expectation of career advancement and enhance jealousy: An experimental study. *European Journal of Work and Organizational Psychology, 25*(6), 798–803.

Buunk, A. P., Zurriaga, R., Gónzalez-Romá, V., & Subirats, M. (2003). Engaging in upward and downward comparisons as a determinant of relative deprivation at work: A longitudinal study. *Journal of Vocational Behavior, 62*(2), 370–388. https://doi.org/10.1016/S0001-8791(02)00015-5

Buunk, A. P., Zurriaga, R., & Peiró, J. M. (2010). Social comparison as a predictor of changes in burnout among nurses. *Anxiety, Stress & Coping, 23*(2), 181–194. https://doi.org/10.1080/10615800902971521

Buunk, A. P., Zurriaga, R., Peiró, J. M., Nauta, A., & Gosalvez, I. (2005). Social comparisons at work as related to a cooperative social climate and to individual differences in social comparison orientation. *Applied Psychology, 54*(1), 61–80. https://doi.org/10.1111/j.1464–0597.2005.00196.x

Campbell, E. M., Liao, H., Chuang, A., Zhou, J., & Dong, Y. (2017). Hot shots and cool reception? An expanded view of social consequences for high performers. *Journal of Applied Psychology, 102*(5), 845–866. https://doi-org.proxy-ub.rug.nl/10.1037/apl0000183

Carmona, C., Buunk, A. P., Peiró, J. M., Rodríguez, I., & Bravo, M. J. (2006). Do social comparison and coping play a role in the development of burnout? Cross-sectional and longitudinal findings. *Journal of Occupational and Organizational Psychology, 79*(1), 83–99. https://doi.org/10.1348/096317905X40808

Collins, R. L. (1996). For better or worse: The impact of upward social comparison on self-evaluations. *Psychological Bulletin, 119*(1), 51–69. https://doi.org/10.1037/0033–2909.119.1.51

Crosby, F. (1976). A model of egoistical relative deprivation. *Psychological Review, 83*(2), 85–113. https://doi.org/10.1037/0033-295X.83.2.85

De la Sablonnière, R., Tougas, F., De la Sablonnière, E., & Debrosse, R. (2012). Profound organizational change, psychological distress and burnout symptoms: The mediator role of collective relative deprivation. *Group Processes & Intergroup Relations*, *15*(6), 776–790. https://doi.org/10.1177/1368430212445074

DeVellis, R., Holt, K., Renner, B., Blalock, S., Blanchard, L., Cook, H., Koltz, M., Mikow, V., & Harring, K. (1990). The relationship of social comparison to rheumatoid arthritis symptoms and affect. *Basic and Applied Social Psychology*, *11*(1), 1–18. https://doi.org/10.1207/s15324834basp1101_1

Dijkstra, P., & Buunk, B. P. (1998). Jealousy as a function of rival characteristics: An evolutionary perspective. *Personality and Social Psychology Bulletin*, *24*(11), 1158–1166. https://doi.org/10.1177/01461672982411003

Dittrich, J. E., & Carrell, M. R. (1979). Organization equity perceptions, employee job satisfaction, and departmental absence and turnover rates. *Organizational Behavior & Human Performance*, *24*(1), 29–40. https://doi.org/10.1016/0030-5073(79)90013-8

Duffy, M. K., Shaw, J. D., & Schaubroeck, J. M. (2008). Envy in organizational life. In R. H. Smith (Ed.), *Envy: Theory and research* (pp. 167–189). Oxford University Press. https://doi.org/10.1093/acprof:oso/9780195327953.003.0010

Dunn, J., Ruedy, N. E., & Schweitzer, M. E. (2012). It hurts both ways: How social comparisons harm affective and cognitive trust. *Organizational Behavior and Human Decision Processes*, *117*(1), 2–14. https://doi-org.proxy-ub.rug.nl/10.1016/j.obhdp.2011.08.001

Eddleston, K. A. (2009). The effects of social comparisons on managerial career satisfaction and turnover intentions. *The Career Development International*, *14*(1), 87–110. https://doi-org.proxy-ub.rug.nl/10.1108/13620430910933592

Feldman, N. S., & Ruble, D. N. (1981). Social comparison strategies: Dimensions offered and options taken. *Personality and Social Psychology Bulletin*, *7*(1), 11–16. https://doi.org/10.1177/014616728171002

Fenigstein, A., Scheier, M. F., & Buss, A. H. (1975). Public and private self-consciousness: Assessment and theory. *Journal of Consulting and Clinical Psychology*, *43*(4), 522–527. https://doi.org/10.1037/h0076760

Festinger, L. (1954). A theory of social comparison processes. *Human Relations*, *7*, 117–140. https://doi.org/10.1177/001872675400700202

Fischer, P., Kastenmüller, A., Frey, D., & Peus, C. (2009). Social comparison and information transmission in the work context. *Journal of Applied Social Psychology*, *39*(1), 42–61. https://doi-org.proxy-ub.rug.nl/10.1111/j.1559-1816.2008.00428.x

Foley, S., Ngo, H., & Loi, R. (2016). Antecedents and consequences of upward and downward social comparisons: An investigation of Chinese employees. *International Journal of Organizational Analysis*, *24*(1), 145–161. https://doi-org.proxy-ub.rug.nl/10.1108/IJOA-02-2014-0743

Folger, R. (1986). A referent cognitions theory of relative deprivation. In J. M. Olson, C. P. Herman, & M. P. Zanna (Eds.), *Relative deprivation and social comparison: The Ontario Symposium* (Vol. 4, pp. 33–55). Erlbaum.

García, S. M., & Tor, A. (2009). The N-effect: More competitors, less competition. *Psychological Science*, *20*(7), 871–877. https://papers.ssrn.com/sol3/papers.cfm?abstract_id=1307223#:~:text=The%20present%20analysis%20introduces%20the%20N-Effect%20-%20the,average%20number%20of%20test-takers%20at%20test-taking%20venues%20increases

Geurts, S. A., Buunk, B. P., & Schaufeli, W. B. (1994). Social comparisons and absenteeism: A structural modeling approach. *Journal of Applied Social Psychology*, *24*(21), 1871–1890. https://doi-org.proxy-ub.rug.nl/10.1111/j.1559-1816.1994.tb00565.x

Gibbons, F. X., & Buunk, B. P. (1999). Individual differences in social comparison: The development of a scale of social comparison orientation. *Journal of Personality and Social Psychology*, *76*(1), 129–142. https://doi.org/10.1037/0022-3514.76.1.129

Gilbert, D., Price, J., & Allan, S. (1995). Social comparison, social attractiveness and evolution: How might they be related? *New Ideas in Psychology, 13*(2), 149–165. https://doi.org/10.1016/0732-118X(95)00002-X

Gino, F., & Pierce, L. (2009). The abundance effect: Unethical behavior in the presence of wealth. *Organizational Behavior and Human Decision Processes, 109*(2), 142–155. https://doi-org.proxy-ub.rug .nl/10.1016/j.obhdp.2009.03.003

Goodman, P. S., & Haisley, E. (2007). Social comparison processes in an organizational context: New directions. *Organizational Behavior and Human Decision Processes, 102*(1), 109–125. https://doi.org/10.1016/j .obhdp.2006.10.005

Greenberg, J., Ashton-James, C. E., & Ashkanasy, N. M. (2007). Social comparison processes in organizations. *Organizational Behavior and Human Decision Processes, 102*(1), 22–41. https://doi.org/10.1016/j .obhdp.2006.09.006

Harris, M. M., Anseel, F., & Lievens, F. (2008). Keeping up with the Joneses: A field study of the relationships among upward, lateral, and downward comparisons and pay level satisfaction. *Journal of Applied Psychology, 93*(3), 665–673. https://doi-org.proxy-ub.rug.nl/10.1037/0021–9010.93.3.665

Hendrix, W. H., & Spencer, B. A. (1989). Development and test of a multivariate model of absenteeism. *Psychological Reports, 64*(3, Pt 1), 923–938. https://doi-org.proxy-ub.rug.nl/10.2466/pr0.1989.64.3.923

Hoorens, V., Pandelaere, M., Oldersma, F., & Sedikides, C. (2012). The hubris hypothesis: You can self-enhance, but you'd better not show it. *Journal of Personality, 80*, 1237–1274. https://doi.org/10.1016/j .concog.2016.07.003

Hyll, W. (2018). Relative concerns at the workplace: On the design of the firm as a social space. *Journal of Evolutionary Economics, 28*(2), 245–264. https://doi-org.proxy-ub.rug.nl/10.1007/s00191-017-0535-3

Iredale, W., Van Vugt, M., & Dunbar, R. I. M. (2008). Showing off in humans: Male generosity as mate signal. *Evolutionary Psychology, 6*(3), 386–392.

Jandeska, K. E., & Kraimer, M. L. (2005). Women's perceptions of organizational culture, work attitudes, and role-modeling behaviors. *Journal of Managerial Issues, 17*(4), 461–478.

Jia, H., Lu, J., Xie, X., & Huang, T. (2016). When your strength threatens me: Supervisors show less social comparison bias than subordinates. *Journal of Occupational and Organizational Psychology, 89*(3), 568–587. https://doi-org.proxy-ub.rug.nl/10.1111/joop.12142

Lam, C. K., Van der Vegt, G. S., Walter, F., & Huang, X. (2011). Harming high performers: A social comparison perspective on interpersonal harming in work teams. *Journal of Applied Psychology, 96*(3), 588–601. https://doi-org.proxy-ub.rug.nl/10.1037/a0021882

Linehan, N., & Scullion, H. (2008). The development of female global managers: The role of mentoring and networking. *Journal of Business Ethics, 83*(1), 29–40. https://doi.org/10.1007/s10551-007-9657-0

Lockwood, P. (2002). Could it happen to you? Predicting the impact of downward comparisons on the self. *Journal of Personality and Social Psychology, 82*(3), 343–358. https://doi.org/10.1037/0022–3514 .82.3.343

Lockwood, P., & Kunda, Z. (1997). Superstars and me: Predicting the impact of role models on the self. *Journal of Personality and Social Psychology, 73*(1), 91–103. https://doi.org/10.1037/0022–3514.73.1.91

Luxen, M. F., & Van de Vijver, F. J. R. (2006). Facial attractiveness, sexual selection, and personnel selection: When evolved preferences matter. *Journal of Organizational Behavior, 27*(2), 241–255. https://doi.org /10.1002/job.357

McGrath, A., Reid, N., & Boor, J. (1989). Occupational stress in nursing. *International Journal of Nursing Studies, 3*(4), 3–31. https://doi.org/10.1016/s0020-7489(03)00058-0

McKenna, J. F. (1987). Equity/inequity, stress and employee commitment in a health care setting. *Stress & Health, 3*(1), 71–74. https://doi.org/10.1002/smi.2460030113

Michinov, N. (2005). Social comparison, perceived control, and occupational burnout. *Applied Psychology: An International Review, 54*(1), 99–118. https://doi.org/10.1111/j.1464–0597.2005.00198.x

Miller, C. T. (1984). Self-schemas, gender, and social comparison: A clarification of the related attributes hypothesis. *Journal of Personality and Social Psychology, 46*(6), 1222–1229.

Molleman, E., Pruyn, J., & Van Knippenberg, A. (1986). Social comparison processes among cancer patients. *British Journal of Social Psychology, 25*(1), 1–13. https://doi.org/10.1111/j.2044–8309.1986.tb00695.x

Parrott, W. G. (1991). The emotional experiences of envy and jealousy. In P. Salovey (Ed.), *The psychology of jealousy and envy* (pp. 3–30). Guilford.

Ridge, J. W., Hill, A. D., & Aime, F. (2017). Implications of multiple concurrent pay comparisons for top-team turnover. *Journal of Management, 43*(3), 671–690. https://doi-org.proxy-ub.rug.nl/10.1177/0149206314539349

Saad, G., & Gill, T. (2001). Gender differences when choosing between salary allocation options. *Applied Economics Letters, 8*, 531–533. https://doi.org/10.1080/13504850010005251

Schachter, S. (1959). *The psychology of affiliation*. Stanford University Press.

Sheppard, L. D., & Aquino, K. (2017). Sisters at arms: A theory of female same-sex conflict and its problematization in organizations. *Journal of Management, 43*(3), 691–715. https://doi-org.proxy-ub.rug.nl/10.1177/0149206314539348

Shin, J., & Sohn, Y. W. (2015). Effects of employees' social comparison behaviors on distributive justice perception and job satisfaction. *Social Behavior and Personality: An International Journal, 43*(7), 1071–1084. https://doi-org.proxy-ub.rug.nl/10.2224/sbp.2015.43.7.1071

Smith, R. H. (2000). Assimilative and contrastive emotional reactions to upward and downward social comparisons. In J. Suls & L. Wheeler (Eds.), *Handbook of social comparison: Theory and research* (pp. 173–200). Kluwer Academic. https://link.springer.com/chapter/10.1007%2F978-1-4615-4237-7_10

Steil, J. M., & Hay, J. L. (1997). Social comparison in the workplace: A study of 60 dual-career couples. *Personality and Social Psychology Bulletin, 23*(4), 427–438. https://doi.org/10.1177/0146167297234008

Stouffer, S. A., Suchman, E. A., Devinney, L. C., Star, S. A., & Williams, R. M., Jr. (1949). *The American soldier: Adjustment during army life. (Studies in social psychology in World War II)*. Princeton University Press.

Suls, J., Collins, R. L., & Wheeler, L. (Eds.). (2020). *Social comparison in judgment and behavior*. Oxford University Press.

Suls, J., Gaes, G., & Gastorf, J. W. (1979). Evaluating a sex-related ability: Comparison with same-, opposite-, and combined-sex norms. *Journal of Research in Personality, 13*(3), 294–304. https://doi.org/10.1016/0092–6566(79)90020–5

Suls, J., & Wheeler, L. (2000). A selective history of classic and neo-social comparison theory. In J. Suls & L. Wheeler (Eds.), *Handbook of social comparison: Theory and research* (pp. 3–22). Kluwer Academic. https://link.springer.com/chapter/10.1007/978-1-4615-4237-7_1

Sweeney, P. D., & McFarlin, D. B. (2005). Wage comparisons with similar and dissimilar others. *Journal of Occupational and Organizational Psychology, 78*(1), 113–131. https://doi-org.proxy-ub.rug.nl/10.1348/096317904X23808

Taylor, S. E., & Lobel, M. (1989). Social comparison activity under threat: Downward evaluation and upward contacts. *Psychological Review, 96*(4), 569–575. https://doi.org/10.1037/0033-295X.96.4.569

Thau, S., Aquino, K., & Wittek, R. (2007). An extension of uncertainty management theory to the self: The relationship between justice, social comparison orientation, and antisocial work behaviors. *Journal of Applied Psychology, 92*, 250–258. https://doi-org.proxy-ub.rug.nl/10.1037/0021–9010.92.1.250

Tornow, W. W. (1971). The development and application of an input-outcome moderator test on the perception and reduction of inequity. *Organizational Behavior and Human Performance, 6*(5), 614–638. https://doi.org/10.1016/S0030-5073(71)80010–7

Van de Ven, N., Zeelenberg, M., & Pieters, R. (2009). Leveling up and down: The experiences of benign and malicious envy. *Emotion, 9*, 419–429. https://doi.org/10.1037/a0015669

Van de Ven, N., Zeelenberg, M., & Pieters, R. (2012). Appraisal patterns of envy and related emotions. *Motivation and Emotion, 36*(2), 195–204. https://doi.org/10.1007/s11031-011-9235-8

Van der Zee, K., Oldersma, F., Buunk, B. P., & Bos, D. (1998). Social comparison preferences among cancer patients as related to neuroticism and social comparison orientation. *Journal of Personality and Social Psychology, 75*(3), 801–810. https://doi.org/10.1037/0022–3514.75.3.801

Vardaman, J. M., Allen, D. G., Otondo, R. F., Hancock, J. I., Shore, L. M., & Rogers, B. L. (2016). Social comparisons and organizational support: Implications for commitment and retention. *Human Relations, 69*(7), 1483–1505. https://doi-org.proxy-ub.rug.nl/10.1177/0018726715619687

Wheeler, L., & Suls, J. (Eds.). (2020). *Handbook of social comparison: Theory and research.* Kluwer Academic.

Williams, M. L., McDaniel, M. A., & Nguyen, N. T. (2006). A meta-analysis of the antecedents and consequences of pay level satisfaction. *Journal of Applied Psychology, 91*(2), 392–413. https://doi.org/10.1037/0021–9010.91.2.392

Wills, T. A. (1981). Downward comparison principles in social psychology. *Psychological Bulletin, 90*(2), 245–271. https://doi.org/10.1037/0033–2909.90.2.245

Wood, J. V. (1989). Theory and research concerning social comparisons of personal attributes. *Psychological Bulletin, 106*(2), 231–248. https://doi.org/10.1037/0033–2909.106.2.231

Ybema, J. F. (1994). *Up and down: Affective responses to social comparison.* Labyrint.

Ybema, J. F., Buunk, B. P., & Heesink, J. A. M. (1996). Affect and identification in social comparison after loss of work. *Basic and Applied Social Psychology, 18*(2), 151–169. https://doi-org.proxy-ub.rug.nl/10.1207/s15324834basp1802_3

Abraham P. Buunk

TEAM DYNAMICS AND PROCESSES IN THE WORKPLACE

INTRODUCTION

Organizations become more reliant on collaborative performance as the nature of their work increases in complexity. Complex tasks are often performed better as a set of smaller, interdependent tasks divided among several workers. These tasks require more than individual efforts—teamwork is essential to integrating individual taskwork and performing effectively as a team. The use of teams has become commonplace in many industries (e.g., aviation crews, military squads, medical teams), with decades of team performance research informing their success. Over the years, this research has made clear that performance does not improve automatically as a result of structuring workers in teams. Employees must foster and master teamwork skills to become effective team players. In this article, we provide a detailed overview of the content area to introduce the research findings that shape what we know about team dynamics and processes.

This article is intended for those interested in what the evidence says about team performance in the workplace. Although a complete and comprehensive review is beyond the scope of this article, we provide depth and breadth by focusing on the teamwork process and identifying the wide range of factors that can influence its effectiveness. To this end, we have reviewed and synthesized the extant literature to summarize the foundations of teamwork research in an organized framework. We supplement our overview with evidence-based recommendations for improving practice. Before introducing our framework, we provide a brief introduction to the science of teams in organizations. In doing so, we differentiate teams from groups, identify the characteristics of effective teams, and introduce teamwork competencies. After introducing the foundations of team science, we begin to dissect the dynamic process that leads to performance outcomes and team effectiveness.

What Is a Team?   Teams are complex, dynamic systems made up of two or more individuals working on interdependent tasks to reach a shared goal (Salas, Dickinson, Converse, & Tannenbaum, 1992). There are many different types of teams that may vary in their respective industries, objectives, compositions, hierarchies, and interdependencies. This has led researchers to advance numerous categorization schemes (e.g., Hackman, 1987). Considering characteristics inherent to team structure, Wildman and colleagues (2012) advanced six discrete categories for differentiating team types: task interdependence, physical distribution, communication structure, role structure, leadership structure, and lifespan (Wildman et al., 2012). Although many team-type taxonomies exist, this classification does a good job of capturing meaningful differences in team functioning.

There are many ways to discuss how teams may differ, but there are seven common factors of all work teams that differentiate them from any other group of individuals. Work teams (a) have at least two members (b) who perform work-relevant tasks (c) that are interdependent, (d) have at least one shared goal or mission, (e) have some form of social interaction among members, (f) maintain boundaries with other units, and (g) are embedded within a larger organizational network that dictates context (Kozlowski & Bell, 2003, p. 334). A group of individuals is not considered a team unless they meet these seven conditions. For instance, consider a company book club with members who share reading goals and meet weekly to discuss each chapter—even though most requirements are met, this group cannot be considered a team because its members do not perform interdependent tasks. Likewise, a few employees who take separate but complementary approaches toward improving workplace safety is not a team if they do not assemble or interact using some form of communication. The research and recommendations outlined in this effort pertain specifically to work teams.

Relatedly, understanding what an effective team is made of goes beyond its typology. A team of experts does not always make an expert team. Consider a basketball team with a star player in every position—history has demonstrated that this often does not work out as the coaches and fans would have hoped. It takes a specific and separate set of individual- and team-level skills to make an effective team (Prince, Brannick, Prince, & Salas, 1997). Before discussing what it takes to build an effective team, "effectiveness" must be defined so that it can be recognized.

What Is Team Effectiveness?   Team effectiveness is a term we use broadly in reference to the outcomes that result from working in a team. There is no metric of overall effectiveness in teams because the meaning of effectiveness depends on the context (i.e., teams can be effective at different things) and varies at different organizational levels. For instance, teams can be effective at the individual level by improving member self-efficacy, just as a reduction in critical errors can indicate effectiveness of safety performance at the team level. Identifying what makes a team effective requires understanding its objectives.

In general, organizations utilize teams when goal achievement exceeds the capacity of an individual and would be more effective as a coordinated effort. With that in mind, there are three main questions that should be answered in any evaluation of team effectiveness: (a) Do team outputs meet the goals or performance standards in place? (b) Do team members evaluate their experience with the team favorably? (c) Is the team's experience conducive to successful performance in the future? (Hackman, 1987). These questions can be adapted to apply to more specific contexts, and provide a nice framework for doing so to define team expectations.

As emphasized, organizations utilize teams with the hope that team performance would be superior to individual performance. Unfortunately, the use of teams does not always lead to better outcomes (Allen & Hecht, 2004). What exactly do high-performing teams do to be successful? What do low-performing teams do that leads to failure? To answer these and more general questions of team effectiveness, researchers have examined the team performance process to identify the particular behaviors that characterize high- and low-performing teams. These efforts have built a strong and growing body of research on the science of teamwork.

What Is Teamwork?   At this point, it is important to differentiate between team performance and team performance *outcomes*. Team performance is the multilevel *process* that arises from individuals working together in a team, whereas team performance *outcomes* refer to the team-produced outputs that result from this process (Campbell, 1990). Team performance consists of two distinct types of behavior: *taskwork* and *teamwork* (McIntyre & Salas, 1995). More proximal to reaching performance goals is *taskwork*. Taskwork consists of engaging in a specific set of behaviors to complete a particular team task. Each team member has a role attached to responsibilities that pertain to completion of shared tasks. Completing taskwork requires knowledge and expertise that is specific to each task and unlikely to generalize to other activities. Unlike taskwork, teamwork behaviors are transferrable across tasks and contexts, and involve efforts to coordinate individual taskwork. Effective teamwork leads to performance gains that are greater than the sum of each individual's taskwork. In summary, both taskwork and teamwork behaviors are required to achieve shared goals (Salas, Shuffler, Thayer, Bedwell, & Lazzara, 2015); but teamworking involves much more than simply engaging in particular behaviors.

Teamwork is a multifaceted phenomenon that allows a group of individuals to function effectively as a unit by using a set of interrelated knowledge, skills, and attitudes (Baker, Day, & Salas, 2006). Some researchers conceptualize how these sets of "KSAs" manifest as core competencies of teamwork. Competency models, although broad, provide a useful framework for discussing the critical components of effective teamwork across all settings and task objectives, as well as for designing team training programs aimed at improving particular skill sets. Salas and colleagues (2015) identify six[1] core competencies of teamwork that impact performance: (a) coordination, (b) cooperation, (c) conflict, (d) communication, (e) cognition, and (f) coaching. Although many competency models of teamwork exist, the literature reflects a high consensus among researchers about the importance of these six factors. We provide a brief summary of each competency to introduce the mechanisms behind teamwork, and describe how they facilitate team functioning.

Coordination.   Coordination involves bringing together each individual's effort to form synchronized team actions (Marks, Mathieu, & Zaccaro, 2001). The literature differentiates between explicit and implicit coordination. Explicit coordination involves overtly planning and strategizing courses of action and team members' interdependent responsibilities. Implicit coordination does not involve communicating explicit plans, but instead uses shared knowledge within the team to anticipate events and adapt to the situation at hand (Rico, Sánchez-Manzanares, Gil, & Gibson, 2008). Both explicit and implicit coordination are essential for effective teamwork, and are just as important to performance outcomes as task expertise. Each teammate could be an expert, but a group of experts cannot succeed as a team without coordination. Just as a choreographed dance is much more than each dancer's role, coordinated teams require more than individual members' task expertise. The greatest performances are not those with the best performers, but those that bring individual expertise together seamlessly to create something greater than the sum of its parts. Work teams with high coordination have minimal process-loss, and operate efficiently with few errors. Teams with poor coordination are dysfunctional, disorganized, and error-prone; often having to make up for losses. Coordination is key for team efficiency.

Cooperation. Cooperation is a broad competency that encompasses a team's propensity and willingness to work well together. Team members must be motivated to cooperate with one another to perform well on interdependent tasks (Salas et al., 2015). Teams high in cooperation have members who trust and help one another, and are high in collective efficacy (i.e., a shared perception that the team is capable of meeting performance goals; Salas, Sims, & Klein, 2004). Teams low in cooperation experience more negative perceptions toward the team and encounter more conflict (Jehn, Rispens, & Thatcher, 2010). Thus, cooperation is related to conflict.

Conflict/Conflict Management. Teams can experience conflict from opposing opinions on tasks and processes, as well as relationship conflict from interpersonal disagreements that are unrelated to the task. Although relationship conflict is typically associated with negative outcomes (e.g., poor trust and cooperation), some research suggests that there can be benefits to task-related conflict (e.g., increased creativity; De Dreu, 2008). Jehn (1997) posits that task conflict can cause team members to think critically about opposing perspectives and encourage creative solutions that enhance team performance, highlighting the importance of effective conflict management. Teams skilled in conflict management respond both proactively and reactively to conflict by finding a middle-ground that benefits all members, and establishing a course of action for resolution and prevention (Marks et al., 2001). Unfortunately, teams that experience conflict early-on often maladapt over time by decreasing trust and cooperation, causing long-lasting effects on team functioning (De Jong & Dirks, 2012; Greer, Jehn, & Mannix, 2008). For this reason, it may be especially beneficial to train teams in conflict-management skills before performing on shared tasks.

Communication. Team communication involves the closed-loop exchange of information, both explicitly and implicitly. After a message is sent, it must be acknowledged and understood, then confirmed by the sender as interpreted correctly by the receiver (Salas, Rosen, Burke, & Goodwin, 2009). Teams that communicate effectively have shared knowledge and individual knowledge that can be exchanged efficiently, make fewer errors, and waste less resources than teams with poor communication. They are also effective at articulating strategic plans and discussing feedback following performance. Interestingly, overcommunicating can be just as detrimental to team performance as undercommunicating (Patrashkova-Volzdoska, McComb, Green, & Compton, 2003). This might indicate that it is inefficient to communicate when unnecessary, or when the information exchanged is redundant or irrelevant (Mesmer-Magnus & DeChurch, 2009). In order to walk this thin line of effective communication, teams rely on cognitive structures.

Cognition. Team cognition refers to the shared knowledge among teammates that connects their understanding and allows them to function as a coordinated unit (Salas et al., 2015). Teams use cognitive structures to hold and exchange knowledge related to the team, the task, the goal, and the process (Wildman et al., 2012). Teams with poor cognition have members with divergent understandings of their mission and strategy, who are often unaware of each other's roles and situational conditions. Teams with effective cognition are able to predict and adapt to situational changes seamlessly, and have members with similar mental models who exchange knowledge efficiently and anticipate each other's needs. Team cognition is positively related to team motivation and performance (DeChurch & Mesmer-Magnus, 2010).

Coaching. Team coaching refers to all actions aimed at improving performance, such as giving feedback, instilling motivation, training, and providing support. Although typically a leadership function, all team members can play a part in coaching; such as in shared leadership (see Burke, Fiore, & Salas, 2003). Coaching encourages teams to work hard and stay committed, improve knowledge and skills, and develop effective strategies (Hackman & Wageman, 2005). Teams that lack coaching have members that are unmotivated to build their skills, are detached from their work group, and perform poorly; while teams with effective coaching exhibit higher levels of teamwork and performance outcomes (Liu, Pirola-Merlo, Yang, & Huang, 2009).

These competencies provide an organized structure for introducing a wide array of teamwork topics. Within each competency are the specific attitudinal, behavioral, and cognitive constructs that combine to create and shape the complex phenomenon that is teamwork. In the following section, we unpack these competencies and take a process-oriented approach to discussing the factors involved in teamwork performance.

TEAMWORK AS A COMPLEX PHENOMENON

Teamwork is the driver that transforms individual inputs into team-produced outcomes. This performance process involves a variety of factors and is complex, dynamic, and recursive. The IMOI framework (Inputs→Mediators→Outputs→Inputs) illustrates how team performance develops throughout time, over a series of interaction cycles (Ilgen, Hollenbeck, Johnson, & Jundt, 2005). It demonstrates the mediating role of teamwork in explaining how inputs (e.g., individual attitudes) result in outputs (e.g., team performance quality) that further serve as inputs in the next performance episode (e.g., good performance leads to more positive attitudes that influence the next team interaction). Additionally, it does not require linear relationships between components; which means it allows for moderators on all paths, as teams exist in specific contexts and are often embedded within multiple systems.

It is important to note that task accomplishment does not always occur in a single IMOI cycle, in the way that the example above may suggest. Rather, team performance consists of multiple tasks, in which teams engage in a series of IMOI episodes and subepisodes to achieve their objectives (Marks et al., 2001). For instance, mission analysis (i.e., a teamwork process) has outputs that re-inform inputs and subsequent processes such as strategy formulation, which has additional outputs that re-inform subsequent performance, and so on. There are multiple phases of teamwork involved in completing a single task, and multiple tasks involved in achieving an overall goal. This makes it critical to consider temporal aspects to gain the most understanding of team performance. This also means that teams engaged in multiple tasks can be in different phases of each task, adding complexity to understanding the requirements of each objective. Although team member responsibilities vary as they pertain to taskwork, being proficient in teamwork skills is beneficial across all tasks and phases. Regardless of the number of tasks and their relative characteristics, teamwork is the key mechanism that drives performance and leads to their accomplishment.

Guided by the IMOI framework (Ilgen et al., 2005), we begin to untangle the various components of teamwork by first considering its inputs. Next, we discuss the mediators that transmit inputs to outcomes—the behavioral processes and emergent psychological states that interact and influence teamwork. Following mediators, we review some of the common attitudes, behaviors, and cognitions that serve as outcomes of teamwork, followed by how these outputs re-inform inputs of subsequent team performance. Finally, we identify organizational and situational factors that can potentially influence relationships in the model. Figure 1 summarizes these topics and their complex relationships.

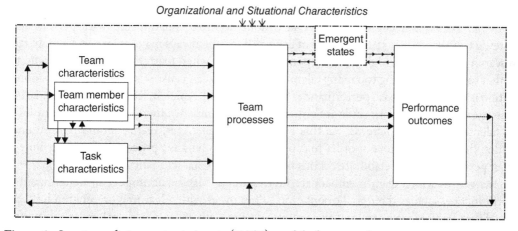

Figure 1. Inputs-mediators-outputs-inputs (IMOI) model of team performance.
Note: The gray box represents the context in which teams operate. Inputs (i.e., team, team member, and task characteristics) lead to outputs (i.e., performance outcomes) both directly (via the dotted line) and indirectly through mediators (i.e., team processes and emergent states). The dashed border around emergent states represents their special properties that allow them to also act as contextual variables. Outputs then lead back to re-inform inputs. The arrow leading from outputs to team processes allows for multiple subepisodes of performance in the completion of a single task.

Inputs. Inputs set the stage for a team interaction. Each member in a team brings a unique set of attributes and perceptions that influences team performance. The combination of their respective attributes also impacts performance. In general, inputs come from three sources: (a) individual team member characteristics, (b) team characteristics, and (c) perceived task characteristics. At the most basic level, a team is a collection of individuals—all team-level phenomena begin with the individual. Therefore, we examine factors from each of these sources while acknowledging that they all originate from, and would not be as such without, individual members. Some researchers consider organizational-level factors as inputs to the teamwork process, as well; but this does not meet the conceptualization in this article. We specify organizational and situational factors in a later segment (see "Contextual Moderators") in which we distinguish them as components of the context in which teams operate, rather than as direct influencers or antecedents[2] of teamwork. In general, a factor's specification in an IMOI model of teamwork depends on the theoretical rationale and the specific objectives of a researcher. Here, we present factors that serve as direct inputs to the teamwork process and have the potential to shape team outcomes.

Member Characteristics. Team member characteristics exist prior to team interaction, and continue to exude influence on performance throughout the life of the team (Ilgen et al., 2005). Some schools of thought (see Steiner, 1972) focus on the unique set of attributes that each member brings to team interactions. The contributions of each individual are thought to create a pool of team resources available for work needs (Guzzo & Shea, 1992). This can include their general task knowledge and skills, general abilities, personality traits, attitudes, motivations, and other individual-difference characteristics. Each member's characteristics can impact the manner in which a team interacts and performs as a whole.

First and foremost, general abilities and task skills are important in any work situation. For a team to be capable of accomplishing tasks, individual members must be competent. Talented team members will inherently contribute the most to performance outputs (Aguinis & O'Boyle, 2014), and cognitive ability also holds a strong relationship with performance (Stewart, 2006); but as stated, a team of experts does not always make an expert team. In fact, research shows that in highly interdependent contexts when team members must come together to succeed, having too many talented performers can cause status conflicts and coordination issues that decrease performance (Swaab, Schaerer, Anicich, Ronay, & Galinsky, 2014). This means that teamwork skills are critical as interdependence increases, and as the number of talented members increase. As this evidence demonstrates, teams should be examined within their social context in order to capture the microdynamic processes that contribute to their performance. We elaborate on this issue in "Team Characteristics."

The way in which team members are motivated can also be an important determinant of performance, such as their goal orientation.[3] Employees with a learning orientation hold the belief that abilities can be trained and improved upon with effort, whereas those with a performance orientation believe ability is fixed. A number of research findings suggest that because team members with high learning-orientation are motivated to master tasks, they may exert more effort to improve than performance-oriented members and approach behavioral processes in such a manner (e.g., Bell & Kozlowski, 2002; Phillips & Gully, 1997; Porter, 2005). This could mean that individuals with certain characteristics may be better suited for teamworking.

Team members with certain attitudes may also perform better than others on teams. Research findings show that employees with a general preference or positive attitude toward working in groups not only have higher job satisfaction, but also exhibit higher performance than their counterparts (Campion, Medsker, & Higgs, 1993; Driskell & Salas, 1992). This attitude is referred to as a collective orientation. As members interact and over time, a team-level feeling of collective orientation specific to the current group also emerges, along with other affective- and cognitive-based psychological states. We discuss these later, in "Emergent States," but it is important to note that these team-level factors have the potential to influence inputs and subsequent performance once they emerge. For this reason, emergent states are often conceptualized as inputs in team performance models. Individual-level attitudes are distinct, as they exist prior to team interaction and after a team adjourns.

An interesting viewpoint is that a characteristic of a single team member can have great influence on team-level performance. Bell (2007) found cursory evidence that a team's minimum agreeableness level (i.e., measured by the team member with the lowest agreeableness score) may predict low performance. This implies that the trait of a single member can be powerful enough to impact the whole team. Some trait-level inputs may be particularly important in the initial stages of a team's life-cycle, before members form their identity within the team. For example, extraverted teammates emerge early as influencers; while conscientiousness, emotional stability, and openness to experience gradually increase in importance as the team matures (Deuling, Denissen, van Zalk, Meeus, & van Aken, 2011). This means that extraverted members likely play a large role in shaping factors that emerge in the early stages of a team's life, like performance norms, although these may not stick, as teammates with other traits gain influence over time.

Team Characteristics. In addition to examining individual inputs to teamwork, performance is also influenced by team-level inputs. Some team-level characteristics are inherent to the structure of the team, such as group size, member distribution, communication structure, or level of task interdependence (Wildman et al., 2012). Other characteristics are inherent to differences at the team level, such as (a) homogeneity and diversity in cultures, (b) microdynamics (i.e., individual-level dynamics), (c) changes in team membership, (d) individual personalities, and (e) skill sets.

Research on member homogeneity explores how individuals of various degrees of (dis) similarity interact in teams. In other words, this research gives insight to how teams are affected by diversity. Team members can be diverse in in race, ethnicity, age, and other demographic factors (i.e., surface-level diversity), or in personality, experiences, values, and psychological factors (i.e., deep-level diversity; Bell, Villado, Lukasik, Belau, & Briggs, 2011; Harrison, Price, & Bell, 1998). In any social situation, differences between people and their perspectives have the potential to create conflict. For instance, demographic diversity can be a detriment to cooperation; but research shows that over time, this effect diminishes in strength (Chatman & Flynn, 2001). This conclusion was echoed by findings exhibiting a negative impact of surface-level diversity on social integration (and subsequent performance) that diminished with each team interaction (Harrison, Price, Gavin, & Florey, 2002). In summary, evidence shows that teams may take an early hit from surface-level diversity, but the effects are short-lived, demonstrating the importance of time consideration in team diversity research.

On the other hand, Harrison and colleagues (2002) found that deep-level diversity (e.g., from clashing perspectives or cultural values) can cause negative effects that get *stronger* over time. This is a problem because organizations rely on diversity to garner competitive advantage. Like a diversified investment portfolio, a diverse team has a variety of perspectives and resources to manage risk and perform effectively. Unfortunately, diversity research shows just as many negative effects as positive effects on performance (van Knippenberg & Schippers, 2007). In an effort to leverage performance benefits and avoid conflict from diversity, researchers investigated the effectiveness of multicultural teams and advanced seven guidelines: (a) build cohesion with leadership, (b) communicate clearly and meaningfully, (c) take one another's perspective, (d) engage in supportive behaviors, (e) emphasize psychological safety, (f) negotiate compromises, and (g) learn together as a team (Burke, Shuffler, Salas, & Gelfand, 2010). Additionally, Ely and Thomas (2001) suggest that teams can maximize the benefits of diversity by fully embracing the integration of diverse perspectives, beyond the purpose of avoiding unfairness and discrimination. Adhering to these practical recommendations can help diverse teams avoid performance losses and increase effectiveness.

Other research looks at more specific forms of diversity, such as functional diversity (i.e., differences in work expertise). Bunderson and Sutcliffe (2002) examined management teams to find that information-sharing and subsequent team performance increased as the breadth of their combined prior experiences increased. In other words, teams composed of members who each have a wide range of work experience may perform better than a team of specialists. Being experienced in a range of job functions (such as in a job-rotation program) may help team members understand each other's roles and responsibilities. This speaks to the above recommendations of Burke and colleagues (2010), which encourage perspective-taking to improve the effectiveness of diverse teams.

Researchers have also begun to recognize the importance of studying individual-level dynamics to understand team-level phenomena (e.g., Guillaume, Brodbeck, & Riketta, 2012; van Dijk & van Engen, 2013). Borrowing from social psychology, organizational researchers examine individuals interacting in teams and how performance can be affected by their social dynamics (e.g., by self-categorizing and stereotyping oneself and others). This field of research pushes for multilevel models of team performance that incorporate time, and theories that emphasize the social dynamics of team interactions (e.g., theories of social exchange, social comparison, social networks; see Humphrey & Aime, 2014). For instance, research of this type revealed that teams are more creative when certain leadership behaviors (i.e., power expressions) shift among team members as the situation demands different resources (Aime, Humphrey, DeRue, & Paul, 2014). These examples are findings that could not have otherwise been uncovered without considering the social environment and relationships among team members.

Another area of interest in team composition research concerns changes in the team roster. Team membership changes can occur for a variety of reasons, such as turnover, organizational restructuring, promotions, or for the general needs of the team. When members depart, those who remain must adapt to the loss of the unique knowledge and skills that are no longer available, often while incorporating replacement members. Dynamic team membership is a natural and unavoidable obstacle that must be managed. Adding new members and removing or replacing current members is disruptive to teamwork processes and performance outcomes

(Arrow & McGrath, 1993). This becomes especially salient as exchanged members increase in cognitive ability and role centrality (i.e., the degree to which responsibilities are critical to team tasks; Summers, Humphrey, & Ferris, 2012). Research demonstrates that teams can mal-adapt their cognitive systems after membership changes, resulting in more errors in knowledge-sharing and performance (Lewis, Belliveau, Herndon, & Keller, 2007).

Teams might be able to lessen the negative impact of losing a central member by considering newcomer cognitive ability. Team members who play the most critical roles in completing interdependent tasks hold the most social connections and therefore, have access to the largest knowledge bank (Ellis, Bell, Ployhart, Hollenbeck, & Ilgen, 2005). Summers and colleagues (2012) found that replacement members with high cognitive ability are able to effectively assume their roles with minimal disruption to team coordination, while those with moderate cognitive ability experienced the greatest amount of fluctuation.[4] Although most research focuses on reducing the potential negative impact of membership change, a different perspective reveals that managing change can be an asset that aids teams in adjusting to the dynamic demands of their environment (e.g., Bedwell, Ramsay, & Salas, 2012; Ramos-Villagrasa, Navarro, & García-Izquierdo, 2012) or by enhancing creativity (e.g., Choi & Thompson, 2005).

The way in which a team-level variable is operationalized (e.g., average score, minimum score, maximum score) impacts its interpretation. Examining personality at the team level has been a long-standing topic of debate among researchers, due to the lack of clarity in theoretical rationale and conceptual meaning of such variables. Nevertheless, researchers have been able to find meaningful differences in team-level measures of personality that predict performance. Meta-analytic evidence of real-world teams (i.e., field studies) shows that aggregated conscientiousness, openness to experience, and collectivism may be especially important to predicting team performance (Bell, 2007). Examining a more granular level of performance, Barry and Stewart (1997) found that team conscientiousness is particularly important for planning tasks, whereas team extraversion has a strong relationship with decision-making tasks. Team-level openness to experience and emotional stability may also aid teams in approaching conflict and leveraging its performance benefits (Bradley, Klotz, Postlethwaite, & Brown, 2013). This research demonstrates that personality compositions are capable of predicting team performance outcomes, but researchers should be advised that the practical value of findings rests largely in the meaning dictated by operationalization.

Historically, configuring optimal team size has been of interest to researchers. Understaffing can lead to process-loss due to overloaded team members, but overstaffing can lead to redundancies and problems with coordination. Stewart (2006) found cursory evidence that teams with ill-defined tasks (e.g., those based on tacit knowledge and skills) may benefit from a large group size, whereas others (e.g., production teams) may be hindered. Large teams have the benefit of large resource pools (e.g., combined expertise, energy); which could be useful for teams that rely on idea-sharing and interpersonal factors, and less useful for teams that rely on routine tasks and product-based performance (Sundstrom, De Meuse, & Futrell, 1990). Guastello (2010) examined emergency-room teams to conclude that teams that are too large may suffer coordination problems, but teams that are not large enough may generate fewer ideas in decision-making tasks. Ultimately, optimal team size depends on the nature of the task, team, objectives, and environment (Kozlowski & Bell, 2003).

We can also examine differences in the team characteristics advanced by Wildman and colleagues (2012) and how they might inform performance (e.g., interdependence, leadership structure, distribution). For example, the level of interdependence required in a team can influence team member relationships and interactions. Greater interdependence requires team members to rely on each other more and necessitates more coordination than teams with less interdependence. Moreover, different types of interdependence have different implications on performance. Teams with high task interdependence rely on task-focused team functioning (i.e., collective efficacy, transition and action processes), whereas high outcome interdependence is more associated with relational team functioning (i.e., interpersonal processes and cohesion; Courtright, Thurgood, Stewart, & Pierotti, 2015).

Leadership structure or hierarchy can also influence team performance. Although leadership is a behavioral teamwork process, the structure and type of leadership have effects on performance distinct from leadership behaviors. Teams can have internal and/or external sources of leadership that can be formal or informal (Morgeson, DeRue, & Karam, 2010). Kirkman and Rosen (1999) found that external leaders can impact team empowerment, which leads to job satisfaction, commitment, and team productivity across a variety of industries. External coaching also helps build shared leadership among team members, and improved performance (Carson, Tesluk, & Marrone, 2007). Meta-analytic evidence considering different types of leadership shows that person-focused leaders (e.g., servant leaders; see van Dierendonck, 2011) engender high levels of team learning and effectiveness, whereas task-focused leaders are only moderately related to team effectiveness (Burke et al., 2006a).

Additionally, whether a team is located in the same work space (i.e., co-located) or geographically distributed can have very different implications on performance, most notably, differences in communication and coordination processes provide unique challenges. For example, Gibson and Gibbs (2006) found that virtual aerospace design teams were less innovative than their co-located counterparts who relied less on electronic-mediated communication. A systematic review of multinational virtual teams found that there are task-related challenges (e.g., knowledge-sharing, establishing expectations) and socioemotional challenges (e.g., building relationships and trust, overcoming biases) to being distributed across the globe (Han & Beyerlein, 2016). Interest in team distribution, or the configuration of geographically distributed team members, has grown with the expansion of global markets and teleworking capabilities. As the workplace follows the greater society's reliance on electronic and social media, structural challenges will become more salient in team communication, roles, and general interactions.

Task Characteristics. The characteristics of a task can also impact team interaction (Campion, Papper, & Medsker, 1996). For example, Stewart (2006) found meta-analytic evidence that teams with more autonomous taskwork have higher performance than those with less autonomy. Furthermore, Langfred (2005) examined manufacturing teams and found that teams with high task interdependence perform well with more team-level autonomy and poorly with high individual-level autonomy. In contrast, high-performing teams with low task interdependence rely more on individual-level autonomy (Langfred, 2005). As this research demonstrates, various inputs (e.g., autonomy and interdependence) discussed here and elsewhere can interact with each other to form different effects on teamwork. This is a testament to the complexity involved in team phenomena and research.

Team member perceptions of task characteristics (e.g., task significance, identity) can also influence performance. Hackman (1987) noted that team members should believe that their task is meaningful and that poor performance will have significant consequences. Moreover, a meta-analysis of 93 studies reveals a modest relationship between task meaningfulness and performance (Stewart, 2006). It is important to realize that teams are often engaged in multiple tasks simultaneously within a given space and time. Perceptions of relative task characteristics often vary as a result of the situation, resulting in significant performance differences. For example, the situation may dictate how meaningful a team perceives each member's task, which would affect the way they prioritize and plan their course of action. Although task characteristics are stable, team member interpretations have the potential to be affected by situational changes. This malleability provides an opportunity for targeted interventions that improve teamwork inputs.

So far, we have discussed the factors that set the stage for team interactions. Although the concepts reviewed are not an exhaustive list, we hope they serve as an insightful introduction to understanding the mechanisms that initiate the complex phenomenon of teamwork. We now shift our discussion to the teamwork phase, where individual members begin to interact as a single unit. As inputs come together and individuals become teams, they must work together to reach performance goals.

Mediators. Mediators of the IMOI model are factors that transmit the effects of inputs to team performance outcomes. Individual, team, and task inputs combine to shape teamwork behavioral processes that explain team-level outcomes. In addition to the behaviors involved, psychological states begin to emerge and evolve as teams interact throughout time (Ilgen et al., 2005).

Team Processes. Recall that team performance consists of taskwork and teamwork behaviors (McIntyre & Salas, 1995). Effective team performance is not only a function of individual member inputs, but also the teamwork behaviors used to interact and work together. Teamwork behaviors are not task-specific, but universal to virtually all teams across industries. One of the most prolific teamwork frameworks, advanced by Marks and colleagues (2001), defines team processes as the behavioral actions performed in achieving shared goals. Team processes are multidimensional, and characterize the nature of team member interaction by the behaviors performed across performance phases. This model of team processes is further validated by meta-analytic evidence (LePine, Piccolo, Jackson, Mathieu, & Saul, 2008) demonstrating that team processes load onto three higher-order factors: (a) transition processes, (b) action processes, and (c) interpersonal processes. The processes within each factor are distinct, but effective team performance depends on their combined effects; therefore, most research considers some aspect of all three processes.

In transition phases of task performance, teams prepare for upcoming tasks and plan their courses of action. The three transition processes advanced by Marks and colleagues (2001) are mission analysis, goal specification, and strategy formulation. Transition processes are rarely examined on their own, as action processes are more proximal to performance outcomes;

but Mathieu and Schulze (2006) report a positive relationship between formal planning and team performance. Formal planning also provides a framework for dynamic planning, or planning mid-task for contingencies or in reaction to an issue (Mathieu & Schulze, 2006). Taking the time to strategize both teamwork and taskwork in the initial stages of performance can improve team effectiveness over time (Mathieu & Rapp, 2009). Transition processes may also play an important role in explaining the negative relationship between team resistance climate and customer satisfaction, as teams may set less goals or develop more ineffective strategies (Maynard, Mathieu, Marsh, & Ruddy, 2007).

Action processes are more directly related to goal attainment, such as coordinating team members and taskwork, and monitoring the team, systems, and goal progress. Maynard and colleagues (2007) found supporting evidence for the positive relationship between action processes and quantitative performance outcomes. Coordination involves the timing and sequencing of integrated efforts, and plays an important role in strategizing and managing problem situations (Tesluk & Mathieu, 1999). Team monitoring involves paying attention to team members' statuses and stepping in to help when needed (i.e., backup behavior). Backup behavior has a positive relationship with task performance (Porter, Hollenbeck, Ilgen, Ellis, West, & Moon, 2003) and fully mediates the relationship between shared mental models and team performance outcomes (Marks, Sabella, Burke, & Zaccaro, 2002). Backup behaviors can also lead to better decision-making (Porter, 2005).

While transition and action processes are definitionally bound to initial and later phases of task performance (respectively), interpersonal teamwork processes occur throughout performance episodes. Interpersonal teamwork processes include managing conflict, managing affect, and motivating the team. Meta-analytic evidence shows that interpersonal processes are important to increasing performance in ongoing teams who engage in long-term tasks (Bradley, White, & Mennecke, 2003). Managing conflict is extremely important, as relationship and task conflict are detrimental to team performance and satisfaction (De Dreu & Weingart, 2003). Conflict is bound to occur when team members with different perspectives interact, and this is likely intensified as diversity increases. Jehn, Northcraft, and Neale (1999) found that informational diversity leads to task conflict, but also increased performance, indicating the potential importance of conflict management in boosting performance. Teammates can also be motivated by getting feedback from one another, which leads to trust and performance in virtual teams (Geister, Konradt, & Hertel, 2006).

Emergent States. As team members begin interacting, psychological states begin to form behind the scenes. These emergent states are shaped by team member behaviors, thoughts, and feelings that arise from their experiences (Kozlowski & Klein, 2000). Marks and colleagues (2001) note that emergent states "represent member attitudes, values, cognitions, and motivations," making them distinct from process variables (p. 357). With each team interaction and throughout time, experiences compile to form new information that updates emergent states (Burke, Stagl, Salas, Pierce, & Kendall, 2006b). Although first emerging in the initial stages of team interaction, they continue to be revised with each performance cycle, varying as a function of inputs, mediators, outputs, and context (Ilgen et al., 2005; Marks et al., 2001). Emergent states can be (a) affect-based or (b) cognition-based.

In a sense, emergent states can be thought of as contextual matter that the team creates and shapes. Once they emerge, they become part of the environment in which teams operate. Like contextual variables, they can intervene with the performance process at various stages; but their dynamism distinguishes them from typical contextual variables, because they continually update as teams perform. They are not only outcomes of team interaction, but inputs to subsequent interactions and performance outcomes. This can make it difficult to place emergent states appropriately in research models. For instance, a team with low trust (i.e., an emergent state) may not coordinate their tasking well (i.e., a process) which could result in process losses that further reduce their trust in one another. In this example, a state that emerges from team interaction (i.e., trust) influenced and was subsequently influenced by a teamwork process (i.e., coordination). Ultimately, model specification decisions depend on the research objective and theoretical rationale.

Emergent states based on affect reflect the shared feelings and attitudes that form as team members interact with one another. One of the most important affect-based emergent states is collective efficacy, or the shared belief that the team is capable and will be successful at achieving goals. As teammates become familiar with each other's expertise and abilities pertaining to taskwork and teamwork, they begin to form a shared attitude of whether or not they are capable of performing successfully. Meta-analytic evidence shows that collective efficacy has a positive relationship with team performance (Gully, Incalcaterra, Joshi, & Beaubien, 2002), and other research shows that it becomes more important as interdependence decreases (Katz-Navon & Erez, 2005). To yield the most effective performance, teammates need to believe that they can and will be successful. This finding suggests that less-interdependent teams may require even more confidence to achieve performance goals.

Trust is also an important factor in team performance (Jones & George, 1998; Kirkman, Rosen, Tesluk, & Gibson, 2004). Intrateam trust involves a willingness to be vulnerable. Teams with low trust often exhibit avoidance behaviors and detrimental team processes that protect against vulnerability (Mayer & Gavin, 2005). Related to feelings of trust, team psychological safety emerges as a shared feeling of interpersonal security and positive intentions of fellow teammates (e.g., members are not punished or embarrassed for speaking their minds or asking questions; Edmondson, 1999). Meta-analytic findings exhibit the importance of psychological safety in improving engagement, commitment, team learning, organizational citizenship behaviors, and performance outcomes (Frazier, Fainschmidt, Klinger, Pezeshkan, & Vracheva, 2017). Gibson and Gibbs (2006) found that a lack of psychological safety can lead to poor innovation in virtual teams. This means that virtual teams may encounter challenges particular to their context that hinder free expression. This becomes especially important in organizations that employ distributed teams, a practice that occurs frequently as businesses globalize their operations.

Another affect-based emergent state is team cohesion, or a team's pride and commitment to the team and its goals. Cohesive teams have members who genuinely like working together and being a part of the team. Meta-analytic evidence shows that cohesion is highly correlated with team performance and efficiency (Beal, Cohen, Burke, & McLendon, 2003). Cohesive teams are also likely to have a collective orientation. Team collective orientation is a shared preference for working in a team (Salas, Guthrie, Wilson-Donnelly, Priest, & Burke, 2005). These teams have members that put team needs above their own, participate in strategizing, and seek feedback from teammates to improve performance (Driskell & Salas, 1992).

Each team interaction influences these shared attitudes toward working together, and these shared attitudes continue to exist and affect future performance. The emergent states discussed in this section are certainly not the only ones that exist. Any attitude or cognition that emerges at the team level as a result of team interaction can be considered an emergent state. We continue with an overview of cognition-based emergent states.

Team-level cognitive states emerge as teammates form shared and interconnected knowledge and perceptions (Salas & Fiore, 2004). The most commonly studied cognition-based emergent states are shared mental models (SMMs). SMMs refer to the structure and content of knowledge regarding how teams should interact in reference to tasks, strategies, goals, problem-solving, norms, roles, and any other decision-making circumstance (Salas, Sims, & Burke, 2005). Team SMMs should be universally similar in both content (i.e., accurate knowledge) and structure (i.e., connections between factors, ordered steps in a process) to allow for implicit coordination and avoid errors. Teams with high-quality SMMs exhibit better team processes and performance outcomes than those with less-shared, low-quality mental models (Mathieu, Heffner, Goodwin, Cannon-Bowers, & Salas, 2005). Meta-analytic evidence reveals the importance of both knowledge content and structure of SMMs in predicting team performance outcomes (DeChurch & Mesmer-Magnus, 2010).

Another cognition-based emergent state is a team's transactive memory system (TMS). A TMS is the embedded structure and process through which groups learn, store, retrieve, and communicate knowledge (Hollingshead, 2001; Wegner, 1987). An efficient TMS gives team members quick access to one another's specialized knowledge and expertise, improving task performance by allowing members to leverage and integrate disparate knowledge in a coordinated, knowledge-intensive effort. Teams with a high-quality TMS exhibit high goal-performance and group effectiveness (Austin, 2003).

Team situation awareness is another cognitive state that emerges from team interaction. Situation awareness is defined as perceiving and comprehending environmental factors and their effects, as well as their potential meanings for future status (Endsley, 1988, 1995). Situation awareness requires much more than simply being aware of the immediate environment. It incorporates aspects of concentration, attention, anticipation, and resistance to distractions (Endsley, 1988). At the team level, situation awareness emerges as the shared understanding of the situation from the combined perceptions of each member (Salas, Prince, Baker, & Shrestha, 1995). Teams high in situation awareness perceive environmental cues and make similar attributions to their meanings; but those low in situation awareness may have some members perceive a cue as critical while others disagree. Burke and colleagues (2006b) posit that team situation awareness is a critical factor facilitating teams in adapting to environmental cues and challenges. Their proposed model depicts team adaptation as a process that results in emergent states that continue to influence subsequent phases of the process. To advance the most informative theories, future models of team performance should follow this precedent in capturing the temporal aspects and dynamic nature of team performance (see also Marks et al., 2001).

Outputs. At this point, we have mentioned various teamwork findings without emphasis on particular performance outcomes. The following section is intended to outline the criterion space of teamwork by discussing a range of common outputs. Outputs are the products of team activity that are considered valuable to stakeholders (e.g., managers, employees, customers; Rousseau, Aubé, & Savoie, 2006), and are used to evaluate team effectiveness. As mentioned in previous sections, classifying a construct as an "output" depends on the theoretical model being specified. In general, we can conceptualize the outcomes of teamwork as (a) attitudes, (b) behaviors, or (c) cognitions. It is important to remember that "effectiveness" must be defined before determining how performance should be assessed. After the purpose of the team and characterizations of "effectiveness" are made clear, it can be decided which attitudes, behaviors, and cognitions might indicate such performance.

Affect-related outcomes (i.e., job attitudes) can be assessed to uncover team member feelings resulting from team interaction. Stakeholders can often avoid costly turnover expenses and counterproductive behaviors by maintaining happy, committed employees with positive attitudes. Team members should also have the right attitude toward teamwork and be willing to cooperate and learn with one another. Attitudes can be assessed at the individual level, or at the team level (i.e., emergent states). Some of the most common outcomes of interest in team studies are satisfaction and commitment. Measuring attitudes is important because it can give insight to the internal processes of team members that are not readily observable. Because attitudes are unobservable, they are typically measured with self-report rating scales (Marshall, Bisbey, & Salas, 2015). Although subjective measurements are susceptible to biases, self-reported tools are acceptable for measuring team member attitudes because they are more proximal to the source than observer measures.

On the contrary, team member behaviors are observable sources of performance evaluation. Behavioral performance measures are of particular interest because they reflect what employees actually "do" or the tangible, observable outcomes. The specific behaviors that might indicate performance depend on the type of team and the nature of its mission. For instance, team performance quality or quantity might be assessed using time-on-task or the frequency of errors. Other behaviors commonly used to indicate team effectiveness involve decision-making and team leadership. Team member behaviors can be assessed using rating scales, checklists, frequency scales, event-based scales, and automated tools; and evaluators can be internal (e.g., supervisors, teammates) or external (e.g., subject-matter experts, consultants, researchers; Marshall et al., 2015).

Cognitive performance outcomes can be assessed to give insight to the thoughts, perceptions, and knowledge resulting from team performance (Salas, Rosen, Burke, Nicholson, & Howse, 2007). Like team-level attitudes, team-level cognitions are also considered emergent states (e.g., SMMs, TMSs). One cognitive outcome of common interest in team studies is team learning. Teams learn from their experiences in each performance episode, but learning is also important in studies of training intervention effectiveness. Like attitudes, cognitions are commonly assessed using self-report tools (Wildman, Salas, & Scott, 2014) although, because cognitive constructs are more abstract, their measures can be more complex. Some tools for assessing cognitive performance are rating scales, concept mapping, social networking methods, and probed protocol analysis (Marshall et al., 2015).

Teamwork as a Recursive Process. The final path in the IMOI framework involves outputs circling back to impact inputs. Outputs are unique because they have the potential to influence, and to be influenced by, teamwork. Some research conceptualizes this as a feedback loop, in which feedback from teamwork outputs re-informs subsequent inputs (e.g., Burke et al., 2006b). This process is crucial to understanding the dynamic nature of team performance. After performing a task, teams often develop new knowledge and skills that impact their future performance, as well as new norms and patterns of behavior (e.g., new communication patterns or strategies). As emphasized earlier in this section, team learning is an output of the teamwork process. The simple act of performing can result in a new way of doing things, and this is further augmented by receiving feedback and reflecting on performance. An important aspect of team dynamics is that every team action impacts future performance. At its core, team performance is an iterative process of learning and adapting.

Contextual Moderators. As emphasized by the research reviewed so far, teamwork is a complex phenomenon. It is important to remember that teams do not operate within a vacuum—they are often embedded in a larger system, and interact across other teams and organizations. This is especially relevant as shifting global markets and advancing technology interfere with team functioning. Researchers should consider instances in which their theorized relationships may not transpire as expected. Contextual moderators to teamwork are factors that have the potential to alter IMOI relationships at various stages in the model. These are the relatively stable, organizational, and situational characteristics that shape the environmental landscape in which teams operate (e.g., reward systems, culture, intergroup relations).

One contributing factor to teamwork relationships is the organization's reward system. Organizations use rewards (e.g., bonuses, opportunities) to motivate employees, and being rewarded or not rewarded for an action plays a large part in explaining employee behavior (see Kerr, 1995). For instance, competitive teams that switch to a cooperative reward structure share less information and make more rash, inaccurate decisions than teams switching from a cooperative to competitive structure (Johnson et al., 2006). Relatedly, human resource policies can affect team processes by signaling to employees the goals they should have and the actions that are encouraged. Mathieu, Gilson, and Ruddy (2006) observed service technician teams and found that having team-based policies empowers employees and relates positively to performance and customer satisfaction. These findings demonstrate the important role of organizational support in team performance.

Organizational cultures and norms can also affect the way in which teams interact. Interestingly, research shows that teamwork in top management teams trickles down to employee teams even when they are not experienced first-hand (Raes, Bruch, & De Jong, 2013). This research found that leaders who help one another and engage in joint decision-making have more satisfied employees who resist turnover (Raes et al., 2013). Similarly, research on supermarket department teams shows that leaders who value service quality foster a service climate, which results in customer-focused citizenship behaviors, customer satisfaction, and unit sales (Schneider, Ehrhart, Mayer, Saltz, & Niles-Jolly 2005). These findings demonstrate that team context can influence both internal and external effectiveness. It is important to consider how the signals sent by organizational leaders, climate, or culture in general are received by teams and influence their interactions.

Examining teams across national cultures can also uncover interesting findings. Sosik and Jung (2002) found that teams from individualistic societies (e.g., the United States) were more confident in their team's ability to succeed than those from collectivistic societies (e.g., Korea), and this transferred to their performance, with U.S. teams outperforming Korean teams. Likewise, Gibson (2003) found that nursing teams in Indonesia provided higher service quality than those in America because of the way the Indonesian organization focused on quality improvement. To develop team theories that are generalizable across cultures, researchers must demonstrate external validity by replicating their findings in various settings.

Teamwork relationships can also be affected by uncertainty in the environment. Uncertainty is a key factor in employee perceptions of justice and trust (see Colquitt and Zipay [2015], and De Jong and Elfring [2010]). There are many organizational and situational sources of uncertainty, such as resource availability, customer demand flux, new technological advancements, market competition, and other environmental factors that may be unfamiliar or unpredictable. Atuahene-Gima and Li (2004) examined product development teams and found that technology uncertainty (e.g., from many rapid changes) hinders the effectiveness of strategic decision-making and product performance. On the other hand, providing stability may provide situational strength that allows team performance to be more predictable. Keck (1997) found that environmental stability strengthens the effect of composition variables on teamwork. Researchers should consider how sources of uncertainty and stability might affect team performance when theorizing teamwork models.

It is also important to account for intergroup relations within and across settings. In many instances, multiple teams are dependent upon one another to achieve their goals and higher-order shared goals (Mathieu, Marks, Zaccaro, 2001). These multi-team systems (MTSs) necessitate another layer of cooperation and teamwork processes for successful performance. As teams in an MTS become more interdependent, cross-team action processes (e.g., coordinating, monitoring) become more important than within-team processes (Marks, DeChurch, Mathieu, Panzer, & Alonso, 2005). This means that examining only a single team within an MTS may provide an incomplete explanation of performance outcomes. Researchers should account for a team's boundaries and how it operates within and across them.

IMPROVING PRACTICE

The IMOI model of team performance illustrates the complexity involved in team dynamics and processes. This may leave a reader feeling discouraged as to how we can accurately predict and improve team performance when there are so many factors to consider. Although there seems to be a multitude of moving parts, note that teamwork is the constant that is central to effective team performance; but structuring workers in teams does not produce teamwork automatically. Rather than occurring naturally, effective teamwork requires proper skills and constant grooming in order to be mastered. In this section, we discuss the evidence-based tools that practitioners can leverage to improve teamwork and team performance outcomes.

Interventions. Team members do not inherently adopt teamwork KSAs by being positioned in a team. Practitioners should ensure that all members are trained for teamwork just as much as they are trained for technical job duties. Team training refers to a systematic learning initiative to build teamwork KSAs (Salas et al., 2008). This might occur through individual-level or team-level interventions, though research suggests that teams trained together may exhibit more efficient TMSs and greater performance outcomes (Moreland, Argote, & Krishnan, 2002). Practitioners can also embed teamwork concepts in the instructional content of a training by utilizing simulations. Simulations (e.g., technology-based games, or role-playing exercises) are engaging, can facilitate transfer, and accelerate team expertise.

Research shows that the teamwork skills garnered through team training impact team-level attitudes, behaviors, and cognitions involved in effective performance (Salas et al., 2008). These findings were validated and expanded upon in an extensive meta-analysis by Hughes and colleagues (2016) who found support for the causal sequence of team training leading to learned teamwork KSAs, which then transfer to on-the-job performance, and then result in improved team performance outcomes. Furthermore, this research uncovered evidence that healthcare team training not only improves task and teamwork performance, but also reduces medical errors and patient mortality (Hughes et al., 2016)—a groundbreaking finding. By and large, team training interventions are effective, can influence bottom-line outcomes, and can even save lives (see Bisbey, Reyes, Traylor, & Salas, 2019 for a historical review of team training).

Another type of intervention shown to improve teamwork and team performance is cross-training, such as in a job-rotation program. This involves team members learning about or assuming the responsibilities of fellow teammates in order to gain a better understanding of the roles involved in shared tasks. Knowledge of fellow teammates' roles may build appreciation for each other's effort and reduce potential conflict resulting from diverse opinions. Learning more about and taking on one another's perspective can aid the effectiveness of diverse teams (Burke et al., 2010), and might also help team members anticipate and recognize when someone needs backup. Although these interventions have the potential to build both teamwork and taskwork expertise, greater performance outcomes may be realized if taskwork cross-training is followed by a greater emphasis on cross-training for teamwork KSAs. Cooke and colleagues (2003) note that teamwork knowledge cannot fully develop without taskwork knowledge and experience; therefore, premature attempts to cross-train may prove counterproductive to improving teamwork. Because cross-training initiatives can be costly, they should be strategically planned to ensure the highest performance benefit.

Distinct from team training is team building. Whereas team training is focused on systematically teaching teamwork KSAs, team building is less methodical and focuses more on the social relationships among teammates. Team building does not train employees to perform taskwork together as a team, but serves to improve less-specific outcomes like morale and cohesion, or to decrease conflict and tension. Meta-analytic findings suggest that team-building initiatives may be especially helpful to clarify roles and set goals, particularly in larger teams (Klein et al., 2009). Depending on the objectives of an organization, a combination of team training and team-building initiatives may be most effective in improving team performance. In general, research suggests that team building may be more effective at enhancing attitudes and perceptions, and less consistent in improving behavioral performance (Tannenbaum, Beard, & Salas, 1992).

Measuring Teamwork.   Regularly administered performance assessments (e.g., annual reviews) set clear expectations for taskwork, and allow employees to review and revise their performance repertoires. Similarly, regular and consistent measurement can also improve teamwork performance. Teamwork measures can reveal training needs, issues with inputs (e.g., composition, team structure), and opportunities for developmental feedback (Smith-Jentsch, Sierra, & Weise, 2013). For instance, feedback can be delivered via debriefing sessions following a performance episode. Debriefing aids teams by confronting the strategies that worked and the ones that can be improved. Meta-analytic evidence shows that debriefing can improve performance by 25% (Tannenbaum & Cerasoli, 2013). Feedback helps employees recognize performance deficiencies and adopt more effective strategies, facilitating outputs in re-informing the inputs of subsequent team performance.

Moreover, regularly collecting and documenting team performance data will create a rich database that can be used to inform training needs, decision-making, and human resource management. For instance, a downward trend of customer satisfaction in the 6 months following a restructuring of leadership might coincide with a decrease in team coordination. With this information, managers can make an informed decision about training for coordination before making a second attempt to reorganize the leadership structure. Consistent measurement of teamwork provides a baseline to compare future measurements against, and allows a level of detail that otherwise would not be recognized in single time-point. Giving team performance consistent attention and a central role in decision-making processes can signal to employees the values held by top management. It shows a commitment to improve teamwork and performance, and conveys the importance of team functioning to a company's mission. This leads to our final recommendation.

Encouraging Teamwork. Practitioners should take all measures to encourage an organizational culture that values teamwork and create conditions that allow it to be sustainable. Teams that feel supported by their organization show high levels of team performance (Howes, Cropanzano, Grandey, & Mohler, 2000). One effective strategy might be holding pre-performance meetings that motivate team members and outline performance expectations. These efforts will foster collaboration and express management's commitment to team success. Encouraging teamwork can also enhance employee attitudes toward working in teams. Team members who hold a positive attitude toward teamwork are more satisfied and show higher levels of performance than those who prefer to work individually (Campion et al., 1993; Driskell & Salas, 1992). A company that builds a culture that encourages teamworking may foster employees that adopt positive attitudes about working together.

The key to creating a sustainable culture lies in the policies and procedures of an organization, such as the reward system. A single training event can be effective at influencing teamwork, but policies are lasting and continually reinforce teamwork values. In the workplace and elsewhere, individuals are encouraged by the rewards that they receive. Managers should ensure that reward systems recognize teamwork by adopting benefits based on team output rather than individual performance. Basing rewards on individual performance can foster a culture of competition and harm intragroup relations, which directly contradicts efforts to encourage cooperative teamwork. Practitioners should consider the message sent by company policies and make changes that reflect values of cooperation and synergistic team performance.

CONCLUSION

This review takes a broad perspective in outlining the foundation of team dynamics and performance processes in the workplace. Teamwork is a complex phenomenon with many moving parts (see Mathieu, Gallagher, Domingo, & Klock, 2019). Using an IMOI framework, we reviewed and summarized key empirical findings and integrated evidence for various inputs, mediators, and outputs of team performance. We present this information in Table 1 alongside key sources for more information on each topic. Additionally, we have suggested several actionable recommendations that would be of use to practitioners interested in improving teamwork with evidence-based methods. Teamwork is essential to effective performance in virtually all organizations. We hope this article provides a useful and informative introduction to the content area of team dynamics and processes in organizations.

850 • TEAM DYNAMICS AND PROCESSES IN THE WORKPLACE

Table 1. Summary of Inputs, Mediators, and Outputs of Teamwork

Component	Definition	Key Readings
Inputs		
Member Characteristics	Attributes each member contributes to the pool of team resources, including knowledge, skills, abilities, personality traits, attitudes, motivations, and other individual-difference characteristics	Aguinis & O'Boyle, 2014; Deuling et al., 2011
Team Characteristics	Team-level attributes inherent to the structure of the team or created through composition of member characteristics	Bell et al., 2011; Bell, Brown, Colaneri, & Outland, 2018; Feitosa, Grossman, & Salazar, 2018; Humphrey & Aime, 2014; Mathieu et al., 2014
Member diversity	The degree of (dis)similarity in team members, such as in their surface-level (e.g., race, age) or deep-level traits (e.g., personality, values)	
Microdynamics	Activities, processes, relationships, or other variable phenomena among individual team members	
Membership change	Changes in the team roster occurring when members depart, are replaced, or new members are added	
Personality	The composition of individual-level personality traits	
Team structure	Characteristics inherent to the team, such as its size, member distribution, level of interdependence, or hierarchy	
Task Characteristics	Attributes of team tasks such as type, autonomy, interdependence, significance	Wildman et al., 2012
Mediators		
Team Processes	Multidimensional behavioral actions performed in achieving shared goals	Bush et al., 2018; Killumets, D'Innocenzo, Maynard, & Mathieu, 2015; Kozlowski & Chao, 2018; LePine et al., 2008
Transition processes	Behaviors performed in transition phases of task performance, including mission analysis, goal specification, and strategy formulation	
Action processes	Behaviors performed in action phases of task performance, including coordinating and monitoring performance	
Interpersonal processes	Behavior performed to manage team member attitudes and perceptions, including managing conflict, managing affect, and motivating the team	

Table 1. Continued

Mediators

Emergent States	Psychological states that emerge from team member interactions and are shaped by their behaviors, thoughts, and feelings	Burtscher & Manser, 2012; De Jong et al., 2016; Kozlowski & Chao, 2018; Tannenbaum & Cerasoli, 2013
Affect-based	Shared feelings and attitudes among team members, such as collective efficacy, team trust, and cohesion	
Cognition-based	Shared cognition, knowledge, and perceptions among team members, such as shared mental models, transactive memory, and situation awareness	

Outputs

Performance Outcomes	Products of team activity including attitudes (e.g., satisfaction), behaviors (e.g., leadership), cognition (e.g., team learning), and the goal-based outcomes (e.g., quantity, quality); these re-inform future performance cycles	Allen, Reiter-Palmon, Crowe, & Scott, 2018; Mathieu et al., 2019

FURTHER READING

Allen, J. A., Reiter-Palmon, R., Crowe, J., & Scott, C. (2018). Debriefs: Teams learning from doing in context. *American Psychologist, 73*, 504–516. https://doi.org/10.1037/amp0000246

Bell, S. T., Brown, S. G., Colaneri, A., & Outland, N. (2018). Team composition and the ABCs of teamwork. *American Psychologist, 73*, 349–362. https://doi.org/10.1037/amp0000305

Bell, S. T., Villado, A. J., Lukasik, M. A., Belau, L., & Briggs, A. (2011). Getting specific about demographic diversity variable and team performance relationships: A meta-analysis. *Journal of Management, 37*, 709–743. https://doi.org/10.1177/0149206310365001

Bisbey, T. M., Reyes, D. L., Traylor, A. M., & Salas, E. (2019). Teams of psychologists helping teams: The evolution of the science of team training. *American Psychologist, 74*(3), 278–289. http://dx.doi.org/10.1037/amp0000419

Bush, J. T., LePine, J. A., & Newton, D. W. (2018). Teams in transition: An integrative review and synthesis of research on team task transitions and propositions for future research. *Human Resource Management Review, 28*, 423–433. https://doi.org/10.1016/j.hrmr.2017.06.005

De Jong, B. A., Dirks, K. T., & Gillespie, N. (2016). Trust and team performance: A meta-analysis of main effects, moderators, and covariates. *Journal of Applied Psychology, 101*, 1134–1150. https://doi.org/10.1037/apl0000110

Feitosa, J., Grossman, R., & Salazar, M. (2018). Debunking key assumptions about teams: The role of culture. *American Psychologist, 73*, 376–389. https://doi.org/10.1037/amp0000256

Frazier, M. L., Fainschmidt, S., Klinger, R. L., Pezeshkan, A., & Vracheva, V. (2017). Psychological safety: A meta-analytic review and extension. *Personnel Psychology, 70*, 113–165. https://doi.org/10.1111/peps.12183

Hughes, A. M., Gregory, M. E., Joseph, D. L., Sonesh, S. C., Marlow, S. L., Lacerenza, C. N., . . . Salas, E. (2016). Saving lives: A meta-analysis of team training in healthcare. *Journal of Applied Psychology, 101*, 1266–1304. https://doi.org/10.1037/apl0000120

Humphrey, S. E., & Aime, F. (2014). Team microdynamics: Toward an organizing approach to teamwork. *Academy of Management Annals, 8*, 443–503. https://doi.org/10.1080/19416520.2014.904140

Ilgen, D. R., Hollenbeck, J. R., Johnson, M., & Jundt, D. (2005) Teams in organizations: From input-process-output models to IMOI models. *Annual Review of Psychology, 56*, 517–543. https://doi.org/10.1146/annurev.psych.56.091103.070250

Killumets, E., D'Innocenzo, L., Maynard, M. T., & Mathieu, J. E. (2015). A multilevel examination of the impact of team interpersonal processes. *Small Group Research, 46*, 227–259. https://doi.org/10.1177/1046496415573631

Kozlowski, S. W. J., & Chao, G. T. (2018). Unpacking team process dynamics and emergent phenomena: Challenges, conceptual advances, and innovative methods. *American Psychologist, 73*, 576–592. https://doi.org/10.1037/amp0000245

Mathieu, J. E., Gallagher, P. T., Domingo, M. A., & Klock, E. A. (2019). Embracing complexity: Reviewing the past decade of team effectiveness research. *Annual Review of Organizational Psychology and Organizational Behavior, 6*, 17–46.

Mathieu, J. E., Tannenbaum, S. I., Donsbach, J. S., & Alliger, G. M. (2014). A review and integration of team composition models: Moving toward a dynamic and temporal framework. *Journal of Management, 40*, 130–160. https://doi.org/10.1177/0149206313503014

Salas, E., Rosen, M. A., Burke, C. S., & Goodwin, G. F. (2009). The wisdom of collectives in organizations: An update of the teamwork competencies. In E. Salas, G. Goodwin, & C. S. Burke (Eds.), *Team effectiveness in complex organizations: Cross-disciplinary perspectives and approaches* (pp. 39–79). New York, NY: Taylor & Francis.

Tannenbaum, S. I., & Cerasoli, C. P. (2013). Do team and individual debriefs enhance performance? A meta-analysis. *Human Factors, 55*, 231–245. https://doi.org/10.1177/0018720812448394

REFERENCES

Aguinis, H., & O'Boyle, E. Jr. (2014). Star performers in twenty-first century organizations. *Personnel Psychology, 67*, 313–350. https://doi.org/10.1111/peps.12054

Aime, F., Humphrey, S. E., DeRue, D. S., & Paul, J. (2014). The riddle of heterarchy: Power transitions in cross-functional teams. *Academy of Management Journal, 57*, 327–352. https://doi.org/10.5465/amj.2011.0756

Allen, N. J., & Hecht, T. D. (2004). The "romance of teams": Toward an understanding of its psychological underpinnings and implications. *Journal of Occupational and Organizational Psychology, 77*, 439–461. https://doi.org/10.1348/0963179042596469

Arrow, H., & McGrath, J. E. (1993). Membership matters: How member change and continuity affect small group structure, process, and performance. *Small Group Research, 24*, 334–361. https://doi.org/10.1177/1046496493243004

Atuahene-Gima, K., & Li, H. (2004). Strategic decision comprehensiveness and new product development outcomes in new technology ventures. *Academy of Management Journal, 47*, 583–597. https://doi.org/10.2307/20159603

Austin, J. R. (2003). Transactive memory in organizational groups: The effects of content, consensus, specialization, and accuracy on group performance. *Journal of Applied Psychology, 88*, 866–878. https://doi.org/10.1037/0021-9010.88.5.866

Baker, D. P., Day, R., & Salas, E. (2006). Teamwork as an essential component of high-reliability organizations. *Health Services Research, 41*, 1576–1598. https://doi.org/10.1111/j.1475-6773.2006.00566.x

Barry, B., & Stewart, G. L. (1997). Composition, process, and performance in self-managed groups: The role of personality. *Journal of Applied Psychology, 82*, 62–78. https://doi.org/10.1037/0021-9010.82.1.62

Beal, D. J., Cohen, R. R., Burke, M. J., & McLendon, C. L. (2003). Cohesion and performance in groups: A meta-analytic clarification of construct relations. *Journal of Applied Psychology, 88*, 989–1004. https://doi.org/10.1037/0021-9010.88.6.989

Bedwell, W. L., Ramsay, P. S., & Salas, E. (2012). Helping fluid teams work: A research agenda for effective team adaptation in healthcare. *Translational Behavioral Medicine, 2*, 504–509. https://doi.org/10.1007/s13142-012-0177-9

Bell, S. T. (2007). Deep-level composition variables as predictors of team performance: A meta-analysis. *Journal of Applied Psychology, 92*, 595–615. https://doi.org/10.1037/0021-9010.92.3.595

Bell, B. S., & Kozlowski, S. W. J. (2002). Goal orientation and ability: Interactive effects on self-efficacy, performance, and knowledge. *Journal of Applied Psychology, 87*, 497–505. https://doi.org/10.1037/0021-9010.87.3.497

Bradley, B. H., Klotz, A. C., Postlethwaite, B. E., & Brown, K. G. (2013). Ready to rumble: How team personality composition and task conflict interact to improve performance. *Journal of Applied Psychology, 98*, 385–392.

Bradley, J., White, B. J., & Mennecke, B. E. (2003). Teams and tasks: A temporal framework for the effects of interpersonal interventions on team performance. *Small Group Research, 34*, 353–387. https://doi.org/10.1177/1046496403034003004

Bunderson, J. S., & Sutcliffe, K. M. (2002). Comparing alternative conceptualizations of functional diversity in management teams: Process and performance effects. *Academy of Management Journal, 45*, 875–893.

Burke, C. S., Fiore, S. M., & Salas, E. (2003). The role of shared cognition in enabling shared leadership and team adaptability. In C. L. Pearce & J. A. Conger (Eds.), *Shared leadership: Reframing the hows and whys of leadership* (pp. 103–122). Thousand Oaks, CA: SAGE.

Burke, C. S., Shuffler, M. L., Salas, E., & Gelfand, M. (2010). Multicultural teams: Critical team processes and guidelines. In K. Lundby & J. Jolton (Eds.), *Going global: Practical applications and recommendations for HR and OD professionals in the global workplace* (pp. 46–71). San Francisco, CA: Jossey-Bass.

Burke, C. S., Stagl, K. C., Klein, C., Goodwin, G. F., Salas, E., & Halpin, S. M. (2006a). What type of leadership behaviors are functional in teams? A meta-analysis. *Leadership Quarterly, 17*(3), 288–307.

Burke, C. S., Stagl, K. C., Salas, E., Pierce, L., & Kendall, D. (2006b). Understanding team adaptation: A conceptual analysis and model. *Journal of Applied Psychology, 91*(6), 1189–1207.

Burtscher, M. J., & Manser, T. (2012). Team mental models and their potential to improve teamwork and safety: A review and implications for future research in healthcare. *Safety Science, 50*, 1344–1354. https://doi.org/10.1016/j.ssci.2011.12.033

Campbell, J. P. (1990). Modeling the performance prediction problem in industrial and organizational psychology. In M. D. Dunnette & L. M. Hough (Eds.), *Handbook of industrial and organizational psychology* (Vol. 1, pp. 687–732). Palo Alto, CA: Consulting Psychologists Press.

Campion, M. A., Medsker, G. J., & Higgs, A. C. (1993). Relations between work group characteristics and effectiveness: Implications for designing effective work groups. *Personnel Psychology, 46*, 823–850.

Campion, M. A., Papper, E. M., & Medsker, G. J. (1996). Relations between work team characteristics and effectiveness: A replication and extension. *Personnel Psychology, 49*, 429–452. https://doi.org/10.1111/j.1744-6570.1996.tb01806.x

Carson, J. B., Tesluk, P. E., & Marrone, J. A. (2007). Shared leadership in teams: An investigation of antecedent conditions and performance. *Academy of Management Journal, 50*, 1217–1234. https://www.researchgate.net/publication/275859545_Shared_Leadership_in_Teams_An_Investigation_of_Antecedent_Conditions_and_Performance

Chatman, J. A., & Flynn, F. J. (2001). The influence of demographic heterogeneity on the emergence and consequences of cooperative norms in work teams. *Academy of Management Journal, 44*, 956–974. https://doi.org/10.2307/3069440

Choi, H.-S., & Thompson, L. (2005). Old wine in a new bottle: Impact of membership change on group creativity. *Organizational Behavior and Human Decision Processes, 98*, 121–132. https://doi.org/10.1016/j.obhdp.2005.06.003

Colquitt, J. A., & Zipay, K. P. (2015). Justice, fairness, and employee reactions. *Annual Review of Organizational Psychology and Organizational Behavior, 2*, 75–99. https://doi.org/10.1146/annurev-orgpsych-032414-111457

Cooke, N. J., Kiekel, P. A., Salas, E., Stout, R., Bowers, C., & Cannon-Bowers, J. (2003). Measuring team knowledge: A window to the cognitive underpinnings of team performance. *Group Dynamics: Theory, Research, And Practice, 7*, 179–199. https://doi.org/10.1037/1089-2699.7.3.179

Courtright, S. H., Thurgood, G. R., Stewart, G. L., & Pierotti, A. J. (2015). Structural interdependence in teams: An integrative framework and meta-analysis. *Journal of Applied Psychology, 100*, 1825–1846. https://doi.org/10.1037/apl0000027

De Dreu, C. K. W. (2008). The virtue and vice of workplace conflict: Food for (pessimistic) thought. *Journal of Organizational Behavior, 29*, 5–18. https://doi.org/10.1002/job.474

De Dreu, C. K. W., & Weingart, L. R. (2003). Task versus relationship conflict, team performance, and team member satisfaction: A meta-analysis. *Journal of Applied Psychology, 88*, 741–749. https://doi.org/10.1037/0021-9010.88.4.741

De Jong, B. A., & Dirks, K. T. (2012). Beyond shared perceptions of trust and monitoring in teams: Implications of asymmetry and dissensus. *Journal of Applied Psychology, 97*, 391–406. https://doi.org/10.1037/a0026483

De Jong, B. A., & Elfring, T. (2010). How does trust affect the performance of ongoing teams? The mediating role of reflexivity, monitoring, and effort. *Academy of Management Journal, 53*, 535–549. https://doi.org/10.5465/AMJ.2010.51468649

DeChurch, L. A., & Mesmer-Magnus, J. R. (2010). The cognitive underpinnings of effective teamwork: A meta-analysis. *Journal of Applied Psychology, 95*, 32–53. https://doi.org/10.1037/a0017328

Deuling, J. K., Denissen, J. J. A., van Zalk, M., Meeus, W., & van Aken, M. (2011). Perceived influence in groups over time: How associations with personality and cognitive ability can change over time. *Journal of Research in Personality, 45*, 576–585. https://doi.org/10.1016/j.jrp.2011.07.005

van Dierendonck, D. (2011). Servant leadership: A review and synthesis. *Journal of Management, 37*, 1228–1261. https://doi.org/10.1177/0149206310380462

van Dijk, H., & van Engen, M. L. (2013). A status perspective on the consequences of work group diversity. *Journal of Occupational and Organizational Psychology, 86*, 223–241. https://doi.org/10.1111/joop.12014

Driskell, J. E., & Salas, E. (1992). Collective behavior and team performance. *Human Factors, 34*, 277–288. https://doi.org/10.1177/001872089203400303

Dweck, C. S. (1989). Motivation. In A. Lesgold & R. Glaser (Eds.), *Foundations for a psychology of education* (pp. 87–136). Hillsdale, NJ: Lawrence Erlbaum.

Edmondson, A. (1999). Psychological safety and learning behavior in work teams. *Administrative Science Quarterly, 44*, 350–383. https://doi.org/10.2307/2666999

Ellis, A. P. J., Bell, B. S., Ployhart, R. E, Hollenbeck, J. R., & Ilgen, D. R. (2005). An evaluation of generic teamwork skill training with action teams: Effects on cognitive and skill-based outcomes. *Personnel Psychology, 58*, 641–672. https://doi.org/10.1111/j.1744-6570.2005.00617.x

Ely, R. J., & Thomas, D. A. (2001). Cultural diversity at work: The effects of diversity perspectives on work group processes and outcomes. *Administrative Science Quarterly, 46*, 229–273. https://doi.org/10.2307/2667087

Endsley, M. R. (1988). Design and evaluation for situation awareness enhancement. *Proceedings of the Human Factors and Ergonomics Society Annual Meeting, 32*, 97–101. https://doi.org/10.1177/154193128803200221

Endsley, M. R. (1995). Toward a theory of situation awareness in dynamic systems. *Human Factors, 37,* 32–64. https://doi.org/10.1518/001872095779049543

Geister, S., Konradt, U., & Hertel, G. (2006). Effects of process feedback on motivation, satisfaction, and performance in virtual teams. *Small Group Research, 37,* 459–489. https://doi.org/10.1177/1046496406292337

Gibson, C. B. (2003). Quality of team service: The role of field independent culture, quality orientation, and quality improvement focus. *Small Group Research, 34,* 619–646. https://doi.org/10.1177/1046496403257226

Gibson, C. B., & Gibbs, J. L. (2006). Unpacking the concept of virtuality: The effects of geographic dispersion, electronic dependence, dynamic structure, and national diversity on team innovation. *Administrative Science Quarterly, 51,* 451–495. https://doi.org/10.2189/asqu.51.3.451

Greer, L. L., Jehn, K. A., & Mannix, E. A. (2008). Conflict transformation: A longitudinal investigation of relationships between different types of intragroup conflict and the moderating role of conflict resolution. *Small Group Research, 39,* 278–302. https://doi.org/10.1177/1046496408317793

Guastello, S. J. (2010). Nonlinear dynamics of team performance and adaptability in emergency response. *Human Factors, 52,* 162–172. https://doi.org/10.1177/0018720809359003

Guillaume, Y. R. F., Brodbeck, F. C., & Riketta, M. (2012). Surface- and deep-level dissimilarity effects on social integration and individual effectiveness related outcomes in work groups: A meta-analytic integration. *Journal of Occupational and Organizational Psychology, 85,* 80–115. https://doi.org/10.1111/j.2044-8325.2010.02005.x

Gully, S. M., Incalcaterra, K. A., Joshi, A., & Beaubien, J. M. (2002). A meta-analysis of team-efficacy, potency, and performance: Interdependence and level of analysis as moderators of observed relationships. *Journal of Applied Psychology, 87,* 819–832. https://doi.org/10.1037/0021-9010.87.5.819

Gully, S. M., & Phillips, J. M. (2005). A multilevel application of learning and performance orientations to individual, group, and organizational outcomes. In J. J. Martocchio (Ed.), *Research in personnel and human resources management* (Vol. 24, pp. 1–51). Bingley, UK: Emerald Publishing.

Guzzo, R. A., & Shea, G. P. (1992). Group performance and intergroup relations in organizations. In M. D. Dunnette & L. M. Hough (Eds.), *Handbook of industrial and organizational psychology* (Vol. 3, pp. 269–313). Palo Alto, CA: Consulting Psychologists Press.

Hackman, J. R. (1987). The design of work teams. In L. Lorsch (Ed.), *Handbook of organizational behavior.* New York, NY: Prentice Hall.

Hackman, J. R., & Wageman, R. (2005). A theory of team coaching. *Academy of Management Review, 30,* 269–287. https://doi.org/10.5465/AMR.2005.16387885

Han, S. J., & Beyerlein, M. (2016). Framing the effects of multinational cultural diversity on virtual team processes. *Small Group Research, 47,* 351–383. https://doi.org/10.1177/1046496416653480

Harrison, D. A., Price, K. H., & Bell, M. P. (1998). Beyond relational demography: Time and the effects of surface- and deep-level diversity on work group cohesion. *Academy of Management Journal, 41,* 96–107. https://doi.org/10.2307/256901

Harrison, D. A., Price, K. H., Gavin, J. H., & Florey, A. T. (2002). Time, teams, and task performance: Changing effects of surface- and deep-level diversity on group functioning. *Academy of Management Journal, 45,* 1029–1045. https://doi.org/10.2307/3069328

Hollingshead, A. B. (2001). Cognitive interdependence and convergent expectations in transactive memory. *Journal of Personality and Social Psychology, 81,* 1080–1089. https://doi.org/10.1037/0022-3514.81.6.1080

Howes, J. C., Cropanzano, R., Grandey, A. A., & Mohler, C. J. (2000). Who is supporting whom? Quality team effectiveness and perceived organizational support. *Journal of Quality Management, 5,* 207–223. https://doi.org/10.1016/S1084-8568(01)00021-9

Jehn, K. A. (1997). A qualitative analysis of conflict types and dimensions in organizational groups. *Administrative Science Quarterly, 42,* 530–557. https://doi.org/10.2307/2393737

Jehn, K. A., Northcraft, G. B., & Neale, M. A. (1999). Why differences make a difference: A field study of diversity conflict and performance in workgroups. *Administrative Science Quarterly, 44*, 741–763. https://doi.org/10.2307/2667054

Jehn, K. A., Rispens, S., & Thatcher, S. M. B. (2010). The effects of conflict asymmetry on work group and individual outcomes. *Academy of Management Journal, 53*, 596–616. https://doi.org/10.5465/AMJ.2010.51468978

Johnson, M. D., Hollenbeck, J. R., Humphrey, S. E., Ilgen, D. R., Jundt, D., & Meyer, C. J. (2006). Cutthroat cooperation: Asymmetrical adaptation to changes in team reward structures. *Academy of Management Journal, 49*, 103–119. https://doi.org/10.5465/AMJ.2006.20785533

Jones, G. R., & George, J. M. (1998). The experience and evolution of trust: Implications for cooperation and teamwork. *Academy of Management Review, 23*, 531–546. https://doi.org/10.5465/AMR.1998.926625

Katz-Navon, T. Y., & Erez, M. (2005). When collective- and self-efficacy affect team performance: The role of task interdependence. *Small Group Research, 36*, 437–465. https://doi.org/10.1177/1046496405275233

Keck, S. L. (1997). Top management team structure: Differential effects by environmental context. *Organization Science, 8*, 143–156. https://doi.org/10.1287/orsc.8.2.143

Kerr, S. (1995). On the folly of rewarding A, while hoping for B. *The Academy of Management Executive, 9*, 7–14. https://www.jstor.org/stable/4165235

Kirkman, B. L., & Rosen, B. (1999). Beyond self-management: Antecedents and consequences of team empowerment. *Academy of Management Journal, 42*, 58–74. https://doi.org/10.2307/256874

Kirkman, B. L., Rosen, B., Tesluk, P. E., & Gibson, C. B. (2004). The impact of team empowerment on virtual team performance: The moderating role of face-to-face interaction. *Academy of Management Journal, 47*, 175–192. https://doi.org/10.2307/20159571

Kirkpatrick, D. L. (1956). How to start an objective evaluation of your training program. *Journal of the American Society of Training Directors, 10*, 18–22. https://www.kirkpatrickpartners.com/Portals/0/Resources/How%20to%20Start%20an%20Objective%20Evaluation%20of%20Your%20Training%20Program.pdf?ver=2018-01-29-083410-360

Kirkpatrick, D. L. (1996). Great ideas revisited: Revisiting Kirkpatrick's four-level model. *Training & Development, 50*, 54–59.

Klein, C., DiazGranados, D., Salas, E., Le, H., Burke, C. S., Lyons, R., & Goodwin, G. F. (2009). Does team building work? *Small Group Research, 40*, 181–222. https://doi.org/10.1177/1046496408328821

van Knippenberg, D., & Schippers, M. C. (2007). Work group diversity. *Annual Review of Psychology, 58*, 515–541. https://doi.org/10.1146/annurev.psych.58.110405.085546

Kozlowski, S. W. J., & Bell, B. S. (2003). Work groups and teams in organizations. In W. C. Borman, D. R. Ilgen, & R. J. Klimoski (Eds.), *Handbook of psychology: Industrial and organizational psychology* (Vol. 12, pp. 333–375). New York, NY: Wiley-Blackwell.

Kozlowski, S. W. J., & Klein, K. J. (2000). A multilevel approach to theory and research in organizations: Contextual, temporal, and emergent processes. In K. J. Klein & S. W. J. Kozlowski (Eds.), *Multilevel theory, research, and methods in organizations: Foundations, extensions, and new directions* (pp. 3–90). San Francisco, CA: Jossey-Bass.

Langfred, C. W. (2005). Autonomy and performance in teams: The multilevel moderating effect of task interdependence. *Journal of Management, 31*, 513–529. https://doi.org/10.1177/0149206304272190

LePine, J. A., Piccolo, R. F., Jackson, C. L., Mathieu, J. E., & Saul, J. R. (2008). A meta-analysis of teamwork processes: Tests of a multidimensional model and relationships with team effectiveness criteria. *Personnel Psychology, 61*, 273–307. https://doi.org/10.1111/j.1744-6570.2008.00114.x

Lewis, K., Belliveau, M., Herndon, B., & Keller, J. (2007). Group cognition, membership change, and performance: Investigating the benefits and detriments of collective knowledge. *Organizational Behavior and Human Decision Processes, 103*, 159–178. https://doi.org/10.1016/j.obhdp.2007.01.005

Liu, C.-Y., Pirola-Merlo, A., Yang, C.-A., & Huang, C. (2009). Disseminating the functions of team coaching regarding research and development team effectiveness: Evidence from high-tech industries in Taiwan. *Social Behavior and Personality: An International Journal*, 37, 41–57. https://doi.org/10.2224/sbp.2009.37.1.41

Marks, M. A., DeChurch, L. A., Mathieu, J. E., Panzer, F. J., & Alonso, A. (2005). Teamwork in multiteam systems. *Journal of Applied Psychology*, 90, 964–971. https://doi.org/10.1037/0021-9010.90.5.964

Marks, M. A., Mathieu, J. E., & Zaccaro, S. J. (2001). A temporally based framework and taxonomy of team processes. *Academy of Management Review*, 26, 356–379. https://doi.org/10.5465/AMR.2001.4845785

Marks, M. A., Sabella, M. J., Burke, C. S., & Zaccaro, S. J. (2002). The impact of cross-training on team effectiveness. *Journal of Applied Psychology*, 87, 3–13. https://doi.org/10.1037/0021-9010.87.1.3

Marshall, A., Bisbey, T., & Salas, E. (2015). Teamwork and team performance measurement. In J. R. Wilson & S. Sharples (Eds.), *Evaluation of human work* (4th ed., pp. 773–789). Boca Raton, FL: CRC Press.

Mathieu, J. E., Gilson, L. L., & Ruddy, T. M. (2006). Empowerment and team effectiveness: An empirical test of an integrated model. *Journal of Applied Psychology*, 91, 97–108. https://doi.org/10.1037/0021-9010.91.1.97

Mathieu, J. E., Heffner, T. S., Goodwin, G. F., Cannon-Bowers, J. A., & Salas, E. (2005). Scaling the quality of teammates' mental models: Equifinality and normative comparisons. *Journal of Organizational Behavior*, 26, 37–56. https://doi.org/10.1002/job.296

Mathieu, J. E., Marks, M. A., & Zaccaro, S. J. (2001). Multi-team systems. In N. Anderson, D. S. Ones, H. K. Sinangil, & C. Viswesvaran (Eds.), *Handbook of industrial and organizational psychology* (Vol. 2, pp. 289–313). Thousand Oaks, CA: SAGE.

Mathieu, J. E., & Rapp, T. L. (2009). Laying the foundation for successful team performance trajectories: The roles of team charters and performance strategies. *Journal of Applied Psychology*, 94, 90–103.

Mathieu, J. E., & Schulze, W. (2006). The influence of team knowledge and formal plans on episodic team process-performance relationships. *Academy of Management Journal*, 49, 605–619. https://doi.org/10.5465/AMJ.2006.21794678

Mayer, R. C., & Gavin, M. B. (2005). Trust in management and performance: Who minds the shop while the employees watch the boss? *Academy of Management Journal*, 48, 874–888. https://doi.org/10.5465/AMJ.2005.18803928

Maynard, M. T., Mathieu, J. E., Marsh, W. M., & Ruddy, T. M. (2007). A multilevel investigation of the influences of employees' resistance to empowerment. *Human Performance*, 20, 147–171. https://doi.org/10.1080/08959280701332885

McIntyre, R. M., & Salas, E. (1995). Measuring and managing for team performance: Emerging principles from complex environments. In R. A. Guzzo, E. Salas, & Associates (Eds.), *Team effectiveness and decision making in organizations* (pp. 9–45). San Francisco, CA: Jossey-Bass. https://doi.org/10.1002/hrdq.3920070310

Mesmer-Magnus, J. R., & DeChurch, L. A. (2009). Information sharing and team performance: A meta-analysis. *Journal of Applied Psychology*, 94, 535–546. https://doi.org/10.1037/a0013773

Moreland, R. L., Argote, L., & Krishnan, R. (2002). Training people to work in groups. In R. S. Tindale, L. Heath, J. Edwards, E. J. Posavac, F. B. Bryant, Y. Suarez-Balcazer, . . . J. Myers (Eds.), *Theory and research on small groups* (pp. 37–60). New York, NY: Kluwer. https://doi.org/10.1007/0-306-47144-2_3

Morgeson, F. P., DeRue, D. S., & Karam, E. P. (2010). Leadership in teams: A functional approach to understanding leadership structures and processes. *Journal of Management*, 36, 5–39. https://doi.org/10.1177/0149206309347376

Patrashkova-Volzdoska, R. R., McComb, S. A., Green, S. G., & Compton, W. D. (2003). Examining a curvilinear relationship between communication frequency and team performance in cross-functional project teams. *IEEE Transactions on Engineering Management, 50,* 262–269. https://doi.org/10.1109/TEM.2003.817298

Phillips, J. M., & Gully, S. M. (1997). Role of goal orientation, ability, need for achievement, and locus of control in the self-efficacy and goal-setting process. *Journal of Applied Psychology, 82,* 792–802. https://doi.org/10.1037/0021-9010.82.5.792

Porter, C. O. L. H. (2005). Goal orientation: Effects on backing up behavior, performance, efficacy, and commitment in teams. *Journal of Applied Psychology, 90,* 811–818. https://doi.org/10.1037/0021-9010.90.4.811

Porter, C. O. L. H., Hollenbeck, J. R., Ilgen, D. R., Ellis, A. P. J., West, B. J., & Moon, H. K. (2003). Backing up behaviors in teams: The role of personality and legitimacy of need. *Journal of Applied Psychology, 88,* 391–403. https://doi.org/10.1037/0021-9010.88.3.391

Prince, A., Brannick, M. T., Prince, C., & Salas, E. (1997). The measurement of team process behaviors in the cockpit: Lessons learned. In M. T. Brannick, E. Salas, & C. Prince (Eds.), *Team performance assessment and measurement: Theory, methods, and applications* (pp. 289–310). Mahwah, NJ: Lawrence Erlbaum Associates.

Raes, A. M. L., Bruch, H., & De Jong, S. B. (2013). How top management team behavioural integration can impact employee work outcomes: Theory development and first empirical tests. *Human Relations, 66,* 167–192. https://doi.org/10.1177/0018726712454554

Ramos-Villagrasa, P. J., Navarro, J., & García-Izquierdo, A. L. (2012). Chaotic dynamics and team effectiveness: Evidence from professional basketball. *European Journal of Work and Organizational Psychology, 21,* 778–802. https://doi.org/10.1080/1359432X.2012.669525

Rico, R., Sánchez-Manzanares, M., Gil, F., & Gibson, C. (2008). Team implicit coordination processes: A team knowledge-based approach. *Academy of Management Review, 33,* 163–184. https://doi.org/10.5465/AMR.2008.27751276

Rousseau, V., Aubé, C., & Savoie, A. (2006). Teamwork behaviors: A review and an integration of frameworks. *Small Group Research, 37,* 540–570. https://doi.org/10.1177/1046496406293125

Salas, E., DiazGranados, D., Klein, C., Burke, C. S., Stagl, K. C., Goodwin, G. F., & Halpin, S. M. (2008). Does team training improve team performance? A meta-analysis. *Human Factors, 50,* 903–933. https://doi.org/10.1518/001872008X375009

Salas, E., Dickinson, T. L., Converse, S. A., & Tannenbaum, S. I. (1992). Toward an understanding of team performance and training. In R. W. Swezey & E. Salas (Eds.), *Teams: Their training and performance* (pp. 3–29). Westport, CT: Ablex Publishing.

Salas, E., & Fiore, S. M. (2004). *Team cognition: Understanding the factors that drive process and performance.* Washington, DC: American Psychological Association.

Salas, E., Guthrie, J. W. Jr., Wilson-Donnelly, K. A., Priest, H. A., & Burke, C. S. (2005). Modeling team performance: The basic ingredients and research needs. In W. B. Rouse & K. R. Boff (Eds.), *Organizational simulation* (pp. 185–228). Hoboken, NJ: John Wiley & Sons.

Salas, E., Prince, C., Baker, D. P., & Shrestha, L. (1995). Situation awareness in team performance: Implications for measurement and training. *Human Factors, 37,* 123–136. https://doi.org/10.1518/001872095779049525

Salas, E., Rosen, M. A., Burke, C. S., Nicholson, D., & Howse, W. R. (2007). Markers for enhancing team cognition in complex environments: The power of team performance diagnosis. *Aviation, Space, and Environmental Medicine, 78,* B77–B85. https://www.researchgate.net/publication/6289884_Markers_for_enhancing_team:cognition_in_complex_environments_The_power_of_team:performance_diagnosis

Salas, E., Shuffler, M. L., Thayer, A. L., Bedwell, W. L., & Lazzara, E. H. (2015). Understanding and improving teamwork in organizations: A scientifically based practical guide. *Human Resource Management, 54,* 599–622. https://doi.org/10.1002/hrm.21628

Salas, E., Sims, D. E., & Burke, C. S. (2005). Is there a "Big Five" in teamwork? *Small Group Research, 36,* 555–599. https://doi.org/10.1177/1046496405277134

Salas, E., Sims, D. E., & Klein, C. (2004). Cooperation at work. In C. D. Spielberger (Ed.), *Encyclopedia of applied psychology* (Vol. 1, pp. 497–505). San Diego, CA: Elsevier Academic Press.

Schneider, B., Ehrhart, M. G., Mayer, D. M., Saltz, J. L., & Niles-Jolly, K. (2005). Understanding organization-customer links in service settings. *Academy of Management Journal, 48,* 1017–1032. https://doi.org/10.5465/AMJ.2005.19573107

Smith-Jentsch, K. A., Sierra, M. J., & Weise, C. W. (2013). How, when, and why you should measure team performance. In E. Salas, S. I. Tannenbaum, D. Cohen, & G. Latham (Eds.), *Developing and enhancing teamwork in organizations* (pp. 552–580). San Francisco, CA: Jossey-Bass.

Sosik, J. J., & Jung, D. I. (2002). Work-group characteristics and performance in collectivistic and individualistic cultures. *The Journal of Social Psychology, 142,* 5–23. https://doi.org/10.1080/00224540209603881

Steiner, I. D. (1972). *Group process and productivity.* New York, NY: Elsevier Academic Press.

Stewart, G. L. (2006). A meta-analytic review of relationships between team design features and team performance. *Journal of Management, 32,* 29–55. https://doi.org/10.1177/0149206305277792

Summers, J. K., Humphrey, S. E., & Ferris, G. R. (2012). Team member change, flux in coordination, and performance: Effects of strategic core roles, information transfer, and cognitive ability. *Academy of Management, 55,* 314–338. https://doi.org/10.5465/amj.2010.0175

Sundstrom, E., De Meuse, K. P., & Futrell, D. (1990). Work teams: Applications and effectiveness. *American Psychologist, 45,* 120–133. https://doi.org/10.1037/0003-066X.45.2.120

Swaab, R. I., Schaerer, M., Anicich, E. M., Ronay, R., & Galinsky, A. D. (2014). The too-much-talent effect: Team interdependence determines when more talent is too much or not enough. *Psychological Science, 25,* 1581–1591. https://doi.org/10.1177/0956797614537280

Tannenbaum, S. I., Beard, R. L., & Salas, E. (1992). Team building and its influence on team effectiveness: An examination of conceptual and empirical developments. In K. Kelley (Ed.), *Advances in psychology: Issues, theory, and research in industrial/organizational psychology* (pp. 117–153). New York, NY: Elsevier.

Tesluk, P. E., & Mathieu, J. E. (1999) Overcoming roadblocks to effectiveness: Incorporating management of performance barriers into models of work group effectiveness. *Journal of Applied Psychology, 84,* 200–217. https://doi.org/10.1037/0021-9010.84.2.200

Wegner, D. M. (1987). Transactive memory: A contemporary analysis of the group mind. In B. Mullen & G. R. Goethals (Eds.), *Theories of group behavior* (pp. 185–208). New York, NY: Springer.

Wildman, J. L., Salas, E., & Scott, C. P. R. (2014). Measuring cognition in teams: A cross-domain review. *Human Factors, 56,* 911–941. https://doi.org/10.1177/0018720813515907

Wildman, J. L., Thayer, A. L., Rosen, M. A., Salas, E., Mathieu, J. E., & Rayne, S. R. (2012). Task types and team-level attributes: Synthesis of team classification literature. *Human Resource Development Review, 11,* 97–129. https://doi.org/10.1177%2F1534484311417561

NOTES

1. Salas and colleagues (2015) proposed three additional considerations to teamwork: (i) context, (ii) composition, and (iii) culture. Although critical to teamwork, these categories represent influencing conditions rather than core competencies. We discuss these crucial topics in the "Teamwork as a Complex Phenomenon" section. Specifically, context and culture are discussed in the "Contextual Moderators" subsection, and composition is discussed in "Member Characteristics."

2. It is important to note that although antecedents to teamwork are inputs, not all inputs are antecedents. Because some inputs are re-informed by outputs and other factors emerging from team interaction

1. (e.g., emergent states), classifying them as antecedents would be a misnomer. Therefore, we use the term "inputs" rather than "antecedents."
3. Certain aspects of goal orientation may also emerge from team interaction (Gully & Phillips, 2005), but it is largely considered a trait-level variable (Dweck, 1989).
4. Interestingly, Summers and colleagues (2012) found minimal coordination flux when incoming members have low cognitive ability, but speculate that these newcomers become quickly marginalized before being socialized into the group.

Tiffany M. Bisbey and Eduardo Salas

VIRTUAL TEAMS AND DIGITAL COLLABORATION

RELEVANCE OF VIRTUAL TEAMS AND DIGITAL COLLABORATION

Modern information and communication technologies (ICTs), such as email, chat, video conferencing, augmented and virtual reality, and collaboration software with shared networked databases, enable synchronous and asynchronous communication and information access in real time and digital collaboration within and across locations, countries, and company boundaries. Members of virtual teams can be geographically dispersed but still coordinate with other team members and quickly access the same information. Especially for organizations operating in a global market, it has been crucial to take advantage of the opportunities of virtual teams. Specialists for complex and customer-specific project tasks can be recruited across the world more easily and contribute their knowledge to different teams working in parallel as needed. Thus, digital collaboration promises companies organizational flexibility and acceleration of work processes. Furthermore, employees may benefit from more flexible work arrangements granting more autonomy to decide where and when to work, reducing commuting time and costs when working from home. Already in the 1990s, virtual teams were announced as the new way to work and the peopleware of the 21st century (Lipnack & Stamps, 1997). Although many knowledge workers had already been collaborating digitally (at least to some extent) for a long time, the beginning of the Covid pandemic in 2020 was a game changer. Almost from one day to the next, offices were shut down and people worked from home. Collaborating digitally became the new normal. Companies and employees that had no experience with virtual teams realized the chances and risks of virtual teamwork and digital collaboration. After the forced experience, companies and employees seem more willing to continue virtual teamwork than before. In the future, digital collaboration will increasingly encompass software agents, which can act and decide autonomously based on artificial intelligence (O'Neill et al., 2022). Only time will tell if the vision of human team members and software agents meeting in the metaverse via avatars will come true.

The focus of this article is on virtual teams and digital collaboration in teams. Virtual team research deals with phenomena and questions on the team level, such as how working with collaborative ICT affects the emergence of trust between members or influences the relationship between team processes and outcomes. In contrast, telework and telecommuting research focuses on the individual level of analysis, such as on the relationship between individual characteristics and individual adjustment, well-being, and performance comparing office work with non-office contexts using individual and mobile technologies (Raghuram et al., 2019). The structure of the article is as follows. First, I define the concept of virtual teams and team virtuality. Then, I describe the factors influencing the processes and the development of emergent states and outcomes of virtual teams using an input-mediator-output-input (IMOI) model of team effectiveness before deriving practical implications and future research perspectives.

DEFINING AND MEASURING TEAM VIRTUALITY

Lipnack and Stamps (1997) define a virtual team, like any team, as "a group of people who interact through interdependent tasks guided by common purpose" but which "works across space, time, and organizational boundaries with links strengthened by webs of communication technologies" (p. 7). The authors combine aspects of ICT-mediated communication and distributed work with core aspects of a definition of teams in general. However, the mentioned aspects of teams in general might also apply for people working interdependently along a process chain in different departments or even companies. Hence, this definition might fit for digital collaborative work better than for virtual teams. To differentiate teamwork from collaborative work in general, core aspects are missing, such that teams have specific common goals linked to organizational goals and members have different roles and responsibilities for attaining them (Kozlowski & Ilgen, 2006). Teams have boundaries and linkages to the broader system context and task environment and are—apart from cross-organizational project teams—embedded in an encompassing organizational system.

With respect to team virtuality, Schulze and Krumm (2017) point out that at least four different types of definitions of virtual teams exist in the literature: (a) definitions treating virtual and face-to-face teams as a dichotomy; (b) definitions based on a single dimension of team virtuality, ranging from low (merely face-to-face) to high (entirely virtual) virtuality; (c) definitions with multiple dimensions of virtuality; (d) definitions which emphasize how individuals perceive and react to discontinuities in which routine behaviors do not produce expected effects (e.g., Watson-Manheim et al., 2012).

Approaches using multiple dimensions differ in terms of facets and measurement. For example, Chudoba and colleagues (2005) consider the aspects of geographic locations, time zones, cultures, work practices, organizations, and ICTs as potential discontinuities. They asked team members to rate these aspects (e.g., how often team members experienced working with people at different sites). They used a factor analysis to develop a three-dimensional measure of team virtuality encompassing team distribution, workplace mobility, and variety of work practices. Others, such as Gibson and Gibbs (2006), use objective indicators to measure team distribution and combine them with external or team members' ratings on electronic dependence, dynamic structure, national diversity, and psychological safety. Criteria such as dynamic structure, national diversity, and psychological safety apply also to merely face-to-face teams. They can be used to differentiate between teams in general but appear less suited to define team virtuality. Therefore, most definitions of team virtuality focus on geographic dispersion and technology use (Gilson et al., 2015).

Geographic dispersion implies that team members cannot interact face-to-face besides when meeting in person or using videoconferencing tools. However, digital collaboration can also take place to varying degrees when team members are co-located. Focusing on ICT use and characteristics might therefore tap the core of team virtuality. For example, Kirkman and Mathieu (2005) define team virtuality as the extent to which team members use virtual tools to coordinate and execute team processes, the amount of informational value provided by such tools, and the synchronicity of team members' virtual interaction. By integrating informational value and media synchronicity as criteria for team virtuality, they build on media richness theory (Daft & Lengel, 1984, 1986) and media synchronicity theory (Dennis et al., 2008), which explain how ICTs influence information and communication processes in organizations.

Handke and colleagues (2021) introduce the concept of team-perceived virtuality. They describe team-perceived virtuality as an emergent state influenced by structural team virtuality and other team characteristics and team processes, which in turn influence team outcomes. Team-perceived virtuality consists of two dimensions: collectively experienced distance and collectively experienced information deficits. However, by focusing on these two dimensions, they adopt only a deficit-oriented view, implying that increasing team virtuality means more distance and information deficits, leaving out any positive effects, such as increased flexibility.

Furthermore, the above-described definitions of virtual teams focus implicitly on human teams. However, the rapid development of artificial intelligence allows researchers and developers to design software agents with higher levels of agent autonomy and to integrate them in digital collaboration and virtual teams. O'Neill and colleagues (2022, p. 911) define human-autonomy teams or human-agent teams (HATs):

> as interdependence in activity and outcomes involving one or more humans and one or more autonomous agents, wherein each human and autonomous agent is recognized as a unique team member occupying a distinct role on the team, and in which the members strive to achieve a common goal as a collective.

To be considered autonomous, the agents must meet at least partial levels of self-directed behavior (agency) and agent autonomy. The concept of levels of automation was suggested by Parasuraman and colleagues (2000) and ranges from low (level 1: agent offers no assistance) to high (level 10: agent decides everything). Partial agent autonomy means that the computer can at least suggest and execute actions and decisions if they are approved by the human (level 5) or do not veto actions and decisions before they are automatically executed (level 6). Whether one perceives an autonomous software agent as a virtual teammate or collaborator or as a machine with artificial intelligence performing collaborative tasks might also depend on the similarity of perceived agent personality characteristics to the individual (Dryer, 1999). Boundaries might get more fluid in the future when humans and software agents interact via avatars in the metaverse and when software agents can recognize emotions and react accordingly (Lee et al., 2021).

Integrating research on HATs and following Kozlowski and Ilgen's (2006) definition of teams, I define virtual teams as two or more human or autonomous software agents who (a) collaborate to perform organizationally relevant tasks; (b) interact at least to a certain degree virtually to achieve one or more common goals; (c) are interdependent with respect to workflow, goals, and outcomes; (d) have different roles and responsibilities; and (e) are embedded together in an encompassing organizational system or cross-organizational agreement with boundaries and linkages to the broader system context and task environment. This definition implies that virtuality can have varying degrees and that different types of virtual interaction are used. Virtual teams with human members can vary the degree and type of virtual interaction over time depending on task and situational demands as well as human member needs. They can interact virtually exclusively or alternate virtual and face-to-face interaction or combine the two interactions. Most of the existing virtual teams have some face-to-face contact (Hertel et al., 2005). Partially virtual teams, which alternate virtual and face-to-face interaction or combine them, with some team members interacting face-to-face and others virtually, are also called hybrid teams (Hosseini et al., 2017). Virtual, digital, or e-collaboration is collaboration among individuals or autonomous software agents to accomplish common tasks using electronic technologies, which could happen even without interacting or communicating (Kock, 2005), for example, by telework.

The facets used to define virtual teams are also used to define virtual organizations, where virtual teams are embedded and members collaborate digitally. For example, Ahuja and Carley (1999, p. 742) define virtual organizations "as a geographically distributed organization whose members are bound by a long-term common interest or goal, and who communicate and coordinate their work through information technology."

AN IMOI MODEL OF VIRTUAL TEAM EFFECTIVENESS

To summarize virtual team research, I adopt an IMOI model (Ilgen et al., 2005; Kozlowski & Ilgen, 2006). In comparison with an input-process-output model (Hackman, 1987), an IMOI model emphasizes that virtual teams are complex dynamic open socio-technical or socio-digital systems embedded in an organizational, economical, and societal context (Antoni & Hertel, 2009). Employees are organized in teams within or between organizations to contribute to organizational goals by achieving common team tasks and goals with the help of ICTs. Virtual team members (humans and autonomous software agents) learn and develop through the execution of their tasks and the use of ICTs. They have to adapt to changing internal and external situational demands, but their actions and performance in turn also contribute to organizational and situational changes. Important factors influencing team outcomes via team processes and the development of emergent states are ICTs and team tasks, team member characteristics, and situational demands as input factors. The IMOI model (see Figure 1) describes the recursive and cyclical processes between inputs, mediators, and outcomes.

Information and Communication Technologies.
ICTs are important elements of the technical system of virtual teams as team members collaborate using ICTs. The characteristics of ICTs influence task and situational demands, team processes as well as the development and outcomes of virtual teams. But as virtual teams learn and develop, also the characteristics of ICTs can change. Key ICT characteristics or functionalities discussed in the literature are the degree of social presence, media richness, naturalness, and synchronicity.

Social presence means the degree to which one is aware of the other person in an interaction. Social presence theory proposes that media differ in their degree of social presence and that communication effectiveness depends on the task-media-fit. Face-to-face interaction is considered to have the most social presence, and text-based communication the least. For

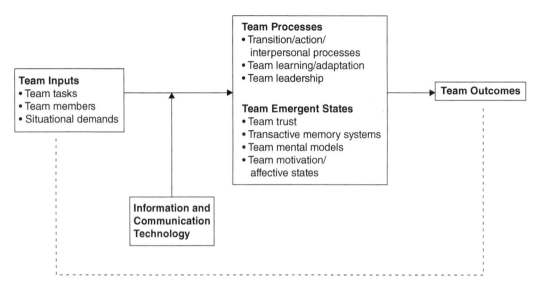

Figure 1. An input-mediator-output-input model of virtual team effectiveness.

effective communication, the degree of social presence should have the level of interpersonal involvement required for a task (Short et al., 1976).

Similarly, media richness theory states that media can be ranked according to their information richness. In their seminal article, Daft and Lengel (1986, p. 560) defined information richness "as the ability of information to change understanding within a time interval." They proposed that communication media differ in their capacity to transmit rich information because of the number of channels they use, the number of cues they can transmit in a given time, their capability for immediate feedback, personalization, and language variety. Using these criteria, they presented a hierarchical classification of media in order of decreasing richness: (a) face-to-face, (b) telephone, (c) personal documents such as letters or memos, (d) impersonal written documents, and (e) numeric documents (Daft & Lengel, 1984, 1986). Daft and Lengel argue that when working under bounded rationality and time constraints, organizations should use rich media to reduce equivocality and quickly clarify ambiguous issues to reach a common understanding of a situation. Videoconferences, telephones, and chat software were not available that time and could probably be ranked second, third, and fifth according to this logic. Kirkman and Mathieu (2005) suggest that subjective ratings of the amount of informational value might be better able to assess media richness than objective ranking as proposed by Daft and Lengel (1984). Research supports that people perceive ICT functionalities differently and that intraindividual differences and differences between situational contexts occur over time and can influence performance (e.g., Carlson & Zmud, 1999; Fuller & Dennis, 2009; Hantula et al., 2011).

Why do team members perceive ICT functionalities differently and change their perception? Channel expansion theory suggests that the knowledge base of ICT users and their ability to communicate with an ICT develop with experience and change the perception of media richness (Carlson & Zmud, 1999). Particularly, the experience of using a medium, the experience with communicating partners, and perceived social influence change the perception of media richness not only between and within users but also between situational contexts (Carlson & Zmud, 1999; D'Urso & Rains, 2008; Hollingshead et al., 1993).

Similarly, adaptive structuration theory argues that people actively select how they appropriate and use the features of a technology and that this appropriation may change over time (DeSanctis & Poole, 1994). In line with this reasoning that ICT use is a function less of physical properties than of media appropriation and perception, Handke and colleagues (2018) report findings that individuals change their perception of ICT richness over time and toward communication partners. Fuller and Dennis (2009) showed that while task-media/technology-fit predicted team performance when teams used a technology the first time, over time teams with an initial fit did not perform better than teams with an initial poor fit. In line with adaptive structuration theory, teams with an initial poor media/technology-fit innovated and adapted their ICT use and improved their performance. This indicates that it is not ICTs that determine the processes and performance of virtual teams but rather that it is a recursive relationship in which the two influence each other (DeSanctis & Poole, 1994).

Although there is no technological determinism, ICTs influence media use, team processes, and outcomes. Media naturalness theory argues that people prefer media similar to face-to-face interactions because they require less cognitive effort for knowledge transfer because of the evolution of our brain (Kock, 2004). Kock suggests that the degree of similarity or naturalness of media can be assessed by the co-location of people communicating, the synchronicity to exchange information quickly, the ability to convey and observe facial and body expressions, and, in particular, the ability to convey and listen to speech. Kock (2004) proposes that cognitive adaption to ICT and the degree of schema alignment between team members decrease the cognitive effort required.

The synchronicity of information exchange is the focus of media synchronicity theory (Dennis & Valacich, 1999; Dennis et al., 2008). It differentiates conveyance and convergence of meaning in communication processes. Conveyance refers to the transmission and exchange of information between team members; convergence refers to the information processes needed for sense making to achieve a common understanding of the information received. Both processes are regarded as necessary for understanding tasks but differ in terms of the media synchronicity required. Media synchronicity can be defined as the extent to which media capabilities enable individuals to work together on the same activity at the same time and to have a shared focus (Dennis & Valacich, 1999; Dennis et al., 2008). Media synchronicity theory proposes that a higher degree of media synchronicity is required for convergence than for conveyance processes. Consequently, it is proposed that the use of higher synchronic media will lead to better communication performance if team members want to achieve common understanding and, vice versa, that lower synchronic media are supposed to lead to better performance if teams want to convey information. Media synchronicity is determined by media capabilities to support information transmission and processing.

Dennis and colleagues (2008) propose that media synchronicity is supported by (a) the speed of media to transmit information (transmission velocity/channel capacity), (b) media with more natural symbol sets, allowing fast encoding and decoding, and (c) symbol sets better suited to the content of a message (e.g., vocal tone to show doubt); they propose that media synchronicity is impaired by (a) a higher extent to which signals from multiple senders can be transmitted simultaneously using a medium (parallelism), (b) messages that can be rehearsed before sending (higher media rehearsability), and (c) messages that can be reexamined during decoding (higher reprocessability) as shared focus is lowered.

Team Tasks, Team Members, and Situational Demands. Key input factors for virtual teams that influence teamwork interacting with ICTs are team tasks, team members, and situational demands. Virtual teams are formed to fulfill tasks relevant for an organization with the help of ICTs that cannot be effectively accomplished by individuals alone. Team tasks influence workflow and coordination demands and thus the structure and design of virtual teams. Team tasks define the minimum requirements that team members must meet in terms of knowledge, skills, attitudes, and other characteristics (KSAOs), such as dispositions or personality characteristics. Tasks are performed under certain situational conditions that pose specific requirements for team members. Moreover, situational conditions might change, and virtual teams have to cope with the resulting situational demands.

Team Tasks. Which types of tasks are suited for virtual teams? Obviously, tasks requiring information processing and specialist knowledge, such as in research and development, are better suited for virtual teams than tasks requiring manual work. Furthermore, if these tasks are separable into subtasks, coordination requirements are reduced. However, subtasks have to be interdependent to some degree; otherwise, only digital collaboration but no virtual teamwork would be needed. Typically, project tasks that are unique and time-limited and require the integration of specialized knowledge for planning and problem solving are well suited for virtual project teams, particularly if the specialists needed are distributed locally (Hertel et al., 2005). Although the time frame for a project task can vary considerably from months to years, all project teams have, by the very definition of a project, a fixed deadline to accomplish the task after which the teams are usually dissolved. Aside from purely project-based organizations, project team members continue to work in their functional job while working part-time in one or more project teams. Hence, project tasks usually imply multiple team membership (Bell & Kozlowski, 2002; Margolis, 2020) in several more or less virtual project and functional teams. Larger projects are often organized as multi-team systems with interdependent project teams working together to achieve a common goal (Shuffler & Carter, 2018; Zaccaro et al., 2020). However, multi-team systems to address larger problem-solving tasks are not restricted to projects. In particular, international companies use virtual multi-team systems to coordinate distributed functional teams and to develop, adapt, and implement global company strategies.

Team Members' KSAOs. Team tasks determine what KSAOs are required from team members, and they are selected or have to be trained accordingly. As virtual teams perform their tasks using ICTs, team members require, besides task and team, ICT-specific KSAOs. Schulze and Krumm (2017) provide a review of the literature on KSAO requirements of team virtuality. They found that successful performance in virtual teams requires media-specific KSAOs; that is, team members should know about the functionalities of the media and use their potential, how and when to use a certain medium for communication and knowledge transfer, and be able to adapt to channel restrictions of certain media (e.g., when using emails as opposed to videoconferences). Besides having media-specific KSAOs, virtual team members should be able to communicate effectively with distributed team members (communication KSAOs), to act in a way that creates trust (e.g., by being responsive and dependable) and to be willing to trust others (trust-related KSAOs), to be able to work with people from different cultural backgrounds (intercultural KSAOs), to manage oneself effectively (e.g., self-, time-, and project-management KSAOs), and to handle conflicts constructively (conflict management KSAOs). These media-unspecific competencies are particularly required when the available media are inappropriate for the team tasks or when team members work in different time zones and cultures.

Situational Demands. As virtual teams are complex dynamic open socio-digital systems embedded in an organizational, economical, and societal context, they have to learn to deal with changing situational demands and adversities. Whereas changes can be perceived as being positive, neutral, or negative (such as additional team tasks and responsibilities) and may require adaptation of task strategies and team processes, adversities have a negative connotation and are associated with disruption, stress, and failure (Hartwig et al., 2020). Changes and adversities can originate from within the team or from outside. Internal adversities, such as the failure or the loss of a team member, or external adversities, such as a conflict with another team or a customer, require virtual teams to be resilient to deal with the adversities (Raetze et al., 2021). This may or may not require virtual teams to adapt their task strategy and team processes.

Team Processes. In the IMOI model, team processes are mediators, which mediate the effects of team inputs on team outcomes. Team processes describe how team members interact and exchange information with or without ICTs to coordinate and monitor their taskwork. Taskwork describes what tasks teams are doing, their interaction with tasks, ICTs, and other technical tools and systems.

Team processes can be differentiated in transition, action, and interpersonal processes. Transition processes encompass team mission analysis, formulation and planning, goal specification, and strategy formulation. Team action processes are the monitoring of goal progress, systems, and team monitoring and coordination. Interpersonal processes include conflict and affect management as well as team motivation and confidence building (Marks et al., 2001).

Team processes are dynamic. Over time, team interaction and information exchange, with or without using ICTs, shape team emergent cognitive and affective states, which in turn influence team processes as well as team outcomes, which reciprocally influence team processes and emergent states (Kozlowski & Ilgen, 2006). DeChurch and Mesmer-Magnus (2010) provided support for this conception. Results of their meta-analysis of 65 independent studies show that both emergent cognitive and affective states were strongly associated with performance. Team cognition was significantly related to team affective states, such as team cohesion, and team action and transition processes, as well as to team performance. Team cognition, team cohesion, and team processes predicted team performance, and team cognition explained unique variance in team performance after controlling for team cohesion and team processes.

ICTs do influence team processes, as suggested by social presence (Short et al., 1976) and media richness (Daft & Lengel, 1986) theories. However, there is no technological determinism. As described above, people learn to appropriate new media by using them in virtual team interaction (Fuller & Dennis, 2009), and this experience can change ICT characteristics by, for example, developing and learning to use emoticons in e-mails and instant messaging (Carlson & Zmud, 1999).

Team Learning and Adaptation. Team learning is both a team process and an outcome (Edmondson et al., 2007; Kozlowski & Bell, 2008). As a process, team learning can be defined as the interaction behaviors of team members to acquire, share, refine, or combine knowledge relevant to the team and the task. Team learning behaviors include the reflection of processes and outcomes, seeking feedback and information from outside the team, and storing and retrieving generated knowledge, encompassing transition, action, and interpersonal processes. As an outcome, team learning describes the acquisition of new knowledge, skills, and attitudes by team learning behaviors, which broadens the action repertoire of a team. Team learning is crucial for the appropriation of ICT functionalities in virtual teams and for team adaptation to ICT, team, and situation requirements (Fuller & Dennis, 2009; Handke et al., 2018). Team learning and team adaptation are closely intertwined as team learning can be regarded as both an antecedent and an outcome of team adaptation.

Burke and colleagues (2006, p. 1190) define team adaptation "as a change in team performance, in response to a salient cue or cue stream, that leads to a functional outcome for the entire team."

Following this definition, team adaptation can be observed as it is manifested in the innovation or modification of actions or existing structures, while team learning can be latent as a change of new knowledge, skills, and attitudes if it is not implemented in actions. Thus, team learning is a necessary but insufficient condition for team adaptation. When teams adapt (e.g., to ICTs and change their ICT use), they may acquire new knowledge, skills, and attitudes because of team adaptation. Oertel and Antoni (2014) showed that interruptive events can trigger team adaptation via reflective team learning. However, depending on the phase of team development, different team learning behaviors may be relevant for changing team knowledge structures. Research indicates that knowledge-based processes (storage and retrieval) play a more important role during early stages of project-based teamwork, followed by a shift to a higher relevance of communication-based processes (reflection and co-construction) in later stages (Oertel & Antoni, 2015).

Team Leadership. Bell and Kozlowski (2002) argue that team virtuality (i.e., spatial distance and ICT-mediated communication) impedes two primary team leader functions (i.e., team performance management and team development). They recommend delegating these functions to the team and implementing team self-regulation processes using team goal and feedback systems (Kozlowski & Ilgen, 2006). Feedback is important not only regarding key performance indicators to coordinate taskwork but also regarding social processes to support team coordination and team cohesion, motivation, and development (Hertel et al., 2005). For example, Ellwart and colleagues (2015) showed that individual online feedback about individual information overload perceptions and task knowledge followed by collective team reflection increased situation awareness and supported virtual team adaptation processes. Self-regulating teams also require shared leadership. Several studies support the positive relation between shared leadership and virtual team performance (Hoch & Kozlowski, 2014).

However, studies report inconsistent results regarding the effects of transformational leadership and virtual team performance. Some studies report negative effects (Gilson et al., 2015; Hoch & Kozlowski, 2014), others positive effects (Avolio et al., 2014; Kahai et al., 2013; Purvanova & Bono, 2009).

The Development of Team Emergent States.

Closely related to team processes is the development or emergence of cognitive and affective states, such as trust, transactive memory systems (TMSs), and shared mental models (SMMs), as well as team motivation and affective states, such as team cohesion. Team emergent states and team processes interact and mediate the effects of team inputs on team outcomes.

When a virtual team starts from scratch, team members do not know each other or what is expected from them as a team and from each team member. Team members have to get to know each other. They have to agree on their team tasks and goals as well as on their task strategies and roles before they are able to coordinate and perform effectively. Most authors agree that it is more difficult to get started as a team, to learn each other's expectations and KSAOs, and to develop team trust only by using ICT-mediated communication. Therefore, they recommend kick-off workshops face-to-face to get to know each other, to clarify tasks and goals as well as team member roles and functions, and to develop rules for virtual teamwork and mutual trust (Hertel et al., 2005). Particularly, the development of trust seems to be both a challenge and a requirement for virtual teams.

Team Trust. Team trust can be defined as an emergent shared willingness of team members to be vulnerable to the actions of the other team members, which are important to the team, irrespective of the ability to monitor or control them (Breuer et al., 2016). A meta-analysis of 48 field and six laboratory studies using cross-sectional (34 studies) and longitudinal (24 studies) data shows that the relationship between team trust and team task performance was stronger in virtual than in face-to-face teams (Breuer et al., 2016). Team trust was also significantly related to information processing (knowledge sharing and team learning), contextual performance (e.g., showing extra effort, volunteering, helping and cooperating with others, following organizational rules, and defending organizational goals), and team attitudes, such as team cohesion, satisfaction, commitment, and effort. However, the studies were too few and the sample size was too low to test whether virtual teams differ from face-to-face teams with respect to these variables. Also, cross-sectional studies, same source data, and subjective ratings showed stronger (and significant) relationships compared with studies using longitudinal data, different data sources, and objective data. Nevertheless, these results are in line with the authors' reasoning that when team members trust each other, they are more likely to take the risk to share their knowledge thus supporting team effectiveness via team coordination and cooperation. As practical implications, the authors recommend, besides trust-building activities, documenting team interactions particularly in virtual teams because their results indicate that the need for trust in virtual teams decreases when interactions in teams are documented. They assume that documenting team interactions facilitates peer monitoring and allows reviewing and verifying team agreements and decisions and thus reduces the risk that individual team members think their efforts are exploited by others.

870 • VIRTUAL TEAMS AND DIGITAL COLLABORATION

Transactive Memory Systems. Virtual teams are often implemented to solve project tasks, which require the knowledge and collaboration of different specialists. The concept of TMS is highly relevant for explaining team coordination and performance of this type of teams because it explains how teams can use the individual memories and the distributed specialized knowledge of their team members efficiently. The TMS concept combines two components: (a) a transactive memory that connects the knowledge held by each team member to the knowledge held by the others and (b) knowledge-relevant transactive communication processes that occur among group members (Wegner, 1987). In order to encode, store, and retrieve distributed specialist knowledge, teams need a shared transactive memory or metaknowledge of expertise location (knowing who knows what). Metaknowledge is defined as the shared perception of expertise location (i.e., the shared knowledge of the expertise and knowledge domains of the other team members). Research on TMS shows that individual team members can function as distributed knowledge repositories, each specializing in particular areas of knowledge and expertise to extend the knowledge capacity of teams and to improve team performance by the cognitive division of labor (Ren & Argote, 2011). Many studies showed that memory specialization, task credibility, and task coordination in teams improved team coordination and performance (Lewis, 2003, 2004; Liang et al., 1995).

Shared Mental Models. While the TMS concept focuses on how teams can profit from team members with specialized and distributed knowledge, the concept of SMMs explains how shared cognitions about work-relevant aspects allow implicit coordination and enhance task performance (Cannon-Bowers et al., 1993; DeChurch & Mesmer-Magnus, 2010). SMMs emerge in a dynamic process of convergence and divergence of individual mental models in team interaction and communication processes and manifest as emergent states in teams as a higher-level, collective phenomenon (Kozlowski & Klein, 2000). Whether teams collaborate face-to-face or via ICTs influences and impedes the development of SMMs (Andres, 2011, 2013).

SMMs can be described in terms of similarity and accuracy. Similarity measures the extent of match between individual team members' mental models. Accuracy describes the extent to which the team members' SMMs correspond to standards, rules, and expert assessments (Mohammed & Dumville, 2001).

Cannon-Bowers and colleagues (1993) initially differentiated four types of mental models: the equipment, task, team interaction, and team mental model. They suggested that particularly task (e.g., task procedures), team interaction (e.g., roles and role interdependencies), and team mental model (e.g., teammates' abilities and preferences) across tasks and situations should be shared in teams.

While the task and interaction mental model were considered as moderately dynamic and the team model as highly dynamic, the equipment mental model was regarded as highly stable across tasks and situations. Cannon-Bowers and colleagues (1993) assumed that equipment mental models (the knowledge of equipment functioning and limitations, operating procedures, and likely failures) focus on individual taskwork and do not need to be shared. Although later research integrated task and technology/equipment aspects in the concept of task mental models and team and team interaction aspects in team mental models (Mathieu et al., 2000), equipment aspects were neglected in research for a long time.

In the face of the multitude of collaborative ICTs that support the interaction and coordination of virtual team members, researchers called for considering ICT SMMs (Schmidtke & Cummings, 2017). Müller and Antoni (2020, 2022) showed that a shared understanding of ICT functionalities, task-specific ICT use, ICT adaptation, and ICT netiquette within a team had an impact on virtual team coordination and performance via team communication. Results also indicated that information about the advantages and disadvantages of ICTs can influence ICT mental models and that explicit planning of ICT use contributes to ICT SMM similarity (Müller & Antoni, 2022).

Furthermore, it has been shown that a temporal SMM, defined as shared knowledge about deadlines, pacing, and sequencing of tasks, contributes to team coordination and performance (Gevers et al., 2006; Mohammed et al., 2015).

Team Motivation and Team Affective States. Several studies showed that team motivation and team affective states, such as team cohesion, can be impaired if team members interact only virtually, because feelings of anonymity and low social control might support social loafing. On the other hand, team motivation and cohesion are considered crucial for virtual team functioning and performance (Hertel et al., 2005). Study findings indicate that positive team affective tone is positively and negative affective tone is negatively related to team cooperation and indirectly to team performance (Lin et al., 2017).

TEAM OUTCOMES

Team outcomes are often conceptualized as team effectiveness encompassing multiple dimensions and perspectives, such as team performance as evaluated by different stakeholders, team satisfaction (i.e., the satisfaction of team members with their team), and team viability (i.e., their willingness to continue work together as a team).

Impact of Team Virtuality on Team Effectiveness. In their meta-analysis of 428 samples from 398 studies on the relationship between team design characteristics and team performance, Carter and colleagues (2019) found only a very small negative relationship ($r = -0.05$) between team performance and dispersed and virtual teams. This finding does not support the results of prior studies and predictions of social presence theory (Short et al., 1976) and media richness theory (Daft & Lengel, 1984) described above. For example, Baltes and colleagues (2002) had reported results of their meta-analysis of 27 studies and 52 effect sizes that computer-mediated communication decreased group effectiveness and member satisfaction and increased time required for task completion compared with face-to-face teams. Lim and colleagues (2007) reported in their meta-analysis of 33 laboratory studies with 62 data points that virtual teams needed more time to reach a decision but achieved higher decision quality, but the authors did not find differences in terms of decision satisfaction between virtual and face-to face teams.

Ortiz de Guinea and colleagues (2012) analyzed 80 data sets from 79 studies and reported negative effects of virtual teams compared with face-to-face teams on team functioning: virtual teams had more task conflicts, lower communication frequency, and less knowledge sharing, and lower performance. The effects for task conflicts, knowledge sharing, and lower performance were stronger for short-term teams than for long-term teams. However, long-term teams had more relationship, process, and other conflicts and a lower communication frequency than short-term teams. Interestingly, in studies with continuous measures of virtuality, they found that the relationship with task conflict was more negative (i.e., lower conflict for more virtual teams) and that the relationships with knowledge sharing and satisfaction were more positive, and they found no association with performance. Other meta-analyses found positive effects of virtual teams compared with face-to-face teams. For example, compared with face-to-face teams, virtual teams generated more ideas, needed less time for task completion, and team members were more satisfied, if there was a fit between the group support system and the task and if the group received appropriate support (Dennis et al., 2001).

Also, Fjermestad (2004) reports an increased number of ideas generated in teams using synchronous group support systems, while no differences were observed between face-to-face teams and teams using synchronous group support systems with respect to satisfaction and usability. However, face-to-face teams showed higher levels of consensus and perceived quality, communicated more, and required less time to complete the tasks. Similarly, Rains (2005) reports that teams using synchronous group support systems generated a larger number of unique ideas and experienced less member dominance than face-to-face teams.

Purvanova and Kenda (2022) criticized studies that reported negative relationships between virtuality and team effectiveness because they analyzed primarily short-lived student teams and because organizational virtual teams were severely underrepresented in these studies. Therefore, Purvanova and Kenda (2022) compared the impact of virtuality on team effectiveness of 73 independent samples of organizational virtual teams and 109 independent samples of non-organizational virtual teams. They found that, in organizational teams, virtuality did not show a direct positive or negative relationship with any of the team effectiveness outcomes they examined. They had analyzed the following outcomes: productive outcomes (earnings, accuracy, and process improvements), performance outcomes (including both externally rated and team member–rated team performance), social outcomes (including cohesion and team trust), and individual team member outcomes (including project/task satisfaction and relational quality). Supplemental analyses showed that these neutral relationships between team virtuality and team effectiveness in organizational teams were not moderated by virtuality operationalization (technology dependence versus geographic dispersion), industry type (information technology [IT]/telecommunication, service, and production), company type (multinational and domestic), occupation of team members (IT/engineering, research and development [R&D], and consulting/management/sales), national diversity within teams (homogeneous vs. heterogeneous), and gender diversity within teams (percent males). They also found that results from non-organizational teams were significantly more negative than results from organizational teams. However, this was not the case when studies used graduate student participants, long-term teams, continuous virtuality measures, and classroom projects instead of laboratory tasks stimulating greater participant investment.

Outcomes of Human-Autonomy Teaming. A special type of virtual teams are HATs. In their review of 76 studies on human-autonomy teaming, O'Neill and colleagues (2022) report that communication among autonomous agents and humans tended to be different than communication among humans. Performance of HATs was typically lower than performance of human–human teams because of their lower-quality communication. High reliability of autonomous agents showed consistently positive effects on outcomes such as trust, workload, and performance. However, reliability interacted with transparency. Lower agent reliability could be partially compensated by higher transparency. When humans were aware of lower agent reliability, they were more trusting and showed higher performance. However, studies on transparency on autonomous agents showed mixed effects. On the one hand, it seems that transparency can clarify the reasoning and decision making of autonomous agents. On the other hand, it may lead to less vigilance in overseeing or questioning the autonomous agents' work.

With respect to HATs, they found that higher levels of agent autonomy and interdependence of autonomous agents and humans led to better team outcomes. Although one could assume that autonomous agents are designed to perform tasks and roles that are difficult or too difficult for humans, they did not find evidence that autonomous agents were particularly useful for teams working under conditions of high task difficulty. However, the studies they reviewed were laboratory-based and did not include field settings. Most of them used only a single human–agent dyad performing an action or execution task with a moderate level of difficulty and very limited levels of communication capabilities and partial autonomy of software agents. As studies focused on performance, workload, trust, situational awareness, team coordination, and shared mental models as dependent variables, research on team viability, development, and learning in HATs is lacking. Owing to these restrictions, caution is advised in generalizing these findings.

PRACTICAL IMPLICATIONS

Research findings that stronger negative effects with respect to virtual team functioning were found in short-term compared with long-term teams indicate that teams would benefit from team-building interventions to support team learning and adaptation to the specific challenges of virtual team work, such as developing task, team, temporal, and ICT shared mental models. Meta-analytic studies show that team-building interventions have stronger effects if teams are large (Klein et al., 2009). This might indicate that team coordination and developing a common understanding are more challenging with increasing team size but that small teams can more easily regulate themselves.

Since the development of trust seems to take more time in virtual compared with face-to-face interactions (Breuer et al., 2016), face-to-face kick-off workshops or team development interventions are recommended (Hertel et al., 2005). Besides trust-building activities, documenting team interactions particularly in virtual teams is recommended, as the need for trust decreases when team interactions are documented. Study findings on HATs suggest that it is important to provide transparency regarding the capabilities and roles of software agents, particularly if systems lack reliability, but also stress human responsibility to prevent complacency (O'Neill et al., 2022). Findings of communication theories suggest that this implication holds for ICTs in general.

FUTURE RESEARCH

Study results indicate a serious method bias, as more negative effects of team virtuality are reported when short-term laboratory teams are compared with long-term organizational teams (Purvanova & Kenda, 2022), and additional longitudinal studies, particularly with organizational teams, are needed. Furthermore, as team virtuality seems to be multidimensional, continuous measures or considering the different dimensions of team virtuality seem to be promising. It might be also worthwhile to examine non-linear effects of team virtuality and to study different forms of hybrid teams. Many studies have focused on the effects of team virtuality; therefore, more studies on mediating and moderating variables are needed to learn more about the causal mechanisms. As virtual teams are a multi-level phenomenon, consisting of individual team members and being embedded in organizations and societies, multi-level studies would be promising. Besides virtual team effectiveness, cross-level effects of virtual working conditions and team processes on individual outcomes such as perceived life-domain balance and stress could be interesting. Particularly, virtual leadership research is still needed (Avolio et al., 2014). Last but not least, research on HATs is still in its beginning stages. Studies analyzing larger teams, more complex tasks, more autonomous agents, and team interaction processes and outcomes both in the laboratory and in the field are needed.

FURTHER READING

Battiste, V., Lachter, J., Brandt, S., Alvarez, A., Strybel, T. Z., & Vu, K. P. L. (2018, July). Human-automation teaming: Lessons learned and future directions. In S. Yamamoto & H. Mori (Eds.), *International Conference on Human Interface and the Management of Information* (pp. 479–493). Springer. https://ntrs .nasa.gov/api/citations/20190001937/downloads/20190001937.pdf

Calhoun, G. (2022). Adaptable (not adaptive) automation: Forefront of human–automation teaming. *Human Factors, 64*(2), 269–277. https://journals.sagepub.com/doi/10.1177/00187208211037457

Dinh, J. V., Reyes, D. L., Kayga, L., Lindgren, C., Feitosa, J., & Salas, E. (2021). Developing team trust: Leader insights for virtual settings. *Organizational Dynamics, 50*(1), 100846. https://www.sciencedirect .com/science/article/abs/pii/S0090261621000218?via%3Dihub

Feitosa, J., & Salas, E. (2021). Today's virtual teams: Adapting lessons learned to the pandemic context. *Organizational Dynamics, 50*(1), 100777. https://www.sciencedirect.com/science/article/pii /S0090261620300292?via%3Dihub

Gibson, C. B., & Grushina, S. V. (2021). A tale of two teams: Next generation strategies for increasing the effectiveness of global virtual teams. *Organizational Dynamics, 50*(1), 100823. https://www.sciencedirect .com/science/article/pii/S0090261620300759?via%3Dihub

Gilson, L., Costa, P., O'Neill, T. A., & Maynard, M. T. (2021). Putting the "TEAM" back into virtual teams. *Organizational Dynamics, 50*(1) 100777. https://www.sciencedirect.com/science/article/abs/pii /S009026162100022X?via%3Dihub

Handke, L., Klonek, F., O'Neill, T. A., & Kerschreiter, R. (2022). Unpacking the role of feedback in virtual team effectiveness. *Small Group Research, 53*(1), 41–87. https://doi.org/10.1177/10464964211057116

Kozlowski, S. W., Chao, G. T., & Van Fossen, J. (2021). Leading virtual teams. *Organizational Dynamics, 50*(1), 100842. https://www.sciencedirect.com/science/article/abs/pii/S0090261621000176?via%3Dihub

Morrison-Smith, S., & Ruiz, J. (2020). Challenges and barriers in virtual teams: A literature review. *SN Applied Sciences, 2*(6), 1–33. https://link.springer.com/article/10.1007/s42452-020-2801-5

Schelble, B. G., Flathmann, C., McNeese, N. J., Freeman, G., & Mallick, R. (2022). Let's think together! Assessing shared mental models, performance, and trust in human-agent teams. *Proceedings of the ACM on Human-Computer Interaction, 6*(GROUP), 1–29. https://dl.acm.org/doi/10.1145/3492832

REFERENCES

Ahuja, M. K., & Carley, K. M. (1999). Network structure in virtual organizations. *Organization Science, 10*(6), 741–757. https://doi.org/10.1287/orsc.10.6.741

Andres, H. P. (2011). Shared mental model development during technology-mediated collaboration. *International Journal of e-Collaboration, 7*(3), 14–30. https://www.igi-global.com/gateway/article/55425

Andres, H. P. (2013). Collaborative technology and dimensions of team cognition. *International Journal of Information Technology Project Management, 4*, 22–37. https://www.emerald.com/insight/content/doi/10.1108/02683941311298850/full/html

Antoni, C., & Hertel, G. (2009). Team processes, their antecedents and consequences: Implications for different types of teamwork. *European Journal of Work and Organizational Psychology, 18*(3), 253–266. https://www.tandfonline.com/doi/abs/10.1080/13594320802095502

Avolio, B. J., Sosik, J. J., Kahai, S. S., & Baker, B. (2014). E-leadership: Re-examining transformations in leadership source and transmission. *The Leadership Quarterly, 25*(1), 105–131. https://www.sciencedirect.com/science/article/pii/S1048984313001185?via%3Dihub

Baltes, B. B., Dickson, M. W., Sherman, M. P., Bauer, C. C., & LaGanke, J. S. (2002). Computer-mediated communication and group decision making: A meta-analysis. *Organizational Behavior and Human Decision Processes, 87*(1), 156–179. https://www.sciencedirect.com/science/article/abs/pii/S0749597801929619?via%3Dihub

Bell, B. S., & Kozlowski, S. W. J. (2002). A typology of virtual teams: Implications for effective leadership. *Group and Organization Management, 27*(1), 14–49. https://journals.sagepub.com/doi/10.1177/1059601102027001003

Breuer, C., Hüffmeier, J., & Hertel, G. (2016). Does trust matter more in virtual teams? A meta-analysis of trust and team effectiveness considering virtuality and documentation as moderators. *Journal of Applied Psychology, 101*(8), 1151–1177. https://psycnet.apa.org/doiLanding?doi=10.1037%2Fapl0000113

Burke, C. S., Stagl, K. C., Salas, E., Pierce, L., & Kendall, D. (2006). Understanding team adaptation: A conceptual analysis and model . *Journal of Applied Psychology, 91*(6), 1189. https://psycnet.apa.org/doiLanding?doi=10.1037%2F0021-9010.91.6.1189

Cannon-Bowers, J. A., Salas, E., & Converse, S. (1993). Shared mental models in expert team decision making. In N. J. Castellan (Ed.), *Individual and group decision making: Current issues* (pp. 221–246). Lawrence Erlbaum.

Carlson, J. R., & Zmud, R. W. (1999). Channel expansion theory and the experiential nature of media richness perceptions. *Academy of Management Journal, 42*(2), 153–170. https://amj.aom.org/cgi/doi/10.2307/257090

Carter, K. M., Mead, B. A., Stewart, G. L., Nielsen, J. D., & Solimeo, S. L. (2019). Reviewing work team design characteristics across industries: Combining meta-analysis and comprehensive synthesis. *Small Group Research, 50*(1), 138–188. https://journals.sagepub.com/doi/10.1177/1046496418797431

Chudoba, K. M., Wynn, E., Lu, M., & Watson-Manheim, M. B. (2005). How virtual are we? Measuring virtuality and understanding its impact in a global organization. *Information Systems Journal, 15*, 279–306. https://doi.org/10.1111/j.1365-2575.2005.00200.x

Daft, R. L., & Lengel, R. H. (1984). Information richness: A new approach to manager information processing and organization design. In B. Staw & L. L. Cummings (Eds.), *Research in organizational behavior* (pp. 191–233). JAI Press.

Daft, R. L., & Lengel, R. H. (1986). Organizational information requirements, media richness and structural design. *Management Science, 32*, 554–571. https://pubsonline.informs.org/doi/10.1287/mnsc.32.5.554

DeChurch, L. A., & Mesmer-Magnus, J. R. (2010). The cognitive underpinnings of effective teamwork: A meta-analysis. *The Journal of Applied Psychology, 95*, 32–53. https://psycnet.apa.org/doiLanding?doi=10.1037%2Fa0017328

Dennis, A. R., Fuller, R. M., & Valacich, J. S. (2008). Media, tasks, and communication processes: A theory of media synchronicity. *MIS Quarterly, 32*, 575–600. https://www.jstor.org/stable/25148857

Dennis, A. R., & Valacich, J. S. (1999). Rethinking media richness: Towards a theory of media synchronicity. In *Proceedings of the 32nd Hawaii international conference on system sciences: HICSS-32. Abstracts and CD-ROM of full papers* (p. 10). IEEE Computer Society Press. https://ieeexplore.ieee.org/document/772701

Dennis, A. R., Wixom, B. H., & Vandenberg, R. J. (2001). Understanding fit and appropriation effects in group support systems via meta-analysis. *MIS Quarterly, 25*(2), 167–193. https://www.jstor.org/stable/3250928

DeSanctis, G., & Poole, M. S. (1994). Capturing the complexity in advanced technology use: Adaptive structuration theory. *Organization Science, 5*(2), 121–147. https://pubsonline.informs.org/doi/10.1287/orsc.5.2.121

Dryer, D. C. (1999) Getting personal with computers: How to design personalities for agents. *Applied Artificial Intelligence, 13*(3), 273–295. https://www.tandfonline.com/doi/pdf/10.1080/088395199117423

D'Urso, S. C., & Rains, S. A. (2008). Examining the scope of channel expansion: A test of channel expansion theory with new and traditional communication media. *Management Communication Quarterly, 21*(4), 486–507. https://doi.org/10.1177/0893318907313712

Edmondson, A. C., Dillon, J. R., & Roloff, K. S. (2007). Three perspectives on team learning: Outcome improvement, task mastery, and group process. In J. P. Walsh & A. P. Brief (Eds.), *The academy of management annals* (pp. 269–314). Lawrence Erlbaum Associates.

Ellwart, T., Happ, C., Gurtner, A., & Rack, O. (2015). Managing information overload in virtual teams: Effects of a structured online team adaptation on cognition and performance. *European Journal of Work and Organizational Psychology, 24*(5), 812–826. https://www.tandfonline.com/doi/full/10.1080/1359432X.2014.1000873

Fjermestad, J. (2004). An analysis of communication mode in group support systems research. *Decision Support Systems, 37*(2), 239–263. https://doi.org/10.1016/S0167-9236(03)00021-6

Fuller, R. M., & Dennis, A. R. (2009). Does fit matter? The impact of task-technology fit and appropriation on team performance in repeated tasks. *Information Systems Research, 20*(1), 2–17. https://www.jstor.org/stable/23015458

Gevers, J. M. P., Rutte, C. G., & von Eerde, W. (2006). Meeting deadlines in work groups: Implicit and explicit mechanisms. *Applied Psychology: An International Review, 55*, 52–72. https://doi.org/10.1111/j.1464-0597.2006.00228.x

Gibson, C. B., & Gibbs, J. L. (2006). Unpacking the concept of virtuality: The effects of geographic dispersion, electronic dependence, dynamic structure, and national diversity on team innovation. *Administrative Science Quarterly, 51*(3), 451–495. https://doi.org/10.2189/asqu.51.3.451

Gilson, L. L., Maynard, M. T., Jones Young, N. C., Vartiainen, M., & Hakonen, M. (2015). Virtual teams research: 10 years, 10 themes, and 10 opportunities. *Journal of Management, 41*(5), 1313–1337. https://journals.sagepub.com/doi/10.1177/0149206314559946

Hackman, J. R. (1987). The design of work teams. In J. Lorsch (Ed.), *Handbook of organizational behavior* (pp. 315–342). Prentice Hall.

Handke, L., Costa, P. L., Klonek, F. E., O'Neill, T. A., & Parker, S. K. (2021). Team perceived virtuality: An emergent state perspective. *European Journal of Work and Organizational Psychology, 30*(5), 624–638. https://www.tandfonline.com/doi/full/10.1080/1359432X.2020.1806921

Handke, L., Schulte, E. M., Schneider, K., & Kauffeld, S. (2018). The medium isn't the message: Introducing a measure of adaptive virtual communication. *Cogent Arts & Humanities, 5*(1), 1–25. https://www.tandfonline.com/doi/full/10.1080/23311983.2018.1514953

Hantula, D. A., Kock, N., D'Arcy, J. P., & DeRosa, D. M. (2011). Media compensation theory: A Darwinian perspective on adaptation to electronic communication and collaboration. In G. Saad (Ed.), *Evolutionary psychology in the business sciences* (pp. 339–363). Springer. https://link.springer.com/chapter/10.1007/978-3-540-92784-6_13

Hartwig, A., Clarke, S., Johnson, S., & Willis, S. (2020). Workplace team resilience: A systematic review and conceptual development. *Organizational Psychology Review, 10*(3–4), 169–200. https://journals.sagepub.com/doi/10.1177/2041386620919476

Hertel, G., Geister, S., & Konradt, U. (2005). Managing virtual teams: A review of current empirical research. *Human Resource Management Review, 15*(1), 69–95. https://www.sciencedirect.com/science/article/abs/pii/S1053482205000033?via%3Dihub

Hoch, J. E., & Kozlowski, S. W. (2014). Leading virtual teams: Hierarchical leadership, structural supports, and shared team leadership. *Journal of Applied Psychology, 99*(3), 390–403. https://psycnet.apa.org/doi Landing?doi=10.1037%2Fa0030264

Hollingshead, A. B., McGrath, J. E., & O'Connor, K. M. (1993). Group task performance and communication technology: A longitudinal study of computer-mediated versus face-to-face work groups. *Small Group Research, 24*(3), 307–333. https://journals.sagepub.com/doi/10.1177/1046496493243003

Hosseini, M. R., Zavadskas, E., Xia, B., Chileshe, N., & Mills, A. (2017). Communications in hybrid arrangements: Case of Australian construction project teams. *Engineering Economics, 28*(3), 290–300. https://inzeko.ktu.lt/index.php/EE/article/view/13791

Ilgen, D. R., Hollenbeck, J. R., Johnson, M., & Jundt, D. (2005). Teams in organizations. *Annual Review of Psychology, 56,* 517–543. https://www.annualreviews.org/doi/10.1146/annurev.psych.56.091103.070250

Kahai, S., Jestire, R., & Huang, R. (2013). Effects of transformational and transactional leadership on cognitive effort and outcomes during collaborative learning within a virtual world . *British Journal of Educational Technology, 44*(6), 969–985. https://bera-journals.onlinelibrary.wiley.com/doi/10.1111/bjet.12105

Kirkman, B. L., & Mathieu, J. E. (2005). The dimensions and antecedents of team virtuality. *Journal of Management, 31*(5), 700–718. https://doi.org/10.1177/0149206305279113

Klein, C., DiazGranados, D., Salas, E., Le, H., Burke, C. S., Lyons, R., & Goodwin, G. F. (2009). Does team building work?. *Small Group Research, 40*(2), 181–222. https://journals.sagepub.com/doi/abs/10.1177/1046496408328821

Kock, N. (2004). The psychobiological model: Towards a new theory of computer-mediated communication based on Darwinian evolution. *Organization Science, 15*(3), 327–348. https://pubsonline.informs.org/doi/10.1287/orsc.1040.0071

Kock, N. (2005). What is e-collaboration. *International Journal of e-collaboration, 1*(1), 1–7. http://cits.tamiu.edu/kock/pubs/journals/2005journalijec/kock2005.pdf

Kozlowski, S. W. J., & Bell, B. S. (2008). *Team learning, development, and adaptation.* Lawrence Erlbaum Associates.

Kozlowski, S. W., & Ilgen, D. R. (2006). Enhancing the effectiveness of work groups and teams. *Psychological Science in the Public Interest, 7*(3), 77–124. https://doi.org/10.1111/j.1529-1006.2006.00030.x

Kozlowski, S. W., & Klein, K. J. (2000). A multilevel approach to theory and research in organizations: Contextual, temporal, and emergent processes. In K. J. Klein & S. W. Kozlowski (Eds.), *Multilevel theory, research and methods in organizations: Foundations, extensions, and new directions* (pp. 3–90). Jossey-Bass.

Lee, L. H., Braud, T., Zhou, P., Wang, L., Xu, D., Lin, Z., Kumar, A., Bermejo, C. & Hui, P. (2021). All one needs to know about metaverse: A complete survey on technological singularity, virtual ecosystem, and research agenda. https://doi.org/10.48550/arXiv.2110.05352

Lewis, K. (2003). Measuring transactive memory systems in the field: Scale development and validation. *Journal of Applied Psychology, 88,* 587–604. https://doi.org/10.1037/0021-9010.88.4.587

Lewis, K. (2004). Knowledge and performance in knowledge-worker teams: A longitudinal study of transactive memory systems. *Management Science, 50,* 1519–1533. https://pubsonline.informs.org/doi/10.1287/mnsc.1040.0257

Liang, D. W., Moreland, R., & Argote, L. (1995). Group versus individual training and group performance: The mediating role of transactive memory. *Personality and Social Psychology Bulletin, 21,* 384–393. https://journals.sagepub.com/doi/10.1177/0146167295214009

Lim, J., Yang, Y. P., & Zhong, Y. (2007). Computer-supported collaborative work and learning: A meta-analytic examination of key moderators in experimental GSS research. *International Journal of Web-Based Learning and Teaching Technologies, 2*(4), 40–71. https://doi.org/10.4018/jwltt.2007100104

Lin, C. P., He, H., Baruch, Y., & Ashforth, B. E. (2017). The effect of team affective tone on team performance: The roles of team identification and team cooperation. *Human Resource Management, 56*(6), 931–952. https://onlinelibrary.wiley.com/doi/10.1002/hrm.21810

Lipnack, J., & Stamps, J. (1997). *Virtual teams: Researching across space, time, and organizations with technology.* John Wiley & Sons.

Margolis, J. (2020). Multiple team membership: An integrative review. *Small Group Research, 51*(1), 48–86. https://journals.sagepub.com/doi/10.1177/1046496419883702

Marks, M. A., Mathieu, J. E., & Zaccaro, S. J. (2001). A temporally based framework and taxonomy of team processes. *Academy of Management Review, 26*(3), 356–376. https://www.jstor.org/stable/259182?origin=crossref

Mathieu, J. E., Heffner, T. S., Goodwin, G. F., Salas, E., & Cannon-Bowers, J. A. (2000). The influence of shared mental models on team process and performance. *Journal of Applied Psychology, 85,* 273–283. https://doi.org/10.1037/0021-9010.85.2.273

Mohammed, S., & Dumville, B. C. (2001). Team mental models in a team knowledge framework: Expanding theory and measurement across disciplinary boundaries. *Journal of Organizational Behavior, 22,* 89–106. https://onlinelibrary.wiley.com/doi/10.1002/job.86

Mohammed, S., Hamilton, K., Tesler, R., Mancuso, V., & McNeese, M. (2015). Time for temporal team mental models: Expanding beyond "what" and "how" to incorporate "when". *European Journal of Work and Organizational Psychology, 24,* 693–709. https://www.tandfonline.com/doi/full/10.1080/1359432X.2015.1024664

Müller, R., & Antoni, C. H. (2020). Individual perceptions of shared mental models of information and communication technology (ICT) and virtual team coordination and performance—The moderating role of flexibility in ICT use. *Group Dynamics: Theory, Research, and Practice, 24*(3), 186. https://psycnet.apa.org/fulltext/2020-48733-001.html

Müller, R., & Antoni, C. H. (2022). Effects of ICT shared mental models on team processes and outcomes. *Small Group Research, 53*(2), 307–335. https://journals.sagepub.com/doi/10.1177/1046496421997889

Oertel, R., & Antoni, C. H. (2014). Reflective team learning: Linking interfering events and team adaptation. *Team Performance Management, 20*(7–8), 328–342. https://www.emerald.com/insight/content/doi/10.1108/TPM-03-2014-0027/full/html

Oertel, R., & Antoni, C. H. (2015). Phase-specific relationships between team learning processes and transactive memory development. *European Journal of Work and Organizational Psychology, 24*(5), 726–741. https://www.tandfonline.com/doi/full/10.1080/1359432X.2014.1000872

O'Neill, T., McNeese, N., Barron, A., & Schelble, B. (2022). Human-autonomy teaming: A review and analysis of the empirical literature. *Human Factors, 64*(5) 904–938. https://doi.org/10.1177/0018720820960865

Ortiz de Guinea, A., Webster, J., & Staples, D. S. (2012). A meta-analysis of the consequences of virtualness on team functioning. *Information & Management, 49*(6), 301–308. https://www.sciencedirect.com/science/article/abs/pii/S0378720612000626?via%3Dihub

Parasuraman, R., Sheridan, T. B., & Wickens, C. D. (2000). A model for types and levels of human interaction with automation. *IEEE Transactions on Systems, Man, and Cybernetics—Part A: Systems and Humans*, *30*(3), 286–297. https://doi.org/10.1109/3468.844354

Purvanova, R. K., & Bono, J. E. (2009). Transformational leadership in context: Face-to-face and virtual teams. *The Leadership Quarterly*, 20(3), 343-357. https://doi.org/10.1016/j.leaqua.2009.03.004

Purvanova, R. K., & Kenda, R. (2022). The impact of virtuality on team effectiveness in organizational and non-organizational teams: A meta-analysis. *Applied Psychology*, *71*(3), 1082–1131. https://iaap-journals.onlinelibrary.wiley.com/doi/10.1111/apps.12348

Raetze, S., Duchek, S., Maynard, M. T., & Kirkman, B. L. (2021). Resilience in organizations: An integrative multilevel review and editorial introduction. *Group & Organization Management*, *46*(4), 607–656. https://journals.sagepub.com/doi/10.1177/10596011211032129

Raghuram, S., Hill, N. S., Gibbs, J. L., & Maruping, L. M. (2019). Virtual work: Bridging research clusters. *Academy of Management Annals*, *13*(1), 308–341. https://journals.aom.org/doi/10.5465/annals.2017.0020

Rains, S. A. (2005). Leveling the organizational playing field—Virtually: A meta-analysis of experimental research assessing the impact of group support system use on member influence behaviors. *Communication Research*, *32*(2), 193–234. https://journals.sagepub.com/doi/10.1177/0093650204273763

Ren, Y., & Argote, L. (2011). Transactive memory systems 1985–2010: An integrative framework of key dimensions, antecedents, and consequences. *The Academy of Management Annals*, *5*, 189–229. https://journals.aom.org/doi/10.5465/19416520.2011.590300

Schmidtke, J. M., & Cummings, A. (2017). The effects of virtualness on teamwork behavioral components: The role of shared mental models. *Human Resource Management Review*, *27*(4), 660–677. https://www.sciencedirect.com/science/article/abs/pii/S1053482216301036?via%3Dihub

Schulze, J., & Krumm, S. (2017). The "virtual team player." A review and initial model of knowledge, skills, abilities, and other characteristics for virtual collaboration. *Organizational Psychology Review*, *7*(1), 66–95. https://journals.sagepub.com/doi/10.1177/2041386616675522

Short, J., Williams, E., & Christie, B. (1976). *The social psychology of telecommunications*. John Wiley & Sons.

Shuffler, M. L., & Carter, D. R. (2018). Teamwork situated in multiteam systems: Key lessons learned and future opportunities. *American Psychologist*, *73*(4), 390. https://psycnet.apa.org/doiLanding?doi=10.1037%2Famp0000322

Watson-Manheim, M. B., Chudoba, K. M., & Crowston, K. (2012). Perceived discontinuities and constructed continuities in virtual work. *Information Systems Journal*, *22*(1), 29–52. https://doi.org/10.1108/09593840210444746

Wegner, D. M. (1987). Transactive memory: A contemporary analysis of the group mind. In B. Mullen & G. R. Goethals (Eds.), *Theories of group behavior* (pp. 185–208). Springer-Verlag.

Zaccaro, S. J., Dubrow, S., Torres, E. M., & Campbell, L. N. (2020). Multiteam systems: An integrated review and comparison of different forms. *Annual Review of Organizational Psychology and Organizational Behavior*, *7*, 479–503. https://doi.org/10.1146/annurev-orgpsych-012119-045418

Conny H. Antoni

JUSTICE IN TEAMS

INTRODUCTION

Organizational theory has increasingly paid attention to the investigation of justice. The interest shown by scholars and practitioners is based on the idea that justice is a strong predictor of employee attitudes and behaviors (e.g., Colquitt et al., 2013). These outcomes lie at different levels of construct and analysis. In fact, one of the most important advances in the justice literature was the transition from an individual-level to a multilevel approach to organizational justice, where the team level has achieved a prominent status (see Li, Cropanzano, & Molina, 2015). At least three interrelated drivers explain the interest in justice at the team level: (a) the shift toward team-based structures in organizations; (b) the expansion of scientific knowledge through the multilevel perspective; and (c) the development of techniques that facilitate statistical analyses beyond the individual level.

The shift toward team-based structures in organizations has stimulated the interest in justice in teams. Although the fragmentation and distribution of simple tasks among individual workers—present in the scientific management (Taylor, 1991)—were efficient strategies for the mass production of standard products, these strategies are being questioned in an era when consumers are more sophisticated and ask for differentiated products and services. To satisfy this complex demand, organizations need multi-tasking and multi-skilled employees working in teams, based on the assumption that this way of organizing the work is better "for an environment in which flexibility, innovation and problem solving at source are important" (Lanz, Miroudot, & Nordås, 2013, p. 211). The increasingly generalized use of teams in organizations creates an ideal context for the emergence and study of justice at the team level. Team members are subjected to similar stimuli, processes, and structures. They also have more opportunities to communicate with each other than in an individual-based organization of work. This context facilitates shared experiences and perceptions of justice beyond individual differences but also can result in potential conflicts and discrepancies among subgroups within the team in their interpretation of fairness.

Regarding the second driver, the consideration of different levels in the study of justice coincides with the expansion of scientific knowledge in organizational theory, where there is general consensus about the importance of going beyond the individual level in order to better understand organizational behavior. If we seriously consider the organization from a systems approach, we cannot restrict research efforts to the individual subsystem. Relevant constructs emerge at different levels (individual, team, organization as a whole), and investigating bridges between levels of construct and analysis is an indicator of the maturity of theory and research (Kozlowski & Klein, 2000). Of course, individual differences in justice perceptions exist, but team members are also able to develop shared perceptions of justice regarding the way the supervisor and other sources of justice (e.g., the organization as a whole, peers) treat the team as a whole (e.g., Naumann & Bennett, 2000; Stoverink, Umphress, Gardner, & Miner, 2014). Approaches such as symbolic interaction or the attraction/selection/attrition model, which we discuss later, help to provide theoretical arguments for the existence of team-level justice. Nevertheless, the internal dynamics of teams are complex, and different views about justice can coexist within the same team (Roberson & Colquitt, 2005).

Finally, the development of techniques and methods of conducting research has also facilitated the consideration of justice at the team level in empirical research. The individual is usually the original level for the measurement of constructs, including justice. Thus, scholars traditionally use mean ratings of measures at the individual level to obtain indicators of variables at the team level. To do so, researchers should not only have theoretical arguments but also statistical information about the existence of agreement among team members. During the past few decades, different techniques have flourished to assess the degree to which raters (e.g., team workers) assign similar judgments to an object (e.g., treatment received by the supervisor). Well-known examples of these techniques are the interrater agreement index (rwg) by James, Demaree, and Wolf (1993) and average deviation indices (AD) by Burke, Finkelstein, and Dusig (1999). Researchers are also interested in investigating cross-level effects, such as how team-level variables (e.g., team-level justice) can impact individual-level variables (e.g., individual commitment). To this end, the use of hierarchical linear models has become popularized (Raudenbush & Bryk, 2002). In addition, to capture the complex and sometimes conflictive dynamic of teams, algorithms have been developed to assess discrepancies and the potential existence of subgroups (see Meyer, Glenz, Antino, Rico, & González-Romá, 2014). Over time, all of these methodological efforts, as well as others, have facilitated adequate research on team-level justice (e.g., Molina, Moliner, Martínez-Tur, Cropanzano, & Peiró, 2015; Yang, Mossholder, & Peng, 2007).

Research on justice at the team level has largely imitated the steps that have been taken in the study of justice at the individual level, examining areas such as the dimensionality of justice, main antecedents and outcomes, and sources of justice. This strategy has led to significant advances. However, other approaches that consider the particularities of teams have significantly contributed to the knowledge and identified new paths in the study of justice at the team level. With this in mind, this article is organized as follows. First, it summarizes the transition from the individual to the team level in the study of justice in organizations. Second, it describes the parallelism between justice at the individual and team levels. Finally, it analyzes how considering unique characteristics of teams contributes to knowledge and implications for future research.

FROM THE INDIVIDUAL TO THE TEAM: A BRIEF SUMMARY

In general terms, organizational justice is defined as the degree to which an element of the organizational environment is perceived as fair, according to a certain rule or standard (Cropanzano, Rupp, Mohler, & Schminke, 2001). Over time, justice research has evolved from the individual level exclusively to a multilevel perspective where the team level has acquired relevance. During this transition, topics and perspectives in the investigation of justice at the team level were similar to those studied at the individual level, but gradually more specific team-related issues have emerged. The team refers to a group of peers who coordinate their efforts to achieve shared objectives. Justice research beyond the individual focuses predominantly on this type of team. Nevertheless, other research studies considered conceptually close levels (e.g., department) where the level of integration of members is lower. In any case, researchers assume the existence of justice perceptions beyond the individual.

Justice at the Individual Level.   About 50 years ago, John Stacey Adams (1965) published his influential paper, helping to establish the foundations of equity theory in understanding interpersonal relations and facilitating the transfer of justice to the investigation of organizational life. For years, justice in the workplace and equity were equivalent concepts, although scholars proposed other rules (e.g., equality) to define justice (Deutsch, 1975). Accordingly, *distributive justice* was prominent during the early stages of the conceptualization and research on organizational justice. Distributive justice emphasizes worker evaluations of outcome fairness. Workers consider their investments (time, effort, etc.) and benefits (promotion, salary, etc.), and they also compare their own investments and benefits with the inputs and outputs of a referent. When these ratios are balanced, the individual experiences equity feelings, while any disturbance in this balance has potentially negative effects. Workers perceiving underbenefiting situations experience anger because they can feel that others are taking advantage of them, while overbenefiting perceptions produce a sense of indebtedness (Buunk & Schaufeli, 1999). However, due to humans' negativity bias (a special human sensitivity to negative events) (Baumeister, Bratslavsky, Finkenauer, & Vohs, 2001), some research studies have questioned the idea that negative effects of under- versus overbenefiting perceptions are symmetrical in their magnitudes. In other words, underbenefiting perceptions have more accentuated negative effects than overbenefiting ones (Martínez-Tur, Estreder, Moliner, Sánchez-Hernández, & Peiró, 2016). Positive reactions toward advantageous inequity may even increase in workers without a process through which to become socialized in deontology (Moliner, Martínez-Tur, Peiró, Ramos, & Cropanzano, 2013) and in situations where cognitive processing is strongly limited (Van den Bos, Peters, Bobocel, & Ybema, 2006). In addition, there are low equity sensitivity individuals who are tolerant to overbenefiting situations and intolerant to underbenefiting ones (see Sauley & Bedeian, 2000).

Although the study of distributive justice remains relevant, over time, scholars have become aware that considering outcome fairness as the only way to define justice in work settings is limited. Research has also focused on procedures, introducing social elements of justice in the workplace (see Folger & Greenberg, 1985, for an early review). Workers consider not only outcomes in their evaluation of justice but also the procedures used to make decisions about the distribution of outcomes. This dimension of justice, called *procedural justice*, pays attention to the rules underlying the implementation of procedures (Thibaut & Walker, 1975). In his influential categorization of rules, Leventhal (1976, 1980) argued that fairness increases when procedures are consistently applied, correctable, free from bias, representative of all parties, and consistent with ethical standards. The distinction between outcomes and procedures has been a challenge for scholars. Usually, distributive justice has been associated with outcome-oriented concerns, while procedural justice is more relation-oriented, indicating that the recipient is a respected member of the organization (Blader & Tyler, 2005). Researchers have explored the role of both types of justice in the nomological network. For example, according to the two-factor model (see Gilliland & Chan, 2001), procedural justice is especially related to system-referenced variables (e.g., commitment), whereas distributive justice is closely associated with personal-referenced variables (e.g., pay satisfaction). However, this duality probably simplifies the motivations that underlie organizational justice. As Cropanzano and Rupp proposed (2002), individuals also act fairly for moral reasons because they view this behavior as the "right thing to do" (Cropanzano & Rupp, 2002, p. 268).

In addition to distributive and procedural justice, Bies and Moag (1986) proposed the existence of a third dimension of justice called *interactional justice*. This justice facet captures the quality of the treatment the worker receives from others. This proposal stimulated a debate about the differentiation between procedural and interactional justice. Some scholars suggested that interactional justice does not have an independent status because it only describes the social component of procedural justice (e.g., Tyler & Bies, 1990), while other researchers argued for a distinction between procedural and interactional justice, indicating that they present differential correlations with criterion variables (see Cropanzano et al., 2001). Some authors even refined the structure of organizational justice by proposing a four-factor model (Greenberg, 1993). Greenberg indicated that interactional justice could be divided into two justice dimensions: interpersonal and informational justice. *Interpersonal justice* describes the quality of the treatment (e.g., dignity), whereas *informational justice* refers to the information provided (e.g., the degree to which decisions are explained and justified). Relevant empirical evidence supported the four-factor model by demonstrating that individuals are able to distinguish among the four justice dimensions (Colquitt, 2001) and by observing that each dimension has a different nomological status (Colquitt, Conlon, Wesson, Porter, & Ng, 2001).

The differentiation between specific dimensions is still persistent in the literature (e.g., Johnson, Lanaj, & Barnes, 2014). However, an increasing number of scholars question whether using the different facets exclusively is beneficial to improving knowledge, and they also propose the consideration of overall justice (e.g., Lind, 2001). Ambrose and Schminke (2007) indicated that overall justice offers a better representation of the way individuals perceive justice than discrete facets do. It helps to evaluate the total effect of justice on outcomes, and it provides a more parsimonious approach to justice. These researchers also argued that although workers differentiate between different dimensions of justice, the overall justice perception is the direct driver of final reactions. Ambrose and Schminke (2009) confirmed this argument by testing the mediating role of overall justice in the relation between specific justice dimensions (distributive, procedural, and interactional) and employee attitudes.

One way to deal with this debate about justice dimensions versus overall justice is to explore the connection between justice and outcomes and the extent to which justice dimensions differ in their predictive power. In the first meta-analysis about organizational justice, Colquitt et al. (2001) did not confirm the predominance of only one justice dimension (e.g., distributive justice) over the rest of the justice facets in predicting several relevant outcomes (e.g., job satisfaction, organizational commitment, evaluation of authority, organizational citizenship behavior, withdrawal, performance). By contrast, their findings partially supported the two-factor model. Distributive justice showed stronger relationships with some personal-referenced outcomes (e.g., outcome satisfaction) than procedural justice did, while procedural justice had stronger links to several system-referenced outcomes (e.g., organizational commitment) than distributive justice. Colquitt et al. (2001) also observed that interpersonal or informational justice predominates (due to its interpersonal character) over procedural justice in predicting agent-referenced outcomes (e.g., citizenship behaviors directed at the supervisor). In a more recent meta-analysis, Colquitt et al. (2013) proposed two routes from justice dimensions (distributive, procedural, interpersonal, and informational) to performance and citizenship behaviors. Based on social exchange theory and a cognitive approach to human behavior, in the first route, the effects to justice dimensions were channeled through several indicators of social exchange quality (trust, organizational commitment, perceived organizational support, and leader-member exchange). By contrast, the second route establishes state affect (positive and negative) as the mediator between justice dimensions and outcomes. The authors found partial empirical support for these two routes.

Thus, the investigation of individuals' justice experiences has mainly been characterized by exploring the dimensionality of justice, the analysis of the role of overall justice in understanding individual interpretations of justice and their consequences, and the differential effects of justice dimensions on relevant outcomes (performance, commitment, etc.). To some extent, this research at the individual level has inspired the efforts at the team level.

The Birth and Early Stages of Justice at the Team Level. During the past 15 years, and parallel to the investigation of the individual-level construct, research on team-level justice has strongly emerged (e.g., Rupp, Bashshur, & Liao, 2007). Although there are antecedents (Mossholder, Bennett, & Martin, 1998), the seminal effort to delimitate team justice has been attributed to Naumann and Bennet (2000). These authors focused on the well-established procedural justice dimension in introducing the concept of *justice climate*. More specifically, they defined procedural justice climate as "a distinct group-level cognition about how a work group as a whole is treated" (Naumann & Bennet, 2000, p. 882). From that time on, many research papers have taken the team level into consideration. This is based on the idea that justice is associated with a collective identity beyond the individual. In fact, fairness positively affects the activation of interdependent identity (Johnson & Lord, 2010). In their recent review, Li et al. (2015) identified 46 relevant papers that used justice climate as a construct beyond the individual level. Of them, 21 referred to the team (or work group) level explicitly, while 17 additional studies considered a conceptually close level (department, work-unit, etc.). Other levels of construct and analysis (e.g., organization as a whole, alliances) have been used infrequently. Focusing on papers reviewed by Li et al. (2015) that used justice at the team or similar levels (work-group, work-unit, department, etc.), 30 of them considered procedural justice, 11 assessed interactional justice or some of its specific facets (interpersonal and/or informational justice), 8 evaluated distributive justice, and 4 recent papers used some version of overall justice. According to this analysis, we can conclude that research on justice in teams has considered procedural justice to be the critical dimension, given the connection between this justice dimension and the particularities of teams. According to the *relational* model (Lind & Tyler, 1988), team members are very sensitive to the procedural treatment they receive as a team because the group satisfies identity needs and develops norms about fairness. Consequently, unfair procedural treatment directed toward any member of the team is also considered an offense to the team as a whole (Tyler & Lind, 1992). Roberson and Colquitt (2005) also considered that procedural justice is the most influential dimension in the emergence of justice at the team level, due to its visibility and the common existence of formal procedural practices across teams. Despite the predominance of procedural justice, other justice dimensions have also been considered in the investigation of team-level justice, and statistical analyses related to data aggregation revealed that teams are able to share perceptions about distributive (e.g., Moliner et al., 2005, pp. 105–106), interactional (e.g., Spell & Arnold, 2007, pp. 735–736), and overall (Priesemuth, Arnaud, & Schminke, 2013, p. 241) justice. The construction of justice climate can emerge across justice dimensions through different mechanisms. For example, social interaction and exchange of information among team members can occur in different types of justice events—including distribution of resources, procedures, and interpersonal treatment received by the supervisor/manager—facilitating a shared view of different justice dimensions (see Spell & Arnold, 2007). Approaches to understanding the emergence of justice at the team level are discussed later.

Therefore, the use of the team level plays a main role in the current justice research, coinciding with the generalization of groups in organizations. Research efforts have followed two main directions. First, scholars have elaborated theoretical arguments and found empirical evidence to understand how shared perceptions of justice emerge at the team level. Second, research has explored the impact of team-level justice on relevant outcomes.

Regarding theoretical foundations, justice at the team level is clearly linked to the long research tradition on organizational climate. During the first decades of the 20th century, Kurt Lewin and colleagues investigated the impact of social climates or atmospheres—introducing different kinds of leadership—on behaviors and attitudes of team members (Lewin, Lippitt, & White, 1939). They assumed an interactionist approach to human behavior, where both the person and the situation are simultaneously considered. Building on this contribution by Lewin and colleagues, the climate concept was introduced into organizational psychology. The influential review by James and Jones (1974) facilitated this incorporation of the climate concept into the research agenda. These scholars distinguished between objective characteristics of the organizational context and interpretations people make of that context. Objective characteristics were considered as independent variables with significant consequences for worker perceptions. Accordingly, a top-down investigation was carried out, with worker interpretations mediating the relationship between objective contexts and individual-level outcomes (see Kozlowski & Klein, 2000). James and Jones also recommended differentiating between "climate regarded as an organizational attribute and climate regarded as an individual attribute" (James & Jones, 1974, p. 1108). This suggestion has had a strong influence on climate research in teams and organizations. Following the proposal by James and Jones, an increasing number of scholars have investigated the existence of homogeneity among organizational members in their climate perceptions, describing an emergent property of teams and organizations beyond the individual level (see Ostroff, Kinicki, & Tamkins, 2003).

In addition, one of the relevant advances in climate research has been the proposal of *specific climates*. In the early stages of climate research, scholars concentrated their efforts on molar dimensions. Over time, however, researchers have introduced several different specific climates associated with organizational or team goals (e.g., service, safety, innovation). As Schneider, Wheeler, and Cox (1992) indicated, "strategically focused climate measures produce stronger relationships with specific organizational outcomes than less-focused measures" (p. 705). A specific climate emerges because the topic in question is relevant to the organization or the team (Dietz, Pugh, & Wiley, 2004). Therefore, different specific climates can exist in the organization simultaneously (Martínez-Tur, Tordera, Peiró, & Potocnik, 2011; Schneider, White, & Paul, 1998). With this in mind, Naumann and Bennet (2000, p. 882) tested the existence of justice climate as a new specific climate, focusing on the procedural justice dimension. To do so, they used the three mechanisms proposed by Schneider and Reichers (1983) to understand the creation of climates: (a) the symbolic interaction approach; (b) the attraction/selection/attrition (ASA) model; and (c) the structuralist approach.

The symbolic interaction approach argues that the team creates the ideal context for the emergence of shared views. Members pertaining to a specific team have more opportunities for social interaction with each other than with members of other teams. This social interaction allows members of a team to develop similar interpretations of organizational life.

Naumann and Bennet (2000) used team cohesion to test this proposal because, in cohesive teams, members present high levels of interaction with each other and mutual influence. Naumann and Bennet (2000) confirmed this hypothesis, observing that cohesion is positively and significantly related to the level of agreement on procedural justice within teams. Other quite similar arguments and approaches have also been considered to support the existence of justice climate, also focusing on the exchange of information and experiences. Degoey (2000) referred to cognitive and emotional contagion processes, where social interaction again plays a critical role. When information is ambiguous and emotionally charged, members of the same team tend to interact and exchange information in order to reduce the ambiguity by creating a shared interpretation among team members. Whitman, Caleo, Carpenter, Horner, and Bernerth (2012) and Li et al. (2015) used social information processing (SIP) to argue that workers from the same team or unit level discuss justice events, facilitating agreement in their interpretations. Roberson (2006) argued that teams activate sense-making in the creation of justice climate. Sense-making "is a process of social construction in which individuals interpret and explain their experiences, which become rationalized and objectified, thereby influencing individuals' view of reality" (Roberson, 2006, p. 178). Because it is not easy to access objective information, the sense-making process helps team members to exchange information and create a consensual view of justice. Whitman et al. (2012), based on fairness heuristic theory (FHT), interpreted this sense-making process as a collective heuristic (or shortcut), where team members search for justice signals through interaction, allowing a shared interpretation of authorities' behavior. Despite the different labels and perspectives, the final argument of all these approaches is similar: team members are motivated to discuss organizational life, including justice, and in doing so they create consensus about justice. Roberson (2006) found empirical evidence supporting this proposal. Teams that participated in discussions about their collective experiences and extended this discussion over time presented high agreement about procedural and distributive justice dimensions.

The ASA model (Schneider, 1987; Schneider, Goldstein, & Smith, 1995) can be summarized as the following process: workers are attracted to others who have similar physical characteristics, personality traits, education level, and so on; selection processes in organizations also tend to incorporate people with similar characteristics; and workers who do not fit the predominant profile are more likely to try to leave the organization. Subsequently, the model predicts that teams evolve toward homogeneity over time. Therefore, it is reasonable to expect that when teams are composed of similar members, shared justice perceptions are likely to emerge. Naumann and Bennet (2000) predicted that (un)fair events directed toward similar peers can be extended to the other team members, creating consensual views about (in)justice. Degoey (2000) suggested that people are more willing to share information and experiences about justice with colleagues who are similar, facilitating similar perceptions. Colquitt, Noe, and Jackson (2002) argued that diversity in teams increases internal discrepancies in the perception, interpretation, and evaluation of reality, including justice events. Empirical evidence supporting the expected positive relationship between homogeneity and shared perceptions of justice at the team level is mixed (Colquitt et al., 2002; Naumann & Bennet, 2000). Thus, it is likely that third factors play a role in the way homogeneity/heterogeneity impacts shared perceptions of justice. For example, socialization can be a successful organizational strategy to create similar mental models (see Li et al., 2015), reducing the effects of diversity on justice climate, even in heterogeneous groups.

The structuralist approach has received less attention than symbolic interaction approaches and the ASA model. According to structuralism (Schneider & Reichers, 1983), the mere exposure to similar policies, practices, and procedures facilitates shared climates because recipients are subjected to the same stimuli. Naumann and Bennet (2000) transferred this argument to the emergence of procedural justice climate. They assumed that supervisors are climate engineers. If supervisors are visible in implementing policies and delivering justice, uniformity in procedural justice perceptions among team members is likely to increase. Naumann and Bennet confirmed this hypothesis: supervisors' visibility in managing the team was positively related to team members' agreement in terms of procedural justice.

All these theoretical approaches (symbolic interaction, contagion, SIP, FHT, ASA, and structuralism) suggest that the creation of justice climate at the team level can follow different routes: interaction and exchange of information and experiences among team members; uniform composition of the team; and exposure to similar stimuli in organizations. These theoretical proposals and empirical evidence were necessary prerequisites to taking further steps. Once the existence of justice at the team level was confirmed as an emergent property beyond individual differences, relationships between justice climate in teams and other variables could be investigated. Whitman et al. (2012) carried out a meta-analysis that helps to understand the impact of justice climate on a number of outcomes. In general, they found moderate-to-substantial relations with four criteria that are relevant in team effectiveness: attitudes (e.g., satisfaction, commitment); processes (e.g., citizenship behaviors, cooperation); withdrawal (e.g., absenteeism, turnover intentions); and performance (e.g., customer satisfaction, financial performance). The magnitude of these relationships is higher when the level of the referent (in the formulation of items) is collective—"we"—compared to the individual referent in items—"I"—and when the level of analysis is the team (as opposed to the organization as a whole). Whitman et al. (2012) also observed that distributive justice at the team level has the strongest relation with performance, while interactional justice has the strongest link to processes. These differential results allowed them to propose that instrumental versus relational motives have a role in the impact of team-level justice on outcomes. The instrumental model proposes that people value justice as a way to achieve economic and material benefits (Thibaut & Walker, 1975). Accordingly, high distributive justice at the team level stimulates the combined effort of team members, maximizing team performance and achieving rewards, which explains the strong association between distributive justice and performance at the team level. By contrast, Whitman et al. (2012, p. 784) attributed the strong relationship between interactional justice at the team level and processes (e.g., citizenship behaviors) to relational motives. When supervisors/managers treat team members adequately, teams are motivated to display helping behaviors and cooperation.

Regarding interactive results, Li et al. (2015) concluded in their review that justice at the team level interacts with environmental and employee personality variables in predicting outcomes. In addition, they observed that the literature, based on the individual level, connects justice climate to leadership and organizational changes. A few papers have tested the link from servant, ethical, and transformational leadership to justice at the team level. Leaders

888 · JUSTICE IN TEAMS

focusing on follower development (servant leadership) and the ability to inspire the followers to contribute to the organization's mission (transformational leadership) increase procedural justice at the team level, whereas ethical leaders increase interactional justice in teams. Li et al. (2015) also analyzed some research studies about change process fairness, a team-level construct that describes the fairness of change processes in organizations. In general, findings indicate that, under some circumstances, the fairness of change processes helps to understand changes and how they are interpreted within the organization.

In sum, during the past decade researchers have introduced the concept of justice climate, and the team level has had a prominent status. Interestingly, theoretical arguments and statistical findings have supported the existence of an emergent reality beyond individual perceptions. In addition, the connection between justice at the team level and critical outcomes and processes has legitimated justice in teams as a relevant construct.

THE PARALLELISM BETWEEN INDIVIDUAL AND TEAM LEVELS

Many research studies on justice in teams have assumed an isomorphic structure across levels and analogous relationships with outcomes at both individual and team levels. This general picture describes a parallelism between the individual and team levels in the investigation of justice, where scholars' concerns and responses have been very similar, despite studying different levels of construct. This parallelism is summarized in different aspects below.

- The interest of researchers in the dimensionality of justice has been transferred from the individual to the team level. Although the research in teams began with procedural justice (Naumann & Bennet, 2000) and this dimension remains predominant, the literature about justice at the team level has progressively incorporated the other dimensions. Several theoretical models (symbolic interaction, contagion, SIP, FHT, ASA, and structuralism) make it possible to support the existence of identical justice dimensions across levels, creating an isomorphic perspective where the dimensionality of justice at the individual level is transferred to the team level. Even the concern for overall justice, initiated at the individual level, was recently transferred to the team level (e.g., Priesemuth et al., 2013).
- This parallelism can also be observed in the prediction of outcomes, comparing the meta-analysis by Colquitt et al. (2001) at the individual level and the meta-analysis by Whitman et al. (2012) about justice climate. The magnitudes of the relationships between justice and relevant outcomes were similar at the individual and team levels: "the patterns of the relationships at the unit level appear to be either similar or slightly greater in magnitude than the individual-level relations" (Whitman et al., 2012, p. 784). In addition, Whitman et al. (2012) also observed parallelisms with the individual level in the differential relations between justice dimensions and outcomes, supporting the two-factor model: "These findings are in line with individual-level research (e.g., Colquitt, 2001)... that has suggested that instrumental and relational motives play a role in the different construct relations" (p. 784). Thus, scholars explore analogous relationships with outcomes for justice at the individual level and justice at the team level.

- Most of the papers about justice in teams use the traditional sources of justice existing in research studies at the individual level. Thus, measures in papers ask team members about their perceptions of the degree to which an external authority—usually the supervisor/manager or the organization as a whole—treats the team adequately (e.g., Moliner et al., 2005).
- The parallelism is again present in the investigation of leadership as a relevant antecedent of justice. The tradition at the individual level (e.g., Pillai, Scandura, & Williams, 1999) was transferred to the first research studies on leadership as a predictor of collective justice (see Ehrhart, 2004, for research at the department level).
- Scholars also transferred the study of the role of justice in organizational changes from the individual to the team level (see Li et al., 2015, p. 146). More specifically, the investigation of procedural justice in organizational changes at the individual level (e.g., Brockner et al., 1994) has been translated into the team-level construct called *change process fairness climate* (Caldwell, Herold, & Fedor, 2004; Herold, Fedor, & Caldwell, 2007) to understand worker reactions to organizational changes.

This parallelism between the individual and team levels is logical. Scholars have used the individual level as a successful model from which to build the concept of justice at the team level. Additionally, justice at the team level is able to predict worker behaviors after controlling for justice at the individual level (e.g., Naumann & Bennet, 2000). Thus, the predictive power has increased with the incorporation of justice at the team level. Nevertheless, future research can produce qualitative changes by considering what is unique about or specific to teams.

PARTICULARITIES OF JUSTICE AT THE TEAM LEVEL: IMPLICATIONS FOR FUTURE RESEARCH

Research may benefit from the consideration of particularities of justice in teams that are not present at the individual level. Some research efforts have focused on these particularities, showing new ways to make contributions to the existing knowledge. Accordingly, two promising areas of research are proposed: (a) faultlines and subgrouping and (b) intergroup justice.

Beyond Justice Climate Strength: Faultlines and Subgrouping in Teams. One exciting research area in team-level justice is justice climate strength. Whereas justice climate refers to the level of justice perceived by a team, justice climate strength describes the level of agreement within the team with regard to the treatment team members receive. Again, Naumann and Bennet (2000) were responsible for introducing this concept in the justice literature. Some scholars have focused on factors that explain strength (agreement). As mentioned above, all these efforts (e.g., Colquitt et al., 2002; Naumann & Bennet, 2000; Roberson, 2006) helped to establish justice at the team level as a construct with an independent status. It was assumed that teams were subjected to circumstances (e.g., information exchange) that facilitated agreement. Thus, it can be concluded that climate at the team level exists as an emergent property beyond individuals.

Other scholars have been interested in examining the role of justice climate strength in models for predicting justice outcomes. Some studies have explored the mediating role of justice climate strength in the relationship between leadership and outcomes (e.g., Ogunfowora, 2013). It was assumed that leaders would have an influence on justice climate strength (e.g., through variability in their behaviors) that could be translated, in turn, into outcomes. Strength has also been considered as a moderator. Colquitt et al. (2002) observed that relationships between the justice climate level and outcomes (absenteeism and team performance) were stronger in teams with high justice agreement. They interpreted this effect of strength according to the fairness heuristic (shortcut). When strength is high, the heuristic is shared among members and the justice climate level is automatically translated into outcomes. By contrast, in teams where strength is low, members have to reconcile perspectives, and this reduces the effects of justice climate on outcomes. Similarly, based on the situational strength concept, Moliner et al. (2005) proposed that agreement increases consistency in affective responses, influencing the predictability of units' average burnout. They confirmed that the link from interactional justice climate to team exhaustion is higher for high interactional justice strength than for low interactional justice strength.

High or low strength is a particularity of teams that contribute to knowledge, avoiding the parallelism with the individual level. However, behavior within teams is complex and cannot be limited to the level and strength of justice climate. For example, different subgroups can exist within the same team. Since the first scientific studies on organizational theory, this phenomenon has been identified and described (e.g., Henderson & Mayo, 1936, pp. 407–408). The shift toward team-based structures in organizations may facilitate shared perceptions within numerous teams, but, paradoxically, this shift toward teams also provides an opportunity to observe their complexity and the difficulty, in many cases, of conceiving of the team members as part of a single group. Changes related to workforce mobility, globalization, and the specialization of team members are factors that may be increasing diversity within teams, creating adequate conditions for subgrouping (Meyer et al., 2014). The incorporation of virtual technologies in teams also has an influence. Electronic communication allows instantaneous exchanges among team members across time and space, but it reduces their direct and shared experiences (Jarvenpaa, Knoll, & Leidner, 1998). The generalized use of teams, combined with high levels of diversity and the use of information and communication technologies, creates conditions for subgrouping within teams because of *faultlines*. Although the faultline concept comes from geography (intersection between two tectonic plates), Lau and Murnighan (1998) adapted it to the study of teams. Thus, they referred to faultlines as "hypothetical dividing lines that may split a group into subgroups based on one or more attributes" (Lau & Murnighan, 1998, p. 328).

An increasing number of scholars are interested in faultlines and the subgrouping phenomenon. Although some research studies have created subgroups through experimental conditions in the lab (Rico, Sánchez-Manzanares, Antino, & Lau, 2012), most efforts have been conducted in the field. Research increasingly explores multiple characteristics or attributes of teams simultaneously in understanding faultlines (e.g., Thatcher, Jehn, & Zanutto, 2003) rather than evaluating just one demographic characteristic. In addition, there are different measures of faultlines to diagnose the potential existence of subgroups in a real context (Meyer et al., 2014). Using one measure or another depends on the research question. For example, the *Fau* measure (Thatcher et al., 2003) of faultlines assumes the existence of two well-differentiated subgroups, while the *ASW* measure (Meyer & Glenz, 2013) helps to detect multiple subgroups.

Some researchers have analyzed factors that can explain the existence of faultlines and sub-groups within teams. In their review, Roberson and Colquitt (2005) referred to member diversity, leader-member exchange (LMX), and dispersion. *Member diversity* usually reduces communication in teams, and communication between dissimilar team members tends to be infrequent, not reciprocated, and weak. Diversity can also facilitate differentiated functions and roles within teams, hindering communication between members with different statuses and facilitating subgrouping. In line with the *LMX theory*, leaders distribute resources according to the contribution of each team member. High- versus low-quality relations between the leader and team members can create subgroups (e.g., core vs. peripheral team members). Finally, *dispersion* also facilitates the emergence of subgroups because the physical proximity that allows formal and spontaneous interaction is limited within the team. Other research efforts have focused on understanding the effects of faultlines and subgroups. In general, a detrimental impact of faultlines on team-level outcomes (performance, satisfaction, etc.) is observed, and it is accentuated if team members actively perceive the faultline (see Thatcher & Patel, 2011, 2012, for meta-analyses). The main theoretical argument used to understand the negative effects of faultlines is related to categorization and social identity approaches. Each group within the team perceives the members of other groups as pertaining to a different social category, hindering the necessary cooperation, especially if the categories are salient for team members (Thatcher & Patel, 2011). In line with this argument, González-Roma and Hernández (2014) observed that subgrouping in a team climate of support from the organization increases team conflict and reduces communication quality within teams, after controlling for climate level and climate strength. Faultlines and climate strength are different—although related—concepts. Strength assumes uniformity, reflecting variability in agreement within the team. In contrast, faultlines assume non-uniformity, describing the existence of different sub-groups within the team (see González-Roma & Hernández, 2014, p. 1044). Regarding justice, research is at the starting point. Bezrukova, Spell, and Perry (2011) investigated the influence of faultlines on coping with injustice. Spell, Bezrukova, Haar, and Spell (2011) found, using a sample from 42 teams, that faultlines moderated the relationships between distributive justice, task conflict, and role conflict.

The investigation of faultlines and subgrouping in teams offers additional relevant input to future research on justice at the team level in at least two ways. First, the adequate identification and assessment of faultlines within teams, based on justice perceptions, is a necessary step. Fortunately, in other research areas, scholars have developed different algorithms and guidelines for choosing the right measure combination (Meyer et al., 2014). These efforts can facilitate an optimal starting point for the identification of faultlines associated with justice perceptions. Second, there are theoretical arguments to propose and test models where faultlines and subgrouping play a role (Roberson & Colquitt, 2005). For example, differential or asymmetrical LMX can produce subgroups based on justice interpretations that, in turn, influence team effectiveness. This type of research can contribute to the knowledge by considering unique aspects of teams.

Beyond Peer Justice: Inter-Group Justice. As mentioned above, most papers about justice in teams have followed the literature at the individual level to define sources of justice (see Li et al., 2015). For this reason, the typical source of justice considered in team-level justice is an external authority (supervisors/managers and the organization as a whole). However, Cropanzano and colleagues initiated the study of an aspect that is specific to and significant for groups: peer justice. Instead of looking for the source of justice in an external authority, they focused on the nature of teams by investigating how team members who cooperate in the achievement of common goals treat each other. In fact, they defined peer justice as a "shared perception regarding how individuals who work together within the same unit and who do not have formal authority over each other judge the fairness with which they treat one another" (Cropanzano, Li, & Benson, 2011, p. 568). In this first empirical study of this topic, they validated the peer justice construct and found two mediating effects. First, peer justice is related to citizenship behaviors via interpersonal team processes (cohesion, efforts, and interpersonal support in the team). Second, peer justice is associated with team performance through communication, coordination, and contribution of team members. The main contribution of a second empirical study (Li, Cropanzano, & Bagger, 2013) was structural. These authors found that the best way to represent peer justice (and justice climate) is through a hierarchical two-level model. The first-order factors were the three typical justice dimensions (distributive, procedural, and interactional), whereas the second-order factor was overall justice. Recently, Molina et al. (2015) investigated peer justice and justice climate in a cross-level relationship between teams and customers in the health care industry. They observed that both justice climate and peer justice are related to customers' quality of life through service quality delivered by teams. However, two different routes were identified. Justice climate improved customers' quality of life through functional service quality (efficiency of the team in delivering the core service), whereas peer justice followed a relational service quality route (emotional benefits above and beyond the core service).

Although research on peer justice is in its infancy, it makes it possible to study aspects that are genuinely associated with the internal life of teams and can stimulate future initiatives in research. The continuity in the study of peer justice will provide advances in justice research, but future research can also make significant progress by questioning the universality of certain principles underlying peer justice research. Peer justice assumes a shared perception among team members about how they treat one other, with variability in the agreement in terms of strength. However, this uniformity is not universal in teams. The identification of faultlines and subgroups within the team (González-Roma & Hernández, 2014; Thatcher & Patel, 2011) forces us to consider non-uniform realities where different subgroups and significant faultlines exist. Peer justice also assumes that teammates do not have formal authority over each other. Nevertheless, faultlines provide an informal structure (Lau & Murnighan, 2005), and the existence of subgroups can also describe informal differences in the status of team members (Roberson & Colquitt, 2005). Taken together, these perspectives about teams stimulate the study of the subgroup as a source of justice and the focus on intergroup justice within the team. At least two relevant topics can be investigated. First, future research could study the quality of the relationships among subgroups (fair, unfair, and neutral)—considered as a relational property—and their antecedents and effects. For example, a previous history of offenses can create a negative spiral affecting the quality of relationships between subgroups that translates into mutual unfair treatment between the parties. Second, interesting asymmetries can be investigated in the way subgroups treat one another. For instance, differences in roles and status are not only precursors of subgrouping (Roberson & Colquitt, 2005), but they could also produce power asymmetry and differential perceptions about the treatment each subgroup receives from the other subgroups in the team.

CONCLUSION

During the past 15 years, research has produced relevant contributions to understanding justice at the team level. This construct has achieved an independent status in the literature, and scholars have studied its dimensionality and clarified some of its connections with antecedents and outcomes. This progress has been inspired largely by research conducted at the individual level. It is reasonable to expect that this parallelism between the individual and team levels will remain. However, there is also a growing interest in aspects that are unique to teams, with the potential to promote a qualitative change that distinguishes justice in teams from the individual approach. Contributions to knowledge about justice in teams can follow different routes. One of them would be the interrelations with the individual level, but another fruitful path would be to focus the research on the particularities of teams.

FURTHER READING

Cojuharenco, I., Patient, D., & Bashshur, M. R. (2011). Seeing the "forest" or the "trees" of organizational justice: Effects of temporal perspective on employee concerns about unfair treatment at work. *Organizational Behavior and Human Decision Processes, 116*(1), 17–31.

Colquitt, J. A., & Zipay, K. P. (2015). Justice, fairness, and employee reactions. *Annual Review of Organizational Psychology and Organizational Behavior, 2,* 75–99.

Cropanzano, R., Bowen, D. E., & Gilliland, S. W. (2007). The management of organizational justice. *Academy of Management Perspectives, 21*(4), 34–48.

Cropanzano, R., & Stein, J. H. (2009). Organizational justice and behavioral ethics: Promises and prospects. *Business Ethics Quarterly, 19*(2), 193–233.

Gilliland, S. W., Gross, M. A., & Hogler, R. L. (2014). Is organizational justice the new industrial relations? A debate on individual versus collective underpinnings of justice. *Negotiation and Conflict Management Research, 7*(3), 155–172.

Goldam, B., & Cropanzano, R. (2015). "Justice" and "fairness" are not the same thing. *Journal of Organizational Behavior, 36*(2), 313–318.

Patient, D. (2011). Pitfalls of administering justice in an inconsistent world: Some reflections on the consistency rule. *Journal of Organizational Behavior, 32*(7), 1008–1012.

Steiner, D. D., Trahan, W. A., Haptonstahl, D. E., & Fointiat, V. (2006). The justice of equity, equality, and need in reward distributions: A comparison of French and American respondents. *Revue Internationale de Psychologie Sociale-International Review of Social Psychology, 19*(1), 49–74.

Truxillo, D. M., Bauer, T. N., & Campion, M. A. (2009). Organizational justice interventions: Practicalities, concerns, and potential. *Industrial and Organizational Psychology—Perspectives on Science and Practice, 2*(2), 211–214.

Van den Bos, K., Cropanzano, R., Kirk J., Jasso, G., & Okimoto, T. G. (2015). Expanding the horizons of social justice research: Three essays on justice theory. *Social Justice Research, 28*(2), 229–246.

REFERENCES

Adams, J. S. (1965). Inequity in social exchange. In L. Berkowitz (Ed.), *Advances in experimental social psychology* (pp. 267–299). New York: Academic Press.

Ambrose, M. L., & Schminke, M. (2007). Examining justice climate: Issues of fit, simplicity, and content. In F. Dansereau & F. J. Yammarino (Eds.), *Multilevel issues in organizations and time* (Vol. 6, pp. 397–413). Oxford: Elsevier.

Ambrose, M. L., & Schminke, M. (2009). The role of overall justice judgments in organizational justice research: A test of mediation. *Journal of Applied Psychology, 94*(2), 491–500.

Baumeister, R. F., Bratslavsky, E., Finkenauer, C., & Vohs, K. D. (2001). Bad is stronger than good. *Review of General Psychology, 5*(4), 323–370.

Bezrukova, K., Spell, C. S., & Perry, J. L. (2011). Violent splits or healthy divides? Coping with injustice through faultlines. *Personnel Psychology, 63*(3), 719–751.

Bies, R. J., & Moag, J. S. (1986). Interactional justice: Communication criteria for fairness. In B. Sheppard (Ed.), *Research on negotiation in organizations* (Vol. 1, pp. 43–55). Greenwich, CT: JAI Press.

Blader, S. L., & Tyler, T. R. (2005). How can theories of organizational justice explain the impact of fairness? In J. Greenberg & J. A. Colquitt (Eds.), *Handbook of organizational justice* (pp. 329–354). Mahwah, NJ: Erlbaum.

Brockner, J., Konovsky, M., Cooperschneider, R., Folger, R., Martin, C, & Bies, R. J. (1994). Interactive effects of procedural justice and outcome negativity on victims and survivors of job loss. *Academy of Management Journal, 37*(2), 397–409.

Burke, M. J., Finkelstein, L. M., & Dusig, M. S. (1999). On average deviation indices for estimating interrater agreement. *Organizational Research Methods, 2*(1), 49–68.

Buunk, B. P., & Schaufeli, W. B. (1999). Reciprocity in interpersonal relationships: An evolutionary perspective on its importance for health and well-being. In M. Hewstone & W. Strogebe (Eds.), *European review of social psychology* (pp. 259–340). Chichester, UK: Wiley.

Caldwell, S. D., Herold, D. M., & Fedor, D. B. (2004). Toward an understanding of the relationships among organizational change, individual differences, and changes in person-environment fit: A cross-level study. *Journal of Applied Psychology, 89*(5), 868–882.

Colquitt, J. A. (2001). On the dimensionality of organizational justice: A construct validation of a measure. *Journal of Applied Psychology, 86*(3), 386–400.

Colquitt, J. A., Conlon, D. E., Wesson, M. J., Porter, C. O. L. H., & Ng, K. Y. (2001). Justice at the millennium: A meta-analytic review of 25 years of organizational justice research. *Journal of Applied Psychology, 86*(3), 425–445.

Colquitt, J. A., Noe, R. A., & Jackson, C. L. (2002). Justice in teams: Antecedents and consequences of procedural justice climate. *Personnel Psychology, 55*(1), 83–109.

Colquitt, J. A., Scott, B. A., Rodell, J. B., Long, D. M., Zapata, C. P., Conlon, D. E., et al. (2013). Justice at the millennium, a decade later: A meta-analytic test of social exchange and affect-based perspectives. *Journal of Applied Psychology, 98*(2), 199–236.

Cropanzano, R., Li, A., & Benson, L. (2011). Peer justice and teamwork process. *Group & Organization Management, 36*(5), 567–596.

Cropanzano, R., & Rupp, D. E. (2002). Some reflections on the morality of organizational justice. In S. W. Gilliland, D. D. Steiner, & D. P. Skarlicki (Eds.), *Emerging perspectives on managing organizational justice* (pp. 225–278). Greenwich, CT: Information Age Publishers.

Cropanzano, R., Rupp, D. E., Mohler, C. J., & Schminke, M. (2001). Three roads to organizational justice. In G. R. Ferris (Ed.), *Research in personnel and human resource management* (pp. 1–113). New York: Elsevier Science.

Degoey, P. (2000). Contagious justice: Exploring the social construction of justice in organizations. In B. M. Staw & R. L. Sutton (Eds.), *Research in organizational behavior* (Vol. 22, pp. 51–102). Greenwich, CT: JAI Press.

Deutsch, M. (1975). Equity, equality, and need: What determines which value will be used as the basis of distributive justice? *Journal of Social Issues, 31*(3), 137–149.

Dietz, J., Pugh, S. D., & Wiley, J. W. (2004). Service climate effects on customer attitudes: An examination of boundary conditions. *Academy of Management Journal, 47*(1), 81–92.

Ehrhart, M. G. (2004). Leadership and procedural justice climate as antecedents of unit-level organizational citizenship behavior. *Personnel Psychology, 57*(1), 61–94.

Folger, R., & Greenberg, J. (1985). Procedural justice: An interpretive analysis of personnel systems. In K. M. Rowland & G. R. Ferris (Eds.), *Research in personnel and human resources management* (Vol. 3, pp. 141–183). Greenwich, CT: JAI Press.

Gilliland, S. W., & Chan, D. (2001). Justice in organizations: Theory, methods, and application. In N. Anderson, D. S. Ones, H. K. Sinangil, & C. Viswesvaran (Eds.), *Handbook of industrial, work and organizational psychology* (Vol. 2, pp. 142–165). London: SAGE.

González-Romá, V., & Hernández, A. (2014). Climate uniformity: Its influence on team communication quality, task conflict, and team performance. *Journal of Applied Psychology, 99*(6), 1042–1058.

Greenberg, J. (1993). The social side of fairness: Interpersonal and informational classes of organizational justice. In R. Cropanzano (Ed.), *Justice in the workplace: Approaching fairness in human resource management* (pp. 79–103). Hillsdale, NJ: Erlbaum.

Henderson, L. J., & Mayo, E. (1936). The effects of social environment. *Journal of Industrial Hygiene and Toxicology, 18*(7), 401–416.

Herold, D. M., Fedor, D. B., & Caldwell, S. D. (2007). Beyond change management: A multilevel investigation of contextual and personal influences on employees' commitment to change. *Journal of Applied Psychology, 92*(4), 942–951.

James, L. R., Demaree, R. G., & Wolf, G. (1993). Rwg: An assessment of within group interrater agreement. *Journal of Applied Psychology, 78*(2), 306–309.

James, L. R., & Jones, A. P. (1974). Organizational climate: A review of theory and research. *Psychological Bulletin, 81*(12), 1096–1112.

Jarvenpaa, S., Knoll, K., & Leidner, D. (1998). Is anybody out there? Antecedents of trust in global virtual teams. *Journal of Management Information Systems, 14*(4), 29–64.

Johnson, R. E., Lanaj, K., & Barnes, C. M. (2014). The good and bad of being fair: Effects of procedural and interpersonal justice behaviors on regulatory resources. *Journal of Applied Psychology, 99*(4), 635–650.

Johnson, R. E., & Lord, R. G. (2010). Implicit effects of justice on self-identity. *Journal of Applied Psychology, 95*(4), 681–695.

Kozlowski, S. W. J., & Klein, K. J. (2000). A multilevel approach to theory and research in organizations: Contextual, temporal, and emergent processes. In K. J. Klein & S. W. J. Kozlowski (Eds.), *Multilevel theory, research, and methods in organizations* (pp. 3–90). San Francisco: Jossey-Bass.

Lanz, R., Miroudot, S., & Nordås, H. K. (2013). Offshoring of tasks: Taylorism versus Toyotism. *World Economy, 36*(2), 194–212.

Lau, D. C., & Murnighan, J. K. (1998). Demographic diversity and faultlines: The compositional dynamics of organizational groups. *Academy of Management Review, 23*(2), 325–340.

Lau, D. C., & Murnighan, J. K. (2005). Interactions within groups and subgroups: The effects of demographic faultlines. *Academy of Management Journal, 48*(4), 645–659.

Leventhal, G. S. (1976). The distribution of rewards and resources in groups and organizations. In L. Berkowitz & W. Walster (Eds.), *Advances in experimental social psychology* (Vol. 9, pp. 91–131). New York: Academy Press.

Leventhal, G. S. (1980). What should be done with equity theory? New approaches and organizations. In K. Gergen, M. Greenberg, & R. Willis (Eds.), *Social exchange advances in theory and research* (pp. 27–55). New York: Plenum.

Lewin, K., Lippitt, R., & White, R. K. (1939). Patterns of aggressive behavior in experimentally created "social climates." *Journal of Social Psychology, 10*(2), 271–299.

Li, A., Cropanzano, R. S., & Bagger, J. (2013). Justice climate and peer justice climate. A closer look. *Small Group Research, 44*(5), 563–592.

Li, A., Cropanzano, R. S., & Molina, A. (2015). Fairness at the unit level: Justice climate, justice climate strength, and peer justice. In R. Cropanzano & M. Ambrose (Eds.), *The Oxford handbook of justice in the workplace* (pp. 137–164). Oxford: Oxford University Press.

Lind, E. A. (2001). Fairness heuristic theory: Justice judgments as pivotal cognitions in organizational relations. In J. Greenberg & R. Cropanzano (Eds.), *Advances in organizational justice* (pp. 56–88). Stanford, CA: Stanford Business Press.

Lind, E. A., & Tyler, T. (1988). *The social psychology of procedural justice*. New York: Plenum.

Martínez-Tur, V., Estreder, Y., Moliner, C., Sánchez-Hernández, R., & Peiró, J. M. (2016). Under-over benefitting perceptions and evaluation of services: Nonlinear relationships in a four-sample investigation. *Journal of Service Theory and Practice, 26*(4), 406–429.

Martínez-Tur, V., Tordera, N., Peiró, J. M., & Potocnik, K. (2011). Linking service climate and disconfirmation of expectations to customer satisfaction: A cross-level study. *Journal of Applied Social Psychology, 41*(5), 1189–1213.

Meyer, B., & Glenz, A. (2013). Team faultline measures: A computational comparison and a new approach to multiple subgroups. *Organizational Research Methods, 16*(3), 393–424.

Meyer, B., Glenz, A., Antino, M., Rico, R., & González-Romá, V. (2014). Faultlines and subgroups: A meta-review and measurement guide. *Small Group Research, 45*(6), 633–670.

Molina, A., Moliner, C., Martínez-Tur, V., Cropanzano, R., & Peiró, J. M. (2015). Unit-level fairness and quality within the health care industry: A justice–quality model. *European Journal of Work and Organizational Psychology, 24*(4), 627–644.

Moliner, C., Martínez-Tur, V., Peiró, J. M., Ramos J., & Cropanzano, R. (2005). Relationships between organizational justice and burnout at the work-unit level. *International Journal of Stress Management, 12*(2), 99–116.

Moliner, C., Martínez-Tur, V., Peiró, J. M., Ramos, J., & Cropanzano, R. (2013). Perceived reciprocity and well-being at work in non-professional employees: Fairness or self-interest? *Stress and Health, 29*(1), 31–39.

Mossholder, K. W., Bennett, N., & Martin, C. L. (1998). A multilevel analysis of procedural justice context. *Journal of Organizational Behavior, 19*(2), 131–141.

Naumann, S. E., & Bennett, N. (2000). A case for procedural justice climate: Development and test of a multilevel model. *Academy of Management Journal, 43*(5), 881–889.

Ogunfowora, B. (2013). When the abuse is unevenly distributed: The effects of abusive supervision variability on work attitudes and behaviors. *Journal of Organizational Behavior, 34*(8), 1105–1123.

Ostroff, C., Kinicki, A. J., & Tamkins, M. M. (2003). Organizational culture and climate. In W. C. Borman, D. R. Ilgen, & R. J. Klimoski (Eds.), *Handbook of psychology* (pp. 565–593). New York: Wiley.

Pillai, R., Scandura, T., & Williams, E. (1999). Leadership and organizational justice: Similarities and differences across cultures. *Journal of International Business Studies, 30*(4), 763–779.

Priesemuth, M., Arnaud, A., & Schminke, M. (2013). Bad behavior in groups: The impact of overall justice climate and functional dependence on counterproductive work behavior in work units. *Group and Organization Management, 38*(2), 230–257.

Raudenbush, S. W., & Bryk, A. S. (2002). *Hierarchical linear models: Applications and data analysis methods*. Newbury Park, CA: SAGE.

Rico, R., Sánchez-Manzanares, M., Antino, M, & Lau, D. (2012). Bridging team faultlines by combining task role assignment and goal structure strategies. *Journal of Applied Psychology, 97*(2), 407–420.

Roberson, Q. M. (2006). Justice in teams: The activation and role of sensemaking in the emergence of justice climates. *Organizational Behavior and Human Decision Processes, 100*(2), 177–192.

Roberson, Q. M., & Colquitt, J. A. (2005). Shared and configural justice: A social network model of justice in teams. *The Academy of Management Review, 30*(3), 595–607.

Rupp, D. E., Bashshur, M., & Liao, H. (2007). Justice climate: Consideration of source, target, type, specificity, and emergence. In F. Dansereau & F. Yammarino (Eds.), *Research in multilevel issues* (Vol. 6, pp. 439–459). Oxford: Elsevier.

Sauley, K. S., & Bedeian, A. G. (2000). Equity sensitivity: Construction of a measure and examination of its psychometric properties. *Journal of Management, 26*(5), 885–910.

Schneider, B. (1987). The people make the place. *Personnel Psychology, 40*(3), 437–453.

Schneider, B., Goldstein, H., & Smith, D. B. (1995). The ASA framework: An update. *Personnel Psychology, 48*(4), 747–773.

Schneider, B., & Reichers, A. (1983). On the etiology of climates. *Personnel Psychology, 36*(1), 19–40.

Schneider, B., Wheeler, J. K., & Cox, J. F. (1992). A passion for service: Using content analysis to explicate service climate themes. *Journal of Applied Psychology, 77*(5), 705–716.

Schneider, B., White, S. S., & Paul, M. C. (1998). Linking service climate and customer perceptions of service quality: Test of a causal model. *Journal of Applied Psychology, 83*(2), 150–163.

Spell, C. S., & Arnold, T. J. (2007). A multi-level analysis of organizational justice climate, structure, and employee mental health. *Journal of Management, 33*(5), 724–751.

Spell, C. S., Bezrukova, K., Haar, J., & Spell, C. (2011). Faultlines, fairness, and fighting: A justice perspective on conflict in diverse groups. *Small Group Research, 43*(3), 309–340.

Stoverink, A. C., Umphress, E. E., Gardner, R. G., & Miner, K. N. (2014). Misery loves company: Team dissonance and the influence of supervisor-focused interpersonal justice climate on team cohesiveness. *Journal of Applied Psychology, 99*(6) 1059–1073.

Taylor, F. W. (1991). *The principles of scientific management.* New York and London: Harper.

Thatcher, S. M. B., Jehn, K. A., & Zanutto, E. (2003). Cracks in diversity research: The effects of diversity faultlines on conflict and performance. *Group Decision and Negotiation, 12*(3), 217–241.

Thatcher, S. M. B., & Patel, P. C. (2011). Demographic faultlines: A meta-analysis of the literature. *Journal of Applied Psychology, 96*(6), 1119–1139.

Thatcher, S. M. B., & Patel, P. C. (2012). Group faultlines: A review, integration, and guide to future research. *Journal of Management, 38*(4), 969–1009.

Thibaut, J., & Walker, L. (1975). *Procedural justice: A psychological analysis.* New York: Erlbaum Wiley.

Tyler, T. R., & Bies, R. J. (1990). Beyond formal procedures: The interpersonal context of procedural justice. In J. S. Carroll (Ed.), *Applied social psychology and organizational settings* (pp. 77–98). Hillsdale, NJ: Lawrence Erlbaum.

Tyler, T. R., & Lind, E. A. (1992). A relational model of authority in groups. In M. P. Zanna (Ed.), *Advances in experimental social psychology* (Vol. 25, pp. 115–191). San Diego, CA: Academic Press.

Van, den Bos, Peters, S. L., Bobocel, D. R., & Ybema, J. F. (2006). On preferences and doing the right thing: Satisfaction with advantageous inequity when cognitive processing is limited. *Journal of Experimental Social Psychology, 42*(3), 273–289.

Whitman, D. S., Caleo, S., Carpenter, N. C., Horner, M. T., & Bernerth, J. B. (2012). Fairness at the collective level: A meta-analytic examination of the consequences and boundary conditions of organizational justice climate. *Journal of Applied Psychology, 97*(4), 776–791.

Yang, J., Mossholder, K. W., & Peng, T. K. (2007). Procedural justice climate and group power distance: An examination of cross-level interaction effects. *Journal of Applied Psychology, 92*(3), 681–692.

Vincente Martínez-Tur and Carolina Moliner